LABORATORY MANUAL FOR INTRODUCTORY GEOLOGY

THIRD EDITION

ALLAN LUDMAN

Queens College, New York

STEPHEN MARSHAK

University of Illinois

W. W. NORTON & COMPANY
NEW YORK · LONDON

W. W. Norton & Company has been independent since its founding in 1923, when William Warder Norton and Mary D. Herter Norton first published lectures delivered at the People's Institute, the adult education division of New York City's Cooper Union. The firm soon expanded their program beyond the Institute, publishing books by celebrated academics from America and abroad. By mid-century, the two major pillars of Norton's publishing program—trade books and college texts—were firmly established. In the 1950s, the Norton family transferred control of the company to its employees, and today—with a staff of four hundred and a comparable number of trade, college, and professional titles published each year—W. W. Norton & Company stands as the largest and oldest publishing house owned wholly by its employees.

Editor: Eric Svendsen
Senior Project Editor: Thomas Foley
Associate Production Director: Benjamin Reynolds
Developmental Editor: Sunny Hwang
Copy Editor: Chris Curioli
Managing Editor, College: Marian Johnson
Managing Editor, College Digital Media: Kim Yi
Media Editors: Robin Kimball and Rob Bellinger
Marketing Manager, Geology: Meredith Leo
Design Director: Hope Miller Goodell
Designer: Lissi Sigillo
Photography Editor: Evan Luberger
Composition and page layout by codeMantra
Illustrations by Precision Graphics/Lachina
Project manager at Precision Graphics/Lachina: Terri Hamer
Manufacturing by LSC Communications
Topographic maps created by Mapping Specialists—Madison, WI

W. W. Norton & Company, Inc., 500 Fifth Avenue, New York, NY 10110
wwnorton.com

W. W. Norton & Company Ltd., Castle House, 75/76 Wells Street, London W1T 3QT

3 4 5 6 7 8 9 0

This laboratory manual is based on our collective 70+ years of teaching and coordinating introductory geology courses—experience that has helped us to understand both how students best learn geologic principles and which strategies help instructors arouse student interest in order to enhance the learning process. This manual provides: (1) an up-to-date, comprehensive background that focuses on the hands-on tasks at the core of any introductory geology course; (2) clearer and more patient step-by-step explanations than can be accommodated in textbooks; (3) a text and exercises that engage students in thinking like a geologist, in order to solve real-life problems important to society; and (4) the passion and excitement that we still feel after decades as geologists and teachers.

Students often ask us how we maintain this enthusiasm. Our answer is to share with them both the joys and the frustrations of facing and solving real-world geologic problems. You will find many of those types of problems in the following pages—modified for the introductory nature of the course, but still reflecting their challenges and the rewards of solving them. This manual brings that experience directly to the students, *engaging* them in the learning process by *explaining* concepts clearly and providing many avenues for further *exploration*.

Unique Elements

As you read through this manual, you will find elements and a pedagogical approach that distinguish it from others, including:

Hands-on, inquiry-based pedagogy

We believe that students learn science best by doing science, not by just memorizing facts. Beginning in Chapter 1 and continuing in each subsequent chapter, students are guided through real-world geologic puzzles in order to understand concepts more deeply and to start learning to think like a geologist. In Chapter 9, for example, students work out the rules of contour lines for themselves by comparing a topographic map with a digital elevation model of the same area. In Chapter 5, they reason out the cooling rates for plutons of different sizes and shapes, and so on.

Innovative exercises that engage students and provide instructors with choice

Tiered exercises are carefully integrated into the text, leading students to understand concepts for themselves by first reading about the concept and then immediately using what they learned in the accompanying exercise. These unique exercises engage students because they show how important geologic principles are to our every-day activities.

There are more exercises per chapter than can probably be completed in a single lab session. This is done intentionally, to provide options for instructors during class or as potential out-of-class assignments. The complexity and rigor of the exercises increases within each chapter, enabling instructors to use the manual for both non-majors and potential majors alike. Just assign the exercises that are most appropriate for your student population.

Superb illustration program

Readers have come to expect a superior illustration program in any Norton geology text, and this manual does not disappoint. The extensive and highly illustrative photos, line drawings, maps, and DEMs continue the tradition of Stephen Marshak's *Earth: Portrait of a Planet* and *Essentials of Geology*.

Reader-friendly language and layout

Our decades of teaching introductory geology help us to identify the concepts that are most difficult for students to understand. The conversational style of this manual and the use of many real-world analogies help to make these difficult concepts clear and enhance student understanding. The crisp, open layout makes the book more attractive and reader-friendly than other laboratory manuals, which are crammed with pages of multiple-column text.

Unique mineral and rock labs

Students learn the difference between minerals and rocks by classifying Earth materials in a simple exercise (Ch. 3). That exercise then leads to the importance of physical properties and a logical system for identifying minerals. In Chapter 4, students make intrusive and extrusive igneous "rocks," clastic and chemical sedimentary "rocks," and a foliated metamorphic "rock" to understand how the rock-forming processes are indelibly recorded in a rock's texture. The goal in studying rocks in Chapters 5–7 is to interpret the processes and conditions by which they formed, not just to be able to find their correct names.

Digital elevation models (DEMs)

Digital elevation models are used to enhance the understanding of contour lines and to build map-reading skills.

Improvements to the Third Edition

We are grateful to the many adopters of the First and Second Editions for their detailed feedback and helpful suggestions, which we have incorporated into this improved Third Edition. This edition represents a significant revision, based on the comments of reviewers and users who asked for an even more visual, hands-on, thought-provoking, and easier-to-use experience. We assembled a team that included the authors, two reviewers, and three professional editors to both update the content and make certain that all of the improvements were integrated seamlessly into the Third Edition. Throughout this revision, we have retained the core approach of the earlier editions—interspersing exercises throughout the text, so that the manual follows the logical sequence of laboratory activities. Adopters have praised this organization and following their suggestions, we have strengthened this approach. Other improvements to the Third Edition include:

- *A completely revised map program:* All of the topographic maps in this edition are brand new and were created specifically for this lab manual by professional mapmakers. They reproduce clearly, are easy to use, and each is tailored to the specific lab exercise that it accompanies. We continue to produce maps in a full page format so that they are easy to use with their corresponding exercises.

- *New and significantly revised figures that explain important concepts:* Figures throughout the text have been revised and enlarged, and new figures added to better illustrate the geologic concepts for today's more visual learners.

- *"What Do You Think" exercises:* Each chapter now contains a special "What Do You Think" scenario where students are asked to make a decision, offer a recommendation, or express their opinion—often as if they were a geologic consultant. These exercises are designed to help students see the connection of geology to the "real" world, to spark discussion in the lab, and to connect geology with other disciplines such as economics, ethics, and history.

- *Improved pedagogy:* Chapters now begin with clear learning objectives that facilitate student assessment and at the request of reviewers, we have also simplified the figure numbering to improve ease of use for both students and instructors.

- *Simplified and improved mineral charts and flowcharts:* The mineral charts and flowcharts in Chapter 3 have greatly benefited from the recommendations of several users, making them easier for students to understand and use.

- *New and revised content based on reviewer feedback:* Many chapters have been reorganized to simplify and improve their approach. In particular, Chapter 2 (Plate Tectonics), Chapter 6 (Metamorphic Rocks), and Chapter 15 (Structural Geology) have all been strengthened by new sequencing and additional basic exercises. Other chapter-by-chapter changes include:

> **Chapter 1:** The introductory material has been reorganized to start with a student-focused mini-case.
>
> **Chapter 2:** The simplistic cut-and-paste exercises have been removed, the exercises were reordered to group examples of each type of plate boundary together, and the figures used in several exercises have been improved.
>
> **Chapter 3:** New photographs were added to illustrate cleavage and hardness. The determinative tables and flow charts have been improved based on user suggestions.
>
> **Chapter 4:** An improved diagram and explanation of the rock cycle is included and better photos of rock textures have been added.
>
> **Chapter 5:** We have added a section on volcanoes and volcanic hazards and improved the Bowen's Reaction Series and igneous rock classification diagrams.
>
> **Chapter 6:** This chapter has a reorganized structure that introduces sedimentary processes and rock types more clearly, and easier-to-use classification diagrams for sedimentary rocks have been added.
>
> **Chapter 7:** This chapter was significantly restructured in order to present metamorphism in a more logical and student-friendly way.
>
> **Chapter 8:** An improved illustration program clarifies basic map elements.
>
> **Chapter 9:** A new exercise explaining isolines using the contours of forest growth has been included.
>
> **Chapter 10:** New photos showing the range of stream sinuosity and figures showing stream features and stream evolution have been added, as well as improved exercises for the principles of stream behavior.
>
> **Chapter 11:** A new section and exercise on climate change and glacial retreat is now included.
>
> **Chapter 12:** The maps and exercises have been revised for greater clarity.
>
> **Chapter 13:** Diagrams showing the evolution of arid landforms have been improved.

Chapter 14: An expanded explanation of factors affecting shoreline landforms is included, as well as a more comprehensive and up-to-date treatment of coastal hazards and strategies to protect shorelines. This chapter has also been updated to include the effects of Hurricane Sandy on the east coast of the United States.

Chapter 15: This chapter has been shortened and simplified in response to reviewer comments, with revised exercises that better explain the basics of rock deformation and the interpretation of geologic maps.

Chapter 16: Improved figures showing the propagation of seismic body and surface waves is now included and other figures have been improved to aid student completion of the exercises.

Chapter 17: A new exercise that applies paleoenvironmental indicators to reconstruct the Cretaceous paleogeography of North America has been added.

- *Revisions to more closely match terminology with other Marshak texts:* While this book is designed to work with any introductory textbook, terminology in particular was reviewed for consistency with Stephen Marshak's *Earth: Portrait of a Planet* and *Essentials of Geology.*

- *New electronic lab versions, pre-lab worksheets, and supplements:* Because some schools now need to offer the lab in a distance-learning environment, we have created a new coursepack compatible with all of the major learning management systems. First, coursepacks include electronic review sheets that you can assign to students before the lab, thus guaranteeing they have reviewed the basic concepts. Then, for help with your distance-learning courses, we have prepared electronic versions of many of the lab exercises. While these labs require students to have the text in print or electronic format to access figures and maps, questions have been tailored to work better in an on-line environment and to work with your learning management system. Please consult with your W. W. Norton sales rep, or review the Instructor's Manual for a complete list of these exercises. A revised instructor's solution manual and new figures in electronic formats are available for download at the Norton Instructor Resource site: wwwnorton.com/instructors.

Supplements

(available for download at wwnorton.com/instructors)

Coursepacks. Available at no cost to professors or students, Norton Coursepacks bring high-quality Norton digital media into your course. This new supplement includes:

- *Prelab quizzes,* available as autograded assignments or printable worksheets, are designed to assess if students have prepared their pre-lab material.
- *On-line versions of selected lab exercises* (a complete list is in the Instructor's Manual). For professors that need to offer this course in a blended- or distance-learning environment, we have adapted the best exercises for these formats into our coursepacks. Responses are either autograded or written to require brief responses. (*Note:* students still need either a print or an electronic version of the lab manual to access figures and background reading.) We have also constructed the labs to work with typical rock kits that can be purchased from many suppliers.

Instructor's Manual, available in electronic format. The revised Instructor's Manual contains word files of the solutions to each exercise, teaching tips for each lab, and a detailed conversion guide showing changes between the Second and Third Editions

Electronic figures. All figures, photographs, charts, and maps in this text are available for you to download and incorporate in your presentations, handouts, or online courses.

Animations of core concepts in geology, which are available to download or stream from our site.

Acknowledgments

We are indebted to the talented team at W. W. Norton & Company whose zealous quest for excellence is matched only by their ingenuity in solving layout problems, finding that special photograph, and keeping the project on schedule. We also appreciate the professors who provided accuracy reviews and feedback for earlier editions: Pete Wehner of Austin Community College–Northridge; Daniel Imrecke, Jinny Sisson, and Julia Smith Wellner of the University of Houston; Kurt Wilkie and Amanda Stahl of Washington State University; Michael Rygel of SUNY–Potsdam; and Karen Koy of Missouri Western State University. We also appreciate the detailed chapter-by-chapter review of the Second Edition by the core teaching faculty and teaching assistants at the University of Houston. We would also like to thank Nathalie Brandes of Lone Star College and Geoffrey W. Cook of the University of California, San Diego, who worked closely with the authors and a team of editors at W. W. Norton to proofread and check the accuracy of the Third Edition.

We are very grateful to and would like to thank all of the following expert reviewers for their input and expertise in making this Lab Manual the best it can be:

Stephen T. Allard, *Winona State University*
Richard Aurisano, *Wharton County Junior College*
Miriam Barquero-Molina, *University of Missouri*
Theodore Bornhorst, *Michigan Tech University*
Nathalie Brandes, *Lone Star College*
Lee Anne Burrough, *Prairie State College*
Geoffrey W. Cook, *University of California, San Diego*
Winton Cornell, *University of Tulsa*
Juliet Crider, *University of Washington*
John Dassinger, *Chandler-Gilbert Community College*
Meredith Denton-Hedrick, *Austin Community College*
Mark Evans, *Central Connecticut State University*
Todd Feeley, *Montana State University*
Jeanne Fromm, *University of South Dakota*
Lisa Hammersley, *Sacramento State University*
Bernie Housen, *Western Washington University*
Daniel Imrecke, *University of Houston*
Jacalyn Gorczynski, Texas *A&M University–Corpus Christi*
Michael Harrison, *Tennessee Technological University*
Daniel Hembree, *Ohio University*
Ryan Kerrigan, *University of Maryland*
Karen Koy, *Missouri Western State University*
Heather Lehto, *Angelo State University*
Jamie Macdonald, *Florida Gulf Coast University*
John A. Madsen, *University of Delaware*
Lisa Mayo, *Motlow State Community College*

Lisa Mayo, *Motlow State Community College*
Amy Moe Hoffman, *Mississippi State University*
Kristen Myshrall, *University of Connecticut*
David Peate, *University of Iowa*
Alfred Pekarek, *St. Cloud State University*
Elizabeth Rhodes, *College of Charleston*
Anne Marie Ryan, *Dalhousie University*
Ray Russo, *University of Florida*
Mike Rygel, *SUNY Potsdam*
Jinny Sisson, *University of Houston*
Roger Shew, *University of North Carolina - Wilmington*
Amanda Stahl, *Washington State University*
Alexander Stewart, *St. Lawrence University*
Christiane Stidham, *SUNY Stony Brook*
Lori Tapanila, *Idaho State University*
JoAnn Thissen, *Nassau Community College*
Peter Wallace, *Dalhousie University*
Pete Wehner, *Austin Community College–Northridge*
Julia Smith Wellner, *University of Houston*
Kurt Wilkie, *Washington State University*
Andrew H. Wulff, *Western Kentucky University*
Victor Zabielski, *Northern Virginia Community College*

1

Setting the Stage for Learning about the Earth

This sunset over the red cliffs of Horseshoe Bend on the Colorado River in Page, Arizona shows the Earth System at a glance—air, water, and rock all interacting together to produce this stunning landscape.

1.1 Thinking Like a Geologist

Learning about the Earth is like training to become a detective. Both geologists and detectives need keen powers of observation, curiosity about slight differences, broad scientific understanding, and instruments to analyze samples. And both ask the same questions: What happened? How? When? Although much of the logical thinking is the same, there are big differences between the work of a detective and that of a geologist. A detective's "cold" case may be 30 years old, but "old" to a geologist means hundreds of millions or billions of years. To a detective, a "body" is a human body, but to a geologist, a body may be a mountain range or a continent. Eyewitnesses can help detectives, but for most of Earth's history there weren't any humans to act as eyewitnesses for geologists. To study the Earth, geologists must therefore develop different strategies from those of other kinds of investigators. The overall goal of this manual is to help you look at the Earth and think about its mysteries like a geologist.

To illustrate geologic thinking, let's start with a typical geologic mystery. Almost 300 years ago, settlers along the coast of Maine built piers (like the modern pier shown in **FIGURE. 1.1**) to load and unload ships. Some of these piers are now submerged to a depth of 1 meter (39 inches) below sea level.

FIGURE 1.1 **Subsidence along the coast of Maine.**

Tourists might not think twice about this before heading for a lobster dinner at the local restaurant, but a geologist would want to know how rapidly the pier was submerged and what caused the submergence. How would a geologist go about tackling this problem? To get started, let's try a sample exercise designed to present some basic geologic reasoning and to show the types of real world problems that it can solve.

Name: _____   Section: _____

Course: _____   Date: _____

2015

1715

The figure on the left illustrates a pier whose walkway sits 1 meter below the ocean's surface today. Since we weren't there when it was built 300 years ago, we have to make some assumptions—geologists often do this to make estimates. So let's assume that the pier's walkway was originally 1 m *above* sea level at high tide, as many are built today (illustrated in the figure on the right), and that submergence occurred at a constant rate. With these assumptions, calculating the rate of submergence for the past 300 years becomes simple arithmetic.

(a) The rate of submergence is the total change in the elevation of the pier (_____ m) divided by the total amount of time involved (_____ years) and is therefore _____ cm/yr. (Remember, 1 m = 100 cm.)

Now consider a problem this might solve:

(b) A local restaurant owner is considering the purchase of a pier, whose walkway is 50 cm above the high-water mark, for use in outdoor events. The owner has been advised that piers with walkways less than 30 cm above the high-water mark should be avoided because they can be flooded by storms and very high tides. If submergence continues at the rate you calculated, how many years will pass before the high-water mark is less than 30 cm from the base of the deck? _____ yrs.

? What Do You Think   Now it's time to really try thinking like a geologist. Given your answers to (a) and (b), would you recommend the restaurant owner purchase this pier? In a sentence or two, explain why. Then describe another issue that you think the owner should investigate before they make their decision.

You've just tried your first geology problem, Congratulations! A geologist, however, would also want to explain *why* the piers were submerged. When faced with such a problem, geologists typically try to come up with as many explanations as possible. For example, which of the following explanations could account for the submergence?

☐ The sea level has risen.

☐ The land has sunk.

☐ Both the sea level and land have risen, but sea level has gone up more.

☐ Both the sea level and land have sunk, but the land has sunk more.

☐ Over time, the piers gradually sink in the mud of the seafloor.

If you thought all five choices might be right (correctly!), you realize that explaining submergence along the Maine coast may be more complicated than it seemed at first. To find the answer, you need more **data**—more observations and/or measurements. One way to obtain more data would be to see if submergence is restricted to Maine or the east coast of North America or if it is perhaps worldwide. As it turns out, submergence is observed worldwide, suggesting that the first choice above (sea-level rise) is the most probable explanation, but not necessarily the only one.

With even more data, we could answer questions like, When did submergence happen? Was the sea-level rise constant? Maybe all submergence occurred in the first 100 years and then stopped. Or perhaps it began slowly and then accelerated. Unfortunately, we may not be able to answer all of these questions because, unlike television detectives who always get the bad guys, geologists don't always have enough data and must often live with uncertainty. We still do not have the answers to many questions about the Earth.

1.1.1 The Scientific Method

Like all scientists (and most people trying to find answers to problems they have identified), geologists follow a logical process that you are probably familiar with—the scientific method. You did so instinctively in Exercise 1.1 and will do so many times throughout this course. The scientific method begins with making observations of Earth features or processes—in Exercise 1.1, for example, we observed that a colonial pier is now below sea level.

STEP 1 Observing an Earth feature or process (e.g., the submerged pier).

STEP 2 Recognizing that a problem exists and asking questions about that problem. Usually the problem is that we don't understand how what we've observed came to be. In Exercise 1.1, by how much has the pier been submerged? How fast did submergence take place? Why was the pier submerged? We respond with the steps that follow.

STEP 3 Collecting more data to see if the observation is valid and to help us understand what is going on. In Exercise 1.1, for instance, it isn't just one pier being submerged, but many along the Maine coast.

STEP 4 Proposing tentative answers to those questions called **hypotheses** (singular, **hypothesis**). Some versions of the scientific method suggest that we propose a single hypothesis. When we first look at problems, we usually come up with more than one hypothesis, a practice called *multiple working hypotheses*.

STEP 5 Testing the hypotheses by getting more data, which may support some, rule out others, or possibly lead to new hypotheses. Some of this testing can be in the form of a formal laboratory experiment, but there are also other forms, such as field trips to gain additional information, detailed measurements where there had been only eyeball estimates, and so forth.

STEP 6 If your test supports the hypothesis, continue to make additional tests to further verify your result. If your test does not support the hypothesis, then revise the hypothesis and try again, or propose an entirely new hypothesis.

The cycle of observations and experiments illustrated schematically in FIGURE 1.2 enables us to eliminate many of the original hypotheses and leads us to propose new ones until, sometimes, only a single viable explanation remains. Even then we are not satisfied and continue to test it, using new technology as it becomes available. If after years of rigorous testing a hypothesis has withstood all tests, it is elevated to the level of a **theory**, like the germ theory of disease, the theory of evolution, or, as you will learn in Chapter 2, the plate tectonic theory for the origin and evolution of mountains, oceans, and continents.

FIGURE 1.2 The scientific method.

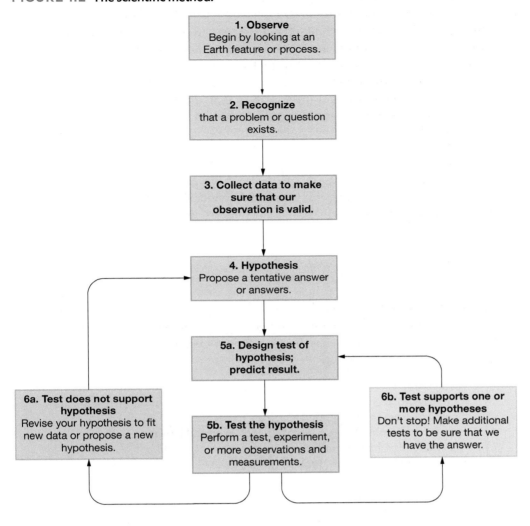

1.1.2 The Challenge of Studying a Planet

Problems like submergence along the Maine coast pose challenges to geologists and geology students who are trying to learn about the Earth. These challenges require us to:

- understand the many kinds of materials that make up the Earth and how they behave.
- be aware of how energy causes changes at Earth's surface and beneath it.
- consider features at a wide range of sizes and scales—from the atoms that make up rocks and minerals to the planet as a whole.
- think in *four* dimensions, because geology involves not just the three dimensions of space but also an enormous span of *time*.
- realize that some geologic processes occur in seconds but others take millions or billions of years and are so slow that we can detect them only with very sensitive instruments.

The rest of this chapter examines these challenges and how geologists cope with them. You will learn basic geologic terminology and how to use tools of observation and measurement that will be useful throughout your geologic studies. Some terms will probably be familiar to you from previous science classes.

1.2 Studying Matter and Energy

Earth is a dynamic planet. Unlike the airless Moon, which has remained virtually unchanged for billions of years, Earth's gases, liquids, and solids constantly move from one place to another. They also change from one state to another through the effects of heat, gravity, other kinds of energy, and living organisms. We refer to all of Earth's varied materials and the processes that affect them as the **Earth System**, and the first step in understanding the Earth System is to understand the nature of matter and energy and how they interact with one another.

1.2.1 The Nature of Matter

Matter is the "stuff" of which the Universe is made; we use it to refer to any material making up the Universe. Geologists, chemists, and physicists have shown that matter consists of ninety-two naturally occurring elements and that some of these elements are much more abundant than others. Keep the following definitions in mind as you read further (**TABLE 1.1**).

TABLE 1.1 Basic definitions

- An **element** is a substance that cannot be broken down chemically into other substances.
- The smallest piece of an element that still has all the properties of that element is an **atom**.
- Atoms combine with one another chemically to form **compounds**; the smallest possible piece of a compound is called a **molecule**.
- Atoms in compounds are held together by **chemical bonds**.
- A simple **chemical formula** describes the combination of atoms in a compound. For example, the formula H_2O shows that a molecule of water contains two atoms of hydrogen and one of oxygen.

Matter occurs on Earth in three states—solid, liquid, or gas. Atoms in *solids*, like minerals and rocks, are held in place by strong chemical bonds. As a result, solids retain their shape over long periods. Bonds in *liquids* are so weak that atoms or molecules move easily, and as a result, liquids adopt the shape of their containers. Atoms or molecules in *gases* are barely held together at all, so a gas expands to fill whatever container it is placed in. Matter changes from one state to another in many geologic processes, as when the Sun evaporates water to produce water vapor, or when water freezes to form ice, or when lava freezes to become solid rock.

We describe the amount of matter in an object by indicating its **mass** and the amount of space it occupies by specifying its **volume**. The more mass packed into a given volume of matter, the greater the **density** of the matter. You notice density differences every day: it's easier to lift a large box of popcorn than a piece of rock of the same size because the rock is much denser; it has much more mass packed into the same volume and therefore weighs much more.

1.2.2 Distribution of Matter in the Earth System

Matter is stored in the Earth System in five major **reservoirs** (**FIG. 1.3a**). Most gas is in the **atmosphere**, a semi-transparent blanket composed of about 78% nitrogen (N_2) and 21% oxygen (O_2), with minor amounts of carbon dioxide (CO_2), water vapor (H_2O), ozone (O_3), and methane (CH_4). Nearly all liquid occurs as water in

FIGURE 1.3 The Earth System.

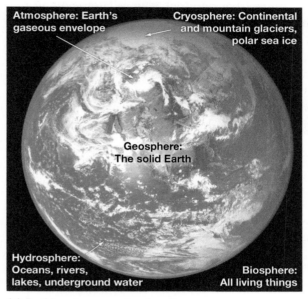

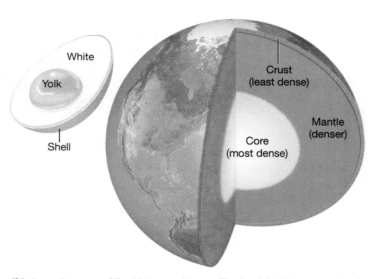

(a) Earth's major reservoirs of matter.

(b) An early image of Earth's internal layers. The hard-boiled egg analogy for the Earth's interior. Earth's interior is denser than the mantle and crust.

the **hydrosphere**—Earth's oceans, rivers, lakes, and groundwater, which is found in cracks and pores beneath the surface. Frozen water makes up the **cryosphere**, including snow, thin layers of ice on the surface of lakes or oceans, and huge masses of ice in glaciers and the polar ice caps.

The solid Earth is called the **geosphere**, which geologists divide into concentric layers like those in a hard-boiled egg (**FIG. 1.3b**). The outer layer, the **crust**, is relatively thin, like an eggshell, and consists *mostly* of rock. Below the crust is the **mantle**, which also consists *mostly* of different kinds of rock and, like the white of an egg, contains most of Earth's volume. We say *mostly* because about 2% of the crust and mantle has melted to produce liquid material called **magma** (known as **lava** when it erupts on the surface). The central part of the Earth, comparable to the egg yolk, is the **core**. The outer core consists mostly of a liquid alloy of iron and nickel, and the inner core is a solid iron-nickel alloy.

Continents make up about 30% of the crust and are composed of relatively low-density rocks. The remaining 70% of the crust is covered by the oceans. Oceanic crust is both thinner and denser than the crust under the continents. Three types of solid materials are found at the surface: **bedrock**, a solid aggregate of minerals and rocks attached to the Earth's crust; **sediment**, unattached mineral grains such as boulders, sand, and clay; and **soil**, sediment and rock modified by interactions with the atmosphere, hydrosphere, and organisms so that it can support plant life.

The **biosphere** is the realm of living organisms, extending from a few kilometers below Earth's surface to a few kilometers above. Geologists have learned that organisms—from bacteria to mammals—are important parts of the Earth System. They exchange gases with the atmosphere, absorb and release water, break rock into sediment, and help convert sediment and rock to soil.

The movement of materials from one reservoir to another is called a **flux** and happens in many geologic processes. For example, rain is a flux in which water moves from the atmosphere to the hydrosphere. Rates of flux depend on the materials, the reservoirs, and the processes involved. In some cases, a material moves among several reservoirs but eventually returns to the first. We call such a path a

geologic cycle. In your geology class you will learn about several cycles, such as the rock cycle (the movement of atoms from one rock type to another) and the hydrologic cycle (the movement of water from the hydrosphere to and from the other reservoirs). Exercises 1.2 and 1.3 will help you understand the distribution of matter.

EXERCISE 1.2	Reservoirs in the Earth System

Name: _____   Section: _____
Course: _____   Date: _____

What Earth materials did you encounter in the past 24 hours? List at least ten in the following table without worrying about the correct geologic terms (for example, "dirt" is okay *for now*). Place each Earth material in its appropriate reservoir and indicate whether it is a solid (S), liquid (L), or gas (G).

Atmosphere	Hydrosphere	Geosphere	Cryosphere	Biosphere

1.2.3 Energy in the Earth System

Natural disasters in the headlines remind us of how dynamic the Earth is: rivers flood cities and fields, lava and volcanic ash bury villages, earthquakes topple buildings, and hurricanes ravage coastal regions. However, many geologic processes are much slower and less dangerous, like the movement of ocean currents and the almost undetectable creep of soil downhill. All are caused by energy, which acts on matter to change its character, move it, or split it apart.

Energy for the Earth System comes from (1) Earth's *internal* heat, which melts rock, causes earthquakes, and builds mountains (some of this heat is left over from the formation of the Earth, but some is being produced today by radioactive decay); (2) *external* energy from the Sun, which warms air, rocks, and water on the Earth's surface; and (3) the pull of Earth's gravity. Heat and gravity, working independently or in combination, drive most geologic processes. Exercise 1.4 explores this idea.

Heat energy is a measure of the degree to which atoms or molecules move about (vibrate) in matter—including in solids. When you heat something in an oven, for example, the atoms in the material vibrate faster and move farther apart. Heat energy drives the flux of material from one state of matter to another or from one reservoir of the Earth System to another. For example, heating ice causes **melting** (solid → liquid; cryosphere → hydrosphere) and heating water causes **evaporation** (liquid → gas; hydrosphere → atmosphere). Cooling slows the motion, causing **condensation** (gas → liquid, atmosphere → hydrosphere) or **freezing** (liquid → solid, hydrosphere → cryosphere).

Name: _____   **Section:** _____

Course: _____   **Date:** _____

Even without a geology course, you already have a sense of how water moves from one reservoir to another in the Earth System. Based on your experience with natural phenomena on Earth, complete the following table that describes fluxes associated with the *hydrologic cycle*. First describe what happens in the process using plain language, then describe how matter may have moved between Earth's reservoirs. The first example is given.

Process	What happens?	Did matter change reservoir? Movement from _____ to _____
Sublimation	*Solid ice becomes water vapor.*	*Yes. cryosphere to atmosphere*
Ice melting		
Evaporation of a puddle		
Water freezing		
Plants absorbing water		
Raindrop formation		
Cloud formation		
Steam erupting from a volcano		

Name: _____   Section: _____
Course: _____   Date: _____

Some of the heat that affects geologic processes comes from the Sun and some comes from inside the Earth. What role does each of these heat sources play in Earth processes?

(a) If you take off your shoes on a beach or any sandy environment and walk on it on a hot, sunny day, is the sand hot or cold? Why?

_____

• Now, dig down in the sand just a few inches. What do you feel now, and why?

_____

• What does this suggest about the depth to which heat from the Sun can penetrate the Earth?

_____

_____

• Based on this conclusion, is the Sun's energy or Earth's internal heat the cause of melting rock within the Earth? Explain.

_____

_____

(b) The deeper down one goes into mines or drill holes, the hotter it gets. This temperature increase is called the **geothermal gradient**. Does this phenomenon support or contradict your conclusion in (a)? Explain.

_____

_____

• In the upper 10 km of the crust, the geothermal gradient is typically about 25°C per km, but it can range from 15°C/km to 50°C/km. In the chart below, plot these three geothermal gradients (15°C/km, 25°C/km, and 50°C/km) for the upper 10 km of the Earth. Use one line for each gradient.

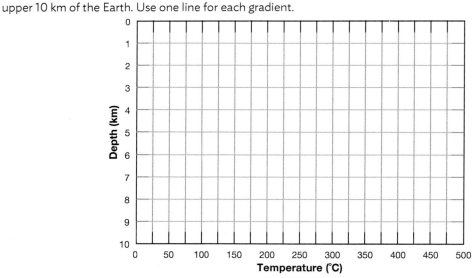

• The deepest mine on Earth penetrates to a depth of about 2 km. Using the geothermal gradients you just drew, what range of temperatures would you expect in the mine? Explain your answer. How hot is it in the bottom of this mine? What assumptions did you make to come up with this answer?

_____

_____

_____

Gravity, as Isaac Newton showed more than three centuries ago, is the force of attraction that every object exerts on other objects. The strength of this force depends on the amount of mass in each object and how close the objects are to one another. The greater the mass and the closer the objects are, the stronger the gravitational attraction. The smaller the mass and the farther apart the objects are, the weaker the attraction. The Sun's enormous mass produces a force of gravity sufficient to hold Earth and the other planets in their orbits. Earth's gravitational force is far less than the Sun's, but it is strong enough to hold the Moon in orbit, hold you on its surface, cause rain or volcanic ash to fall, and enable rivers and glaciers to flow.

1.3 Units for Scientific Measurement

Before we begin to examine components of the Earth System scientifically, we must first consider its dimensions and the units used to measure them. We can then examine the challenges of scale that geologists face when studying Earth and the atoms of which it is made.

1.3.1 Units of Length and Distance

If you described this book to a friend as being "big," would your friend have a clear picture of its size? Is it big compared to a quarter or to a car? Without providing a frame of reference for the word *big*, your friend wouldn't have enough information to visualize the book. A *scientific* description would much more accurately give the book's dimensions of length, width, and thickness using units of distance.

People have struggled for thousands of years to describe size in a precise way with standard units of measurement. Scientists everywhere and people in nearly all countries except the United States use the **metric system** to measure length and distance. The largest metric unit of length is the kilometer (km), which is divided into smaller units: 1 km = 1,000 meters (m); 1 m = 100 centimeters (cm); 1 cm = 10 millimeters (mm). Metric units differ from each other by a factor of 10, making it very easy to convert one unit into another. For example, 5 km = 5,000 m = 500,000 cm = 5,000,000 mm. Similarly, 5 mm = 0.5 cm = 0.005 m = 0.000005 km.

The United States uses the U.S. customary system (sometimes known as the English Unit System) to describe distance. Distances are given in miles (mi), yards (yd), feet (ft), and inches (in), where 1 mi = 5,280 ft; 1 yd = 3 ft; and 1 ft = 12 in. As scientists, we use metric units in this book, but when appropriate, equivalents are also given (in parentheses).

Appendix 1.1, at the end of this chapter, provides basic conversions between U.S. Customary and metric units.

1.3.2 Other Dimensions, Other Units

Distance is just one of the dimensions of the Earth that you will examine during this course. We still need other units to describe other aspects of the Earth, its processes, and its history: units of time, velocity, temperature, mass, and density.

Time is usually measured in seconds (s), minutes (min), hours (h), days (d), years (yr), centuries (hundreds of years), and millennia (thousands of years). A year is the amount of time it takes for the Earth to complete one orbit around the Sun. Because the Earth is very old, geologists also have to use much larger units of time: thousand years ago (abbreviated **ka**, for "kilo-annum"), million years ago (**Ma**, for "mega-annum"), and billion years ago (**Ga**, for "giga-annum"). The 4,570,000,000-year age of the Earth can thus be expressed as 4.57 Ga, or 4,570 Ma.

Velocity, or the rate of change of the position of an object, is described by units of distance divided by units of time, such as meters per second (m/s), feet per second (ft/s), kilometers per hour (km/h), or miles per hour (mph). You will learn later that the velocity at which geologic materials move ranges from extremely slow (mm/yr) to extremely fast (km/s).

Temperature is a measure of how hot an object is relative to a standard. It is measured in degrees Celsius (°C) in the metric system and degrees Fahrenheit (°F) in the U.S. customary system. The reference standards are the freezing and boiling points of water: 0°C and 100°C or 32°F and 212°F, respectively. Note that there are 180 Fahrenheit degrees between freezing and boiling but only 100 Celsius degrees. A change of 1°C is thus 1.8 times larger than a change of 1°F (180°/100°). To convert Fahrenheit to Celsius or vice versa, see Appendix 1.1.

Mass refers to the amount of matter in an object, and **weight** refers to the force with which one object is attracted to another. The weight of an object on Earth therefore depends not only on its mass but also on the strength of Earth's gravitational force. Objects that have more mass than others also weigh more on Earth because of the force of Earth's gravity. While the mass of an object remains the same whether it is on the Earth or on the Moon, the object *weighs* less on the Moon because of the Moon's weaker gravity.

Grams and kilograms (1 kg = 1,000 g) are the units of mass in the metric system; the U.S. Customary System uses pounds and ounces (1 lb = 16 oz). For those who don't read the metric equivalents on food packages, 1 kg = 2.2046 lb and 1 g = 0.0353 oz.

We saw earlier that the **density** (δ) of a material is a measure of how much mass is packed into each unit of volume, generally expressed as units of g/cm³. We instinctively distinguish unusually low-density materials like Styrofoam and feathers from low-density materials like water (δ = 1 g/cm³) and high-density materials like steel (δ = ~7 g/cm³) because the former feel very light *for their sizes* and the latter feel unusually heavy *for their sizes* (**FIG. 1.4**).

FIGURE 1.4 **Weight of materials with different densities.**

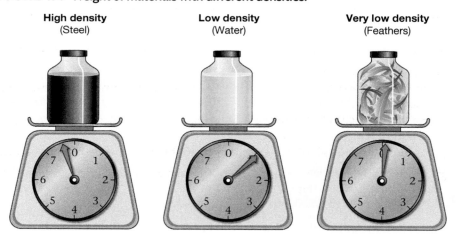

To measure the density of a material, we need to know its mass and volume. We measure mass on a balance or scale, and we can use simple mathematical formulas to determine the volumes of cubes, bricks, spheres, or cylinders. For example, to calculate the volume of a bar of gold, you would multiply its length times its width, times its height (**FIG. 1.5a**). But for an irregular chunk of rock, it is easiest to submerge the rock in a graduated cylinder partially filled with water. Measure the volume of water before the rock is added and then with the rock in the cylinder. The rock displaces a volume of water equivalent to its own volume, so simply subtract the volume of the water before the rock was added from that of the water plus rock to obtain the volume of the rock (**FIG. 1.5b**). The density of a rock can be calculated simply from the definition of density: density = mass ÷ volume.

FIGURE 1.5 **Measuring the volume of materials.**

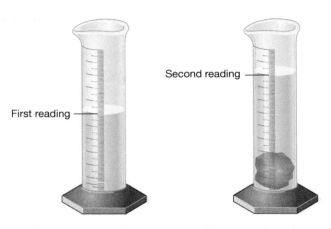

First reading

Second reading

(a) For a rectangular solid, volume = length × width × height.

(b) For an irregular solid, the volume of the rock is the volume of the displaced liquid, which equals the difference between the first and second readings.

Thousands of years ago, the Greek scientist Archimedes recognized that density determines whether an object floats or sinks when placed in a liquid. For example, icebergs float in the ocean because ice is less dense than water. Nearly all rocks sink when placed in water because the density of most rocks is at least 2.5 times greater than the density of water. Exercise 1.5 helps you practice your understanding of density.

EXERCISE 1.5   **Measuring the Density of Earth Materials**

Name: _____   Section: _____
Course: _____   Date: _____

(a) You are given a graduated cylinder, a balance, and a container of water. Determine the density of water. _____ g/cm^3

(b) Your instructor will provide you with two samples of rock: *granite*, a light-colored rock that makes up a large amount of the continental crust, and *basalt*, a dark-colored rock that makes up most of the oceanic crust and the lower part of the continental crust.
  • What is the density of granite?   _____ g/cm^3
  • What is the density of basalt?   _____ g/cm^3
  • What is the ratio of the density of granite to the density of basalt?   _____

(c) Most modern ships are made of steel, which has a density of about 7.85 g/cm^3. This is much greater than the density of water, so how can ships float?

_____

_____

1.4 Expressing Earth's "Vital Statistics" with Appropriate Units

Now that you are familiar with some of the units used to measure the Earth, we can look at some of the planet's "vital statistics."

■ *The Solar System:* Earth is the third planet from the Sun in a Solar System of eight planets (Pluto has been reclassified as a "dwarf planet"). It is one of four terrestrial planets, along with Mercury, Venus, and Mars, whose surfaces are made of rock rather than of frozen gases. Earth is, on average, 150,000,000 km (93,000,000 mi) from the Sun.

■ *Earth's orbit:* It takes Earth 1 year (365.25 days, or 3.15×10^7 seconds) to complete one slightly elliptical orbit around the Sun.

■ *Earth's rotation:* It takes Earth 1 day (24 hours, or 86,400 seconds) to rotate once on its axis. The two points where the axis intersects the surface of the planet are the north and south **geographic poles**. At present, Earth's axis is tilted at about 23.5° to the plane in which it orbits the Sun (the **plane of the ecliptic**), but Earth wobbles a bit so this tilt changes over time.

■ *Shape:* Our planet is almost, but not quite, a sphere. Earth's rotation causes it to bulge slightly at the equator. The equatorial radius of 6,400 km (~4,000 mi) is 21 km (~15 mi) longer than its polar radius.

■ *Temperature:* Earth's surface temperature ranges from 58°C (136°F) in deserts near the equator to −89°C (−129°F) near the South Pole. *Average* daily temperature in New York City ranges from 0°C (32°F) in the winter to 24°C (76°F) in the summer. The geothermal gradient is about 15°C to 30°C per km in the upper crust, and temperatures may reach 5000°C at the center of the Earth.

■ *Some additional dimensions:* The highest mountain on Earth is Mt. Everest, at 8,850 m (29,035 ft) above sea level. The average depth of the world's oceans is about 4,500 m (14,700 ft), and the deepest point on the ocean floor—the bottom of the Mariana Trench in the Pacific Ocean—is 11,033 m (35,198 ft) below the surface. The *relief,* the vertical distance between the highest and lowest points, is thus just a little less than 20 km (12 mi). It would take only about 10 minutes to drive this distance at highway speed! This relief is extremely small compared to the overall size of the planet.

1.5 The Challenge of Scale when Studying a Planet

Geologists deal routinely with objects as incredibly small as atoms and others as incredibly large as the Appalachian Mountains or the Pacific Ocean. Sometimes we have to look at a feature at different scales, as in FIGURE 1.6a, b, to understand it fully.

FIGURE 1.6 **The white cliffs of Dover, seen at two different scales.**

(a) The chalk cliffs of Dover, England; the person in the foreground gives an idea of the size of the cliffs.

(b) Microscopic view of the chalk (plankton shells) that the cliffs are made of. The eye of a needle gives an idea of the minuscule sizes of the shells that make up the cliffs.

The challenge of scale is often a matter of perspective: to a flea, the dog on which it lives is its entire world; but to a parasite inside the flea, the flea is *its* entire world. For most of our history, humans have had a flea's-eye view of the world, unable to recognize its dimensions or shape from our vantage point on its surface. As a result, we once thought Earth was flat and at the center of the Solar System. It's easy to laugh at such misconceptions now, but Exercise 1.6 gives a feeling for the challenges of scale that still exist.

1.5.1 Scientific Notation and Orders of Magnitude

Geologists must cope with the enormous ranges in the scale of distance (atoms to sand grains to planets), temperature (below 0°C in the cryosphere and upper atmosphere to more than 1000°C in some lavas, to millions of degrees Celsius in the Sun), and velocity (continents moving at 2 cm/yr to light moving at 299,792 km/s). We sometimes describe scale in approximate terms, and sometimes more precisely. For example, the terms *mega-scale*, *meso-scale*, and *micro-scale* denote enormous, moderate, and tiny features, respectively, but don't tell exactly how large or small they are, because they depend on a scientist's frame of reference. For example, *mega-scale* to an astronomer might mean intergalactic distances, but to a geologist it may mean the size of a continent or a mountain range. *Micro-scale* could refer to a sand grain, a bacterium, or an atom. Geologists commonly approximate scale in terms that clearly specify the frame of reference. For example, your instructor may use "outcrop-scale" for a feature in a single exposure of rock or "hand-specimen-scale" for a rock the size of your fist. Exercise 1.6 helps you practice with scale.

EXERCISE 1.6 **The Challenge of Perspective and Visualizing Scale**

Name: _____ Section: _____
Course: _____ Date: _____

The enormous difference in size between ourselves and our planet gives us a limited perspective on large-scale features and makes understanding major Earth processes challenging. To appreciate this challenge, consider the relative sizes of familiar objects (use Appendix 1.1 for conversions):

1 mm

1 m

Relative sizes of a dog and a flea.

12,800 km

2 m

Relative sizes of the Earth and a tall human being.

(a) Assume that the flea is 1 mm long and that a dog is 1 m long.
  • To relate this to our English system of measurement, how long is this flea in inches? _____ in
  • How many times larger is the dog than the flea? _____
  • How long is the bar scale representing the flea? _____
  • How long would the bar representing the dog have to be, if the dog and the flea were shown at the same scale? _____

(continued)

Name: _____   Section: _____

Course: _____   Date: _____

(b) Now, think about the relative dimensions of a geologist and the Earth.
   • How many times larger than the geologist is the Earth? _____
   • How large would the drawing of the Earth have to be, if it were drawn at the same scale as the geologist? Give your answer in kilometers and in miles. _____ km _____ mi
   • Based on the relative sizes of flea and dog versus human and Earth, does a flea have a better understanding of a dog than a human has of the Earth? Or vice versa? Explain.

   _____

   _____

   _____

Geologists use a system based on powers of 10 to describe things spanning the entire range of scales that we study, sometimes using the phrase **orders of magnitude** to indicate differences in scale. A feature that is an order of magnitude larger than another is 10 times larger; a feature one-tenth the size of another is an order of magnitude *smaller*. Something 100 times the size of another is two orders of magnitude larger, and so on. **TABLE 1.2** shows that the range of dimensions in our Universe spans an almost incomprehensible 44 orders of magnitude, from the diameter of the particles that make up an atom (about 10^{-18} m across) to the radius of the observable Universe (about 10^{26} m).

TABLE 1.2   Orders of magnitude defining lengths in the Universe (in meters).

$\sim 2 \times 10^{26}$	Radius of the observable Universe
2.1×10^{22}	Distance to the nearest galaxy (Andromeda)
9.0×10^{20}	Diameter of the Milky Way
1.5×10^{11}	Diameter of Earth's orbit
6.4×10^{6}	Radius of the Earth
5.1×10^{6}	East–west length of the United States
8.8×10^{3}	Height of Mt. Everest above sea level (Earth's tallest mountain)
1.7×10^{0}	Average height of an adult human
1.0×10^{-3}	Diameter of a pinhead
6.0×10^{-4}	Diameter of a living cell
2.0×10^{-6}	Diameter of a virus
1.0×10^{-10}	Diameter of a hydrogen atom (the smallest atom)
1.1×10^{-14}	Diameter of a uranium atom's nucleus
1.6×10^{-15}	Diameter of a proton (a building block of an atomic nucleus)
$\sim 1 \times 10^{-18}$	Diameter of an electron (a smaller building block of an atom)

We simplify the numbers that describe such a wide range with a method called **scientific notation** based on powers of 10. In scientific notation, 1 is written as 10^0, 10 as 10^1, 100 as 10^2, and so on. Numbers less than 1 are shown by negative exponents: for example, $\frac{1}{10} = 0.1 = 10^{-1}$; $\frac{1}{100} = 0.01 = 10^{-2}$; and $\frac{1}{1,000} = 0.001 = 10^{-3}$. A positive exponent tells how many places the decimal point has to be moved to the right of the number, and a negative exponent how many places to the left.

In scientific notation, the 150,000,000-km (93,000,000-mi) distance from the Earth to the Sun is written as 1.5×10^8 km (9.3×10^7 mi)—start with 1.5 and move the decimal eight places to the *right*, adding zeroes as needed. Similarly, a small number such as 0.0000034 would be written as 3.4×10^{-6} (start with 3.4 and move the decimal six places to the *left*, adding zeroes as needed).

Exercise 1.7 practices scientific notation and gives a sense of our perspective relative to the Earth's basic processes.

EXERCISE 1.7 **Moving Along**

Name: _____ Section: _____
Course: _____ Date: _____

Complete the following calculations to get a sense of the distances that the Earth travels and the speed at which it moves.

45° N

150,000,000 km

Person 2

(6,400 km)

Person 1

Earth's orbit. Earth orbits the Sun in an elliptical path. To simplify calculation, here we assume a circular orbit with a radius of 150,000,000 km (93,000,000 mi).

Earth's rotation. Earth rotates on its axis every 24 hours.

(a) For simplicity, in this exercise we picture the Earth's orbit around the Sun as a circle, with a radius of 150,000,000 km (93 million mi). It takes 1 year for the Earth to orbit the Sun.
- What distance does the Earth travel during a single complete orbit? Remember that the circumference of a circle is $2\pi r$, and that $\pi \approx 3.14$. Orbital distance = _____ km (_____ mi).
- What is the velocity of the Earth as it orbits the Sun? Give your answer in both kilometers per hour and miles per hour. _____ km/h _____ mph
- Express the above results using scientific notation. _____ km/h _____ mph

(b) Earth rotates on its axis in 1 day. At what velocity is a person standing at the equator in the figure above (Person 1) moving due to our planet's rotation? _____ km/h _____ mph

(c) Now consider a person standing on Earth's surface at a point halfway between the equator and the geographic pole (Person 2). Is this person moving faster or slower than the person standing at the equator? Explain your answer.

_____

_____

(continued)

Name: _____   Section: _____

Course: _____   Date: _____

(d) Many components of the Earth System are too *small* for us to comprehend. For example, atoms are too small to be seen even with the most powerful optical microscope. A sodium atom has an approximate diameter of 2×10^{-8} cm. The diameter of the period at the end of this sentence is approximately 4×10^{-4} cm.

- If you lined up sodium atoms one next to the other, how many sodium atoms would it take to span the diameter of a period? _____ Express this number in scientific notation: _____
- How many orders of magnitude larger is the period than the atom? _____

1.5.2 Coping with Scale Problems: Maps, Diagrams, and Models

Figure 1.6 showed how we use microscopes to help see very *small* features. One way to cope with the challenge of very *large* geologic features is to construct scale models like that in **FIGURE 1.7a**. Using these models, we can re-create the conditions of floods or the ground shaking during earthquakes to understand these processes better. Scaled-down diagrams like the one of the geothermal gradient in Exercise 1.4 help show relationships within the Earth, and we use maps, aerial photographs, and satellite images to visualize the Earth's surface (**FIG. 1.7b**). Depending on the degree to which we scale down the area, these images can show the entire Earth on a single sheet of paper or just the part of it we wish to study. If you have a good high-speed Internet connection, you can download *Google Earth*™ or *NASA World Wind* to see spectacular images of any part of the world at almost any scale. Exercise 1.8 gives simple examples of how scaled-down maps and diagrams are made.

FIGURE 1.7 Coping with scale problems associated with very large features.

(a) A scale model of St. Paul Harbor, Alaska, used to study water and sediment movement.

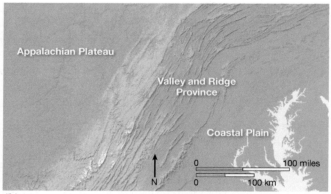

(b) Maps scale down portions of the Earth to make them easier to visualize and understand.

Scaling Down Features to Visualize Them

Name: _____   Section: _____

Course: _____   Date: _____

(a) The United Kingdom is about 900 km long from north to south. By how many orders of magnitude would you have to scale down a map of the United Kingdom so it would fit on a sheet of paper 20 cm long? _____

(b) Earth's radius is about 6,500 km. Using a compass and ruler, draw a cross section of the Earth in the left-hand box below, using Point E to locate the center of the Earth. *Indicate the scale that you used in the lower left corner of the box.*

(c) The Moon has a radius of 1,750 km. At the same scale that you used in (a), draw a cross section of the Moon in the right-hand box below, using Point M to locate the center of the Moon.

(d) Compare the size of the Moon with that of Earth's core, which has a radius of 3,400 km. Which is larger and by approximately how much?

_____

• E

• M

■■■■ _____ km

1.6 The Challenge of Working with Geologic Time

Geologists have amassed a large body of evidence showing that Earth is about 4.57 billion years old (4,570,000,000, or 4.57×10^9 years). This enormous span is referred to as **geologic time** (**FIG. 1.8**), and understanding its vast scope is nearly impossible for humans, who live less than 100 years. Our usual frame of reference for time is based on human lifetimes: a war fought two centuries ago happened two lifetimes ago, and 3,000-year-old monuments were built about 30 lifetimes ago. To help visualize geologic time, we can compare its scale to more familiar dimensions. For example, if geologic time (4.57 billion years) was represented by a 1-km-long field, each millimeter would represent 4,570 years, each centimeter 45,700 years, and each meter 4,570,000 years. If all of geologic time was condensed to a single year, each second would represent 145 years. Exercise 1.9 helps demonstrate this scale.

Name: _____ Section: _____

Course: _____ Date: _____

Complete the following calculations to appreciate the duration of geologic time and how slow processes can lead to major changes.

(a) If you want to represent the 4.57 billion years of geologic time with a roll of masking tape so that 1 inch represents 1 million years, how long would the tape have to be? *Answer using scientific notation.* _____ in _____ mi _____ km

(b) If you want to represent geologic time with a 24-hour clock, how many years would be represented by a single second? _____ a minute? _____ an hour? _____

(c) If you saved a penny a day, how long would it take you to save $1 million? _____ days
 • If you collected a penny a year for a hundred years, how much money would you have? $ _____
 • How much would you have in a million years? $ _____ a billion years? $ _____

FIGURE 1.8 **Geologic time line.** Milestones in the history of the Earth.

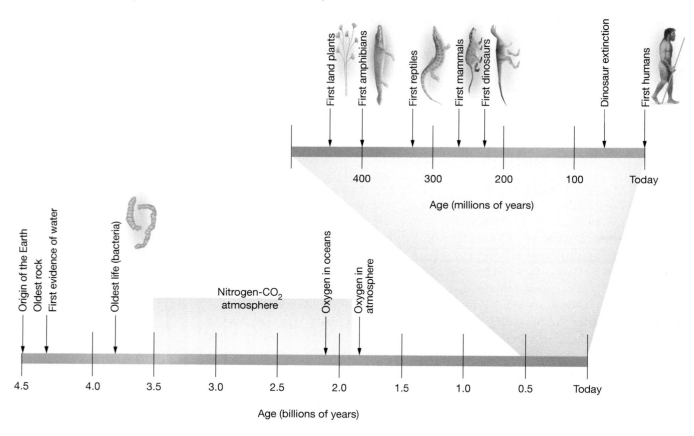

1.6.1 Uniformitarianism: The Key to Understanding the Geologic Past

The challenge in studying Earth history is that many of the processes that made the rocks, mountains, and oceans we see today occurred millions or billions of years ago. How can we figure out what those processes were if they happened so long ago? The answer came nearly 300 years ago when a Scottish geologist, James Hutton,

FIGURE 1.9 The principle of uniformitarianism.

(a) Ripple marks in 145-million-year-old sandstone at Dinosaur Ridge, Colorado.

(b) Ripple marks in modern sand on the shore of Cape Cod, Massachusetts.

noted that some features observed in rocks resembled those forming in modern environments (**FIG. 1.9a, b**). For example, the sand on a beach or a stream's bed commonly forms a series of ridges called ripple marks. You can see identical ripple marks preserved in ancient layers of sandstone, a rock made of sand grains.

Based on his observations, Hutton proposed the **principle of uniformitarianism** as a basis for interpreting Earth history. According to uniformitarianism, most ancient geologic features formed by the same processes as modern ones. The more we know about the physical and chemical processes by which modern features form, the more we can say about the ancient processes. This principle is often stated more succinctly as "the present is the key to the past."

1.6.2 Rates of Geologic Processes

Many geologic processes occur so slowly that it's difficult to know they are happening. For example, mountains rise and are worn away (**eroded**) at rates of about 1 to 1.5 *mm*/yr, and continents move about one to two orders of magnitude faster—1 to 15 *cm*/yr. Some geologic processes are much faster. A landslide or volcanic eruption can happen in minutes; an earthquake may be over in seconds; and a meteorite impact takes just a fraction of a second.

Before the significance of uniformitarianism became clear, scholars thought that Earth was about 6,000 years old. Uniformitarianism made scientists rethink this estimate and consider the possibility that the planet is much older. When geologists observed that it takes a very long time for even a thin layer of sand to be deposited or for erosion to deepen a modern river valley, they realized that it must have taken much more than all of human history to deposit the layers of rock in the Grand Canyon. Indeed, the submergence of coastal Maine discussed at the opening of this chapter turns out to be one of the *faster* geologic processes. Understanding rates of geologic processes thus helped us recognize Earth's vast age hundreds of years before the discovery of radioactivity enabled us to measure the age of a rock in years.

Small changes can have big results when they are repeated over enormous spans of time, as shown by Exercise 1.9. And at the very slow rates at which some geologic processes take place, familiar materials may behave in unfamiliar ways. For example, if you drop an ice cube on your kitchen floor, it behaves brittlely and shatters into pieces. But given time and the weight resulting from centuries of accumulation, ice in a glacier can flow plastically at tens of meters a year (**FIG. 1.10a**). Under geologic conditions and over long enough periods, even layers of solid rock can be bent into folds like those seen in **FIGURE 1.10b**.

FIGURE 1.10 Solid Earth materials change shape over long periods under appropriate conditions.

(a) Athabasca Glacier, Alberta, Canada.

(b) Folded sedimentary rocks in eastern Ireland.

1.6.3 "Life Spans" of Mountains and Oceans

You will learn later that mountains and oceans are not permanent landscape features. Mountains form by uplift or intense folding, but as soon as land rises above the sea, running water, ice, and wind begin to erode it away. When the forces that cause the uplift cease, the mountains are gradually leveled by the forces of erosion. Oceans are also temporary features. They form when continents split and the pieces move apart from one another, and they disappear when the continents on their margins collide. Exercise 1.10 explores the rates at which mountains and oceans form and are then destroyed.

EXERCISE 1.10   **Rates of Mountain and Ocean Formation**

Name: _____   Section: _____

Course: _____   Date: _____

(a) **Rates of uplift and erosion.** The following questions give you a sense of the rates at which uplift and erosion take place. We will assume that uplift and erosion do not occur at the same time—that the mountains are first uplifted and only then does erosion begin—whereas the two processes actually operate simultaneously.
  - If mountains rose by 1 mm/yr, how high would they be (in meters) after 1,000 years? _____ m
    10,000,000 years? _____ m   50 million years? _____ m
  - The Himalayas now reach an elevation of 8.8 km, and radiometric dating suggests that their uplift began about 45 Ma. Assuming a constant rate of uplift, how fast did the Himalayas rise? _____ km/yr
    _____ m/yr   _____ mm/yr
  - Evidence shows that there were once Himalayan-scale mountains in northern Canada, an area now eroded nearly flat. If Earth were only 6,000 years old as was once believed, how fast would the rate of erosion have had to be for these mountains to be eroded to sea level in 6,000 years? _____ m/yr
    _____ mm/yr
  - Observations of modern mountain belts suggest that ranges erode at rates of 2 mm per 10 years. At this rate, how long would it take to erode the Himalayas down to sea level? _____ years

(b) **Rates of seafloor spreading.** Today the Atlantic Ocean is about 5,700 km wide at the latitude of Boston. At one time, however, there was no Atlantic Ocean because the east coast of the United States and the northwest coast of Africa were joined in a huge supercontinent. The Atlantic Ocean started to form "only" 185,000,000 years ago, as modern North America split from Africa and the two slowly drifted apart in a process called *seafloor spreading*.
  - Assuming that the rate of seafloor spreading has been constant, at what rate has North America been moving away from Africa? _____ mm per year   _____ km per million years

---

1.7 Applying the Basics to Interpreting the Earth

The concepts presented in this chapter are the foundations for understanding the topics that will be covered throughout this course. This section shows how you can apply these concepts with a little geologic reasoning to arrive at significant conclusions about the Earth.

1.7.1 Pressure in the Earth

The pull of Earth's gravity produces **pressure**. For example, the pull of gravity on the atmosphere creates a pressure of 1.03 kg/cm^2 (14.7 lb/in^2) at sea level. This means that every square centimeter of the ocean, the land, or your body is affected by a weight of 1.03 kg. We call this amount of pressure 1 **atmosphere** (atm). Scientists commonly specify pressures using a unit called the *bar* (from the Greek *barros*, meaning weight), where 1 bar ≈1 atm. Two kinds of pressure play important roles in the hydrosphere and geosphere. **Hydrostatic pressure**, pressure caused by the weight of water, increases as you descend into the ocean and can crush a submarine in the deep ocean. **Lithostatic pressure**, pressure caused by the weight of overlying rock, increases as you go deeper in the geosphere and is great enough in the upper mantle to change the graphite in a pencil into diamond. The rate at which lithostatic pressure increases is called the **geobaric gradient**, which along with the geothermal gradient plays a major role in determining what materials can exist at depth. Lithostatic pressures are so great that we must measure them in **kilobars** (Kbar), where 1 Kbar = 1,000 bars. Exercise 1.11 shows how pressure varies in the Earth.

EXERCISE 1.11 | **Thinking about Pressure in the Earth**

Name: _____   Section: _____
Course: _____   Date: _____

Hydrostatic and lithostatic pressures are caused by the weight of the overlying water and rock, respectively, and these pressures, in turn, depend on the density of the overlying material. You calculated earlier that water has a density of 1 g/cm^3, whereas rock in the crust beneath continents has an average density of about 2.8 g/cm^3.

(a) Why does lithostatic pressure increase more rapidly with depth than hydrostatic pressure?

_____

_____

_____

(b) The geobaric gradient beneath continents is about 1 Kbar for every 3.3 km of depth.
  • On the top of the diagram used in Exercise 1.4 for the *geothermal* gradient, construct a scale showing pressure from 1 to 3 Kbar and draw the *geobaric* gradient in a different color.
  • What is the lithostatic pressure at a depth of 8 km below the surface of a continent? _____ Kbar
  • What are the temperature and pressure conditions in the Earth at a depth of 3.5 km?
    _____ °C   at 5.6 km? _____ °C
    _____ Kbar   _____ Kbar

Metric–English Conversion Chart

To convert U.S. Customary units to metric units	To convert metric units to U.S. Customary units
Length or distance inches × 2.54 = centimeters feet × 0.3048 = meters yards × 0.9144 = meters miles × 1.6093 = kilometers	centimeters × 0.3937 = inches meters × 3.2808 = feet meters × 1.0936 = yards kilometers × 0.6214 = miles
Area in^2 × 6.452 = cm^2 ft^2 × 0.929 = m^2 mi^2 × 2.590 = km^2	cm^2 × 0.1550 = in^2 m^2 × 10.764 = ft^2 km^2 × 0.3861 = mi^2
Volume in^3 × 16.3872 = cm^3 ft^3 × 0.02832 = m^3 U.S. gallons × 3.7853 = liters	cm^3 × 0.0610 = in^3 m^3 × 35.314 = ft^3 liters × 0.2642 = U.S. gallons
Mass ounces × 28.3495 = grams pounds × 0.45359 = kilograms	grams × 0.03527 = ounces kilograms × 2.20462 = pounds
Density lb/ft^3 × 0.01602 = g/cm^3	g/cm^3 × 62.4280 = lb/ft^3
Velocity ft/s × 0.3048 = m/s mph × 1.6093 = km/h	m/s × 3.2804 = ft/s km/h × 0.6214 = mph
Temperature 0.55 × (°F − 32) = °C	(1.8 × °C) + 32 = °F
Pressure lb/in^2 × 0.0703 = kg/cm^2	kg/cm^2 × 14.2233 = lb/in^2
For U.S. Customary units 1 foot (ft) = 12 inches (in) 1 yard (yd) = 3 feet 1 mile (mi) = 5,280 feet	**For metric units** 1 centimeter = 10 millimeters (mm) 1 meter (m) = 100 centimeters 1 kilometer (km) = 1,000 meters 1 milliliter (ml) = 1 cm^3

2

The Way the Earth Works: Examining Plate Tectonics

A path through the Þingvellir Valley in Iceland, the location of a rift valley that marks the crest of the Mid-Atlantic Ridge.

2.1 Introduction

Earthquakes and volcanic eruptions show that Earth is a dynamic planet with enough energy beneath its surface to cause disasters for those who live on its surface. For thousands of years humans wondered about the causes of these events, until the 1960s and 1970s when geologists developed the **theory of plate tectonics**— a unifying theory that answered geologic questions that had puzzled us for many years. Plate tectonics explains the outer layer of the Earth as a group of separate plates that move with respect to each other and change the Earth's surface as they move. At first it was difficult to accept the concept that Earth's oceans, continents, and mountains are only temporary features that move and change over time, as the proposed changes are so slow that they could not be detected. Yet, according to the plate tectonics theory, planet-wide processes break continents apart, open and close oceans, and build and shrink great mountain chains. Local earthquakes and volcanoes are simply results of energy released as these processes occur.

No one ridicules plate tectonics now because evidence proved these processes are happening today, and geologists showed that these processes have been operating for billions of years. In this chapter, we will explore the evidence and the geologic reasoning that led to the plate tectonics theory.

2.2 The Plate Tectonics Theory

Plate tectonics is based on many kinds of information about the Earth that you will examine during this course, including the origin and distribution of different rock types, the topography of the continents and ocean basins, and the geographic distribution of earthquakes and volcanic eruptions. The basic concepts of the theory include the following:

- Earth's crust and the uppermost part of the layer below it, called the **mantle**, form a relatively rigid outermost layer called the **lithosphere** that extends to a depth of 100 to 150 km.

- The lithosphere is not a single shell, but consists of several large pieces called **lithosphere plates** or simply, **plates** (**FIG. 2.1**). There are about 12 major

FIGURE 2.1 Earth's major lithosphere plates.

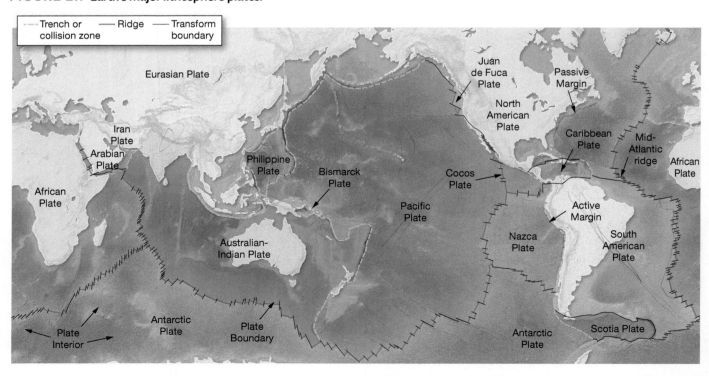

plates that are thousands of kilometers wide and several minor plates that are hundreds of kilometers wide.

▪ Continental lithosphere is thicker than oceanic lithosphere because continental crust alone (without the mantle component) is 25 to 70 km thick, whereas the oceanic crust is only about 7 km thick.

▪ The plates rest on the **asthenosphere**, a zone in the upper mantle (**FIG. 2.2**) that, although solid, has such low rigidity that it can flow like soft plastic. The asthenosphere acts as a lubricant, permitting the plates above it to move. Plates move relative to one another at 1 to 15 cm/yr, roughly the rate at which fingernails grow.

FIGURE 2.2 Cross section showing activity at convergent, divergent, and transform plate boundaries. At divergent boundaries (ocean ridges), new lithosphere is created; at convergent boundaries (subduction zones or areas of continent-continent-collision), old lithosphere is destroyed; and at transform faults (neutral plate boundaries), lithosphere is neither created nor destroyed.

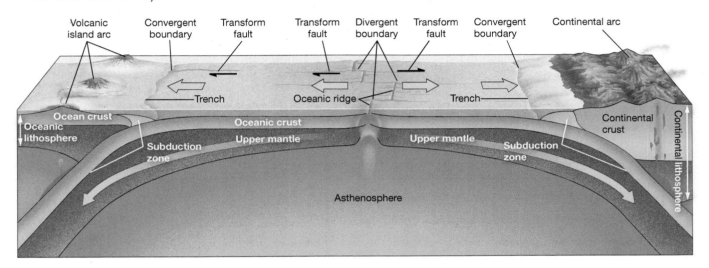

▪ A place where two plates make contact is called a **plate boundary**, and in some places *three* plates come together at a **triple junction**. There are three different kinds of plate boundaries, defined by the relative motions of the adjacent plates (Figs. 2.1 and 2.2):

1. At a **divergent plate boundary**, plates move away from one another at the axis of submarine mountain ranges called **mid-ocean ridges**, or oceanic ridges. Molten material rises from the asthenosphere to form new oceanic lithosphere at the ridge axis. The ocean grows wider through this process, called **seafloor spreading**, during which the new lithosphere moves outward from the axis to the flanks of the ridge.

2. At a **convergent plate boundary**, two plates move toward each other, and the oceanic lithosphere of one plate sinks (the subducted plate) into the mantle below the other (the overriding plate) in **subduction zones**. The lithosphere of the overriding plate may be oceanic or continental. The boundary between the two plates is a deep-ocean **trench**. At a depth of about 150 km, gases (mostly steam) released from the heated, subducted plate rise into the lower lithosphere. These gases help melt the lower mantle component of the lithosphere, and the resulting magma rises to the surface to produce volcanoes as either a **volcanic island arc** (like the Japanese Islands), where the overriding plate is made of oceanic lithosphere, or as a **continental arc** (like the Andes Mountains), where the overriding plate is made of continental lithosphere.

3. At a **transform boundary**, two plates slide past one another along a vertical zone of fracturing called a **transform fault**. Most transform faults break ocean ridges into segments and are also called *oceanic fracture zones*. A few, however, such as the San Andreas Fault in California, the Alpine Fault in New Zealand, and the Great Anatolian Fault in Turkey, cut through continental plates.

■ Continental crust cannot be subducted because it is too buoyant to "sink" into the mantle. When subduction completely consumes an oceanic plate between two continents, **continental collision** occurs, forming a **collisional mountain belt** like the Himalayas, Alps, or Appalachians. Folding during the collision thickens the crust to the extent that the thickest continental crust is found in these mountains.

■ **Continental rifts** are places where continental lithosphere is stretched and pulled apart in the process of breaking apart at a new divergent margin. If rifting is "successful," a continent splits into two pieces separated by a new oceanic plate, which gradually widens by seafloor spreading.

■ In the **tectonic cycle**, new oceanic lithosphere is created at the oceanic ridges, moves away from the ridges during seafloor spreading, and returns to the mantle in subduction zones. Oceanic lithosphere is neither created nor destroyed at transform faults, where movement is almost entirely horizontal.

EXERCISE 2.1	**Recognizing Plates and Plate Boundaries**

Name: _____   Section: _____

Course: _____   Date: _____

Using Figure 2.1 as a reference, answer the following questions:

(a) What is the name of the plate on which the United States resides? _____

(b) Does this plate consist of continental lithosphere? Oceanic lithosphere? Or both? _____

(c) Where does the lithosphere of the Atlantic Ocean form? _____

(d) What kind of plate boundary occurs along the west coast of South America? _____

(e) Is the west coast of Africa a plate boundary? _____

2.3 Early Evidence for Plate Tectonics

A simple problem of scale and this low rate of plate movement delayed the discovery of plate tectonics until the late 1960s: lithosphere plates are so big and move so slowly that we didn't realize they were moving. Today there is no question because global positioning satellites and sensitive instruments can measure their directions and rates. We will look at some of the evidence that led geologists to accept the hypothesis that plates move and then see how we deduce the nature and rates of processes at the three types of plate boundaries.

2.3.1 Evidence from the Fit of the Continents

As far back as 500 years ago, mapmakers drawing the coastlines of South America and Africa noted that the two continents looked as if they might have fit together once in a larger continent. Those foolish enough to say it out loud were ridiculed, but today this fit is considered one of the most obvious lines of evidence for plate tectonics. You will explore this in the following exercise.

Name: _____   Section: _____
Course: _____   Date: _____

In this exercise, you will examine the shorelines of South America and Africa for evidence of the theory of plate tectonics.

(a) Sketch the shorelines of South America and Africa from the figure below on separate pieces of tracing paper. Rearrange the continents so that they fit as well as possible without overlapping or leaving large gaps. How well do the continents fit? Where are the problem areas?

_____

_____

(b) Are the current shorelines of South America and Africa accurate representations of those continents when they were rifted apart? What factors other than rifting and seafloor spreading could have modified the shape of the current shorelines?

_____

_____

Physiographic map of the South Atlantic Ocean floor and adjacent continents.

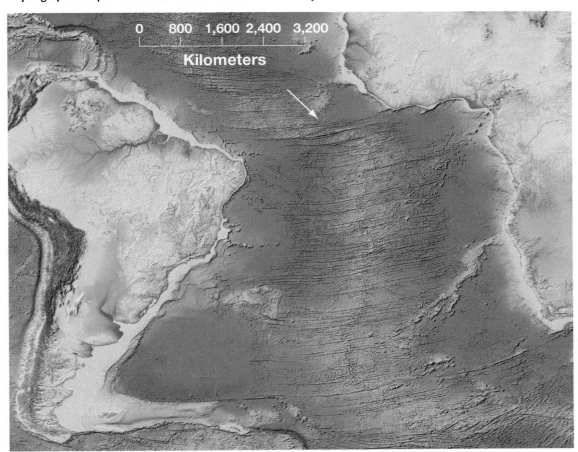

(continued)

Name: _____   Section: _____

Course: _____   Date: _____

(c) Trace the outlines of the continents again, this time using the edges of their continental shelves (the shallow, flat areas adjacent to the land) rather than the shoreline, and attempt to join them. Which reconstruction produces the best fit? In what ways is it better than the other?

_____

_____

_____

(d) Based on this evidence, what is the true edge of a continent?

_____

(e) When you fit the continents together, you could rotate them however you wished. However, this figure also contains clues that show exactly how Africa and South America spread apart. Place the *best-fit* tracings of South America and Africa over those continents on the figure. Now bring them closer to one another until they join, *using the oceanic fracture zones to guide the direction in which you move the two plates.* Do the continents fit well when moved this way?

_____

(f) What does this suggest about the age and origin of the fracture zones?

_____

_____

_____

2.3.2 Evidence from Reconstructing Paleoclimate Belts

FIGURE 2.3 **Earth's major climate zones.**

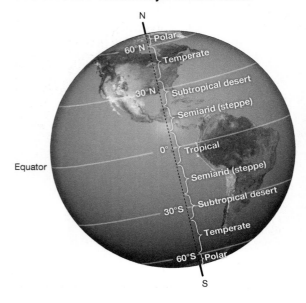

Earth's climate zones are distributed symmetrically about the equator today (**FIG. 2.3**), and the tropical, temperate, and polar zones support animals and plants unique to each environment. For example, walruses live in Alaska but palm trees don't, and large coral reefs grow in the Caribbean Sea but not in the Arctic Ocean. Climate zones also produce distinctive rock types: regional sand dunes and salt deposits form in arid regions, rocks made of debris deposited by continental glaciers accumulate in polar regions, and coal-producing plants grow in temperate and tropical forests.

However, geologists have found many rocks and fossils far outside the modern climate belts where we expect them to form. For example, 390-million-year-old (390-Ma) limestone containing reef-building organisms crops out along the entire Appalachian Mountain chain, some far north of where reefs exist today; 420-Ma salt underlies humid, temperate Michigan, Ohio, and New York; and deposits of 260- to 280-Ma continental glaciers are found in near-equatorial Africa, South America, India, and Madagascar.

According to the principle of uniformitarianism, these ancient salt deposits, reefs, and glacial deposits should have formed in locations similar to those where they form today. Either uniformitarianism doesn't apply to these phenomena or the landmasses have moved from their original climate zone into another. Observations like these led Alfred Wegener, a German meteorologist, to suggest in the 1920s that the continents had moved—a process he called *continental drift*. Modern geologists interpret these anomalies as the result of plate motion—when continents change position on the globe by moving apart during seafloor spreading or by coming together as subduction closes an ocean.

2.3.3 Geographic Distribution of Earthquakes and Active Volcanoes

By the mid-1800s, scientists realized that Earth's active volcanoes are not distributed randomly. Most are concentrated in narrow belts near the edges of continents, like the chain called the Ring of Fire surrounding the Pacific Ocean, while the centers of most continents have none (FIG. 2.4). In the late 1900s, technological advances provided new insights into the nature of the ocean floors, and we learned that submarine volcanoes are found in every major ocean basin.

More clues soon came from seismologists (geologists who study earthquakes). Records of where earthquakes occurred over a certain X period of time revealed a pattern. While this pattern (FIG. 2.5) was more complex than that for volcanoes, particularly in the deep ocean and continental interiors, it demonstrated important similarities. Something unique was happening along the volcanic chains and where earthquakes occurred, but geologists couldn't agree on what that was. Exercise 2.3 follows the reasoning geologists used to build the basic framework of the plate tectonic theory.

FIGURE 2.4 **Worldwide distribution of active volcanoes. The solid, orange line surrounds the Ring of Fire.**

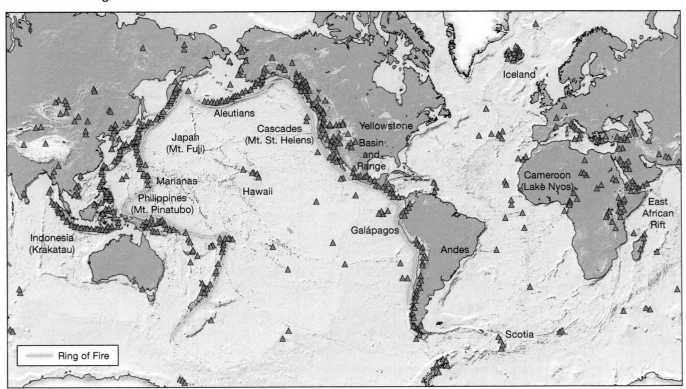

FIGURE 2.5 Worldwide distribution of earthquakes.

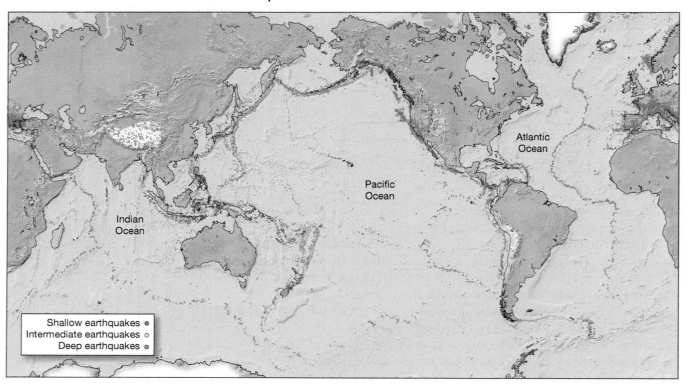

Atlantic
Ocean

Pacific
Ocean

Indian
Ocean

Shallow earthquakes •
Intermediate earthquakes ◦
Deep earthquakes •

EXERCISE 2.3 | **Putting the Early Evidence Together**

Name: _____   Section: _____
Course: _____   Date: _____

In this exercise, you will study Figures 2.4 and 2.5 in order to understand more of the initial reasoning for plate tectonics theory.

(a) Look at the volcanic and earthquake activity that occurred on the west coast of North America. How do these compare? Examine the earthquake and volcanic material in the center of the United States. How do these compare?

_____

_____

(b) Examine the chain of volcanoes and line of earthquakes in the middle of the Atlantic Ocean in Figures 2.4 and 2.5. From reading the past sections, describe what you believe is causing these. _____

_____

_____

(c) Geologists have found rocks and fossils of species native to Africa in South America and rocks and fossils native to South America in Africa. Considering your response to (b), explain what they theorized had happened.

_____

_____

2.4 Modern Evidence for Plate Tectonics

The geographic fit and paleoclimate evidence convinced some geologists that plate tectonics was a reasonable hypothesis, but more information was needed to convince the rest. That evidence came from an improved understanding of Earth's magnetic field, the ability to date ocean-floor rocks, careful examination of earthquake waves, and direct measurements of plate motion using global positioning satellites and other exciting new technologies. The full body of evidence has converted nearly all doubters to ardent supporters.

2.4.1 Evidence for Seafloor Spreading: Oceanic Magnetic Anomalies

Earth has a magnetic field that can be thought of as having "north" and "south" poles like a bar magnet (**FIG. 2.6**). Navigational compasses are aligned by magnetic lines of force that emanate from one pole and reenter the Earth at the other. The magnetic field has been known for centuries, but two discoveries about the field in the mid-twentieth century provided new insights about how the field works and, soon afterward, the evidence that confirmed the plate tectonic theory.

First, geologists learned that when grains of magnetite or hematite crystallize, they are aligned magnetically parallel to Earth's lines of force. Some rocks that contain magnetite or hematite therefore preserve a weak record of Earth's ancient magnetic field, a record called **paleomagnetism**. Then geologists learned that the magnetic field reverses polarity from time to time, so that what is now the north magnetic pole becomes the south magnetic pole and vice versa. During periods of **normal polarity**, the field is the same as it is today, but during periods of **reversed polarity**, a compass needle that points to today's north magnetic pole would swing around and point south. So by finding and determining the polarities of rocks throughout the world, geologists have accurately learned the dates of the magnetic reversals back to 4.0 Ma (**FIG. 2.7**).

This was interesting and certainly surprising, but how does it support plate tectonics? Earth's magnetic field varies irregularly on the continents, with a complex pattern of areas where the field is anomalously stronger or weaker than average (positive and negative **magnetic anomalies**). In contrast, research in the late 1960s discovered that the pattern of magnetic anomalies in the oceans is much simpler and more regular than that on the continents—parallel linear belts of positive and negative anomalies

FIGURE 2.6 Earth's magnetic field is defined by magnetic lines of force shown by the arrows.

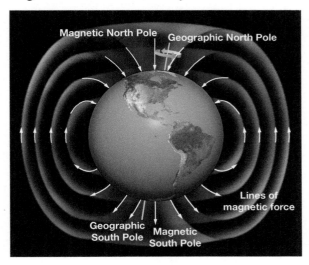

FIGURE 2.7 Radiometric dating of lava flows shows magnetic reversals for only the past 4 Ma.

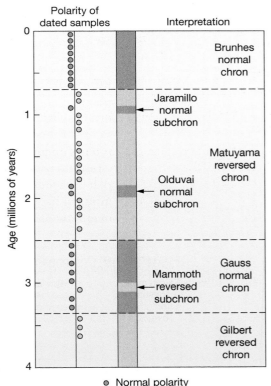

Major intervals of positive or negative polarity are called *chrons* and are named after scientists who contributed to the understanding of the magnetic field. Short-duration reversals are called *subchrons*.

FIGURE 2.8 **Magnetic anomaly stripes in the Atlantic and Pacific oceans.**

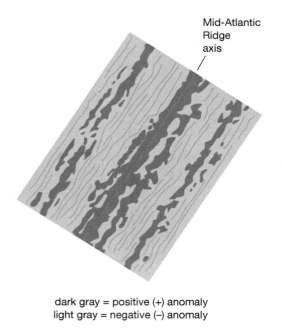

Mid-Atlantic
Ridge
axis

dark gray = positive (+) anomaly
light gray = negative (–) anomaly

(a) The Mid-Atlantic Ridge southwest of Iceland.

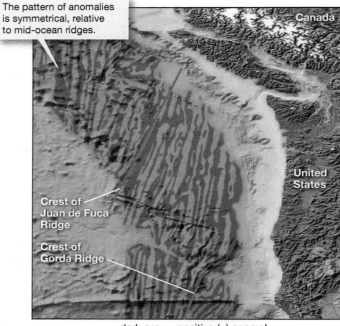

The pattern of anomalies is symmetrical, relative to mid-ocean ridges.

Canada

United States

Crest of
Juan de Fuca
Ridge

Crest of
Gorda Ridge

dark gray = positive (+) anomaly
light gray = negative (–) anomaly

(b) The Juan de Fuca and Gorda ridges in the North Pacific off the state of Washington and the province of British Columbia.

informally called **magnetic stripes** (FIG. 2.8a, b). The measured strength of the magnetic field in the oceans is the result of two components: (1) Earth's modern magnetic field strength and (2) the paleomagnetism (remanent magnetic field) of the oceanic crust. If the paleomagnetic polarity of a rock is the same as today's magnetic field, the rock's weak paleomagnetism *adds* to the modern field strength, resulting in an observed magnetic field *stronger* than today's field. If the paleomagnetic polarity is reversed, the rock's paleomagnetism *subtracts* from the modern field, and the result is a measurement *weaker* than the average modern magnetic field (FIG. 2.9).

FIGURE 2.9 **Components of Earth's magnetic field strength in the oceans.**

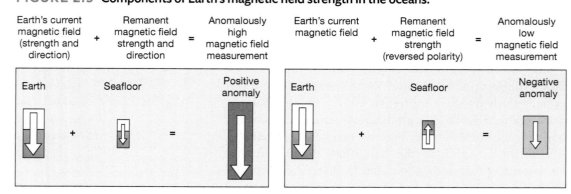

| Earth's current magnetic field (strength and direction) | + | Remanent magnetic field strength and direction | = | Anomalously high magnetic field measurement | | Earth's current magnetic field | + | Remanent magnetic field strength (reversed polarity) | = | Anomalously low magnetic field measurement |

Earth   Seafloor   Positive anomaly

Earth   Seafloor   Negative anomaly

This pattern of reversals has been found at every oceanic ridge, proving that the reversals are truly worldwide events, and this paleomagnetism was convincing evidence for seafloor spreading. As lava erupting at ocean ridges cools, it records the magnetic field polarity in effect at that time. If Earth's polarity reverses, new lava will adopt the new polarity, and the older lava will yield a negative magnetic anomaly as shown in Figure 2.9.

Using this information, Exercise 2.4 shows the reasoning by which geologists connected magnetic anomaly stripes in the oceans with the plate tectonic model.

EXERCISE 2.4   **Interpreting Ocean Ridge Magnetic Stripes**

Name: _____   Section: _____

Course: _____   Date: _____

In Figure 2.8a, compare the orientation of the magnetic anomaly stripes for the Mid-Atlantic Ridge with the orientation of the ridge crest (illustrated with a red line.) In Figure 2.8b, do the same for the Juan de Fuca Ridge and its anomalies.

(a) Are the individual anomalies oriented randomly? Are they parallel to the ridge crests? Oblique to the ridge crests?

_____

_____

_____

(b) Explain how the process of seafloor spreading can produce these orientations and relationships.

_____

_____

_____

(c) Some magnetic stripes are wider than others. Knowing what you do about seafloor spreading and magnetic reversals, suggest an explanation. _____

_____

_____

2.4.2 Direct Measurement of Plate Motion

Skeptics can no longer argue that Earth's major features are fixed in place. Satellite instruments can measure Earth's features with precision not even dreamed of 10 years ago, and they make it possible to measure the directions and rates of plate motion. Data for the major plates are shown in FIG 2.10. The length of each arrow indicates the relative rate of plate motion caused by seafloor spreading. We will see later how geologists were able to deduce the same information using other data.

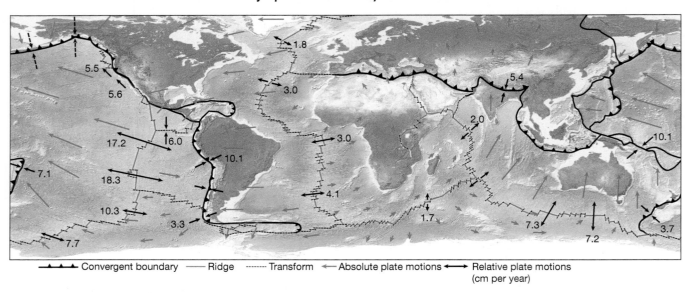

—▲—▲— Convergent boundary ——— Ridge ------- Transform ←— Absolute plate motions ←——→ Relative plate motions (cm per year)

2.5 Processes at Plate Boundaries Revealed in Earth Features

The next few exercises examine the three kinds of plate boundaries and show how geologists deduce details of their geometry, the rates of plate motion involved, and their histories. Let's start with information that we can gather about seafloor spreading.

EXERCISE 2.5 | **Estimating Seafloor Spreading Rates**

Name: _____ Section: _____

Course: _____ Date: _____

The South Atlantic Ocean formed by seafloor spreading at the Mid-Atlantic Ridge. Geologists can get a rough estimate of the spreading rate (i.e., the relative motion of South America with respect to Africa) by measuring the distance between the two continents in a direction parallel to the fracture zones and determining the time over which the spreading occurred.

(a) Measure the distance between South America and Africa along the fracture zone (indicated by the arrow) on the map in Exercise 2.2 (see p.29) _____ km

The oldest rocks in the South Atlantic Ocean, immediately adjacent to the African and South American continental shelves, are 120,000,000 years old.

(b) Calculate the average rate of seafloor spreading for the South Atlantic Ocean over its entire existence. Express your answer in _____ km/million years = _____ km/yr = _____ cm/yr = _____ mm/yr.

(c) Assuming someone born today lives to the age of 100, how much wider will the Atlantic Ocean become during his or her lifetime? _____ cm

---

2.5.1 Seafloor Spreading and Continental Rifting

These results dramatically demonstrate how slowly the South Atlantic Ocean is spreading and why plate tectonics met widespread disbelief initially. They also reinforce the importance of understanding the vast expanse of geologic time discussed in Chapter 1. Even extremely slow processes can have great impact given enough time to operate!

A new ocean forms when rifting takes place beneath a continent. The continental crust first thins and then breaks into two pieces separated by an oceanic ridge. As seafloor spreading proceeds, an ocean basin grows between the fragments of the original continent. This process is in an early stage today in eastern Africa.

Exercises 2.6, 2.7, and 2.8 examine these concepts and processes further.

EXERCISE 2.6 **Comparing Seafloor Spreading Rates of Different Ocean Ridges**

Name: _____ Section: _____
Course: _____ Date: _____

Magnetic reversals are found worldwide, so magnetic stripes should be the same width in every ocean *if the rate of seafloor spreading is the same at all ridges.* If a particular anomaly is wider in one ocean than another, however, it must result from faster spreading. The figure on the right shows simplified magnetic stripes from the South Atlantic and Pacific oceans, the ages of the rocks, and the distance from the spreading center (the red line). For simplicity, only the most recent 80 million years of data are shown for the two oceans, and we will only estimate the spreading rate for that time span.

(a) Measure the width of the South Atlantic
Ocean _____ km

(b) Estimate the average rate at which the South Atlantic Ridge has been opening over the 80 million years for which data are provided. _____cm/yr.

(c) Now look at the data for the South Pacific Ocean and its spreading center, the East Pacific Rise. Considering the width of this ocean, will the spreading rate be the same, greater, or less than that of the South Atlantic? _____ Explain.

_____

_____

_____

(d) Now get the details. Measure the width of the South Pacific Ocean. _____ km

(e) What is the spreading rate of the East Pacific Rise? _____ km/million years

These spreading rates are typical of the range measured throughout the world's oceans and represent "fast spreaders" and "slow spreaders."

Map view of magnetic anomaly stripes in two oceans.

South Atlantic Ridge   East Pacific Rise

(red line = axis of ocean ridges; black = positive anomaly; white = negative anomaly)

Name: _____   **Section:** _____

Course: _____   **Date:** _____

The figures below show bathymetric maps of parts of the East Pacific Rise and Mid-Atlantic Ridge at the same scale.

(a) The East Pacific Rise in the South Pacific Ocean.

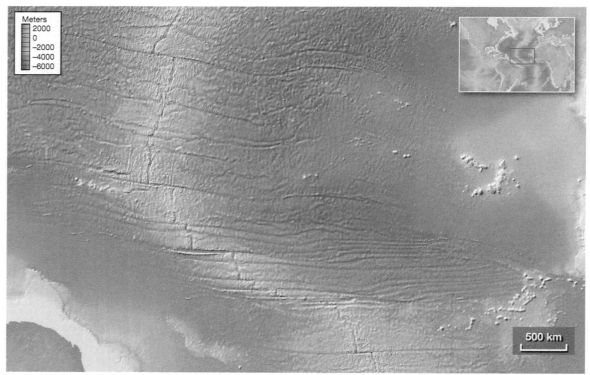

(b) The Mid-Atlantic Ridge off South America.

(continued)

Name: _____   Section: _____
Course: _____   Date: _____

(a) Ocean ridges typically have a rift valley at their axes—a valley created when two continents split. Which of the two ridges in the previous figures has the deepest and longest rift valley?

_____

_____

_____

_____

Different spreading rates cause variations in shape because of the way the cooling lithosphere behaves. Lithosphere near the ridge axis is young, thin, still hot, and therefore has a lower density than older, colder lithosphere far from the axis. As a result, the ridge axis area floats relatively high on the underlying asthenosphere, and the water above it is relatively shallow. As seafloor spreading moves the oceanic lithosphere away from the ridge axis, the rocks cool and get thicker and denser. The farther it is from the ridge axis, the lower the oceanic lithosphere sits on the asthenosphere and the deeper the water will be. This concept is known as the **age-versus-depth relationship**.

(b) Keeping in mind the age-versus-depth relationship, why is the belt of shallow sea wider over the East Pacific Rise than over the Mid-Atlantic Ridge?

_____

_____

_____

_____

(c) On the graph provided, plot depth (on the vertical axis) against distance from the ridge axis (on the horizontal axis) for both the East Pacific Rise and the Mid-Atlantic Ridge. Use five to ten points for each ridge, marking the points you use on the maps on page 38. Connect the dots for the East Pacific Rise with red pencil and those for the Mid-Atlantic Ridge with green pencil to make cross sections of each ridge.

Depth (m): −2,500 −3,000 −3,500 −4,000 −4,500
Distance from ridge (km): 1,000   500   0   500   1,000

(d) Does the rate at which the depth increases with distance from the ridge stay the same over time, decrease over time, or increase over time?

_____

_____

_____

_____

Name: _____   Section: _____

Course: _____   Date: _____

Examine the bathymetric/physiographic map of the region that includes eastern Africa, the Red Sea, and the western Indian Ocean below. The Arabian Peninsula was split from Africa by the Red Sea rift, which continues to widen today. The East African rift was an earlier attempt that failed to split off a piece of the continent.

Red Sea rift zone.

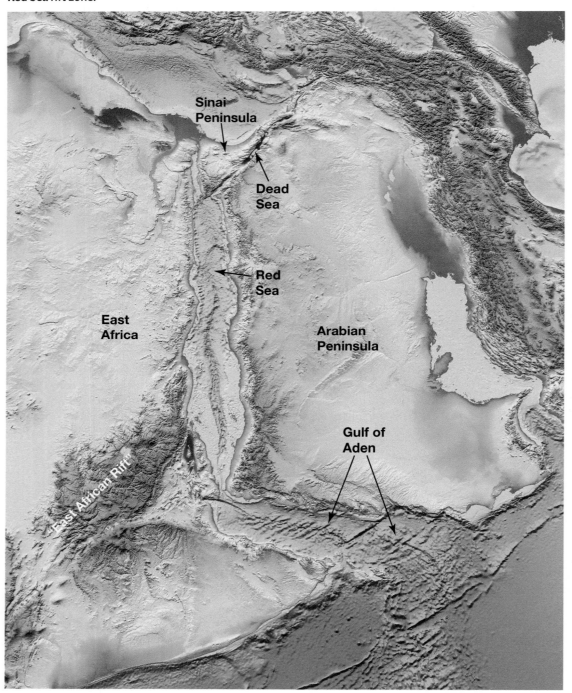

(continued)

Name: _____   Section: _____

Course: _____   Date: _____

Rifting has split Africa from the Arabian Peninsula to form the Red Sea. A new ocean ridge and ocean lithosphere have formed in the southern two-thirds of the Red Sea. A narrow belt of deeper water defines the trace of this ridge. At the northern end of the Red Sea, the ridge/rift axis is cut by a transform fault that runs along the eastern side of the Sinai Peninsula and through the Dead Sea.

(a) Use a red line to show the trace of the Red Sea rift/ridge axis. Use a purple line to show the trace of the Dead Sea transform fault.

(b) The narrow ocean bordering the southeast edge of the Arabian Peninsula is the Gulf of Aden. Use red and purple lines to trace the ridge segments and transform fault in this narrow sea.

(c) Based on the geometry of the ridges and transform faults in the Red Sea and Gulf of Aden, draw an arrow showing the motion of the Arabian Peninsula (the Arabian Plate) relative to Africa.

2.5.2 Subduction Zones: Deducing the Steepness of Subduction

When two oceanic plates collide head-on, one is subducted beneath the other and returns to the mantle, completing the tectonic cycle begun when the ocean crust initially erupted at a mid-ocean ridge. Melting occurs above the subducted plate when it reaches a depth of about 150 km. As a result, the volcanic arc forms at some distance from the ocean trench. The area between the volcanic arc and trench typically contains an accretionary prism, which is composed of highly deformed sediment scraped off the sinking plate, and a forearc basin, in which debris eroded from the arc accumulates (**FIG. 2.11**).

No two subduction zones are identical. Differences can include the width of the accretionary prism, the rate of subduction, and the steepness of the subducted plate as it moves into the mantle. Earthquakes occur in the subducted plate as it moves, concentrated in what geologists call a *Wadati-Benioff zone*. We can track the plate as it is subducted by locating the depth and location of the earthquake foci (points where the energy is released).

FIGURE 2.11 Anatomy of an island arc–trench system.

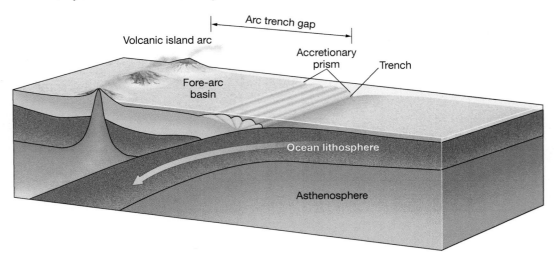

Even without any earthquake information, it is possible to estimate the steepness of a subduction zone. All you need is an accurate map of the seafloor and a little geologic reasoning based on knowledge of its arc-trench system. We will see how this is done in Exercise 2.9.

EXERCISE 2.9 **Estimating the Steepness of Subduction Zones**

Name: _____ Section: _____
Course: _____ Date: _____

(a) Based on island arc–trench geometry (Fig. 2.11) and the fact that melting typically occurs at about the same depth in subduction zones, what is the major factor that controls the width of the arc-trench gap? Explain. _____

_____

_____

(b) Based on your answer to (a), sketch two island arc–trench systems, one with a wider arc-trench gap than the other.

Narrow arc-trench gap   Wide arc-trench gap

The Aleutian Island arc extends westward from mainland Alaska into the Pacific Ocean. Profiles across four segments of the Aleutian arc are given in the illustration that follows, which shows the positions of the volcanic arc and trench for each segment. Gray dots in the profile of the Amchitka segment show the earthquakes in the Wadati-Benioff zone.

(continued)

Name: _____   **Section:** _____
Course: _____   **Date:** _____

(c) Using this earthquake information, you will see the boundaries of the subducted plate sketched on the Amchitka profile. Assuming that the deepest part of the Aleutian Trench is at the middle of the trench, explain the reason for these boundaries.

_____

_____

_____

(d) The volcanic arc sits directly above the point where the subducted plate begins to melt. At what depth does melting apparently begin beneath the Amchitka segment of the arc? _____ km. How does this point relate to the position of the volcanic arc?

_____

_____

_____

The positions of volcanic arcs and trenches are shown for three other segments of the Aleutian arc. Although earthquake information is not available for these segments, you have enough information to sketch the subducted plates in all three areas.

(e) Sketch the outlines of the subducted plate for each segment in the profiles.

Hints:
  • Assume that melting occurs at the same depth in each segment.
  • Draw a vertical line from the volcanic arc to the melting depth.
  • Draw a horizontal line from the melting depth.
  • Draw the subducted slab so that its upper surface passes through the intersection point.
  • Using your protractor, measure the angle of subduction downward from the horizontal.

(f) From the profiles, record the following data in the table provided:
  • The width of the arc-trench gap
  • The angle of subduction

	Amchitka	Shumagin Islands	Cook Inlet	Skwentna
Arc-trench gap				
Subduction angle				

(g) Based on this information, what is the relationship between the steepness of subduction and the width of the gap between the volcanic island arc and the trench?

_____

_____

_____

2.5.3 Transform Faults

We have thus far looked at transform faults only in the oceans—the ocean fracture systems—but some also cut continental lithosphere. Continental transform faults can be found in New Zealand (the Alpine Fault), Turkey (the Great Anatolian Fault), and Haiti (Enriquillo-Plantain Garden Fault). However, the most famous of these is the San Andreas Fault system of California, an active continental transform fault that has caused major damage and loss of life over the past 100 years. The San Andreas Fault *system* (shown in Exercise 2.10) is not a single fault but rather a zone containing several faults. It extends for more than 1,000 km, connecting segments of the Juan de Fuca Ridge and Cascade Trench at its northern end to an unnamed ridge segment in the Gulf of California to the south.

EXERCISE 2.10 | **Estimating the Amount and Rate of Motion in a Continental Transform Fault**

Name: _____   Section: _____

Course: _____   Date: _____

The more we know about the history of a continental transform fault close to heavily populated regions, the better we can prepare for its next pulse of activity. Geologists try to find out how long a continental transform fault has been active, how much it offsets the plates it separates, and how fast it has moved in the past.

Geologists estimate that the San Andreas Fault system has been active for about 20 million years. This exercise shows how geologists use geologic markers cut by faults to measure the amount and rate of motion along a transform fault.

(a) Simplified geologic setting of the San Andres Fault system.

(b) Amount of fault movement indicated by offset bodies of identical rock.

(continued)

Name: _____   **Section:** _____
Course: _____   **Date:** _____

Field geologists have mapped an active continental transform fault (red line in the figure below) for several hundred kilometers. A 50-million-year-old (50-Ma) body of granite and a 30-Ma vertical layer of marble have been offset by the fault as shown.

(a) Draw arrows to indicate the direction in which the plate on the northeast side of the fault has moved relative to the plate on the southwest side.

(b) Measure the amount of offset of the 50-Ma granite body. _____ km

(c) The geologists have proved that faulting began almost immediately after the granite formed and continues today. If the fault blocks moved at a constant rate for the past 50 million years, calculate the rate of offset. _____ km/million years; mm/year _____

(d) Was the rate constant for 50 million years? Measure the offset of the 30-Ma marble. _____ km

Geologic markers displaced by a continental transform fault.

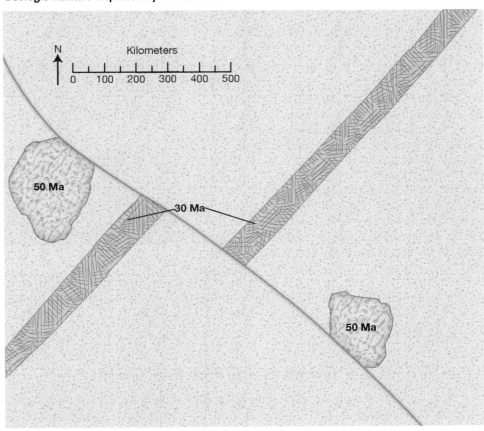

(e) Assume that the fault blocks moved at a constant rate for the past 30 million years. Offset rate: _____ km/30 million years; _____ km/million years; _____ mm/year

(continued)

Name: _____   **Section:** _____
Course: _____   **Date:** _____

(f) Compare the two rates. Has the rate of fault offset been constant or has it increased or decreased over time? Explain.

_____

_____

_____

Now let's look at the San Andreas Fault system again (the maps at the beginning of this exercise):

(g) On map (a), draw arrows to indicate the direction along the San Andreas Fault in which the Pacific and North American Plates have been offset.

(h) San Francisco and Los Angeles are on opposite sides of the San Andreas Fault. If the San Andreas Fault is undergoing offset at the rates that you measured above, how many years will it take before the two cities are directly opposite one another? _____

? **What Do You Think** Because of the earthquake threats from the San Andreas Fault, the city of San Francisco has rigorous building codes requiring that buildings be designed to withstand earthquakes in the area. On the other side of the country, however, the codes are less rigorous. An earthquake in Virginia in August 2011 was felt along most of the east coast of the United States, prompting questions about whether existing building codes should be changed to meet rigorous San Francisco standards. Meeting San Francisco standards makes construction a lot more expensive than that in New York. Imagine you had to make a recommendation to the New York City Council about whether they should or should not adopt San Francisco building codes. Using the information you have in this chapter, on a separate sheet of paper, note what would your recommendation be and why?

2.5.4 Hotspots and Hot-Spot Tracks

Paleoclimate anomalies show that plates have moved, magnetic stripes help measure the rate of seafloor spreading, and satellites measure the rates and directions of plate motion today. But how can we determine if a plate always moved at its current rate? Or if it has changed direction over time? The answers come from the study of hot-spot volcanic island chains.

FIGURE 2.12 shows how hot-spot island chains form. Each volcano in the chain forms at a **hot spot**—an area of unusual volcanic activity not associated with processes at plate boundaries. The cause is still controversial, but many geologists propose that hot spots form above a narrowly focused source of heat called a **mantle plume**—a column of very hot rock that rises by slow plastic flow from deep in the mantle.

FIGURE 2.12 Origin of hot-spot island chains and seamounts.

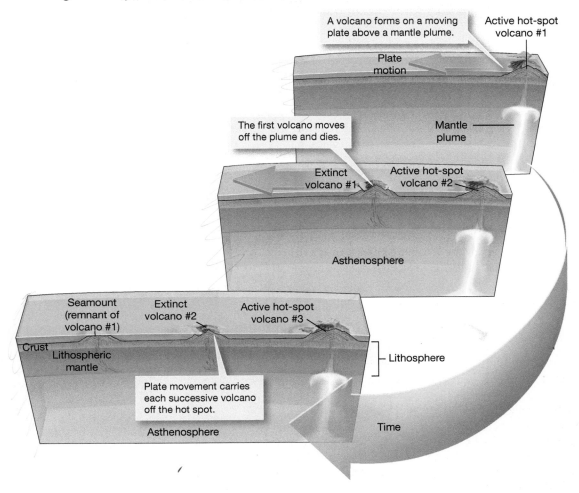

When the plume reaches the base of the lithosphere, it melts the lithosphere rock and produces magma that rises to the surface, erupts, and builds a volcano. The plume is thought to be relatively motionless. If the plate above it moves, the volcano is carried away from its magma source and becomes extinct. A new volcano then forms above the hot spot until it, too, is carried away from the hot spot.

Over millions of years, a chain of volcanic islands forms, the youngest at the hot spot, the oldest farthest from it. As the volcanoes cool, they become denser, subside, and are eroded by streams and ocean waves. Eventually, old volcanoes sink below the ocean surface, forming **seamounts**. The chain of islands and seamounts traces plate motion above the hot spot, just as footprints track the movement of animals.

For Example, the Hawaiian Islands are the youngest volcanoes in the Hawaiian–Emperor seamount chain. Most of the older volcanoes are seamounts detected by underwater oceanographic surveys. The Hawaiian–Emperor seamount chain tracks the motion of the Pacific Plate and lets us interpret Pacific Plate motion for a longer time span than that recorded by the Hawaiian Islands alone.

In Exercises 2.11 and 2.12, you will examine both the Hawaiian Islands (as hot-spot volcanic islands) and the Hawaiian-Emperor seamount chain.

Name: _____   Section: _____

Course: _____   Date: _____

The Hawaiian Islands, located in the Pacific Ocean far from the nearest oceanic ridge, are an excellent example of hot-spot volcanic islands (see figure below). Volcanoes on Kauai, Oahu, and Maui haven't erupted for millions of years, but the island of Hawaii hosts five huge volcanoes, one of which (Kilauea) has been active for the past 31 years. In addition, a new volcano, Loihi, is growing on the Pacific Ocean floor just southeast of Kilauea. As the Pacific Plate moves, Kilauea will become extinct and Loihi will be the primary active volcano.

(a) Where is the Hawaiian hot-spot plume located today relative to the Hawaiian Islands? Explain your reasoning.

_____

_____

(b) Draw a line connecting the volcanic center (highlighted in red) on Maui to the spot between Kilauea and Loihi (the volcanic center for Hawaii). Connect the volcanic centers of Maui to Molokai, Molokai to Oahu, and Oahu to Kauai as well.

Ages of Hawaiian volcanoes in millions of years before present.

(c) Geologists use the *azimuth system* to describe direction precisely. In the azimuth system, north is 0°, east is 090°, south is 180°, and west is 270°, as shown in the following figure. The green arrow points to 052° (northeast). To practice using the azimuth system, estimate and then measure the directions shown by arrows A through D. Use the protractor in your toolkit.

Name: _____   **Section:** _____

Course: _____   **Date:** _____

The azimuth system.

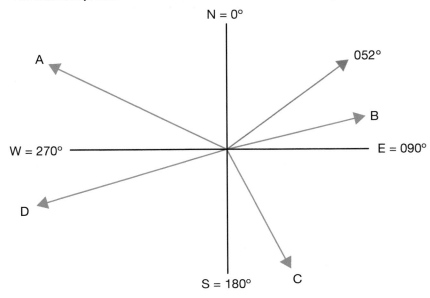

(d) Measure the direction and distance between the volcanic centers of the Hawaiian Islands using a ruler, a protractor, and the map scale. Calculate the rate of plate motion (distance between volcanoes divided by the time interval between eruption ages) and fill in **Table 2.1.** Express the rates in millimeters per year.

TABLE 2.1 Movement of the Pacific Plate over the Hawaiian hot spot.

	Distance between volcanic centers (km)	Number of years of plate motion	Rate of plate motion (mm/yr)	Azimuth direction of plate motion (e.g., 325°)
Hawaii to Maui				
Maui to Molokai				
Molokai to Oahu				
Oahu to Kauai				

Name: _____ Section: _____

Course: _____ Date: _____

The oldest volcano of the Hawaiian–Emperor seamount chain was once directly above the hot spot but is now in the northern Pacific, thousands of kilometers away (see the figure below). Seamount ages show that the hot spot has been active for a long time and reveal the direction and rate at which the Pacific Plate has moved.

(a) What evidence is there that the Pacific Plate has not always moved in the same direction?

_____

_____

_____

(b) How many years ago did the Pacific Plate change direction? Explain your reasoning.

_____

_____

_____

Physiography of the Pacific Ocean floor, showing ages of volcanoes in the Hawaiian–Emperor seamount chain.

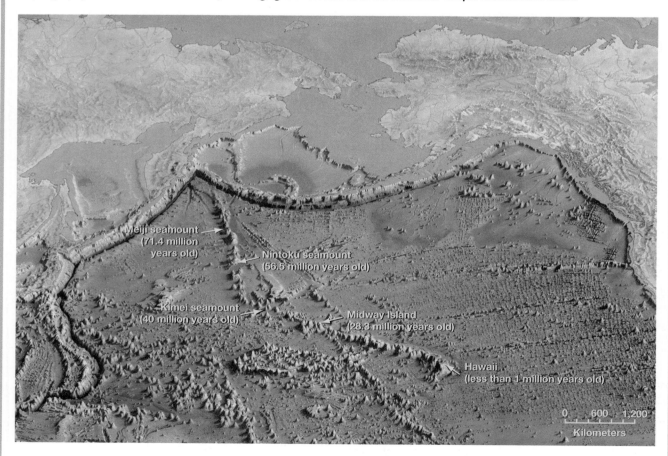

(continued)

Name: _____   Section: _____

Course: _____   Date: _____

(c) Based on the information in the map on page 50, in what direction did the Pacific Plate move originally?

_____

(d) How far has the Meiji seamount moved from the hot spot? Explain your reasoning.

_____

_____

_____

(e) At what rate has the Pacific Plate moved
    (i) based on data from the Hawaii-Midway segment? _____ km/Ma
    (ii) based on data from the Hawaii-Kimei segment? _____ km/Ma
    (iii) based on data from the Kimei-Meiji segment? _____ km/Ma

(f) Has the Meiji seamount moved at a constant rate? Explain your reasoning.

_____

_____

_____

(g) In what direction is the Pacific Plate moving today? Explain your reasoning.

_____

_____

_____

(h) Assuming that the current direction of motion continues, what will be the eventual fate of the Meiji seamount? Explain in as much detail as possible.

_____

_____

_____

2.6 Active versus Passive Continental Margins

Earthquakes and volcanic eruptions are common on the west coast of North America, but there are no active volcanoes on the east coast, and earthquakes there are rare. Geologists call the west coast a (tectonically) **active continental margin** and the east coast a **passive continental margin**. These differences can be found on several continents. Most passive continental margins have broad continental shelves, whereas active continental margins typically have narrow continental shelves.

In Exercise 2.13, you will examine why this phenomena occurs.

Name: _____ Section: _____

Course: _____ Date: _____

Based on what you know about plate tectonics, explain why some continental margins are active and others passive.

(a) Are all continental coastlines plate boundaries? Explain.

_____

_____

_____

(b) Compare the west coast of South America with the west coast of Africa. Which has a broad continental shelf? A narrow shelf? Which is close to an ocean trench? Which coast would you expect to have the most earthquakes? Explain.

_____

_____

_____

Physiographic map of the South Atlantic Ocean floor and adjacent continents.

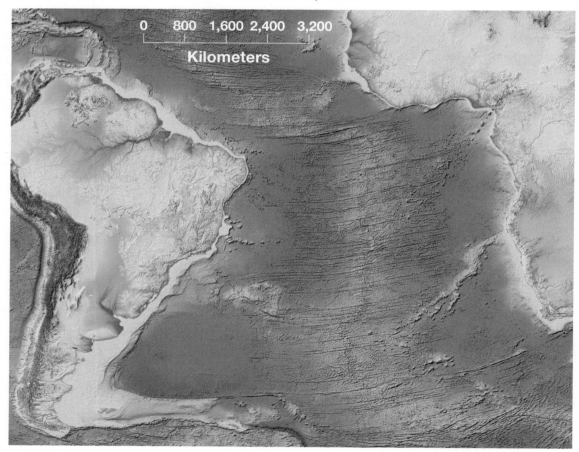

(continued)

| EXERCISE 2.13 | Why Are There More Earthquakes and Volcanoes on One Side of Some Continents than on the Other? (continued) |

Name: _____ Section: _____

Course: _____ Date: _____

(c) On **FIGURE 2.13**, a plate tectonic map of the world, label active continental margins with a red letter A and passive margins with a blue letter P. Two have been identified to get you started.

FIGURE 2.13 Earth's major lithosphere plates.

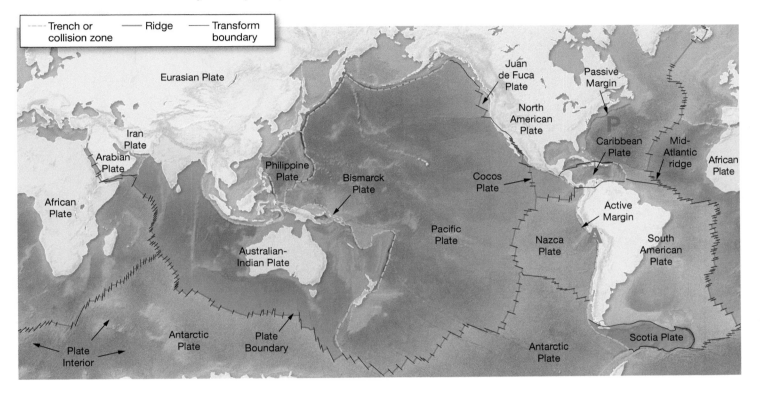

3 Minerals

Giant gypsum crystals in the Cave of the Crystals, Chihuahua, Mexico.

- Understand what makes minerals different from other materials
- Become familiar with and learn to describe the physical properties of minerals
- Identify the most common rock-forming minerals using a systematic approach
- Recognize the economic value of minerals
- Learn what minerals can reveal about Earth processes and Earth history

MATERIALS NEEDED

- Sets of mineral and rock specimens
- Hand lens, streak plate, glass plate, knife or steel nail, and a penny to determine the physical properties of minerals
- Dilute hydrochloric acid (HCl) for a simple chemical test
- Small magnet

3.1 Introduction

This chapter begins our study of Earth materials. It starts by examining the different kinds of materials in the geosphere and then focuses on minerals, the basic building blocks of most of the Earth. You will learn how minerals are different from other substances, how to study their physical properties, and how to use those properties to identify common minerals.

3.2 Classifying Earth Materials

Imagine that an octopus is swimming in the ocean when a container falls off a freighter overhead. The container breaks up and spills its entire cargo of sneakers, sandals, flip-flops, shoes, moccasins, and boots into the sea. The octopus is curious about these objects and wants to learn about them. How would it classify them? Remember, an octopus doesn't have heels or toes, has eight legs, doesn't understand "left" and "right," and doesn't wear clothes. One system might be to separate items that are mostly enclosed (shoes, boots, sneakers, moccasins) from those that are open (sandals, flip-flops). Another might be to separate objects made of leather from those made of cloth; or brown objects from black ones; or big ones from small ones. There are many ways to classify footwear, some of which might lead our octopus to a deeper understanding of the reasons for these differences.

Early geologists faced a similar task in the seventeenth century when they began to study Earth materials systematically by classifying them. Why classify things? Because classification shows us relationships between things that lead to understanding them and the processes by which they were made. Biologists classify organisms, art historians classify paintings, and geologists classify Earth materials. Exercise 3.1 introduces the thought processes involved in developing a classification scheme.

EXERCISE 3.1	Classifying Earth Materials

Name: _____   Section: _____

Course: _____   Date: _____

(a) Examine the specimens of Earth materials provided by your instructor. Group them into categories you believe are justified by your observations, and explain the criteria you used to set up the groups.

Group	Defining criteria for each group	Specimens in group

(continued)

Name: _____   Section: _____

Course: _____   Date: _____

(b) Compare your results with those of others in the class. Did you all use the same criteria? Are your classmates' specimens in the same groups as yours?

_____

_____

(c) What does your comparison tell you about the process of classification?

_____

_____

_____

3.3 What Is a Mineral and What Isn't?

Most people know that the Earth is made of minerals and rocks, but they don't know the difference between them. The words *mineral* and *rock* have very specific meanings to geologists, often much more precise than those used in everyday language. For example, what a dietitian calls a mineral is not a mineral to a geologist. To most geologists, a **mineral** is a naturally occurring homogeneous solid formed by geologic processes with an ordered internal arrangement of atoms, ions, or molecules, and a composition definable by a chemical formula. There has traditionally been another criterion: a mineral must be inorganic, not produced by any animal or plant. Today, some geologists have dropped this requirement in recognition that bones and teeth are identical to the mineral apatite, many clam shells are identical to the mineral calcite, and many microscopic creatures build shells from material identical to the mineral quartz. Let's look at the definition more closely.

■ *Naturally occurring* means that a mineral forms by natural Earth processes. Thus, human-made materials like steel and plastic are not minerals.

■ *Homogeneous* means that a piece of a mineral contains the same pure material throughout.

■ *Formed by geologic processes* traditionally implied processes such as solidification or precipitation, which did not involve living organisms. As noted above, however, many geologists now consider solid, crystalline materials produced by organisms to be minerals too.

■ *Solid* means that minerals retain their shape indefinitely under normal conditions. Therefore, liquids like oil and water and gases like air and propane cannot be minerals.

■ An *ordered internal arrangement of atoms* is an important characteristic that separates minerals from substances that may fit all other parts of the definition. Atoms in minerals occupy positions in a grid called a *crystalline structure*. Solids in which atoms occur in random clusters rather than in a crystalline structure are called *glasses*.

■ *Definable chemical composition* means that the elements present in a mineral and the proportions of their atoms can be expressed by a simple formula—for example, quartz is SiO_2 and calcite is $CaCO_3$—or by one that is more complex: the mineral muscovite is $KAl_2(AlSi_3O_{10})(OH)_2$.

When a mineral grows without interference from other minerals, it develops smooth flat surfaces and a symmetrical geometric shape that we call a **crystal**. When a mineral forms in an environment where other minerals interfere with its growth, it has an irregular shape but still has the appropriate crystalline structure for that mineral, as would a piece broken off a crystal during erosion. An irregular or fragmented piece of mineral is a **grain**, and a single piece of a mineral, either crystal or grain, is called a **specimen.**

In the geosphere, most minerals occur as parts of rocks. It is important to know the difference between a mineral specimen and a rock. A **rock** is *a coherent, naturally occurring, inorganic solid consisting of an aggregate of mineral grains, pieces of older rocks, or a mass of natural glass.* Some rocks, like granite, contain grains of several different minerals; and some, like rock salt, are made of many grains of a single mineral. Others are made of fragments of previously existing rock that are cemented together. And a few kinds of rock are natural glasses, cooled so rapidly from a molten state that their atoms did not have time to form the gridlike crystalline structures required for minerals. Exercise 3.2 helps you practice this terminology with specimens provided by your instructor.

EXERCISE 3.2	Is It a Mineral or a Rock?

Name: _____ **Section:** _____
Course: _____ **Date:** _____

(a) Based on the definitions of *mineral* and *rock*, determine which specimens you used in Exercise 3.1 are minerals, which are rocks, and which are *other*—neither minerals nor rocks. Write the specimen number in the appropriate column.

Minerals	Rocks	Other

(b) Choose and look carefully at one of the *rock* specimens. How many different minerals are in this rock? _____

(c) How do you know? What visual or other clues did you use to determine how each mineral is different from its neighbors?

_____

_____

_____

(d) Describe each of the minerals in this rock in your own words. (Up to four, if possible.)

Mineral 1

_____

_____

_____

(continued)

Name: _____   Section: _____

Course: _____   Date: _____

Mineral 2

_____

_____

_____

Mineral 3

_____

_____

_____

Mineral 4

_____

_____

_____

3.4 Physical Properties of Minerals

Mineralogists (geologists who specialize in the study of minerals) have named more than four thousand minerals that differ from one another in composition and crystalline structure. These characteristics, in turn, determine a mineral's **physical properties**, which include how it looks (color and luster), breaks, feels, smells, and even tastes. Some minerals are colorless and nearly transparent; others are opaque, dark colored, and shiny. Some are hard, others soft. Some form long, needlelike crystals, others blocky cubes. You probably instinctively used some of these physical properties in Exercise 3.2 to decide how many minerals were in your rocks and then to describe them. We discuss the major physical properties of minerals below so you can use them to identify common minerals—in class, at home, or while on vacation.

3.4.1 Diagnostic versus Ambiguous Properties

Geologists use physical properties to identify minerals, much as detectives use physical descriptions to identify suspects. And, as with people, some physical properties are *diagnostic properties*—they immediately help identify an unknown mineral or rule it out as a possibility. Other properties are *ambiguous properties* because they may vary in different specimens of the same mineral. For example, color is a notoriously ambiguous property in many minerals (**FIG. 3.1**). Size doesn't really matter either; a large specimen of quartz has the same properties as a small one. Exercise 3.3 shows how diagnostic and ambiguous properties affect everyday life.

3.4.2 Luster

One of the first things we notice when we pick up a mineral is its luster—the way light interacts with its surface. For mineral identification, we distinguish minerals that have a metallic luster from those that are nonmetallic. Something with a *metallic* luster is shiny and opaque like an untarnished piece of metal. Materials with a *nonmetallic* luster look earthy (dull and powdery like dirt), glassy (vitreous), waxy, silky, or pearly—terms relating luster to familiar materials. Luster is a diagnostic property for many minerals, but be careful: some minerals may tarnish, and their metallic luster may be dulled.

3.4.3 Color

The color we see when we look at a mineral is controlled by how the different wavelengths of visible light are absorbed or reflected by the mineral's atoms. Color is generally a diagnostic property for minerals with a metallic luster and for *some* with a nonmetallic luster. Specimens of some nonmetallic minerals, like the fluorite in Figure 3.1, have such a wide range of colors that they were once thought to be different minerals. We now know that the colors are caused by impurities. For example, rose quartz contains a very small amount of titanium.

3.4.4 Streak

The streak of a mineral is the color of its powder, which we can determine by rubbing a mineral against an unglazed porcelain plate. Streak and color are the same for most minerals, but for some they are different. In these cases, the difference between streak and color is an important diagnostic property. A mineral's color may vary widely, as in Figure 3.1; but its streak is generally similar for all specimens regardless of their color, as seen in **FIGURE 3.2**.

FIGURE 3.2 Color and streak.

(a) Red hematite has a reddish-brown streak.

(b) But this dark, metallic-looking specular hematite also has a reddish-brown streak.

EXERCISE 3.3   **People Have Diagnostic Properties Too**

Name: _____   Section: _____

Course: _____   Date: _____

Your father has asked you to pick up his old college roommate at the airport. You've never met him, but your father gave you a yearbook photo and described what he looked like 30 years ago: height, weight, hair color, beard, eye color. Which of these features would still be diagnostic today? Which, considering the passage of time, might be ambiguous? What other properties might also be diagnostic? Indicate in the following chart which properties, considering the passage of time, might be diagnostic and which might be ambiguous. Then suggest two others that would be diagnostic despite the years that have passed.

Property	Diagnostic (explain)	Ambiguous (explain)
Height		
Weight		
Hair color		
Beard		
Eye color		
Others		

3.4.5 Hardness

The hardness of a mineral is a measure of how easily it can scratch or be scratched by other substances. A nineteenth-century mineralogist, Friedrich Mohs, created a mineral hardness scale that we still use today, using ten familiar minerals. He assigned a hardness of 10 to the hardest mineral and a hardness of 1 to the softest (TABLE. 3.1). This is a **relative scale**, meaning that a mineral can scratch those lower in the scale but cannot scratch those that are higher. It is not an *absolute scale* in which diamond would be ten times harder than talc, and corundum would be three times harder than calcite. The hardness of common materials, such as the testing materials listed in FIGURE 3.3, can also be described using the Mohs hardness scale. To determine the hardness of a mineral, see which of these materials it can scratch and which ones can scratch it. You will practice this in Exercise 3.4.

TABLE 3.1   Mohs hardness scale and its relationship to common testing materials.

Mineral	Mohs hardness number (H)	Mohs hardness of testing materials	
Diamond	10		HARD
Corundum	9		
Topaz	8		
Quartz	7		
Orthoclase	6	Streak plate (6.5–7)	MODERATE
Apatite	5	Window glass; steel cut nail (5.5)	
Fluorite	4	Common nail or pocket knife (5.0–5.5)	
Calcite	3	U.S. penny (3.0)	
Gypsum	2	Fingernail (2.5)	SOFT
Talc	1		

EXERCISE 3.4   Constructing and Using a Relative Hardness Scale

Name: _____   Section: _____

Course: _____   Date: _____

Your instructor will tell you which specimens from your mineral set to use for this exercise. Arrange them in order of increasing hardness by seeing which can scratch the others and which are most easily scratched.

Softest ———————————————————————▶ *Hardest*

Specimen no.:   _____   _____   _____   _____   _____

Now use the testing materials listed in Table 3.1 to determine the Mohs hardness of minerals in your set.

Mohs hardness: _____   _____   _____   _____   _____

FIGURE 3.3 **Testing for hardness.**

(a) A fingernail (H=2.5) can scratch gypsum (H=2.0) but not calcite (H=3.0).

(b) A knife blade (H=5.0) can scratch fluorite (H=4.0) but not quartz (H=7.0).

3.4.6 Crystal Habit

Crystal shapes found in the mineral kingdom range from simple cubes with six faces to complex 12-, 24-, or 48-sided (or more) crystals (**FIG. 3.4a–h**). Some crystals are flat like a knife blade, others are needlelike. Each mineral has its own diagnostic **crystal habit**, a preferred crystal shape that forms when it grows unimpeded by other grains. For example, the habit of halite is a cube, and that

FIGURE 3.4 **Crystal habits of some common minerals with diagrams of perfect crystal shapes.**

(a) Cubes of pyrite

(b) Twelve-sided garnet crystals.

FIGURE 3.4 **Crystal habits of some common minerals** (*cont.*).

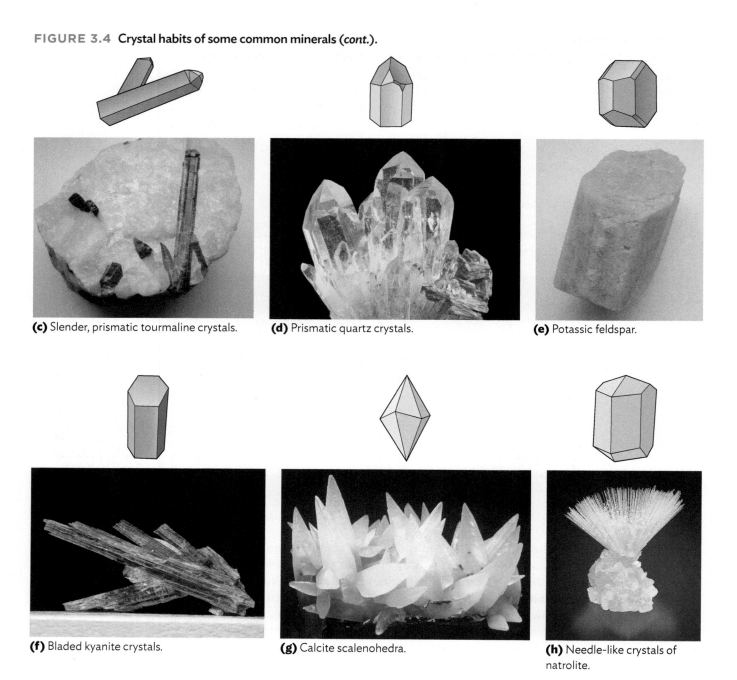

(c) Slender, prismatic tourmaline crystals.

(d) Prismatic quartz crystals.

(e) Potassic feldspar.

(f) Bladed kyanite crystals.

(g) Calcite scalenohedra.

(h) Needle-like crystals of natrolite.

of garnet is an equant 12-sided crystal. The habit of quartz is elongate hexagonal crystals topped by a six-sided pyramid. *Remember:* Crystal growth requires very special conditions. As a result, most mineral specimens are irregular grains; few display their characteristic crystal habit.

3.4.7 Breakage

Some minerals break along one or more smooth planes, others along curved surfaces, and still others in irregular shapes. The way a mineral breaks is controlled by whether there are zones of weak bonds in its structure. Instead of breaking the minerals in your sets with a hammer, you can examine specimens to see how they have already broken—using a microscope or magnifying glass to see more clearly. Two kinds of breakage are important: fracture and cleavage.

Fracture occurs when there are no zones of particularly weak bonding within a mineral. When such a mineral breaks, either irregular (**irregular fracture**) or curved surfaces (*conchoidal fracture*) form (**FIG. 3.5**). Conchoidal fracture surfaces are common in thick glass and in minerals whose bond strength is nearly equal in all directions (e.g., quartz).

FIGURE 3.5 Types of fractures in minerals.

(a) Irregular fracture in garnet.

(b) Conchoidal fracture in quartz.

Cleavage occurs when bonds holding atoms together are weaker in some directions than in others. The mineral breaks along these zones of weakness, producing flat, smooth surfaces. Some minerals have a single zone of weakness, but others may have two, three, four, or six (**FIG. 3.6**). If there is more than one zone of weakness, a mineral cleaves in more than one direction. It is important to note *how many* directions there are and *the angles between those directions.* Two different minerals might each have two directions of cleavage, but those directions might be at 90° in one mineral but not in the other (see Fig. 3.6). For example, amphiboles and pyroxenes (two important groups of minerals) are similar in most other properties and have two directions of cleavage, but amphiboles cleave at 56° and 124° whereas pyroxenes cleave at 90°.

Note that in Figure 3.6 there may be many cleavage *surfaces*, but several of those surfaces are parallel to one another, as shown for halite. All of these parallel surfaces define a single *cleavage direction.* To help observe a mineral's cleavage, hold it up to the light and rotate it. Parallel cleavage surfaces reflect light at the same time, making different cleavage directions easy to see.

Both crystal faces and cleavage surfaces are smooth, flat planes and might be mistaken for one another. If you can see many small, parallel faces, these are cleavage faces because crystal faces are not repeated. In addition, breakage occurs after a crystal has grown, thus cleavage or fracture surfaces generally look less tarnished or altered than crystal faces. Exercise 3.5 will help you recognize the difference between cleavage and fracture.

FIGURE 3.6 Cleavage in common minerals. Some minerals cleave in four or six directions, but all of the directions are rarely visible in a single specimen.

Types of cleavage	Diagram	Visual	Examples
1 Direction	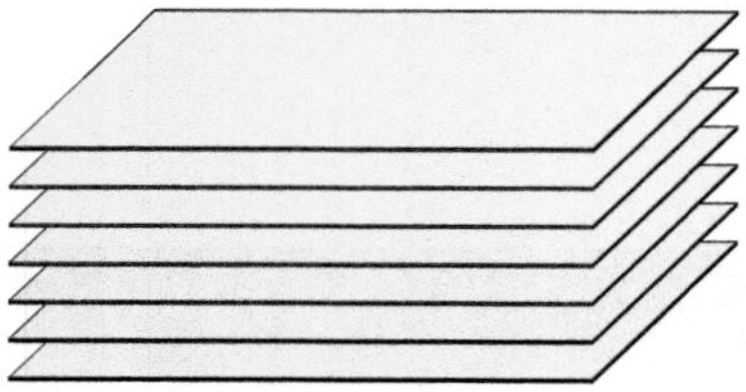		Muscovite
2 Directions at 90°	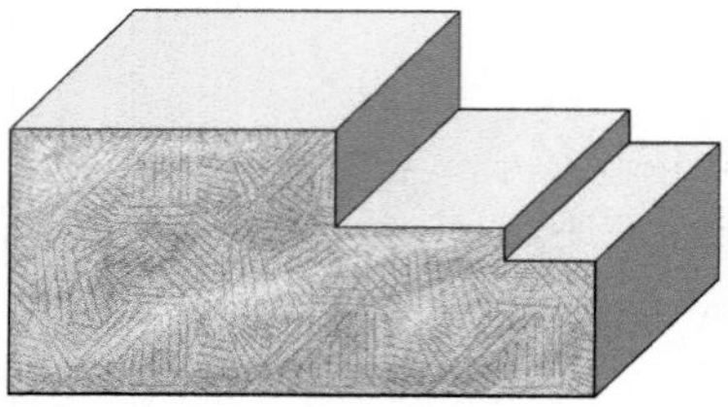		Pyroxene
2 Directions not at 90°	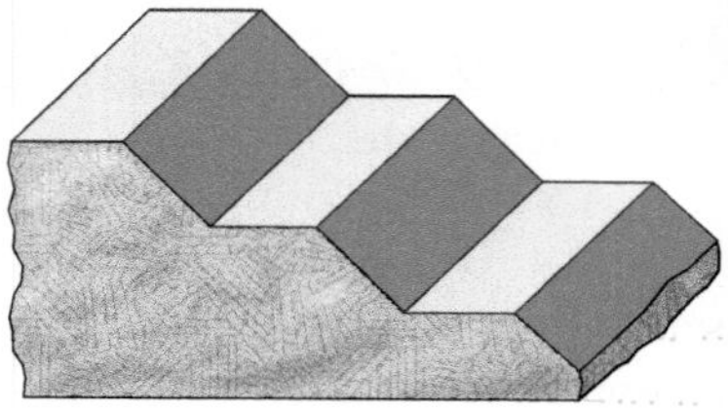		Amphibole
3 Directions at 90°	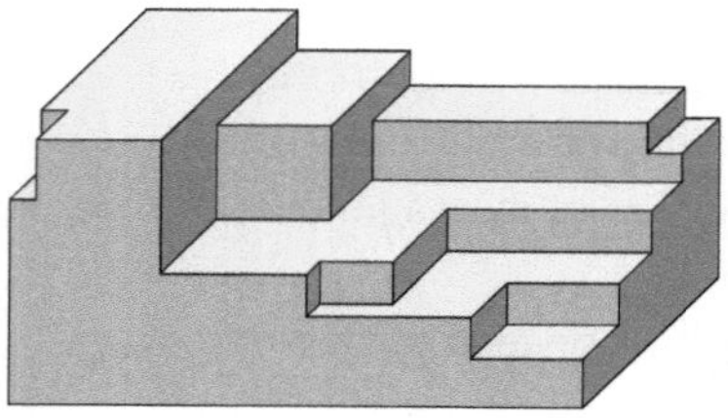		Halite
3 Directions not at 90°	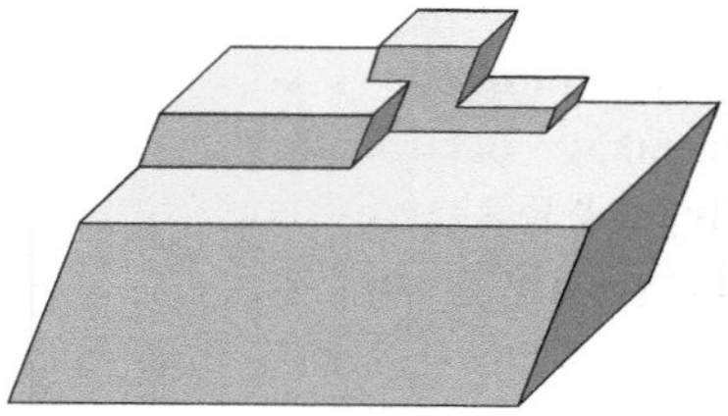	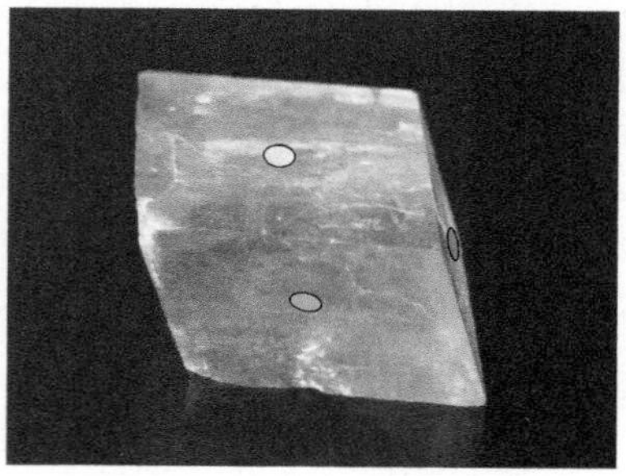	Calcite

Name: _____   Section: _____

Course: _____   Date: _____

Examine the specimens indicated by your instructor. Which have cleaved and which have fractured? For those with cleavage, indicate the number of directions and the angles between them.

_____

_____

_____

_____

_____

3.4.8 Specific Gravity

The specific gravity (**SpG**) of a mineral is a comparison of its density with the density of water. The density of pure water is 1 g/cm^3, so if a mineral has a density of 4.68 g/cm^3, its specific gravity is 4.68.

$$\frac{4.68 \; \cancel{g/cm^3}}{1.00 \; \cancel{g/cm^3}}$$

The units cancel, so **SpG = 4.68**.
This means that the mineral is 4.68 times denser than water.

You can measure specific gravity by calculating the density of a specimen (density = mass ÷ volume). But geologists generally estimate specific gravity by *hefting* a specimen and determining if it seems heavy or light. To compare the specific gravities of two minerals, pick up similar-sized specimens to get a general feeling for their densities. You will feel the difference—just as you would feel the difference between a box of Styrofoam packing material and a box of marbles. In Exercise 3.6 you will practice estimating specific gravity by heft, and then measure it precisely.

Name: _____   Section: _____

Course: _____   Date: _____

Separate the minerals provided by your instructor into those with relatively high specific gravity and those with relatively low specific gravity by hefting them.

(a) What luster do most of the minerals in the high specific gravity group have? _____ This is not a coincidence. In general, minerals with this luster have higher specific gravities than minerals with other lusters.

(b) To become familiar with the range of specific gravity in common minerals, select the most dense and least dense specimens based on their heft. Measure their specific gravities. To calculate density, measure the mass of the specimen by submerging it in a graduated cylinder and calculating the change in volume (see Chapter 1 for a detailed procedure). Density = mass ÷ volume.

Specific gravity of
most dense specimen _____

Specific gravity of
least dense specimen _____

(c) Do not try this procedure with halite (rock salt). Why wouldn't it work?

_____

3.4.9 Magnetism

A few minerals are attracted to a magnet or act like a magnet and attract metallic objects like nails or paper clips. The most common example is, appropriately, called *magnetite*. Because so few minerals are magnetic, this is a diagnostic property.

3.4.10 Feel

Some minerals feel greasy or slippery when you rub your fingers over them. They are greasy because their chemical bonds are so weak in one direction that the pressure of your fingers is enough to break them and to slide planes of atoms past one another. Talc and graphite are common examples.

3.4.11 Taste

Yes, geologists sometimes taste minerals. Taste is a *chemical* property, determined by the presence of certain elements. The most common example is halite (common salt), which tastes salty because of the chloride ion (Cl^-). **Do not taste minerals in your set unless instructed to do so!** We taste minerals only *after* we have narrowed the possibilities down to a few for which taste would be the diagnostic property. Why not taste every mineral? Because some taste bitter (like sylvite—KCl), some are poisonous, and you don't want to get other students' germs!

3.4.12 Odor

As geologists we use all of our senses to identify minerals. A few minerals, and the streak of a few others, have a distinctive odor. For example, the streak of minerals containing sulfur smells like rotten eggs, and the streak of some arsenic minerals smells like garlic.

3.4.13 Reaction with Dilute Hydrochloric Acid

Many minerals containing the carbonate anion (CO_3^{2-}) effervesce (fizz) when dilute hydrochloric acid is dropped on them. The acid frees carbon dioxide from the mineral, and the bubbles of gas escaping through the acid produce the fizz.

3.4.14 Tenacity

Tenacity refers to the way in which materials respond to being pushed, pulled, bent, or sheared. Most adjectives used to describe tenacity are probably familiar: *malleable* materials can be bent or hammered into a new shape; *ductile* materials can be pulled into wires; *brittle* materials shatter when hit hard; and *flexible* materials can bend. Flexibility is a diagnostic property for some minerals. After being bent, thin sheets of *elastic* minerals return to their original unbent shape, but sheets of *flexible* minerals retain the new shape.

3.5 Identifying Mineral Specimens

You are now ready to use these physical properties to identify minerals. Although there are more than 4,000 minerals, only about 30 occur commonly and an even smaller number make up most of the Earth's crust—the part of the geosphere we are most familiar with. Identification is easier if you follow the systematic approach used by geologists:

STEP 1 Assemble the equipment available in most geology classrooms to study minerals.

- A glass plate, penny, and knife or steel nail to test hardness
- A ceramic streak plate to test streak
- A magnifying glass, hand lens, or microscope to help determine cleavage
- Dilute hydrochloric acid to identify carbonate minerals
- A magnet to identify magnetic minerals

STEP 2 Observe or measure the specimen's physical properties. Profile the properties on a standardized data sheet like the one at the end of this chapter, as shown in the example given in TABLE 3.2.

TABLE 3.2 **Profile of a mineral's physical properties.**

Specimen number	Luster	Color	Hardness	Breakage	Other diagnostic properties
1	Metallic	Dark gray	Less than a fingernail	Excellent cleavage in one direction	Leaves a mark on a sheet of paper

STEP 3 Eliminate from consideration all minerals that do not have the properties you have recorded. This can be done systematically by using a **flowchart** (FIG. 3.7) that asks key questions in a logical sequence, so that each answer eliminates entire groups of minerals until only a few remain (one, if you're lucky). Or you can use a **determinative table** in which each column answers the same questions, like those at the branches of a flowchart. Appendices 3.1, 3.2, and 3.3 at the end of this chapter provide flowcharts and determinative tables. Experiment to find out which tool works best for you.

Use these steps to help you complete Exercise 3.7.

FIGURE 3.7 **Flowchart showing the steps used to identify minerals.**

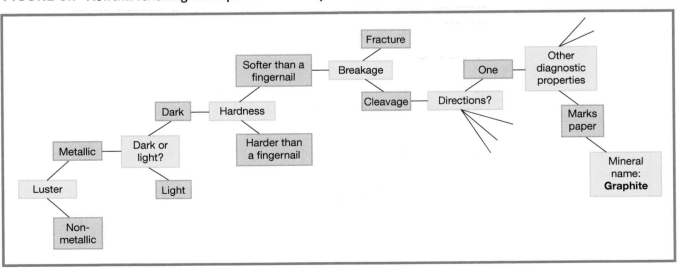

Note: For simplicity, only the path for the unknown mineral is shown.

Name: _____   Section: _____

Course: _____   Date: _____

Your instructor will provide a set of minerals to identify. Record the profile of physical properties for each specimen on the data sheets at the end of this chapter. Then use either the flowcharts (Appendix 3.1) or determinative tables (Appendix 3.2) to identify each mineral. If these lead to more than one possibility, look at Appendix 3.3 for additional information.

3.6 Mineral Classification

The minerals in your set were chosen because they are important rock-forming minerals that make up most of the geosphere, are economically valuable resources, or illustrate the physical properties used to study minerals. Geologists classify all minerals into a small number of groups based on their chemical composition. These groups include

- *silicates*, such as quartz, feldspars, amphiboles, and pyroxenes, which contain silicon and oxygen. Silicates are divided into *ferromagnesian* minerals, which contain iron and magnesium, and *nonferromagnesian* minerals, which do not contain those elements.
- *oxides*, such as magnetite (Fe_3O_4) and hematite (Fe_2O_3), in which a cation is bonded to oxygen anions.
- *sulfides*, such as pyrite (FeS_2) and sphalerite (ZnS), in which a cation is bonded to sulfur anions.
- *sulfates*, such as gypsum ($CaSO_4 \cdot 2H_2O$), in which cations are bonded to the sulfate complex (SO_4^{2-}).
- *halides*, such as halite ($NaCl$) and fluorite (CaF_2), in which cations are bonded to halogen anions (elements in the second column from the right in the periodic table).
- *carbonates*, such as calcite ($CaCO_3$) and dolomite ($CaMg[CO_3]_2$), containing the carbonate complex ($CO_3)^{2-}$.
- *native elements*, which are minerals that consist of atoms of a single element. The native elements most likely to be found in your mineral sets are graphite (carbon) and copper. You are unlikely to find more valuable native elements like gold, silver, and diamond (which is carbon, just like graphite).

3.7 Minerals in Everyday Life

When people think about minerals, many picture brilliantly colored gemstones like diamond, ruby, and emerald. Most minerals are less spectacular, but despite their "ordinary" appearance many play important roles in modern society and are extremely valuable. Indeed, stages in the development of our technologically advanced civilization are named for the resources that our ancestors learned to obtain from rocks and minerals: the Stone Age, when rocks were the major resource, was followed by the Copper Age, Bronze Age (copper plus tin melted from ores of these metals), and Iron Age (the iron initially from meteorites and later smelted from iron ores).

Ore minerals are those containing metals that can be separated from the rest of the elements in the minerals, usually by melting. These, mostly oxides and sulfides, are important resources, but so too are minerals whose physical properties make them valuable. Our ancestors were the first economic geologists, learning how to use minerals based on their physical properties and then figuring out where to find them. In Exercise 3.8, let's look at some of the physical properties that make minerals useful.

EXERCISE 3.8 **Everyday Uses of Minerals**

Name: _____ Section: _____

Course: _____ Date: _____

In following table, indicate what physical property you think would make a mineral appropriate for the use indicated, and name a mineral from your set that could be used for this purpose. In some instances, more than one mineral will meet the requirements and more than one property is required.

Economic use	Physical property or properties needed	Minerals
Abrasives (e.g., sandpaper)		
Old-time window coverings before glass was widely available		
Modern window panes		
Writing on paper		
Lubricant for locks		
After-bath powder		
Bright eye shadow		
Pigment for paints		
Navigation with a compass		

?**What Do You Think** Copper is used widely for electrical wires, pipes, construction (and pennies), and is finding new uses today in high-tech electronics. Exploration geologists recently discovered a very large deposit of copper minerals in a remote part of the woods in northern Maine shown in the accompanying illustration. Imagine that you own land in the area and that a mining company has made an offer to buy or lease the property so it can extract the copper ore. On a separate sheet of paper, explain what you think the pros and cons are to deciding whether to sell or not to sell.

In these appendices, we present two ways of identifying or determining minerals. First, in Appendix 3.1, we provide flowcharts for students who may be more visually oriented. Then, in Appendix 3.2, we present the same information in the more standard determinative tables. Because both students and geologists think and work in different ways, we felt it was important to provide both options. Use whichever works best for you!

Mineral Identification Flowcharts

A. Minerals with Metallic Luster

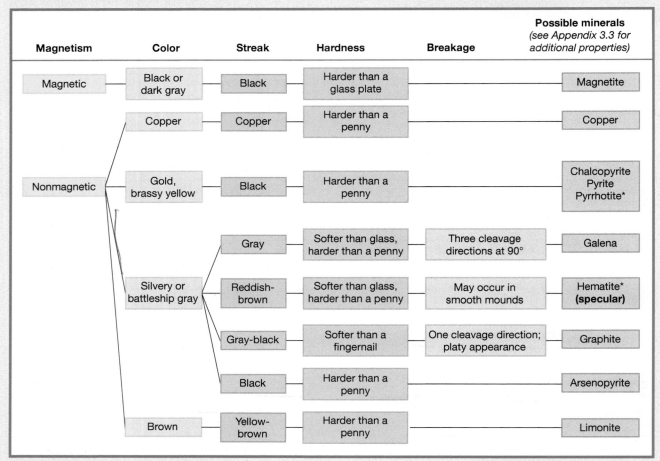

* Pyrrhotite and hematite are sometimes weakly magnetic.

Mineral Identification Flowcharts

B. **Minerals with Nonmetallic Luster, Dark Colored**

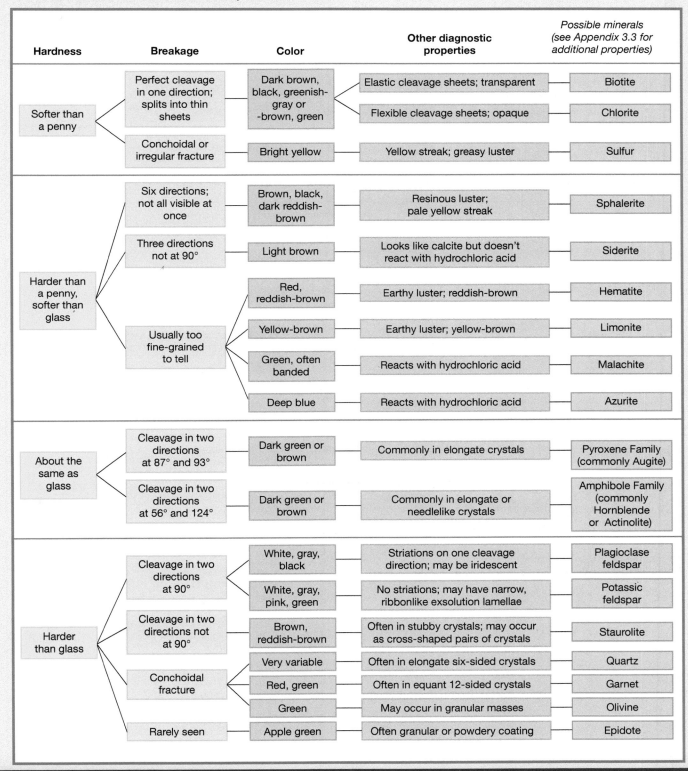

Hardness	Breakage	Color	Other diagnostic properties	Possible minerals (see Appendix 3.3 for additional properties)
Softer than a penny	Perfect cleavage in one direction; splits into thin sheets	Dark brown, black, greenish-gray or -brown, green	Elastic cleavage sheets; transparent	Biotite
			Flexible cleavage sheets; opaque	Chlorite
	Conchoidal or irregular fracture	Bright yellow	Yellow streak; greasy luster	Sulfur
Harder than a penny, softer than glass	Six directions; not all visible at once	Brown, black, dark reddish-brown	Resinous luster; pale yellow streak	Sphalerite
	Three directions not at 90°	Light brown	Looks like calcite but doesn't react with hydrochloric acid	Siderite
	Usually too fine-grained to tell	Red, reddish-brown	Earthy luster; reddish-brown	Hematite
		Yellow-brown	Earthy luster; yellow-brown	Limonite
		Green, often banded	Reacts with hydrochloric acid	Malachite
		Deep blue	Reacts with hydrochloric acid	Azurite
About the same as glass	Cleavage in two directions at 87° and 93°	Dark green or brown	Commonly in elongate crystals	Pyroxene Family (commonly Augite)
	Cleavage in two directions at 56° and 124°	Dark green or brown	Commonly in elongate or needlelike crystals	Amphibole Family (commonly Hornblende or Actinolite)
Harder than glass	Cleavage in two directions at 90°	White, gray, black	Striations on one cleavage direction; may be iridescent	Plagioclase feldspar
		White, gray, pink, green	No striations; may have narrow, ribbonlike exsolution lamellae	Potassic feldspar
	Cleavage in two directions not at 90°	Brown, reddish-brown	Often in stubby crystals; may occur as cross-shaped pairs of crystals	Staurolite
	Conchoidal fracture	Very variable	Often in elongate six-sided crystals	Quartz
		Red, green	Often in equant 12-sided crystals	Garnet
		Green	May occur in granular masses	Olivine
	Rarely seen	Apple green	Often granular or powdery coating	Epidote

Mineral Identification Flowcharts

C. Minerals with Nonmetallic Luster, Light Colored

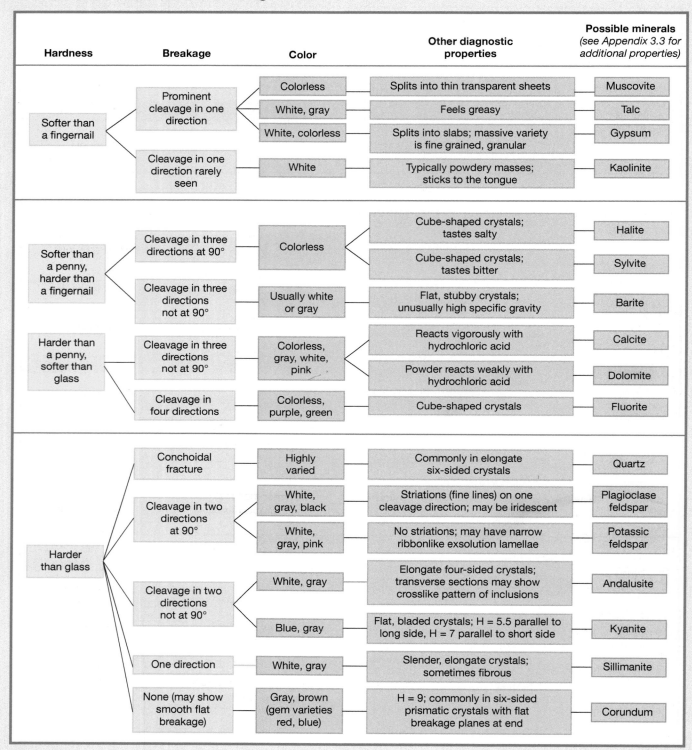

Determinative Tables for Systematic Mineral Identification

Sequence of questions: Luster? Approximate hardness? Streak? Breakage? Color? Other?

TABLE 1 **Minerals with metallic luster**

(a) Hardness less than 2.5 (softer than a fingernail)

Streak	Cleavage or fracture	H	Color	Other diagnostic properties	Mineral name (composition)
Black	Perfect cleavage in one direction	1	Dark gray-black	Greasy feel; leaves a mark on paper; SpG = 2.23	Graphite C
Yellow-brown	Diffcult to see	—	Yellow-brown	Very rarely in masses with metallic luster; more commonly dull, earthy; SpG = 3.6–4	Limonite $FeO(OH) \cdot nH_2O$

(b) Hardness between 2.5 and 5.5 (harder than a fingernail; softer than glass)

Streak	Cleavage or fracture	H	Color	Other diagnostic properties	Mineral name (composition)
Gray	Three directions at 90° angles	2.5	Lead gray	Commonly in cubic crystals; SpG = 7.4–7.6	Galena PbS
Black	Rarely seen	3	Bronze-brown when fresh	Commonly with purplish, iridescent tarnish; SpG = 5.06–5.08	Bornite Cu_5FeS_4
Black	Rarely seen	3.5–4	Brassy yellow	Often tarnished; similar to pyrite but not in cubes	Chalcopyrite $CuFeS_2$
Black	Rarely seen	4	Brown-bronze	Slightly magnetic; SpG = 4.62	Pyrrhotite $Fe_{1-x}S$
Copper-red	Rarely seen	2.5–3	Copper	Often in branching masses; SpG = 8.9	Copper (Cu)

(c) Hardness greater than 5.5 (harder than glass; cannot be scratched by a knife)

Streak	Cleavage or fracture	H	Color	Other diagnostic properties	Mineral name (composition)
Black	Conchoidal fracture	6–6.5	Brassy yellow	Commonly in 12-sided crystals or cubes with striated faces; SpG = 5.02	Pyrite FeS_2
Black	Rarely seen	6	Iron black	Strongly magnetic; SpG = 5.18	Magnetite Fe_3O_4
Black	Rarely seen	5.5–6	Silver white	Streak smells like garlic because of arsenic; SpG = 6.07	Arsenopyrite FeAsS
Reddish-brown	Rarely seen	5.5–6.5	Black, red	Black variety is metallic; red variety is more common and has nonmetallic, earthy luster	Hematite Fe_2O_3

Determinative Tables for Systematic Mineral Identification

TABLE 2 Minerals with nonmetallic luster

(a) Hardness less than 2.5 (softer than a fingernail)

Streak	Cleavage or fracture	H	Color	Other diagnostic properties	Mineral name (composition)
Yellow	Conchoidal or uneven fracture	1.5–2.5	Bright yellow	Resinous luster; SpG = 2.05–2.09	**Sulfur** S
White or colorless	Perfect cleavage in one direction	2–2.5	Colorless, light tan, yellow	Can be peeled into transparent, elastic sheets; SpG = 2.76–2.88	**Muscovite** $KAl_2(AlSi_3O_{10})(OH)_2$
	Perfect cleavage in one direction	1	Green, gray, white	Greasy feel; may occur in irregular masses (soapstone); SpG = 2.7–2.8	**Talc** $Mg_3Si_4O_{10}(OH)_2$
	Perfect cleavage in one direction; may show two other directions not at 90°	2	Colorless, white, gray	Occurs in clear crystals or gray or white, earthy masses (alabaster); SpG = 2.32	**Gypsum** $CaSO_4 \cdot 2H_2O$
	Three directions at 90°	2	Colorless, white	Cubic crystals like halite but has very bitter taste; SpG = 1.99	**Sylvite** KCl
	Perfect in one direction, but rarely seen	2–2.5	White	Usually in dull, powdery masses that stick to the tongue; SpG = 2.6	**Kaolinite** $Al_2Si_2O_5(OH)_4$
	Perfect in one direction, but not always visible	2–5	Green, white	Platy and fibrous (asbestos) varieties; greasy luster; SpG = 2.5–2.6	**Serpentine** $Mg_3Si_2O_5(OH)_4$
	—	—	White, brown, gray	Not really a mineral; rock often made of small, spherical particles containing several clay minerals; SpG = 2–2.55	**Bauxite** Mixture of aluminum hydroxides
Brown or green	Perfect cleavage in one direction	2.5–3	Brown, black, green	Can be peeled into thin, elastic sheets; SpG = 2.8–3.2	**Biotite** $K(Fe,Mg)_3AlSi_3O_{10}(OH)_2$
	Perfect cleavage in direction	2–2.5	Green, dark green	A mica-like mineral, but sheets are flexible not elastic; SpG = 2.6–3.3	**Chlorite** Complex Fe-Mg sheet silicate

(b) Hardness between 2.5 and 5.5 (harder than a fingernail; softer than glass)

Streak	Cleavage or fracture	H	Color	Other diagnostic properties	Mineral name (composition)
Green	—	3.5–4	Bright green	Occurs in globular or elongate masses; reacts with HCl; SpG = 3.9–4.03	**Malachite** $Cu_2CO_3(OH)_2$

Determinative Tables for Systematic Mineral Identification

TABLE 2 **Minerals with nonmetallic luster**

Streak	Cleavage or fracture	H	Color	Other diagnostic properties	Mineral name (composition)
Blue	—	3.5	Intense blue	Often in platy crystals or spherical masses; reacts with HCl; SpG = 3.77	**Azurite** $Cu_3(CO_3)_2(OH)_2$
Reddish-brown	—	—	Reddish brown	Usually in earthy masses; also occurs as black, metallic crystals; SpG = 5.5–6.5	**Hematite** Fe_2O_3
Yellow-brown	—	—	Brown, tan	Earthy, powdery masses and coatings on other minerals; SpG = 3.6–4	**Limonite** $FeO(OH) \cdot nH_2O$
	Three directions not at 90°	3.5–4	Light to dark brown	Often in rhombic crystals; reacts with hot HCl; SpG = 3.96	**Siderite** $FeCO_3$
	Six directions, few of which are usually visible	3.5	Brown, white, yellow, black, colorless	Resinous luster; SpG = 3.9–4.1	**Sphalerite** ZnS
White or colorless	Three directions at 90°	2.5	Colorless, white	Cubic crystals or massive (rock salt); salty taste; SpG = 2.5	**Halite** NaCl
	Three directions not at 90°	3	Varied; usually white or colorless	Rhombic or elongated crystals; reacts with HCl; SpG = 2.71	**Calcite** $CaCO_3$
	Three directions not at 90°	3.5–4	Varied; commonly white or pink	Rhombic crystals; *powder* reacts with HCl but crystals may not; SpG = 2.85	**Dolomite** $CaMg(CO_3)_2$
	Three directions at 90°	3–3.5	Colorless, white	SpG = 4.5 (unusually high for a nonmetallic mineral)	**Barite** $BaSO_4$
	Four directions	4	Colorless, purple, yellow, blue, green	Often in cubic crystals; SpG = 3.18	**Fluorite** CaF_2
	One direction, poor	5	Usually green or brown	Elongate six-sided crystals; may be purple, blue, colorless; SpG = 3.15–3.20	**Apatite** $Ca_5(PO_4)_3(OH,Cl,F)$

(c) Hardness between 5.5 and 9 (harder than glass or a knife; softer than a streak plate)

Streak	Cleavage or fracture	H	Color	Other diagnostic properties	Mineral name (composition)
	Conchoidal fracture	7	Red, green, brown, black, colorless, pink, orange	Equant 12-sided crystals; SpG = 3.5–4.3	**Garnet family** Complex Ca, Fe, Mg, Al, Cr, Mn silicate
	Two directions at 90°	6	Colorless, salmon, gray, green, white	Stubby prismatic crystals; three polymorphs: orthoclase, microcline, sanidine; may show exsolution lamellae; SpG = 2.54–2.62	**Potassic feldspar** $KAlSi_3O_8$

Determinative Tables for Systematic Mineral Identification

TABLE 2 **Minerals with nonmetallic luster** *(continued)*

Streak	Cleavage or fracture	H	Color	Other diagnostic properties	Mineral name (composition)
White or colorless	Two directions at 90°	6	Colorless, white, gray, black	Striations (fine lines) on one of the two cleavage directions; solid solution between sodium (albite) and calcium (anorthite) plagioclase; SpG = 2.62–2.76	**Plagioclase feldspar** $CaAl_2Si_2O_8$ $NaAlSi_3O_8$
	Conchoidal fracture	7	Colorless, pink, purple, gray, black, green, yellow	Elongate six-sided crystals; SpG = 2.65	**Quartz** SiO_2
	Rarely seen	7.5	Gray, white, brown	Elongate four-sided crystals; SpG = 3.16–3.23	**Andalusite** Al_2SiO_5
	One direction	6–7	White, rarely green	Long, slender crystals, often fibrous; SpG = 3.23	**Sillimanite** Al_2SiO_5
	One direction	5 *and* 7	Blue, blue-gray to white	Bladed crystals; *two hardnesses*: H = 5 parallel to long direction of crystal, H = 7 across the long direction	**Kyanite** Al_2SiO_5
Colorless to light green	Conchoidal fracture	6.5–7	Most commonly green	Stubby crystals and granular masses; solid solution between Fe (fayalite) and Mg (forsterite)	**Olivine family** Fe_2SiO_4 Mg_2SiO_4
	Two directions at 56° and 124°	5–6	Dark green to black	An amphibole with elongate crystals; SpG = 3–3.4	**Hornblende** Complex double-chain silicate with Ca, Na, Fe, Mg
	Two directions at 56° and 124°	5–6	Pale to dark green	An amphibole with elongate crystals; SpG = 3–3.3	**Actinolite** Double-chain silicate with Ca, Fe, Mg
	Two directions at 87° and 93°	5–6	Dark green to black	A pyroxene with elongate crystals; SpG = 3.2–3.3	**Augite** Single-chain silicate with Ca, Na, Mg, Fe, Al
	One direction perfect, one poor; not at 90°	6–7	Apple green to black	Elongate crystals and fine-grained masses; SpG = 3.25–3.45	**Epidote** Complex twin silicate with Ca, Al, Fe, Mg
No streak; mineral scratches streak plate	One direction, imperfect	7.5–8	Blue-green, emerald green, yellow, pink, white	Six-sided crystals with flat ends; SpG = 2.65–2.8; gem variety: emerald (green)	**Beryl** $Be_3Al_2Si_6O_{18}$
	—	7–7.5	Dark brown, Reddish-brown, brownish-black	Stubby or cross-shaped crystals; SpG = 3.65–3.75	**Staurolite** Hydrous Fe, Al silicate
	No cleavage	9	Gray, light brown; gem varieties red (ruby), blue (sapphire)	Six-sided crystals with flat ends	**Corundum** Al_2O_3

Common Minerals and Their Properties

Mineral	Additional diagnostic properties and occurrences
Actinolite	Elongate green crystals; cleavage at 56° and 124°; H = 5.5–6. An amphibole found in metamorphic rocks.
Amphibole*	Stubby rod-shaped crystals common in igneous rocks; slender crystals common in metamorphic rocks; two cleavage directions at 56° and 124°.
Andalusite	Elongate gray crystals with rectangular cross sections.
Apatite	H = 5; pale to dark green, brown, white; white streak; six-sided crystals.
Augite	H = 5.5–6; green to black rod-shaped crystals; cleavage at 87° and 93°. A pyroxene common in igneous rocks.
Azurite	Deep blue; reacts with HCl. Copper will plate out on a steel nail dipped into a drop of HCl and placed on this mineral.
Barite	H = 3–3.5; SpG is unusually high for nonmetallic mineral.
Bauxite	Gray-brown earthy *rock* commonly containing spherical masses of clay minerals and mineraloids.
Beryl	Six-sided crystals; H = 7.5–8.
Biotite	Dark-colored mica; one perfect cleavage into flexible sheets.
Bornite	High SpG; iridescent coating on surface gives it "peacock ore" nickname.
Calcite	Reacts with HCl. Produces double image from text viewed through transparent cleavage fragments.
Chalcopyrite	Similar to pyrite, but softer and typically has iridescent tarnish.
Chlorite*	Similar to biotite, but does not break into thin, flexible sheets; forms in metamorphic rocks.
Copper	Copper-red color and high specific gravity are diagnostic.
Corundum	Six-sided prismatic crystals with flat ends; hardness of 9 is diagnostic. Most lab specimens have dull luster and are gray, brown.
Dolomite	Similar to calcite, but only weak or no reaction with HCl placed on a grain of the mineral; *powder* reacts strongly. Slightly curved rhombohedral crystals.
Epidote	Small crystals and thin, granular coatings form in some metamorphic rocks and [by alteration of] some igneous rocks.
Fluorite	Commonly in cube-shaped crystals with four cleavage directions cutting corners of the cubes.
Galena	Commonly in cube-shaped crystals with three perfect cleavages at 90°.
Garnet*	Most commonly dark red; 12- or 24-sided crystals in metamorphic rocks.
Graphite	Greasy feel; leaves a mark on paper.
Gypsum	Two varieties: *selenite* is colorless and nearly transparent with perfect cleavage; *alabaster* is a rock—an aggregate of grains with an earthy luster.
Halite	Cubic crystals and taste are diagnostic.
Hematite	Two varieties: most common is reddish-brown masses with earthy luster; rare variety is black crystals with metallic luster.

* Indicates mineral family.

Common Minerals and Their Properties (continued)

Mineral	Additional diagnostic properties and occurrences
Hornblende	Dark green to black amphibole; two cleavages at 56° and 124°.
Kaolinite	Earthy, powdery white to gray masses; sticks to tongue.
Kyanite	Bladed blue or blue-green crystals; H = 5 parallel to blade, H = 7 across blade.
Limonite	Earthy, yellow-brown masses, sometimes powdery; forms by the "rusting" (oxidation) of iron-bearing minerals.
Magnetite	Gray-black; H = 6; magnetic.
Malachite	Bright green. Copper will plate out on a steel nail dipped into a drop of HCl and placed on this mineral.
Muscovite	A colorless mica; one perfect cleavage; peels into flexible sheets.
Olivine	Commonly as aggregates of green granular crystals.
Plagioclase feldspar*	Play of colors and striations distinguish plagioclase feldspars from potassic feldspars, which do not show these properties.
Potassic feldspar*	
Pyrite	Brassy gold color, hardness, and black streak are diagnostic. Cubic crystals with striations on their faces or in 12-sided crystals with five-sided faces.
Pyrrhotite	Brownish-bronze color; black streak; may be slightly magnetic.
Pyroxene*	Two cleavages at 87° and 93°; major constituent of mafic and ultramafic igneous rocks.
Quartz	Wide range of colors; six-sided crystal shape, high hardness (7) and conchoidal fracture are diagnostic.
Serpentine	Dull white, gray, or green masses; sometimes fibrous (asbestos).
Siderite	Three cleavages not at 90°; looks like brown calcite; powder may react to HCl.
Sillimanite	Gray, white, brown; slender crystals, sometimes needlelike.
Sphalerite	Wide variety of colors (including colorless); distinctive pale yellow streak.
Staurolite	Reddish-brown to dark brown stubby crystals in metamorphic rocks.
Sulfur	Bright yellow with yellow streak; greasy luster.
Sylvite	Looks like halite but has very bitter taste.
Talc	Greasy feel; H = 1.

*Indicates mineral family.

Name _____

MINERAL PROFILE DATA SHEET

Sample	Luster	Hardness	Streak	Color	Cleavage or fracture (describe)	Other properties	Mineral name and composition

MINERAL PROFILE DATA SHEET

Name _____

Sample	Luster	Hardness	Streak	Color	Cleavage or fracture (describe)	Other properties	Mineral name and composition

MINERAL PROFILE DATA SHEET

Name _____

Sample	Luster	Hardness	Streak	Color	Cleavage or fracture (describe)	Other properties	Mineral name and composition

MINERAL PROFILE DATA SHEET

Name _____

Sample	Luster	Hardness	Streak	Color	Cleavage or fracture (describe)	Other properties	Mineral name and composition

4

Minerals, Rocks, and the Rock Cycle

From left to right: sedimentary (conglomerate), metamorphic (gneiss), and igneous (granite) rocks are the three main classes of rock.

- Understand the differences between minerals and rocks

- Become familiar with the three main classes of rock: igneous, sedimentary, metamorphic

- Understand the different processes that form rocks. Learn how the grains in a rock act as records of geologic processes

- Use textures and mineral content to determine if rocks are igneous, sedimentary, or metamorphic

- Understand the rock cycle: how rocks are recycled to make new ones

MATERIALS
NEEDED

- An assortment of igneous, sedimentary, and metamorphic rocks

- Supplies to make artificial igneous, sedimentary, and metamorphic rocks; tongs for moving hot petri dishes, hot plate, sugar, thymol, Na-acetate in a dropper bottle, sand grains, glass petri dishes, $Ca(OH)_2$ solution, straws, Play-Doh, plastic coffee stirring rods, plastic chips

- Magnifying glass or hand lens

- Mineral-testing supplies: streak plate, steel nail, and so on

4.1 Introduction

A rock is an aggregate of mineral grains, fragments of previously existing rock, or a mass of natural glass. Rocks can form in a variety of ways—through cooling and solidification of a melt, by cementation of loose grains, by precipitation from water solutions, or from changes that happen in response to temperature and pressure underground. Geologists can identify rocks and interpret aspects of Earth's history by studying two principal characteristics of rocks: **rock composition** (the proportions of different chemicals and thus the identity of minerals or glass that make up a rock) and **rock texture** (the dimensions and shape of grains, and the ways that grains are arranged, oriented, and held together). On our dynamic planet, rocks don't survive forever—nature recycles materials, using those in one rock to form new rocks through a series of steps called the *rock cycle.*

In this chapter, we first introduce the three basic classes of rocks. Then we describe how to observe the characteristics of rocks and how to use these characteristics to classify rocks. Then you will make your own "rocks" in the classroom and see how different processes produce different textures. By combining your mineral identification skills and knowledge of rock textures, you can face the challenge of determining how specimens of common rocks have formed.

4.2 The Three Classes of Rocks

Geologists struggled for centuries with the question of how to classify rocks. They finally concluded that rocks can best be classified on the basis of how they formed. Rock composition and texture provide the basis for this classification, for these characteristics reflect the process of formation. In modern terminology, we distinguish three classes of rocks: igneous, sedimentary, and metamorphic.

- **Igneous rocks** form through the cooling and solidification of molten rock, which is created by the melting of preexisting rock in the mantle or lower crust. We refer to molten rock below Earth's surface as **magma** and to molten rock that has erupted onto the surface as **lava**. Some volcanoes erupt explosively, blasting rock fragments into the air, and when these fragments fall back to Earth, coalesce, and solidify, the resulting rock is also considered to be igneous.

- **Sedimentary rocks** form at or near the surface of the Earth in two basic ways: (1) when grains of preexisting rocks accumulate, are buried, and then are cemented together by minerals precipitating out of groundwater; and (2) when minerals precipitate out of water near the Earth's surface, either directly or through the life function of an organism, and either form a solid mass or are cemented together later. The grains that become incorporated in sedimentary rocks form when preexisting rocks are broken down into their smallest pieces by processes and interactions with air, water, and living organisms. These interactions are called **weathering**. Some weathering simply involves the physical fragmentation of rock. Other kinds of weathering involve chemical reactions that produce new minerals, most notably clay. The products of weathering can be transported (eroded) by water, ice, or wind to the site where they are deposited (settle out), buried, and transformed into new rock.

- **Metamorphic rocks** form when preexisting rocks are subjected to physical and chemical conditions within the Earth, such as the increase in pressure and temperature and/or shearing at elevated temperature. For example, when buried very deeply, rock is warmed to high temperature and squeezed by high pressure. The texture and/or mineral content of the initial rock changes in response to the new conditions in *the solid state*. Metamorphic rock thus forms without the melting or weathering that makes igneous and sedimentary rocks.

Name: _____   Section: _____

Course: _____   Date: _____

Three settings are described below in which three different classes of rocks form. Fill in the blanks by indicating which class of rocks is the result.

(a) Along the coast, waves carry sand out into deeper, quieter water, where it accumulates and gradually becomes buried. A rock formed from sand grains cemented together is _____.

(b) Thick flows of glowing red lava engulf farms and villages on the flanks of Mt. Etna, a volcano in Sicily. The cold, black rock formed when these flows are cool enough to walk on is _____.

(c) The broad tundra plains of northern Canada expose gray, massive rock that formed many kilometers below a mountain belt. This rock, exposed only after the overlying rock was stripped away, is _____.

4.2.1 The Rock Cycle

An igneous rock that has been exposed at the surface of the Earth will not last forever. Minerals that crystallized from magma to form the rock can be broken apart at the surface by weathering, undergo **erosion** (the grinding effects of moving ice, water, or air), be transported by streams, be deposited in the ocean, and be cemented together to form a sedimentary rock. These same minerals, now in a sedimentary rock, can later be buried so deeply beneath other sedimentary rocks that they are heated and squeezed to form a metamorphic rock with new minerals. Erosion may eventually expose the metamorphic rock at the Earth's surface, where it can be weathered to form new sediment and eventually a different sedimentary rock. Or the metamorphic rock may be buried so deeply that it melts to produce magma and eventually becomes a new igneous rock with still different minerals.

This flux (flow) of material from one rock type to another over geologic time is called the **rock cycle** (**FIG. 4.1**). The rock cycle involves the reuse of mineral grains or the breakdown of minerals into their constituent atoms and the reuse of those atoms to make other minerals. Rocks formed at each step of the rock cycle look very different from their predecessors because of the different processes by which they formed.

4.3 A Rock Is More than the Sum of Its Minerals

The first thing a geologist wants to determine about a rock is whether it is igneous, sedimentary, or metamorphic. Composition *alone* (i.e., the component minerals of the rock) is rarely enough to define a rock's origin, because some of the most common minerals (quartz, potassic feldspar, sodium-rich plagioclase feldspar) are found in all three rock classes. For example, a rock made of these minerals could be igneous (granite), sedimentary (sandstone), or metamorphic (gneiss). Texture *alone* can identify which type of process was involved for many rocks, but some textures can also develop in all three types of rock. The best clue to the origin of a rock is its unique combination of texture *and* mineralogy.

4.3.1 Describing Texture

Geologists begin characterizing a rock's texture by asking: Does the rock consist of a mass of glass or does it consist of grains? If it consists of glass, it will be shiny and develop conchoidal fractures (curving, ridged surfaces). Rocks composed of glass

FIGURE 4.1 The rock cycle.

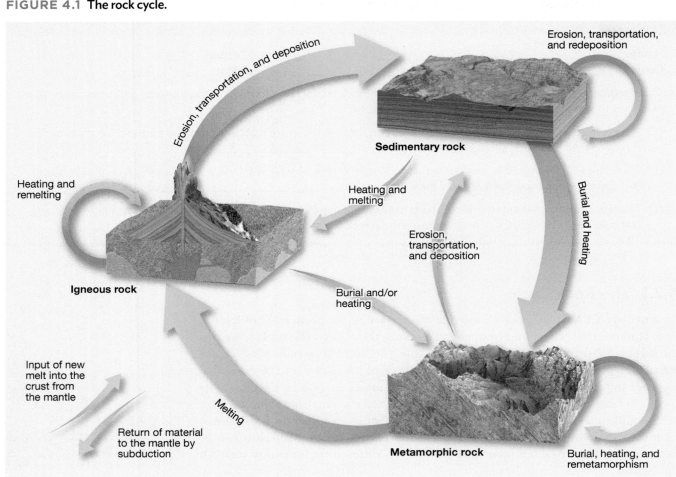

are relatively rare—they form only at certain kinds of volcanoes. In most cases, we jump to the next question: What are the grains like, and how are they connected? To answer this question, we first describe the size and shape of grains and then determine if the grains are interlocking, like pieces of a jigsaw puzzle, or if they are stuck together by cement (mineral "glue").

Grain Size A rock description should include the size(s) of grains and whether the rock has a single (homogeneous) grain size, a wide range of sizes, or two distinctly different sizes. Are the grains **coarse** enough to be identified easily;

TABLE 4.1 **Common grain size terminology**

Grain size term	Practical definition	Approximate size range
Coarse grained	Grains are large enough so you can identify the minerals or grains present.	Larger than 5 mm
Medium grained	Individual grains can be seen with the naked eye but are too small to be identified.	0.1–4.9 mm
Fine grained	Individual grains are too small to be seen with the naked eye or identified with a hand lens; feels "gritty" to the edge of a fingernail.	Smaller than 0.1 mm
Very fine grained	Individual grains cannot be seen with the naked eye *or* a hand lens; feels smooth to the edge of a fingernail.	Much smaller than 0.1 mm
Glassy	No grains at all; rock is a homogeneous mass of glass.	—

FIGURE 4.2 Grain sizes in sedimentary rocks (a–d) and an igneous rock (e).

(a) Very fine grained.

(b) Fine grained.

(c) Medium grained.

(d) Coarse grained.

(e) Glassy.

medium sized, so you can see that there are separate grains but can't easily identify them; **fine**, so that they can barely be recognized; or **very fine**, so small that they cannot be seen even with a magnifying glass? Special terms are used for grain size in igneous and sedimentary rocks, but here we use common words that work just as well (**TABLE 4.1** and **FIG. 4.2**).

Note that some rocks contain grains of different sizes, as in Figure 4.2d where very coarse grains are embedded in a very-fine-grained matrix. As we will see later, these mixed grain sizes give important information about the rock-forming processes.

Grain Shape When we describe the shape of grains, we ask: Are the grains **equant**, meaning they have the same dimension in all directions, or **inequant**, meaning that the dimension in different directions is different? Grains that resemble spheres or cubes are equant, like the garnets in FIGURE 4.3a or the halite crystals in FIGURE 4.3b. Those that resemble rods, sheets, ovals, or have an irregular form are inequant, like the shapes in FIGURE 4.3c, d. Next, we look at the grains to see if they are rounded, angular, or some combination of these shapes. Finally we ask: Are *all* grains the same shape, or do they vary depending on mineral type or on position within the rock? Each of these characteristics tells us something about the formation of the rock.

Relationships among Grains During most igneous- and metamorphic-rock-forming processes, and during some sedimentary-rock-forming processes, crystallizing minerals interfere with one another and interlock like a three-dimensional jigsaw puzzle (FIG. 4.4a, b). We refer to the result as a **crystalline texture**. A very different texture results from sedimentary processes that deposit grains and then cement them together (FIG. 4.4c, d). Such sedimentary rocks are said to have a **clastic texture**, and individual grains in these rocks are called **clasts**.

Grain Orientation and Alignment The orientation of grains relative to one another often provides a key clue to the classification of a rock. For example, in most igneous rocks, the inequant grains are randomly oriented in that they point in a variety of directions. In many metamorphic rocks, however, inequant minerals,

FIGURE 4.3 Typical grain shapes.

(a) Garnet crystals in metamorphic rock.

(b) Halite crystals in sedimentary rock.

(c) Rounded grains.

(d) Angular grains. (Photo courtesy of Michael C. Rygel.)

FIGURE 4.4 Grain relationships.

(a) Crystalline texture: interlocking quartz and feldspar grains in an igneous rock. The dark grains are biotite and hornblende.

(b) Crystalline texture: photomicrograph of interlocking calcite grains in a metamorphic rock.

(c) Clastic texture: cemented grains in a sedimentary rock.

(d) Clastic texture: cemented fossils.

such as platy micas or elongate amphiboles, are oriented parallel to one another. Thus, when looking at a rock, you should ask: Are the inequant grains aligned parallel to one another or are they randomly oriented throughout the rock? If the grains are aligned parallel to one another, the rock develops a type of layering called **foliation** (**FIG. 4.5**).

Now that we've developed a basic vocabulary for important characteristics of rocks, we can begin to describe a rock the way a geologist would. You will try this in Exercise 4.2.

FIGURE 4.5 A foliated rock (schist).

Name: _____ **Section:** _____

Course: _____ **Date:** _____

Describe the *texture* of the rocks provided by your instructor. Be sure to consider the size and shape of grains, the relationships among grains, and whether grains are randomly oriented or aligned. Use your own words—the formal geologic terms for the textures will be introduced later.

(a) Rock 1:

_____

_____

_____

(b) Rock 2:

_____

_____

_____

(c) Rock 3:

_____

_____

_____

(d) What textural features are common to all three rock samples, and which are not?

_____

_____

_____

(e) Did all three rocks form by the same process? Explain your reasoning.

_____

_____

_____

_____

4.4 The Processes That Produce Textures

The best way to understand how a rock's texture forms is to observe the rock-forming process in action. You can't go inside a lava flow to watch an igneous rock crystallize, or deep below a mountain belt to see rock metamorphose, or under the ocean floor to watch sediment become a sedimentary rock—but you can *model* the formation of igneous, sedimentary, and metamorphic rocks well enough in the classroom to understand how textures form. You will use textural features more fully later in detailed interpretations of igneous, sedimentary, and metamorphic rocks. In Exercise 4.3, you will conduct simple experiments to understand how igneous, sedimentary, and metamorphic processes create different and distinctive textures.

EXERCISE 4.3   **Understanding the Origin of Rock Textures**

Name: _____   Section: _____

Course: _____   Date: _____

In this exercise, you will conduct simple experiments to better understand rock textures.

(a) **Crystalline igneous rock.** Partially fill ($\frac{1}{2}$ inch) a glass petri dish with the powder provided by your instructor. Heat on a hot plate until the material melts completely. Carefully remove the dish from the hot plate using forceps, and allow the liquid to cool. Observe the crystallization process closely. You may have to add a crystal seed if crystallization does not begin in a few minutes. Congratulations—you have just made a "magma" and then an "igneous rock" with an interlocking crystalline texture.
  • Describe the crystallization process. How and where did individual grains grow, and how did they eventually join with neighboring grains?

_____

_____

_____

Sketch and describe the texture of the cooled "rock."

Sketch: Describe: _____

                                         _____

                                         _____

                                         _____

                                         _____

                                         _____

                                         _____

                                         _____

                                         _____

This crystalline texture formed when crystals in the cooling "magma" grew until they interfered with one another and eventually interlocked to form a cohesive solid. Crystals grow only when the magma cools slowly enough for atoms to have time to fit into a crystalline lattice.

(continued)

Name: _____   Section: _____
Course: _____   Date: _____

(b) Glassy igneous texture. Add sugar ($\frac{1}{2}$ inch) to another petri dish, melt it on a hot plate, and allow it to cool.

Describe the cooling process and sketch the resulting texture.

Sketch: Describe: _____

_____

_____

_____

_____

_____

_____

_____

This glassy texture is typical of igneous rocks that cool so quickly that atoms do not have time to arrange into crystalline lattices. In some cooling lavas, the bubbles that you saw may be preserved as the lava freezes.

(c) Clastic sedimentary texture. Cover the bottom of another petri dish with a mixture of sand grains and small pebbles. Add a small amount of the liquid provided by your instructor, and allow the mixture to sit until the liquid has evaporated. Now turn the dish upside down.
  • Why don't the grains fall out of the dish?

_____

_____

Examine the "rock" with your hand lens. Sketch and describe the texture.

Sketch: Describe: _____

_____

_____

_____

_____

_____

_____

_____

You have just made a clastic sedimentary rock composed of individual grains cemented to one another.

(continued)

Name: _____   Section: _____
Course: _____   Date: _____

(d) **Fine-grained chemical sedimentary texture.** Using a straw, blow *gently* into the beaker of clear liquid provided by your instructor until you notice a change in the water. Continue blowing for another minute and then observe what happens.

• Describe the change that occurred in the liquid as you were blowing into it.

_____

_____

• Describe what happened to the liquid after you stopped blowing.

_____

_____

• Pour off the liquid and add a drop of dilute hydrochloric acid to the mineral that you formed. What is the mineral?

_____

You have just made a chemical sediment, one that forms when minerals precipitate (grow and settle out) from a solution. This sediment would be compacted and solidified to make a very fine-grained sedimentary rock.

(e) **Crystalline chemical sedimentary texture.** Suspend a piece of cotton twine in a supersaturated salt solution, and allow the salt to evaporate over a few days.

Sketch and describe the texture of the salt crystals attached to the twine; compare it with the interlocking igneous texture from Exercise 4.3a.

Sketch: Describe: _____

_____

_____

_____

_____

_____

_____

_____

_____

You've now seen that crystalline textures can form in both sedimentary and igneous rocks. How might you distinguish the rocks? (*Hint:* Think about whether the chemical composition of lava is the same as that of seawater.) By the way, crystalline textures also form in metamorphic rocks.

_____

_____

_____

(continued)

Name: _____ Section: _____

Course: _____ Date: _____

(f) **Metamorphic foliation.** Take a handful of small plastic chips and push them with random orientation into a mass of Play-Doh. Then flatten the Play-Doh with a book.

Sketch and describe the orientation of the plastic chips in the "rock." Are they randomly oriented, as they were originally? How is their alignment related to the pressure you applied?

Sketch: Describe: _____

_____

_____

_____

_____

_____

_____

_____

The parallel alignment of platy minerals is called *foliation* and is found in metamorphic rocks that have been strongly squeezed, as at a convergent boundary between colliding lithosphere plates.

• What real minerals would you expect to behave the way the plastic chips did?

_____

_____

Name: _____ Section: _____

Course: _____ Date: _____

Now look at the rocks used in Exercise 4.2. Compare their textures with those that you made in Exercise 4.3, and suggest whether each is igneous, sedimentary, or metamorphic. Explain your reasoning.

Rock 1:

_____

_____

_____

_____

(continued)

Name: _____   Section: _____

Course: _____   Date: _____

Rock 2:

_____

_____

_____

_____

Rock 3:

_____

_____

_____

_____

4.5 Clues about a Rock's Origin from the Minerals It Contains

Some minerals can form in only one class of rocks, so their presence in a sample tells us immediately whether the rock is igneous, sedimentary, or metamorphic. For example, halite forms only by the evaporation of salt water, and staurolite forms only by the metamorphism of aluminum-rich sedimentary rocks at high temperature. However, as mentioned earlier, several common minerals can form in more than one class of rocks. For example, quartz crystallizes in many magmas; but it also forms during metamorphic reactions and can precipitate from water to form a fine-grained chemical sedimentary rock or to cement grains together in clastic sedimentary rocks.

TABLE 4.2 shows which common minerals indicate a unique rock-forming process and which can form in two or more ways. Remember the rock cycle: a grain of quartz that originally *formed* by cooling from magma may now be *found* in a sedimentary or metamorphic rock.

The presence of some minerals in a rock is evidence that the rock can only be igneous, sedimentary, or metamorphic. Thus, a rock containing gypsum *must be* sedimentary. The presence of sillimanite in a rock means the rock *is* metamorphic. The blue triangles in Table 4.2 highlight minerals whose presence gives less definite evidence. These can survive the breakup of the igneous or metamorphic rocks in which they formed originally, be deposited along with other clasts, and be found in small amounts in sedimentary rocks. Other minerals, like quartz, can form in igneous, sedimentary, *or* metamorphic rocks, so their presence doesn't help at all in determining a rock's origin.

TABLE 4.2 **Occurrence of common rock-forming minerals.**

Mineral	Igneous	Sedimentary	Metamorphic
Plagioclase feldspar	▲	▼ ■	▲
Potassic feldspar	▲	▼ ■	▲
Quartz	▲	▼ ▲	▲
Quartz can form (▲) in any rock. It can also form in an igneous or metamorphic rock and be deposited and found (▼) when the rocks break up in a sedimentary rock.			
Hornblende	▲		▲
Actinolite			▲
Augite	▲		
Muscovite	▲	▼	▲
Biotite	▲		▲
Chlorite			▲
Olivine	▲		▲
Garnet	▲	▼	▲
Andalusite	■		▲
Kyanite			▲
Sillimanite			▲
A rock containing sillimanite must be metamorphic.			
Epidote	■		▲
Halite		▲	
Calcite		▲	▲
Dolomite		▲	▲
Gypsum		▲	
A rock containing gypsum must be sedimentary.			
Talc			▲
Serpentine	■		▲

▲ Commonly *forms* in these rocks   ■ Rarely *forms* in these rocks
▼ Commonly *found* in these rocks as clasts

4.6 Identifying Minerals in Rocks

The techniques you used to identify individual specimens of minerals are also used when minerals are combined with others in rocks, but the relationships among grains may make the process more difficult, especially when the grains are small. For example, it is usually easy to determine how many minerals are in coarse-grained rocks because color and luster are as easy to determine in rocks as in minerals. But it is difficult to determine hardness and cleavage of small grains without interference from their neighbors. And when a rock contains many mineral grains cemented together, it may be difficult to distinguish between the hardness of individual minerals and the strength of the cement holding them together.

Extra care must be taken with rocks to be sure you are measuring the mineral properties you think you are measuring. In very-fine-grained rocks, geologists have to use microscopes and even more sophisticated methods (e.g., X-rays) to identify the minerals. Keep the following tips in mind as you determine the properties of minerals in rocks in Exercises 4.5 and 4.6.

- *Color:* Whenever possible, look at a rock's weathered outer surface *and* a freshly broken surface, because weathering often produces a surface color different from the color of unaltered minerals. This difference can be helpful for identification. For example, regardless of whether plagioclase feldspar is dark gray, light gray, or colorless, weathering typically produces a very fine white coating of clay minerals. Weathering of a fine-grained rock can help distinguish dark gray plagioclase (white weathering) from dark gray pyroxene (brown weathering) that might otherwise be hard to tell apart.

A rock's color depends on its grain size as well as the color of its minerals. All other things being equal, a fine-grained rock appears darker than a coarse-grained rock made of the same minerals.

- *Luster:* Using a hand lens, rotate the rock in the light to determine how many different kinds of luster (and therefore how many different minerals) are present.

- *Hardness:* Use a steel safety pin or the tip of a knife blade and a magnifying glass to determine mineral hardness in fine-grained rocks. Be sure to scratch a single mineral grain or crystal; and when using a glass plate, be sure a single grain is scratching it. Only then are you testing the mineral's hardness. Otherwise, you might be dislodging grains from the rock and demonstrating how strongly the rock is cemented together rather than measuring the hardness of any of its minerals.

- *Streak:* Similarly, be very careful when using a streak plate, because it may not be obvious which mineral in a fine-grained rock is leaving the streak. Some minerals are also harder than the plate. As a result, streak is generally not useful for identifying single grains in a rock that contains many minerals.

- *Crystal habit:* Crystal habit is valuable in identifying minerals in a rock when it has well-shaped crystals. But when many grains interfere with one another during growth, the result is an interlocking mass of irregular grains rather than crystals. Weathering and transportation break off corners of grains and round their edges, destroying whatever crystal forms were present.

- *Breakage:* Use a hand lens to observe cleavage and fracture. Rotate the rock in the light while looking at a single grain. Remember that multiple *parallel* shiny surfaces represent a single cleavage direction. Breakage can be a valuable property in distinguishing light-colored feldspars (two directions of cleavage at 90°) from quartz (conchoidal fracture), and amphibole (two directions of cleavage not at 90°) from pyroxene (two directions of cleavage at 90°).

- *Specific gravity:* A mineral's specific gravity can be measured only from a pure sample. When two or more minerals are present in a rock, you are measuring the *rock's* specific gravity, and that includes contributions from all of the minerals present. However, the heft of a very-fine-grained rock can be very helpful in interpreting what combination of minerals might be in it.

- *Hydrochloric acid test for carbonates:* Put a *small* drop of acid on a fresh, unaltered surface. Be careful: a thin film of soil or weathering products may contain calcite and make a noncarbonate mineral appear to fizz. Use a hand lens to determine exactly where the carbon dioxide is coming from. Are all of the grains reacting with the acid or is gas coming only from the cement that holds the grains together?

Name: _____   Section: _____

Course: _____   Date: _____

I. Your instructor will provide similar-sized samples of granite and basalt. Granite has grains that are large enough for you to identify. It forms by slow cooling of molten rock deep underground. Basalt also forms from cooling molten material, but it cools faster and has much smaller grains.

(a) Examine the granite. Does it have well-shaped crystals or irregular grains? Suggest an explanation for their shapes.

_____

_____

_____

(b) Identify three or four minerals in the granite. Use a hand lens or magnifying glass if necessary.

_____

_____

(c) Now examine the basalt. Identify the minerals present if you can, using a hand lens or magnifying glass. What problems did you have?

_____

_____

_____

(d) Heft the granite and basalt. Are their specific gravities similar or is one denser than the other? If so, which is denser?

_____

_____

(e) Based on specific gravity, do you think that the most abundant minerals in the basalt are the same as those in the granite? Explain.

_____

_____

_____

(continued)

Name: _____   **Section:** _____

Course: _____   **Date:** _____

II. Your instructor will provide samples of sandstone (made mostly of quartz) and limestone (made mostly of calcite).

(f) Suggest two tests that will enable you to tell which sample is which. Explain.

_____

_____

_____

_____

_____

(g) Okay: Which is the sandstone and which is the limestone?

_____

_____

_____

_____

4.7 Interpreting the Origin of Rocks

You are now ready to begin your examination of rocks. In Exercise 4.6, the goal is to determine which of the three types of rock-forming processes was involved in the origin of each specimen. Later in the book, you will examine each group separately and be more specific about details of those processes. The flowchart on p. 100 combines textural and mineralogical features to make your task easier. Then Exercise 4.7 asks you to apply your knowledge to make a recommendation.

EXERCISE 4.6   Classifying Rocks: Igneous, Sedimentary, or Metamorphic?

Name: _____   **Section:** _____

Course: _____   **Date:** _____

Use the flowchart on page 103 to separate the rocks provided by your instructor into igneous, sedimentary, and metamorphic piles based on their textures, mineral content, and the information in Table 4.2. You will look at these rocks again in more detail in the next three chapters.

(continued)

Name: _____ Section: _____

Course: _____ Date: _____

Igneous rocks	
#	Reasons for classifying as igneous

Sedimentary rocks	
#	Reasons for classifying as sedimentary

Metamorphic rocks	
#	Reasons for classifying as metamorphic

(continued)

Name: _____   Section: _____

Course: _____   Date: _____

What is the rock's texture?

1. Rock has **glassy** texture ─────────────────────────────▶ Rock is **IGNEOUS**.
(smooth, shiny, no grains).

No minerals (glass) ────▶ Rock is **IGNEOUS**.

Nonsilicate minerals ────▶ Rock is **SEDIMENTARY**.

2. Rock has **porous** | Look at material between grains. |

texture (numerous holes).

Silicate minerals ────▶ Rock is **IGNEOUS**.

Halite, gypsum ─▶ Rock is **SEDIMENTARY**.

Nonsilicates

Calcite, dolomite ─▶ Rock may be ⟨ **SEDIMENTARY***.
                                           METAMORPHIC*.

Identify minerals.

3. Rock has **interlocking** grains.

Foliated ───────────▶ Rock is **METAMORPHIC**.

Silicates

Metamorphic minerals (garnet, staurolite, etc.) ── Rock is **METAMORPHIC**.

NONFOLIATED

No metamorphic minerals ────▶ Rock is **IGNEOUS**.

     * Look for metamorphic minerals. Are interlayered rocks in the field sedimentary or metamorphic?

4. Rock consists of **visible grains separated by finer-grained material.**

(a) Matrix is **glassy.** ────────────────────────▶ Rock is **IGNEOUS**.

Silicate mineral matrix ───────▶ Rock is **IGNEOUS** or **METAMORPHIC***.

(b) Matrix is **interlocking crystals.** | Identify matrix minerals. |

Nonsilicate mineral matrix ──▶ Rock is **SEDIMENTARY**.

*If metamorphic minerals are present, then the rock is metamorphic.

(c) Matrix is **small, rounded grains that do not interlock.** ─────────▶ Rock is **SEDIMENTARY**.

(d) Matrix is **too fine grained to identify.** ──▶ Rock could be **SEDIMENTARY** or **IGNEOUS**. Use microscope.

5. Rock is **very fine grained:**   i.   Use microscope to observe relations between grains if thin section is available.
                                ii.   Use field observations to determine relations with rocks of known origin.
                               iii.   Estimate specific gravity to get an indication of what minerals are present.

Name: _____   **Section:** _____

Course: _____   **Date:** _____

? What Do You Think A veterans' group has contacted you about the best stone to use for memorials honoring the men and women who have served our country. They want to use local stone whenever possible and they have found a nearby source of marble and granite. Assuming this is taking place near your institution, what factors should you consider before making a recommendation? (Consider the ease of carving and polishing, the response of the materials to weathering, etc.) What factors would you consider if you lived in a very wet and humid climate? What factors would you consider if you lived in a hot and arid climate?

_____

_____

_____

_____

_____

_____

_____

_____

_____

_____

_____

_____

_____

_____

_____

_____

_____

_____

5

Using Igneous Rocks to Interpret Earth History

Solidified pahoehoe lava engulfs an intersection in Hawaii—an example of extrusive igneous rock.

- Become familiar with igneous textures and mineral assemblages
- Use texture and mineral content to interpret the history of igneous rocks
- Understand the classification of igneous rocks
- Associate igneous rocks with different plate tectonic settings
- Recognize the kinds of volcanoes and why they have different shapes

MATERIALS
NEEDED

- Set of igneous rocks
- Magnifying glass or hand lens and, ideally, a microscope and thin sections of igneous rocks
- Standard supplies for identifying minerals (streak plate, glass plate, etc.)

5.1 Introduction

Every rock has a story to tell. The story of an igneous rock begins when rock in the lower crust or upper mantle melts to form molten material called **magma**, which rises up through the crust. Some magma flows or spatters out on the surface as **lava** or it explodes—often through a crack or vent in the Earth—into the air as tiny particles of **volcanic ash** or larger blocks. Igneous rock that forms from solidified lava or ash is called **extrusive igneous rock** because it comes out (*extrudes*) onto the surface. Other magma never reaches the surface and solidifies underground to form **intrusive igneous rock**, so called because it squeezes into (*intrudes*) the surrounding rocks. Intrusions come in many shapes. Massive blobs are called **plutons**, and the largest of these—called **batholiths**—are generally composites of several plutons. Other intrusions that form thin sheets cutting across layering in the wall rock (the rock around the intrusion) are called **dikes**, and those that form thin sheets parallel to the layers of wall rock are called **sills** (**FIG. 5.1**).

When looking at an igneous rock, geologists want to know: Where did it cool (was it intrusive or extrusive)? Where in the Earth did the rock's parent magma form? In what tectonic setting—ocean ridge, mid-continent, subduction zone, hot spot—did it form? In this chapter, you will learn how to answer these questions and how to identify common types of igneous rock. Few new skills are needed—just observe carefully and apply some geologic reasoning. Exercise 5.1 shows how easy the process is.

Most of the questions geologists ask about an igneous rock can be answered with three simple observations: grain size, color, and specific gravity. The following sections provide the additional information you need to interpret the history of an igneous rock.

FIGURE 5.1 Intrusive and extrusive igneous rock bodies.

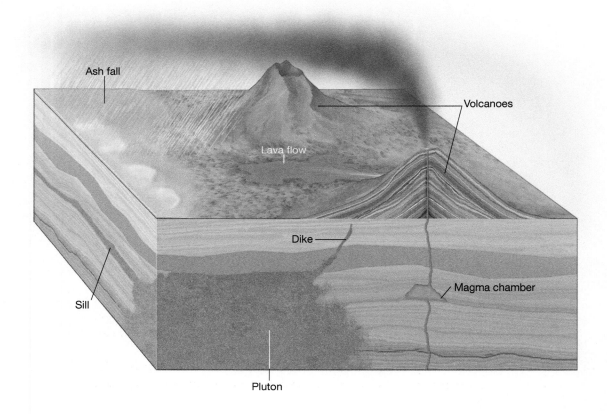

Name: _____   **Section:** _____
Course: _____   **Date:** _____

There are many ways to classify igneous rocks, but for now let's use three easily observable criteria: grain size, color, and specific gravity. Using the set of igneous rocks provided by your instructor, first group the specimens by grain size and record the specimen numbers in the appropriate column of the following table. Then group the specimens by color and specific gravity.

Grain size		Color		Specific gravity (heft)	
Coarse	Fine	Light colored	Dark colored	Relatively high	Relatively low

(a) Which two properties seem to be related to one another? Which is different?

_____

_____

(b) Consider which magma properties and rock-forming processes control the grain size, color, and specific gravity of an igneous rock. Which two of these properties have a common cause and are related to one another? Explain. (This connection will be helpful later when you are identifying igneous rocks.)

_____

_____

_____

_____

5.2 Interpreting the Cooling Histories of Igneous Rocks

Imagine that you are looking at an ancient igneous rock in an outcrop. That rock might have formed from volcanic debris blasted into the air, lava that frothed out of a volcano or flowed smoothly across the ground, magma that cooled just below the surface, or magma that solidified many kilometers below the surface. But millions of years have passed since the rock formed, and if a volcano had been involved, it has long since been eroded away. If the rock was intrusive, kilometers of overlying rock would have been removed to expose it at the surface. How can you determine which of these possibilities is the right one?

The key to understanding the cooling history of an igneous rock is its **texture**—the size, shape, and arrangement of its grains. The texture of an igneous rock, is formed by the settling of ash and other volcanic fragments, looks very different from that of a rock formed by magma cooling deep underground or by lava cooling at the surface.

Specimens composed of interlocking grains—whether large enough to be identified or too small to be identified—are called **crystalline** rocks. Those that are shiny and contain no grains are called **glasses**; sponge-like masses are said to be **porous**; and those that appear to have pieces cemented together are said to be **fragmental**. Each of these textures indicates a unique cooling history—if you understand how to "read" the textural information. Exercise 5.2 will help you start this process.

5.2.1 Grain Size in Crystalline Igneous Rock

Grain size is the key to understanding the cooling history of most igneous rocks that solidified underground or on the surface (you will experiment with this in Exercise 5.3 and 5.4). When magma or lava begins to cool, small crystal seeds form (a process called *nucleation*), and crystals grow outward from the seeds until they interfere with one another. The result is a three-dimensional interlocking texture found in *most* igneous rocks. But why do some igneous rocks have coarser (larger) grains than others?

Crystals grow as ions migrate through magma to the crystal seeds, so anything that assists ionic migration increases grain size in an igneous rock. **Cooling rate** is the most important factor controlling grain size. The slower a magma cools, the more time ions have to migrate to crystal seeds; the faster it cools, the less time there is and the smaller the grains will be. Another factor is a magma's **viscosity** (the resistance of material to flow). The *less* viscous a magma is (i.e., the more *fluid*), the easier it is for ions to migrate and the larger the crystals can become.

Cooling rate and viscosity cause some igneous rocks to have coarse grains (sometimes called a **phaneritic texture**) and others to have fine grains (**aphanitic texture**). **FIGURE 5.2** illustrates the difference between course and fine grains.

EXERCISE 5.2	A First Look at Igneous Rock Textures

Name: _____ Section: _____
Course: _____ Date: _____

We look first at rocks that have the same composition, because their different textures could only be caused by the different ways in which they cooled. For example, the rocks in Figure 5.2 have the same minerals and thus similar compositions. Separate the light-colored igneous rocks in your set. Describe their textures, paying careful attention to the sizes and shapes of the grains and the relationships among adjacent grains. Use everyday language—the appropriate geologic terms will be introduced later.

Specimen	Textural description

Some igneous rocks have grains of two different sizes, one much larger than the other (FIG. 5.3). This is called a **porphyritic texture**. The larger grains are called *phenocrysts* and the finer grains are called, collectively, the rock's *groundmass*.

FIGURE 5.2 **Grain sizes in light-colored igneous rocks.**

(a) Very coarse-grained (pegmatitic crystals).

(b) Coarse-grained (phaneritic crystals).

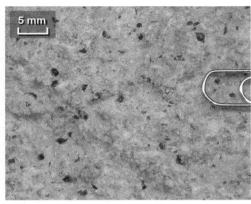
(c) Fine-grained (most of the aphanitic grains are too small to see with the naked eye).

EXERCISE 5.3	Interpreting Igneous Cooling Histories from Grain Size

Name: _____ **Section:** _____
Course: _____ **Date:** _____

It is a short step from understanding how cooling rate affects grain size to deriving the basic rules of how magma and lava cool in nature. Three simple thought experiments will help you understand the cooling process.

(a) Imagine you have two balls of pizza dough 20 cm in diameter. As shown in the figure on the right, one is rolled out to form a crust 1 cm thick and 50 cm in diameter. Both pieces of dough still have the same mass and volume, even though their shapes are very different. Both are baked in a 450°F oven for 20 minutes and removed.

   (i) Which will cool faster, the large cube or one of the small cubes? _____

   Why? _____

   _____

Rule 1 of magma cooling: *Circle the correct two choices in the following statement.* A thin sheet of magma loses heat (**faster/ slower**) than a blob containing the same amount of magma. This is because the amount of surface area available for cooling in the sheet is (**larger/smaller**) than the surface area available in a blob of the same volume.

(b) Equal amounts of hot coffee are poured into thin plastic and Styrofoam cups.
   (i) Which cools faster, the coffee in the plastic cup or in the Styrofoam cup? _____

      (*Hint:* Which cup can you hold the longest before burning your fingers?) Explain. _____

   _____

(continued)

Name: _____ **Section:** _____
Course: _____ **Date:** _____

Rule 2 of magma cooling: *Circle the correct choice.* Magma loses heat much (**faster/slower**) when exposed to air or water than it does when surrounded by other rock, because wall rock is a good insulator.

(c) Consider two cubes of steel measuring 1 m on a side. One is cut in half in each dimension to make eight smaller cubes.

1m

1m

(i)   What is the surface area of the large cube? _____ cm² Of the eight small cubes? _____ cm²
(ii) Imagine the large and small cubes are heated in a furnace to 500°C and removed. Which will cool faster, the large cube or the smaller ones? _____
(iii) Explain why this happens.

_____

_____

_____

Rule 3 of magma cooling: *Circle the correct choice.* A small mass of magma loses heat (**faster/slower**) than a large one.

(d) Now you can put the rules to use.
(i)   In general, lava flows and shallow intrusive igneous rocks have (finer/coarser) grains than deep intrusive rocks.
(ii) In general, thick lava flows, sills, and dikes have (finer/coarser) grains than thin ones.
(iii) Which of the rocks in Figure 5.2 was probably extrusive?

_____

_____

(iv) Which were probably intrusive?

_____

_____

(continued)

Name: _____   Section: _____

Course: _____   Date: _____

(v) Many dikes, sills, and plutons have *chilled margins*—smaller grains at the contact with their wall rock than in their interiors. Explain how this happens.

_____

_____

_____

_____

_____

FIGURE 5.3 Porphyritic texture (two different grain sizes).

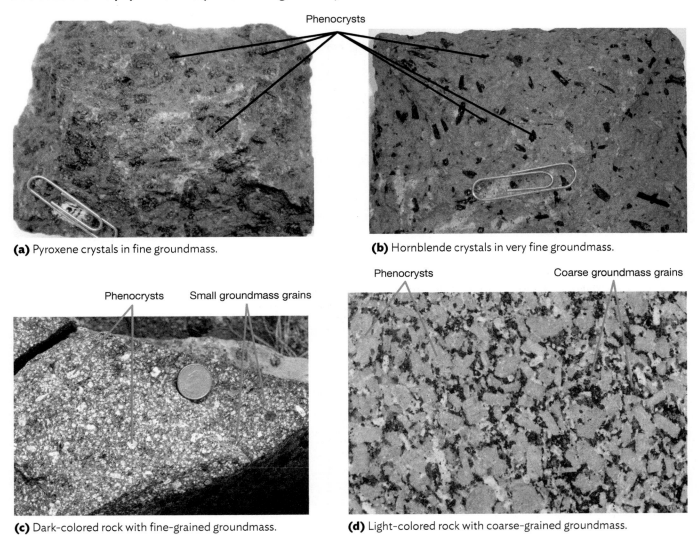

(a) Pyroxene crystals in fine groundmass.

(b) Hornblende crystals in very fine groundmass.

(c) Dark-colored rock with fine-grained groundmass.

(d) Light-colored rock with coarse-grained groundmass.

FIGURE 5.4 Glassy texture (no mineral grains).

5.2.2 Glassy Igneous Textures

Some magmas cool so fast or are so viscous that crystal seeds can't form. Instead, atoms in the melt are frozen in place, arranged haphazardly rather than in the orderly arrangement required for mineral grains. Because haphazard atomic arrangement is also found in window glass, we call a rock that has cooled this quickly **igneous glass**, and it is said to have a **glassy texture** (**FIG. 5.4**). Like thick glass bottles, volcanic glass fractures conchoidally. Volcanic glass commonly looks black, but impurities may cause it to be red-brown or streaked.

Most igneous glass forms at the Earth's surface when lava exposed to air or water cools very quickly, but some may form just below the surface in the throat of the volcano. In addition, much of the ash blasted into the air during explosive eruptions is made of volcanic glass, formed when tiny particles of magma freeze instantly in the air.

EXERCISE 5.4   **Interpreting Porphyritic Textures**

Name: _____   Section: _____
Course: _____   Date: _____

(a) Based on what you have deduced about magma cooling, how does a porphyritic texture form?

_____

_____

_____

(b) Describe the cooling histories of the rocks shown in Figure 5.3 in as much detail as you can.

5.3a

_____

_____

_____

5.3b

_____

_____

_____

5.3c

_____

_____

_____

(continued)

Name: _____   Section: _____

Course: _____   Date: _____

    5.3d

_____

_____

_____

5.2.3 Porous (Vesicular) Textures

As magma rises toward the surface, the pressure on it decreases. This allows dissolved gases (H_2O, CO_2, SO_2) to come out of solution and form bubbles, like those that appear when you open a can of soda. If bubbles form just as the lava solidifies, their shapes are preserved in the lava (**FIG. 5.5**). The material between the vesicles may be fine-grained crystalline material (Fig. 5.5a) or volcanic glass (Fig. 5.5b). These rocks are said to have a **porous** or **vesicular texture**, and the individual bubbles are called **vesicles**. "Lava rock" used in outdoor grills and pumice used to smooth wood and remove calluses are common and useful examples of porous igneous rocks.

5.2.4 Fragmental Textures

Violent volcanic eruptions can blast enormous amounts of material into the air. This material is collectively called **pyroclastic debris** (from the Greek *pyro*, meaning fire, and *clast*, meaning broken). Pyroclastic debris includes volcanic glass, large blocks or bombs erupted as liquid and cooled as fine-grained crystalline rock (**FIG. 5.6a**), crystals formed in the magma before eruption (**FIG. 5.6b**), tiny ash particles, and pieces of rock broken from the walls of the volcanic vent or ripped from the ground surface during an eruption (**FIG. 5.6c**).

FIGURE 5.5 **Porous (vesicular) igneous textures.**

(a) Dark-colored porous igneous rock.

(b) Light-colored porous igneous rock.

FIGURE 5.6 Fragmental (pyroclastic) igneous rocks in a range of grain sizes and textures.

(a) Coarse volcanic bombs in finer-grained pyroclastic matrix at Kilauea in Hawaii.

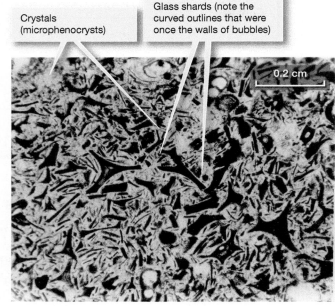

(b) Photomicrograph of glass shards (black) welded together with a few tiny crystals.

(c) Hand sample with volcanic rock fragments in a very fine-grained brown ash.

In an **ash fall**, fine-grained pyroclastic material falls quietly like hot snow and blankets the ground. The ash may be compacted and turned to rock by the pressure of ash from later eruptions. In more violent eruptions, avalanches of ash called **pyroclastic flows** rush down the side of a volcano while still so hot that the fragments weld together immediately to form rock.

5.2.5 Grain Shape

Some grains in igneous rocks are well-shaped crystals (phenocrysts in Fig. 5.3a–c), but others are irregular (Fig. 5.2a, b; groundmass grains in Fig. 5.3c, d). When magma begins to cool, its grains start as well-shaped crystals; but they interfere with one another as they grow, resulting in irregular shapes. This process enables us to determine the sequence in which grains grew in an igneous rock: the well-shaped crystals formed early when there was no interference from others. Can you tell which grains grew first in Figure 5.3?

You are now able to read the story recorded by igneous textures and can do so without identifying a single mineral or naming the rocks. **TABLE 5.1** summarizes the origin of common igneous textures and the terms used by geologists to describe them. In Exercise 5.6 you will sharpen your skills by interpreting the history of igneous rocks provided by your instructor.

TABLE 5.1 Interpreting igneous rock textures

Texture	Pegmatitic	Coarse grained (phaneritic)	Fine grained (aphanitic)	Porphyritic	Glassy	Porous (vesicular)	Fragmental (pyroclastic)
Description	Very large grains (>2.5 cm)	Individual grains are visible with the naked eye	Individual grains cannot be seen without magnification	A few large grains (phenocrysts) set in a finer-grained groundmass	Smooth, shiny; looks like glass; no mineral grains present	Spongy; filled with large or small holes	Mineral grains, rock fragments, and glass shards welded together
Interpretation	Very slow cooling or cooling from an extremely fluid magma (usually the latter)	Slow cooling; generally *intrusive*	Rapid cooling; generally *extrusive*	Two cooling rates; slow at first to form the phenocrysts; then more rapid to form the groundmass	Extremely rapid cooling; generally *extrusive*	Rapid cooling accompanied by the release of gases	Explosive eruption of ash and rock into the air
Example							

Name: _____ Section: _____

Course: _____ Date: _____

Examine the igneous rocks provided by your instructor. Apply what you have learned about the origins of igneous textures to fill in the "cooling history" column in the study sheets at the end of the chapter. Use the following questions as a guide to your interpretation.
  • Which specimens cooled quickly? Which cooled slowly?
  • Which specimens cooled very rapidly at the Earth's surface (i.e., are extrusive)?
  • Which specimens cooled slowly beneath the surface (i.e., are intrusive)?
  • Which specimens cooled from a magma rich in gases?
  • Which specimens experienced more than one cooling rate?

5.3 Igneous Rock Classification and Identification

You now know how to determine the conditions under which igneous rocks form by examining their textures. Igneous rock composition is the key to answering other questions, because it helps reveal how magma forms and why some igneous rocks occur in specific tectonic settings. We look first at how geologists use composition to classify igneous rocks and then at how igneous rocks are named by their composition and texture.

5.3.1 Igneous Rock Classification: The Four Major Compositional Groups

In Exercise 5.1, you saw that some of the igneous rocks in your set are relatively dark colored and others are light colored. Some have high specific gravities, others relatively low specific gravities. A rock's color and specific gravity are controlled mostly by its minerals, which are, in turn, determined by its chemical composition. Oxygen and silicon are by far the two most abundant elements in the lithosphere, so it is not surprising that nearly all igneous rocks are composed primarily of *silicate minerals* like quartz, feldspars, pyroxenes, amphiboles, micas, and olivine.

There are many different kinds of igneous rock, but all fit into one of four major compositional groups—felsic, intermediate, mafic, and ultramafic—defined by how much silicon and oxygen (*silica*) they contain and by which other elements are most abundant (**TABLE 5.2**).

Felsic igneous rocks (from *fel*dspar and *si*lica) have the most silica and the least iron and magnesium. They contain abundant potassic feldspar and sodic plagioclase, commonly quartz, and only sparse ferromagnesian minerals—usually biotite or hornblende. Like their most abundant minerals, felsic rocks are light colored and have low specific gravities.

Intermediate igneous rocks have chemical compositions, colors, specific gravities, and mineral assemblages between those of felsic and mafic rocks: plagioclase feldspar with nearly equal amounts of calcium and sodium, both amphibole and pyroxene, and only rarely quartz.

Mafic igneous rocks (from *ma*gnesium and the Latin *f*errum, meaning iron) have much less silica, potassium, and sodium than felsic rocks but much more calcium, iron, and magnesium. Their dominant calcium-rich plagioclase and ferromagnesian minerals are dark green or black and have higher specific gravities than minerals in felsic rocks. Even fine-grained mafic rocks can therefore be recognized by their dark color and relatively high specific gravity.

TABLE 5.2   The four major groups of igneous rocks.

Igneous rock group	Approximate weight % silica (SiO2)	Other major elements	Most abundant minerals
Felsic	>70	Aluminum (Al), potassium (K), sodium (Na)	K-feldspar, Na-plagioclase, quartz
Intermediate	~55–70	Al, Na, calcium (Ca), iron (Fe), magnesium (Mg)	Ca-Na plagioclase, amphibole, pyroxene
Mafic	~45–55	Al, Ca, Mg, Fe	Ca-plagioclase, pyroxene, olivine
Ultramafic	<45	Mg, Fe	Olivine, pyroxenes

Ultramafic igneous rocks have the least silica and the most iron and magnesium, but very little aluminum, potassium, sodium, or calcium. As a result, they contain mostly ferromagnesian minerals like olivine and pyroxene with very little, if any, plagioclase. Ultramafic rocks are very dark colored and have the highest specific gravities of the igneous rocks.

5.3.2 Identifying Igneous Rocks

The name of an igneous rock is based on its mineral content *and* texture (**FIG. 5.7**). Each of the four igneous rock groups is shown by a column, each of which has coarse, fine, porphyritic, glassy, porous, and fragmental varieties. Rocks in a column may have exactly the same minerals but look so different that they are given different names. For example, granite and rhyolite are both felsic but look different because of their different textures. Although gabbro and granite have the same *texture*, they contain different minerals and therefore look different.

Identifying an igneous rock requires no new skills, just a few simple observations and your ability to identify the common rock-forming minerals.

If you are wondering why there aren't pictures of all the rock types to help you identify the specimens in your rock set, it's because granite may be gray, red, white, or even purple or black depending on the color of its feldspars. A picture can thus help only if it is exactly the same as the rock in your set. But if you understand the combination of minerals that defines granite, you will get it right every time. You will try this in Exercise 5.7.

EXERCISE 5.7   Identifying Igneous Rocks

Name: _____   Section: _____

Course: _____   Date: _____

Name the specimens in your igneous rock set by following the steps below.

   Step 1: Place the rock in the correct *column* in Figure 5.7a by noting its color and heft and estimating mineral abundance if its grains are coarse enough.

   Step 2: Determine the texture of the rock and note which *row* in Figure 5.7b it corresponds to.

   Step 3: The name of the rock is found in the box at the intersection of the column and row.

Record the names of the rocks on the study sheets given at the end of the chapter.

FIGURE 5.7 Classification of igneous rocks.

(a) Abundances of minerals in felsic, intermediate, mafic, and ultramafic igneus rocks.

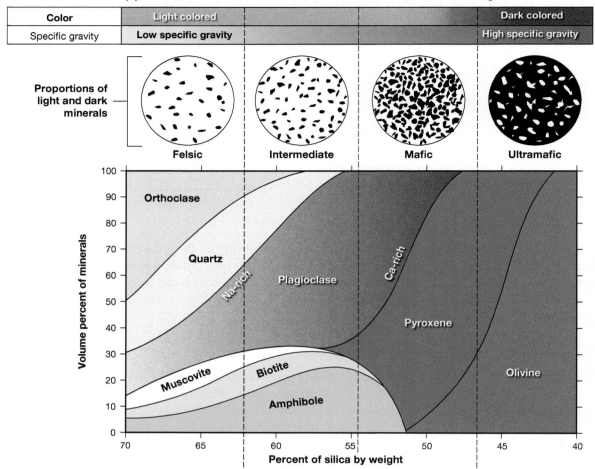

(b) Choose a column based on the abundance of minerals, and select the rock name based on the appropriate texture.

Silica (SiO$_2$) content		**High silica content**			**Low silica content**
	Pegmatitic	**Granitic pegmatite**		**Mafic pegmatite**	**Dunite** (olivine only) **Pyroxenite** (pyroxene) **Peridotite** (olivine + pyroxene)
	Coarse-grained (Phaneritic)	Granite	Diorite	Gabbro	
Texture	Fine-grained (aphanitic)	Rhyolite	Andesite	Basalt	Rocks with these textures and compositions are very rare.
	Porphyritic	Porphyritic granite or* Porphyritic rhyolite	Porphyritic diorite or* Porphyritic andesite	Porphyritic gabbro or* Porphyritic basalt	
	Glassy	Obsidian		Tachylite	
	Porous	Pumice		Scoria/Vesicular basalt	
	Fragmental — Fine	Rhyolite tuff	Andesite tuff	Basalt tuff	
	Fragmental — Coarse	Volcanic breccia			

*Porphyritic rocks are named for the size of the groundmass grains. For example, a felsic porphyry in which the groundmass grains are coarse is called *granite porphyry*. If the groundmass grains are small, it is called a *rhyolite porphyry*.

5.4 Origin and Evolution of Magmas

To understand why there are four basic kinds of igneous rocks and why they can be used to interpret ancient plate tectonic events, we need to know (1) *where* and *why* rocks and minerals melt in the Earth, (2) *how* rocks and minerals melt, and (3) how plate tectonic settings produce specific rock types. The next three sections explore these issues.

5.4.1 *Where* and *Why* Do Rocks and Minerals Melt?

Some science fiction movies and novels suggest that the rigid outer shell of the Earth floats on a sea of magma. In fact, most of the crust and mantle is solid rock. Melting occurs only in special places, generally by one of the following three processes.

Decompression melting: Stretching of the lithosphere at a divergent plate boundary (ocean ridge) or continental rift lowers the confining pressure on the asthenosphere below. The amount of heat in the asthenosphere couldn't originally overcome the chemical bonds *and* the confining pressure; but once the pressure decreases, the heat already present in the rock is sufficient to overcome the bonds and cause melting. This process is called **decompression melting** *and requires no additional input of heat.*

Flux melting: Subducted oceanic crust contains hydrous minerals, some formed when ocean-ridge basalt reacts with seawater shortly after erupting, others formed during weathering of island-arc volcanoes. Water and other volatiles are released from these minerals when the subducted plate reaches critical depth (about 150 km) and rise into the asthenosphere, where they help melt the asthenosphere in the process of **flux melting**. In flux melting, no additional heat is needed because the flux of water lowers the melting point of the rocks.

Heat transfer melting: Iron in a blast furnace melts when enough heat is added to break the bonds between atoms, and some magmas form the same way in continental crust. Some very hot mafic magmas that rise into continental crust from the mantle bring along enough heat to start melting the crust, much as hot fudge does when poured onto ice cream. This process, called **heat-transfer melting**, occurs mostly in four settings: (1) oceanic or continental hot spots where mantle plumes bring heat to shallower levels; (2) continental volcanic arcs where mafic magma transfers heat from the mantle to the continental crust of the arc; (3) during late stages of continent-continent collision when the base of the lithosphere peels off and the asthenosphere rises to fill that space, melts, and sends large amounts of basaltic magma upward; and (4) in continental rifts where mafic magma from the asthenosphere rises into the base of thinned continental crust.

5.4.2 *How* Do Rocks and Minerals Melt?

We can't directly observe melting in the mantle or a subduction zone, but we can study it in the laboratory. In the 1920s, N. L. Bowen and other pioneers melted minerals and rocks and chilled them at different stages of melting to learn how magma forms. They learned that magma melting (and crystallization) is very different from the way ice melts into water, and their results paved the way for understanding the origins of the different igneous rock groups.

■ **Most rocks melt over a range of temperature**, because some of their minerals have lower melting points than others. The minerals with low melting points melt first while others remain solid. The entire rock melts only when the temperature rises enough to melt all the minerals—a range of several hundred degrees in some cases.

■ **Some minerals, like quartz, melt simply, like ice.** When heated to their melting temperatures, these minerals melt completely to form a liquid with the same composition as the mineral. This is not surprising, but the next two findings are.

■ **Plagioclase feldspars melt *continuously*, over a span of temperature.** When plagioclase containing equal amounts of calcium and sodium begins to melt, more sodium atoms are freed from the crystalline structure than calcium. The first liquid is thus more sodium-rich than the original plagioclase. More and more calcium is freed from the residual mineral as temperature rises, so the compositions of both the liquid and residual mineral change continuously. Only when the entire mineral has melted does the liquid have the same composition as the original mineral.

■ **Ferromagnesian minerals melt** *discontinuously,* **and new minerals form in the process.** Melt ice and you get water; but melt pyroxene, for example, and when the first liquid forms, the remaining solid changes from pyroxene to olivine. Keep heating it and the olivine gradually melts. Similar things happen to the other common ferromagnesian minerals: biotite, amphibole, and olivine. As with plagioclase, the melt only has the same composition as the starting material when the process is complete.

Bowen summarized these findings graphically in what is now named Bowen's reaction series in his honor (**FIG. 5.8**). Note the relationship between the melting temperatures of the common rock-forming minerals and the assemblages that define the four major igneous rock groups. In Exercise 5.8, you will practice with results and insights learned from these experiments.

5.4.3 Origin of the Igneous Rock Groups: Factors Controlling Magma Composition

Laboratory melting and crystallization experiments last days, weeks, or months and are carried out in sealed containers to prevent contamination. Melting in the Earth is more complicated because it may take millions of years, and many things can happen to the magma. For example, material from the surrounding rocks can be absorbed by the melt, or magma can escape before melting is complete. Several factors control the composition of a magma and the rocks that can form from it, but four processes play the most important roles.

FIGURE 5.8 Bowen's reaction series showing the sequence and types of crystallization from magma.

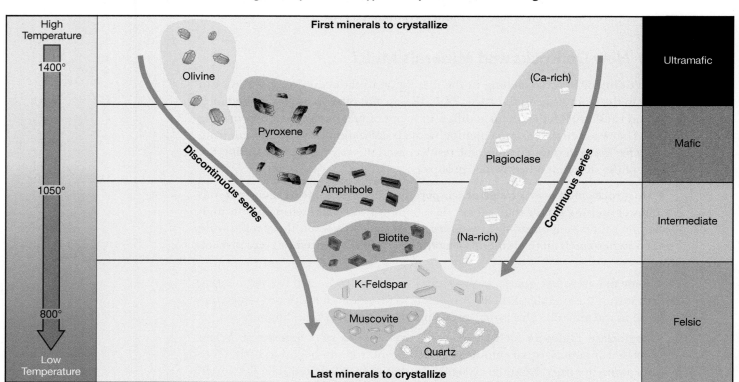

Partial melting: Magma forms by **partial melting** of preexisting rock, not *complete* melting. When ferromagnesian minerals and plagioclase start to melt, the initial liquid has lower density than the source rock and therefore rises, escaping from the melting zone before the rock has melted entirely. In general, partial melting produces a magma that is more felsic (i.e., contains more silica and less iron and magnesium) than its source rock.

Thus, partial melting of ultramafic rock normally produces basalt, but different kinds of basalt could form depending on whether 10%, 20%, or 30% of the source rock melted before the magma escaped. (We said it was more complicated than in the lab!)

EXERCISE 5.8 **Insights from Melting Experiments**

Name: _____ Section: _____
Course: _____ Date: _____

Results from melting experiments help explain several aspects of igneous rock texture and composition. Remember that *crystallization* is the exact opposite of melting. Answer the following questions.

(a) The figure below shows textural features displayed by plagioclase feldspar (left) and pyroxene and amphibole (right) found in many igneous rocks. Considering the continuous and discontinuous legs of Bowen's reaction series, suggest an explanation for the origin of these textures.

_____

_____

_____

_____

Photomicrographs of common mineral textures in igneous rocks.

Compositionally zoned plagioclase feldspar with Ca-rich core and progressively richer Na rims.

Pyroxene grain (px; dark green) with amphibole rim (am; light green).

(b) From Bowen's reaction series, is it likely that minerals with high melting points will occur in rocks with minerals with low melting points? Explain.

_____

_____

_____

(continued)

Name: _____   **Section:** _____
Course: _____   **Date:** _____

(c) List the four major igneous rock groups in compositional order from lowest magma temperature to highest.

1. _____

2. _____

3. _____

4. _____

When the initial magma escapes, it rises to cooler levels and begins to crystallize. Even then it may not "follow the rules" of Bowen's reaction, because three other processes can change its composition and thus the minerals that can crystallize from it.

Magmatic differentiation (also called **fractional crystallization**): Early-formed minerals may separate from a magma, usually by sinking, because they are denser than the liquid. If early-crystallized olivine sinks to the bottom of the magma, it can no longer react with residual liquid to make pyroxene as it should according to Bowen's reaction series. Instead, the results are (1) dunite (an ultramafic rock composed entirely of olivine) at the bottom of the magma chamber and (2) a magma more silicic than the original magma. This residual magma might then crystallize minerals that would not have formed from the original. In extreme cases, differentiation of mafic magma can actually produce very small amounts of felsic magma.

Assimilation: As a magma rises, it may add ions by melting some of the surrounding rocks. As the new material is incorporated, the magma composition may change enough locally to enable minerals to crystallize that could not otherwise have been produced.

Magma mixing: Field and chemical evidence suggests that some intermediate rocks did not crystallize from an intermediate magma but rather formed when felsic and mafic magmas mixed. Exercise 5.9 covers these concepts.

Name: _____   **Section:** _____
Course: _____   **Date:** _____

Use your knowledge of melting and magmatic processes to explain the origin of the following features.

(a) Most continental rift zones contain basalt and rhyolite, but it is also possible to find small amounts of andesite in this setting. Suggest an origin for the andesite.

_____

_____

_____

(continued)

Name: _____   Section: _____

Course: _____   Date: _____

(b) The Palisades Sill on the west bank of the Hudson River in New Jersey is a shallow basaltic intrusive. The sill varies texturally, as shown in the figure below (left). Explain how the observed mineralogic and textural variations were produced by crystallization of the sill.

_____

_____

_____

_____

Schematic cross section of the Palisades Sill

	Wall rock
	Coarse basalt
	Fine basalt
	Zone of concentrated olivine

Mafic inclusions (xenoliths) in a granitic pluton

Iron-rich zones   Xenoliths

(c) In the figure above (right), a thin brown zone of weathering highlights iron-rich zones that separate the host granite from the mafic xenoliths. Based on the magmatic processes described above, suggest an origin for these zones.

_____

_____

_____

5.5 Igneous Rocks and Plate Tectonics

Igneous rock types are not distributed equally or randomly on Earth, because melting occurs in different ways in different tectonic settings. As you read the next sections, remember that assimilation, magma mixing, and magmatic differentiation can produce exceptions to just about every generalization; so keep in mind the phrase "are generally found." With that warning, look at **FIGURE 5.9**, which illustrates the tectonic settings of igneous rocks, and **TABLE 5.3**, which lists the igneous rocks that are *generally* found in those settings. In Exercises 5.10, 5.11, and 5.12, you will apply what you've learned about the origin of igneous rocks to suggest tectonic settings for specimens in your rock sets.

FIGURE 5.9 Tectonic settings for major igneous rock types.

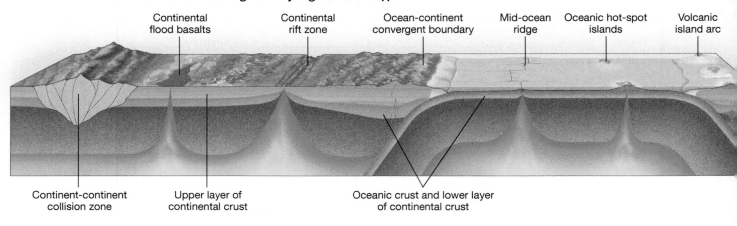

Continental flood basalts • Continental rift zone • Ocean-continent convergent boundary • Mid-ocean ridge • Oceanic hot-spot islands • Volcanic island arc

Continent-continent collision zone • Upper layer of continental crust • Oceanic crust and lower layer of continental crust

TABLE 5.3 **Tectonic associations of igneous rocks.**

Type of Plate Boundary	Geologic Setting	Rock Types
Convergent	Volcanic island arcs (ocean–ocean convergence)	Basalt, minor andesite, very minor rhyolite (and intrusive equivalents)
	Andean-type mountains (ocean-continent convergence)	Andesite, rhyolite, minor basalt (and intrusive equivalents)
	Continental collision zones (continent-continent convergence)	Granite, rhyolite, peridotite in ophiolites
Divergent	Mid-ocean ridge	Basalt—a special kind called MORB (mid-ocean ridge basalt)
	Continental rift	Rhyolite and basalt
Igneous rocks not associated with plate boundaries	Oceanic hot-spot islands	Basalt
	Ocean floors	Basalt (MORB), peridotite (locally along faults)
	Continents	Granite, rhyolite, basalt, and gabbro; andesite and diorite by magma mixing

5.5.1 Tectonic Settings of Ultramafic Rocks (Peridotites)

Several lines of evidence indicate that the mantle consists of the ultramafic rock peridotite, making it the most abundant rock on Earth. But peridotite is not a common rock, because its magma is so much denser than the crust that it doesn't have the buoyancy to rise to the surface. It *is* found in divergent mid-ocean ridges and continental rifts where extreme crustal stretching has exposed the underlying mantle, and at convergent plate boundaries where mountain building has thrust slices of the upper mantle (called **ophiolites**) into the crust.

5.5.2 Tectonic Settings of Mafic Igneous Rocks (Basalt and Gabbro)

Basalt and gabbro are the most abundant igneous rocks in the lithosphere and occur in all tectonic settings—oceanic crust (formed at mid-ocean ridges), continental rifts, oceanic and continental volcanic arcs, and hot spots. These rocks are the result of partial melting in the asthenosphere, but the cause of melting is different in each setting.

5.5.3 Tectonic Settings of Intermediate Rocks (Andesite and Diorite)

In the mid-twentieth century, geologists were puzzled by the fact that nearly all andesites occur next to trenches in continental arcs and in some oceanic island arcs. Today we understand that most intermediate magmas are produced at subduction zones by the mixing of magmas produced during subduction with rocks of the overlying plate.

5.5.4 Tectonic Settings of Felsic Rocks (Granite and Rhyolite)

Granite and rhyolite are most abundant on the continents—in continental volcanic arcs, continent-continent collision zones, rifts, and where plumes rise beneath continents. They form largely by partial melting of the upper (granitic) layer of continental lithosphere and to a lesser extent by differentiation of mafic magmas. Some rhyolite and granite form in subduction zones by differentiation of mafic and intermediate magmas and/or by assimilation. Only very small amounts of rhyolite form in oceanic hot-spot islands by extreme fractional crystallization.

EXERCISE 5.10   Origin of Mafic Magmas in Different Tectonic Settings

Name: _____   Section: _____

Course: _____   Date: _____

Explain which type of melting (addition of volatiles, decompression, heat transfer) is responsible for mafic magmas in each of the following tectonic settings and why the resulting magma is mafic.

(a) Mid-ocean ridges

_____

_____

_____

(b) Continental rifts

_____

_____

_____

(c) Oceanic and continental volcanic arcs

_____

_____

_____

(d) Hot spots

_____

_____

_____

Origin of Intermediate Magmas in Subduction Zones

Name: _____   Section: _____

Course: _____   Date: _____

Melting above the subducted slab produces mafic magma, as described above, yet intermediate rocks (andesite, diorite) are common in many subduction zones. Considering the magmatic processes discussed in section 5.4, and the difference between oceanic and continental lithosphere, explain how this intermediate magma forms.

(a) A relatively small amount of intermediate magma occurs in oceanic volcanic arcs. Remembering that melting above the subducted slab produces mafic magma, explain the origin of the intermediate magma.

_____

_____

_____

(b) Much more intermediate magma erupts in continental arcs. Why?

_____

_____

_____

Origin of Granite and Rhyolite in Continental Rifts

Name: _____   Section: _____

Course: _____   Date: _____

Continental rifts typically contain large amounts of basalt and rhyolite. Your answer to Exercise 5.10b explained the origin of the basalt, but fractional crystallization of mafic magma can produce only a very small amount of felsic magma. Explain the origin of large volumes of felsic magma in continental rifts.

_____

_____

_____

Interpreting Tectonic Setting of Igneous Rocks

Name: _____   Section: _____

Course: _____   Date: _____

Based on the information in Table 5.3 and your answers to Exercises 5.10, 5.11, and 5.12, add possible tectonic settings for the igneous rocks in your study set to your rock identification charts.

5.6 Volcanic Hazards

As we saw in earlier in the chapter, when magma reaches the surface, it spews onto the Earth in an event called a volcanic eruption. As it erupts, it sometimes flows across the land as a glowing **lava flow**, at temperatures ranging from 700°C to 1200°C, or it may be blasted by gases into the air and fall back to Earth pyroclastic debris—solid particles ranging from tiny grains of ash to blocks several feet across. Eruptions can be beneficial. The state of Hawaii is a series of volcanoes, and the lava and pyroclastic material that created (and are still creating) it are extremely fertile. But lava and pyroclastic material can also be extremely dangerous, burying cities and killing thousands of people.

To understand these hazards, we first need to know the types of volcanoes, the types of eruptions that produce them, and where they occur. Then we can consider the risk of volcanoes in parts of North America and how a large eruption might affect how and where we live.

5.6.1 Volcanic Landforms

When asked to describe eruptions, most people immediately think of the mountains we call volcanoes, built from within the Earth by lava and/or pyroclastic material. It is first important to note that not all eruptions build volcanoes; for example, highly fluid lavas flowed out from long fissures and today underlie broad flat areas like the Columbia Plateau in Washington, Oregon, and Idaho (FIG. 5.10).

However, most eruptions *do* build volcanoes, which fall into four types based on whether they are made of lava, pyroclastic material, or a unique combination of the two kinds of material (FIG. 5.11). Two are made almost entirely of lava. **Shield volcanoes** (Fig. 5.11a) are made mostly of highly fluid lava. The lava's fluidity produces broad structures with gentle slopes—the largest volcanoes on Earth (and Mars) are shield volcanoes. Because ketchup or maple syrup are similar to the consistency of lava, you can simulate the formation of a shield volcano by pouring them on a flat surface. **Lava domes** (Fig. 5.11b) are much smaller, often forming in the craters of other kinds of volcano. Lava in these volcanoes is extremely viscous—thicker and stickier than normal lava—so it can form steeper slopes than those of shield volcanoes. To simulate formation of a lava dome, squeeze a blob of epoxy or model-building plastic cement onto a flat surface. While eruptions of lava domes and shield volcanoes are the least violent of all volcanoes, lava from Hawaiian shield volcanoes has buried homes, forests, and fields, displacing people and blocking roads at a cost of millions of dollars.

FIGURE 5.10 The Columbia Plateau, a volcanic landform without volcanoes.

FIGURE 5.11 Four types of volcanoes.

(a) Shield volcano (fluid lava), Mauna Loa, Hawaii.

(b) Lava dome (viscous lava) in the crater of Kelud Volcano, Indonesia.

(c) Cinder cone (pyroclastic material), Sunset Crater, Arizona.

(d) Stratovolcano (pyroclastic material plus lava), (Mt. Mayon, Philippines.

Cinder cones (Fig. 5.11c) are made mostly from relatively fine-grained pyroclastic material and, unlike other volcanoes, form from *above*, when ash erupted from the volcano's vent falls to the ground, similar to sugar being poured into a pile. Eruptions that build cinder cones are relatively peaceful, and the resulting volcanoes are much smaller than shield volcanoes and stratovolcanoes, with moderate slopes.

Stratovolcanoes (Fig. 5.11d) are made of large amounts of both lava and pyroclastic material. They have the steepest slopes of all volcanoes because the ash is so hot when it accumulates that the particles are welded together, and the pile is not flattened by the pull of gravity. Stratovolcanoes are commonly found in subduction zones, and their explosive eruptions are caused by large amounts of steam produced by flux melting associated with the subducted slab.

5.6.2 Impact of Eruptions

While many volcanic eruptions are peaceful, they of course can be quite dangerous. Stratovolcanoes often generate pyroclastic flows—avalanches of hot ash and gas—and **lahars,** which are mudslides made of volcanic ash, water, and debris picked up along the way that can obliterate anything in their path. Volcanic gases include poisonous acids, and explosive eruptions in the oceans can produce massive, destructive events called tsunamis, which will be discussed in a later chapter. Famously, falling ash from Mt. Vesuvius buried the Roman town of Pompeii and its citizens in A.D. 79, and when Mount St. Helens in Washington State erupted in 1980, it killed fifty-seven people, spread ash that caused people to wear surgical masks to avoid the caustic, glassy airborne particles, and destroyed close to fifty bridges. Very recently, ash from Iceland's Eyjafjallajökull in 2010 disrupted European air traffic for a week at a cost of more than $200 million. In Exercise 5.14, we will consider some of the practical aspects of living in an area with volcanic activity and then examine the damage that might occur if a disastrous eruption occurred today.

EXERCISE 5.14   **Living with Volcanoes**

Name: _____   Section: _____
Course: _____   Date: _____

Let's consider the map below. It shows current and potential volcanic activity for the United States.

(a) What area of the United States has the most volcanic activity? Why is this so?

_____

_____

_____

(b) What volcanic hazards do residents of the Pacific Northwest have to be concerned about that residents of Hawaii do not? Explain.

_____

_____

_____

(continued)

Name: _____   Section: _____

Course: _____   Date: _____

(c) Is there a risk of volcanoes occurring on the Atlantic Coast? Why or why not?

_____

_____

_____

? What Do You Think Every time Old Faithful spews steam into the air in Yellowstone National Park, it reminds us that there is hot magma beneath the park capable of producing an eruption. This activity in Yellowstone is not the first volcanism in the Yellowstone area. An enormous explosive eruption 640,000 years ago blasted ash over much of the central and south western United States, blanketing the area shown in the figure below.

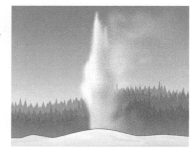

Suppose an eruption of the same size occurred tomorrow in Yellowstone National Park and blasted a layer of ash across the country in an area similar to that of the eruption 640,000 years ago. The map below projects this area onto a standard map showing major cities and highways.

Extent of ash deposits from the Yellowstone eruptive center 640,000 years ago.

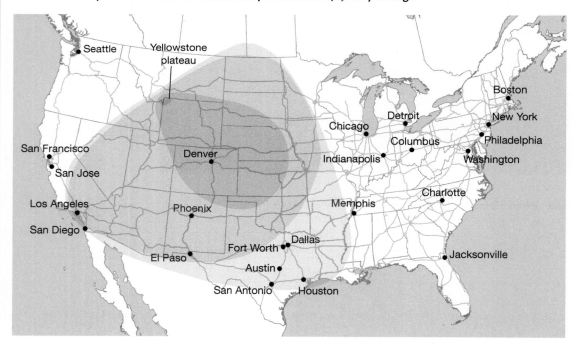

(d) What do you think would be the effect on this area of the country? Which cities and states would suffer the most and why? Consider effects on the economy, health, food supply, and transportation network in this area.

_____

_____

(continued)

Name: _____   Section: _____
Course: _____   Date: _____

_____

_____

_____

_____

_____

(e) Similarly, though not covered by the explosion, what do you think would be the effect on the rest of the country that would not be directly covered by ash?

_____

_____

_____

_____

_____

_____

_____

5.7 Visiting Localities Where Igneous Rocks Are Forming or Have Formed in the Past

Software such as *Google Earth*™ and *NASA World Wind* make it possible to tour the world to see current igneous activity at these tectonic settings and view ancient igneous rocks revealed by erosion. For example, use either software to visit

■ **Yellowstone National Park in Wyoming, a continental hot spot.** About 2.1 million years ago, an incredibly powerful explosive volcanic eruption shook the northwestern corner of Wyoming, spreading immense quantities of ash across the landscape. The sudden removal of so much magma caused the ground to subside, producing a large basin called a **caldera**. This was just the first of three similar explosive events; the most recent, only 640,000 years ago, formed the huge bowl-shaped depression in which Yellowstone National Park is located. Magma close to the surface is responsible for heating the groundwater, which gushes to the surface as hot springs and geysers like Old Faithful.

■ **The Palisades in New Jersey, a divergent plate margin.** About 180 million years ago, a supercontinent began to split apart to form the modern Atlantic Ocean. Rift valleys, like those in east Africa, formed along the east coast of North America from Nova Scotia to South Carolina. Part of the asthenosphere melted, and basaltic magma moved upward toward those valleys. Some flowed as lava, but the Palisades along the Hudson River intruded nearly horizontal sedimentary rocks beneath the surface.

- **Hawaii, an oceanic hot spot.** The "Big" island of Hawaii is the youngest of a long chain of hot-spot volcanic islands that helps us track the motion of the Pacific Plate. The island consists of five huge volcanoes, one of which (Kilauea) has been erupting nearly continually since 1983.

- **the Central Rift Valley in Iceland.** Iceland is a unique place where a hot spot lies beneath a segment of an ocean ridge. The Central Rift Valley is the divergent boundary—Iceland is growing wider as the valley sides move apart, and the lava here and at nearby volcanoes comes from magma rising into the space caused by divergence.

- **the Cascade Mountains of Washington, Oregon, and northern California, a subduction-related continental volcanic arc.** The volcanoes of the Cascade Mountains are a continental arc that developed as a small plate subducted beneath North America. Prominent peaks such as Mt. Rainier, Mt. Hood, and Mt. Baker overlook densely populated areas, much as Mt. Vesuvius stood over Pompeii (and still towers over Naples) in Italy. Thankfully, the most recent eruption in the Cascades arc was of Mount St. Helens, which is in a sparsely populated part of Washington.

- **the Sierra Nevada mountains in California.** Large volumes of the continental crust under eastern and east-central California melted between 210 and 85 million years ago, because of heat and hydrothermal fluids generated from a now-defunct subduction zone. The result was granitic magma, which cooled to form several large batholiths. Tens of millions of years of erosion have exposed the resulting granitic rocks in the Sierra Nevada mountains as seen in the Yosemite, Kings Canyon, and Sequoia national parks.

Name _____

IGNEOUS ROCKS STUDY SHEET

Sample number	Texture	Minerals present (approximate %)	Name of rock	Cooling history; source of magma; tectonic setting

IGNEOUS ROCKS STUDY SHEET

Name _____

Sample number	Texture	Minerals present (approximate %)	Name of rock	Cooling history; source of magma; tectonic setting

6

Using Sedimentary Rocks to Interpret Earth History

The beds of Grand Canyon National Park in Arizona are one of the most extensive sequences of sedimentary rocks in the world.

6.1 Introduction

Like igneous rocks, sedimentary rocks form from previously existing rocks—but by very different processes. If you've ever seen shells on a beach, gravel along a riverbank, mud in a swamp, or sand in a desert, you've seen **sediment**. Sediment consists of loose mineral grains such as **clasts**, (fragments or grains produced by weathering of a rock—boulders, pebbles, sand, silt), shells and shell fragments, plant debris, and/or mineral crystals precipitated from bodies of water. **Sedimentary rock** forms at or near the Earth's surface by the cementation and compaction of accumulated layers of these different kinds of sediment. Sedimentary rocks preserve a record of past environments and ancient life and thus tell the story of Earth history. For example, the fact that a type of sedimentary rock called limestone occurs throughout North America means that, in the past, a warm, shallow sea covered much of the continent. Geologists have learned to read the record in the rocks by comparing features in sedimentary rocks to those found today in environments where distinct types of sediment form, move, or accumulate. Remember, the present is the key to the past. In this chapter, you will learn to read this record, too.

6.2 Sediment Formation and Evolution

6.2.1 The Origin of Sediment

The material from which sedimentary rocks form ultimately comes from **weathering**—the chemical and/or physical breakdown of preexisting rock. Weathering produces both **clasts** and **dissolved ions**, which are charged atoms or molecules in a water solution. Once formed, clasts may be transported by water, wind, or ice to another location, where they are deposited and accumulate. Dissolved ions, meanwhile, enter streams and groundwater. Some of these ions precipitate from groundwater in the spaces between clasts forming a **cement** that holds the clasts together. Others get carried to lakes or seas, where organisms extract them to form shells. Finally, some dissolved ions precipitate directly from water to form layers of new sedimentary minerals. In some environments, sediment may also include organic material, the carbon-containing compounds that remain when plants, animals, and microorganisms die.

6.2.2 Weathering and Its Influence on Sediment Composition

The minerals that occur in sediment at a location depend both on the composition of the source rock(s) *and* on the nature of weathering the minerals were exposed to. Here, we look at the weathering process and how it influences sediment composition.

Physical weathering, like hitting a rock with a hammer, breaks the rock into fragments (clasts) *but does not change the minerals* that make up the rock. Initially, clasts are simply small rock pieces and may contain many grains or crystals that retain their original sizes and shapes. But when physical weathering progresses, the clasts break into smaller pieces, perhaps consisting only of a single mineral. While moving along in wind and water, clasts grind and crash against each other and become progressively smaller. As a result, the size and shape of transported clasts do not tell us whether the source rock itself was coarse or fine or whether grains in the source rock interlocked or were cemented together (**FIG. 6.1**). But because physical weathering does not change the composition of clasts, we can get a sense of the

FIGURE 6.1 Physical weathering of coarse-grained granite.

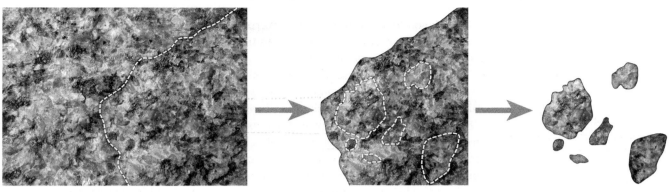

(a) A rock breaks along the dashed lines

(b) The rock fragment preserves grain sizes and relationships.

(c) The fragment breaks into both smaller rock fragments and mineral grains.

composition of the source rock by looking at these clasts. For example, sediment derived from physical weathering of granite would contain clasts of quartz, K-feldspar, plagioclase, and biotite, whereas sediment derived from physical weathering of basalt would contain clasts of plagioclase, pyroxene, amphibole, and olivine.

Chemical weathering is the process during which rock chemically reacts with air, water, and acidic solutions. In other words, chemical weathering involves **chemical reactions**, the breaking and forming of chemical bonds. These reactions can destroy some of the original minerals and can produce new minerals. Minerals that are easily weathered are called *unstable* or *nonresistant*, whereas those that can survive weathering or are produced by weathering are called *stable* or *resistant*. Chemical

FIGURE 6.2 Chemical weathering of felsic and mafic igneous rocks.

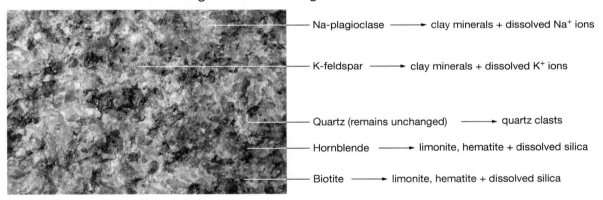

Na-plagioclase $\longrightarrow$ clay minerals + dissolved Na$^+$ ions

K-feldspar $\longrightarrow$ clay minerals + dissolved K$^+$ ions

Quartz (remains unchanged) $\longrightarrow$ quartz clasts

Hornblende $\longrightarrow$ limonite, hematite + dissolved silica

Biotite $\longrightarrow$ limonite, hematite + dissolved silica

(a) Granite weathers to clay minerals, limonite, hematite, and quartz plus dissolved potassium, sodium, and silica.

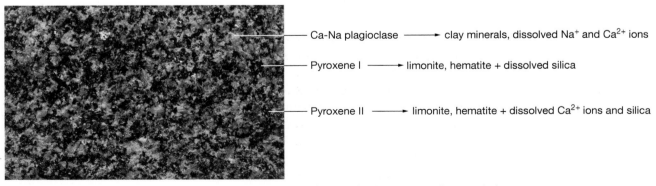

Ca-Na plagioclase $\longrightarrow$ clay minerals, dissolved Na$^+$ and Ca^{2+} ions

Pyroxene I $\longrightarrow$ limonite, hematite + dissolved silica

Pyroxene II $\longrightarrow$ limonite, hematite + dissolved Ca^{2+} ions and silica

(b) Gabbro weathers to clay minerals, limonite, and hematite plus dissolved calcium, sodium, and silica.

weathering has hardly any effect on quartz because quartz is stable, but it transforms feldspar, which is an unstable mineral, into clay and ions (K^+, Ca^{2+}, Na^+). Similarly, chemical weathering converts ferromagnesian minerals such as olivine, pyroxene, amphibole, and biotite into hematite and limonite (iron oxide minerals) along with ions of silicon and oxygen.

Relatively few minerals are stable at the Earth's surface, so *chemical weathering generally reduces the number of minerals in sediment* over time. As a result, weathering of very different source rocks can yield surprisingly similar sedimentary mineral assemblages (**FIG. 6.2**). Weathering of granite, for example, produces quartz, clay minerals, and iron oxides. Gabbro also weathers into clay minerals and iron oxides. Note that only the proportions of minerals (more iron oxides in the weathered gabbro) and the occurrence of quartz (none in weathered gabbro) help us distinguish sediments derived by chemical weathering of granite from those derived from gabbro.

6.2.3 Mineralogical Maturity

Not all sediments have undergone the same amount of weathering. Sediments that contain minerals which are susceptible to chemical weathering (unstable minerals) are said to be **mineralogically immature**. While sediments that contain minerals which are resistant to chemical weathering (stable minerals) are known as **mineralogically mature**. The effects of weathering are examined further in Exercise 6.1.

EXERCISE 6.1	Looking at Weathering Products

Name: _____   **Section:** _____

Course: _____   **Date:** _____

During chemical weathering, water, oxygen, and carbon dioxide combine with minerals in previously existing rocks to destroy some minerals and create new ones.

(a) How does the mineral assemblage in chemically weathered sediment change with the *amount* of chemical weathering?

_____

_____

(b) What weathering history can you interpret from the following mineral assemblages found in *clastic* sedimentary rocks? For example: What was the source rock? Was it weathered for a short time or a long time? Think broadly and remember that there may be more than one possible interpretation.
　(i) All quartz grains
　(ii) Nearly equal amounts of quartz, K-feldspar, and Na-plagioclase with a small amount of hematite
　(iii) All fine-grained clay minerals with some hematite and limonite
　(iv) A mixture of quartz grains and clay minerals
　(v) Rock fragments composed of Ca-plagioclase and pyroxene

_____

_____

_____

_____

_____

(continued)

Name: _____   Section: _____

Course: _____   Date: _____

(c) Rank the following environments in the order in which you would expect sediments to become mineralogically mature, from slowest to fastest. (*Hint*: Think about the temperature and the amount of rainfall available.)

   desert _____   tropical rain forest _____   temperate climate _____

Explain your reasoning.

_____

_____

_____

(d) Which of the following mineral assemblages (as seen in Exercise 6.1b) are mineralogically mature? Which are mineralogically immature?
   (i) All quartz grains _____
   (ii) Nearly equal amounts of quartz, K-feldspar, and Na-plagioclase with a small amount of hematite _____
   (iii) All fine-grained clay minerals with some hematite and limonite _____
   (iv) A mixture of quartz grains and clay minerals _____
   (v) Rock fragments composed of Ca-plagioclase and pyroxene _____

6.3 The Basic Classes of Sedimentary Rocks

Geologists distinguish among many kinds of sedimentary rocks, each with a name based on the nature of the material that the rock contains and the process by which the rock forms. To organize this information, we sort various rocks into classes, though not all geologists use the same classification. A simple scheme groups rocks into four classes—clastic, chemical, biochemical, and organic—based on the nature of the particles that make up rocks. Note that this classification scheme is not based on composition (the mineral present). In this section, we will first examine these classes and then we will conclude by introducing an overlapping classification scheme that focuses on composition.

6.3.1 Clastic Sedimentary Rock

Clastic sedimentary rocks are formed from clasts (mineral grains or rock fragments) derived from previously existing rocks. These rocks have a characteristic clastic texture in which discrete grains are held together by a chemical cement or by a very fine-grained clastic matrix. Of the most common clastic sedimentary rocks, the majority are derived from silicate rocks and thus contain clasts composed of silicate minerals. (To emphasize this, geologists sometimes refer to them as *siliciclastic rocks.*) Formation of clastic sedimentary rock involves the following processes (**FIG. 6.3**):

1. **Weathering:** The process of weathering reduces solid bedrock into a pile of loose (separate mineral) grains or loose clasts, also known as *detritus.*
2. **Erosion:** This occurs as moving water (streams and waves), moving air (wind), and moving ice (glaciers) pluck and/or pick up the clasts.

FIGURE 6.3 The five steps in clastic sedimentary rock formation.

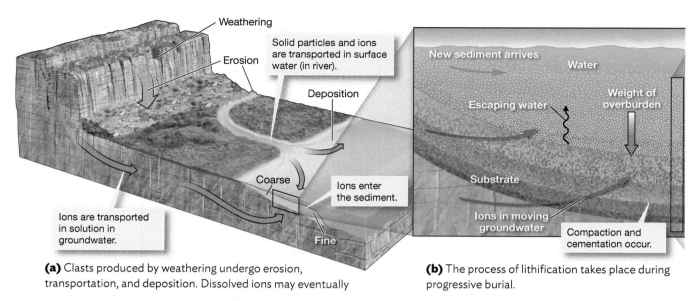

(a) Clasts produced by weathering undergo erosion, transportation, and deposition. Dissolved ions may eventually

(b) The process of lithification takes place during progressive burial.

3. **Transportation:** Moving water, wind, or ice carry clasts away from their source.
4. **Deposition:** When moving water or wind slows or when the ice melts, clasts settle out and accumulate. The places where this occurs are called **depositional environments** (such as the land surface, the sea floor, or a riverbed).
5. **Lithification:** This process transforms loose sediment into solid rock through compaction and cementation. Over time, accumulations of clasts are buried. When this happens, the weight of overlying sediment squeezes out air and/or water, thereby fitting the clasts more tightly together. This process is called **compaction**. As ion-rich groundwater passes through the compacted sediment, minerals precipitate and bind, or "glue," the clasts together. This process is called **cementation**, and the mineral glue between clasts is called **cement**. Cement in sedimentary rock typically consists of either calcite or quartz and may contain minor amounts of hematite or pyrite.

A final process is called **diagenesis,** where the application of pressure and the circulation of fluids over time may gradually change characteristics of sediments and sedimentary rock (e.g., grain size and composition of cement or the nature of grain boundaries), even at temperatures below those required for metamorphism. Any chemical, physical, or biological process that alters the rock after it is formed is called diagenesis.

As we see later in this chapter, the names of *clastic* sedimentary rocks are based primarily on the size of the clasts they contain. Geologists refer to the Wentworth scale (**TABLE. 6.1**) to distinguish among grain size. From coarsest to finest, clastic sedimentary rocks and their grain sizes include:

- **Conglomerate/breccia/diamictite** consists of pebbles and/or cobbles. Clasts in conglomerate are rounded (have no sharp corners), whereas those in breccia are angular (have sharp corners). Diamictite has large clasts in mud. Modifiers are sometimes added when one kind of clast dominates (e.g., quartz conglomerate or limestone breccia).
- **Sandstone/arkose/lithic sandstone/wacke** The name **sandstone** applies to any clastic sedimentary rock composed predominantly of sand-sized grains.

TABLE 6.1 Classification of clastic sedimentary rocks

Clast size terminology (Wentworth scale)	Clast size	Appearance	Size in mm	Clast character	Rock name (alternative name)
Coarse to very coarse	Boulder			Rounded pebbles, cobbles, and boulders	Conglomerate
			256		
Medium to coarse	Cobble			Angular pebbles, cobbles, and boulders	Breccia
			64		
Medium to coarse	Pebble			Pebbles, cobbles, and boulders in muddy matrix	Diamictite
			2		
Medium	Sand			Sand-sized grains • quartz grains only • quartz and feldspar sand • sand-sized rock fragments • quartz sand and sand-sized rock fragments in a clay-rich matrix	Sandstone • quartz sandstone (quartz arenite) • arkose • lithic sandstone • wacke (informally called graywacke)
			0.06		
Fine	Silt			Silt-sized clasts	Siltstone
			0.004		
Very fine	Clay			Clay and/or very fine silt	Shale, if it breaks into platy sheets Mudstone, if it doesn't break into platy sheets

Four types of sandstone are distinguished based on the composition of the grains they contain:

- **Quartz sandstone** (or quartz arenite) consists of > 95% quartz grains. It is the most common type because quartz is the most common resistant mineral in chemical weathering and the most mineralogically mature.
- **Arkose** contains quartz with > 25% feldspar grains. It is less mineralogically mature than quartz sandstone and forms close to a source of sediment in which feldspar has not been removed by chemical weathering.
- **Lithic sandstone** contains clasts of quartz, feldspar, and > 5% fragments of previously existing rocks (*lithic* fragments).
- **Wacke** (informally graywacke) is a sandstone containing quartz, feldspar, and lithic clasts surrounded by a matrix of mud.

■ **Siltstone** consists of silt-sized clasts.

■ **Shale/mudstone** consist mostly of clay-sized particles, invisible even with a hand lens.

6.3.2 Chemical Sedimentary Rock

This class consists of rocks formed from mineral crystals precipitated directly from a water solution. Chemical sedimentary rock forms when water solutions of dissolved ions become oversaturated and excess ions bond together to form solid mineral grains, which often display a crystalline texture as they grow and interlock with each other. These crystals either settle out of the solution or grow outward from the walls of the container holding the solution. Exercise 6.2 allows you to simulate the chemical precipitation process in the lab to see how the textures of these rocks develop.

Groundwater, oceans, and saline lakes all contain significant quantities of dissolved ions and can serve as a source of chemical sedimentary rock. Precipitation to form chemical sedimentary rocks happens in many environments, including (1) hot springs, where warm groundwater seeps out at the Earth's surface and cools; (2) cave walls, where groundwater seeps out, evaporates, and releases CO_2; (3) the floors of saline lakes or restricted seas, where salt water evaporates; (4) within sedimentary rocks, when reactions with groundwater result in the replacement of the original minerals with new minerals; and (5) on the deep-sea floor, where the shells of plankton dissolve to form a gel-like layer that then crystallizes. The composition of a chemical sedimentary rock depends on the composition of

---

EXERCISE 6.2   **Simulating Chemical Sedimentary Textures**

Name: _____   Section: _____
Course: _____   Date: _____

(a) Place a beaker with seawater (or homemade salt water) on a hot plate and heat it gently until the water evaporates. Partially fill a second beaker with a clear, concentrated solution of calcium hydroxide [$Ca(OH)_2$]. Using a straw, blow *gently* into the solution until you notice a change.

Describe what happened in each demonstration, and sketch the resulting textures.

(i)   Evaporated seawater description   Sketch

_____

_____

_____

_____

_____

(ii) $Ca(OH)_2$ solution description   Sketch

_____

_____

_____

_____

_____

(continued)

Name: _____   Section: _____

Course: _____   Date: _____

(b) Compare the texture in (i) with that of a granite, a rock formed by cooling of a melt. Describe and explain the similarities in texture.

_____

_____

_____

_____

the solution it was derived from—some chemical sedimentary rocks consist of salts (e.g., halite, gypsum), whereas others consist of silica or carbonate. In some chemical sedimentary rocks, the grains are large enough to see (**FIG. 6.4a**). But in others, the grains are so small that the rock looks somewhat like porcelain (**FIG. 6.4b**). Such rocks are called **cryptocrystalline rocks**, from the Latin *crypta-*, meaning hidden.

Geologists distinguish among different types of chemical sedimentary rocks based primarily on composition:

- **Evaporites** Chemical sedimentary rocks in thick deposits composed of crystals formed when salt water evaporates. Rock salt and rock gypsum are two common examples.
- **Travertine (chemical limestones)** Rocks composed of crystalline calcium carbonate ($CaCO_3$) formed by chemical precipitation from groundwater that has seeped out of the ground surface either in hot- or cold-water springs or from the walls of caves.

FIGURE 6.4 **Textures of chemical sedimentary rocks.**

(a) Coarse, interlocking halite grains in rock salt.

(b) Cryptocrystalline silica grains (chert). Note the almost glassy appearance and conchoidal fracturing.

- **Dolostone** Carbonate rocks differing from limestone in that they contain a significant amount of dolomite, a mineral with equal amounts of calcium and magnesium. Most dolostone forms from limestone during diagenesis when groundwater adds magnesium to calcite ($CaCO_3$), forming the mineral dolomite [$CaMg(CO_3)_2$].
- **Chert** Sedimentary rocks composed of very fine-grained silica. Some chert, called replacement chert, forms when cryptocrystalline quartz replaces calcite in limestone. Another kind (biochemical chert) is formed during diagenesis when microscopic shells made of quartz dissolve partially, form an ultrafine-grained gel, and then solidify. *Note:* Biochemical and chemical forms of chert cannot be distinguished in hand samples.

6.3.3 Biochemical and Organic Sedimentary Rocks

While alive, organisms extract chemicals from their environment and use these to produce new molecules for building bodies and shells. For example, some invertebrates (such as clams and oysters), along with certain types of algae and plankton, extract dissolved ions from water to produce shells composed of either carbonate or silica. Plants extract CO_2 from the air to produce the cellulose of leaves and wood. And all organisms produce *organic chemicals*, meaning chemicals containing rings or chains of carbon atoms bonded to hydrogen, nitrogen, oxygen, and other elements. When organisms die, the materials that compose their cells and/or shells can accumulate in depositional settings, just like sediment. Carbonate or silicate shells are quite durable—after all, they're composed of fairly hard minerals such as calcite or quartz. Organic chemicals are less durable, and they commonly decompose and oxidize. But in special depositional settings where there is relatively little oxygen and the organisms get buried rapidly, organic chemicals can be preserved in rocks.

Rock composed primarily of the remains of once-living organisms are classified as **biochemical sedimentary rocks** if they consist of the hard shells of those organisms or **organic sedimentary rocks** if they contain significant quantities of the organic material from the soft, carbon-rich parts of those organisms. Continuing diagenesis tends to modify both biochemical and organic rocks significantly after initial lithification. For example, rocks containing abundant calcite may undergo pervasive recrystallization, so that the original grains are replaced by new, larger interlocking crystals. Diagenesis may also dissolve some grains and precipitate new cements in pores, and it may drive the transformation of calcite ($CaCO_3$) into dolomite [$CaMg(CO_3)_2$]. Organic chemicals, over time, lose certain elements and transform into either pure carbon or hydrocarbon (carbon + hydrogen). The texture of biochemical and organic rocks, like other sedimentary rocks, reflects the nature of the depositional environment. In some environments, shells are transported by currents or waves and break into fragments that behave like sedimentary clasts.

Geologists distinguish among many types of biochemical and organic sedimentary rocks based on composition and texture. Common examples are as follows.

Biochemical rocks

- Limestone is a general class of rocks formed from shells composed of calcite. Commonly, limestone tends to form as chunky blocks, light gray to dark-bluish gray in color. Geologists recognize distinct subcategories of biochemical limestone, based on texture.
  - **Fossiliferous limestone** contains abundant visible fossils in a matrix of fossil fragments and other grains.
  - **Micrite** is very fine-grained limestone formed from the lithification of carbonate mud. The mud may come from tiny spines of sponges or from the shells of algae or bacteria, or it may form after burial by diagenesis.

- **Chalk** is a soft, white limestone composed of the shells of plankton.
- **Coquina** consists of a mass of shells that are only poorly cemented together and have undergone minimal diagenesis.

■ **Biochemical chert** forms from a silica gel that forms when shells of silica-secreting plankton accumulate on the sea floor. We use the word *biogenic* to distinguish this chert from another occurrence, replacement chert, which forms by diagenesis in already lithified limestone.

Organic rocks

■ **Coal** is composed primarily of carbon, derived from plant material (wood, leaves) that was buried and underwent diagenesis. Geologists distinguish three *ranks* of coal based on the proportion of carbon: lignite (50%); bituminous (85%); anthracite (95%).

■ **Oil shale**, like regular shale, is composed mostly of clay; but unlike regular shale, oil shale contains a significant amount of kerogen (a waxy organic chemical derived from fats in the bodies of plankton and algae).

6.4 Sedimentary Rock Identification

You are now familiar with the nature and origin of sediment, the major classes of sedimentary rocks, and the names of the most common sedimentary rock types. TABLE 6.2 summarizes information from the preceding sections in a simplified

TABLE 6.2 Classification of common sedimentary rocks.

(A) Clastic Sedimentary Rocks (silicate mineral grains or rock fragments held together by cement)			
Composition	**Texture or Clasts (grain size in mm)**	**Clues to Identify**	**Rock Name**
Usually silicate minerals	Boulders, Cobbles, Pebbles (> 2)	Clasts are bigger than peas; you can measure clasts with a ruler.	**Conglomerate** (if clasts are rounded); **Breccia** (if clasts are angular) **Diamictite** (larger clasts are surrounded by a muddy matrix)
Usually silicate minerals	Sand (1/16 to 2)	Grains are easily visible and identifiable, but too small to measure with a ruler.	**Sandstone** (a general term) - **Quartz sandstone** (= arenite; > 95% quartz) - **Arkose** (quartz plus > 25% feldspar) - **Lithic sandstone** (contains > 5% lithic clasts*) - **Graywacke** (informal name; sand grains ± rock chips, surrounded by a clay matrix)
Usually silicate minerals	Silt (1/256 to 1/16)	Grains are visible but too small to identify; feels gritty.	**Siltstone**
Usually silicate minerals	Clay (<1/256)	Individual grains are not visible; composed dominantly of clay.	**Mudstone** (breaks into blocky pieces); **Shale** (breaks into thin plates)

* Lithic clasts are sand-sized rock fragments

TABLE 6.2 Classification of common sedimentary rocks (*continued*).

(B) Chemical Sedimentary Rocks (composed of grains that precipitated from a water solution)

Composition	Texture or Clasts (grain size in mm)	Clues to Identify	Rock Name
Halite	Crystal (generally > 2)	Clear to gray, with visible interlocking crystals; tastes salty.	**Rock salt**
Gypsum	Crystal (generally > 2)	Clear to whitish–pale gray or pinkish; soft, can be scratched with a fingernail.	**Rock gypsum**
Calcite	Grains appear like tiny balls	Very fine-grained; HCl test yields a vigorous fizz.	**Oolitic limestone**
Quartz	Grains not visible	Won't be scratched by a nail or knife; grains are too small to see; tends to be porcelainous; fractures conchoidally.	**Chert** - **Jasper** (reddish) - **Flint** (black)

(C) Biochemical Sedimentary Rocks (composed of minerals originally extracted by organisms to form shells)

Composition	Texture or Clasts (grain size in mm)	Clues to Identify	Rock Name
Calcite	Visible shells or a few shells in very fine grains (generally 1/256 to 2); some crystal appearance	Commonly grayish, but may be white, yellow, or pink; vigorously reacts with acid; some examples may consist of shell fragments cemented together and have a clastic texture; some have recrystallized to form a crystalline texture.	**Limestone** (general name) - **Fossiliferous limestone** - **Micrite** (very fine-grained; grains aren't visible)
Calcite	Visible shells (>2)	A weakly cemented mixture of shells.	**Coquina** (a type of limestone)
Calcite	Grains not visible	Whitish; can be used to write on slate. Vigorously reacts with HCl acid	**Chalk** (a type of limestone)
Dolomite	Grains not visible	Grayish to rusty tan; scratched-off powder has a moderate reaction with HCl acid.	**Dolostone**

(D) Organic (containing organic chemicals derived from the bodies of organisms)

Composition	Texture or Clasts (grain size in mm)	Clues to Identify	Rock Name
Clay and kerogen	Grains not visible	Dark gray to black; may have an oily smell; may burn; can't see grains.	**Oil shale**
Carbon (± clay and quartz)	Grains not visible	Black; may have a subtle bedding; typically breaks into blocks; may contain plant fossils.	**Coal** - **Lignite coal** (50% carbon; fairly soft) - **Bituminous coal** (85% carbon; medium hard; dull) - **Anthracite coal** (95% carbon; quite hard; shiny)

classification chart for sedimentary rocks based on texture and mineralogy. With this information, careful observations, and sometimes using the same tests you used for mineral identification (see Chapter 3, section 3.4), you will be able to identify the most common sedimentary rock types.

6.4.1 Steps in Identifying Sedimentary Rocks

Geologists approach sedimentary rock identification systematically, following the steps outlined below. As with mineral identification, we offer two different visual reference tools to help as you follow these steps: (1) Table 6.2 presents different classes of sedimentary rocks, with their basic characteristics, clues for identification, and their names, and (2) **FIG. 6.5** presents the same information in a flowchart. Identical colors identify the different classes of sedimentary rock in both schemes.

STEP 1 **Examine the rock's texture**. A simple textural observation will be easy for sedimentary rocks with grains coarse enough to see with the naked eye or a hand lens. Does the specimen consist of cemented-together grains, clasts, intergrown crystals, or fossils? If your specimen has grains too small to be seen even with a hand lens, go directly to step 2. Otherwise follow steps (a), (b), or

FIGURE 6.5 **Flow chart for identifying sedimentary rocks.**

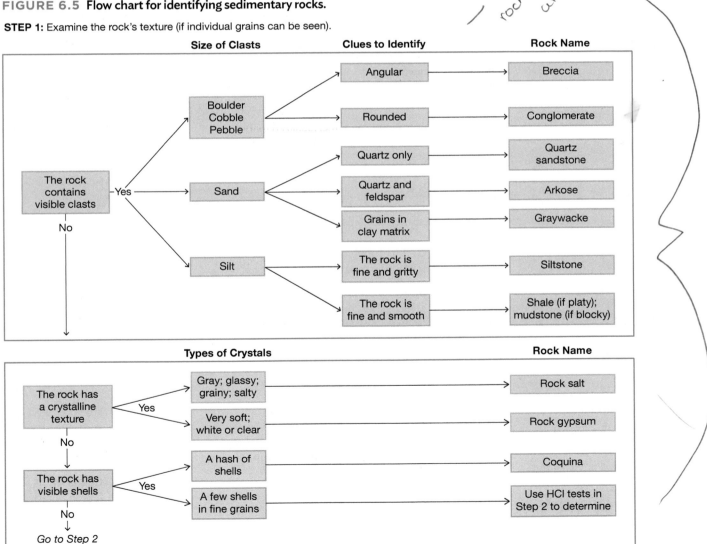

STEP 1: Examine the rock's texture (if individual grains can be seen).

FIGURE 6.5 Flow chart for identifying sedimentary rocks. (cont.)

STEP 2: If the grains are too small to see, use physical **(a)** and HCl **(b)** tests to determine rock type.

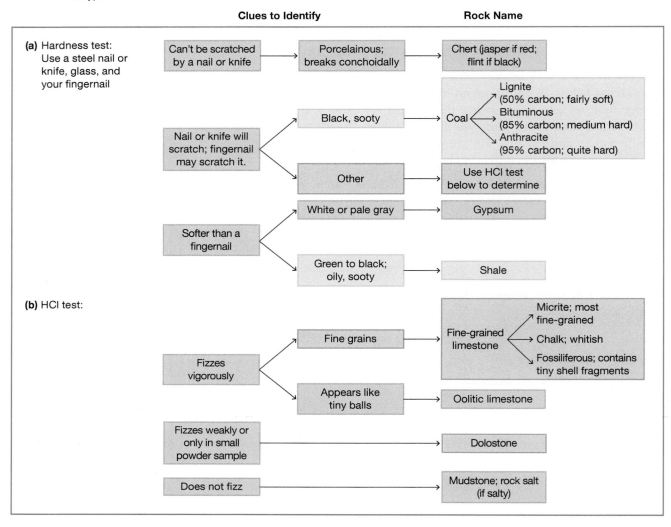

(c) depending on the texture of your specimen. Use Table 6.2 or Figure 6.5 to help make your determination.

(a) If the rock is clastic, determine grain *size* and *roundness*. First use the grain size chart in Table 6.1 to find the correct name for the grain size. Then, use other clues as identified in the Table 6.2 or Figure 6.5 to find the rock name. Remember that larger, rounded grains define a conglomerate and angular grains a breccia. If the clasts are smaller (at the size of sand or silt), you are identifying either a form of sandstone, siltstone, shale, or mudstone. Use the specifics in Table 6.2 or Figure 6.5 to choose the correct one.

(b) If the rock is crystalline, locate the crystalline rocks in Table 6.2 or Figure 6.5, and use the tests and observation skills you have learned for hardness, cleavage, luster, HCl reaction, and, if necessary, taste to identify the minerals. Then apply the appropriate name from the table or flowchart.

(c) If the rock is made entirely of cemented fossils and fossil fragments, it is *coquina*. If a few fossils are set in a fine-grained matrix, use HCl to determine if it is a fossiliferous limestone (it fizzes) or mudstone (it doesn't).

STEP 2 What to do when grains are too small to be seen. If the grains are too small to see, you will need to use the physical tests you have learned in Chapter 3.

(a) Use a steel nail (or knife) and fingernail to determine the rock's hardness.

  (i) If it is harder than the nail, it is chert—made entirely of silica—and has a Mohs hardness of about 7.
  (ii) If it is harder than the fingernail but softer than the steel nail (and it's not black and sooty—meaning it's a form of coal), go to step 2b to determine its chemical composition.
  (iii) If it is softer than the fingernail and white or pale gray, it is rock gypsum.
  (iv) If it is softer than the fingernail, black, and sooty, it is coal.

(b) Carefully add a very small drop of HCl to find out if the rock is a limestone or dolostone.

  (i) If the rock fizzes vigorously, it is a very fine-grained limestone. It could be chemical (micrite) or biochemical (chalk). However, if the texture appears like tiny balls it is oolitic limestone.
  (ii) If the rock fizzes weakly, scratch it again and put a drop of acid on the powder. If it reacts more strongly, it is a very fine-grained dolostone (dolomicrite).
  (iii) If the rock doesn't fizz, go to step 2c.

(c) Moisten your finger, rub it against the rock, and taste. If it tastes salty, the specimen is rock salt.

Exercise 6.3 will help you practice identifying rock samples by using these steps. Remember you can look to either the table or the chart for help. Both present the same information, so use whichever style you are more comfortable with.

EXERCISE 6.3   **Identifying Sedimentary Rock Samples**

Name: _____   Section: _____
Course: _____   Date: _____

Examine the rock samples in your set that you classified as sedimentary rocks. Read Section 6.4.1 closely to remind yourself of the steps. Fill in the rock study sheets at the end of this chapter to identify each sample. Keep these samples and your study sheets until you have finished the chapter. At that point, you will be able to add an interpretation of the histories of the rocks.

6.5 Interpreting Clastic Sedimentary Textures

If you are given a clastic sedimentary rock, identifying it is only part of the task. The texture of the rock is a rich source of information about the geologic history that eventually led to the deposition of the sediment from which the rock formed. Specific aspects of texture—grain size, sorting, and grain shape—provide clues to the amount of transport and the amount of weathering that the sediment has undergone between the time it eroded from its source to the time it became buried at the site of deposition.

6.5.1 Grain Size and Sorting

Clasts in sedimentary rocks range from the size of a house to specks so small they can't be seen without an electron microscope. As noted earlier, geologists use familiar words like *sand* and *pebble* to define clast size (see illustration in Table 6.1). The size of grains in a rock reflects the kinetic energy of the agent that transports it—an agent with more kinetic energy can move bigger clasts.

The kinetic energy of a transporting agent depends on both its mass and velocity. Air has much less mass than running water, so at the same velocity a stream can move larger particles than air can. Similarly, a small stream flowing at the same velocity as a large river has less kinetic energy (less mass) and therefore cannot move clasts as large as the river can. Another important factor for glaciers—the only *solid* transporting agent—is that ice is less dense than running water (remember, ice cubes float). A given volume of water therefore weighs more than the same volume of ice, and running water moves far faster than a glacier can advance. Yet, glaciers transport blocks of material far larger than those that even the largest river can move. There are two reasons for this: first, the mass of the ice is enormous; second, its solid nature provides a permanent strength absent in running water. Even though glacial ice moves slowly, it can carry debris weighing tons.

The **sorting** of a clastic sedimentary rock is a measure of the uniformity of grain size (**FIG. 6.6**). It shows the degree to which clasts have been separated by flowing currents, and it can also help identify the transporting agent. For example, aeolian (wind-deposited) sediment is very well sorted because wind can pick up only clasts of a narrow size range. A fast-moving, turbulent stream can carry clasts ranging from mud- to boulder-sized. But as a stream slows, sediment of different sizes progressively settles out. The coarsest grains (boulders and cobbles) drop out first, then the mid-size grains (pebbles and sand), and only when the water is moving very slowly can silt and mud settle out. Thus streams do sort clasts, but not as completely as the wind. Glacial ice is solid, so it can carry clasts of all sizes. As a result, glacially transported deposits are not sorted.

6.5.2 Grain Shape

The shape of clasts is another clue to the agent and distance of transportation. Clasts carried by water or wind collide frequently with one another as they move. As transport progresses, collisions knock off sharp corners and edges, eventually rounding the clasts. First the grains become **subrounded**, with smoothed edges and corners. Eventually, when they are almost spherical, they are called **rounded**. Thus, the farther streams and wind carry clasts, in general, the more rounded the grains become. The clasts also become smaller as a result of these collisions. **FIGURE 6.7**

FIGURE 6.6 **Sorting in sedimentary rocks.**

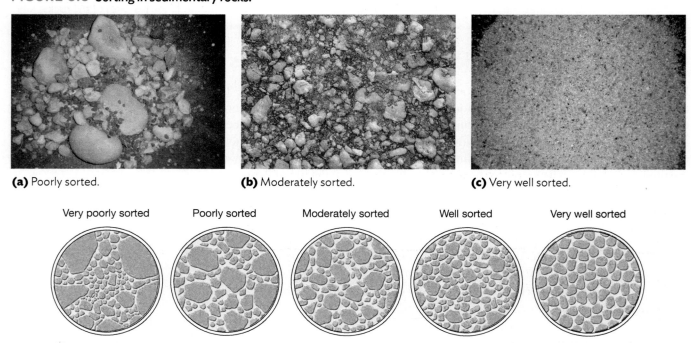

(a) Poorly sorted.

(b) Moderately sorted.

(c) Very well sorted.

Very poorly sorted   Poorly sorted   Moderately sorted   Well sorted   Very well sorted

(d) In a poorly sorted sediment, there is a great variety of different clast sizes, whereas in a well-sorted sediment, all the clasts are the same size.

FIGURE 6.7 Degrees of grain roundness in clastic sedimentary rocks.

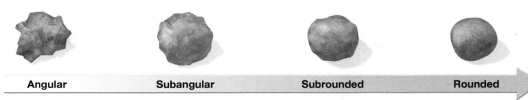

Angular   Subangular   Subrounded   Rounded

(a) Angular clasts   **(b)** Rounded clasts

shows different degrees of roundness in two sedimentary rocks. In contrast, grains that have not moved far from their source tend to have sharp edges and corners because they have not had the opportunity to collide as much and are called **angular**.

EXERCISE 6.4   **What Could Move the Clasts?**

Name: _____   Section: _____
Course: _____   Date: _____

Some agents of transport can move sediment that ranges widely in grain size. Match the letter of the transport agent from the left-hand column with the **maximum grain size** it can transport listed in the right-hand column.

(a) house-sized block   ____ turbulent stream during a flood
(b) boulder   ____ very slow-moving stream
(c) cobble   ____ ocean waves or desert winds
(d) sand   ____ glacial ice
(e) silt   ____ quiet water
(f) mud   ____ fast-moving stream

EXERCISE 6.5   **Interpreting Sorting**

Name: _____   Section: _____
Course: _____   Date: _____

Look at the three sets of clasts in Figure 6.6. Suggest possible transporting agents that could be responsible for each.

(a) Poorly sorted: _____

(b) Moderately sorted: _____

(c) Very well sorted: _____

Name: _____   Section: _____

Course: _____   Date: _____

Look back at the definitions of breccia and conglomerate. Based on these definitions, which of these two rock types contains clasts that have been transported a longer distance? Explain.

_____

_____

_____

Angular clasts also occur in sediments deposited by glaciers, because these clasts are frozen into position and thus can't collide with one another.

6.5.3 Sediment "Maturity"

We discussed mineralogical maturity earlier in this chapter. We can expand this concept into the broader idea of **sediment maturity**—the degree to which a sediment has evolved from a crushed-up version of the original rock into a sediment that has lost its easily-weathered minerals and become well sorted and rounded. The changes occur as the sediment is transported and include the loss of easily-weathered minerals by chemical reaction and progressive rounding and sorting.

Specifically, if the resulting sediment accumulates close to the source, it can contain a variety of grain sizes and remain poorly sorted. Also, because chemical weathering has not progressed to completion, relatively unstable minerals (e.g., feldspar, mica, and amphibole) remained mixed with stable minerals (e.g., quartz). Finally, since grains have not traveled far, they may retain an angular shape. Geologists refer to a sediment with these characteristics as *immature*. If, however, the sediment is carried a long distance by a river and/or is washed by wave action along a shore, and if the sediment has time to undergo substantial chemical weathering so that unstable minerals transform into clay and wash away, it will be quite different—it will be well sorted, it will consist almost entirely of stable minerals, and grains will be well rounded. Geologists refer to sediments with this character as *mature* (**FIGURE 6.8**).

FIGURE 6.8 Mature sediment. As sediments are transported progressively farther, weatherable sediments such as feldspar break down and convert to clay, which washes away, so the proportion of sediment consisting of resistant minerals such as quartz increases. Further, the physical bouncing and grinding that accompanies the transport of sediment progressively rounds the quartz grains and sorts them.

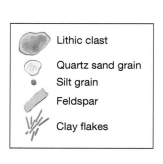

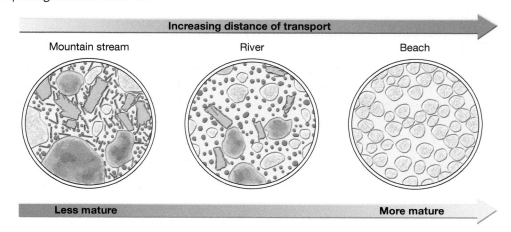

Name: _____   Section: _____

Course: _____   Date: _____

Fill in the following table to summarize the characteristics of sediment deposited by the different continental agents of erosion.

Textural feature	Agent of transportation		
	Streams	**Wind**	**Glaciers**
Grain size			
Sorting			
Grain shape			

6.5.4 Cements in Clastic Rocks

The most common cements found in clastic sedimentary rocks are quartz or calcite, for the ions making these minerals can occur in relatively high concentrations in the groundwater from which cements precipitate. Which mineral occurs as the dominant component of the cement depends on the source of the groundwater and on the chemical environment in which precipitation takes place.

In some cases, the cement that holds clasts together provides a clue to the depositional environment. For example, the formation of a hematite cement requires oxygen, so sedimentary rocks in which the cement contains hematite, and thus has a reddish color, come from environments where water contained dissolved oxygen. In contrast, sedimentary rocks containing pyrite in the cement formed in environments low in oxygen, because if oxygen had been present, the pyrite would have dissolved. Reddish sedimentary rocks, or *redbeds*, generally indicate deposition in terrestrial environments (e.g., rivers, alluvial fans). You can practice this concept in Exercise 6.8.

EXERCISE 6.8   **Identifying Cements**

Name: _____   Section: _____

Course: _____   Date: _____

How can you tell what minerals occur in a cement? Simply remember the basic physical properties of the minerals (e.g., hardness, the ability to react with acid, color). With this in mind, answer the following questions concerning sandstone, a type of sedimentary rock consisting of cemented-together grains of quartz sand.

(a) The cement (but not the grains) in a sedimentary rock reacts when in contact with dilute HCl. The cement consists of
_____.

(b) The rock, overall, has a reddish color. The cement contains _____.

(c) The cement is very strong, and when scratched with a steel needle it has the same hardness as the grains. The cement consists of _____.

6.6 Sedimentary Structures: Clues to Ancient Environments

6.6.1 Beds and Stratification

Gravity causes all sediment to settle to the floor of the basin in which it was deposited. Over time, layers of sediment called **beds** accumulate. Beds range from a millimeter to several meters thick, depending on the process involved. Each bed represents a single depositional event, and the different colors, grain sizes, and types of sediment from each event distinguish one bed from another (**FIG. 6.9**).

Many beds are fairly homogeneous, with uniform color, mineralogy, and texture, and have smooth surfaces. But some contain internal variations or have distinct features on their surfaces. These **sedimentary structures** provide important information about the rock's history. In the next section, we look at a few examples of sedimentary structures.

6.6.2 Sedimentary Structures

Graded Beds Graded beds are layers in which the grain size decreases progressively from the bottom to the top. These form during a submarine avalanche when poorly sorted sediment speeds down a submarine slope (**FIG. 6.10**). When the avalanche, called a *turbidity current*, slows, the coarsest grains settle first while the finer materials remain in suspension longer. With time, the finer sediments settle, and the finest ones settle last. To make a graded bed in the lab, put water, sand, silt, and gravel in a jar or graduated cylinder. Shake to mix thoroughly and watch as the grains settle.

Ripple Marks, Dunes, and Cross Beds *Ripple marks* are regularly spaced ridges on the surface of a sedimentary bed at right angles to the direction of the current flow. They form when sand grains are deposited by air or water currents. Small ripple

FIGURE 6.9 Sedimentary rock beds.

(a) Horizontal beds of sandstone and siltstone in the Painted Desert of Arizona. White, dark red, and light red beds contain different amounts of hematite cement.

(b) Horizontal beds of sandstones, siltstones, and limestones in the Grand Canyon in Arizona. Beds are distinguished by differential resistance to weathering as well as color.

FIGURE 6.10 Graded bedding.

Top of bed

Silt and mud-sized clasts

Fine sand-sized clasts

Pebble- and granule-sized clasts

Bottom of bed

marks are shown in **FIGURE 6.11**. Some ripple marks have systematically oriented steep and gentle sides (Fig. 6.11a). These **asymmetric ripple marks** are produced by a current that flowed from the gentle side toward the steep side. **Symmetric ripple marks** (Fig. 6.11b) have steep slopes on both sides and form from oscillating currents. Larger mounds of sediments that resemble asymmetric ripple marks in shape are called *dunes*. The largest dunes occur in deserts, where they build from windblown sand; however, dunes can also form underwater.

In some beds of sediment, subtle curving surfaces, delineated by coarser and/or denser grains, lie at an angle to the main bedding surfaces. These inclined surfaces are called **cross beds**. They form when sediment moves up the windward (or up-current) side and then slips down the lee side as dunes and ripples build (**FIG. 6.12**).

Mud Cracks and Bedding-Plane Impressions Mud cracks are arrays of gashes in the surface of a bed formed when mud dries out and shrinks. Typically, mud cracks are arrayed in a honeycomb-like pattern. Sand deposited over the mud layer fills the cracks, so when the sediment lithifies, the shape of the cracks remains visible (**FIG. 6.13**).

FIGURE 6.11 Ripple marks.

Steep side   Gentle side

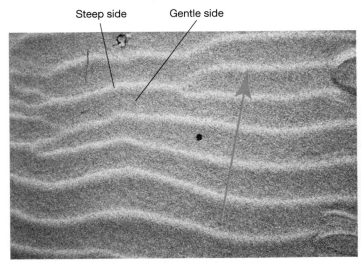

(a) Asymmetric ripple marks in modern sand. The arrow indicates the direction of the current that formed the ripples.

(b) Symmetric ripple marks in ancient sandstone. Note the equally steep slopes on both sides of the ripples.

FIGURE 6.12 Cross bedding, a type of sedimentary structure within a bed.

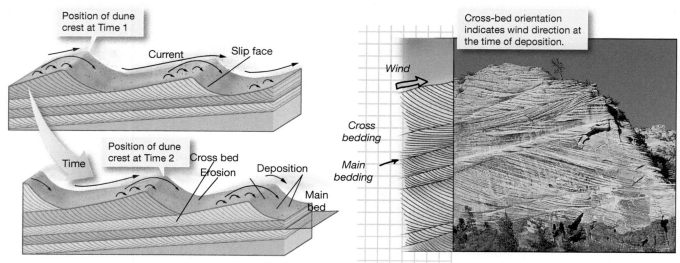

(a) Cross beds form as sand blows up the windward side of a dune or ripple and then accumulates on the slip face. With time, the dune crest moves.

(b) A cliff face in Zion National Park, Utah, displays large cross beds formed between 200 million and 180 million years ago, when the region was a desert with large sand dunes.

FIGURE 6.13 Formation of mud cracks.

(a) Mud cracks in modern sediment. The circular impressions were made by raindrops hitting the mud before it dried.

(b) Mud cracks preserved in 180 million-year-old mudstone.

Moving objects can leave impressions on unconsolidated sediment before the bed hardens into rock. The imprints of these objects can, in some instances, provide fascinating glimpses of animals living in the sediment or of processes acting on it.

Imprints may be made by raindrops falling on a muddy floodplain (Fig. 6.13a), logs dragged by currents along the bottom of a stream, worms crawling along the sea floor in search of food (**FIG. 6.14a**), and the footprints of animals walking through a forest (**FIG. 6.14b**). Indentations also may be scoured into a bed surface by the turbulence of the fluid flowing over it.

6.7 Fossils: Remnants of Past Life

Fossils are the remains or traces of animals and plants that are preserved in rocks—in effect, they are sedimentary structures. Generally, fossils reveal the shape of the hard

FIGURE 6.14 **Impressions on bedding planes.**

(a) Worm burrows on siltstone in Ireland (lens cap for scale).

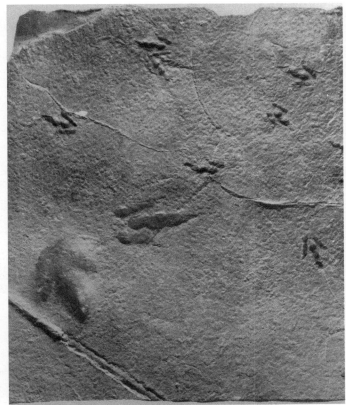

(b) Footprints of different-sized dinosaurs.

EXERCISE 6.9	Gaining Insight into Depositional Environments of Sedimentary Rocks

Name: _____   **Section:** _____

Course: _____   **Date:** _____

Sedimentary structures, fossils, cements, and other features of sedimentary rocks provide insight into the environment in which the sediment was deposited. Match each of the features in the left-hand column to an aspect of the depositional environment listed in the right-hand column by placing the corresponding letter in the proper blank.

Rock and/or feature of the rock

(a) poorly sorted arkose

(b) contains fossils of intact coral

(c) red mudstone containing dinosaur footprints

(d) black shale containing some pyrite crystals

(e) sandstone containing symmetrical ripples

(f) cross-bedded sandstone

(g) contains > 50% carbon and fossil leaves

(h) contains large, rounded pebbles and cobbles

(i) contains fossils of feathers

(j) very angular grains

Aspect of the depositional environment

_____ deposited in a desert dune or in a current

_____ formed from sediments accumulated in a swamp

_____ deposited in very quiet (stagnant) water

_____ deposited in an anoxic marine setting

_____ deposited by a swiftly moving stream

_____ formed from warm-water, shallow marine reef

_____ has not undergone a lot of transport

_____ immature, deposited close to the source

_____ formed from terrestrial mud (riverbank deposits)

_____ deposited on a beach

FIGURE 6.15 Fossils reveal remarkable details of life throughout geologic time.

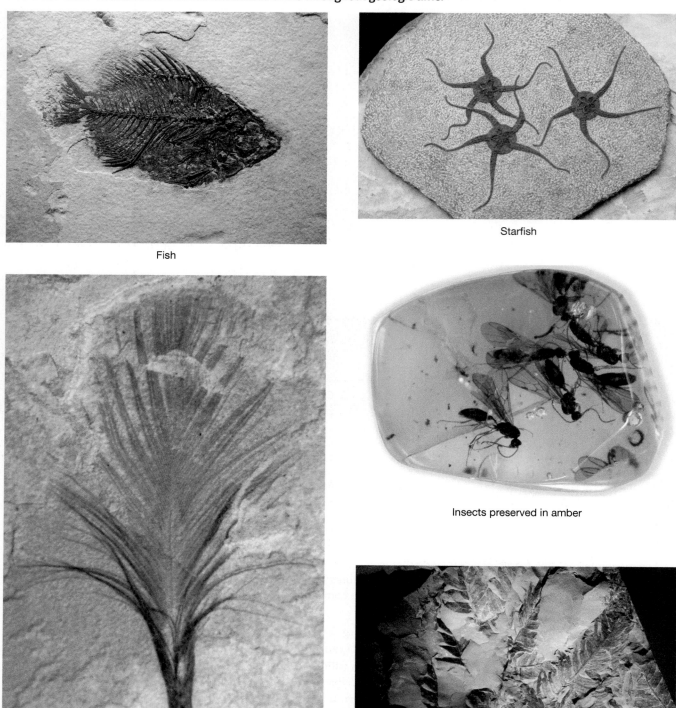

Fish

Starfish

Feather

Insects preserved in amber

Leaves

(a) Relatively fragile organisms.

Brachiopod

Apatosaurus (formerly called Brontosaurus)

Tree trunks

(b) Relatively robust organisms.

parts (shells or skeleton) of an organism. Soft-bodied organisms are preserved only in special cases, where deposition happens before the organism decays (**FIG. 6.15**). Fossils are the subject of a whole subdiscipline of geology called paleontology, for the study of fossils reveals the history of life on Earth and, as discussed elsewhere in this book, provides clues to the age of strata. We mention them briefly here because most fossils are found in sedimentary rocks, due to the environments in which sedimentary accumulation occurs are the same as those in which animals and plants lived.

Because different kinds of organisms live in different environments, the types of fossils in a sedimentary rock provide clues to the depositional environment in which the sediment composing the rock accumulated. Applying the *principle of uniformitarianism,* we can deduce that sediments containing fossil corals probably formed in warm, clear seawater; sediments with fossils of tropical plants were probably deposited in equatorial latitudes; sediments with fossils of dinosaurs generally accumulated on land rather than in the deep ocean; and sediments containing fossil starfish accumulated in the oceans, not on land.

FIGURE 6.16 **Examples of depositional environments.**

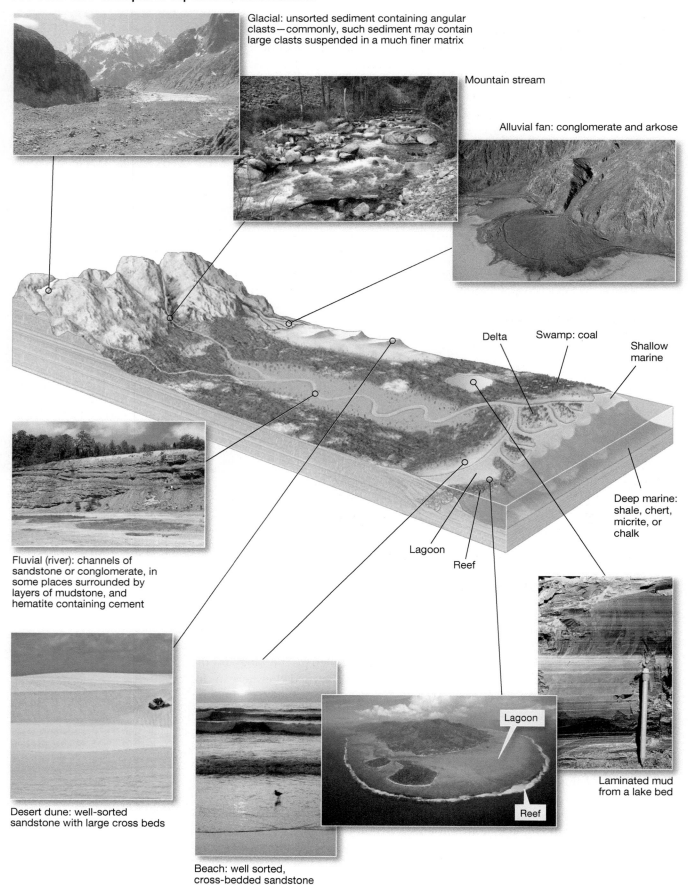

Glacial: unsorted sediment containing angular clasts—commonly, such sediment may contain large clasts suspended in a much finer matrix

Mountain stream

Alluvial fan: conglomerate and arkose

Delta

Swamp: coal

Shallow marine

Deep marine: shale, chert, micrite, or chalk

Lagoon

Reef

Fluvial (river): channels of sandstone or conglomerate, in some places surrounded by layers of mudstone, and hematite containing cement

Lagoon

Reef

Laminated mud from a lake bed

Desert dune: well-sorted sandstone with large cross beds

Beach: well sorted, cross-bedded sandstone

6.8 Applying Your Knowledge to Stratigraphy

Ultimately, geologists use observational data about sedimentary rocks to interpret the depositional setting (conditions of deposition) in which the sediment forming the rock accumulated. Examples of depositional settings are listed in **FIGURE 6.16**, along with a simplified description of characteristics found there. Successions of beds, or strata, are like pages in a book that record the succession of depositional environments. Further study in geology will add additional detail to this image, but even with your basic knowledge, you can interpret outcrops in the field. You will do this in Exercise 6.10.

EXERCISE 6.10 | **Interpreting Outcrops**

Name: _____   Section: _____

Course: _____   Date: _____

(a) Look at the sedimentary rocks in the figures below. Brief "field notes" are provided with each photograph. In each case, identify the rock and any sedimentary structures present, and interpret the depositional setting in which the rock formed.

Interpreting sedimentary outcrops.

Entrance to Zion National Park in Utah. Large cliff face containing thick beds of medium-grained white, gray, and beige sandstones displaying excellent cross bedding.

_____

_____

_____

_____

Sandstone with preserved dinosaur trackway and asymmetric ripple marks. Note different orientation of ripple marks in the foreground.

_____

_____

_____

(continued)

Name: _____ **Section:** _____

Course: _____ **Date:** _____

Excavation along a lumber road in eastern Maine. Very poorly sorted sediment with large clasts of granite, sandstone, and shale in a matrix of gravel, sand, and large amounts of clay. Based on this information and the photo to the left, what is the most likely depositional environment and what is the most likely agent of erosion responsible.

_____

_____

_____

_____

(b) Using *Google Earth*™, fly to the following coordinates. Describe what you see.

- Lat 24°44'40.42" S, Long 15°30'5.34" E _____

- Lat 23°27'03.08" N, Long 75°38'15.68" W _____

- Lat 67°3'38.31" N, Long 65°33'2.88" W _____

- Lat 25°7'48.94" N, Long 80°59'3.18" W _____

- Lat 30°10'2.73" N, Long 94°48'58.24" W _____

- Lat 5°24'54.48" N, Long 6°31'26.25" E _____

(c) What do regions underlain by sedimentary rocks look like? Fly to the following coordinates (Lat 47°48'02.31" N, Long 112°45'30.97" W) using *Google Earth*™ and see an example of a region where sedimentary beds are well exposed. Note that the bedding appears as a series of parallel ridges if the layers are tilted. That's because softer beds (shale) weather faster than harder beds (sandstone).

? **What Do You Think** You are the project manager for a company and you're in charge of completing large projects on time, with millions of dollars on the line in costs and profits. While bulldozing land for a new housing development, one of your crews uncovered a large dinosaur trackway, like the one shown on page 161. It is clearly an important find because nothing like this has ever been reported in the area. Reporting the trackway to the State, however, could delay the project, lowering the anticipated profits. But, not reporting it would mean losing this priceless artifact forever.

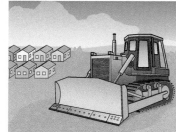

What do you think? Is it possible to preserve the trackway without affecting the timeline, cost, and profit of your project? Or should you just continue with the excavation? What would you recommend and why? (Answer on a separate sheet of paper.)

SEDIMENTARY ROCKS STUDY SHEET

Name _____

Sample	Texture (grain size, shape, sorting)	Components			Minerals/rock fragments present (approximate %)	Name of sedimentary rock	Rock history (transporting agent, environment, etc.)
		Clastic	Chemical	Biogenic			

SEDIMENTARY ROCKS STUDY SHEET

Name _____

Sample	Texture (grain size, shape, sorting)	Components			Minerals/rock fragments present (approximate %)	Name of sedimentary rock	Rock history (transporting agent, environment, etc.)
		Clastic	Chemical	Biogenic			

7

Using Metamorphic Rocks to Interpret Earth History

This polished specimen of gneiss is a layered and foliated metamorphic rock.

- Understand the agents that bring about metamorphism
- Understand the changes that occur during formation of metamorphic rocks
- Become familiar with metamorphic textures and mineral assemblages
- Interpret the history of metamorphic rocks from their textures and mineral assemblages

MATERIALS NEEDED

- A set of metamorphic rocks
- Magnifying glass or hand lens and, ideally, a microscope and thin sections of metamorphic rocks
- Standard supplies for identifying minerals (streak plate, glass plate, etc.)
- Play-Doh, small rods (plastic coffee stirrers cut into short pieces), pennies

7.1 Introduction

Biologists use the term *metamorphosis* (from the Greek *meta*, meaning change, and *morph*, meaning form) to describe what happens when a caterpillar turns into a butterfly. Geologists use the similar term **metamorphism** for certain processes of change that a rock undergoes when exposed to physical and chemical conditions significantly different from those under which it first formed. Logically, the end product of metamorphism is a **metamorphic rock**. Note that we used the word *certain* in the definition of metamorphism. That's because not all changes that a rock can undergo are considered to be metamorphism. For example, metamorphism does not include the processes of weathering, diagenesis, melting, or solidification from a magma. By definition, metamorphism occurs at higher temperatures than those of diagenesis (i.e., greater than about 250°C) and only under conditions in which the rock remains solid (i.e., metamorphic rocks are not igneous). Because metamorphism takes place without either fragmentation or melting, geologists describe metamorphism as a "solid-state" process.

Metamorphism can cause many kinds of changes in a rock or, in some cases, just one type of change. For example, during metamorphism one or more of the following may take place as the parent rock (called the *protolith*) is converted to a metamorphic rock:

- The **texture** of the protolith may change, sometimes dramatically, by:
  - *Recrystallization*: when small grains of a mineral coalesce to form larger grains or large grains separate into smaller ones.
  - *Pressure solution*: if water is present, some minerals dissolve partially and the dissolved ions re-precipitate, changing relationships between grains.
  - *Alignment of grains*: in some instances, randomly oriented protolith minerals are aligned parallel to one another. The result is foliation and lineation—two metamorphic textures described Section 7.4.2.

- The **mineralogy** of the protolith may change. The original minerals in the protolith may be changed into new **metamorphic minerals** that are more stable under the new temperature and pressure conditions. This may occur by:
  - *Phase change*: one polymorph (remember Chapter 3) changes to another more stable at the new conditions. There is no change in the chemical composition. Example: andalusite (Al_2SiO_5) converts to sillimanite (Al_2SiO_5) with increasing heat.
  - *Neocrystallization*: a process of chemical reactions between protolith minerals during which ions from two or more minerals combine to create new minerals.

Example: Muscovite + quartz → sillimanite + potassic feldspar + water

$$KAl_2(AlSi_3O_{10})(OH)_2 + SiO_2 \rightarrow Al_2SiO_5 + KAlSi_3O_8 + H_2O$$

Sometimes a rock changes only slightly during metamorphism, so that most of its original characteristics are still recognizable. In many cases, however, the changes are so drastic that a metamorphic rock can look as different from its protolith as a butterfly is from a caterpillar (**FIG. 7.1**).

Most metamorphism is caused by tectonic and igneous processes that we cannot observe because they take place deep within the Earth. For example, what happens to rocks as the opposite sides of the San Andreas Fault grind past one another? Or to rocks along the west coast of South America as part of the Nazca Plate is subducted beneath the continent? Or to rocks deep below Mt. Everest as India collides with Asia? How did rocks in California change when they were intruded by granitic magma that today forms the Sierra Nevada batholith?

FIGURE 7.1 Examples of changes from protolith (left) to metamorphic rock (right).

(a) Changes in texture (grain size and shape).

    i. Very fine-grained calcite in micrite recrystallizes to coarse-grained calcite in marble.

    ii. Coarse quartz and feldspar grains in granite change to very fine grains in ultramylonite.

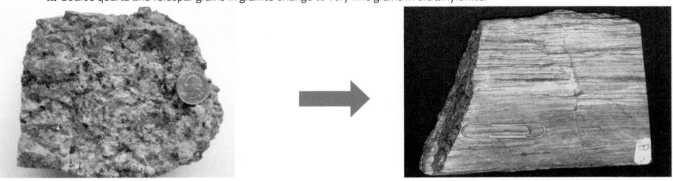

    iii. Grain shape changes: round clasts in conglomerate are flattened in metamorphosed conglomerate.

(b) New minerals form—protolith minerals react to form new minerals more stable at the metamorphic conditions.

    i. Clay minerals in mudstone react with quartz to form biotite and garnet in gneiss.

ii. Dolomite and quartz in micrite react to produce actinolite (green) in marble.

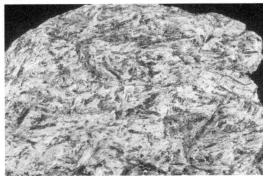

(c) Both texture changes and new minerals form.

i. Foliation: muscovite flakes formed from clay minerals in mudstone are aligned parallel to one another to produce foliation in schist.

ii. Lineation: rod-shaped amphiboles produced from pyroxene in diorite are aligned parallel to one another to produce lineation in a metamorphosed diorite.

Metamorphic rocks provide answers to these and many other questions about Earth history and Earth processes. Because they form at depths below which sedimentary rocks form and above which melting occurs, metamorphic rocks yield important clues to conditions and processes that igneous and sedimentary rocks cannot.

This chapter explains how you can read the Earth history recorded in metamorphic rocks. We begin by examining the causes of metamorphism and then examine characteristic features of metamorphic rocks, kinds of metamorphic rocks, and the information we can glean from a sample about the conditions under which it was metamorphosed. Finally, we introduce the concept of the intensity or **grade** of metamorphism and discuss how to interpret metamorphic grade from a specimen.

7.2 Agents of Metamorphism

Geologists refer to the heat, pressure, and fluids that cause metamorphism as agents of metamorphism. Let's consider how each of these may trigger change in a rock. Keep in mind, however, that even though we address each agent of metamorphism separately, all of them may act simultaneously in many geologic environments.

7.2.1 The Effect of Heat

A rock heats up when it either becomes buried to great depth, as can happen either during mountain building—when part of the crust is pushed up and over another part—or when magma intrudes nearby. As the temperature rises, atoms vibrate

FIGURE 7.2 Growth of metamorphic minerals.

(a) Garnet crystals.   **(b)** Andalusite crystals.

more rapidly, and chemical bonds holding the atoms into the lattice of minerals begin to stretch and break. The freed atoms migrate slowly through the solid rock by a process called **diffusion**, much as atoms of ink spread when dropped into a glass of water. Eventually, the wandering atoms bond with other atoms to produce metamorphic minerals that are more stable under the higher temperatures. Put another way, heat drives chemical reactions that can produce a new assemblage of metamorphic minerals.

If the protolith has a very simple composition (e.g., quartz only, or calcite only), metamorphic reactions may produce new crystals of the same minerals. For example, metamorphism of a pure quartz sandstone (a sedimentary rock composed of SiO_2 grains) produces a metamorphic rock composed of new grains of quartz. But if the protolith contains a variety of elements, metamorphism can produce completely different minerals. For example, metamorphism of shale (composed of clay, which can contain Ca, Fe, Al, Mg, and K) produces a metamorphic rock composed of mica, quartz, and garnet. Diffusion is much slower in solid rock than in magmas or aqueous solutions, but over thousands to millions of years, it can completely change a rock. In some cases, new metamorphic minerals can grow to impressive sizes (**FIG. 7.2**).

7.2.2 The Effect of Pressure

Two kinds of pressure are important in metamorphism (**FIG. 7.3**). **Lithostatic pressure** results from the burial of rocks within the Earth and, like hydrostatic pressure in the oceans or atmospheric pressure in air, it is equal in all directions. Lithostatic pressure can become so large at great depths beneath mountain belts or in association with subduction that it forces atoms closer together than the original mineral's structure can allow. As a consequence, a new mineral with a more compact atomic arrangement can form that is more stable under the high-pressure conditions. Such a change is called a **phase change**. Diamond, for example, is a metamorphic mineral formed at very high pressures from graphite. Diamond and graphite are both made of pure carbon, but the diamond structure is much more compact than that of graphite and therefore more stable at high pressure. Minerals like diamond and graphite that have identical compositions but different internal structures are called **polymorphs**.

When subjected to lithostatic pressure, the shape of mineral grains in a rock doesn't necessarily change, because the rock is being pushed *equally* from all directions (Fig. 7.3a). During mountain-building processes and along plate boundaries, bodies of rock undergo more intense squeezing in one direction than in others. To picture this vise-like squeezing, imagine what happens when you press a ball of

FIGURE 7.3 Effects of lithostatic pressure and differential stress.

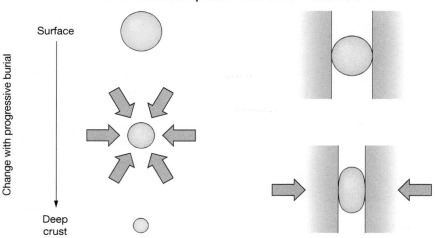

Change with progressive burial

Surface

Deep crust

(a) Lithostatic pressure. Pressure acts equally from all directions; grain remains spherical but gets smaller.

(b) Differential stress. Greater pressure in one direction than others; spherical grain is flattened.

clay or dough between a book and a table—it flattens into a pancake. In addition, the crust may move, producing shear, during which one part of a rock body moves sideways relative to another—to picture shear, imagine what happens when you smear a deck of cards across a table. Simplistically, we can refer to the type of pressure in such rock due to vise-like squeezing and/or shear as **directed pressure**, or **differential stress**. Under conditions of elevated temperature, differential stress can cause grains to change shape, flattening them in one direction and elongating or stretching them in others (Fig. 7.3b).

7.2.3 The Effect of Temperature and Pressure Combined

It's important to keep in mind that pressure changes in most metamorphic environments are accompanied by temperature changes, because as the depth of burial increases, *both* temperature and pressure rise. But the temperature change that occurs with increasing depth at one location is not necessarily the same as that which occurs at another. For example, at a given depth, the temperature near an intruding pluton of magma may be higher than in a region at a great distance from the magma. The particular minerals that form during metamorphism depend on both pressure and temperature. We can represent this fact on a graph, called a **phase diagram**, that has pressure and depth on the vertical axis and temperature on the horizontal axis. **FIGURE 7.4** shows the phase diagram for the aluminum silicate minerals—three different minerals that exist in nature but have the same chemical formula. Note that at points Y and Z, the pressure is the same but the temperature is different—at a lower temperature, kyanite forms, whereas at a higher temperature, sillimanite forms. Point X is at the same temperature as Y, but at a lower pressure; under these conditions, andalusite forms at low pressure while kyanite forms at high pressure.

FIGURE 7.4 Phase diagram for aluminum silicate (Al_2SiO_5).

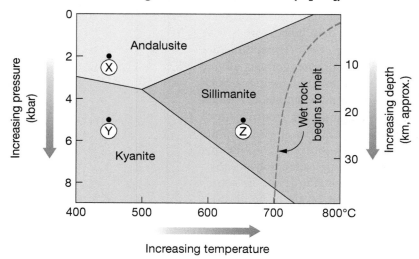

7.2.4 Metasomatism: The Effect of Hydrothermal Fluids

In many environments, rocks contain high-temperature liquids, gases, and "supercritical fluids" (fluids that have characteristics of both a gas and liquid) composed of H_2O and/or CO_2 in which ions of other elements have been dissolved. Collectively, these fluids are called **hydrothermal fluids** (from *hydro*, meaning water, and *thermal*, meaning hot). They may be released from magma when the magma solidifies, may be produced by metamorphic reactions, or may be formed where groundwater has percolated deep into the crust. Hydrothermal fluids can be "chemically active" in that they can dissolve ions and transport them throughout the crust and can provide ions that bond to other ions and produce new, metamorphic minerals. Thus, reactions with hydrothermal fluids tend to change the chemical composition of rocks—the fluids can be thought of as buses that pick up and drop off ions as they pass through a rock. In some cases, the fluids pick up certain chemicals and flush them entirely out of the rock. When the chemical composition of a metamorphic rock changes significantly due to reaction with hydrothermal fluids, we say that the rock has undergone **metasomatism**.

Exercise 7.1 will help you understand how metamorphic agents bring about changes in metamorphic rocks.

EXERCISE 7.1 **Effects of Metamorphic Agents**

Name: _____   Section: _____

Course: _____   Date: _____

(a) Andalusite, sillimanite, and kyanite are polymorphs of Al_2SiO_5 with identical chemical compositions but different crystal structures. Based on the phase diagram in Figure 7.4, and keeping in mind how pressure tends to affect the compactness of crystals, which of these minerals has the lowest specific gravity? Explain.

_____

_____

_____

_____

(b) During metamorphism at a given location, the overall amount of the element calcium in a metamorphic rock changes substantially. Which metamorphic agent is likely to have caused this metamorphism? Why?

_____

_____

_____

_____

(c) Would you expect to find aligned, flattened grains in a rock that has undergone heating but has not been subjected to differential stress during metamorphism? Why?

_____

_____

_____

_____

7.3 Types and Environments of Metamorphism

Metamorphism may be caused by a single agent or by a combination of two or three, depending on the tectonic and geologic settings in which agents are applied. Geologists recognize six types of metamorphism, each characterized by a unique agent or combination of agents and associated with a different geologic or tectonic environment. Each type produces distinctive metamorphic rocks, enabling geologists to interpret ancient tectonic settings from the rock types exposed on the surface.

Heat plays a role in all types of metamorphism, helping to break bonds in minerals. It is a dominant agent in some types, but plays a relatively minor role in others where lithostatic pressure or differential stress dominate. The types of metamorphism are as follows:

■ **Contact metamorphism** (also called thermal metamorphism) occurs where rocks are subjected to elevated heat without a change in pressure and without the application of differential stress. This happens where an igneous intrusion comes in contact with a rock (**FIG. 7.5a, b**).

■ **Regional metamorphism** (also called dynamothermal metamorphism) occurs where rocks in a large region of crust are subjected to increases in temperature and pressure *and* are subjected to differential stress (squeezing and shearing). Such metamorphism typically happens during mountain-building processes (Fig. 7.5a,b).

■ **Burial metamorphism** happens when rocks are simply buried very deeply by overlying sediment (**FIG. 7.5c**).

■ **Dynamic metamorphism** occurs where rock undergoes differential stress in response to shear along a fault zone but does not undergo a change in temperature and/or lithostatic pressure (**FIG. 7.5d**).

■ **Shock** (or impact) **metamorphism** occurs where a meteorite hits the Earth and its enormous kinetic energy is converted instantaneously to heat and differential stress. Impact metamorphism is rare on Earth (**FIG. 7.5e**).

■ **Metasomatism** occurs where hydrothermal fluids are present, especially as

FIGURE 7.5 Environments of metamorphism.

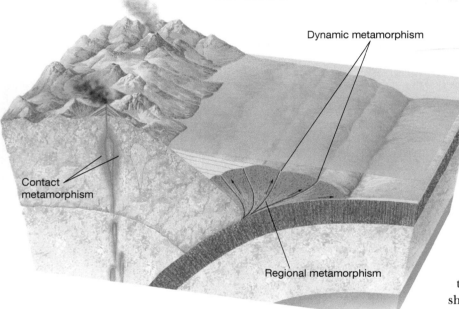

(a) Convergent plate boundaries (e.g., Japan).

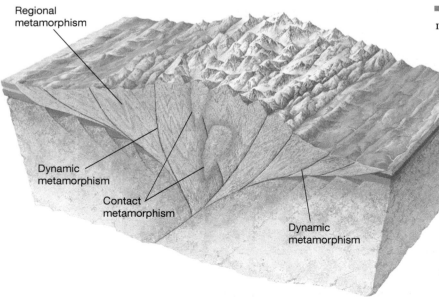

(b) Continent-continent collision zone (e.g., Appalachian Mountains).

FIGURE 7.5 **Environments of metamorphism** (*continued*).

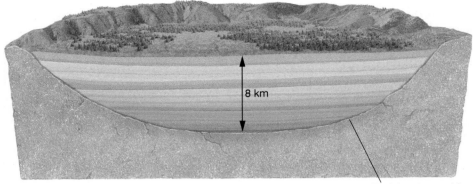

(c) Deep sedimentary basin (e.g., Rio Grande Rift).

8 km

Burial metamorphism

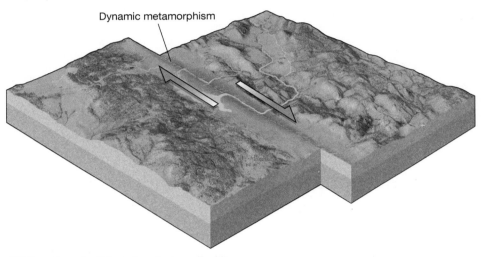

Dynamic metamorphism

(d) Transform fault (e.g., San Andreas Fault).

Impact metamorphism

(e) Meteorite crater (e.g., Barringer Crater, Arizona).

superheated water from metamorphic reactions adds dissolved ions to or removes ions from rock, changing its composition.

TABLE 7.1 summarizes the types of metamorphism and notes how the agents of metamorphism present in each type tend to operate.

TABLE 7.1 Types, environments, and agents of metamorphism.

Agent(s) of metamorphism*	How the agents of metamorphism are applied	Type of metamorphism	Geologic environment
Heat (pressure not a major cause)	Heat given off from cooling magma affects rocks adjacent to an intrusive body or lava flow.	Contact or thermal	Contact between pluton or lava flow and host rock
Lithostatic pressure and a little heat	Gravity causes increased lithostatic pressure as rocks are buried deeper.	Burial	Lower parts of deep sedimentary basins
Differential stress and a little heat	Two large blocks of rock grind past one another in a fault zone. The moving blocks generate the differential stress; heat comes from depth in the Earth and a very minor amount from friction.	Dynamic or fault zone	Fault zones, including transform faults
Hydrothermal fluids	Superheated water from magma or metamorphic reactions adds dissolved ions to or removes ions from rock, changing its composition.	Metasomatism	Continental collision zones; pluton-host rock contacts; mid-ocean ridges
Heat, lithostatic pressure, differential stress	Lithosphere plates collide in subduction zone or continent-continent collision. Collision creates intense differential stress; heat and lithostatic pressure come from depth in the Earth.	Regional	Convergent plate boundaries: subduction zones and continent-continent collisions
Heat, differential stress	Meteorite survives passage through the atmosphere and collides with Earth.	Impact	Meteorite impact crater

* Hydrothermal fluids may play a role in any type of metamorphism.

7.4 Metamorphic Rock Classification and Identification

Classification of metamorphic rocks, like that of their igneous and sedimentary relatives, is based on mineral content and texture. Both kinds of information are needed to identify a rock successfully. In this section, we will first review mineral content or composition, then texture, and then see how we can use both to identify metamorphic rocks.

7.4.1 Compositional Classes of Metamorphic Rocks

Geologists recognize four major classes of metamorphic rocks based on their mineral (and therefore chemical) composition:

- **Aluminous** (or **pelitic**) metamorphic rocks contain a relatively large proportion of aluminum, silicon, and oxygen, with lesser amounts of potassium, iron, and magnesium. These rocks were derived from shale or mudstone, which are made up mostly of clay minerals rich in aluminum. Common metamorphic minerals of aluminous rocks include muscovite, biotite, chlorite, garnet, andalusite, sillimanite, and kyanite.

- **Quartzo-feldspathic** metamorphic rocks contain large amounts of silicon, oxygen, potassium, and sodium, less aluminum than aluminous rocks, and small amounts of calcium, iron, and magnesium. Possible protoliths include felsic igneous rocks like granite and rhyolite or sedimentary rocks like arkose. Typical minerals, as the name suggests, are quartz, potassic feldspar, and plagioclase feldspar.

- **Calcareous** metamorphic rocks are composed mostly of calcium, carbon, and oxygen, with some magnesium. These are derived from carbonate sedimentary rocks—limestones and dolostones. If the protolith contained significant amounts of clay and quartz, the additional aluminum, silicon, and oxygen permit crystallization of "calc-silicate" metamorphic minerals like garnet, the amphibole actinolite, or the pyroxene diopside.

■ **Mafic** metamorphic rocks contain calcium, iron, magnesium, aluminum, silicon, and oxygen. As the name suggests, their protoliths were basalts and gabbros. Typical mafic metamorphic minerals include epidote, amphiboles, pyroxenes, and garnet.

A fifth class—**organic**—is needed for the relatively uncommon instances in which an organic sedimentary rock is metamorphosed. The most common of these is anthracite coal.

Exercise 7.2 will show how minerals in metamorphic rocks can help identify the composition of the rock's protolith.

EXERCISE 7.2   **Metamorphic Minerals as a Key to Protolith Composition**

Name: _____   Section: _____
Course: _____   Date: _____

(a) Identify the minerals in the four metamorphic rocks provided by your instructor, and record the data in the following table. Add the chemical compositions for these minerals from Appendix 3.2.

	Specimen 1	Specimen 2	Specimen 3	Specimen 4
Major minerals and their compositions				

(b) Based on the minerals and their chemical compositions, what were the most abundant elements in the protoliths of these specimens?

Specimen 1	Specimen 2	Specimen 3	Specimen 4

(c) Is it likely that these metamorphic rocks came from the same parent rock? Explain.

_____

_____

_____

_____

7.4.2 Textural Classes of Metamorphic Rocks

All aspects of a rock's texture—grain size, grain shape, grain orientation—may change during metamorphism. The textural criterion used in naming metamorphic rocks is whether or not their minerals display **preferred orientation**. Unlike igneous and sedimentary rocks, grain *size* is not important in classification even though it may change drastically. It *is*, however, helpful in interpreting a rock's metamorphic history (see section 7.5).

Preferred Orientation You saw in Figure 7.3 that differential stress can flatten grains. It also causes original grains from the protolith and newly crystallized metamorphic minerals to show two kinds of **preferred orientation** that geologists refer to as **foliation** and **lineation**. A rock is said to display **foliation** if it contains a stack of parallel features, either alternating bands of different minerals [see the chapter opening photograph and the right side of Fig. 7.1b (i)] or alignment of platy minerals as shown in Figure 7.1c (i). A rock has a **mineral lineation** if rod-shaped minerals are aligned parallel to one another [as in Fig. 7.1c (ii)]. **FIGURE 7.6** shows the relationships among aligned grains in rocks displaying foliation and lineation.

FIGURE 7.6 Mineral alignment: foliation and lineation.

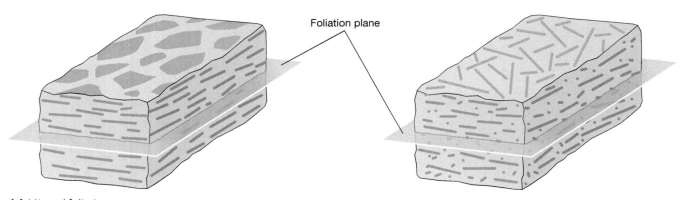

Foliation plane

(a) Mineral foliation.
Stack of platy minerals (e.g., mica) aligned parallel to one another.

Rod-shaped minerals are not parallel to one another, but their long dimensions all lie in parallel planes (foliation planes).

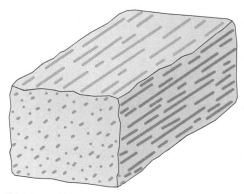

(b) Mineral lineation.
The long dimensions of rod-shaped minerals (e.g., amphibole) are parallel to one another, producing a streaky appearance on some surfaces and a dotted pattern on others.

Exercise 7.3 shows how differential stress produces preferred mineral orientation in metamorphic rocks. *Note:* Foliations are given different names depending on the intensity of metamorphism (see section 7.4.3), but all that is needed to name a rock is the presence or absence of any kind of foliation or lineation.

EXERCISE 7.3 **Visualizing Preferred Orientation Due to Reorientation**

Name: _____ Section: _____

Course: _____ Date: _____

We can gain insight into how preferred orientation develops with a simple laboratory experiment.

(a) Randomly insert pennies (flat grains) and small sticks (elongate grains) into a ball of Play-Doh. Flatten the dough into a pancake by pressing on it with a book (i.e., apply differential stress). What happens to the alignment of the objects? Are the sticks parallel to each other in the plane of the pancake?

_____

_____

(b) Clean off the pennies and sticks, and reinsert them into another ball of Play-Doh. This time, roll the dough into a cigar shape. What happens to the alignment of the objects now? Are the sticks parallel to each other? How are they oriented relative to the length of the cigar?

_____

_____

Absence of Preferred Orientation Minerals in some metamorphic rocks are oriented randomly and therefore have neither foliation nor lineation. Such rocks are said to have a **granoblastic** texture (**FIG. 7.7**). Preferred orientation may be absent because (a) there was no differential stress during metamorphism, or (b) there were no platy or rod-shaped minerals to align, or (c) both (a) and (b).

7.4.3 Identifying Metamorphic Rocks

TABLE 7.2 is a classification scheme for common metamorphic rocks based on observable mineralogy and texture. Each column corresponds to one of the five major compositional classes and each row to textural variations. Different names are given to some textural varieties depending on whether they result from low-, moderate-, or high-grade metamorphism. For example, slate, phyllite, and schist are all foliated aluminous rocks, but they represent different metamorphic grades.

To name a metamorphic rock, begin by identifying its minerals. This will place the rock in the correct compositional type and column in Table 7.2. Move downward through the table until you come to the row with the appropriate texture. In some cases there is only one choice; in others there may be a few possibilities. The following descriptions will help you choose.

Slate: A low-grade metamorphosed shale or mudstone composed of strongly aligned flakes of clay. The foliation is revealed by slate's tendency to split into thin plates. Typically, slate is gray, black, red, or green.

Phyllite: As grade increases, clay is replaced by tiny flakes of muscovite and/or chlorite. Grains are larger than those in slate but may still be too small to be seen without magnification. Phyllite has a silky sheen caused by reflection of light from the aligned platy minerals.

FIGURE 7.7 Granoblastic texture (random mineral alignment).

(a) Interlocking calcite grains in coarse-grained marble.

(b) Photomicrograph of interlocking calcite grains in a marble.

(c) Interlocking quartz grains in quartzite.

(d) Photomicrograph of quartz grains fused together in quartzite.

Schist: This is a medium- to high-grade rock with a strong foliation defined by large mica flakes that can be identified with the naked eye. Porphyroblasts (large crystals) of other metamorphic minerals (e.g., garnet) may occur in schist. We distinguish among different types of schist based on composition. Aluminous schist contains mica and chlorite; mafic schist contains chlorite, talc, and hornblende; and calcareous schist contains Ca-mica and Ca-amphiboles.

Gneiss: A high-grade metamorphic rock of any composition in which minerals have segregated into light and dark layers. The foliation is defined by compositional banding.

Mylonite: Dynamically metamorphosed rock in which very tiny grains formed. The foliation is defined by flattened and stretched grains. (A *protomylonite* is only slightly sheared, so less than 50% of the rock is very fine-grained. Some grains from the protolith may still be present. An *ultramylonite* is intensely sheared, so more than 90% is extremely fine grained.)

Nonfoliated aluminous rocks: These rocks are typically dense, hard, very fine-grained, dark gray or brown. Some contain porphyroblasts of metamorphic index minerals (like the andalusite in Fig. 7.2b). Many rocks that fall into this category are found next to igneous plutons and are clearly the result of contact metamorphism. These are properly called **hornfels** (plural, **hornfelses**). Others, however, could form during burial metamorphism. Without the field data, you can't tell. For an introductory course in geology where we want to keep names to a minimum, there are essentially two choices: hornfels or "something similar to hornfels."

Name: _____   Section: _____

Course: _____   Date: _____

Using Table 7.2 and what you read in this section, determine the mineralogy and texture of the metamorphic rocks in your study set. Record the information in the rock study sheets at the end of the chapter, and name each specimen. Don't worry about the columns for type of metamorphism and metamorphic grade. We will look next at how to interpret the metamorphic history of these rocks.

Greenschist: Low-grade mafic metamorphic rock composed of chlorite and plagioclase feldspar with epidote and/or actinolite. Foliation is defined by alignment of chlorite and actinolite.

Greenstone: A nonfoliated (granoblastic) equivalent of greenschist.

Serpentinite: Typically fine-grained; various shades of light to medium green. May contain fibrous minerals ("asbestos").

Soapstone: Very soft (can be scratched with a fingernail) and greasy; composed almost entirely of talc. Color ranges widely: gray, white, green.

Hornblende schist: A higher-grade version of greenschist in which foliated and often aligned hornblende crystals and plagioclase replace the lower-grade chlorite-epidote-actinolite assemblage. This rock is more commonly called *amphibolite*. Of note, some amphibolites have no lineation.

Quartzite: A monomineralic, granoblastic, metamorphic rock composed of quartz.

Marble: A calcareous metamorphic rock composed mostly of calcite or dolomite. Marble may also contain some of the calc-silicate index minerals. Marble is commonly granoblastic.

Anthracite coal: A black, shiny, hard rock made of carbon that has no visible mineral grains and has relatively low specific gravity. It may exhibit conchoidal fracture.

TABLE 7.2   **Simplified classification scheme for metamorphic rocks.**

Texture		Composition				
		Aluminous muscovite, chlorite, biotite, garnet, staurolite, kyanite, sillimanite	**Calcareous** calcite, dolomite, amphibole (actinolite), garnet, pyroxene	**Mafic** talc, serpentine, chlorite, biotite, amphibole, pyroxene, garnet + plagioclase	**Quartzo-feldspathic** dominantly quartz, potassic feldspar, plagioclase feldspar	**Organic**
Foliated	Fine grained	Slate* Phyllite*	Rarely observed	Greenschist Hornblende Schist Amphibolite	Rarely observed	
Foliated	Medium and coarse grained	Schist*				
	Foliated and layered	Gneiss*	Calc-silicate gneiss	Mafic gneiss	Gneiss*	
	Foliated, layered, smeared	Mylonite	Mylonite	Mylonite	Mylonite	
	Nonfoliated (granoblastic)	Hornfels or other nonfoliated rock (see text)	Marble	Serpentinite Soapstone (talc) Greenstone	Quartzite Metasandstone Metaconglomerate	Anthracite coal

(Increasing metamorphic grade — indicated by downward arrow in Aluminous column)

* Add more detail with dominant minerals (e.g., muscovite-biotite phyllite; garnet-staurolite schist).

7.5 What Can We Learn from a Metamorphic Rock?

Metamorphic rocks may preserve evidence of both their metamorphic history and that of their protoliths. There's a lot to learn when we study a metamorphic rock. First, we would like to know the *nature of the protolith*. For example, did the metamorphic rock we see today originate as a granite, sandstone, basalt, or shale? Second, we would like to know the *agents and type of metamorphism* responsible for causing the change. Did metamorphism result from a change in temperature, pressure, or both? Was the rock subjected to differential stress during deformation or not? Third, we would like to know the *"intensity" of metamorphic conditions*. In this context, the informal term *intensity* refers to the highest temperature and pressure at which the metamorphism took place and/or the overall amount of shearing and squeezing during deformation. Finally, we hope to define the *tectonic setting* in which metamorphism occurred. For example, did metamorphism occur in a collisional mountain belt, along a fault zone, or next to a hot pluton? This, however, cannot be done without information about field relationships and will not be discussed further.

7.5.1 Identifying the Protolith

During metamorphism, ions in the protolith minerals commonly recombine with one another to form new minerals that are more stable under the new temperature and pressure conditions. The original protolith minerals may disappear completely, but because the new mineral assemblage recycles the available protolith ions, it can tell us a lot about the protolith. But chemistry alone cannot tell exactly what kind of rock it was. For example, a quartzo-feldspathic rock could have been igneous or sedimentary. If igneous, it might have been either intrusive (granite) or extrusive (rhyolite). A calcareous rock can be identified as a limestone or dolostone, but not as a specific kind (fossiliferous, micrite, oolitic, coquina, etc.). Other factors not available to you in the classroom can help in these cases, as shown in Exercise 7.5. It will show how the minerals in a metamorphic rock can be used to determine the composition of that rock's protolith.

7.5.2 Identifying the Type of Metamorphism

It is not always possible to determine the type of metamorphism that created a laboratory specimen because field evidence is often critical to that decision, and that information is lost if you didn't collect the specimens yourself. For example, a metamorphic rock with random grain orientation adjacent to an igneous intrusion almost certainly resulted from contact metamorphism. But if you look at a piece of that rock in the laboratory, you have no idea whether it was the result of contact or burial metamorphism. Or, if it is a calcareous or quartzo-feldspathic rock, you don't know whether it was subjected to regional metamorphism.

Some conclusions, however, can be made based on what you have learned about the agents of metamorphism and metamorphic textures. *The key is the presence or absence of preferred mineral orientation*—foliation or lineation—which is produced by differential stress. Differential stress is an important agent of regional and dynamic metamorphism (see Table 7.1). If it is present in a metamorphic rock, one of these types of metamorphism was responsible.

The absence of foliation or lineation (i.e., a granoblastic texture) is trickier to interpret and depends on whether or not platy (e.g., mica) or rod-shaped (e.g., amphibole) grains that could have been foliated or lineated are present. If these minerals are present and the rock is granoblastic, then differential stress was not involved, and contact

Interpreting the Protoliths of Metamorphic Rocks

Name: _____   Section: _____

Course: _____   Date: _____

(a) In Exercise 7.2, your instructor provided you with four rocks and you identified their minerals and chemical composition. Compare the mineral content and most abundant ions from the four rocks you were given with the four main compositional classes of metamorphic rocks. What protoliths produced the four specimens you studied?

	Specimen 1	Specimen 2	Specimen 3	Specimen 4
Protolith				

(b) How would your interpretation of protoliths be affected if you learned that the area had experienced significant metasomatism? Explain.

_____

_____

_____

_____

or burial metamorphism is the likely origin. If they are not present, but rather equant grains that cannot be aligned, then any type of metamorphism is possible.

Exercise 7.6 will help clarify which types of metamorphism produce preferred mineral orientation and which do not.

7.5.3 Determining the Intensity of Metamorphism

Geologists can determine the temperatures and pressures at which metamorphism occurred but only with the use of sophisticated (and very expensive) instruments. In an introductory geology class without those instruments, you can still describe the **metamorphic grade**—a broad, informal approximation of how much a rock has changed. This generally relates to how much heat and pressure the rock experienced during metamorphism. We estimate that metamorphic *low-grade* rock has changed little, still preserving much of the character of its protolith; a *moderate-grade* rock retains fewer aspects of the protolith; and *high-grade* rock has changed so much that no traces of its protolith's minerals or texture are preserved. As an example, consider a rock that starts out as a sequence of alternating layers of sandstone and shale. At low grade, the sandstone may have recrystallized and the shale may have developed a subtle foliation, but the bedding is still visible and the original minerals are still present. At high grade, the rock may contain a totally different assemblage of minerals with a very strong foliation and no hint at all of the original bedding.

Textural Evidence for Metamorphic Grade Three textural features help estimate metamorphic grade: grain size, relationships between grains, and degree of preferred orientation. In general, the longer a rock remains at its peak metamorphic

Name: _____   Section: _____

Course: _____   Date: _____

(a) Summarize the relationship between mineral alignment and type of metamorphism by checking the appropriate box(es) in each row in the following table.

Texture	Type of metamorphism				
	Contact	Regional	Dynamic	Burial	Can't tell from texture alone
Foliation					
Lineation					
Granoblastic with micas					
Granoblastic without micas					
Compositionally layered but not foliated					
Compositionally layered and foliated					

(b) Examine the metamorphic rocks in your study set. Which are foliated? Lineated? Granoblastic? Write your answers in the appropriate column of the study sheets at the end of the chapter. Suggest, wherever possible, the type of metamorphism that produced each sample.

temperature, the greater the amount of solid-state diffusion that can occur and the larger its grains can grow. Thus, in most cases, **grain size** increases with increasing metamorphic grade. This is illustrated in **FIGURE 7.8**: compare the original fine-grained micrite protolith (Fig. 7.8a, b) with its metamorphosed equivalent (Fig. 7.8c, d). Details of fine-grained rocks are best examined with a microscope, as seen in photomicrographs in Figure 7.8b and d.

Some metamorphic minerals called **porphyroblasts** grow much larger than others in the rock. Garnet porphyroblasts in **FIGURE 7.9** resemble phenocrysts in an igneous rock, but they have nothing to do with the rate of cooling. Instead, they result from solid-state diffusion and concentration of ions. In general, the larger the porphyroblast, the higher the metamorphic grade and the longer the rock stayed at its peak metamorphic temperature.

Relationships between grains also change, as shown in photomicrographs of a quartzose sandstone protolith and its metamorphic product, quartzite. During metamorphism, the rounded quartz clasts and fine-grained cement that hold them together (**FIG. 7.10a**) recrystallize, and the cement grains grow larger. The final result is an angular, interlocking granoblastic texture that has obliterated the original clast/cement relationships (**FIG. 7.10b**). At low metamorphic grade, some of the clast outlines are preserved, but with progressively higher grades they eventually disappear.

Foliation may develop during the earliest stages of metamorphism in which differential stress plays a role, particularly in aluminous rocks (**FIG. 7.11**). Grain size increases and foliation becomes more permanent with the increasing of the metamorphic grade. Initially fine-grained aligned micas in slate (Fig. 7.11a) grow with increasing metamorphic grade, becoming large enough to produce a

FIGURE 7.8 Fine-grained parent rock of a common metamorphic rock.

(a) Hand specimen of micritic limestone (metamorphic equivalent shown in Fig. 7.8c).

(b) Photomicrograph of micritic limestone (metamorphic equivalent shown in Fig 7.8d).

(c) Hand specimen of coarse-grained marble.

(d) Photomicrograph of marble.

visible sheen in phyllite (Fig. 7.11b) and finally a coarse-grained shiny surface in schist (Fig. 7.11c).

At high metamorphic grades, **gneissic banding** may develop— a compositional banding defined by alternating light- and dark-colored layers. If mica is present, it is usually foliated parallel to the banding. But at very high grades, the micas may be consumed in making new minerals, and the gneiss will have a granoblastic texture.

Dynamic metamorphism is an exception to the principle that grain size increases with increasing metamorphic grade (see Fig. 7.8), but the progressively more intense foliation is the same. At temperatures high enough that rocks do not fracture and break up when sheared, dynamic metamorphism can transform a coarse-grained rock into a very fine-grained rock with strong foliation and lineation. The product is called **mylonite**. Such transformation occurs, simplistically, because the stress causes large crystals of quartz to subdivide into very

FIGURE 7.9 Porphyroblastic texture (red garnet porphyroblasts in a metamorphosed mafic igneous rock).

FIGURE 7.10 Photomicrographs showing recrystallization of a clastic sedimentary texture.

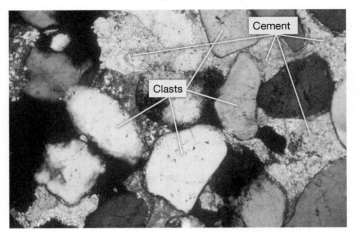

(a) Sandstone protolith: rounded clasts distinguished clearly from interstitial cement that holds them together.

(b) Metamorphosed sandstone (quartzite): cement and clasts recrystallized, forming network of interlocking quartz grains. Original clasts and cement are indistinguishable.

FIGURE 7.11 Change in foliation in aluminous rocks with increasing metamorphic grade.

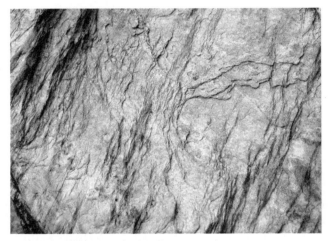

(a) Low grade (slaty texture).

(b) Low-moderate grade (phyllitic texture).

(c) High grade (schistose texture).

(d) Very high grade (gneissic texture).

small grains that fit together like a mass of soap bubbles. **FIGURE 7.12** shows how progressively intense dynamic metamorphism affected a coarse-grained granite from the Norumbega fault system in east-central Maine (Fig. 7.12a).

The process of transforming a rock into mylonite takes place gradually, so we may see intermediate stages preserved in outcrops. [In fact, geologists sometimes distinguish between *protomylonite*, rock that has just started transformation (Fig. 7.12b); *mylonite*, in which the transformation has affected most of the rock (Fig. 7.12c); and *ultramylonite*, in which the transformation is complete (Fig. 7.12d).] Blocky feldspar grains tend to be aligned during the process and grow tails of fine-grained mica, whereas some quartz grains smear into very thin ribbons (Fig. 7.12b). In some cases, relatively large feldspar grains remain after the surrounding rock has changed into a mass of very fine mica and quartz; these leftover grains of feldspar are called **porphyroclasts** (Fig. 7.12c).

Mineralogic Evidence for Metamorphic Grade We have seen that metamorphic minerals form from protolith minerals as temperature and pressure increase.

FIGURE 7.12 Effects of dynamic metamorphism on coarse-grained granite.

(a) Undeformed granite showing original coarse-grained igneous texture.

(b) Protomylonite: potassic feldspars (pink grains) are stretched and aligned parallel to the white line; quartz grains (gray) have coalesced to form continuous ribbons.

(c) Mylonite: grain size of the original granite has been reduced to form a dark, very fine-grained matrix with remnant feldspars smeared into ovoid grains.

(d) Ultramylonite : the intensely metamorphosed granite now consists entirely of fine grains and has strong foliation and lineation.

Some minerals (e.g., chlorite) are stable only at relatively low grade (low temperature), others (e.g., biotite) only at moderate grade, and still others (e.g., sillimanite) only at high grade. Minerals that therefore indicate the conditions of metamorphism are called **metamorphic index minerals** (**TABLE 7.3**). Note that some minerals like quartz and feldspar, which are stable over a wide range of temperature and pressure conditions, are *not* helpful at all in determining metamorphic grade.

Table 7.3 also shows that each compositional class of metamorphic rock has its own set of index minerals due to its unique chemical composition. Some minerals, like chlorite, biotite, and garnet, can occur in more than one compositional class because the appropriate ions can be present in more than one kind of protolith. The complete *assemblage* of minerals in a rock, however, makes it clear what the parent rock was. For example, biotite can be found in low- to moderate-grade aluminous and mafic metamorphic rocks. If biotite occurs in an assemblage with muscovite and quartz, the protolith must have been aluminous; but if it is found with plagioclase feldspar and actinolite, the protolith must have been mafic.

Variations in Metamorphic Grade The pattern of variation in metamorphic grade depends on the type of metamorphism (**FIG. 7.13**) and can be predicted by using a little common sense. For example, metamorphic grade in a wall rock due to thermal metamorphism is greatest at the contact between a pluton and its wall rock and decreases from the pluton (Fig. 7.13a).

Regional metamorphism occurs in a collisional mountain belt. In such a setting, the crust squeezes together horizontally and thickens vertically. Rocks that were originally near the surface of one continental margin may end up at great depth when thrust beneath the edge of the other continent. The rocks that are carried to

TABLE 7.3   Mineral assemblages as indicators of metamorphic grade.

Parent rock type	Increasing metamorphic grade ⟶				
	Low grade		**Medium grade**		**High grade**
Quartzo-feldspathic (quartz, potassic feldspar, plagioclase, ± micas)	Impossible to determine based on mineralogy alone				
Aluminous (muscovite, quartz, chlorite, garnet, staurolite, etc., ± quartz, feldspars)	Muscovite Chlorite	Muscovite Biotite	Muscovite Biotite Fe-Mg garnet Staurolite	Muscovite Biotite Fe-Mg garnet Kyanite or sillimanite	Sillimanite K-feldspar Fe-Mg garnet
Calcareous (calcite, dolomite, ± calc-silicate minerals such as those listed to the right)	Calcite Talc Olivine	Calcite Tremolite	Calcite Diopside Ca-Al garnet		Diopside Wollastonite Ca-Al garnet
Mafic (plagioclase + ferromagnesian minerals such as those listed to the right)	Chlorite Na-plagioclase Epidote	Actinolite Na-Ca plagioclase Biotite	Hornblende Ca-Na plagioclase Fe-Mg garnet		Pyroxene Ca-plagioclase Fe-Mg garnet

FIGURE 7.13 Geographic distribution of metamorphic intensity.

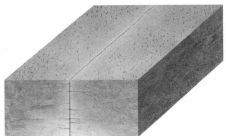

(a) Contact metamorphism: intensity decreases outward from the intrusive pluton or lava flow.

(b) Regional metamorphism: intensity increases with depth and closeness to suture between colliding plates.

(c) Burial metamorphism: intensity increases with depth

(d) Dynamic metamorphism: intensity decreases outward from the fault and increases with depth.

the greatest depth not only reach the highest temperature and the highest grade, but they also tend to be squeezed and sheared the most (Fig. 7.13b). Because burial metamorphism is due principally to lithostatic pressure associated with the thickness of overlying rocks, and to temperature due to the geothermal gradient, the burial metamorphic grade increases with depth (Fig. 7.13c). Dynamic metamorphic intensity is greatest where fault blocks are in contact, and it decreases outward in the two fault blocks (Fig. 7.13d).

You will put all of this information together in Exercise 7.7 to interpret the histories of the metamorphic rocks in your study set.

EXERCISE 7.7 | **Interpreting Metamorphic Rock History**

Name: _____   Section: _____

Course: _____   Date: _____

(a) You have already identified the metamorphic rocks in your study set. Now, based on the information presented earlier, fill in the rest of the rock study sheet at the end of the chapter, saying as much as you can for each sample about possible types of metamorphism and approximate metamorphic grade.

(b) The map on the next page shows the distribution of rocks of different metamorphic grades. The local geologist has mapped a concentric pattern in which the highest metamorphic grade is in the center of the area and surrounded by rocks of progressively lower grade. All metamorphic rocks have a granoblastic texture; the coarsest grains are found in the central region. Although the granoblastic texture suggests contact metamorphism, the geologist has found no igneous rock anywhere in the region. Suggest an explanation for this metamorphic pattern.

(continued)

Name: _____   Section: _____

Course: _____   Date: _____

Mapped distribution of rocks with varying metamorphic grades.

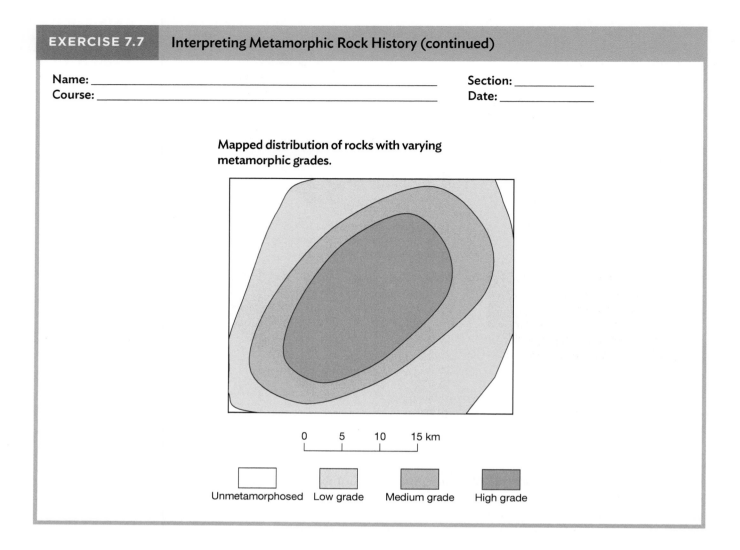

0   5   10   15 km

Unmetamorphosed   Low grade   Medium grade   High grade

7.6 Applying Your Knowledge of Metamorphic Rocks to Geologic Problems

With your new skills, you can interpret the history of metamorphic rocks from textural and mineralogic data and information from the field. Now you're ready for a little detective work and geologic reasoning in Exercise 7.8.

Name: _____   Section: _____

Course: _____   Date: _____

? **What Do You Think** Geologists in Africa have found economically valuable concentrations of chromite (the principal ore of chromium) that
formed by gravity settling in thick mafic sills. In the same area of Africa, there are
also mafic lava flows that look very much like the sills but which contain none of the
valuable minerals. You have been hired as a geologic consultant by an investment
firm that is considering purchasing the mineral rights for the mountain that includes
the sills. The firm specifically needs to know whether the mafic igneous rock (in the
photograph below) is a sill (i.e., intrusive) and therefore worth the cost of exploration or a lava-flow (i.e., extrusive) and therefore not worth a penny. What *metamorphic* evidence would you look for that would distinguish the two possibilities? On a
separate sheet of paper, write a brief report to the firm explaining your reasoning and
what you would expect to find in either case.

METAMORPHIC ROCKS STUDY SHEET

Name _____

Sample #	Minerals present (compositional group)	Texture (grain orientation, size, shape)	Type of metamorphism	Metamorphic grade (low, medium, or high grade)	Rock name

METAMORPHIC ROCKS STUDY SHEET   Name _____

Sample #	Minerals present (compositional group)	Texture (grain orientation, size, shape)	Type of metamorphism	Metamorphic grade (low, medium, or high grade)	Rock name

METAMORPHIC ROCKS STUDY SHEET

Name _____

Sample #	Minerals present (compositional group)	Texture (grain orientation, size, shape)	Type of metamorphism	Metamorphic grade (low, medium, or high grade)	Rock name

8

Studying Earth's Landforms: Maps and Other Tools

Horseshoe Bend in Arizona, showing the effectiveness of stream erosion.

- Become familiar with different ways to portray landforms and landscapes

- Learn the strengths and weaknesses of these representations of the Earth's surface

- Understand the essential elements of an accurate map (location, distance, direction, elevation), how they are measured, and how they are portrayed on maps

MATERIALS
NEEDED

- Clear plastic ruler with divisions in tenths of an inch and millimeters (in your toolkit at the back of this book)

- Circular protractor (in your toolkit at the back of this book)

- A globe and maps provided by your instructor that show major cities

8.1 Introduction

It is easier to study Earth's surface today than at any time in history. To examine surface features, we can now make detailed surface models from satellite elevation surveys and download images of any point on the planet with the click of a mouse. Geologists were quick to understand the scientific value of satellite imaging technology and adopted new methods as quickly as they were developed. Some of the images in this manual were not even available to researchers a decade ago. The study of the Earth's surface is almost as dynamic as the surface itself!

This chapter is an introduction to traditional maps and aerial photographs and some of the new methods used by geologists to view Earth's surface and understand how its landscapes form. Much of the new technology is available to you *free* for use on your computer. *Google Earth*[TM] and *NASA World Wind* provide free satellite images of the entire globe and can generate three-dimensional views of landforms. Archived topographic maps of most states are available online from the U.S. Geological Survey at http://ngmdb.usgs.gov/maps/TopoView/. And *Google Maps* is another exciting new tool for geologists; you can use it to zoom anywhere on Earth.

8.2 Ways to Portray Earth's Surface

The best way to study landforms is to fly over them for a bird's-eye view and then walk or drive over them to see them from a human perspective. That isn't practical for a college course, so we have to bring the landforms to you instead. To portray landforms, we will use a combination of traditional topographic maps, aerial photographs, satellite images, and digital elevation models (**FIG. 8.1**).

Figure 8.1 portrays an area of eastern Maine by four different methods. A **topographic map** (Fig. 8.1a) uses contour lines to show landforms (see Chapter 9). Topographic maps used to be drawn by surveyors who measured distances, directions, and elevations in the field. They are now made by computers from aerial photographs and radar data. **Aerial photographs** (Fig. 8.1b), including U.S. Geological Survey (USGS) Orthophotoquads, are photographs taken from a plane and pieced together to form a mosaic of an area. **Landsat images** (Fig. 8.1c) are made by a satellite that takes digital images of Earth's surface using visible light and other wavelengths of the electromagnetic spectrum. Scientists adjust the wavelengths to color the image artificially and emphasize specific features. For example, some infrared wavelengths help reveal the amount and type of vegetation. **Digital elevation models** (DEMs; Fig. 8.1d) are computer-generated, three-dimensional views of landforms made from radar satellite elevation data spaced at 10- or 30-meter (m) intervals on the Earth's surface. A new generation based on 1-m data is now being released that provides a more accurate model of the surface than anything available to the public 5 years ago. Exercise 8.1 asks you to make recommendations based on the images in Figure 8.1.

8.2.1 Map Projections

The portrayals of the area in Figure 8.1 are flat, two-dimensional pictures, but Earth is a nearly spherical three-dimensional body. Only a three-dimensional representation—a globe—can accurately show the *areas* and *shapes* of figures and the *directions* and *distances* between points. The process by which the three-dimensional Earth is converted to a two-dimensional map is called making a **projection**. There are many different projections, each of which distorts one or more

FIGURE 8.1 One area in eastern Maine represented by different imaging methods. [Scale bar and north arrow in (a) apply to all figures.]

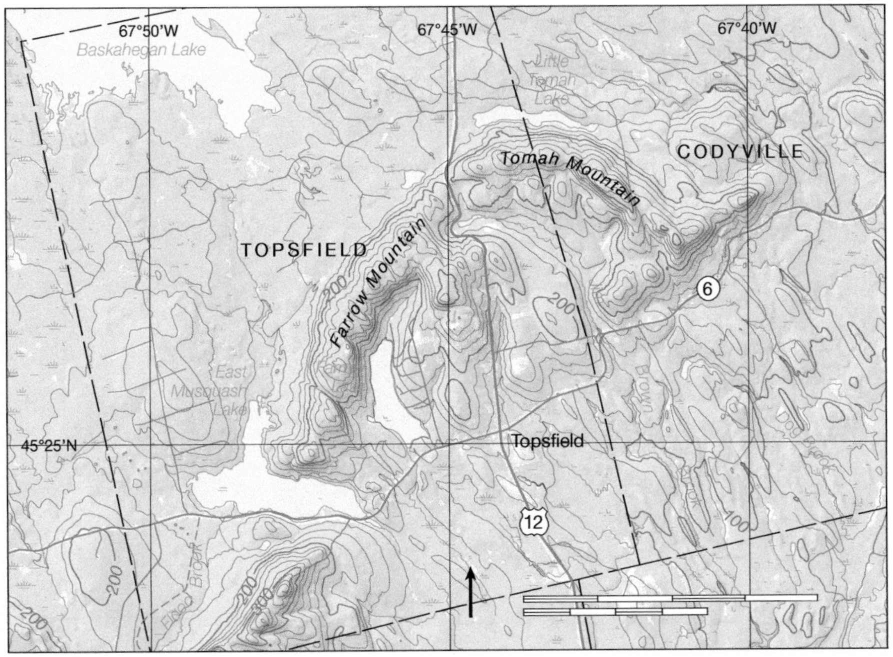

(a) Topographic map.

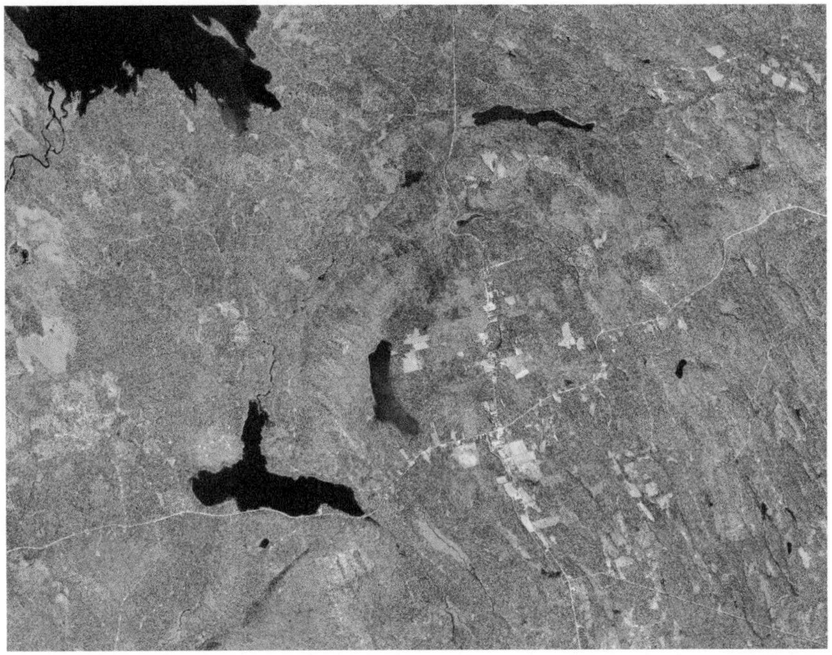

(b) Aerial photograph.

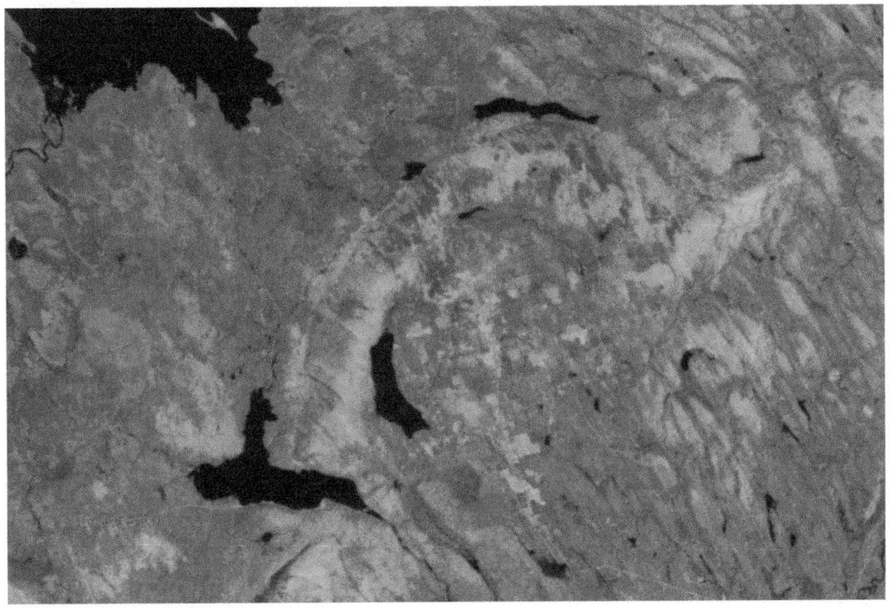

(c) Landsat image (artificial color).

(d) Digital elevation model.

Name: _____ **Section:** _____

Course: _____ **Date:** _____

Each type of portrayal has strengths that make it useful for some purposes and weaknesses that prevent its use in others. This exercise examines the strengths and weaknesses of the four landscape representations in Figure 8.1.

(a) Examine the images in Figure 8.1 and rank them (on a scale of 1 to 4) in the table below by how well they show the map elements indicated (1 is most effective, 4 is least effective; ties are allowed).

	Topographic map	Aerial photograph	Landsat image	DEM
Location				
Direction				
Elevation				
Changes in slope				
Distance				
Names of features				

(b) Which of the images enables you to recognize the topography most easily? Why?

_____

_____

(c) Which is least helpful in trying to visualize the hills, valleys, and lakes? Why?

_____

_____

(d) Erosional agents often produce a "topographic grain," an alignment of elongate hills, ridges, and valleys. Which images show the topographic grain in this area most clearly? Once you've seen it on those images, can you recognize it on the others?

_____

(e) Which images show highways most clearly?

_____

(f) Which images show unpaved lumber roads most clearly?

_____

(g) Which image do you think is the oldest? The most recent? Explain your reasoning.

_____

_____

(continued)

Name: _____   **Section:** _____
Course: _____   **Date:** _____

? What Do You Think You work at a state university forestry department and are also a scout leader for young teenagers. As part of your "day job," you have been asked by the state forestry commissioner to discuss recent changes in forest cover with her staff. In addition, you were asked to organize an overnight wilderness hike by your scouting group. Which type of image would you want to use for each of the two activities? In the space below, indicate your choices and why you made them.

(a) Staff presentation: _____

_____

_____

(b) Wilderness hike: _____

_____

_____

of the four elements italicized above and each of which is useful for some purposes but unusable for others. Three common map projections are shown in **FIGURE 8.2**, and **TABLE 8.1** indicates what they distort and for what purposes they are best used.

FIGURE 8.2 Three common map projections and their different views of the world. (The equator is indicated in each projection by a red line.)

(a) Orthographic.

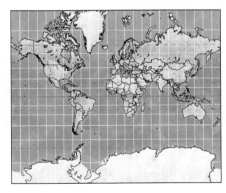

(b) Mercator.

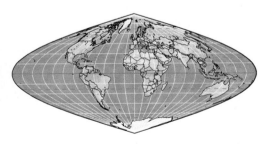

(c) Uninterrupted sinusoidal.

8.3 Map Elements

All accurate depictions of Earth's surface must contain certain basic elements: *location*, a way to show precisely where the area is; a way to measure the *distance* between features; and an accurate portrayal of *directions* between features. It is also important to know *elevations* of hilltops and other features and the *steepness of slopes*.

TABLE 8.1 **The strengths and weaknesses of three common map projections.**

	Orthographic	Mercator	Uninterrupted sinusoidal
Strengths	Directions between points are preserved. East–west distances are accurate.	Accurate near the equator. *Directions* preserved in most areas.	Areas of continents are represented accurately.
Weaknesses	Shapes and areas are distorted, especially near the edge of the projection. Distances other than in east–west direction are distorted.	Severe shape and area distortions away from the equator. Useless for north and south polar areas.	Scale is constant only along a central north–south line and the equator and changes elsewhere. Shapes are distorted for features distant from these reference lines.
Comments	Perspective view is similar to view of a globe from a great distance. Note accurate representation of size of Greenland compared with the Mercator projection.	Note vastly distorted polar areas of Greenland (shown much more accurately on the other projections) and Antarctica.	Note that the area of Greenland (much smaller than Africa and South America) is portrayed accurately compared with the Mercator projection.
Uses	Often used to provide context for images taken of Earth from space.	Nautical navigation charts because point-to-point directions are accurate.	Commonly used for features elongated north–south (e.g., maps of Africa and South America).

8.3.1 Map Element 1: Location

Road maps and atlases use a simple grid system to locate cities and towns (e.g., Chicago is in grid square A8). This is not very precise because many other places may be in the same square, but it is good enough for most drivers. More sophisticated grids are used to locate features on Earth precisely. Maps published by the USGS use three grid systems: latitude/longitude, the Universal Transverse Mercator (UTM) grid, and, for most states, the Public Land Survey System. The UTM grid is least familiar to Americans but is used extensively in the rest of the world.

Latitude and Longitude The latitude/longitude grid is based on location north or south of the **equator** and east or west of an arbitrarily chosen north–south line (**FIG. 8.3**). A *parallel of latitude* connects all points that are the same angular distance north or south of the equator. The maximum value for latitude is 90° N or 90° S (the North and South Poles, respectively). A *meridian of longitude* connects all points that are the same angular distance east or west of the **prime meridian**, a line that passes through the Royal Observatory in Greenwich, England. The maximum value for longitude is 180° E or 180° W, the international date line. *Remember: You must indicate whether a point is north or south of the equator **and** east or west of the prime meridian.*

Latitude and longitude readings are typically reported in **degrees** (°), **minutes** ('), and **seconds** ("), and there are 60' in a degree and 60" in a minute (e.g., 40°37'44" N, 73°45'09" W). ***For reference, 1 degree of latitude is equivalent to approximately 69 miles (111 km), 1 minute of latitude is about 1.1 mile (1.85 km), and 1 second of latitude is about 100 feet (31 m).*** The same kind of comparison can be made for longitude only *at the equator*, because the meridians converge at the poles and the distance between degrees of longitude decreases gradually toward the poles (Fig. 8.3b). Handheld global positioning system (GPS) receivers and those used in cars and planes can locate points to within a second. In Exercise 8.2 you will practice working with latitude and longitude.

FIGURE 8.3 **The latitude/longitude grid.**

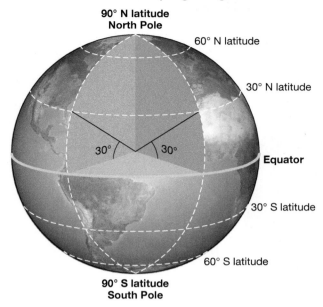

(a) Latitude is measured in degrees north or south of the equator.

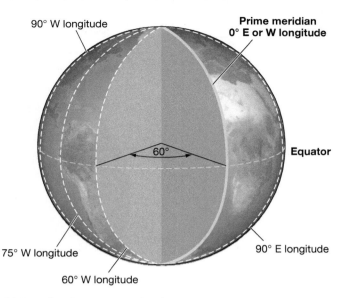

(b) Longitude is measured in degrees east or west of the prime meridian (Greenwich, England).

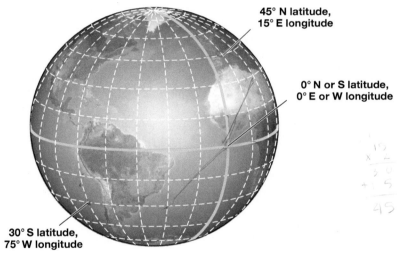

(c) Locating points using the completed grid.

EXERCISE 8.2 **Locating Cities Using Latitude and Longitude**

Name: _____ Section: _____

Course: _____ Date: _____

(a) For practice using the latitude/longitude system, describe the locations of the points (indicated by the stars) on the figure below. (*Remember* to indicate N or S for latitude, W or E for longitude.) *Note:* Latitude parallels and longitude meridians are spaced 15° apart.

i _____   ii _____   iii _____

(continued)

Name: _____   Section: _____
Course: _____   Date: _____

(b) With the aid of a globe or map, what geographic features are located at
  i. 45°00′00″ N latitude, 90°00′00″ W longitude? _____
  ii. 15°00′00″ N latitude, 30°00′00″ E longitude? _____
  iii. 30°00′00″ S latitude, 90°00′00″ W longitude? _____

(c) With the aid of a globe or map, determine the latitude and longitude of your geology laboratory as accurately as you can. How could you locate the laboratory more accurately?

_____

_____

(d) If you have access to a GPS receiver, locate the corners of your laboratory building. Draw a map below (or on a separate piece of paper) showing the location, orientation, and distances between the corners.

(e) Locate the latitude and longitude coordinates of the following U.S. and Canadian cities as accurately as possible.

Nome, Alaska _____	Seattle, Washington _____
Chicago, Illinois _____	Los Angeles, California _____
St. Louis, Missouri _____	Houston, Texas _____
New York, New York _____	Miami, Florida _____
St. Johns, Newfoundland _____	Ottawa, Ontario _____
Calgary, Alberta _____	Victoria, British Columbia _____

(continued)

Name: _____   Section: _____

Course: _____   Date: _____

(f) Which of the cities in (e) do you think is closest in latitude to each of the following world cities? Predict first, without looking at a map, globe, or *Google Earth*™, then check. Were you surprised by any?

City	Predicted best match	Latitude and longitude	Actual best match
Oslo, Norway			
Baghdad, Iraq			
London, England			
Paris, France			
Rome, Italy			
Beijing, China			
Tokyo, Japan			
Quito, Ecuador			
Cairo, Egypt			
Cape Town, South Africa			

Public Land Survey System The Public Land Survey System was created in 1785 to provide accurate maps as America expanded from its thirteen original states. Much of the country is covered by this system, except for the original thirteen colonies, Kentucky, Maine, Tennessee, West Virginia, Alaska, Hawaii, Texas, and part of the southwestern states surveyed by Spanish colonists before the states joined the Union. Points can be located rapidly to within an eighth of a mile in this system (**FIG. 8.4**).

The grid is based on accurately surveyed north–south (**principal meridian**) and east–west (**base line**) lines for each survey region. Lines parallel to these at 6-mile intervals create grid squares 6 miles on a side, forming east-west rows called **townships** and north–south columns called **ranges** (Fig. 8.4). Townships are numbered north or south of the base line, and ranges are numbered east and west of the principal meridian. Each 6-mile square is divided into 36 **sections**, each 1 mile on a side, numbered as shown in Figure 8.4. Each section is divided into **quarter sections** ½ mile on a side, and each of these is further quartered, resulting in squares ¼ mile on a side. The location of the yellow star in the orange box in Figure 8.4 is described in the series of blow-ups:

- **T2S R3E** locates it somewhere within an area of 36 square miles (inside a 6 mi × 6 mi square).
- **Section 12, T2S R3E** locates it somewhere within an area of 1 square mile.
- **SW ¼ of Section 12, T2S R3E** locates it somewhere within an area of ¼ square mile.
- **SW ¼ of the SW ¼ of Section 12, T2S R3E** locates it within an area of ¹⁄₁₆ square mile.

In Exercise 8.3, you will practice using the Public Land Survey System.

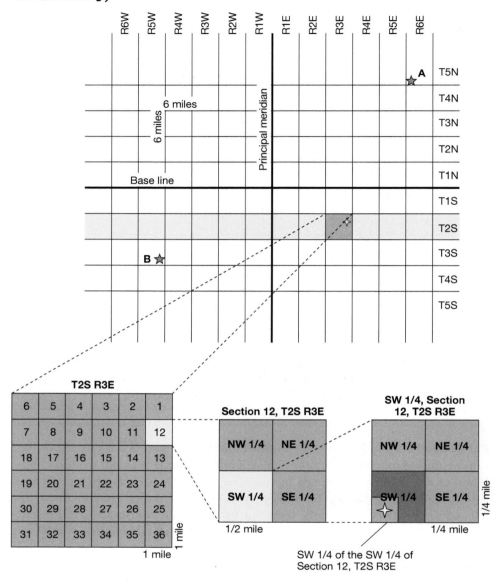

FIGURE 8.4 The Public Land Survey System grid. (Points A and B are for use with Exercise 8.3.)

Universal Transverse Mercator Grid The UTM grid divides the Earth into 1,200 segments, each containing 6° of longitude and 8° of latitude (**FIG. 8.5**). North–south segments are assigned letters (C through X); east–west segments are called **UTM zones** and are numbered 1 to 60 eastward from the international date line (180° W). Thus, UTM zone 1 extends from 180° to 174° W longitude, zone 2 from 174° to 168° W longitude, and so on. The forty-eight conterminous United States lie within UTM zones 10 through 19, roughly 125° to 67° W longitude. The UTM grid is based on a Mercator projection, in which the north and south polar regions are extremely distorted: Greenland and Antarctica appear much larger than their actual sizes. Because of this distortion, the grid does not extend beyond 80° N and 80° S latitudes.

To locate a point, begin with the grid box in which the feature is located. For example, the red box in Figure 8.5 is grid S22. UTM grid readings tell *in meters* how

Name: _____   **Section:** _____

Course: _____   **Date:** _____

(a) Determine the location of points A and B in Figure 8.4.

A _____   B _____

(b) Locate the following points on Figure 8.4 by writing the number on the figure:
1. NE ¼ of Section 36, T3N R4W
2. SE ¼ of Section 18, T1N R1E
3. NW ¼ of Section 3, T4S R5E

(c) Determine the location of points indicated by your instructor on topographic maps.

_____

_____

_____

far north of the equator (*northings*) and east of the central meridian for each zone (*eastings*) a point lies. The central meridian for each UTM zone is a line of longitude that runs through the center of the zone (**FIG. 8.6**) and is arbitrarily assigned an easting of 500,000 m so that no point has a negative easting. Points east of a central meridian thus have eastings greater than 500,000 m, and those west of the central meridian have eastings less than 500,000 m.

FIGURE 8.5 The UTM grid.

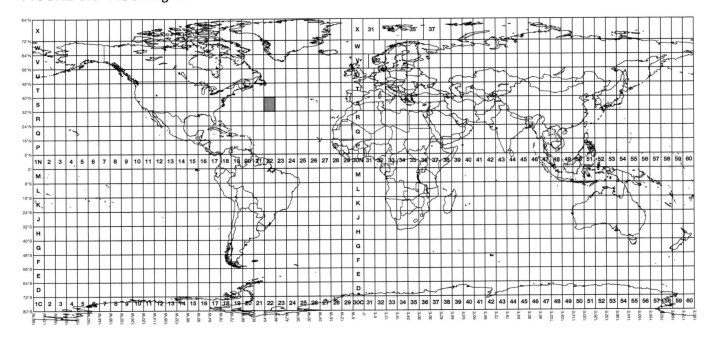

FIGURE 8.6 UTM zones for the forty-eight conterminous United States.

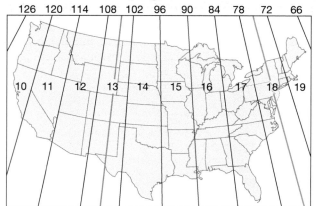

The red line is the central meridian (105° W) for UTM zone 13; the blue line is the central meridian for zone 18.

FIGURE 8.7 shows how the UTM grid appears on the most recent USGS topographic maps. Each grid square is exactly 1,000 m (1 km) on a side. Labels along the top and (as here) bottom of the map are **eastings (E)**—the distance in meters from the central meridian for the UTM zone (19 as shown in Fig. 8.6). Labels along the east and west sides of the map are **northings (N)**—the distance in meters north or south of the equator. These values are written out fully near the corner and elsewhere in

FIGURE 8.7 Southeast corner of the Greenfield quadrangle, Maine, showing UTM grid and marginal UTM grid values. (Map scale = 1:24,000. UTM tool is shown in position to locate the blue point.)

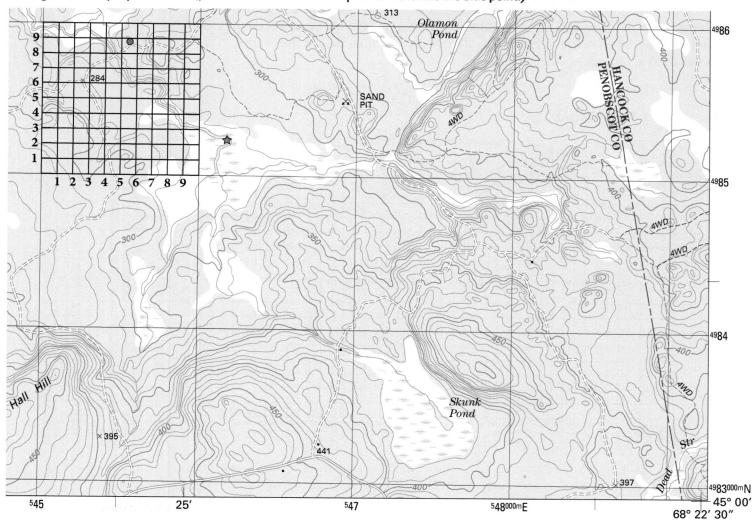

a shorthand form. For example, the easting near the right-hand corner of the map, $^{5}48^{000\text{m}}\text{E}$, is the full value: 548,000 m east of the central median for UTM zone 19. The eastings to the west are the shorthand version: $^{5}47$ and $^{5}45$ are, respectively, 547,000 and 545,000 m east of the central meridian. Note that the grid label for $^{5}46$ is missing; this is because it should have appeared in the place where a longitude value is shown (25′, representing longitude 68°25′00″ west). Similarly, the full northing value just above the 45°00′00″ is $^{49}83^{000}\text{N}$ (4,983,000 m north of the equator), and the values above are the shorthand version (e.g., $^{49}84$).

It is possible to measure locations to within 100 m or better using a simple UTM tool calibrated for the map scale (Exercise 8.4). A UTM tool for this map scale is found in the geologist's toolbox at the end of the book. To determine the location of the blue dot in Figure 8.7, place the lower left corner of the UTM tool on the map so that it covers the grid box in which the point lies. The side of each grid box is 1,000 m, and the UTM tool divides it into smaller boxes 100 m on a side. The easting for the point is between 545,000 and 546,000; the northing between 4,985,000 and 4,986,000. The blue point easting is approximately 550 m (5 ½ boxes) east of the 545,000 mark = **545,550 mE**, and its northing is 120 m (1.2 boxes) south of the 4,986,000 mark = **4,985,880 mN**. In Exercise 8.4, you will practice using the UTM grid.

EXERCISE 8.4   **Locating Points with the UTM Grid**

Name: _____   Section: _____

Course: _____   Date: _____

Refer to Figure 8.7 to complete this exercise.

(a) Using the 1:24,000 UTM tool (from the back of this manual), give the location in northings and eastings of the red star on Figure 8.7.

_____N   _____E

(b) What is the location of the point where the stream leaves Olamon Pond and flows to the southwest?

_____N   _____E

(c) What feature is located at UTM 547,575 E and 4,983,450 N? _____

8.3.2 Map Element 2: Direction

Geologists use the **azimuth method** to indicate direction, based on the dial of a compass (**FIG. 8.8**). The red-tipped compass needle in Figure 8.8a is pointing northeast—that is, somewhere between north and east—but how much closer to north than to east? On an azimuth compass (Fig. 8.8b), 0° or 360° is due north, 090° due east, 180° due south, and 270° due west. The direction 045° is exactly halfway between north and east. The direction of the needle in Figure 8.8b can be read as 032°.

Use the circular protractor in your toolkit to determine the direction between any two points. Draw a line between the points, align the protractor's registration lines in a north–south or east–west position, and place its center point on one of the two points (Fig. 8.8c). The direction from the first point to the second is where the line intersects the azimuth scale; in this case, the direction from A to B is 235°. You will practice this technique in Exercise 8.5.

8.3.3 Map Element 3: Distance and Scale

A map of the entire world or your school campus can fit onto one sheet of paper—if we scale the Earth down so it fits. A **map scale** indicates how much an area has been

FIGURE 8.8 Using the azimuth method to describe the direction between two points.

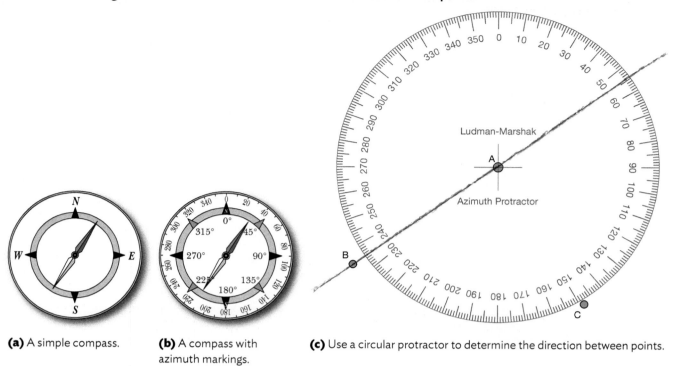

(a) A simple compass.

(b) A compass with azimuth markings.

(c) Use a circular protractor to determine the direction between points.

EXERCISE 8.5 | **Giving Directions**

Name: _____   **Section:** _____
Course: _____   **Date:** _____

Use the circular (azimuth) protractor from your toolkit to determine the direction between the following two points.

(a) In the figure below, from A to C _____°   C to A _____°   B to C _____°   C to B _____°

(b) In Figure 8.4, from A to B _____°

(c) In Figure 8.7, what is the direction from the red star to the blue dot? _____°

(d) In Figure 8.7, what is the direction from the peak of Hall Hill near the southwest corner of the map to the northernmost point of Skunk Pond? _____°

A
●

B
●

C
●

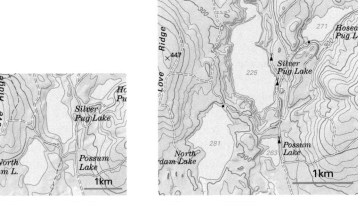

(a) Scale = 1:100,000.

(b) Scale = 1:62,500.

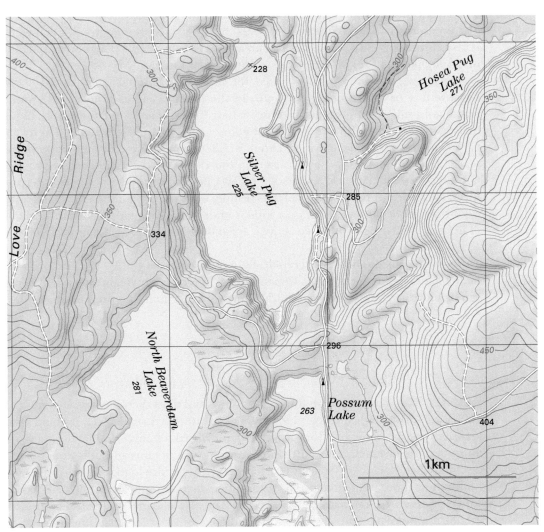

(c) Scale = 1:24,000.

scaled down so we can relate inches or centimeters on the map to real distances on the ground. **FIGURE 8.9** shows three maps of the same general area made at different scales. The more we scale down an area, the more detail we lose; the closer the map is to the real size, the more detail we can see.

The three map segments in Figure 8.9 show approximately the same area of land, but are different sizes because each is scaled down a different amount. Figure 8.9a has been scaled down more than four times as much as Figure 8.9c (1:100,000 versus 1:24,000) and therefore can cover the same area in much less space.

Different Ways to Describe Map Scale Map scale may be expressed verbally, proportionally, or graphically. A **verbal scale**, used on many road maps, uses words like "1 inch equals approximately 6.7 miles" to describe the scaling of map and real distances. A driver can estimate distances between cities, but not very accurately.

The most accurate way to describe scale is a **proportional scale**, one that tells exactly how much the ground has been scaled down to fit onto the sheet of paper. For example, a proportional scale of 1:100,000 (read "one to one hundred thousand") means that distances on the map are 1/100,000 of the distance on the ground. The proportions are the same for all units of measurement: 1 inch on such a map corresponds to 100,000 inches on the ground (1.58 miles) *and* 1 centimeter (cm) on the map corresponds to 100,000 cm on the ground (1 km). The larger the number in a proportional scale, the less space is needed to portray a given area on a map (compare Fig. 8.9a, b, and c). Note in Figure 8.9 that while it takes more space on a map to show an area at a scale of 1:24,000 than at 1:62,500 or 1:100,000, the 1:24,000 map shows much more detail.

The metric system is ideally suited for scales like 1:100,000,000 or 1:100,000 because it is based on multiples of 10. In the United States, we measure ground distance in miles but map distance in inches. Unfortunately, relationships among inches, feet, and miles are not as simple as in the metric system. There are 63,360 inches in a mile (12 in per foot × 5,280 ft per mile), so the proportional scale 1:63,360 means that 1 inch on a map represents exactly 1 mile on the ground. Old topographic maps use a scale of 1:62,500. For most purposes, we can interpret this scale to be approximately 1 inch = 1 mile, even though an inch on such a map would be about 70 feet short of a mile. Other common map scales are 1:24,000 (1 in. = 2,000 ft), 1:100,000 (see above), 1:250,000 (1 in. = 3.95 mi), and 1:1,000,000 (1 in. = 15.8 mi).

Map scale can also be shown **graphically**, using a **bar scale** (FIG. 8.10) to express the same relation as the verbal scale. Depending on how carefully you measure, a bar scale can be more accurate than a verbal scale, but not as accurate as a proportional scale.

8.4 Vertical Exaggeration: A Matter of Perspective

DEMs show the land surface in three dimensions and must therefore use an appropriate *vertical* scale to indicate how much taller one feature is than another. It would seem logical to use the same scale for vertical and horizontal distances, but we don't usually do so because mountains wouldn't look much like mountains and hills would barely be visible. Landforms are typically much wider than they are high, standing only a few hundred or thousand feet above or below their surroundings. At a scale of 1:62,500, 1 inch represents about a mile. If we used the same scale to make a three-dimensional model, a hilltop 400 feet above its surroundings would be less than one-tenth of an inch high. A mountain rising a mile above its base would be only 1 inch high.

We therefore exaggerate the vertical scale compared to the horizontal to show features from a human perspective. For a three-dimensional model of a 1:62,500

FIGURE 8.10 Scale bars used with three common proportional scales.

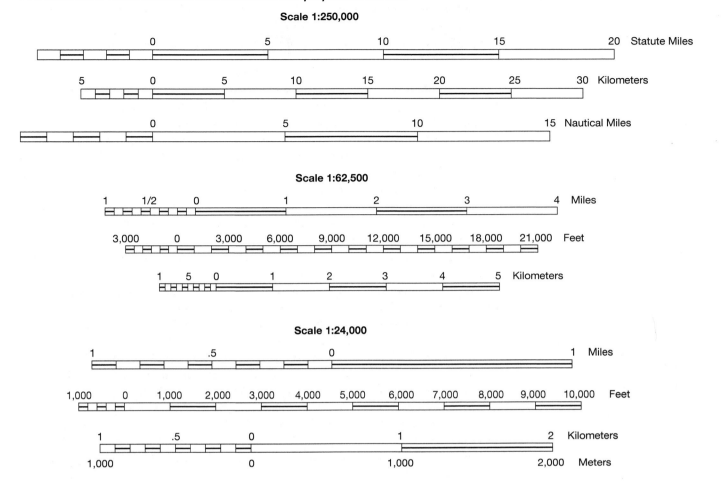

map, a vertical scale of 1:10,000 would exaggerate apparent elevations by a little more than six times (62,500/10,000 = 6.25). A mountain rising 1 mile above its surroundings would stand 6.25 inches high in the model; a 400-foot hill would be about half an inch tall, which is more realistic than the 0.1 inch if the 1:62,500 horizontal scale had been used vertically.

The degree to which the vertical scale has been exaggerated is, logically enough, called the **vertical exaggeration**. FIGURE 8.11 shows the effects of vertical exaggeration on a DEM. With no vertical exaggeration, the prominent hill in the center of Figure 8.11a is barely noticeable. One of the authors of this manual has climbed that hill several times and guarantees that climbing it is far more difficult than Figure 8.11a would suggest. In contrast, Figure 8.11d exaggerates too much; the hill did not seem that steep, even with a pack loaded with rocks.

Is there such a thing as too much vertical exaggeration? The basic rule of thumb is not to make a mountain out of a molehill. Vertical exaggerations of two to five times generally preserve the basic proportions of landforms while presenting features clearly. We return to the concept of vertical exaggeration when we discuss drawing topographic profiles from topographic maps in Chapter 9.

FIGURE 8.11 DEMs of part of the area in Figure 8.1 showing the effects of vertical exaggeration (VE).

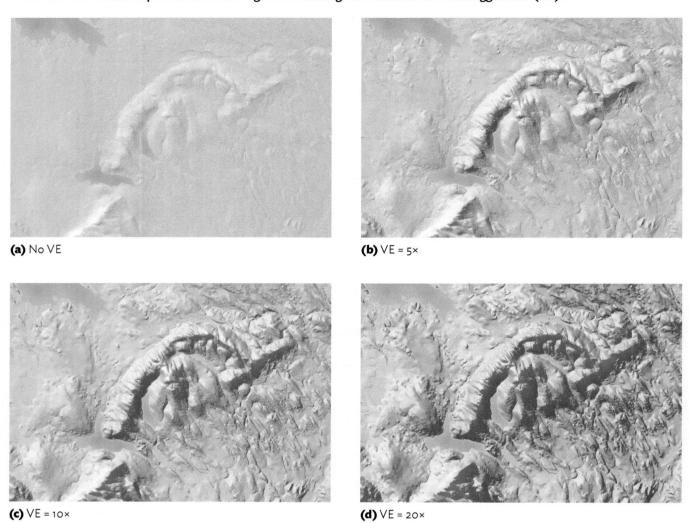

(a) No VE

(b) VE = 5×

(c) VE = 10×

(d) VE = 20×

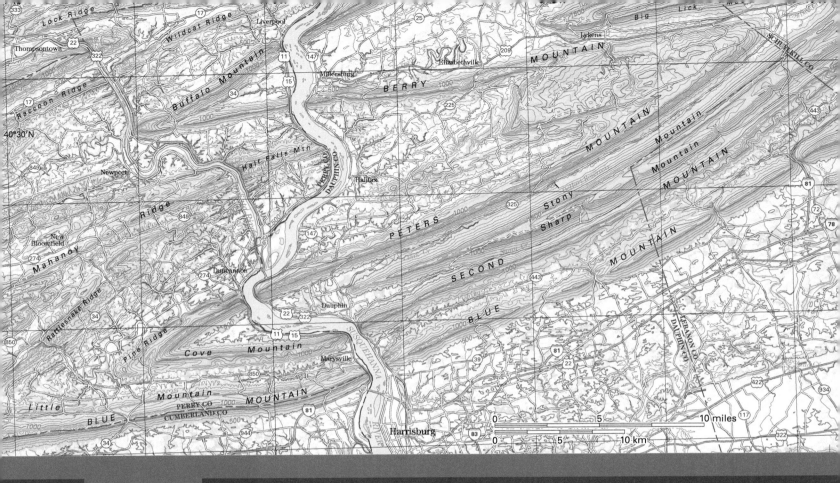

9

Working with Topographic Maps

A topographic map of the Appalachian Valley and Ridge province in Pennsylvania

9.1 Introduction

In today's modern world, we have become very familiar with tools that help picture the world around us. With the click of a mouse, *Google Earth*™ and *NASA World Wind* provide satellite images of any point on the planet; digital elevation models (DEMs) are available to help to visualize topography; GPS satellites circling the Earth can help locate exactly where you are standing; and sophisticated Geographic Information System (GIS) software can locate points, give elevations, measure lengths of meandering streams, and construct detailed profiles of an area. But what would you do if you were in the field and did not have access to any sophisticated equipment or could not get a reliable signal? A geologist in the field would use a **topographic map**—a special type of map that uses contour lines to show landforms. Topographic maps cost almost nothing, weigh much less than a digital device, and withstand rain, swarming insects, and being dropped better than computers. A recent topographic map gives the names and elevations of lakes, streams, mountains, and roads, and it outlines fields and distinguishes swamps and forests as well as a satellite image does. With a little practice, you can learn more about landforms from topographic maps than from a satellite image or DEM. This chapter explains how topographic maps work and helps you develop map-reading skills for identifying landforms, planning hikes, solving environmental problems—and possibly, even saving your life.

9.2 Contour Lines

Like aerial photographs and satellite images, topographic maps show location, distance, and direction very accurately. Topographic maps show the shapes of landforms, elevations, and the steepness of slopes with a special kind of line called a **contour line**.

A contour line is a line on a map that connects points of the same value for whatever is being measured. Contour lines can show many types of features on a map, like population density and average income, as well as elevation. You are already familiar with one common type of contour line on weather maps, which shows a change in temperature in different areas (**FIG. 9.1**).

The contour lines in Figure 9.1b are *isotherms* or lines of equal temperature. Thus, the predicted temperature for every point on the 60° line is 60°F, every point on the 40° line 40°F, and so on. Each isotherm separates areas where the temperature is higher or lower than that along the line itself. Thus, all points in the area north of the 30° contour line have predicted high temperatures for the day lower than 30°F, and those on the south side are predicted to be higher than 30°F. The map has a **contour interval** of 10°, meaning that contour lines represent temperatures at 10° increments.

To get experience with contour lines before looking at topographic maps, the following two exercises ask you to create two basic contour maps. In Exercise 9.1, you will create a contour map showing areas of different tree heights in a small woodland area. Then, Exercise 9.2 asks you to create your own contour map of different temperature areas in the United States, like you see in Figure 9.1b and like you see on many news websites as shown in Figure 9.1c.

FIGURE 9.1 Contour map showing predicted high temperatures for the United States.

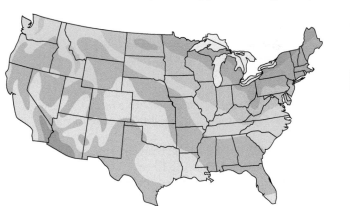

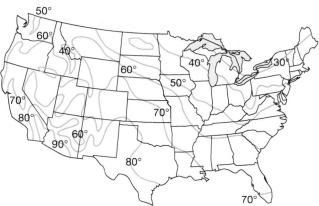

(a) Colored zones show predicted high temperature ranges in increments of 10°F.

(b) Contour lines outline the same zones.

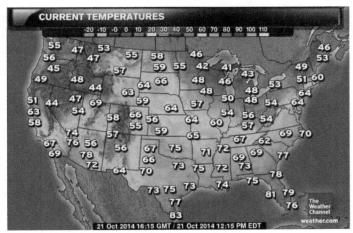

(c) You will see these types of maps frequently on the news. This map is from weather.com.

EXERCISE 9.1	Making a Simple Contour Map

Name: _____   Section: _____

Course: _____   Date: _____

Last year, foresters planted pine tree saplings in a grid pattern in a small area. This year, they noted that some trees were taller than others and want to understand the factors that caused those trees to grow faster. The map in this exercise shows the heights of saplings throughout the area.

To help the foresters, create a contour map that shows areas of different tree heights (and thus growth rates). Use the map with a contour interval of 10 cm on the next page, and sketch your contour lines in pencil. You may want to copy the next page to practice your initial attempts.

(continued)

Name: _____   Section: _____

Course: _____   Date: _____

Hints

- As you saw with the temperatures in Figure 9.1b, heights that are multiples of 10 cm will lie on a contour line.
- Heights that are not multiples of 10 cm will lie between two contour lines. For example, tree heights between 10 and 20 cm will lie between the 10-cm and 20-cm contour lines.
- To estimate where a contour line passes between two points, examine the differences in height between the points. For example, we have placed a red line connecting the 6-cm and 14-cm tree heights. Because 10 cm is between these two numbers, the 10-cm contour line must pass between them. And because 10 cm is exactly 4 cm less than 14 cm and 4 cm more than 6 cm, the 10-cm contour will pass midway between these two points.
- Similarly, the 20-cm contour will be between the 14-cm and 22-cm areas. But as 20 cm is only 2 cm less than 22 cm but 6 cm more than 14 cm, this contour line should be drawn close to the 22-cm data point.
- When you are ready, sketch the 10-cm contour line first, then the 20 cm, then the 30 cm, then the 40 cm. Remember, multiple contour lines can pass between two heights—contour lines for 20 cm and 30 cm will pass between the 15-cm and 32-cm measurements.
- Some contour lines will form completely closed areas but others may end at a side of the map.

Map showing the heights (in centimeters) of pine saplings in different areas after 1 year of growth.

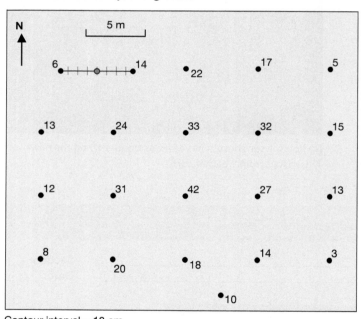

Contour interval = 10 cm

Name: _____   Section: _____

Course: _____   Date: _____

On a certain day in the middle of the summer, the U.S. Weather Bureau predicted maximum daily temperatures shown on the map that follows later in this exercise. Using the data included on the map, create a contoured map with a contour interval of 10°F. Sketch your contour lines in pencil on the map. You may want to copy this page to practice your initial attempts.

(continued)

Name: _____   Section: _____
Course: _____   Date: _____

Hints: As with Exercise 9.1, your main task is to estimate where contour lines will pass between temperatures that are not multiples of 10°.

- To get you started, we show how to locate the 80° isotherm between San Francisco and Los Angeles. San Francisco is 4° cooler than the 80° contour, whereas Los Angeles is 6° warmer, so the 80° contour is closer to San Francisco than Los Angeles as shown.
- Each contour line will be some multiple of 10° (70°, 80°, 90°, 100°), so that contour lines will pass through predicted temperatures that are multiples of 10°.
- Remember, more than one contour line could fall between cities with large differences in temperature. For example, the 80°, 90°, and 100° contour lines have to fit between San Francisco (76°) and Reno, Nevada (102°). Some lines can form completely closed areas while others may end at the sides of the map.

Predicted high temperatures (°F) for a day in the United States.

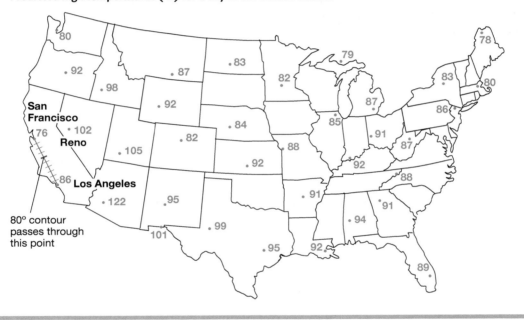

9.2.1 Contour Lines on Topographic Maps

Now that you understand the basic concept of contour lines and how to create them from map data, let's look at how they work on topographic maps.

A contour line on a **topographic** map connects points that are the same elevation above sea level (the reference for all elevations), and the complete set of lines accurately shows the three-dimensional shape of the surface. **FIGURE 9.2a** shows the shape of the island of Hawaii using a contour interval of 1,000 m. The first contour line is easy to draw for any island because the 0-m contour line is sea level and defines the outer shape of the island.

The elevation difference between contour lines is called the **contour interval.** Small contour intervals are used where there isn't much change in elevation, and large contour intervals are used where the difference in elevation is high. Typical contour intervals on topographic maps are 10, 20, 50, and 100 feet. A 1,000-m

FIGURE 9.2 Topographic maps of the island of Hawaii with different contour intervals.

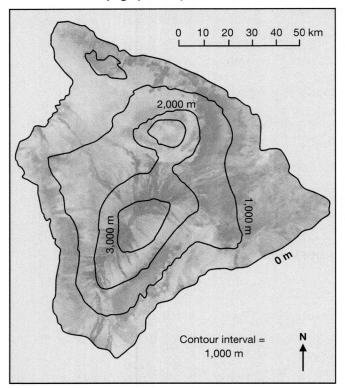

0 10 20 30 40 50 km

2,000 m

3,000 m

1,000 m

0 m

Contour interval =
1,000 m

N

(a) 1,000 m contour interval

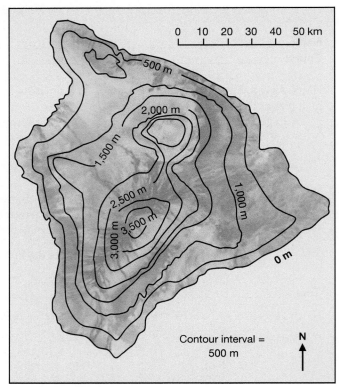

0 10 20 30 40 50 km

500 m

2,000 m

1,500 m

2,500 m

1,000 m

3,000 m

3,500 m

0 m

Contour interval =
500 m

N

(b) 500 m contour interval

FIGURE 9.3 Useful information outside the borders of a topographic map.

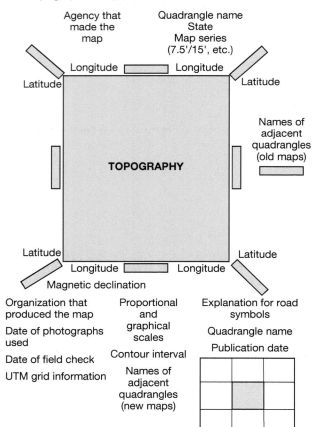

Agency that
made the
map

Quadrangle name
State
Map series
(7.5'/15', etc.)

Longitude   Longitude

Latitude   Latitude

Names of
adjacent
quadrangles
(old maps)

TOPOGRAPHY

Latitude   Latitude

Longitude   Longitude

Magnetic declination

Organization that
produced the map

Date of photographs
used

Date of field check

UTM grid information

Proportional
and
graphical
scales

Contour interval

Names of
adjacent
quadrangles
(new maps)

Explanation for road
symbols

Quadrangle name

Publication date

interval is used in Figure 9.2a because the island of Hawaii is so mountainous. If the contour interval had been 10 m, the map would have been unreadable with 100 contour lines for each contour line in the figure. The 1,000-m contour interval can give only a rough idea of the topography, but a smaller interval could give better details (**FIG. 9.2b**).

Geologists use the term **relief** to describe the range in elevation in an area. **High relief** indicates mountainous areas with great elevation differences between the highest and lowest places. **Low relief** refers to flat areas like plains and plateaus where there is very little elevation change over broad expanses.

9.3 Reading Topographic Maps

Because topographic maps come in many sizes and scales, cover areas of different sizes, and can use different contour intervals, the first thing you should do when looking at a map is to examine its borders for useful information like the contour interval, scale, and location. **FIGURE 9.3** is a guide for finding this information on the most recent topographic maps produced by the U.S. Geological Survey (USGS). Further, Appendix 9.1 shows the standard map symbols used to represent natural and man-made features on most maps. As an example, consider **FIGURE 9.4**, which shows a topographic map of an area in eastern Maine.

USGS maps use green to highlight forests, blue for bodies of water like streams, rivers, and lakes, and white for fields or marshes. If there were any urban areas in this part of Maine, they would be shown in pink. Human-built features like roads and buildings in and around the town of Topsfield are shown as white lines.

Take a moment to see how this map compares to a digital elevation model of the same area in **FIGURE 9.5**, a model created using sophisticated computing power. Note how instead of using contour lines to show hills, valleys, and ridges, the DEM uses shading and perspective to show elevations. In this next exercise, we will help you compare different areas of both maps to see how differences in contour lines communicate a variety of shapes in the landscape (hills, valleys, lakes, and flat areas), shapes that are easily seen on a DEM.

EXERCISE 9.3 | **How Topographic Maps Show Landform Shapes**

Name: _____   Section: _____

Course: _____   Date: _____

For this exercise, you will use the topographic map in Figure 9.4 and the DEM in Figure 9.5, of the same location.

(a) Slope: Find a flat place on the DEM in Figure 9.5 and a place where the slope is steep. Now locate these places on the topographic map (Fig. 9.4). Compare the contour lines in the flat and steep places.

(i) How does the spacing of the contour lines show the difference between gentle and steep slopes?

_____

_____

(ii) Describe the slopes on both sides of Farrow Lake, the first lake west of Topsfield. Are the slopes equally steep on both sides of the lake or is one side steeper than the other? Explain your reasoning.

_____

_____

_____

(iii) Describe the slopes of Farrow Mountain in words, and draw a sketch (using the graph paper provided at the end of this chapter) showing what it would look like to climb over the mountain from northwest to southeast.

_____

_____

_____

_____

_____

_____

(b) Nested contour lines: Colored circles in Figure 9.4 identify places where there are a series of concentric (nested) contour lines. Look at these features on the DEM (Figure 9.5).

(i) What type of feature do nested contour lines indicate? _____

(ii) Mark similar features with colored dots on the map.

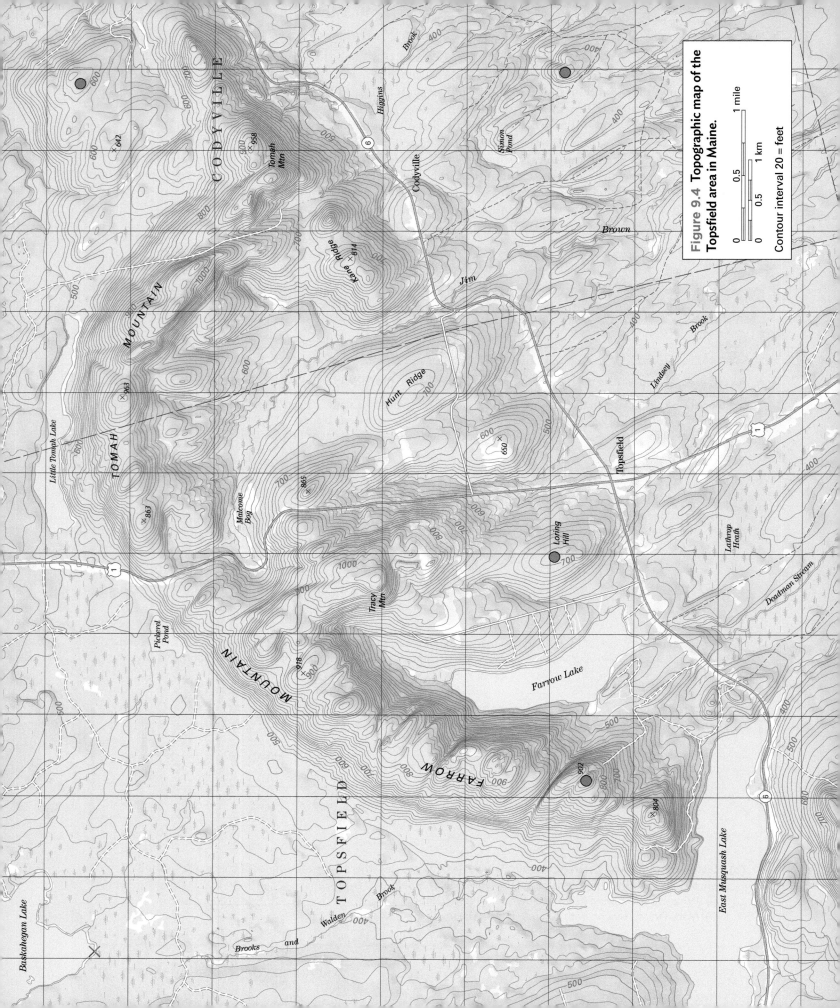

Figure 9.4 Topographic map of the Topsfield area in Maine.

Contour interval 20 = feet

Figure 9.5 Digital elevation model (DEM) of the Topsfield area in Maine.

1 mile

0   0.5

0   0.5   1 km

9.3.1 Contour Lines and Elevation

Maps provide several key features to help determine elevations. Two of the easiest to use are benchmarks and index contour lines.

A benchmark is an accurately surveyed point marked on the ground by a brass plaque cemented in place. It records the latitude, longitude, and elevation of that spot. On topographic maps, elevations of selected points (like hilltops, lake surfaces, and highway intersections) are indicated with a symbol and a number, such as $X_{1438'}$ or Δ_{561}. The latter symbol is the benchmark.

To find the elevation of other points on the map, however, we need to learn how to use the contour lines. First, check the contour interval shown at the bottom of every map for the difference in elevation between adjacent contour lines (see Fig. 9.3). Then notice that on maps like Figure 9.4, every fifth contour line is darker than those around it and has its elevation labeled. These are index contours, which represent elevations that are five times the contour interval (multiples of 5 × 20 in Fig. 9.4—300 feet, 400 feet, and so on). To determine the elevation of an unlabeled contour line, determine its position relative to an index contour. For example, a contour line immediately adjacent to the 500-foot index contour must be 480 or 520 feet—20 feet lower or higher than the index contour on a map where the contour interval is 20 feet.

What about the elevation of a point between two contour lines? All points on one side of a contour line are at higher elevations than the line itself, and those on the opposite side are at lower elevations—but how much higher or lower? This is just as easy as finding the temperature between two isotherms on a weather map. The contour interval in **FIGURE 9.6** is 50 feet, so a point between two adjacent contour lines must be less than 50 feet higher or lower than those lines. Either use a ruler or estimate as you did in Exercise 9.2: a point midway between the 500- and 550-foot contour lines would be estimated as 525 feet above sea level.

Depressions Concentric contour lines may indicate a hill (as in Exercise 9.3b) or a depression. To avoid confusion, it must be clear that contour lines outlining a depression indicate progressively *lower* elevations toward the center of the concentric lines rather than the *higher* elevations that would indicate a hill. To show this, small marks called hachures are added to the line, pointing toward the lower elevation (see the innermost two lines in **FIGURE 9.7**).

The feature in Figure 9.7 could be a volcano with a crater at its summit. Note that the nested contour lines on the flanks of the feature indicate increasing elevation just like those of Figure 9.4, but that the 300-foot contour line is repeated, with the

FIGURE 9.6 **Reading elevations of hills and valleys from topographic maps.**

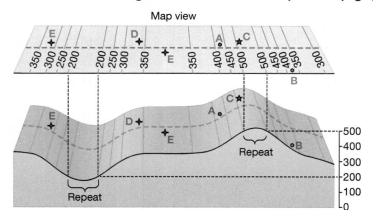

The elevation of Point A is between 400 and 450 feet. Because the slope of the hill is constant between the 400- and 450-foot contour lines and A is halfway between the contour lines, its elevation is 425 feet above sea level.

The elevation of Point B is between 350 and 400 feet. The slope of the hill is gentler close to the 350-foot line and steeper near the 400-foot line. We must therefore estimate elevation taking this into account. The approximate elevation of B is 355 feet above sea level.

The elevation of Point C is greater than 500 feet, but how much greater? If it was more than 550 feet above sea level, there would be another contour line (550 feet). Therefore, the most we can say about the elevation of C is that it is between 500 and 550 feet above sea level.

FIGURE 9.7 Hachured contour lines indicate depressions.

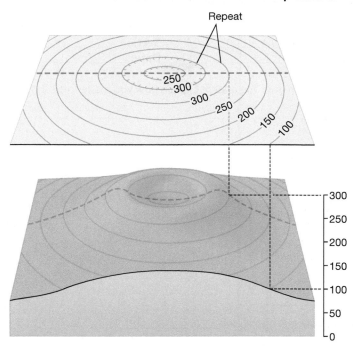

inner one hachured. This shows that the rim of the crater is higher than 300 feet but lower than 350 feet.

Using what you have learned and some of the figures you have studied, Exercise 9.4 helps you to practice determining different elevations on contour maps.

EXERCISE 9.4 **Determining Elevations from Topographic Maps**

Name: _____ Section: _____

Course: _____ Date: _____

To determine the elevation of a point on a topographic map:

1. Determine the map contour interval.

2. Find the known elevation closest to the point. This may be a benchmark or a contour line. Remember that every fifth contour line is a heavier **index contour**. You may have to follow contour lines some distance before finding an elevation label.

3. Determine whether the point is higher or lower than the known elevation based on place names, such as "fire tower," "valley," and so forth.

4. Interpolate between the contour lines that bracket the point to get elevation.

Using this procedure and what you have learned in your reading, answer the following questions using figures found earlier in the chapter:

(a) In Figure 9.7, what is your estimate of the elevation of the highest point on the rim of the crater? Explain how you made this estimation.

_____

_____

_____

(continued)

Name: _____   Section: _____
Course: _____   Date: _____

(b) In Figure 9.7, what is your estimate of the lowest point of the crater? Explain how you made this estimation.

_____

_____

_____

(c) In Figure 9.5, a red "x" marks a spot on the shore of Baskahegan Lake, but a printed DEM doesn't give information about its elevation. See the topographic map (Fig. 9.4) to determine the elevation of that point as accurately as possible. _____ feet

(d) In Figure 9.4, what is the elevation of:

the highest point on Hunt Ridge? _____

the highest point on Farrow Mountain? _____

the intersection of U.S. Route 1 and Maine Route 6 in Topsfield? _____

Malcome Bog? _____

(e) What is the relief between Little Tomah Lake and the top of Tomah Mountain in Figure 9.4? _____

(f) What is the relief between the intersection of U.S. Route 1 and Maine Route 6 in Topsfield and East Musquash Lake in Figure 9.4? _____

9.3.2 Contour Lines and Streams: Which Way Is the Water Flowing?

Geologists study the flow of streams and drainage basins to prevent the downstream spread of pollutants and to determine where to collect water samples to find traces of valuable minerals. Streams flow downhill from high elevations to low elevations. You could determine the flow direction by looking for benchmarks along the stream or where different contour lines cross the stream, but there is an easier way as you will see in Exercise 9.5.

Name: _____   Section: _____
Course: _____   Date: _____

(a) Refer to Figure 9.4, and look closely at the unnamed stream at the north end of Farrow Lake. Based on the elevations of the contour lines that cross the stream and the general nature of the topography, in which compass direction does this stream flow?

_____

(b) Apply the same reasoning to the stream at the east end of Malcome Bog. In which compass direction does this stream flow?

_____

(continued)

Name: _____   Section: _____

Course: _____   Date: _____

(c) Now look at the contour lines as they cross these two streams. Their distinctive V shape tells which way the stream is flowing. Suggest a "rule of V" that describes how the direction of stream flow is revealed by the contour lines that cross it.

_____

_____

_____

(d) Based on your rule of V, does the stream at the west side of Pickerel Pond flow into or away from the pond?

_____

(e) In what direction does Jim Brown Brook flow (in the southeast corner of the map)?

_____

9.4 Rules and Applications of Contour Maps

In the past few sections and exercises, you learned the most important points and techniques to get started with topographic maps. The basic "rules" for reading contour lines are mostly common sense, and you figured out the most important ones for yourself in Exercises 9.3 to 9.5. Now in Exercise 9.6, you will summarize what you have learned and then apply it. Exercise 9.7 asks you to create your own topographic map, and Exercise 9.8 shows how understanding these maps could help save your life.

EXERCISE 9.6   Rules of Contour Lines on Topographic Maps

Name: _____   Section: _____

Course: _____   Date: _____

In Exercise 9.3, you deduced for yourself the most important "rules" of contour lines, and you will use them in the next several chapters to study landforms produced by streams, glaciers, groundwater, wind, and shoreline currents. Complete the following sentences *using what you've just learned* to summarize the rules of contour lines.

(a) Two different contour lines cannot cross because _____.

(b) The spacing between contour lines on a map reveals the _____ of the ground surface. Closely spaced contour lines indicate _____ and widely spaced contour lines indicate _____.

(c) Concentric contour lines indicate a _____.

(d) Concentric *hachured* contour lines indicate a _____.

(e) Contour lines form a V when they cross a stream. The open part of the V faces the (upstream/downstream) direction.

Name: _____   **Section:** _____

Course: _____   **Date:** _____

Now that you understand the basic rules of contour lines, you can make your own contoured map from elevation data. The figure below shows elevation data for a coastal area. Using the figure below, construct a contour map showing the topography. Remember that nature has already drawn the first contour line: the coastline is, by definition, the 0-foot contour. You've already done something similar on the weather map, but topographic contours must follow the rules you have just learned. Use a contour interval of 20 feet. *Remember: Contour lines do not go straight across a stream—they form a V.*

Topographic contouring exercise.

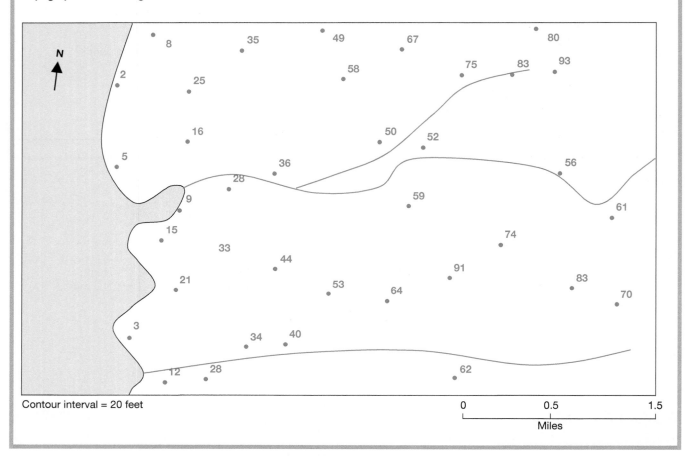

Contour interval = 20 feet

0   0.5   1.5
Miles

Name: _____   **Section:** _____

Course: _____   **Date:** _____

A small plane carrying you and a friend crashes near the northeast corner of an island at the spot indicated on the following map. The nearest human beings are a lighthouse keeper and his family living on the opposite side of the island, as shown on the map. Unfortunately, the plane's radio was destroyed during the crash, and your cell phones don't work. No one knows where you are, and the only way to save yourselves is to walk to the lighthouse.

(continued)

Name: _____   Section: _____
Course: _____   Date: _____

You and your friend were injured in the crash and can't climb hills higher than 75 feet or swim across rivers. You can only walk about 12 miles a day and carry only enough water to last 3 days. It gets worse: the rivers have crocodiles, there's a large area filled with quicksand, and there's a jungle filled with—yes—lions and tigers and bears. The good news is that you have a compass and a topographic map (on the next page) showing the hazards. You have figured out exactly where the plane crashed and know where you have to go. The map also shows a well where you can get drinking water—if you can get there in 3 days.

(a) With a pencil, protractor, and ruler, plan the shortest route from the crash site to the lighthouse, avoiding steep hills, rivers, quicksand, and hungry jungle carnivores. Record the direction (using the azimuth system) and distance of each leg of your trip in the table below.

(b) How many days will the trip take? _____

(c) Do you have to stop for water? If so, on what day do you to get to the well? _____

(d) How many days will it take to get from the well to the lighthouse? _____

(e) Where is the highest point on the island? _____ Give its elevation as precisely as you can. _____

(f) What is the elevation of the lowest point in Sinking Feeling Basin? _____

(g) Which is the steepest side of Deadman's Mountain? _____

Your route to safety on Survivor Island.

Leg #	Direction of leg (in azimuth degrees)	Length of leg (in miles)	Leg #	Direction of leg (in azimuth degrees)	Length of leg (in miles)
1			11		
2			12		
3			13		
4			14		
5			15		
6			16		
7			17		
8			18		
9			19		
10			20		
Total distance					

(h) Unfortunately, the plane didn't carry a life raft. If it had, what would have been the shortest route to sail or paddle from the crash site to the lighthouse? Give your answer with directions and distances for each leg on a separate piece of paper.

(continued)

Name: _____   Section: _____
Course: _____   Date: _____

Survivor Island.

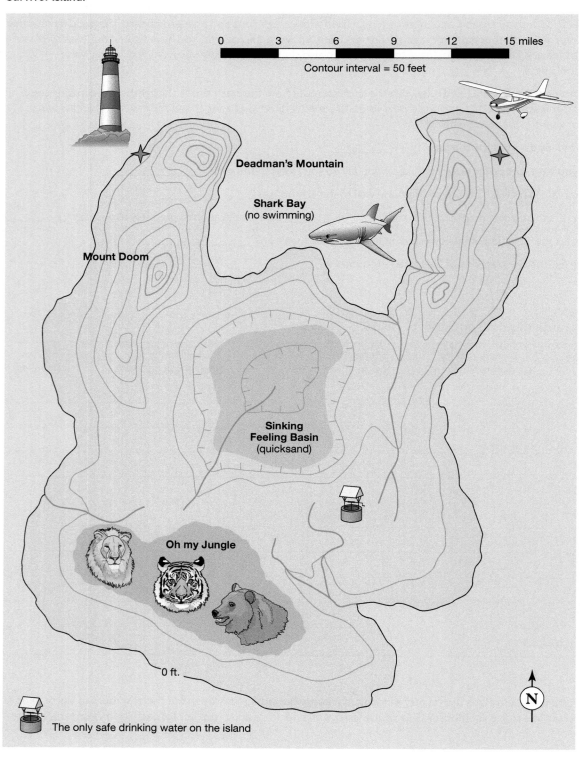

0   3   6   9   12   15 miles

Contour interval = 50 feet

Deadman's Mountain

Shark Bay
(no swimming)

Mount Doom

Sinking
Feeling Basin
(quicksand)

Oh my Jungle

0 ft.

N

The only safe drinking water on the island

9.5 Topographic Profiles

Topographic maps show a view of an area from above; however, in many cases, seeing a cross section is extremely helpful. The next two sections of this chapter show how to create a simple cross section and how to understand vertical exaggeration. Then Exercise 9.9 examines a situation where this knowledge might help you get a job (or a raise).

9.5.1 Constructing a Topographic Profile

One benefit of using a topographic map is that it is easy to construct an accurate **topographic profile**, a cross-section view of the topography. Freeware, such as MICRODEM, or other GIS software, could draw the profile for you, but it is important to understand just what a profile can and cannot do. This is best learned by constructing profiles by hand—a simple process outlined below.

STEP 1: Place a strip of paper along the line of profile (A–B) shown in **FIGURE 9.8**, and label the starting and finishing points.

STEP 2: Draw a short line where the strip of paper crosses contour lines, streams, roads, and so on, and label each mark with its elevation (**FIG. 9.9**). For clarity, index contour labels are shown here.

STEP 3: Create a profile paper. Set up a vertical scale using the graph paper at the end of this chapter or blank paper with a series of evenly spaced horizontal lines corresponding to the elevations represented by contour lines along the traverse. Label each line so its elevation is recognizable (right side of **FIG. 9.10**).

STEP 4: Place the strip of paper with the labeled lines at the bottom of the vertical scale, and use a ruler to transfer the elevations to their correct positions on the profile paper. Place a dot where each contour line marker intersects the corresponding elevation line in the profile (Fig. 9.10).

STEP 5: Connect the dots, using what you know about contour lines to estimate the elevations at the tops of hills and bottoms of stream valleys along the profile (Fig. 9.10).

FIGURE 9.8 **Map of the microwave tower project area. Scale = 1:62,500; contour interval = 50 feet**

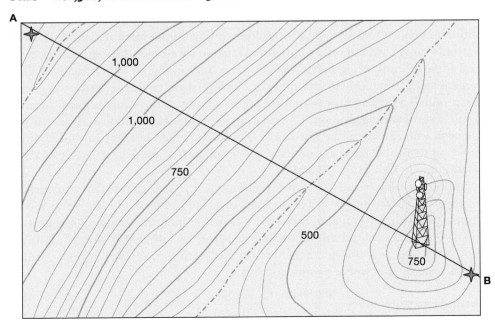

FIGURE 9.9 Constructing the profile.

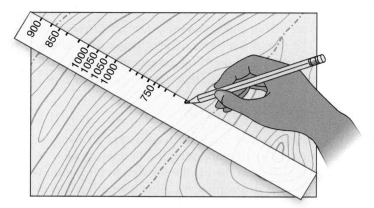

FIGURE 9.10 Completing the profile.

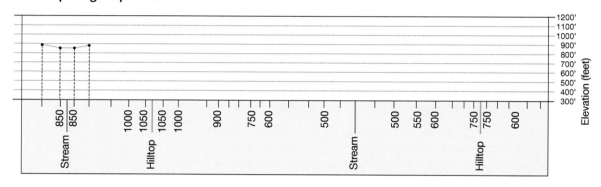

9.5.2 Vertical Exaggeration

Constructing a topographic profile is quick, even without a computer, and can yield important information that can't be obtained just by looking at a map. But care must be taken to make sure that the profile is a realistic view of the topography. It is possible to minimize a mountain so that it looks like an anthill or exaggerate an anthill to make it look like Mt. Everest, depending on the vertical scale you choose. A profile must have not only a horizontal scale to agree with the map but also a vertical scale to show topography. The elevation lines in Figure 9.10 actually define a vertical scale. When the horizontal (map) and vertical (profile) scales are the same, the profile is a perfect representation of topography. If the scales are different, the result is **vertical exaggeration**. Vertical exaggeration overemphasizes the vertical dimension with respect to the horizontal. This is illustrated by three profiles drawn at different vertical exaggerations across the same part of the Hanging Rock Canyon quadrangle in California (**FIG. 9.11**).

To find out how much the profile in Figure 9.10 exaggerates the topography, we need to know the vertical scale used in profiling. First, measure the vertical dimension with a ruler; this shows that 1 *vertical* inch on the profile represents nearly 900 feet of elevation, a proportional scale of 1:10,800 (900 ft × 12 in. per foot = 10,800 in.). To calculate vertical exaggeration, divide the map proportional scale by the profile proportional scale.

$$\textbf{Vertical exaggeration} = \frac{\text{Map scale}}{\text{Profile scale}} = \frac{62,500}{10,800} = 5.8\times$$

FIGURE 9.11 The effect of vertical exaggeration on topographic profiles.

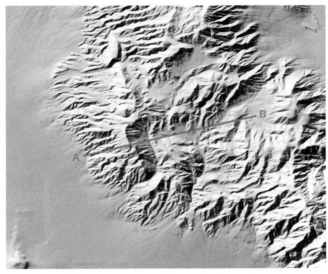

(a) DEM of the Hanging Rock Canyon quadrangle showing the line of profile.

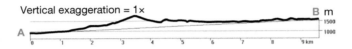

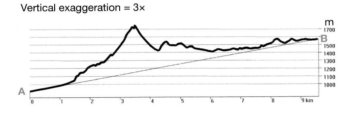

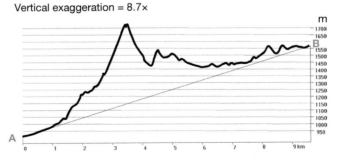

(b) Topographic profiles along the line A–B drawn with different vertical exaggerations. Note that the horizontal scale is the same in all three profiles; only the vertical scale chagnes.

Name: _____   Section: _____

Course: _____   Date: _____

A telecommunications company wants to place microwave relay towers in a new region to improve cell phone reception and plans to put a tower on the hilltop in the southeast corner of the map shown in Figure 9.8. Project managers are concerned that a prominent ridge might block the signal to areas to the northwest. It is not immediately obvious from the map if there will be a "dead zone." You have been hired as a consultant to answer this question. The best way to do so is to construct a topographic profile showing the hills and valleys.

(a) Construct a profile along the line indicated in Figure 9.8. The horizontal scale is set on Figure 9.8 but you must choose the vertical scale for the profile. *Do not use the same scale as the horizontal*; that is, one large box on the vertical scale will *not* represent the same distance as on the horizontal scale. (Use the graph paper at the end of the chapter to construct the profile.)

(b) What is the vertical exaggeration of your profile? This will depend on what you chose for the vertical scale in (a).

_____

(c) Now construct a profile (using the graph paper at the end of this chapter) along the same line with twice the vertical exaggeration.

? What Do You Think Now that you've got the profile, what advice do you give the telecommunications company? Is there a direct line of sight so there won't be a dead zone for customers in that valley? If there isn't, how high would the tower have to be to guarantee service to everyone in the area? Write a brief summary of your recommendations.

_____

_____

_____

_____

_____

Examine the map again. Are there other potential problem areas? If so, sketch on the figure other lines of profile that would need to be evaluated more fully and submit this updated figure as your work.

Topographic Map Symbols

BATHYMETRIC FEATURES

Area exposed at mean low tide; sounding datum line***	
Channel***	
Sunken rock***	

BOUNDARIES

National	
State or territorial	
County or equivalent	
Civil township or equivalent	
Incorporated city or equivalent	
Federally administered park, reservation, or monument (external)	
Federally administered park, reservation, or monument (internal)	
State forest, park, reservation, or monument and large county park	
Forest Service administrative area*	
Forest Service ranger district*	
National Forest System land status, Forest Service lands*	
National Forest System land status, non-Forest Service lands*	
Small park (county or city)	

BUILDINGS AND RELATED FEATURES

Building	
School; house of worship	
Athletic field	
Built-up area	
Forest headquarters*	
Ranger district office*	
Guard station or work center*	
Racetrack or raceway	
Airport, paved landing strip, runway, taxiway, or apron	
Unpaved landing strip	
Well (other than water), windmill, or wind generator	
Tanks	
Covered reservoir	
Gaging station	
Located or landmark object (feature as labeled)	
Boat ramp or boat access*	
Roadside park or rest area	
Picnic area	
Campground	
Winter recreation area*	
Cemetery	Cem

COASTAL FEATURES

Foreshore flat	Mud
Coral or rock reef	Reef
Rock, bare or awash; dangerous to navigation	
Group of rocks, bare or awash	
Exposed wreck	
Depth curve; sounding	18 23
Breakwater, pier, jetty, or wharf	
Seawall	
Oil or gas well; platform	

CONTOURS

Topographic

Index	6000
Approximate or indefinite	
Intermediate	
Approximate or indefinite	
Supplementary	
Depression	
Cut	
Fill	
Continental divide	

Bathymetric

Index***	
Intermediate***	
Index primary***	
Primary***	
Supplementary***	

CONTROL DATA AND MONUMENTS

Principal point**	3-20
U.S. mineral or location monument	USMM 438
River mileage marker	Mile 69

Boundary monument

Third-order or better elevation, with tablet	BM 9134 BM 277
Third-order or better elevation, recoverable mark, no tablet	5628
With number and elevation	67 4567

Horizontal control

Third-order or better, permanent mark	Neace Neace
With third-order or better elevation	BM 52 Pike BM393
With checked spot elevation	1012
Coincident with found section corner	Cactus Cactus
Unmonumented**	

Topographic Map Symbols

CONTROL DATA AND MONUMENTS – *continued*

Vertical control

Third-order or better elevation, with tablet	BM × 5280
Third-order or better elevation, recoverable mark, no tablet	× 528
Bench mark coincident with found section corner	BM + 5280
Spot elevation	× 7523

GLACIERS AND PERMANENT SNOWFIELDS

Contours and limits	
Formlines	
Glacial advance	
Glacial retreat	

LAND SURVEYS

Public land survey system

Range or Township line	
Location approximate	
Location doubtful	
Protracted	
Protracted (AK 1:63,360-scale)	
Range or Township labels	R1E T2N R3W T4S
Section line	
Location approximate	
Location doubtful	
Protracted	
Protracted (AK 1:63,360-scale)	
Section numbers	1 - 36 1 - 36
Found section corner	
Found closing corner	
Witness corner	WC
Meander corner	MC
Weak corner*	

Other land surveys

Range or Township line	
Section line	
Land grant, mining claim, donation land claim, or tract	
Land grant, homestead, mineral, or other special survey monument	
Fence or field lines	

MARINE SHORELINES

Shoreline	
Apparent (edge of vegetation)***	
Indefinite or unsurveyed	

MINES AND CAVES

Quarry or open-pit mine	×
Gravel, sand, clay, or borrow pit	×
Mine tunnel or cave entrance	
Mine shaft	
Prospect	X
Tailings	Tailings
Mine dump	
Former disposal site or mine	

PROJECTION AND GRIDS

Neatline	39°15′ 90°37′30″
Graticule tick	55′
Graticule intersection	
Datum shift tick	

State plane coordinate systems

Primary zone tick	640 000 FEET
Secondary zone tick	247 500 METERS
Tertiary zone tick	260 000 FEET
Quaternary zone tick	98 500 METERS
Quintary zone tick	320 000 FEET

Universal transverse mercator grid

UTM grid (full grid)	273
UTM grid ticks*	269

RAILROADS AND RELATED FEATURES

Standard gauge railroad, single track	
Standard gauge railroad, multiple track	
Narrow gauge railroad, single track	
Narrow gauge railroad, multiple track	
Railroad siding	
Railroad in highway Railroad in road Railroad in light-duty road*	
Railroad underpass; overpass	
Railroad bridge; drawbridge	
Railroad tunnel	
Railroad yard	
Railroad turntable; roundhouse	

RIVERS, LAKES, AND CANALS

Perennial stream	
Perennial river	
Intermittent stream	
Intermittent river	
Disappearing stream	
Falls, small	
Falls, large	
Rapids, small	
Rapids, large	
Masonry dam	
Dam with lock	
Dam carrying road	

Topographic Map Symbols

RIVERS, LAKES, AND CANALS – *continued*

Perennial lake/pond	
Intermittent lake/pond	
Dry lake/pond	
Narrow wash	
Wide wash	*Wash*
Canal, flume, or aqueduct with lock	
Elevated aqueduct, flume, or conduit	
Aqueduct tunnel	
Water well, geyser, fumarole, or mud pot	
Spring or seep	

ROADS AND RELATED FEATURES

Please note: Roads on Provisional-edition maps are not classified as primary, secondary, or light duty. These roads are all classified as improved roads and are symbolized the same as light-duty roads.

Primary highway	
Secondary highway	
Light-duty road	
Light-duty road, paved*	
Light-duty road, gravel*	
Light-duty road, dirt*	
Light-duty road, unspecified*	
Unimproved road	
Unimproved road*	
4WD road	
4WD road*	
Trail	
Highway or road with median strip	
Highway or road under construction	*Under Const*
Highway or road underpass; overpass	
Highway or road bridge; drawbridge	
Highway or road tunnel	
Road block, berm, or barrier*	
Gate on road*	
Trailhead*	

SUBMERGED AREAS AND BOGS

Marsh or swamp	
Submerged marsh or swamp	
Wooded marsh or swamp	
Submerged wooded marsh or swamp	
Land subject to inundation	*Max Pool 431*

SURFACE FEATURES

Levee	*Levee*
Sand or mud	*Sand*
Disturbed surface	
Gravel beach or glacial moraine	*Gravel*
Tailings pond	*Tailings Pond*

TRANSMISSION LINES AND PIPELINES

Power transmission line; pole; tower	
Telephone line	*Telephone*
Aboveground pipeline	
Underground pipeline	*Pipeline*

VEGETATION

Woodland	
Shrubland	
Orchard	
Vineyard	
Mangrove	*Mangrove*

* USGS–USDA Forest Service Single-Edition Quadrangle maps only.

In August 1993, the U.S. Geological Survey and the U.S. Department of Agriculture's Forest Service signed an Interagency Agreement to begin a single-edition joint mapping program. This agreement established the coordination for producing and maintaining single-edition primary series topographic maps for quadrangles containing National Forest System lands. The joint mapping program eliminates duplication of effort by the agencies and results in a more frequent revision cycle for quadrangles containing National Forests. Maps are revised on the basis of jointly developed standards and contain normal features mapped by the USGS, as well as additional features required for efficient management of National Forest System lands. Single-edition maps look slightly different but meet the content, accuracy, and quality criteria of other USGS products.

** Provisional-Edition maps only.

Provisional-edition maps were established to expedite completion of the remaining large-scale topographic quadrangles of the conterminous United States. They contain essentially the same level of information as the standard series maps. This series can be easily recognized by the title "Provisional Edition" in the lower right-hand corner.

*** Topographic Bathymetric maps only.

Topographic Map Information

For more information about topographic maps produced by the USGS, please call 1-888-ASK-USGS or visit us at http://ask.usgs.gov/.

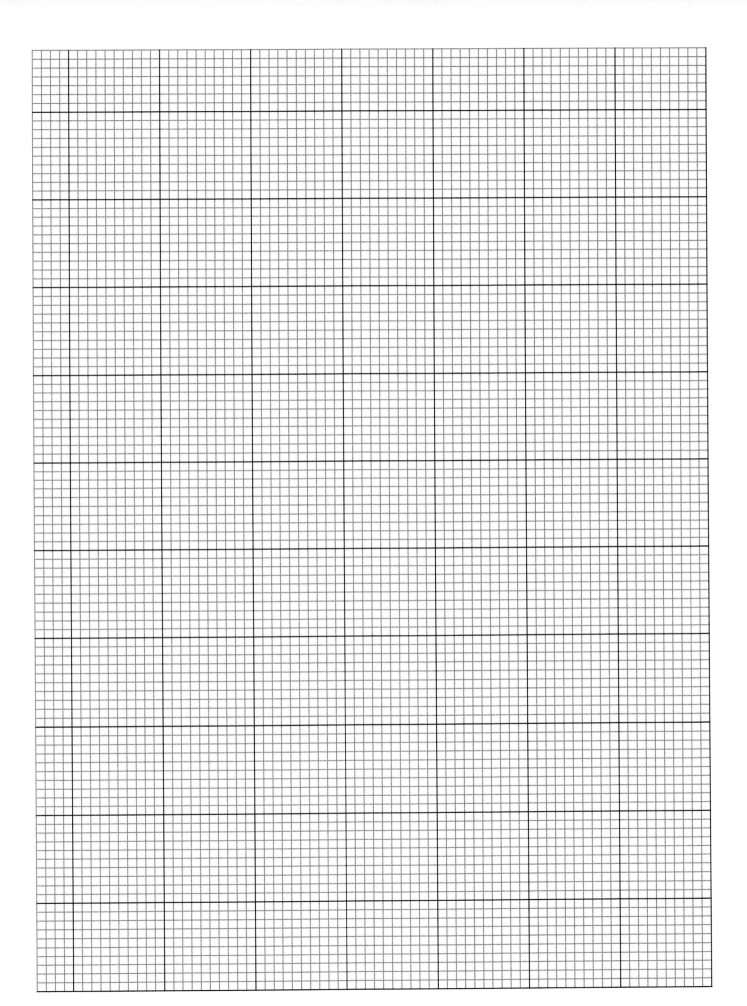

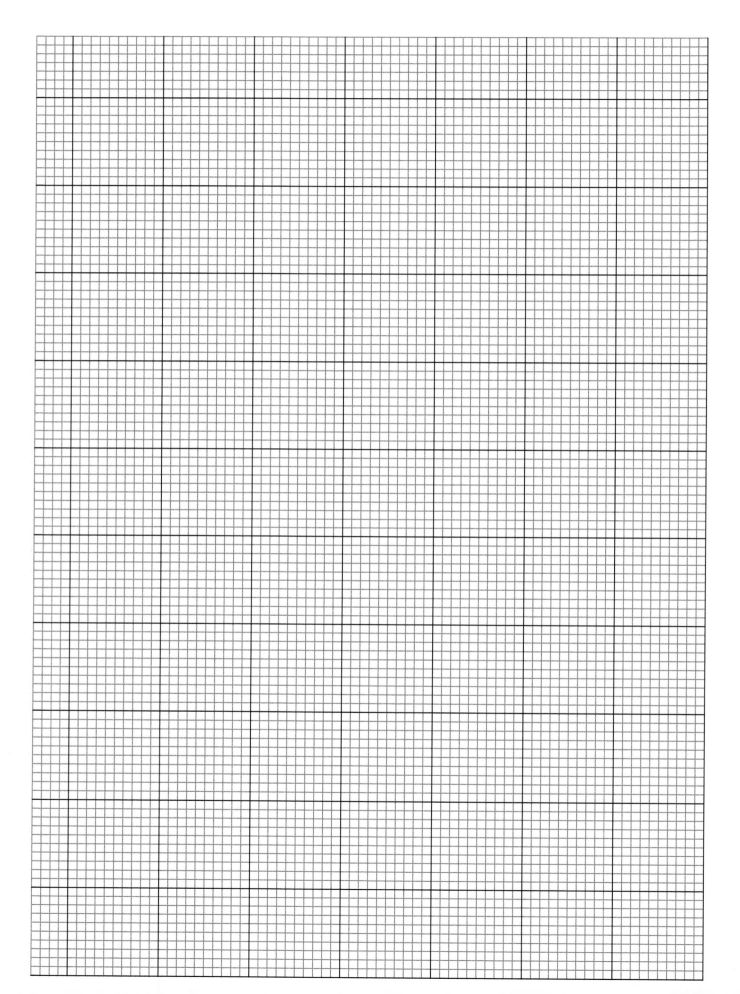

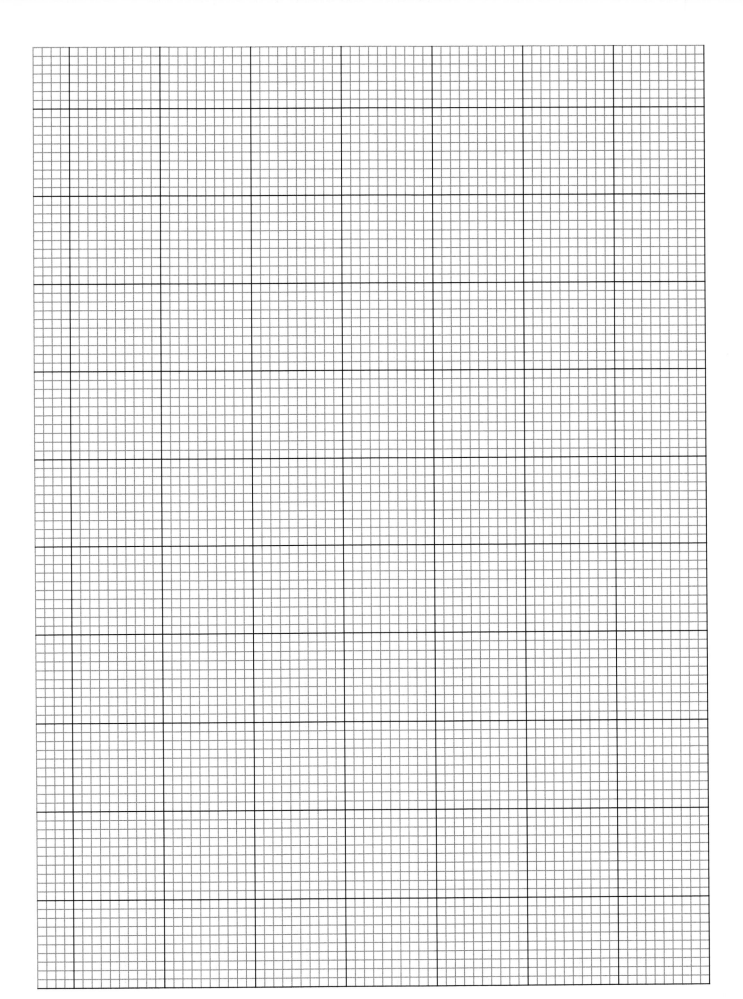

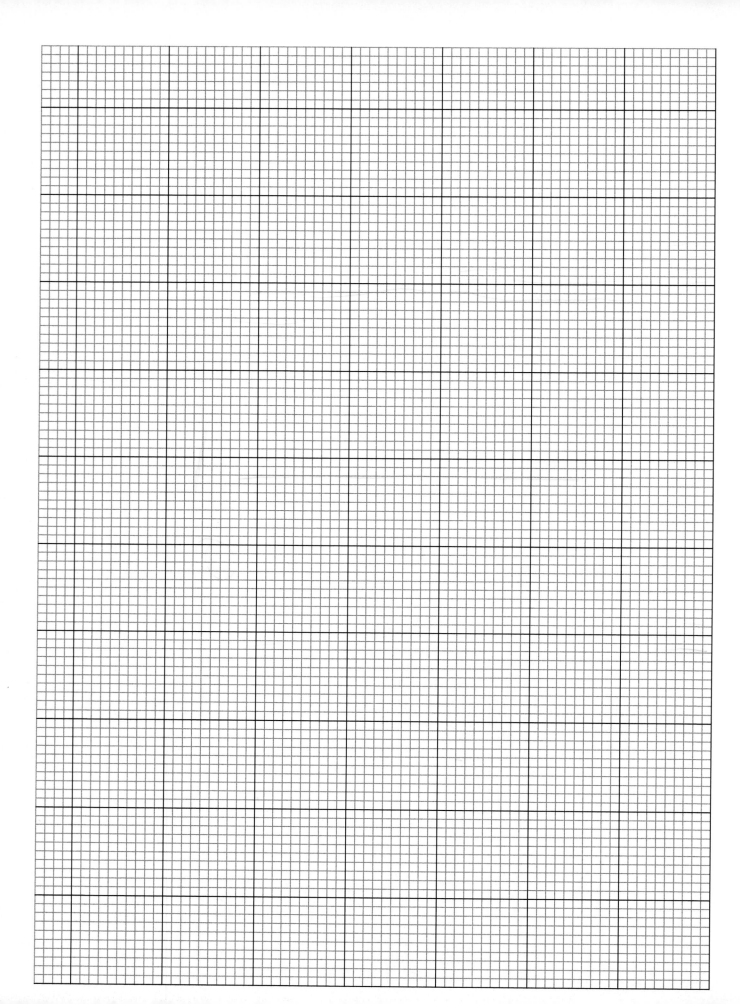

10

Landscapes Formed by Streams

Streams come in different sizes and shapes. They create different landscapes through erosion and by moving and depositing material.

LEARNING OBJECTIVES

- Learn how streams erode and deposit material
- Become familiar with landforms formed by stream erosion and deposition
- Interpret active and ancient stream processes from landscape features

MATERIALS NEEDED

- Thin string
- Ruler with divisions in tenths of an inch or millimeters
- Graph paper for constructing topographic profiles
- Colored pencils
- Magnifying glass or hand lens to read closely spaced contour lines

10.1 Introduction

Water flowing in a channel is called a **stream** whether it is as large as the Amazon River or as small as the smallest creek, run, rill, or brook. Streams are highly effective agents of erosion and may move more material after one storm in an arid region than wind does all year. This chapter explores why not all streams behave the same way and how streams can produce very different landscapes.

10.2 How Do Streams Work?

All streams operate according to a few simple principles regardless of their size.

- Water in streams flows downhill because of gravity.
- Streams normally flow in a well-defined channel, except during floods when the water overflows the channel and spills out across the surrounding land.
- The motion of water gives a stream kinetic energy, enabling it to do the geologic work of erosion and deposition. The amount of energy depends on the amount (mass) of water and its velocity (remember: kinetic energy = $\frac{1}{2}mv^2$), so big, fast-flowing streams erode more than small, slow-flowing streams.
- Its kinetic energy allows a stream to transport sediment, from the finest mud-sized grain to small boulders. These particles slide or roll on the bed of the stream, bounce along, or are carried in suspension within the water.
- The flow of water erodes unconsolidated sediment from the walls and bed of the channel, and the stream uses that sediment to abrade solid rock.
- Streams deposit sediment when they lose kinetic energy by slowing down (or evaporating). The heaviest particles are deposited first, then the smaller grains, as the energy wanes.

Now for a few geologic terms: A stream **channel** is the area within which the water is actually flowing. A stream **valley** is the region within which the stream has eroded the land. In some cases, the channel completely fills the bottom of the valley; in others, it is much narrower than the broad valley floor. Some valley walls are steep, others gentle.

Exercise 10.1 asks you to describe some differences in streams and Exercise 10.2 begins to look at factors that control stream activity. Streams are complex dynamic systems in which changes in one factor bring about changes in

---

EXERCISE 10.1	Differences between Streams

Name: _____ Section: _____

Course: _____ Date: _____

The basic principles of how streams work, as listed in Section 10.2, are the same for all streams, but the principles can be applied differently, resulting in streams that look very different from one another. In your own words, describe how the streams pictured in **FIGURE 10.1** differ.

_____

_____

_____

FIGURE 10.1 A tale of two streams.

(a) Yellowstone River in Wyoming.

(b) River Cuckmere, England.

others, affecting the way the stream looks and behaves. For example, changes in a stream's gradient—the steepness of a stream's channel—can completely change the nature of erosion and deposition, the width of the valley, and the degree to which the channel meanders (its sinuosity).

EXERCISE 10.2 Getting Familiar with Properties of Streams

Name: _____   Section: _____

Course: _____   Date: _____

The following questions ask you to compare the streams pictured in Figure 10.1.

(a) Which stream in Figure 10.1 has the wider channel? _____

(b) Which stream has the broader valley? _____

(c) Which stream has the most clearly developed valley walls? _____

(d) Describe the relationship between valley width and channel width for both streams.

_____

_____

_____

(e) Which stream has the straighter channel? _____
Which has a more *sinuous* (meandering) channel? _____

(f) Which stream appears to be flowing faster? _____ What evidence did
you use to determine this?

_____

_____

_____

(g) Which stream appears to be flowing more steeply downhill? _____ *Note:*
The steepness of a stream channel is called its *gradient* and is a major factor in stream behavior.

FIGURE 10.2 Longitudinal stream profile.

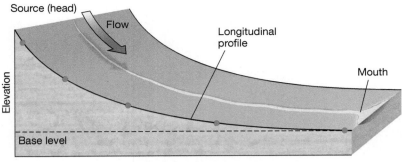

10.2.1 Stream Erosion: Downward or Sideways

A brief lesson in stream anatomy helps to explain stream erosion and deposition. A stream begins at its **headwaters** (or head), and the point at which it ends—by flowing into another stream, the ocean, or a topographic low—is called its **mouth**. The headwaters of the Mississippi River are in Lake Itasca in Minnesota, and its mouth is the Gulf of Mexico in Louisiana. The *longitudinal profile* of a stream from headwaters to mouth is generally a smooth, concave-up curve (**FIG. 10.2**). The gradient (steepness) may vary from a few inches to hundreds of feet of **vertical drop** per mile and is typically steeper at the head than at the mouth.

A stream can erode its channel only as low as the elevation at its mouth, because if it cut deeper it would have to flow uphill to get to the mouth. The elevation at the mouth thus controls erosion along the entire stream and is called the **base level**. Sea level is the ultimate base level for streams that flow into the ocean; base level for a *tributary* that flows into another stream is the elevation where the tributary joins the larger stream.

One difference between the Yellowstone River and the River Cuckmere is the straightness of their channels: the Yellowstone has a relatively straight channel, whereas the Cuckmere channel meanders across a wide valley floor. As noted earlier, the sinuosity of a stream measures how much it meanders, as shown in the following formula. Because sinuosity is a ratio of the two lengths, it has no units. An absolutely straight stream would have a sinuosity of 1.00 (if such a stream existed), whereas streams with many meanders have high values for sinuosity (**FIG. 10.3**).

$$\text{Sinuosity} = \frac{\text{Length of stream channel (meanders and all)}}{\text{Straight-line distance between the same points}}$$

FIGURE 10.3 Stream sinuosity. The straighter a stream, the lower its sinuosity; the more it meanders, the higher its sinuosity.

Low sinuosity (straight)

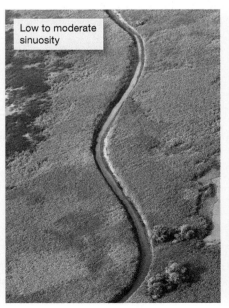

Low to moderate sinuosity

High sinuosity

Name: _____   Section: _____

Course: _____   Date: _____

In this exercise, you will use the maps in **FIGURES 10.4, 10.5,** and **10.6.** Approximate mile measurements to the nearest 1/10 of a mile.

(a) Compare the course of the Bighorn River between points A and B with that of its tributary between points C and D (Fig. 10.4). Fill in the table below.

	Bighorn River	Unnamed tributary
Channel length (~miles)		
Straight-line length (~miles)		
Sinuosity (no units) Channel length divided by straight-line length		
Highest elevation* (feet)		
Lowest elevation* (feet)		
Vertical drop Highest elevation minus lowest elevation (feet)		
Gradient* (feet per mile) Vertical drop divided by channel length		
*Streams aren't considerate; they don't begin and end on contour lines. Scan the entire stream looking for and estimating the highest and then the lowest point on each stream. Then calculate the vertical drop and gradient.		

(b) What is the apparent relationship between a stream's gradient and whether it has a straight or meandering channel?

_____

_____

_____

(c) Test this hypothesis on the Genesee River of New York (Fig. 10.5) and the Casino Lakes area of Idaho (Fig. 10.6). Complete the following table and describe how the Genesee River differs from the Idaho streams.

	Genesee River	Casino Lakes area	
		Stream A–B	Stream C–D
Valley shape (V-shaped or broad with flat bottom)			
Gradient (ft/mile)			
Valley width (miles)		Channel essentially fills valley floor.	
Channel width (feet)			
Valley width/channel width		~1.0	~1.0
Sinuosity Length of stream channel divided by straight-line distance between the same points			

(continued)

Figure 10.4 Part of the Bighorn River in Wyoming (Manderson and Orchard Bench 7.5' quadrangles).

Contour interval = 20 feet

Figure 10.5 The Genesee River south of Rochester, New York.

0   0.5   1 mile
0   0.5   1 km

Contour interval = 10 feet

A

GENESEE

RIVER

HUSTON   ROAD

719

BM
571

552

ROOTS   TAVERN   ROAD

704

748

Jaycox

NATIONS

Creek

Falls

Retsof

705

650

550

600

ROAD

700

690

RIVER   ROAD

817

BM Piffard
569

691

712

561

ROAD

700

CHANDLER   ROAD
BM
569

BM
559

63

RIVER

600

550

39

650

800

GENESEE

750

COUNTRY   CLUB

550

Hemp
Pond

BM
556

LIMA   ROAD

BM   570

Geneseo Airport

BIG   TREE   LANE

GENESEO

600

650

850

BM 756

BM
866

RIVER   ROAD

BM   561

700

900

937

LONG   POINT

550

800

B

Dewey Hill

Brook

ALT
20   39

63

390

Cuylerville

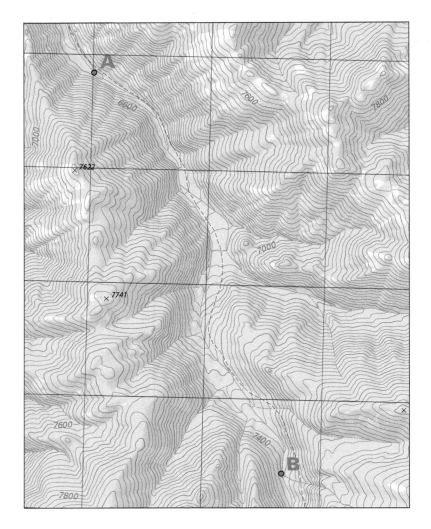

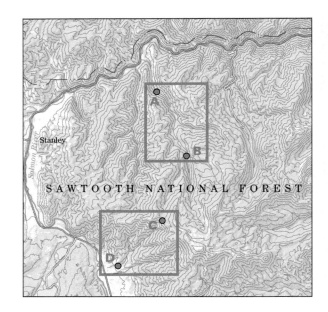

Figure 10.6 Casino Lakes, Idaho (7.5′ quadrangle).

0   0.5   1 mile

0   0.5   1 km

Contour interval = 40 feet

SAWTOOTH NATIONAL FOREST

Stanley

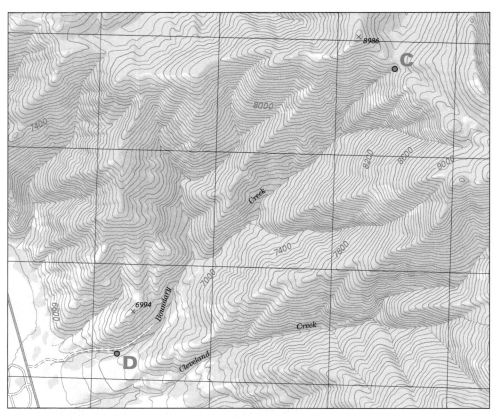

Name: _____   Section: _____

Course: _____   Date: _____

(d) Did these maps support your hypothesis about the relationship between meandering (sinuosity) and gradient? Explain.

_____

_____

_____

(e) What is the apparent relationship between sinuosity and the valley width/channel width ratio?

_____

_____

_____

(f) What is the apparent relationship between stream gradient and the shape of a stream valley?

_____

_____

_____

Now apply what you've learned to the photographs of the streams in Figures 10.1 and 10.3.

(g) Which probably has the steeper gradient–the River Cuckmere or the Yellowstone River? Explain your reasoning.

_____

_____

_____

(h) Which of the streams in Figure 10.3 probably has the steepest gradient? The gentlest gradient? Explain your reasoning.

_____

_____

_____

10.3 Stream Valley Types and Features

The Yellowstone River and River Cuckmere in Figure 10.1 illustrate the two most common types of stream valleys: steep-walled, V-shaped valleys whose bottoms are occupied fully by the channel, and broad, flat-bottomed valleys much wider than the channel and within which the stream meanders widely between the valley walls. **FIGURE 10.7** shows how these valleys form.

FIGURE 10.7 Evolution of stream valleys.

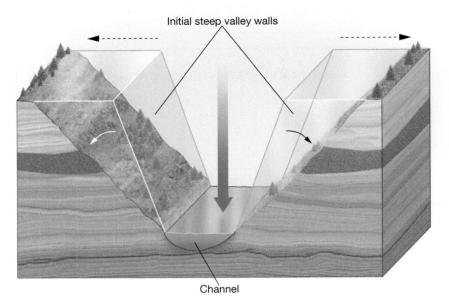

Initial steep valley walls

Channel

(a) Steep, V-shaped valley: Vertical erosion carves the channel and valley downward vertically (large blue arrow), producing steep valley walls. Mass wasting (slump, creep, landslides, and rock falls) reduces slope steepness to the angle of repose (curved arrows) and widens the top of the valley (dashed arrows).

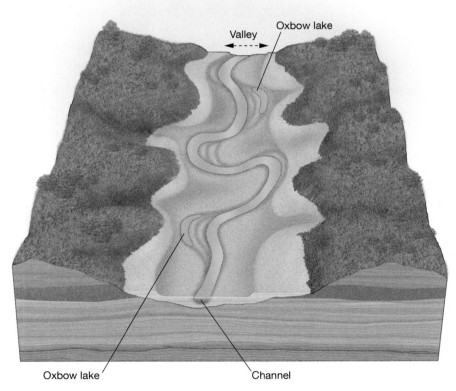

Valley   Oxbow lake

Oxbow lake   Channel

(b) Broad, flat-bottomed valley: As the stream meanders, it widens the valley (arrows). Mass wasting gentles the slope of the valley walls as in part (a). Oxbows mark the position of former meanders.

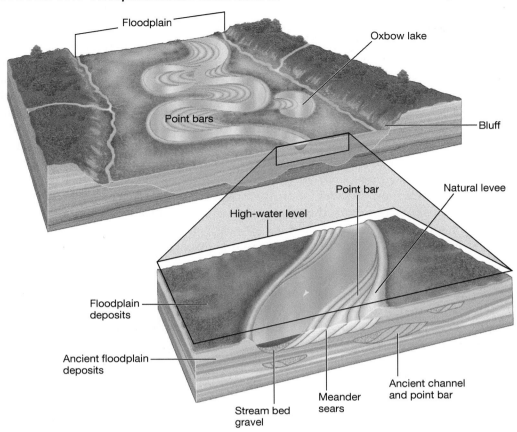

FIGURE 10.8 **Floodplain and associated features.**

When water is added to a stream in a V-shaped valley, the channel expands and fills more of the valley. When more water enters a stream with a broad, flat valley and a relatively small channel, it spills out of the channel onto the broad valley floor in a **flood**. Sediment carried by the floodwater is deposited on the **floodplain**, and other depositional and erosional features can be recognized easily on topographic maps or photographs (**FIG. 10.8**).

10.3.1 Features of Floodplains

Natural levees are ridges of sediment that outline the channel, and they form when a stream overflows its banks and deposits its coarsest sediment next to the channel. Several generations of natural levees are visible in Figure 10.8, showing how the meanders changed position with time. **Point bars** form when water on the inside of a meander loop slows down, causing sediment to be deposited. At the same time, erosion occurs on the outside of the meander loop because water there moves faster. The result is that meanders migrate with time, moving outward (toward their convex side) and downstream. Sometimes a stream cuts off a meander and straightens itself. The levees that formerly flanked the meanders help outline the former position of the river, leaving **meander scars**. Meander scars that have filled with water are called **oxbow lakes**.

10.4 Changes in Streams over Time

Streams erode *vertically* by leveling the longitudinal profile to the elevation of the mouth. Streams also erode *laterally*, broadening their valleys by meandering. Most streams erode both laterally and vertically at the same time, but the balance between vertical and lateral erosion commonly changes as the stream evolves.

Headwaters of a high-gradient stream are much higher than its mouth, and stream energy is used largely in vertical erosion, lowering channel elevation all along its profile. Over time, the gradient lessens as erosion lowers the headwater area. The stream still has enough energy to alter the landscape and uses some of that energy to erode laterally. The valley then widens by a combination of mass wasting and meandering. Even when headwaters are lowered to nearly the same elevation as the mouth, a stream still has energy for geologic work; but because it cannot cut vertically below its base level, most energy at this stage must be used for lateral erosion.

Initially, a stream meanders within narrow valley walls; but with time it erodes those walls farther and farther, eventually carving a very wide valley. As its gradient decreases, a stream redistributes sediment that it had deposited, moving it back and forth across the floodplain.

Although most streams follow this sequence of progressively lowering their gradients and therefore their erosional behavior, not all do so. Some streams have very gentle gradients and meander widely from the moment they begin. Streams on the Atlantic and Gulf coastal plains are good examples of this kind of behavior.

EXERCISE 10.4 **Interpreting Stream Behavior**

Name: _____   Section: _____

Course: _____   Date: _____

FIGURES 10.9a–c on the following pages show three meandering streams, each of which balances energy use differently between vertical and lateral erosion.

(a) From their valley width/channel width ratios alone, which stream would you expect to have the steepest gradient? The gentlest gradient? Explain your reasoning. (You don't have to calculate these; but if it helps, feel free to do so.)

_____

_____

_____

(b) Which stream do you think is doing the most vertical erosion? The least? Explain.

_____

_____

_____

(c) For each of the three maps, describe features that indicate former positions of the river channels. Do all three maps show this information? If not, explain why.

_____

_____

_____

(d) Label one example of the following stream erosional and depositional features on Figure 10.9a: valley; channel; meander; point bar; oxbow lake; meander scar.

(e) Indicate on Figure 10.9c where the velocity of the Arkansas River is the greatest and where it is the least.

FIGURE 10.9 (a) The St. Francis River in Arkansas and Mississippi.

Contour interval = 50 feet

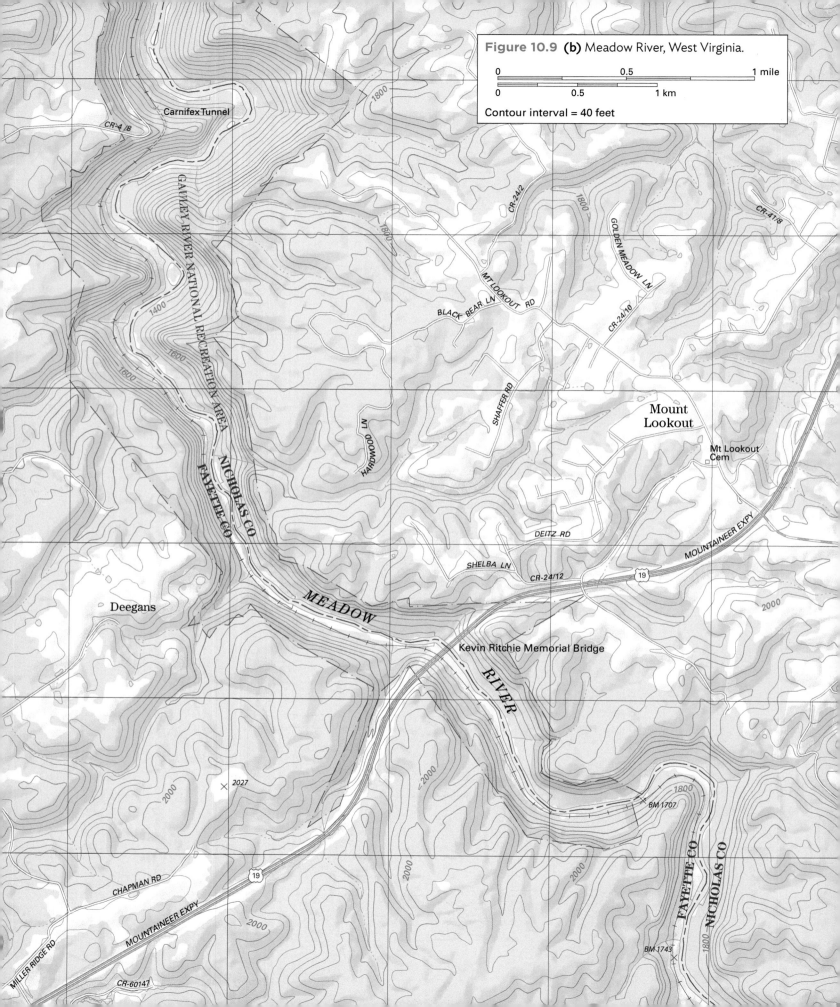

Figure 10.9 (b) Meadow River, West Virginia.

Contour interval = 40 feet

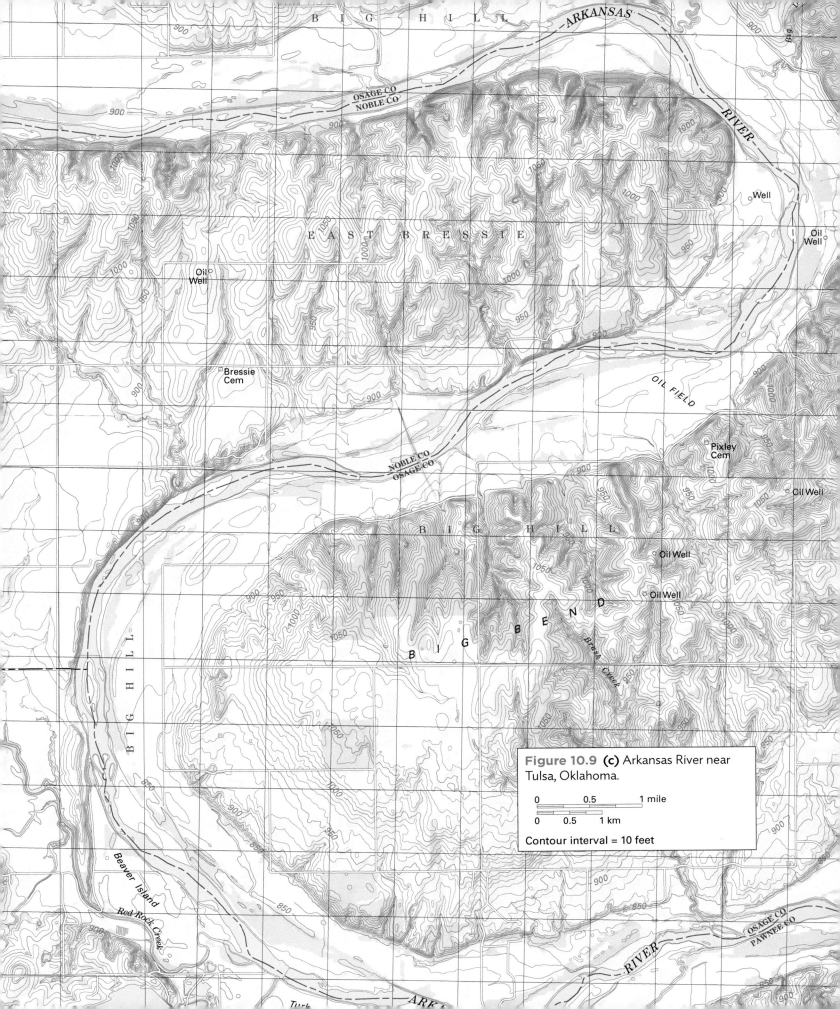

Figure 10.9 (c) Arkansas River near Tulsa, Oklahoma.

0   0.5   1 mile

0   0.5   1 km

Contour interval = 10 feet

10.5 Stream Networks

Streams are particularly effective agents of erosion because they form networks that cover much of Earth's surface. Rain falling on an area runs off into tiny channels that carry water into bigger streams and eventually into large rivers. Each stream—from tiniest to largest—expands headward over time as water washes into its channel, increasing the amount of land affected by stream erosion. Understanding the geometric patterns of stream networks and the way they affect the areas they drain is the key to understanding how to prevent or remedy stream pollution, soil erosion, and flood damage.

10.5.1 Drainage Basins

The area drained by a stream is its **drainage basin**, which is separated from adjacent drainage basins by highlands called **drainage divides**. The drainage basin of a small tributary may cover a few square miles, but that of the master stream may be hundreds of thousands of square miles. **FIGURE 10.10** shows the six major drainage basins of North America. Five deliver water to an ocean (Pacific, Arctic, Hudson Bay/Atlantic, Gulf of Mexico/Atlantic), but the Great Basin is bounded by mountains and there is no exit for the water.

FIGURE 10.10 Major drainage basins of North America.

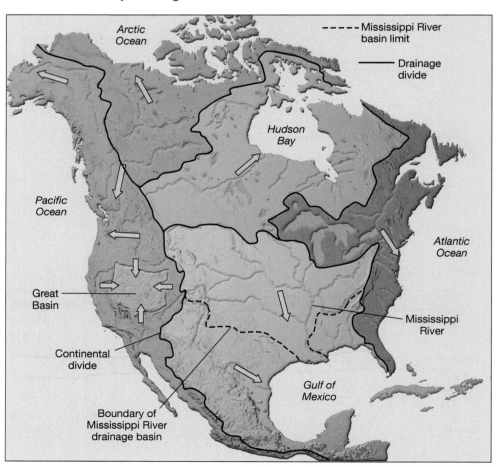

The yellow arrows show the dominant flow direction—note that some of these drain *northward*. The Mississippi drainage basin is the largest and drains much of the interior of the United States. The *continental divide* separates streams that flow into the Atlantic Ocean from those that flow to the Pacific. The Appalachian Mountains are the divide separating the Gulf of Mexico and direct Atlantic Ocean drainage; the Rocky Mountains separate Gulf of Mexico and Pacific drainage. A favorite tourist stop in Alberta, Canada, is a *triple* divide that separates waters flowing north to the Arctic Ocean, west to the Pacific, and south to the Gulf of Mexico.

10.5.2 Drainage Patterns

Master and tributary streams in a network typically form recognizable patterns (FIG. 10.11). **Dendritic** patterns (from the Greek *dendros*, for veins in a leaf), develop where surface materials are equally resistant to erosion. This may mean horizontal sedimentary or volcanic rocks; loose, unconsolidated sediment; or igneous and metamorphic areas where most rocks erode at the same rate. **Trellis** patterns form where ridges of resistant rock alternate with valleys underlain by weaker material. **Rectangular** patterns indicate zones of weakness (faults, fractures) perpendicular to one another. In **radial** patterns, streams flow either outward (**centrifugal**) from a high point (e.g., a volcano) or inward (**centripetal**) toward the center of a large basin. **Annular** drainage patterns occur where there are concentric rings of alternating resistant and weak rocks—typically found in structures called domes and basins. Parallel drainage patterns occur on a uniform slope when several streams with parallel courses develop simultaneously.

FIGURE 10.11 **Common drainage patterns.**

Dendritic   Trellis   Parallel

Radial: centrifugal   Radial: centripetal   Annular   Rectangular

Name: _____   Section: _____

Course: _____   Date: _____

FIGURE 10.12 is a map showing several tributaries on the north and south sides of the Missouri River near Jefferson City, Missouri. One large tributary, the Osage River, joins the Missouri from the south, near the eastern margin of the map, but most of the tributaries on the north are much smaller.

(a) With a colored pencil, trace one of the tributary creeks feeding *directly* into the Missouri from the north. With the same pencil, trace tributaries that flow directly into this creek, and then the tributaries of these smaller streams. Remember the "rule of V" as you trace the smaller streams to their headwaters.

(b) With a different color, trace an adjacent tributary of the Missouri and its tributaries. Repeat for more streams and their tributaries on the north side of the Missouri River, using a different color for each stream.

(c) You have just outlined most of the drainage on the north side of the Missouri. Now, with again a different colored pencil, trace the divides that separate the individual drainage basins for each master stream. This should be easy because you've already identified streams in each drainage basin with a different color.

Note that some divides are defined sharply by narrow ridges, but others are more difficult to locate within broad upland areas where most of the headwaters are located.

(d) Local residents are worried that a recent toxic spill at an electrical substation (asterisk in Fig. 10.12) will work its way into the drainage system. Based on your drainage basin analysis, shade in areas that might be affected. Be conservative: if there is any doubt, err on the side of including areas rather than excluding them.

Name: _____   Section: _____

Course: _____   Date: _____

(a) What drainage pattern is associated with the Mississippi River drainage basin in Figure 10.10? What does that tell you about the materials that underlie the central part of the United States?

_____

_____

_____

(b) What drainage patterns are associated with the areas shown in Figures 10.12 and 10.17? What do these patterns indicate about the rocks underlying those areas?

_____

_____

_____

_____

_____

_____

_____

_____

_____

_____

Figure 10.12 Drainage divides of the Missouri River near Jefferson City, Missouri.

Contour interval = 65 feet

10.6 Changes in Stream-Carved Landscapes with Time

Just as a single stream or entire drainage network changes over time, so too do **fluvial** (stream-created) *landscapes*. Consider a large block of land uplifted to form a plateau. Several things will change with time: the highest elevation, the number of streams, the stream gradients, and the amount of flat land relative to the amount of land that is part of valley walls. These changes reflect the different ways in which stream energy is used as the landscape is eroded closer to base level. **FIGURE 10.13** summarizes these idealized changes. In the real world, things rarely remain constant long enough for this cycle to reach its end: sea level may rise or fall due to glaciation or tectonic activity, the land may be uplifted tectonically, and so on. Nevertheless, the stages in Figure 10.13 are typical of landscapes produced by stream erosion and can be recognized on maps and other images.

FIGURE 10.13 Idealized stages in the evolution of a stream-carved landscape.

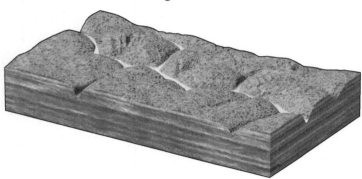

Stage 1: A fluvial landscape is uplifted, raising stream channels above base level.
- Few streams, but with relatively steep gradients.
- Broad, generally flat divides between streams.
- Channels are relatively straight.
- Relief is low to modest (not much elevation difference between divides and channels).

Stage 2: Main streams cut channels downward, and tributaries form drainage networks.
- Numerous tributaries develop with moderate gradients, dissecting most of the area.
- Stream divides are narrow and sharp; most of the area is in slope, with little flat ground.
- Main streams and some tributaries meander moderately.
- Relief is high, and little if any land is at the original uplifted elevation.

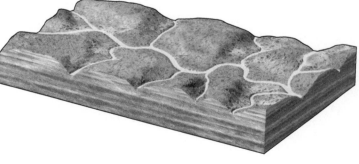

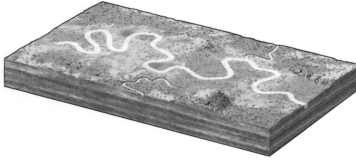

Stage 3: Stream erosion has lowered land surface close to base level.
- Few streams, as in Stage 1, but with gentle gradients.
- Stream divides are broad and flat; relief is low.
- Streams meander broadly.

Name: _____ **Section:** _____

Course: _____ **Date:** _____

(a) Examine the topographic maps of **FIGURES 10.14**, **10.15**, and **10.16**. Fill in the following table comparing aspects of the three areas.

	Southeast Texas (Fig. 10.14)	Colorado Plateau (Fig. 10.15)	Appalachian Plateau (Fig. 10.16)
Approximate relief: elevation difference between highest and lowest points			
Number of streams (few, intermediate, most)			
Estimated amount of land area that is valley slopes as a percentage			
Estimated stream gradients			
Stream divides: broadly rounded, angular, can't see divides			
Stage of stream dissection (Stage 1, 2, or 3)			

(b) With this practice, look at the fluvial landscapes in Figures 10.1a, 10.6, and 10.9a and suggest which stages of erosion each map represents.

_____

_____

_____

_____

_____

_____

_____

_____

_____

_____

_____

Figure 10.14 Stream dissection in southeast Texas (Fred, Spurger, Magnolia Springs, and Potato Patch Lake quadrangles).

Contour interval = 10 feet

0   1   2 km

0   1   2 miles

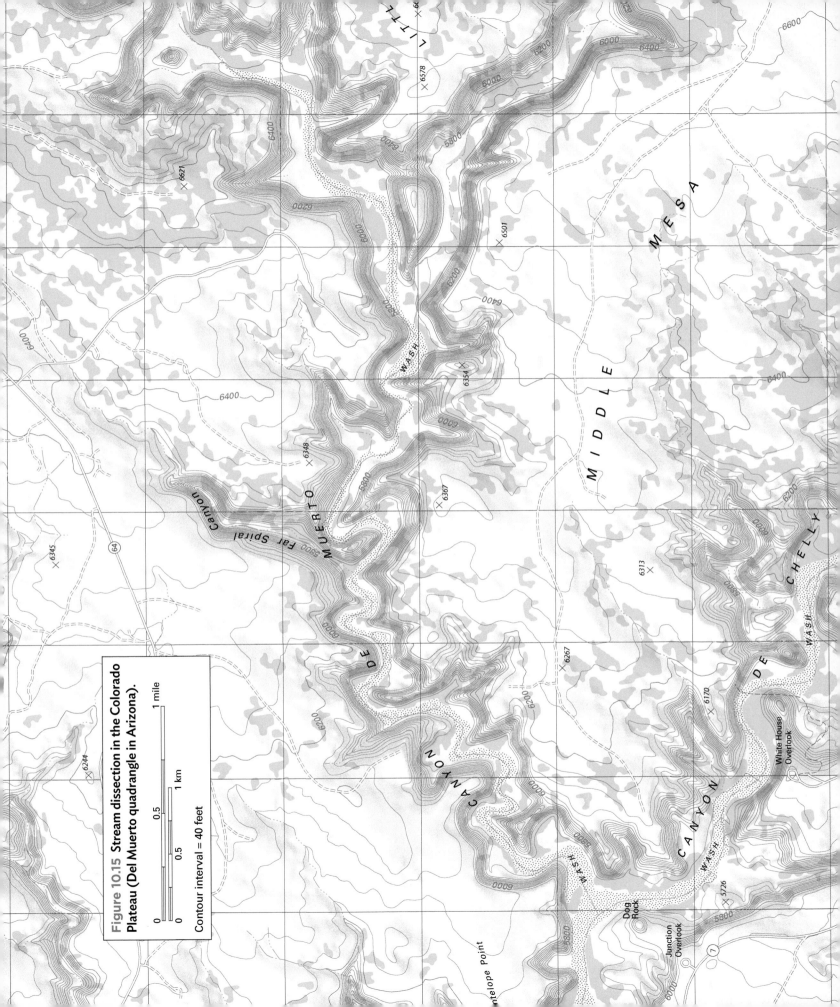

Figure 10.15 Stream dissection in the Colorado Plateau (Del Muerto quadrangle in Arizona).

Contour interval = 40 feet

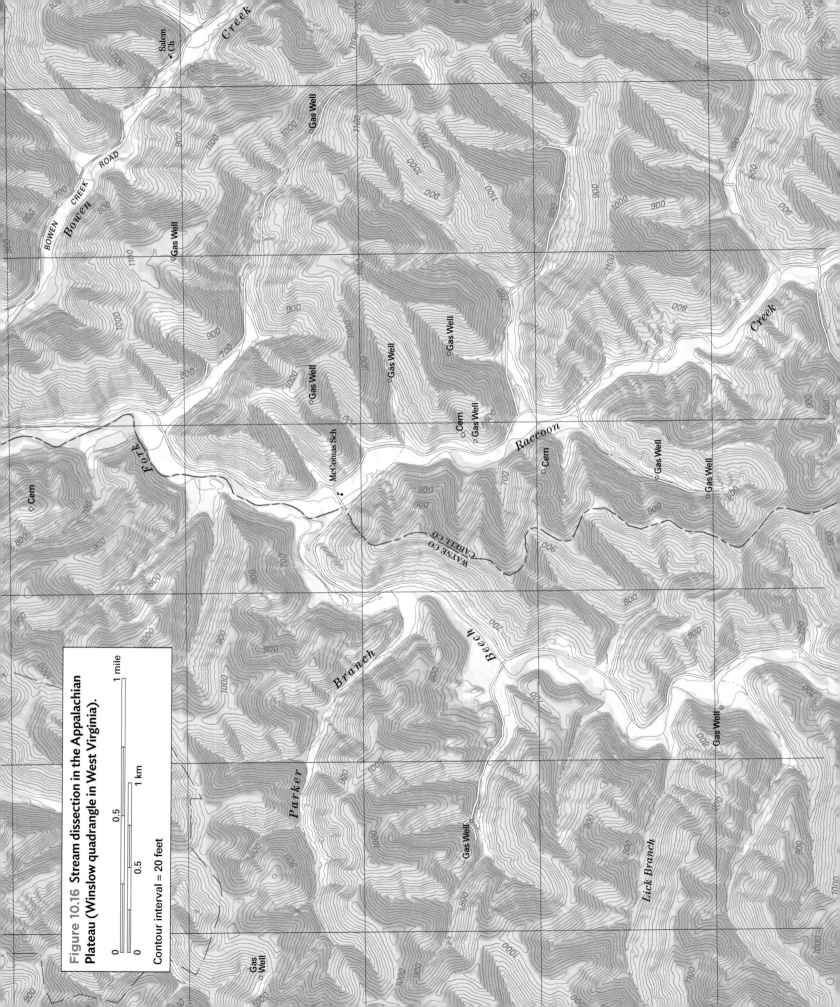

Figure 10.16 Stream dissection in the Appalachian Plateau (Winslow quadrangle in West Virginia).

Contour interval = 20 feet

10.7 When Streams Don't Seem to Follow the Rules

Most stream erosion and deposition follow the principles you just deduced, but there are some notable exceptions. Actually, these streams aren't violating any rules; they are following them to the letter, but their situations are more complex than the basic ones we have examined.

Consider, for example, the Susquehanna River as it flows across the Pennsylvania landscape shown in **FIGURE 10.17**. This area is part of the Valley and Ridge Province of the Appalachian Mountains and is characterized by elongate ridges and valleys made of resistant and nonresistant rocks, respectively. Streams are the dominant agent of erosion in the area. Also look at the Green River, illustrated in **FIGURE 10.18**, where meanders are incised in bedrock. In the following two exercises, you will deduce and suggest what the origins of these two rivers may have been.

EXERCISE 10.8   **Deducing the History of the Susquehanna River**

Name: _____   Section: _____

Course: _____   Date: _____

(a) Figure 10.17 shows a part of the Valley and Ridge Province in Pennsylvania. What is unusual about the relationship between the Susquehanna and Juniata rivers and the valley-and-ridge topography?

_____

_____

_____

Most of the small streams flow in the elongate valleys; but the Susquehanna and its tributary, the Juniata River, cut across the ridges at nearly right angles. It is tempting to think that the big streams had enough energy to cut through the ridges while the small ones couldn't, but this is not the case. The answer lies in a multistage history of which only the last phase is visible today.

(b) Why do most of the smaller streams flow in the elongate valleys?

_____

_____

_____

(c) Suggest as many hypotheses as you can to explain why the two larger rivers cut across the valley-and-ridge topography. *Hint*: How might the landscape have been different at an earlier time?

_____

_____

_____

_____

_____

_____

Rivers with enough energy to cut through the ridges should certainly have been able simply to meander around them, but the Susquehanna and Juniata rivers didn't take the easy way out. It's almost as if they didn't even know the ridges and valleys were there.

(continued)

Name: _____   Section: _____

Course: _____   Date: _____

(d) With that clue, suggest a series of events that explains the behavior of the Susquehanna and Juniata rivers. *Hint:* This type of stream is called a *superposed* stream.

_____

_____

_____

_____

FIGURE 10.17 The Susquehanna River cutting across the Appalachian Valley and Ridge Province in Pennsylvania.

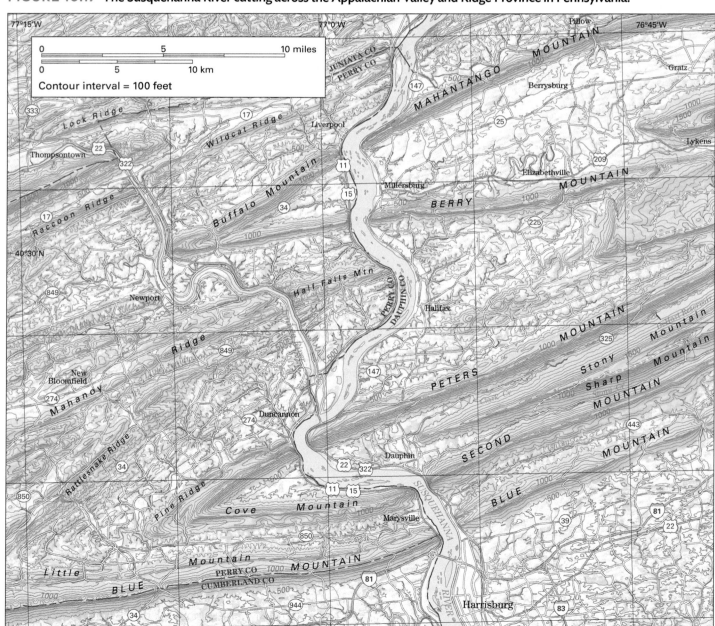

Name: _____ **Section:** _____

Course: _____ **Date:** _____

The Green River is in the Colorado Plateau, an area where meanders of many rivers cut deeply (are *incised*) into the bedrock (**FIG. 10.18**). The most famous is the Colorado River itself, particularly where it flows through the Grand Canyon. This behavior is totally unlike that of the meandering streams encountered earlier in this chapter. The Green River seems to violate rules of stream behavior; but, as with the Susquehanna, it is following them perfectly. Some geologic detective work will let you figure out the difference.

(a) Describe the path of the Green River as shown in Figure 10.18.

_____

_____

_____

(b) What is the sinuosity of the Green River? _____

(c) When a river meanders with such sinuosity, how is it using most of its energy—in lateral or vertical erosion?

_____

_____

(d) What evidence is there that the Green River is eroding laterally?

_____

_____

_____

(e) What evidence is there that the Green River is eroding vertically?

_____

_____

_____

(f) What is the probability that the Green River will straighten its path by cutting through the walls of the Bowknot Bend? Explain.

_____

_____

_____

(g) The Green River flows into the Colorado, which flows into the Gulf of Southern California. How far above base level is the river in this area? Is this what you expect for a meandering stream? Explain.

_____

_____

_____

(h) Suggest an origin for the incised meanders. (Don't forget possible effects of tectonic activity.)

_____

_____

_____

Figure 10.18 **Incised meanders of the Green River in southern Utah.**

Contour interval = 40 feet

10.8 When There's Too Much Water: Floods

A flood occurs when more water enters a stream than its channel can hold. Many floods are seasonal, caused by heavy spring rains or melting of thick winter snow. Others, called **flash floods**, follow storms that can deliver a foot or more of rain in a few hours. FIGURE 10.19 is a map compiled by the Federal Emergency Management Agency (FEMA) showing the estimated flood potential in the United States, based on the number of square miles that would be inundated. It might appear that states lightly shaded in Figure 10.19 would have little flood damage, but that would be an incorrect reading of the map because two of the worst river floods in U.S. history occurred in Rapid City, South Dakota, and Johnstown, Pennsylvania. Indeed, these two cities have been flooded many times. The *area* of potential flooding may not be as large as in some other states, but the *conditions* for flooding may occur frequently. South Dakota's Rapid Creek has flooded more than 30 times since the late 1800s, including a disastrous flash flood on June 9, 1972, triggered by 15 inches of rain in 6 hours. The creek overflowed or destroyed several dams, ruined more than 1,300 homes and 5,000 cars, and killed more than 200 people in Rapid City (FIG. 10.20).

FIGURE 10.19 **Flood risk in the United States.**

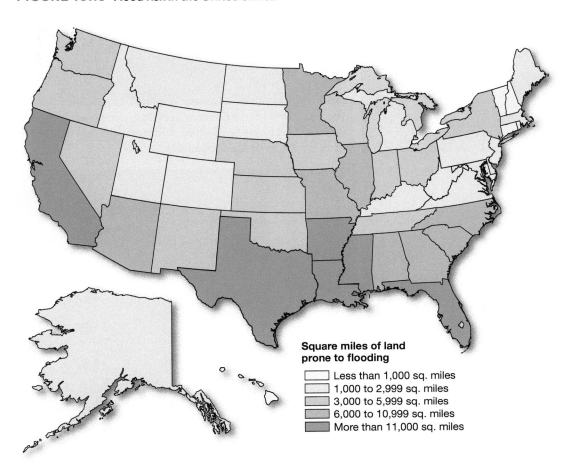

Square miles of land prone to flooding

- Less than 1,000 sq. miles
- 1,000 to 2,999 sq. miles
- 3,000 to 5,999 sq. miles
- 6,000 to 10,999 sq. miles
- More than 11,000 sq. miles

FIGURE 10.20 **Effects of the June 9, 1972, flood in Rapid City, South Dakota.**

(a) Rapid Creek has a narrow floodplain where it follows through Dark Canyon, 1 mile upstream of Rapid City. Floodwaters filled the entire floodplain. Concrete slabs (arrows) are all that is left of the homes built in the floodplain.

(b) The spillway of the Canyon Creek Dam (arrow) was clogged by debris carried by the floodwater, causing water to flow over the dam, which then failed completely.

(c) Not the usual lineup of cars for gasoline.

(d) This railroad trestle was washed away, along with highway bridges, slowing relief efforts.

Name: _____   **Section:** _____

Course: _____   **Date:** _____

Streams shown on maps earlier in the chapter are all subject to flooding, but the potential problems for cities along their banks are not the same. In the following questions, you will use the maps from this chapter to estimate problems caused by potential floods.

(a) Refer to Figures 10.9a, b, and c. For which of these would a flood 20-feet higher than the current stream channels cause damage to human structures and roads? In each case, describe what would happen.

_____

_____

_____

_____

(b) Describe the effect of a flash flood that raised the level of the Bighorn River (Fig. 10.4) 20 feet above its banks. Estimate and describe the affected areas.

_____

_____

_____

_____

(c) Would the Geneseo airport on the east bank of the Genesee River (Fig. 10.5) have to be evacuated if water rose 20 feet? Explain.

_____

_____

_____

(d) Compare the map of the Missouri River with a recent satellite image of the same area in **FIGURE 10.21**, below. What kind of information does the map add? What information does the satellite image add?

_____

_____

_____

(e) What things have been built in the Missouri River floodplain that could be destroyed or made unusable in a flood where the river rose 20 feet? How would the loss of these affect relief efforts?

_____

_____

_____

_____

FIGURE 10.21 Aerial image of the floodplain of the Missouri River near Jefferson City, Missouri.

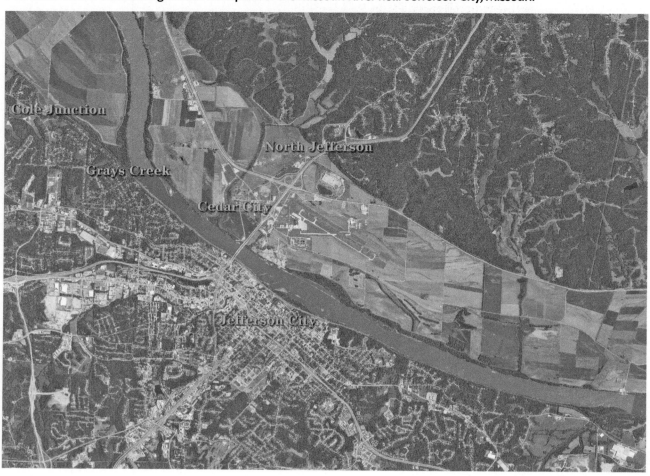

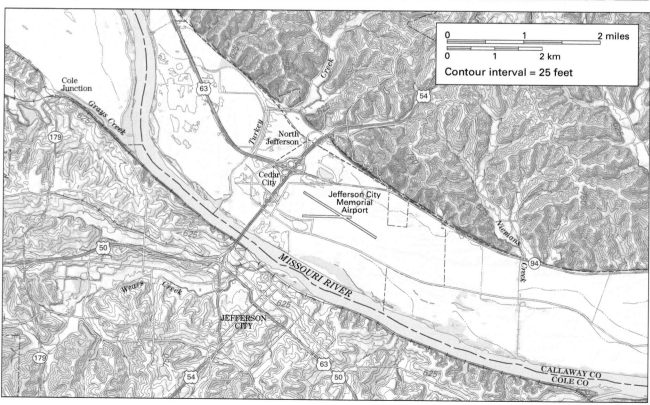

Name: _____   **Section:** _____

Course: _____   **Date:** _____

It may be surprising to learn that normal stream behavior can have "interesting" effects on international relationships. For example, consider the boundary between the United States and Mexico in the vicinity of Brownsville, TX, and Matamoros, Coahuila State, Mexico. The boundary is the center of the Rio Grande River, clearly a meandering stream with significant sinuosity.

   You have seen earlier in this chapter that the channels of meandering streams change over time.

(a) How do you think the Rio Grande River might change its course over the next 50-100 years?

_____

_____

(b) Indicate on the map places where these changes might cause parts of the U.S. to become part of Mexico, and parts of Mexico to become part of the U.S.

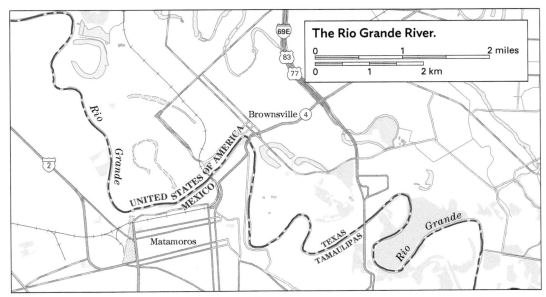

(continued)

Name: _____   Section: _____
Course: _____   Date: _____

? **What Do You Think** You have been hired by the U.S.-Mexico International Boundary and Water Commission (IBWC) as a consultant for issues related to the Rio Grande River. Based on your answers to (a) and (b) above, what do you recommend the IBWC do to anticipate changes in the river channel? Should the river remain the international border? How can property rights be preserved? How will business and agriculture be affected? Use a separate piece of paper for your report.

11

Glacial Landscapes

These jagged mountains are typical of features carved by glaciers, which are powerful and aggressive agents of erosion.

LEARNING OBJECTIVES

- Learn how glaciers erode and deposit material
- Become familiar with landforms carved and deposited by glaciers
- Distinguish glaciated landscapes from those formed by other agents of erosion
- Recognize the effect of climate change on glacial activity

MATERIALS NEEDED

- Colored pencils
- Ruler and paper for constructing topographic profiles

11.1 Introduction

Glaciers are broad sheets or narrow "rivers" of ice that last year round and flow slowly across the land. They hold more than 21,000 times the amount of water in all streams and account for about 75% of Earth's freshwater. Today, huge continental glaciers cover most of one continent (Antarctica) and nearly all of Greenland. Smaller glaciers carve valleys on the slopes of high mountains, causing a characteristically sharp, jagged topography (**FIG. 11.1**). Distinctive landforms show that continental glaciers were even more widespread during the Pleistocene Epoch—the so-called ice ages—covering much of northern Europe and North America.

Today, glaciers are receding at rates unprecedented in human history. As they shrink, the balance of the water cycle changes among glaciers, oceans, streams, and groundwater, altering our water supply and modifying ecologic systems worldwide. Glaciated landscapes contain clues to past climate changes and help us understand what is happening now and plan for the future. We know, for example, that continental glaciers advanced and retreated several times during the Pleistocene, and we know how fast those changes were. This enables us to measure human impact on the rates of these processes.

FIGURE 11.1 The Grand Teton Mountains in Wyoming display jagged topography typical of areas affected by alpine glaciers.

11.1.1 Types of Glaciers

Some small glaciers form on mountains and flow downhill, carrying out their erosion and depositional work in the valleys they carve. These are called, appropriately, **mountain**, **valley**, or **alpine glaciers** (**FIG. 11.2a**). Although they flow in valleys like streams, mountain glaciers work differently and form distinctly different landscapes. The Antarctic and Greenland **continental ice sheets** described earlier are not confined to valleys. They flow across the countryside, as masses of ice thousands of feet thick, dwarfing hills and burying all but the tallest peaks (**FIG. 11.2b**). The North American and European ice sheets did the same during the Pleistocene. Exercise 11.1 compares the ways in which glaciers and water do their geologic work.

FIGURE 11.2 Mountain and continental glaciers.

(a) The Crowfoot Glacier in Banff National Park, Canada.

(b) Continental ice sheet, Antarctica.

EXERCISE 11.1 | **Comparison of Glaciers and Streams**

Name: _____   Section: _____

Course: _____   Date: _____

Glaciers behave differently from stream water—even glaciers that occupy valleys. Based on what you know about streams and have learned about glaciers in lecture and from your geology text, complete the following table.

		Streams	Glaciers
State of matter		Liquid	
Composition		H_2O	
Areal distribution		In channels with tributaries flowing into larger streams	
Rate of flow		Fast or slow, depending on gradient	
Erodes by . . .		1. Abrasion using sediment load 2. Dissolving soluble minerals, rocks	
Maximum depth to which erosion can occur		Base level: sea level for streams that flow into the ocean; master stream for tributaries	
Deposits when . . .		Stream loses kinetic energy either by slowing down or evaporating	
Type(s) of sediment	Maximum clast size range	Small boulders to mud	
	Sorting	Generally well sorted	
	Clast shape	Moderately to well rounded, depending on distance transported	

11.1.2 How Glaciers Create Landforms

Glaciers erode destructional landforms and deposit constructional landforms. A glacier can act as a bulldozer, scraping the regolith from an area and plowing it ahead. When it encounters bedrock, a glacier uses its sediment like grit in sandpaper to abrade the rock and carve unique landforms. Glacial erosion occurs wherever ice is flowing, whether the glacier front is advancing or retreating.

FIGURE 11.3 **Till and outwash.**

(a) Till with characteristic poor sorting (small boulders through sand, silt, and mud) and angular rock fragments.

(b) Layers of outwash. Each layer is very well sorted; most contain well-rounded, sand-sized grains and some show cross bedding. Note the coarser, pebbly layer (arrow) resulting from an increase in meltwater discharge.

Depositional landforms are equally distinctive—some are ridges tens or hundreds of miles long, and others are broad blankets of sediment. All form when the ice in which the sediment is carried melts, generally when the glacier front is retreating. Some sediment, called **till**, is deposited directly from melting ice; but some is carried away by meltwater and is called **outwash** (or *glaciofluviatile* [glacial + stream] *sediment*). Till and outwash particles differ in size, sorting, and shape (**FIG. 11.3**) because of the different properties of the water and ice that deposited them.

11.2 Landscapes Produced by Continental Glaciation

Landscapes formed by continental glaciation differ from those formed by streams in every imaginable way: the shapes of hills and valleys are different, and both continental and mountain glaciers produce unique landforms not found in fluvial landscapes. **FIGURE 11.4** shows an area affected by continental glaciation for comparison with fluvial landscapes, and Exercise 11.2 explores the differences more fully.

Continental glaciers scour the ground unevenly as they flow, producing an irregular topography filled with isolated basins that often become lakes when the ice melts. Many of these post-Pleistocene lakes are still not incorporated into normal networks of streams and tributaries, even though the ice melted thousands of years ago. Glaciers also deposit material unevenly, clogging old streams and choking new ones with more sediment than they can carry. *Poorly integrated drainage, with many swampy areas, is thus characteristic of recently glaciated areas.* In addition, continental glaciers carve bedrock into characteristic streamlined shapes that indicate the direction the ice flowed.

FIGURE 11.4 Comparison of valleys carved by glaciers and streams.

(a) Glacial landscape: an unnamed valley in Glacier National Park, Montana.

(b) Fluvial landscape: Yellowstone River valley in Wyoming.

EXERCISE 11.2	Comparison of Landscapes Formed by Glaciers and Streams

Name: _____   Section: _____

Course: _____   Date: _____

(a) What difference do you notice in the shape of the valleys pictured in Figure 11.4a and b? In particular, compare the overall shape of the valleys pictured and the characteristics of each valley's base.

_____

_____

(continued)

Name: _____   Section: _____

Course: _____   Date: _____

(b) Suggest a reason for the difference in valley shape. *Hint:* Use a colored pencil to fill in the portion of both valleys in which active erosion occurred. (We will return to this issue below.)

_____

_____

(c) Now compare the extensively glaciated area (below) with the photographs, maps, and digital elevation models of fluvial landscapes (in Chapter 10). Describe the differences without worrying about technical terms for the glacial features. *Consider:* Is there a well-developed stream network?

_____

_____

_____

Aerial view of part of the Canadian Shield after extensive continental glaciation.

11.2.1 Erosional Landscapes

When a continental glacier passes through an area, it carves the bedrock into characteristic shapes called *sculptured bedrock*. The DEM in Exercise 11.3 shows the topography of an area of sculptured bedrock eroded by continental glaciers in southern New York State. The hills are underlain by gneisses that were resistant to erosion and the valleys by marbles and schists that were more susceptible to glacial erosion.

11.2.2 Depositional Landscapes

Landscapes formed by continental glaciers contain several depositional landforms. Those composed of till deposited directly from the melting ice are called **moraines** or **drumlins**; those made of outwash carried by meltwater streams include **outwash plains** and **eskers**.

Moraines: Moraines form when melting ice drops the boulders, cobbles, sand, silt, and mud that it has been carrying. Some moraines are irregular ridges; others are broad carpets pockmarked by numerous pits separated by isolated hills. The type of moraine—ridge or carpet—depends on whether the front (**terminus**) of the glacier is *retreating* (i.e., the ice is melting faster than it is being replaced) or *stagnating* (i.e., the terminus is in a state of dynamic equilibrium in which new ice is replenishing what is melting so that the position of the terminus doesn't change).

Till deposited from a retreating glacier forms an irregular carpet of debris called a **ground moraine** that may be hundreds of feet thick. Large blocks of ice are isolated as a glacier retreats, and some may be buried by outwash or till. When a block melts, the sediment subsides and forms a depression in the ground moraine called a **kettle hole**. For this reason, the irregular surface of a ground moraine is often referred to as "knob and kettle" topography.

The terminus of a stagnating glacier may remain in the same place for hundreds or thousands of years, and the till piles up in a ridge that outlines the terminus. This ridge is called a **terminal moraine** and shows the maximum extent of the glacier.

FIGURE 11.5 shows depositional features created at the termini of continental glaciers. Use these models to identify landforms in the following DEMs and maps. A glossary of glacial depositional and erosional features can be found in **TABLE 11.1** (on page 293) at the end of this chapter.

Drumlins: Drumlins are streamlined, asymmetric hills made of till that occur in four large swarms in Nova Scotia, southern Ontario/New York State, southeastern New England (most famously Bunker Hill), and the Midwestern states of Wisconsin, Iowa, and Minnesota. Their origin is debated, but their shapes clearly reflect the dynamics of ice flowing through till, and their shape and orientation are good indicators of glacial direction.

Outwash Plains: A melting continental glacier generates an enormous amount of water, which flows away from the terminus carrying all the clasts the water is powerful enough to carry, usually sand, gravel, and small boulders. Meltwater streams round and sort this sediment and eventually deposit it beyond the terminal moraine as a generally flat outwash plain (Fig. 11.5).

Eskers: Tunnels may form at the base of a continental glacier and act as pipelines to carry meltwater even as the glacier ice surrounding the tunnels continues to flow. Well-sorted sediment carried by these subglacial streams may build up to form ridges 50 feet high or more. These ridges, called *eskers*, trace the courses of meandering subglacial streams and stand above the unsorted till of the adjacent ground moraine (Fig. 11.5).

FIGURE 11.5 Formation of depositional landforms after continental glaciation.

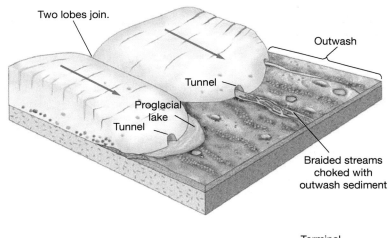

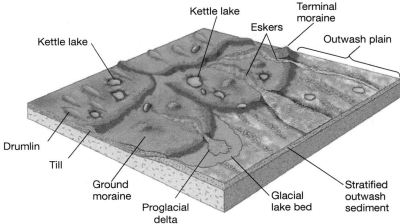

Name: _____   **Section:** _____

Course: _____   **Date:** _____

(a) Describe the topography in the DEM below in your own words, paying particular attention to the shapes of the bedrock hills. When features in a glacial landscape display a strong alignment as in **FIGURE 11.6**, geologists say that the landscape has a "topographic grain" related to the direction in which ice moved. Describe the topographic grain in the map and the direction the ice probably moved.

_____

_____

_____

Look again at the topographic map (Fig. 11.6) for more detail.

(b) Construct a topographic profile, using the graph paper provided at the end of this chapter, from St. John's Church to Lake Rippowam (Line A–B) on the topographic map in Figure 11.6, using 10 × vertical exaggeration. Are the hills symmetrical or asymmetrical?

_____

(c) Are the steep and gentle slopes distributed randomly or systematically? Describe the distribution.

_____

_____

(d) What is controlling the steep slopes of these asymmetric hills?

_____

_____

(e) Based on your description and observations, draw arrows on the DEM below and on Figure 11.6 showing the direction in which the glacier moved across the map area. Explain your reasoning.

_____

_____

_____

_____

_____

_____

_____

_____

_____

(f) Fill in the blanks to complete the following sentence that describes how sculptured rock records glacial movement: The direction of ice flow indicated by sculptured rock is *from* the _____ side of the hill *toward* the_____ side.

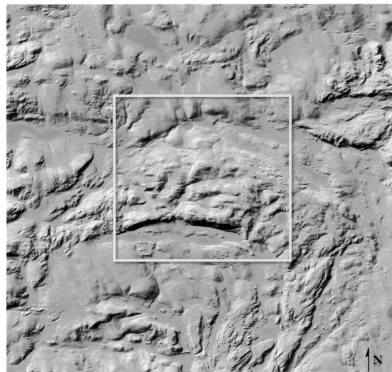

DEM of the Peach Lake quadrangle in New York (area in rectangle shown in Fig. 11.6).

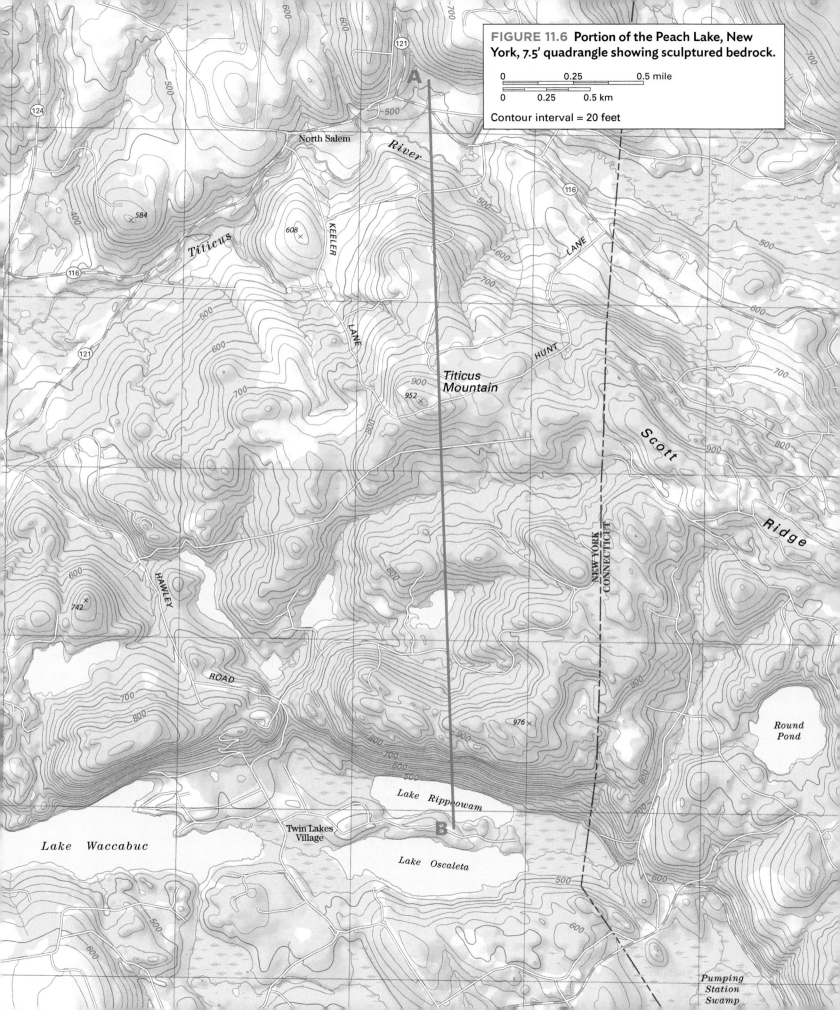

FIGURE 11.6 Portion of the Peach Lake, New York, 7.5′ quadrangle showing sculptured bedrock.

Contour interval = 20 feet

Name: _____   Section: _____

Course: _____   Date: _____

FIGURE 11.7 is a DEM of southeastern New York and southwestern Connecticut showing the irregular glacial topography at the southernmost extent of glaciers in the United States. Long Island is composed largely of till and outwash deposited during the advance and retreat of *two* continental ice sheets. This makes the area more complex than that in Figure 11.5, but landforms that formed at the two glacial termini are recognizable.

(a) Outline or otherwise identify the two terminal moraines, the southernmost outwash plain, and the outwash and glacial deltas deposited between the terminal moraines during a time of glacial retreat. Use different colors to separate features deposited during the two different glacial advances.

(b) Which of the two moraines is younger? Explain your reasoning.

_____

_____

(continued)

FIGURE 11.7 DEM of Long Island, New York, showing two terminal moraines.

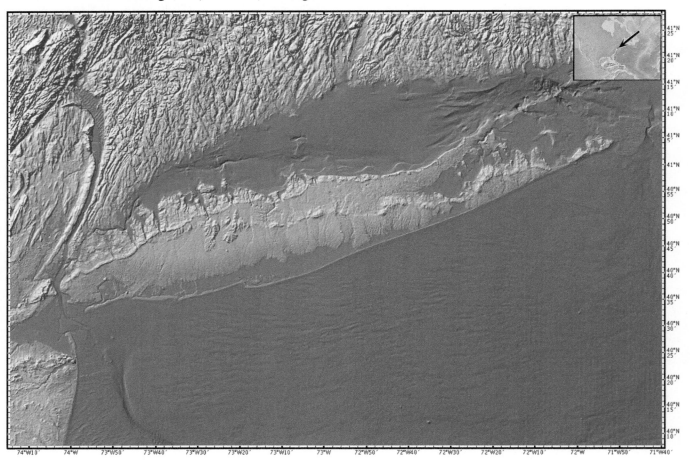

Name: _____ Section: _____

Course: _____ Date: _____

FIGURE 11.8 is a map of the Arnott moraine in Wisconsin, formed approximately 14,000 years ago. It shows the classic irregular "knob and kettle" topography of terminal moraines. Compare this morainal area with stream-produced landscapes as seen in the maps from Chapter 10.

(a) Are the stream networks and divides as well developed and clearly defined in this area?

_____

(b) Suggest an explanation for the absence of a well-integrated drainage system.

_____

_____

_____

(c) Suggest an explanation for the numerous swampy areas.

_____

_____

_____

(d) Compare the sizes and shapes of the hills (knobs) in this area with those in the fluvial landscapes.

_____

_____

(e) Suggest an origin for the several small lakes in the moraine. What will be their eventual fate?

_____

_____

_____

(f) There are several gravel pits in the area. Why might gravel be more easily and profitably mined from these specific areas than from others?

_____

_____

(g) What difficulties do you think might be involved in farming in ground moraine?

_____

_____

FIGURE 11.8 Glaciated terrain in Wisconsin (Amherst and Blaine 7.5' quadrangles).

Contour interval = 20 feet

Name: _____   **Section:** _____

Course: _____   **Date:** _____

Not all ridges in glaciated areas are moraines (some may be eskers) and not all hills are knobs in a ground moraine (some may be drumlins). Eskers are quite long. **FIGURE 11.9** shows part of an esker that extends for more than 40 miles. You can't tell from a map or DEM that eskers are made of outwash rather than till, but they are much narrower than terminal moraines and lack the kettle holes associated with melting ice. The asymmetric shape of drumlins makes them easy to recognize.

(continued)

FIGURE 11.9 Part of the Passadumkeag, Maine, 7.5′ quadrangle showing the Enfield Horseback esker (the DEM inset shows the esker in its regional setting).

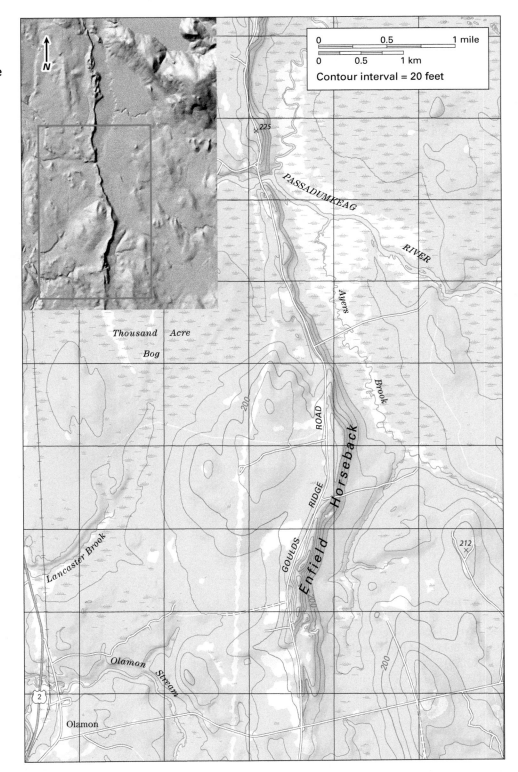

Name: _____   **Section:** _____

Course: _____   **Date:** _____

Examine Figures 11.7 and 11.8, and suggest other ways to differentiate eskers from moraines.

(a) Now examine the DEM (below) and the map of the Weedsport, New York area (**FIG. 11.10**) and describe the topography.

_____

_____

_____

_____

(b) Sketch the long axis of one of the hills on the DEM. What is its orientation? _____ Do the same for the others. What was the direction of glacial movement in this area? _____ Show this with a large arrow on the map.

(c) Sketch or construct profiles of the five hills numbered on Figure 11.10. Are the hills symmetrical or asymmetrical? Describe the distribution of their steep and gentle slopes.

_____

_____

_____

(d) The direction of ice flow indicated by a drumlin is *from* the _____ side of the drumlin *toward* the _____ side.

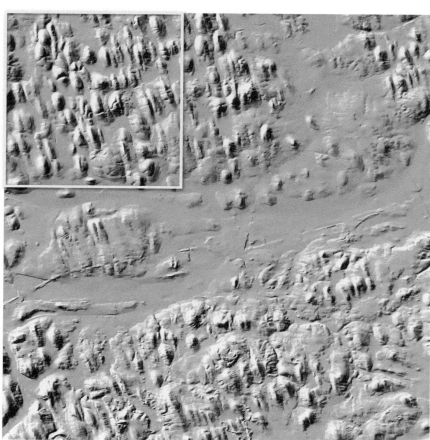

DEM of the Weedsport, New York 7.5′ quadrangle, showing the southern end of the Ontario/New York State drumlin field (area in rectangle shown in Fig. 11.10).

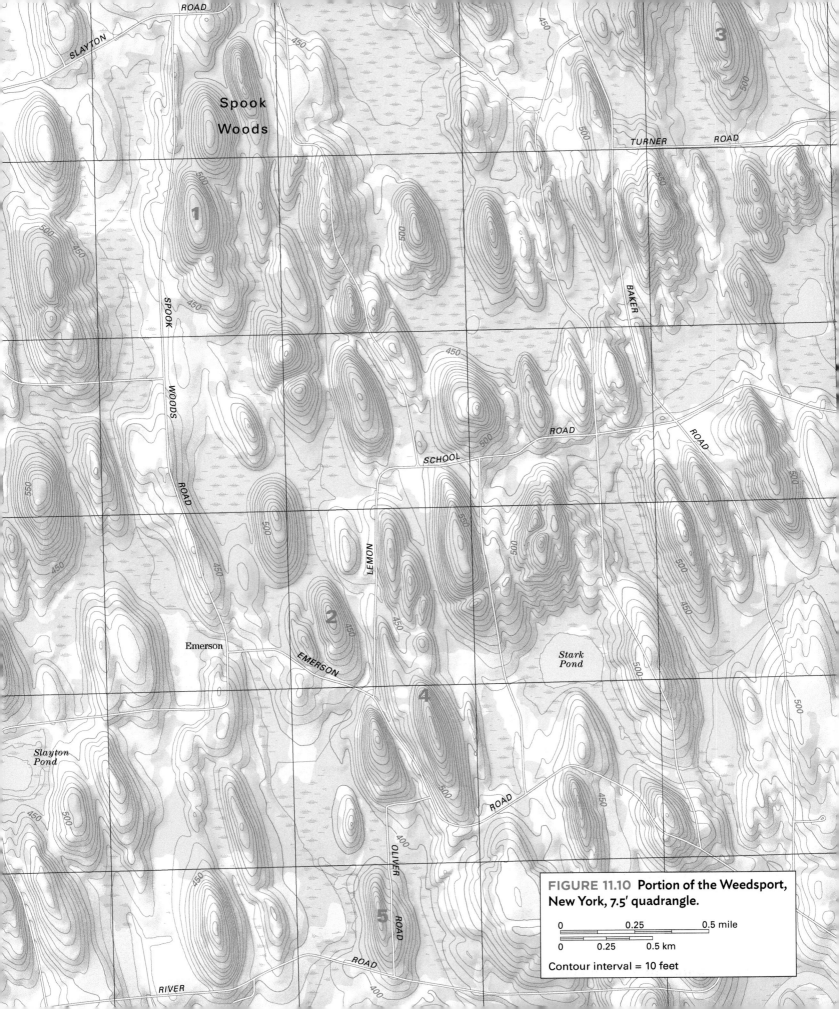

FIGURE 11.10 Portion of the Weedsport, New York, 7.5' quadrangle.

Contour interval = 10 feet

11.3 Landscapes Produced by Mountain Glaciation

Alpine, Himalayan, Rocky Mountain, or Sierra Nevadan vistas with their jagged peaks, steep-walled valleys separated by knife-sharp divides, and spectacular waterfalls are the result of valley glacier erosion. Small glaciers form in depressions high up in the mountains and flow downhill, generally following existing stream valleys. The depressions are deepened and expanded headward by *plucking*, which eats into the mountainside, and the ice flows downhill, filling the former stream valleys and modifying them by abrasion (FIG. 11.11). When the ice melts, the expanded depressions become large, bowl-shaped amphitheaters (**cirques**); formerly rounded stream divides are replaced by knife-sharp ridges (**arêtes**); and the headward convergence of several cirques leaves a sharp, pyramidal peak (**horn peak**, or **horn**, named after the Matterhorn in the Alps).

Valley glaciers transform stream valleys in unmistakable ways, including their cross-sectional and longitudinal profiles, and the way that streams flow into one another. Figure 11.11c shows the characteristic U-shaped cross-sectional profile. Why are stream valleys V-shaped whereas glaciated valleys are U-shaped? Let's see if your ideas in Exercise 11.2 were right.

The answer is in how the two agents of erosion operate (FIG. 11.12). A stream actively erodes only a small part of its valley at any given time, cutting its channel downward or laterally (on the left in Fig. 11.12). Mass wasting gentles the valley walls, creating the V shape. In contrast, a valley glacier fills the entire valley, abrading the walls not only at the bottom, but everywhere it is in contact with the bedrock (center). When the ice melts, it leaves a U-shaped valley (right).

FIGURE 11.11 Erosional features formed by valley glaciers.

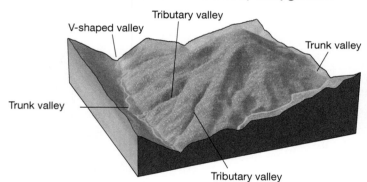

(a) Before valley glaciation, the area has a normal fluvial topography.

(b) The extent of the glaciers during valley glaciation.

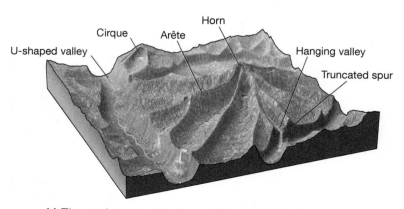

(c) The area's erosional features after valley glaciation.

FIGURE 11.12 **Glacial modification of a fluvial valley.**

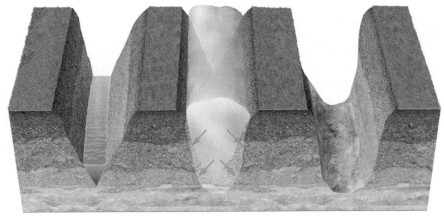

Ice fills the entire valley, eroding everywhere, not just at the bottom like a stream. As it erodes, the valley is deepened and widened everywhere, resulting in the U shape on the right.

Most streams have smoothly concave **longitudinal profiles**. Valley glaciers, being solid, can overcome gravity locally and flow uphill for short distances. Their longitudinal profile is more irregular than a stream's, commonly containing a series of shallow scooped-out basins. Water can collect in some of these basins, producing a chain of lakes called **paternoster** (or **cat-step**) **lakes** (**FIG. 11.13**).

(a) Smooth, concave stream profile.

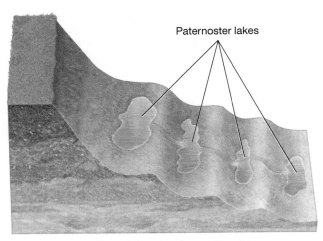

Paternoster lakes

(b) Irregular, scalloped glacial valley profile with paternoster lakes filling the basins.

FIGURE 11.13 **Longitudinal profiles of stream and glacial valleys.**

The base level for a tributary stream is the elevation of the stream, lake, or ocean into which it flows, and most tributary streams flow smoothly into the water body at their base level. In contrast, glaciers have no base level, so large glaciers can carve downward more rapidly than smaller ones. Previously existing main stream valleys, with large glaciers, can therefore be carved more deeply than their tributary valleys. When the ice melts, the result is a **hanging valley**, where the tributary stream hangs over the deeper main valley (**FIG. 11.14**). Today, Bridal Veil Creek falls almost 200 m to the floor of Yosemite Valley. The mouth of the creek and the floor of the valley were once at the same elevation, but the small valley glacier that filled Bridal Veil Creek could not keep pace with the main glacier that eroded downward more rapidly.

FIGURE 11.14 The hanging valley at Bridal Veil Falls, Yosemite National Park, California.

EXERCISE 11.6	Recognizing Features of Valley Glaciation

Name: _____   Section: _____

Course: _____   Date: _____

(a) The following DEM shows part of Glacier National Park and several valley glacier erosional features. Label examples of horn peaks, arêtes, cirques (with a C), and U-shaped valleys (with a U), and look also for flat places (uniform color) that could be filled with lakes (label with an L).

(continued)

DEM (false color) of a portion of Glacier National Park showing classic features of valley glaciation.

Lowest
elevation

Highest
elevation

(b) Look also at the chapter-opening photograph (on page 269) and identify as many features of valley glaciation as you can.

EXERCISE 11.7   **Case Histories in Geologic Reasoning: A Glacial Dilemma**

Name: _____   Section: _____

Course: _____   Date: _____

Mt. Katahdin is the highest peak in Maine, reaching almost a mile above sea level. At first glance, the glacial history of the area seems to be straightforward. A closer look suggests it is a bit more complicated. Examine the shaded relief map of the Mt. Katahdin area (**FIG. 11.15**).

(a) What glacial landform is represented by North Basin, South Basin, and Little North Basin? _____

(b) What glacial feature is represented by the Knife Edge, Hamlin Ridge, and Keep Ridge? _____

(c) What kind of glacial feature is Mt. Katahdin? _____

(d) What type of glacier produced these features? _____

The regional setting of Mt. Katahdin is shown in **FIGURE 11.16**. The area of northern New England, Quebec, and New Brunswick shown in this map was covered by continental ice sheets that pushed as far south as Long Island. The Passadumkeag esker in Figure 11.9 is located just a bit south of Mt. Katahdin, as shown by the green dot in Figure 11.16.

Suggest an explanation for the origin of the alpine glacial features on Mt. Katahdin and surrounding peaks in the midst of an area affected by continental glaciation. There is more than one possible answer.

_____

_____

_____

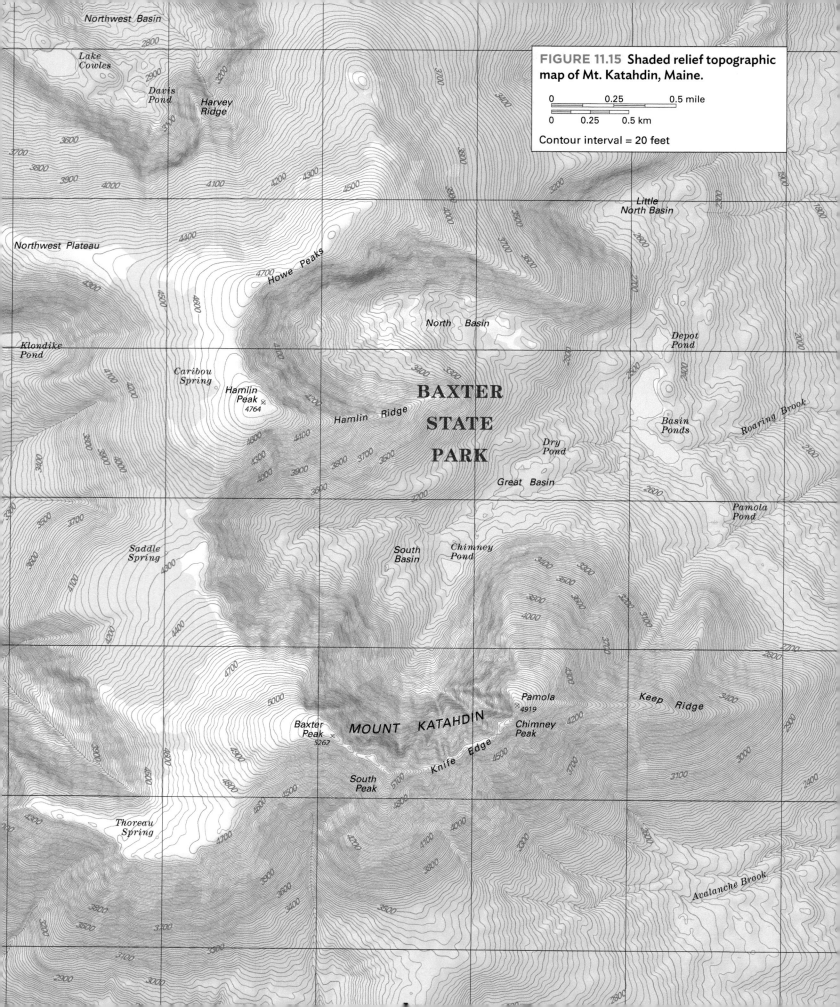

Northwest Basin

Lake Cowles

Davis Pond

Harvey Ridge

Little North Basin

Northwest Plateau

Howe Peaks

North Basin

Depot Pond

Klondike Pond

Caribou Spring

Hamlin Peak
× 4764

Hamlin Ridge

BAXTER STATE PARK

Basin Ponds

Roaring Brook

Dry Pond

Great Basin

Pamola Pond

Saddle Spring

South Basin

Chimney Pond

Keep Ridge

Pamola
× 4919

Baxter Peak ×
5262

MOUNT KATAHDIN

Chimney Peak

South Peak

Knife Edge

Thoreau Spring

Avalanche Brook

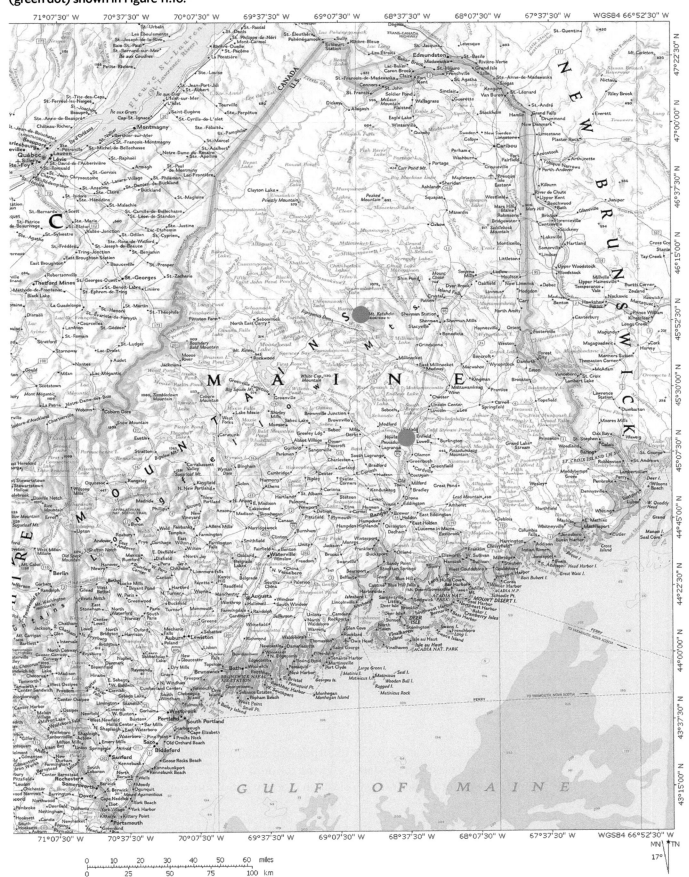

11.4 Glaciers and Climate Change

Intense weather events such as tornadoes, hurricanes, and typhoons, the rise of sea level, and persistent drought have brought the issue of global climate change from the field and laboratories of geologists and meteorologists to media headlines and the world political arena. Glacial landforms and sophisticated studies of polar ice provide the best record of atmospheric changes over the past several hundred thousand years, enabling us to base hypotheses about future changes on solid fact rather than guesswork.

Terminal moraines and outwash plains provide evidence that what movies call "the ice age" and geologists call the Pleistocene Epoch involved four intervals (glacials), in which continental glaciers advanced across the northern hemisphere, each followed by an "interglacial," a period in which the ice retreated or melted completely. Carbon dating of wood from glacial and interglacial sediments gives us a time frame for these events: the first glacial began around 700,000 years ago, and the last continental ice sheets in Europe and North America disappeared around 12,000 years ago.

Although the Pleistocene glaciers have disappeared from North America and Europe, ice sheets remain in Antarctica and Greenland, and they record temperature and greenhouse gas levels (CO_2, methane) over the hundreds of thousands of years that they have existed. Geologists have drilled into these ice sheets and collected ice cores (**FIG. 11.17**) for study in refrigerated laboratories.

FIGURE 11.17 An ice core showing seasonal layering and a dark layer of volcanic ash.

When the ice froze, it incorporated small bubbles of the air that existed at the time. These can be dated and the amount of greenhouse gases can be measured, providing a timeline against which modern conditions can be compared (**FIG. 11.18**).

FIGURE 11.18 Atmospheric temperature and CO_2 concentration from Vostok ice cores, Antarctica.

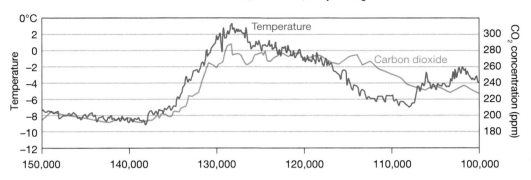

Vostok ice cores 150,000 to 100,000 years ago

Name: _____   Section: _____

Course: _____   Date: _____

We don't need sophisticated instruments to understand how glaciers respond to climate change. All we have to do is look. The Athabasca Glacier in Jasper National Park, Alberta, Canada, is one of the most popular tourist destinations in the province and *the* most visited glacier in North America. The glacier has been retreating since 1843, and the Alberta tourist bureau is concerned that if the retreat continues, it won't be long before there won't be a glacier to visit. The photographs below dramatically document the glacier's retreat — the black and white photograph from 1906 and the color photograph from 2006 are of approximately the same location. Notice how the glacier is now only in the far left-hand portion of the image.

The map given locates the changes in the end of the glacier — what is known as the glacier's terminus — from 1843 to 1999. You have been asked to advise the tourist bureau and National Parks Canada on how much longer the glacier will be a tourist attraction.

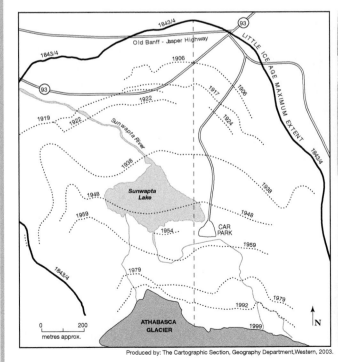

Produced by: The Cartographic Section, Geography Department, Western, 2003.

(continued)

Name: _____   Section: _____
Course: _____   Date: _____

(a) You will note on the map that the glacier's terminus does not follow a straight line but flows around the contours of the landscape. But, to obtain an estimate, you decide to base your estimate along a straight-line (the red, dashed line that intersects the glacial termini for different years).

Measure the amount of retreat from 1843 to 1999 along the dashed line. It is _____ m.
Determine the average rate of the retreat during that period (_____ m/156 years = _____ m/yr).

You note that the rate has not always been consistent. In some time periods it appears to retreat more quickly than others. You decide to compute the rates during different shorter time periods.

- Determine the rate of retreat along the dashed line from 1906 to 1999. _____ m/yr
- Determine the rate of retreat along the dashed line from 1843 to 1906. _____ m/yr

(b) You have computed three rates of retreat over three different time periods. The following picture shows a recent view of this glacier. It is now approximately 6.2 km from its terminus to its top, or head.

First, determine estimates for the potential life of this glacier using the three rates you determined in part (a). Divide 6.2 km by each rate (remember to be careful to *use the same units*) to give you three different time periods. These are

1 _____ years   2 _____ years   3 _____ years

Head of
Athabasca Glacier

2010 terminus

1938 terminus

?What Do You Think Using the information that you have, what are your recommendations to the Alberta tourist bureau? Specifically, how long can they expect the glacier to last and why? What might happen that could cause the rate of retreat either to accelerate or to slow? To the best of your knowledge, propose reasons for both (on a separate sheet of paper).

TABLE 11.1 **Glossary of glacial landforms.**

Erosional Landforms		
Landform	**Type of glacier**	**Description**
Arête	Valley	Sharp ridge separating cirques or U-shaped valleys
Cirque	Valley	Bowl-shaped depression on mountainside; site of snowfield that was source of valley glacier
Hanging valley	Valley	Valley with mouth high above main stream valley; formed by tributary glacier that could not erode down as deeply as larger main glacier
Horn peak	Valley	Steep, pyramid-shaped peak; erosional remnant formed by several cirques
Sculptured bedrock	Continental	Asymmetric bedrock with *steep* side facing the direction toward which the ice flowed; also called roche moutonnée
U-shaped valley	Valley	Steep-sided valley eroded by a glacier that once filled the valley
Depositional Landforms		
Landform	**Type of glacier**	**Description**
Drumlin	Continental	Streamlined (elliptical), asymmetric hill composed of till; the long axis parallels glacial direction, the gentle side faces the direction toward which the ice flowed
Esker	Continental	Narrow, sinuous ridge made of outwash deposited by a subglacial stream in a tunnel at the base of a glacier
Ground moraine	Valley and continental	Sheet of till deposited by a retreating glacier
Kettle hole	Valley and continental	Depression left when a block of ice that had been isolated from a melting glacier is covered with sediment and melts
Lateral moraine	Valley	Till deposited along the walls of a valley when a valley glacier retreats
Outwash plain	Valley and continental	Outwash deposited by meltwater beyond the terminus of a glacier
Proglacial delta	Continental	Outwash deposited into a proglacial lake
Terminal moraine	Valley and continental	Wall of till deposited when the terminus of a glacier remains in one place for a long time
Lakes Associated with Glacial Landscapes		
Landform	**Type of glacier**	**Description**
Ice-marginal lake	Valley and continental	Lake formed by disruption of local drainage by a glacier
Kettle lake	Valley and continental	Lake filling a kettle hole
Paternoster lake	Valley	Series of lakes filling basins in a glaciated valley
Tarn	Valley	Lake occupying part of a cirque

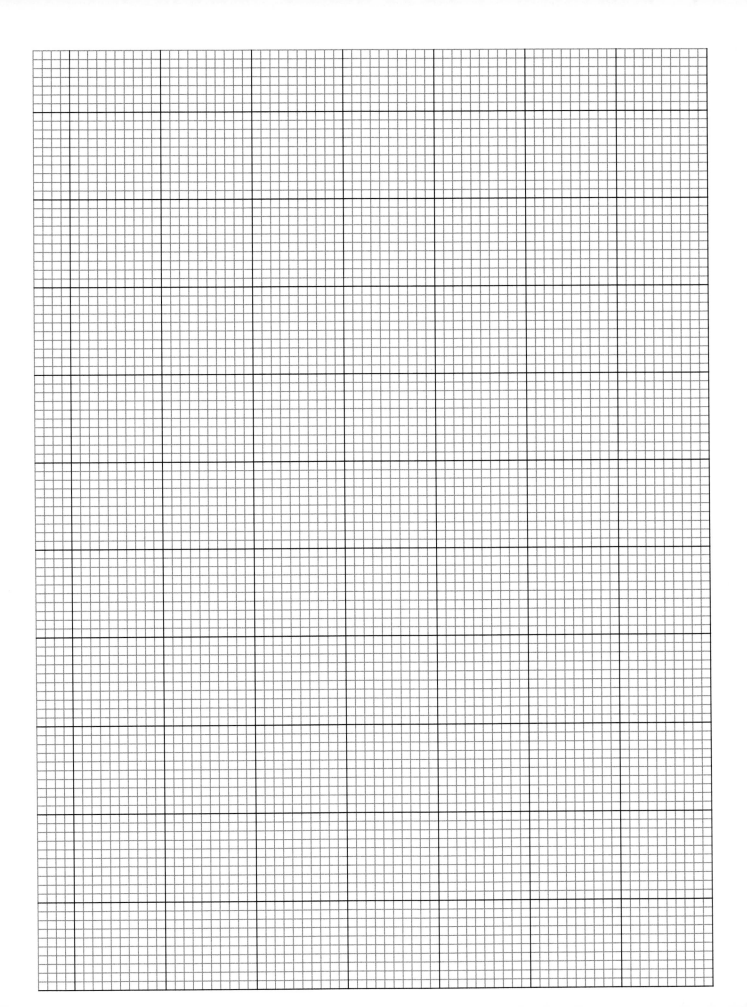

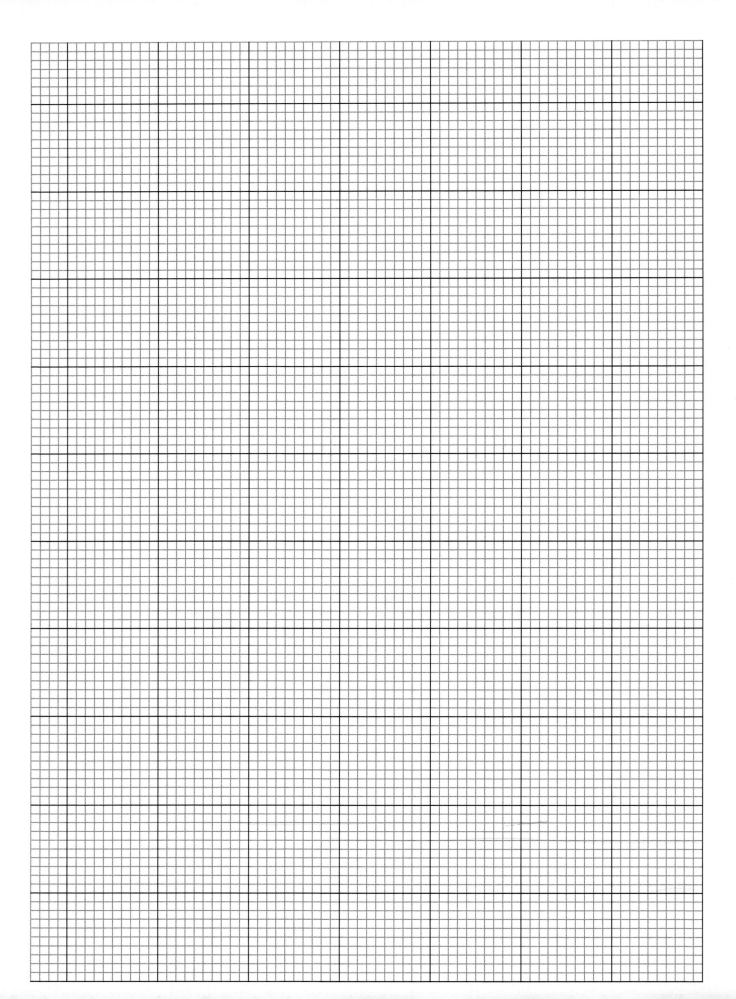

12

Groundwater as a Landscape Former and Resource

Stalactites, stalagmites, and columns in Luray Caverns, Virginia.

- Understand how groundwater infiltrates and flows through Earth materials
- Explain why groundwater erodes and deposits differently from streams and glaciers
- Learn to recognize landscapes formed by groundwater and to interpret groundwater flow direction from the topographic features
- Understand how geologists carry out groundwater resource and pollution studies

MATERIALS
NEEDED

- Specimens of four different materials for the infiltration exercise
- Tracing paper and colored pencils

12.1 Introduction

Some rain and snow that falls on the land runs off into streams, some evaporates into the air, and some is absorbed by plants. The remainder sinks into the ground and is called **groundwater**. Water moves much more slowly underground than in streams because it must drip from one pore space to another rather than flow in a channel. Groundwater therefore has much less kinetic energy than stream water and cannot carry the particles with which streams scrape and wear away at bedrock. Instead, groundwater erodes chemically, by dissolving soluble rocks such as limestone, dolostone, and marble, which are largely made of carbonate minerals like calcite and dolomite.

If groundwater erodes underground, how can it form landscapes at the surface? As groundwater erodes rocks from below, it undermines their support of the surface above, and the land may collapse to produce very distinctive landscapes, often pockmarked with cavities called sinkholes (**FIG. 12.1a**). Landscapes in areas of extreme groundwater erosion are among the most striking in the world, with narrow, steep-sided towers unlike anything produced by streams or glaciers (**FIG. 12.1b**). Groundwater-eroded landscape is called **karst topography,** after the area in Slovenia and northeastern Italy where geologists first studied it in detail, but spectacular examples are also found in Indiana, Kentucky, Florida, southern China, Puerto Rico, and Jamaica.

Groundwater is also a vital resource, used throughout the world for drinking and washing and for irrigating crops. Strict rules govern its use in many places because it flows so slowly that renewal of the groundwater supply takes a long time. In addition, its slow flow and underground location make it difficult to purify once it has been polluted. We examine both roles of groundwater in this chapter: as landscape former and as resource. Exercise 12.1 starts by introducing some factors that affect groundwater flow.

FIGURE 12.1 **Landscapes carved by groundwater.**

(a) Karst topography characterized by sinkholes and underground caves in southern Indiana.

(b) Karst towers in the Guilin area of southern China.

12.2 Aquifers and Aquitards

Materials that transmit water readily are called **aquifers** (from the Latin, meaning "to carry water"), and those that prevent water from infiltrating are called **aquitards** or **aquicludes** (they re*tard* or ex*clude* water). Groundwater flows through pores and fractures in bedrock as well as through unconsolidated sediment. Some rocks, like a poorly cemented sandstone, contain pores when the rock forms (**primary porosity**), but others that have no pores at all when they form (e.g., granite, obsidian) become porous and permeable when broken by faulting or fracturing (**secondary porosity**).

Name: _____ **Section:** _____

Course: _____ **Date:** _____

Let's look first at factors that control the flow of water underground. Your instructor will provide four containers screened at the bottom and filled with materials that have different grain shapes and sizes like in the figure below.

(a) If equal amounts of water were poured into each of the four containers, which material do you think would permit the greatest amount of water to pass through to the graduated cylinder? Rank your predictions here:

Greatest amount   *Least amount*

_____

_____

In a few sentences, explain your reasoning for these choices.

_____

_____

_____

(b) Which material will transmit water fastest? Slowest? Explain.

Fastest water transmission   *Slowest water transmission*

_____

_____

In a few sentences, explain your reasoning for these choices.

_____

_____

_____

(continued)

Name: _____   Section: _____

Course: _____   Date: _____

In the top section of the table, describe the indicated properties of the contents in each container.

Now let's see how good your predictions are. Pour equal amounts of water into the four bottles and measure the amount of water that passes through and its rate of flow. Record your observations in the lower parts of table below.

	Observation	Container A	Container B	Container C	Container D
Properties of material that might affect water flow	Grain size				
	Sorting				
	Grain shape				
	Porosity				
	Permeability				
Volume of water transmitted (ml)	30 seconds				
	60 seconds				
	90 seconds				
	120 seconds				
	150 seconds				
	180 seconds				
	210 seconds				
	240 seconds				
Other observations	Water color				
	Amount of water retained				

(continued)

Name: _____   **Section:** _____
Course: _____   **Date:** _____

(c) Which materials transmitted the most water? Which retained the most water?

_____

_____

(d) What properties of the materials are correlated with good water transmission? Which are correlated with water retardation and retention?

_____

_____

_____

Being porous is not necessarily enough for a material to be a good aquifer. Pumice and scoria are very porous, but their pores are not connected. Pore spaces must be connected for water to move from one to another—a property called **permeability**. The materials in Exercise 12.1 that transmitted water easily had to be both porous (there was room for the water between grains) *and* permeable (the water could move through the material). *An aquifer must be both porous and permeable.* Exercise 12.2 explores these concepts.

EXERCISE 12.2   The Difference between Porosity and Permeability

Name: _____   **Section:** _____
Course: _____   **Date:** _____

Are all porous rocks aquifers? Hold pieces of highly porous pumice and scoria above two beakers or rest them on the rims as shown in the following figure. Using a water dropper, slowly add water to the top of the rock and carefully observe how much water passes into the beaker.

Porosity and permeability in pumice and scoria.

(continued)

Name: _____   Section: _____

Course: _____   Date: _____

(a) Are pumice and scoria porous? Permeable? Explain.

_____

_____

_____

(b) Is a material that is similar to scoria more likely to function as an aquifer or an aquitard? Explain your answer.

_____

_____

_____

_____

(c) Is a material that is similar to pumice more likely to function as an aquifer or an aquitard? Explain your answer.

_____

_____

_____

_____

Groundwater's slow pore-to-pore movement helps chemical erosion because the longer water sits in contact with minerals, the more it can dissolve them. Similarly, even a few drops of water placed on a sugar cube will eventually dissolve their way through the cube. Unfortunately, chemical erosion can cause dangerous health problems if humans or animals drink water in which poisonous material is dissolved. For example, when groundwater wells were drilled in Bangladesh to provide safer drinking water than that from streams contaminated with bacteria, the groundwater turned out to contain high concentrations of arsenic. An international effort is under way to identify the source of the arsenic and devise methods for removing it from the groundwater.

12.3 Landscapes Produced by Groundwater

Groundwater is the only agent of erosion that creates landforms from below the surface of the Earth, and all karst topographic features are destructional. Caves and caverns, the largest groundwater erosional features, are underground, unseen, and often unsuspected at the surface (**FIG. 12.2a**). In some areas, extensive cave networks result from widespread chemical erosion. **Sinkholes** form when these underground cavities grow so large that there is not enough rock to support the ground above them. **Karst towers** are what remain when the rock around them has been dissolved (**FIG. 12.2b**). **Karst valleys** form when several sinkholes develop along an elongate fracture (**FIG. 12.2c**).

Unlike streams and glaciers, deposition by groundwater does not produce land-forms. Groundwater deposition occurs in caverns when drops of water evaporate, leaving behind a tiny residue of calcite—sometimes on the roof of the cavern, sometimes on the floor. These build up slowly over time to produce stalactites and stalagmites, respectively (FIG. 12.3). In some instances, a stalactite and stalagmite may grow together to form a column. In Exercise 12.3, you will explore karst topography.

FIGURE 12.2 Groundwater landscape erosion from beneath the Earth's surface.

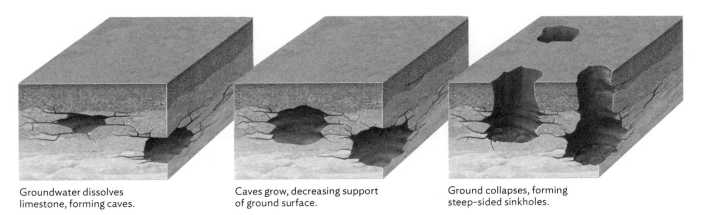

Groundwater dissolves limestone, forming caves.

Caves grow, decreasing support of ground surface.

Ground collapses, forming steep-sided sinkholes.

(a) Origin of sinkholes by solution and collapse.

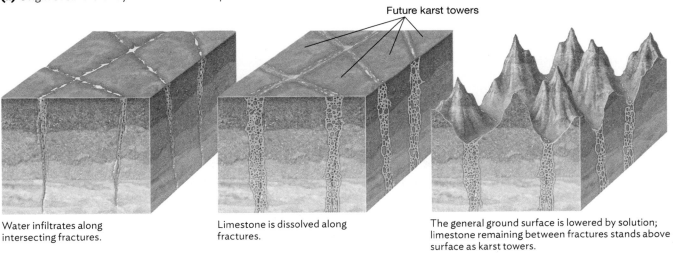

Future karst towers

Water infiltrates along intersecting fractures.

Limestone is dissolved along fractures.

The general ground surface is lowered by solution; limestone remaining between fractures stands above surface as karst towers.

(b) Origin of karst towers as erosional remnants.

(c) Origin of karst valleys along fractures.

FIGURE 12.3 Groundwater deposition in caverns.

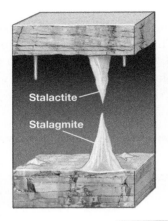

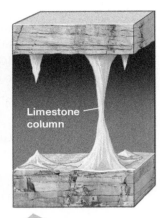

Time

Stalactites grow *downward* from the roof; stalagmites grow *upward* from the floor. Columns form when stalactites and stalagmites merge.

EXERCISE 12.3 | Karst Topography

Name: _____ Section: _____

Course: _____ Date: _____

This chapter examines two classic karst areas in the United States to help you become familiar with groundwater erosional landscapes—one in Kentucky (**FIG. 12.4**) and one in Florida (**FIG. 12.7** on page 307). In this exercise, we will focus on the location in Kentucky.

Compare the map of the Mammoth Cave area (Fig. 12.4) with the diagrams showing how karst features develop (Fig. 12.2).

(a) This area receives a moderate amount of rainfall, yet there are very few streams. Suggest an explanation for this phenomenon. (This is a characteristic of nearly all karst regions.)

_____

_____

_____

(b) Look for changes in topographic grain (texture) across the map area. Draw lines separating places with different topographic textures.

(c) Describe the topography in the southernmost quarter of the area. What karst features are present?

_____

_____

_____

(d) Some of the circular depressions in this part of the map are partially filled with water. Suggest an origin for these lakes (we will return to this point later).

_____

_____

_____

(continued)

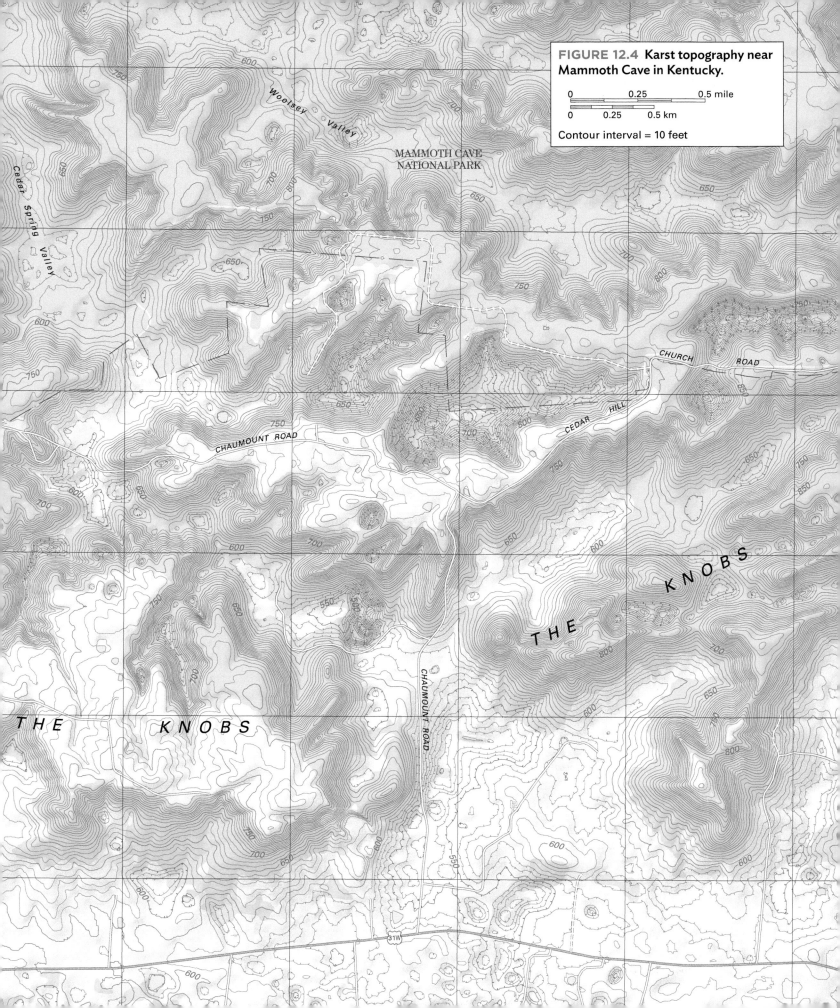

FIGURE 12.4 Karst topography near Mammoth Cave in Kentucky.

0   0.25   0.5 mile
0   0.25   0.5 km

Contour interval = 10 feet

MAMMOTH CAVE
NATIONAL PARK

Woolsey Valley

Cedar Spring Valley

CHAUMOUNT ROAD

CHURCH ROAD

CEDAR HILL

CHAUMOUNT ROAD

THE KNOBS

THE KNOBS

31W

Name: _____   **Section:** _____

Course: _____   **Date:** _____

(e) Describe the topography in the northern three-quarters of the map. What karst feature is represented by The Knobs? What feature is represented by the Woolsey Valley?

_____

_____

_____

_____

_____

_____

(f) Karst features are found throughout the entire map but have a different appearance in the southern quarter compared to the north. Describe the differences and suggest a possible explanation.

_____

_____

_____

_____

_____

_____

(g) Some of the sinkholes contain lakes, but others are dry. Suggest an explanation for the difference. *Hint:* Determine the elevation of lakes in the sinkholes and write it in each lake. Compare those to the elevations of the bottoms of the sinkholes that do not have lakes.

_____

_____

_____

_____

_____

_____

12.4 The Water Table

Look at Figure 12.7, a map showing a karst area in northern Florida in which sinkholes are filled with water. The level of water in the lakes in Figure 12.7 is controlled by a feature called the **water table**. Gravity pulls groundwater downward until it reaches an aquitard that it cannot penetrate, and the water begins to fill pores in the aquifer just above the aquitard. More water percolating downward finds pores at the bottom of the aquifer already filled, and so it saturates those even higher. The water table is the boundary between the **zone of saturation** (where all pore spaces are filled with water) and the **zone of aeration,** where some pores are partly filled with air (**FIG. 12.5**). You can model the water table by adding water to a beaker filled with sand and watching the level of saturation change.

FIGURE 12.5 The water table separates the zones of saturation and aeration.

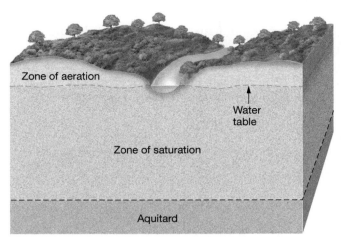

Zone of aeration

Water
table

Zone of saturation

Aquitard

A stream or lake forms where the water table intersects the
land surface.

12.5 Groundwater Resources and Environmental Problems

Groundwater is vital for human existence, both for drinking and to irrigate crops. We drill wells to depths below the water table and use pumps to extract the water from an aquifer. But groundwater flows so slowly that it can rarely replenish itself as rapidly as our needs dictate. Indeed, some water that we drink today entered its aquifer system hundreds of years ago. If we take too much groundwater, our wells run dry—a serious problem for many farms between the Rocky Mountains and the Mississippi River that depend on the same aquifer (the Dakota sandstone aquifer) for their water.

When we pump water from an aquifer, it comes from the saturated pore spaces below the water table, and water must flow downward to replace it from other parts of the aquifer (**FIG. 12.6**). This lowers the water table, especially in the area around the well. Each well creates a **cone of depression** in the water table, as shown in Figure 12.6. You model this phenomenon every time you order a thick milk shake from your local fast-food restaurant. Next time, take the top off the shake and insert the straw just below the surface of the shake. Sip slowly and look at what happens to the surface. Because the shake flows sluggishly (not unlike groundwater), the area

FIGURE 12.6 Formation of a cone of depression by removal of water from an aquifer.

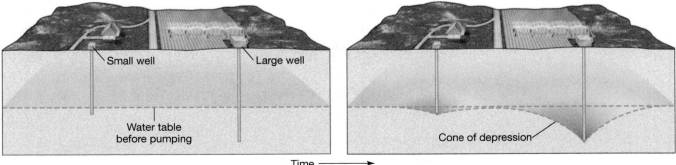

Small well

Large well

Water table
before pumping

Cone of depression

Time ⟶

below the straw is drawn down more than the area near the edges of the cup. You've just made a small cone of depression.

Two types of problems are associated with groundwater resources: issues of *quantity* (whether there is enough groundwater to meet our needs) and *quality* (whether the groundwater is pure enough for us to drink or whether it has become contaminated through natural or human causes). We will explore these issues with two case histories, both based on real-world situations, in Exercises 12.6 and 12.7. But first, let's learn more about how to find the water table in Exercise 12.4 and how to solve a geologic puzzle in Exercise 12.5.

EXERCISE 12.4   Locating the Water Table

Name: _____   Section: _____

Course: _____   Date: _____

Look at the map of the Interlachen area in Florida (Fig. 12.7), a karst landscape underlain by highly soluble limestone. In addition to showing another karst region, this map illustrates other important concepts about groundwater—its value as a resource and environmental and other problems associated with living in karst topography.

The water table generally mimics the surface topography in a slightly subdued shape (Fig. 12.5). Groundwater flows downhill from higher parts of the water table to lower parts.

(a) Construct a profile of the Interlachen area from Point A to Point B in Figure 12.7. From your data of lake level elevations, sketch the water table on this profile.

(continued)

FIGURE 12.7 Karst topography in the Interlachen area of Florida.

0   0.25   0.5 mile

0   0.25   0.5 km

Contour interval = 10 feet

Boyds Lake

Long Pond

Lake Grandin

Clearwater Lake

B

CO. ROAD 315

Silver Lake

Flamingo Lake

Hart Lake

Junior Lake

Lovers Lake

Perch Lake

Hubbard Pond

Trout Lake

Mariner Lake

Sand Hill Pond

A

Name: _____   **Section:** _____

Course: _____   **Date:** _____

(b) Draw an arrow on Figure 12.7 to indicate the direction of groundwater flow. The case histories at the end of this chapter illustrate the importance of knowing which way groundwater is flowing.

(c) The area of Interlachen has grown dramatically in the past 20 years, and part of its suburban street grid can be seen in Figure 12.7. What construction problems do developers face in an area like this?

_____

_____

_____

_____

(d) In the past few years, some lakes in this area have shrunk dramatically or dried up entirely. Suggest possible reasons for this change.

_____

_____

_____

_____

EXERCISE 12.5   A Geological Puzzle

Name: _____   **Section:** _____

Course: _____   **Date:** _____

Carlsbad Caverns National Park in New Mexico (**FIG. 12.8**) contains spectacular caverns with stalactites, stalagmites, and columns, yet the area where it is located does not exhibit the karst features found at Mammoth Cave and southern Florida. Suggest an explanation. What conditions might be causing caverns to form below ground without a karst topography above ground?

_____

_____

_____

_____

_____

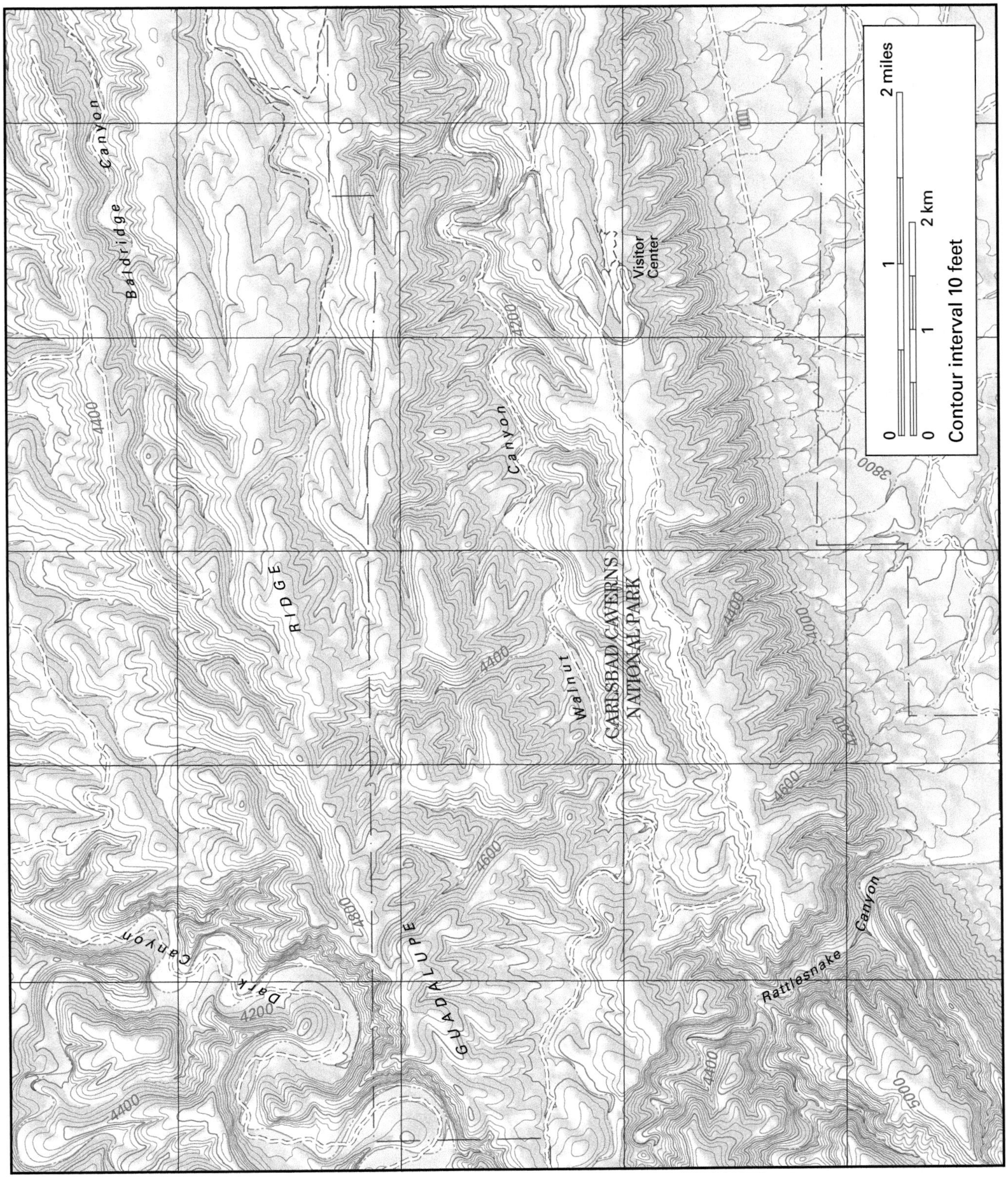

FIGURE 12.8 Topography of the Carlsbad Caverns area of New Mexico.

Contour interval 10 feet

Name: _____   Section: _____
Course: _____   Date: _____

This exercise presents a real-life problem, although details have been changed to protect the privacy of the parties involved.

The figure below is a map showing an area in which farmers have relied on groundwater for generations for drinking and to irrigate their crops. In an attempt to diversify the local economy, the town selectmen offered tax incentives to bring two new industries into the area: Grandma's Soup Company and the Queens Sand and Gravel Quarry. Trouble arose when Farmer Jones (see location on map) found that his well had run dry even though it was the rainy season. Having taken Geology 101 at the State University several years ago, he suspected that pumping by the new companies had lowered the water table. He hired a lawyer and sued Grandma's Soup Company to prevent it from pumping "his" water. Grandma's lawyers responded that the company had nothing to do with his problem.

Depth to water table *before* commercial pumping.

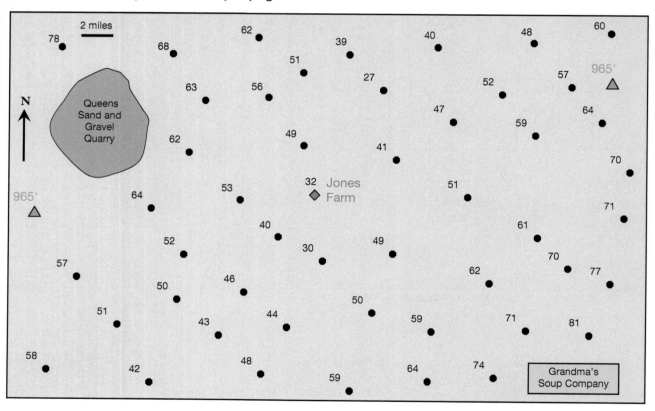

The judge, who has never taken a geology class, has appointed *you* to resolve the problem. Your tasks are (1) find out why Farmer Jones has lost his water, and (2) figure out how to keep everyone happy. After all, Jones and his friends have been benefiting from the fact that Grandma's Soup Company has been paying an enormous amount of taxes. Your assistants have already gathered a lot of useful data.

- A survey shows that the land is as flat as a pancake, with an elevation of 965 feet.

- Records show the depth to the water table in wells *before* the companies opened (above) and *after* the two companies had been pumping for a year (next page).

(continued)

Name: _____   Section: _____
Course: _____   Date: _____

Depth to water table *after* commercial pumping.

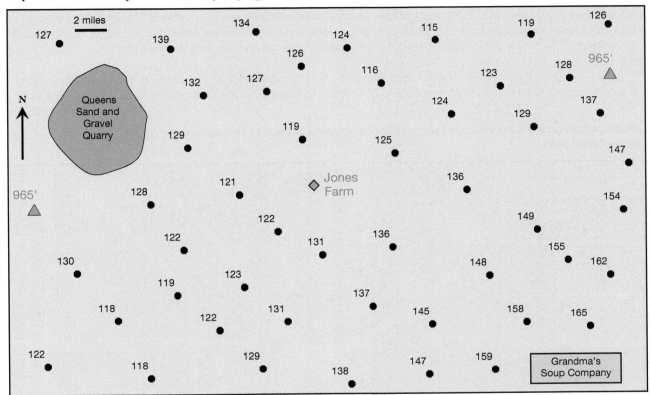

? What Do You Think Based on the data in the two maps, answer the following questions on a separate sheet of paper:

- Why has Farmer Jones's well run dry?
- What steps do you recommend could be taken to keep the Jones Farm and the new industries in business?

Hint 1: Use your contouring skills to make a topographic map of the water table before and after the quarry and soup company began pumping.

Hint 2: Consider what the quarry and soup company do with the water they pump.

Name: _____   Section: _____
Course: _____   Date: _____

Groundwater *quality* is becoming a critical issue as growing populations place stress on the environment. Commercial pollution or leakage from residential septic tanks may make water unsuitable for drinking. The following case history happens all too commonly.

(continued)

Name: _____   **Section:** _____

Course: _____   **Date:** _____

The Smiths bought a home in a suburban development where the water supply was a shallow groundwater aquifer. A few months ago, they noticed a strange smell when they took showers, and the drinking water has begun to taste foul. Last week, while washing dishes, the Smiths thought they smelled gasoline in their kitchen. The local TV news channel ran an investigative report on leakage from storage tanks at gas stations, and the Smiths suspected that this might be the cause of their problem. They hired a groundwater consulting company to solve the problem, and you have been put in charge of the project.

The following map illustrates the Smiths' neighborhood, showing the location of their home and two local gas stations the Smiths suspect to be the cause of their water problem. You have surveyed the neighborhood using state-of-the-art

Concentrations (in parts per billion) of semivolatile compounds in the area surrounding the Smith home (nd = not detected).

Goodmile Gas Co.

GoFast Gas Co.

1 mile

△ Smith home

(continued)

Name: _____ **Section:** _____

Course: _____ **Date:** _____

detection instruments to measure the amount of volatile compounds in the soil around the Smiths' home. These chemicals are released into the ground when corroded gas tanks leak and are indicators of soil and groundwater contamination. Concentrations greater than 50 parts per billion (ppb) are considered dangerous. The data are shown in red numbers on the map.

Hint: Make a contour map of the soil contamination level using a 10-ppm contour interval. This is not a map showing elevation, but the rules are very much the same. Color-code the map to show levels of potential danger: red for values above the danger threshold (50 ppb); a second color for probable future threat (between 30 and 50 ppb); and a third color for possible future threat (between 10 and 30 ppb).

(a) Does either gas station have a leakage problem? Explain your conclusion.

_____

_____

(b) In what direction does the local groundwater flow? How do you know?

_____

_____

(c) Which homes will be the next to feel the effects of the gasoline leakage?

_____

_____

(d) What additional problems has your research discovered?

_____

_____

_____

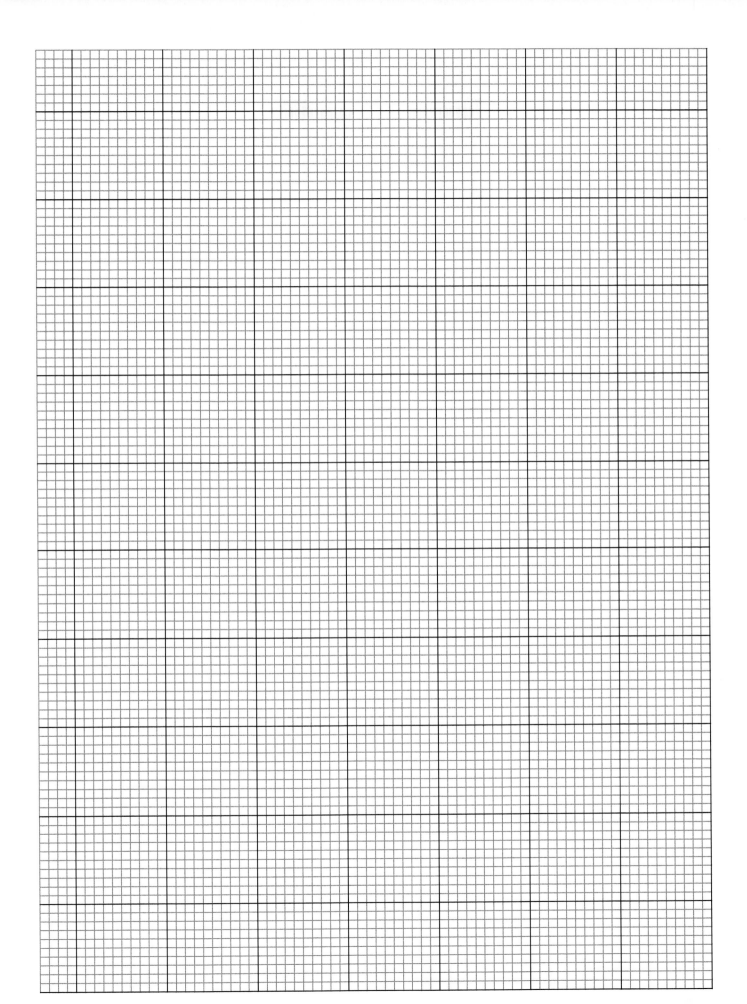

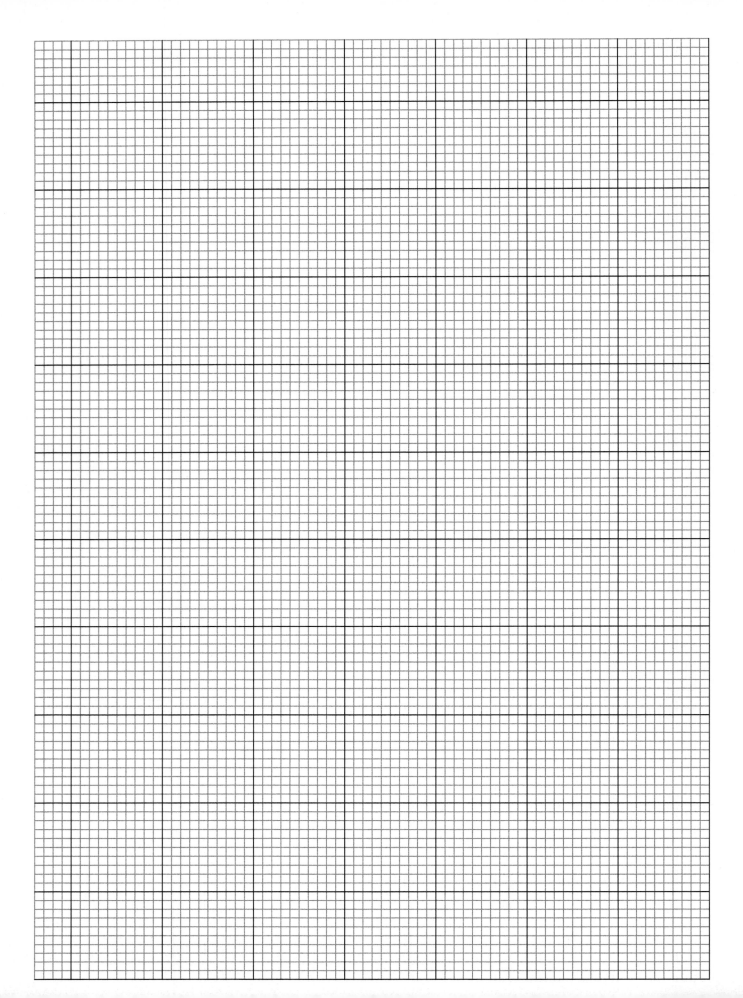

13

Processes and Landforms in Arid Environments

Buttes are common landforms in arid environments. The buttes pictured in this photo are from Monument Valley along the Arizona–Utah state line.

13.1 Introduction

Arid regions are defined as those that receive less than 25 cm (10 in.) of rain per year, which provides very little water for stream and groundwater erosion or for chemical and physical weathering. Weathering, mass wasting, and wind and stream erosion are still the major factors in arid landscape formation, but because they are applied in very different proportions than in humid regions, the results are strikingly different from those in temperate and tropical landscapes (FIG. 13.1).

Movies and television portray arid regions with camels resting at oases amid mountainous sand dunes. Some arid regions, like parts of the Sahara and Mojave deserts, do look like that (minus camels in the Mojave, of course). But some arid regions actually have more rock than sand, while others lie next to shorelines where there is no shortage of water—and even the North and South Poles rank among Earth's most arid regions (FIG. 13.2).

With these factors in mind, complete Exercise 13.1, comparing features of arid and humid landscapes.

FIGURE 13.1 **Arid landforms from the southwestern United States.**

(a) Erosional remnants in Monument Valley, Arizona.

(b) Hoodoo panorams in Bryce Canyon, Utah.

(c) Delicate Arch in Arches National Park, Utah.

FIGURE 13.2 Types of arid regions.

(a) Landscape in Death Valley, in the Mojave Desert, California.

(b) Polar desert, Norway.

(c) Rocky desert, Utah.

Name: _____   Section: _____
Course: _____   Date: _____

(a) In which areas are the landforms more angular? In which are they more rounded? Suggest an explanation for the difference.

_____

_____

_____

(b) In which areas do you think landscape changes are more rapid? Are slower? Explain your answer.

_____

_____

_____

(c) What other differences do you see between the arid and humid regions?

_____

_____

_____

(d) What type of erosion appears to be dominant in the arid regions? In the humid regions? How is this possible?

_____

_____

Comparison of arid and humid landscapes.

(a) Canyonlands National Park, Utah.

(b) Grand Canyon, Arizona.

(c) Delaware Water Gap, New Jersey/Pennsylvania.

(d) Humid region in Utah.

13.2 Processes in Arid Regions

Now let's examine the underlying causes for the different evolution of landscapes in arid and humid areas. Features tend to survive longer in arid areas than in humid ones because weathering, erosion, and deposition are slowed by the scarcity of water needed to abrade, dissolve, and carry debris away. In the absence of water, soluble rocks like limestone, dolostone, and marble—easily weathered and eroded in humid regions to form valleys—become ridge formers.

Both physical and chemical weathering occur in arid regions. The dominant processes of physical weathering are usually different from those in humid areas; for example, where do you think root wedging is more common? In areas where rain is rare, the major source of water for chemical weathering may be the thin film of dew formed on rocks each morning. The scarcity of water limits chemical weathering severely, and soil formation is slow. Exercise 13.2 explores some of these differences.

EXERCISE 13.2	Comparing Processes in Arid and Humid Regions

Name: _____   Section: _____

Course: _____   Date: _____

In a few short sentences, describe how the following processes are different in arid regions and humid regions? Consider the nature and intensity of the processes and the role that water plays in each. What are the dominant processes in each category in the two different areas?

	Arid regions	Humid regions
Physical weathering		
Chemical weathering		
Mass wasting		
Soil formation		
Stream erosion		
Wind erosion		
Groundwater activity		

13.3 Progressive Evolution of Arid Landscapes

The evolution of arid landscapes differs from that in humid regions. FIGURE 13.3 shows the stages in the development of an arid landscape, starting with a block made of resistant and nonresistant rocks that has been uplifted by faulting (Fig. 13.3a). Physical weathering takes advantage of fractures, causing cliffs to retreat and forming a rubble-strewn plain (Fig. 13.3b).

Streams—perhaps flowing after only a few storms during the rainy season but still very effective—erode materials from the highlands and redeposit them as **alluvial fans** that begin to fill in the lowlands (Fig. 13.3c). With further deposition, alluvial fans coalesce to form a broad sand and gravel deposit (a **bajada**) flanking the uplifted block (Fig. 13.3c).

Where several fault blocks and valleys are present, bajada sediment from neighboring blocks eventually fills in the intervening valley, burying all but a few eroded remnants of the original blocks (Fig. 13.3d). These remnants stand out as isolated peaks, called **inselbergs**, above the sediment fill. Streams flowing into the basin from surrounding blocks have no way to leave and so form **playa lakes**, which may evaporate to form **salt flats**. Monument Valley (Fig. 13.3e) is a classic example of remnants of resistant rock isolated from their source layers by arid erosion.

Arid landscapes are typically more angular than humid landscapes. Compare, for example, photos (b) and (c) in Exercise 13.1. In the Grand Canyon, there is little soil. Rockfall is the dominant process of mass wasting, and sharp, angular slope breaks indicate contacts between resistant and nonresistant rocks. In Exercise 13.3, you will practice interpreting these features.

Nearly vertical slopes characterize the resistant sandstones, and more gently sloping surfaces characterize the less resistant shales. In contrast, a well-developed soil profile has formed above the bedrock in the Delaware Water Gap, partially masking erosional differences in the underlying rock. Soil creep is the dominant mass wasting process, and this smooths the topography.

EXERCISE 13.3	Interpreting Arid Landscapes

Name: _____   Section: _____

Course: _____   Date: _____

In the following series of exercises you will practice interpreting aspects of different arid landscapes.

Grand Canyon, Arizona

(a) Why hasn't soil creep smoothed the slopes of the Grand Canyon as pictured in this photo?

_____

_____

_____

Death Valley, California/Nevada

Examine the topographic overview (**FIG. 13.4**) of the Death Valley area. This is one of the driest places in North America and, with an elevation of more than 250 feet *below* sea level, one of the lowest spots on the continent. It also contains classic examples of arid landscapes.

(continued)

FIGURE 13.3 Stages in the evolution of an arid landscape.

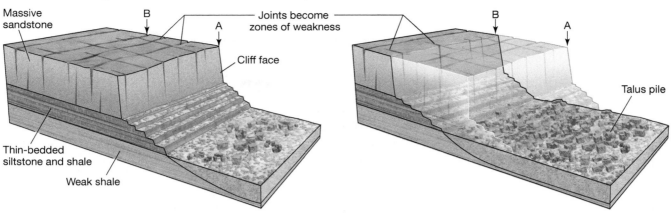

(a) An uplifted block of resistant sandstone and more easily eroded shales.

(b) Idealized cliff retreats from A to B as underlying rocks weather physically. Rockfall produces talus piles at the base of the cliff.

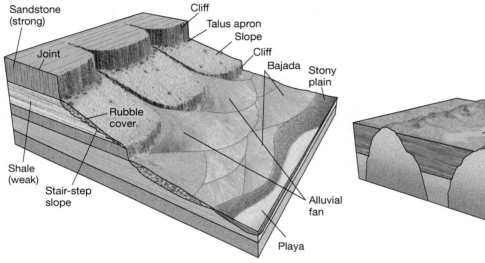

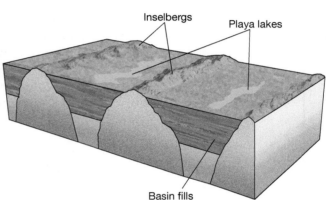

(c) A debris apron covers the lowlands and protects the bedrock slope from further erosion.

(d) A late stage of landscape development involving several uplifted blocks.

(e) Buttes in Monument Valley, Arizona. Buttes are small- to medium-sized erosional remnants with flat tops. Similar but larger features are called *mesas*, from the Spanish word for table.

FIGURE 13.4 Topographic overview and profile of part of the Death Valley area (Death Valley National Monument in dark pink at center of map).

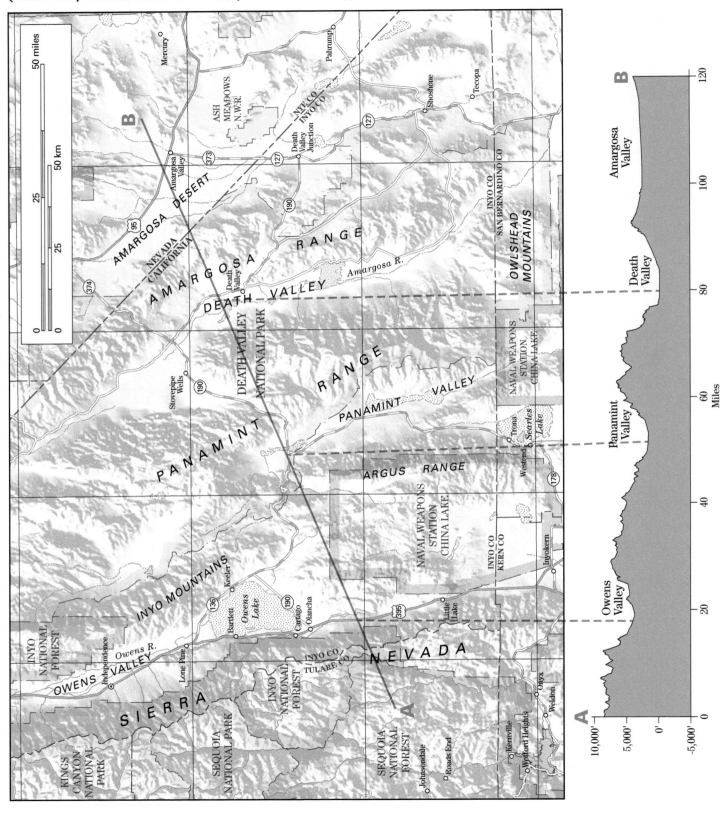

Name: _____ **Section:** _____
Course: _____ **Date:** _____

(b) Compare this region in Figure 13.4 with Figure 13.3. Is this a single fault block like in Figure 13.3a or several blocks like in Figure 13.3d? Explain your reasoning.

_____

_____

_____

(c) Sketch in the border fault(s) with a colored pencil on both the map view and the profile in Figure 13.4.

(d) Why is Death Valley lower in elevation than the other major valleys shown in the topographic profile in Figure 13.4? Consider factors that played roles in forming the valley: stream erosion, tectonic activity.

_____

_____

_____

Now examine Death Valley more closely, starting with the Stovepipe Wells area (**FIG. 13.5**).

(e) What are the broad, rounded landforms that project into Death Valley from the mountains adjacent on the west and southeast? How did they form?

_____

_____

_____

(f) Several streams flow into Death Valley from these mountains. Where do they go? What is their base level?

_____

_____

_____

(g) A stippled pattern identifies areas of rapidly moving sand dunes. Where did this sand come from?

_____

_____

_____

(h) A more detailed view of the sand areas would show individual dunes, but these would not be accurate representations of the current land surface. Why not?

_____

_____

_____

(continued)

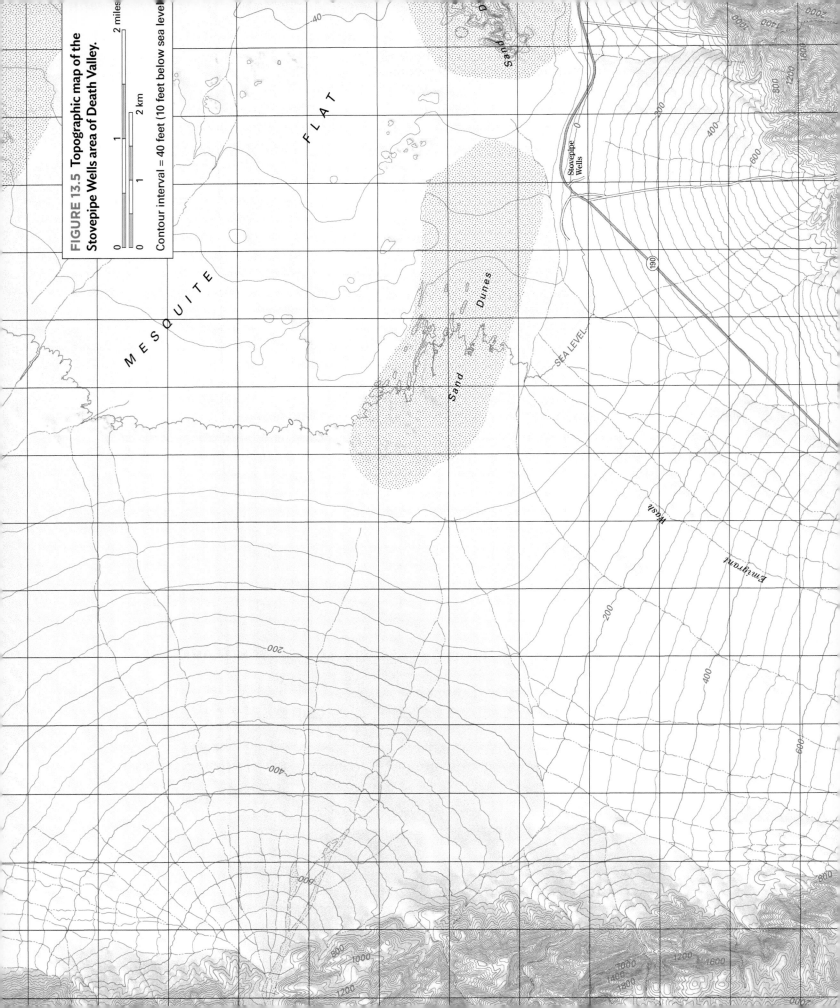

FIGURE 13.5 Topographic map of the Stovepipe Wells area of Death Valley.

Contour interval = 40 feet (10 feet below sea level)

Name: _____ Section: _____

Course: _____ Date: _____

Examine the map of the area surrounding the town of Death Valley, including the Death Valley Airport and Furnace Creek Inn (**FIG. 13.6**).

(i) What arid environment depositional landforms are present? Label these on the map.

(j) A large lake that is not present throughout the year is shown with a blue-stipple pattern in Cotton Ball Basin. What is this type of lake called and how does it form?

_____

_____

_____

(k) What evidence on the map suggests that the water in the streams and lakes is unsafe to drink?

_____

_____

_____

(l) Is all of the water in these lakes brought in by the streams shown on the map? Explain your reasoning.

_____

_____

_____

(m) Compare Figures 13.4, 13.5, and 13.6 with Figure 13.3. How far advanced in the arid erosion cycle is the Death Valley area? What changes can we expect to take place in the future?

_____

_____

_____

Buckeye Hills, Arizona

The Buckeye Hills southwest of Phoenix are in an arid area similar to Death Valley, but this area differs in some ways. A topographic overview of the Buckeye Hills is shown in **FIGURE 13.7**.

(n) Describe the landscape shown in this overview.

_____

_____

_____

_____

(o) How are the Buckeye Hills similar to the part of Death Valley shown in Figure 13.4?

_____

_____

_____

_____

(continued)

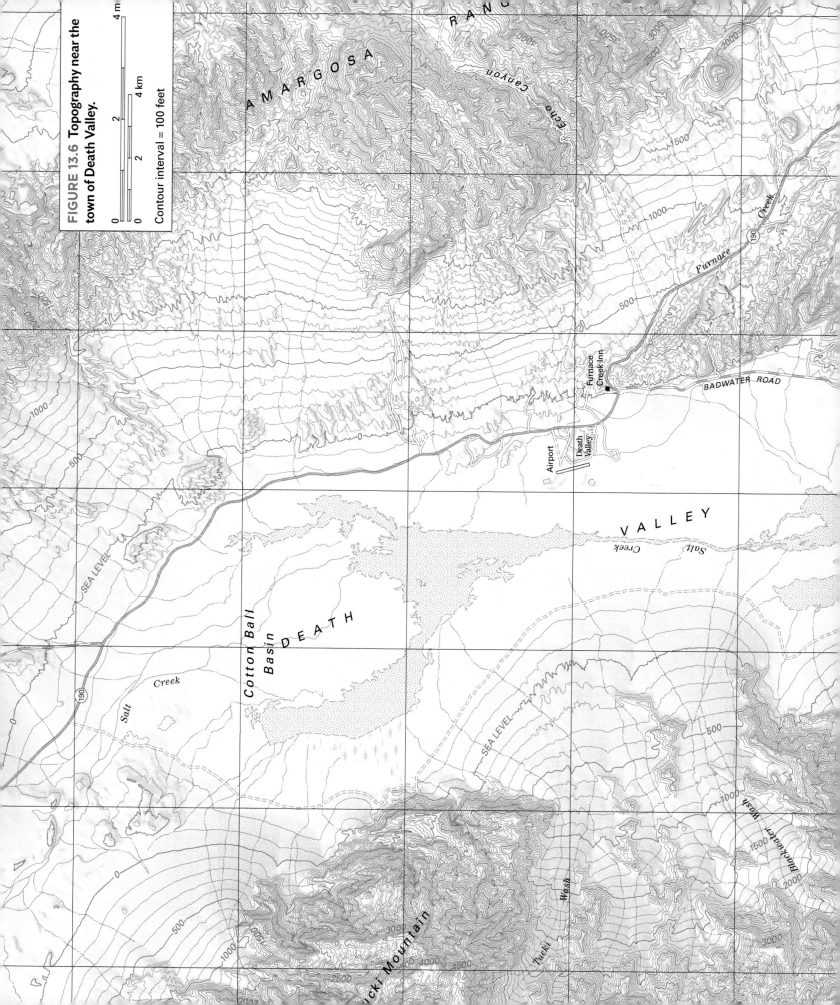

FIGURE 13.6 Topography near the town of Death Valley.

Contour interval = 100 feet

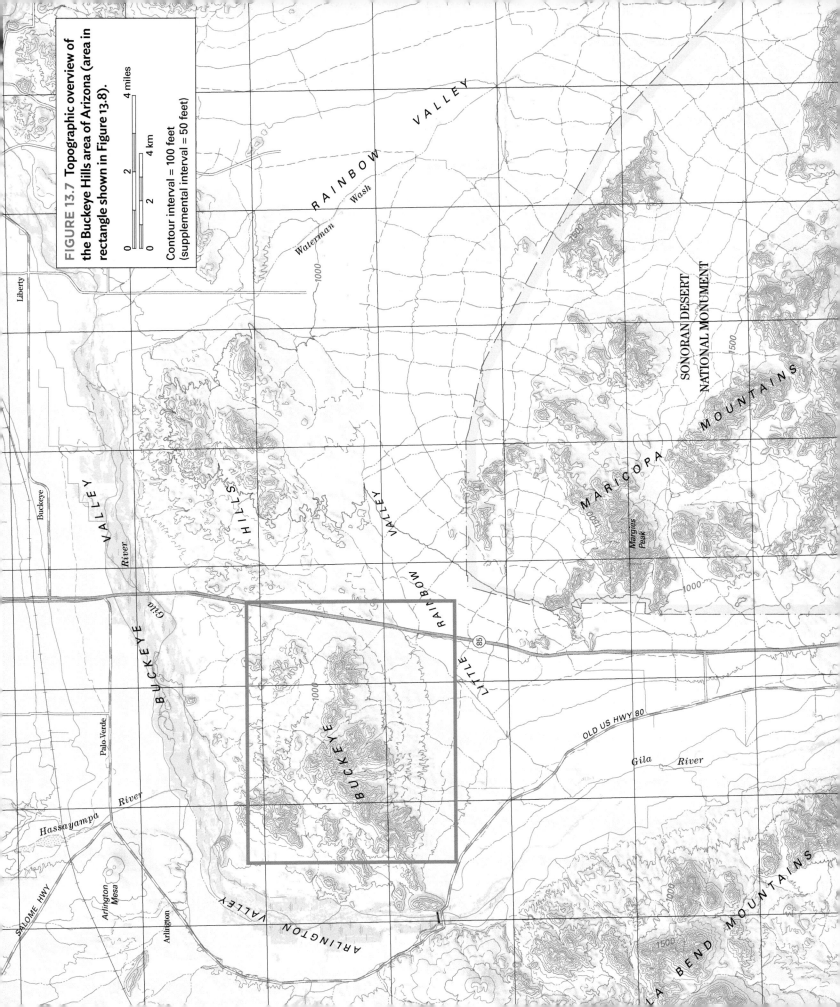

FIGURE 13.7 Topographic overview of the Buckeye Hills area of Arizona (area in rectangle shown in Figure 13.8).

4 miles

4 km

2

2

0

0

Contour interval = 100 feet
(supplemental interval = 50 feet)

RAINBOW VALLEY

Waterman Wash

1000

1500

SONORAN DESERT NATIONAL MONUMENT

MARICOPA MOUNTAINS

1500

Margies Peak

1500

1000

Liberty

VALLEY

HILLS

Buckeye

River

Gila

RAINBOW VALLEY

LITTLE

85

OLD US HWY 80

Gila River

BUCKEYE

1000

1000

Hassayampa

River

SALOME HWY

Palo Verde

Arlington Mesa

Arlington

ARLINGTON VALLEY

1500

LA BEND MOUNTAINS

Name: _____ Section: _____

Course: _____ Date: _____

(p) How are they different?

_____

_____

_____

_____

Now look at the detailed map of the central part of the Buckeye Hills (**FIG. 13.8**).

(q) Identify three erosional and depositional features of arid landscapes. List them here and label them on the map.

_____

_____

_____

(r) What is the probable origin of the small hills just east of Highway 85 that are pictured on this map?

_____

_____

_____

(s) What evidence is there of current stream activity in the Buckeye Hills?

_____

_____

_____

_____

(t) Refer to the diagram showing the evolution of arid landscapes (Fig. 13.3). Which area, Death Valley or the Buckeye Hills, is in a more advanced state of development? Explain your reasoning.

_____

_____

_____

_____

13.4 Wind and Sand Dunes

Wind has a greater impact in arid areas than in humid areas because there is less cohesion between sand grains and little vegetation to hold the sand in place. This is because a small amount of moisture between grains at the surface holds the grains together weakly in humid climates, but that phenomenon is absent in arid regions. There are also fewer trees or other obstacles to block the full force of the wind. Wind erodes the way streams do—using its kinetic energy to pick up loose grains and then using this sediment load to abrade solid rock—literally sandblasting cliffs away.

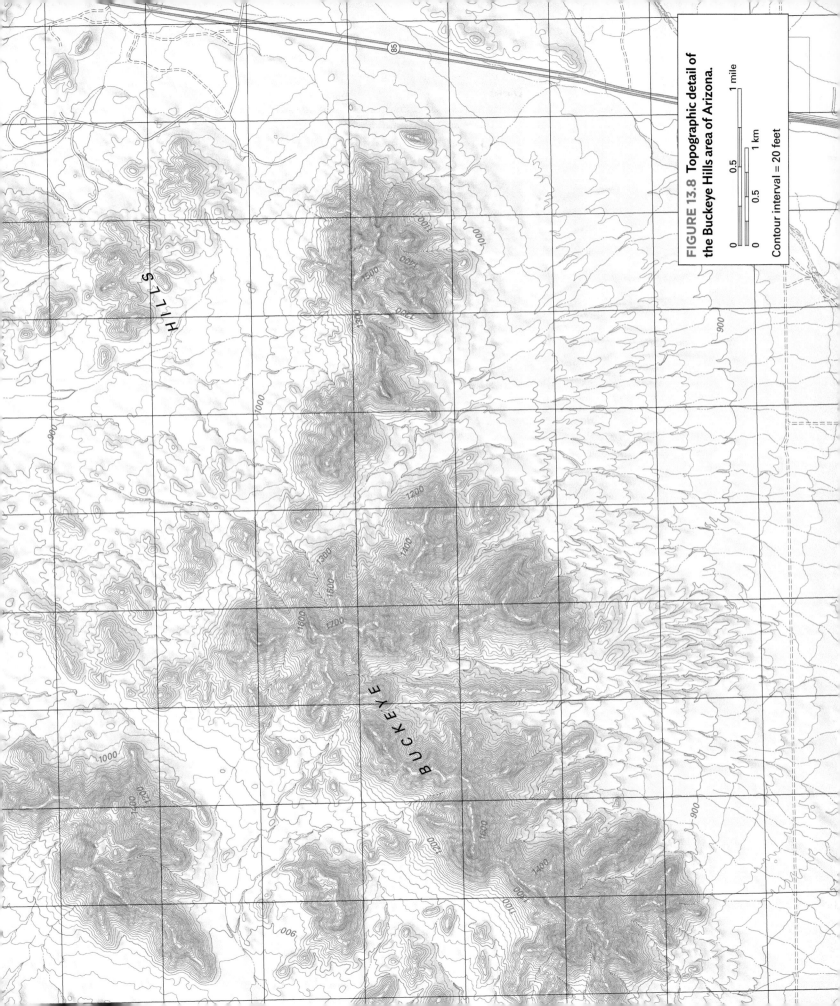

FIGURE 13.8 Topographic detail of the Buckeye Hills area of Arizona.

Contour interval = 20 feet

Dunes are the major depositional landform associated with wind activity in deserts, but they also form along shorelines where there is an abundant source of sand. There are several kinds of dunes, depending on the amount of sand available, the strength of the wind, and how constant the wind direction is (**FIG. 13.9**). **FIGURE 13.10** shows the ripple-marked surface of a large transverse dune from the stippled area on the Stovepipe Wells map in Death Valley (Fig. 13.5). Exercise 13.4 explores the history of sand dunes.

EXERCISE 13.4 **Interpreting the History of Sand Dunes**

Name: _____ Section: _____
Course: _____ Date: _____

The Nebraska Sand Hills

The Nebraska Sand Hills are the remnant of a vast mid-continent sea of sand that existed beyond the Pleistocene ice front approximately 30,000 years ago. More humid conditions today permit grasses, trees, and shrubs to stabilize the dunes so that they no longer move across the countryside like those in Death Valley or the Sahara, but the hills preserve evidence of the more arid conditions under which they formed. Examine the overview of the Nebraska Sand Hills (**FIG. 13.11**).

(a) What evidence is there that this is still a relatively arid region?

_____

_____

_____

_____

(b) Describe the general topographic grain of the area, including the size and shape of the ridges and valleys present.

_____

_____

_____

_____

(c) These ridges are the remnants of the Pleistocene sand sea. What features do they represent?

_____

_____

_____

Examine the map detail (**FIG. 13.12**) of the area outlined in red in Figure 13.11.

(d) Describe the shape of the ridges. Draw a topographic profile, using the graph paper provided at the end of this chapter, along the line indicated to help answer the next question.

_____

_____

(e) What does the shape of the dunes tell you about the wind during the Pleistocene?

_____

_____

(continued)

FIGURE 13.9 Types of sand dunes (red arrows indicate wind direction).

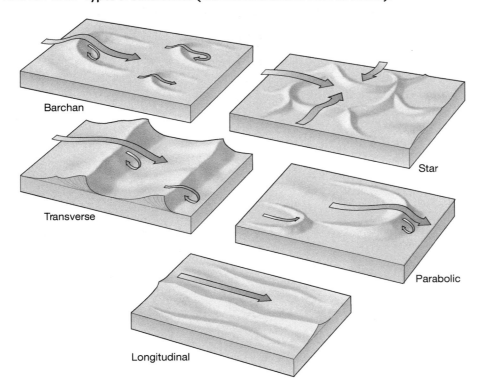

Barchan

Star

Transverse

Parabolic

Longitudinal

FIGURE 13.10 Origin and movement of transverse dunes.

Wind

Windward side

Slip face

Dune

Surface ripples

Slip face

Cross-bed surface

Main bedding surface

(a) Transverse dunes at Stovepipe Wells in Death Valley. The shape of a sand dune depends on wind direction. Small ripples may form on the dune surface.

(b) Movement of sand grains in a transverse dune. Sand is moved from the upwind dune face to the slip face, causing the dune to migrate downwind.

FIGURE 13.11 Topographic overview of part of the Nebraska Sand Hills (area in rectangle shown in Figure 13.12).

Contour interval = 100 feet

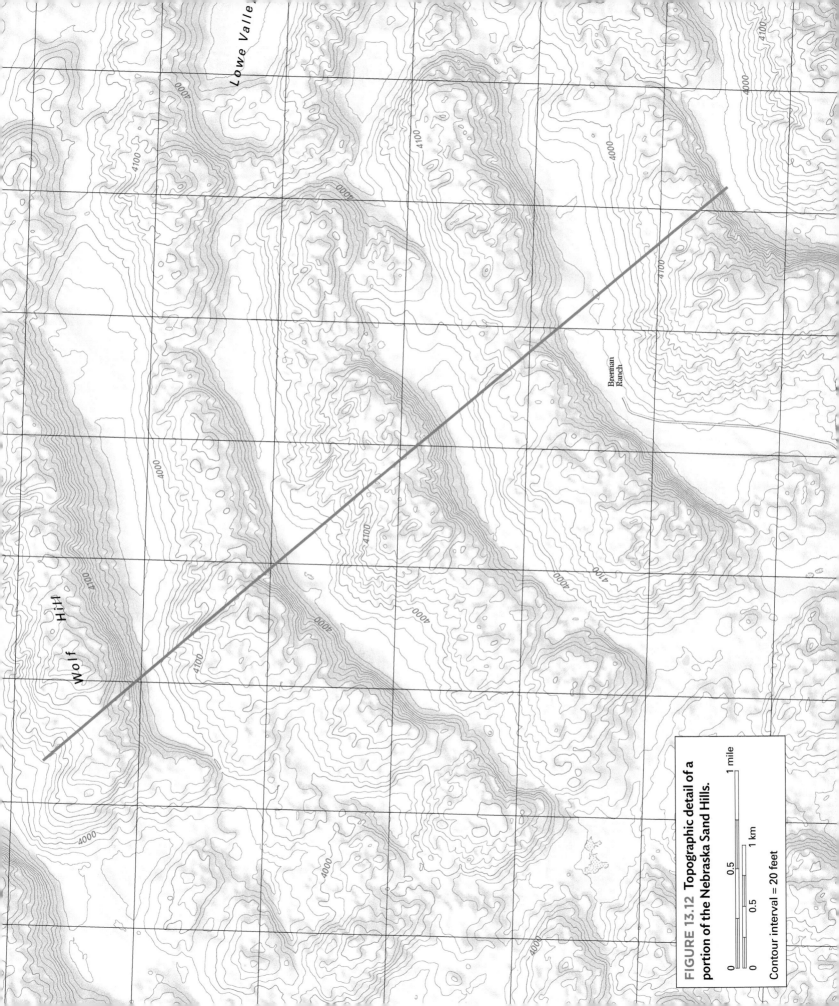

Lowe Valley

Brennan Ranch

Wolf Hill

4000
4100

FIGURE 13.12 Topographic detail of a portion of the Nebraska Sand Hills.

0   0.5   1 km

0   0.5   1 mile

Contour interval = 20 feet

Name: _____   Section: _____

Course: _____   Date: _____

? What Do You Think   Nebraska ranks #4 in the United States in generating electricity with wind–the same wind that forms sand dunes. The wind turbines shown in the first photograph below are only some of the over 500 turbines that generate electricity for 250,000 homes across the state.

In this exercise, suppose that a local initiative is exploring the building of a series of 500 windmills across the Sand Hills area (as seen in Figure 13.12). The windmills would supply low cost electricity for the area, and also allow for future development in the region. However, in this project, the windmills and their arrangement on the landscape will be more similar to those seen in the second photograph below, showing an area outside of Palm Springs, California.

As an informed citizen, you want to start a blog covering this initiative, so that your neighbors understand its pros and cons. To start, on a separate sheet of paper, create two columns, one labeled "Pro" and the other "Con." Then, in each column, briefly describe at least three positive and negative aspects of this project. Consider what you have learned about arid regions, how the turbines might impact other uses of the land, and the possible environmental risks. One thing that many people don't consider is how will the electricity get from the turbines to cities and towns? Then describe your current position either for, against, or possibly somewhere in between, based on your current information.

Wind turbines in Nebraska.

Wind turbines in Palm Springs, CA.

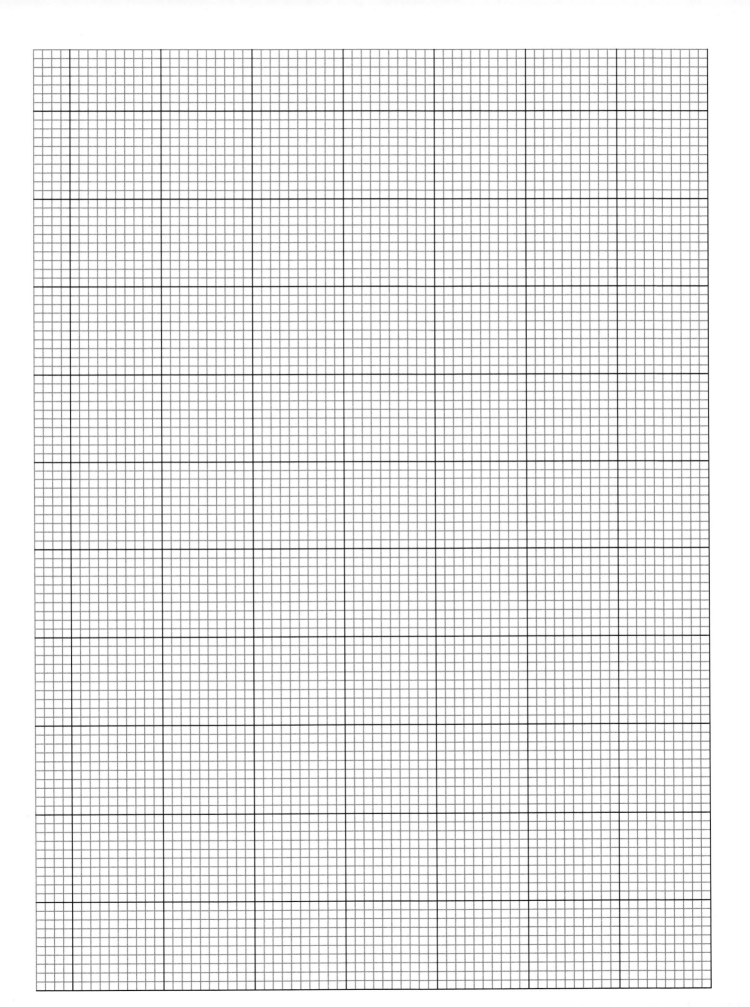

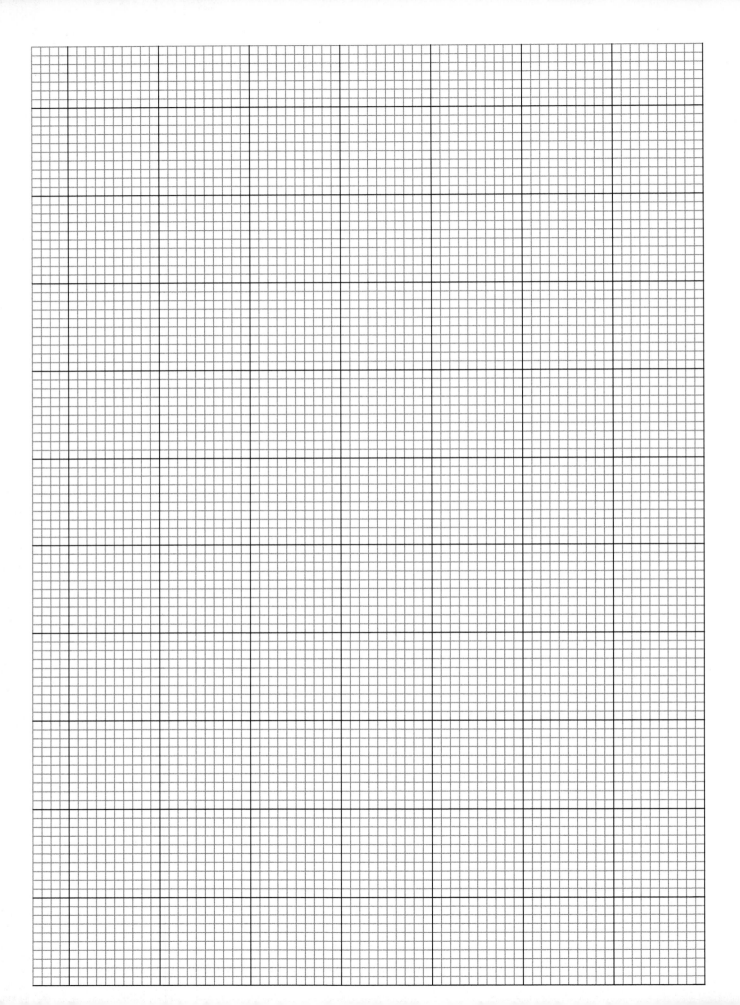

14

Shoreline Landscapes

Coastlines come in a wide variety of types, including rocky, sandy, and mangrove swamps.

14.1 Introduction

Hundreds of millions of people live along North America's Atlantic, Gulf of Mexico, Pacific, and Great Lakes shorelines, and millions more vacation there every year. Recent hurricanes like Katrina and Sandy remind us that shorelines are the most dynamic places on Earth, able to change dramatically in a few hours or days and endanger lives and property. Shoreline landscapes are unique places where the relatively stable geosphere interacts with the much more rapidly changing hydrosphere and atmosphere: wind generates waves that crash onshore, eroding and transporting materials.

Humans will always live along shorelines, but we must do so intelligently to lessen the impact of the rapid changes and must plan wisely as global climate change increases the risk of future catastrophic events. This chapter examines the nature of shorelines, the processes that create and destroy their distinctive landforms, the effects of human activity on those processes, and the disastrous events to which shorelines are uniquely subjected.

14.2 Factors Controlling Shoreline Formation and Evolution

There are many types of shorelines, with examples ranging from rocky cliffs to gentle sandy beaches, untouched coral reefs, marshes, and mangrove groves to heavily urbanized coastlines (FIG. 14.1). But the nature and rapidity of shoreline change are controlled by four important factors, regardless of the type of shoreline:

- Material of which the shoreline is made
- Weather, wind, climate, and climate change
- Tidal range
- Tectonic activity

14.2.1 Shoreline Materials

The type of material present is one of the most important factors in the effectiveness of erosional and depositional processes and therefore shoreline stability. Not all beaches are made of tan sand—consider Hawaii's green, black, and red sand beaches and Bermuda's pink sands—and some shores have little or no sand at all and are made of materials like corals, rocks or boulders, marshes or mangroves, or man-made piers or jetties. And, of course, some shorelines like the southern end of Manhattan Island in New York City, parts of San Francisco, and other harbor cities are now completely man-made. In Exercise 14.1, you will examine the images of shorelines pictured in Figure 14.1.

14.2.2 Weather, Wind, Climate, and Climate Change

Waves are the dominant force in shoreline erosion, and the height and velocity of waves in a region are controlled by weather factors such as the types of weather systems, the strength and direction of winds, and the frequency of storms. Wind also controls how loose materials will be moved along the shoreline in a process called longshore drift (discussed in section 14.3.3) and can have devastating effects on man-made parts of the shoreline.

Climate change has a profound effect on shorelines. For example, during an ice age, glaciers advance across the continents locking enormous amounts of water in ice that would otherwise have been in the oceans. Today, global warming is having the opposite effect, melting the Greenland and Antarctic ice caps as well as most mountain glaciers. It isn't just adding meltwater: as the oceans get warmer, the water in the upper 700 m expands. Between 1961 and 2003, thermal expansion accounted for about 25% of sea-level rise. Between 1993 and 2003, that proportion had risen to nearly 50%.

FIGURE 14.1 Types of shorelines.

(a) Rocky shoreline at West Quoddy Head in Maine.

(b) Sandy and rocky shoreline, Hawaii.

(c) Coral reef along the Hawaiian shoreline.

(d) Salt marsh along the coast of Cape Cod in Massachusetts.

(e) Mangrove swamp in northeastern Brazil.

(f) A seawall built at the southern tip of Manhattan (New York City).

Name: _____   **Section:** _____

Course: _____   **Date:** _____

Review the types of shoreline shown in Figure 14.1 and answer the following questions.

(a) Which of these shorelines do you think would be the most difficult to erode? Which would be the easiest? Explain your choices in a few sentences.

_____

_____

_____

_____

(b) Compare the bedrock cliffs in Figure 14.1 a and b. What factors will determine how resistant to erosion these cliffs are? How can waves erode the bedrock cliffs?

_____

_____

_____

_____

(c) Consider man-made shorelines like the one in Figure 14.1f as compared to the natural shorelines in the other photographs of the figure. Identify one shoreline that may be stronger than the man-made shoreline in (f) and one that may be weaker. Explain your reasoning for each choice.

_____

_____

_____

_____

(d) Indicate with arrows the wind directions that generate the waves shown in Figure 14.1b. Explain your reasoning.

_____

_____

_____

(e) Which area do you think would be most damaged by high winds and high waves? Explain why you made your choice.

_____

_____

_____

_____

FIGURE 14.2 **Tidal range at Mont-Saint-Michel, France.**

(a) At low tide.

(b) At high tide.

14.2.3 Tidal Range

The gravitational attraction of the Sun and Moon cause the tides—water rising and falling along the shore twice a day in most coastal areas. Tidal range is typically a few feet, but in some places coastal geometry results in a far higher range. The Bay of Fundy between the Canadian provinces Nova Scotia and New Brunswick has the highest range, as much as 53 feet between high and low tides. Mont-Saint-Michel in France ranks "only" fourth at 46 feet, but as **FIGURE 14.2** shows, the result is dramatic.

The tides move enormous amounts of sediment all along the shoreline, and fluvial processes extend across exposed tidal flats at low tide. As we shall see later, tidal stage is a major factor in determining how much damage coastal storms will cause when they come onshore.

14.2.4 Tectonic Activity

Tectonic activity creates ocean basins, enlarges or shrinks them, and may uplift or lower the land along the coast. In addition, when submarine volcanoes build their cones above sea level, they create new lands (**FIG. 14.3**), including heavily populated island nations such as Japan, Indonesia, the Philippines, and the state of Hawaii. These islands are in a constant state of change, as waves erode the land that the new lavas build. When an ocean widens or begins to close, the water must occupy the greater or smaller volume of the ocean basin, lowering or raising sea level along the ocean shoreline.

FIGURE 14.3 **Growth of the island of Hawaii by addition of lava from Kilauea Volcano to the shoreline.**

(a) Red-hot lava entering the ocean.

(b) New land created by lava flows in the 1940s.

14.2.5 Emergent and Submergent Shorelines

Short-term fluctuations in sea level occur sporadically during major storms and twice daily in the tidal cycle, but long-term sea-level changes are caused by tectonic activity and climate change. Geologists commonly group shorelines into two categories based on how they respond to these long-term changes. If the land sinks or sea level rises, the shoreline appears to be drowned, with irregular coastline, prominent bays, and abundant islands, marshes, and lagoons. These are called **submergent shorelines**. Land along **emergent shorelines** appears to have risen from the sea by tectonic uplift or a drop in sea level. Emergent shorelines are typically straight and bounded by steep cliffs; where tectonic uplift has occurred, remnants of former shoreline features may be found well above sea level.

The following exercises will give you experience recognizing different types of shorelines, the processes that create them, and how they have changed over time.

EXERCISE 14.2 **Effects of Climate Change on Shorelines**

Name: _____ Section: _____

Course: _____ Date: _____

(a) What would be the effect on the oceans if continental glaciers worldwide expanded by 10%? Explain.

_____

_____

_____

(b) What would be the effect on the world's shorelines if continental glaciers worldwide expanded by 10%?

_____

_____

_____

(c) Conversely, what would be the effect on the world's oceans and shorelines if continental glaciers shrunk by 10%?

_____

_____

_____

(d) Starting about 2 million years ago, much of northern North America, Europe, and Asia were covered with continental glaciers. In what way was the location of the world's shorelines at that time different from that of today's shorelines? Explain your reasoning.

_____

_____

_____

_____

_____

EXERCISE 14.3	Effects of Plate Tectonic Processes on Shorelines

Name: _____ **Section:** _____
Course: _____ **Date:** _____

(a) What effect will continued sea-floor spreading in the Atlantic Ocean have on east and gulf coast sea level? Explain your reasoning. *Hint:* Look at Exercise 2.7.

_____

_____

_____

_____

(b) What effect would partial closing of the Atlantic Ocean have on sea level? Explain.

_____

_____

_____

_____

EXERCISE 14.4	Recognizing Emergent and Submergent Shorelines

Name: _____ **Section:** _____
Course: _____ **Date:** _____

Emergent shorelines look very different from submergent shorelines. Examine the following maps: part of the Atlantic Coast in Maine (**FIG 14.4**), and part of the Pacific Coast in California (**FIG 14.5**). One of these is a typical submergent shoreline, the other a classic emergent shoreline. Apply your geologic reasoning to tell which is which.

(a) Compare and contrast the shapes of the two shorelines.

_____

_____

_____

_____

(b) Which of these shorelines is emergent and which is submergent? Explain your reasoning.

_____

_____

_____

_____

FIGURE 14.4 Maine coastline near Boothbay Harbor.

Contour interval = 25 feet

FIGURE 14.5 California coastline south of Half Moon Bay.

Contour interval = 40 feet

Name: _____   Section: _____

Course: _____   Date: _____

The Pacific Coast, California

The map below shows details of the California coast not far from where Figure 14.11d was photographed.

Portion of the Dos Pueblos Canyon quadrangle of California.

Contour interval = 20 feet

Santa Barbara Channel

(a) Describe the shoreline in your own words.

_____

_____

_____

(b) Sketch profiles along lines A–B and C–D on the graph paper provided at the end of this chapter.

(c) What evidence shows that a change in sea level has taken place?

_____

_____

_____

(d) Based on the map and profile, is this an emergent or submergent shoreline? By how much has sea level changed? Explain your reasoning.

_____

_____

_____

_____

(continued)

Name: _____   Section: _____
Course: _____   Date: _____

Lake Erie, Ohio

The shorelines of many lakes that formed shortly after the retreat of Pleistocene glaciers from North America have changed markedly in the past few thousand years. Some glacial lakes have shrunk to a fraction of their former size (such as Glacial Lake Bonneville, which is now the Great Salt Lake in Utah) or disappeared entirely (Glacial Lake Hitchcock in Massachusetts). The Great Lakes have adjusted to post-glacial conditions, and their shorelines reveal those changes. **FIGURE 14.6** shows an area in Ohio just south of Lake Erie.

(e) Examine the spacing of the contour lines. What do they suggest about the evolution of Lake Erie?

_____

_____

_____

(f) Draw a profile along line A–B (using the graph paper provided at the end of this chapter) and then compare it with the profile you drew for Exercise 14.5b. What features are probably represented by the ridges? What features are probably represented by the gently sloping areas between the ridges?

_____

_____

_____

(g) Based on your answers in (f), how are Sugar, Chestnut, and Butternut ridges related to the post-glacial history of Lake Erie?

_____

_____

_____

(h) Label the previous shoreline position(s).

(i) The current elevation of Lake Erie is 174 feet. How much has lake level changed, based on the evidence on this map?

_____

(j) Was the change continuous or did it take place in sporadic episodes? Explain.

_____

_____

_____

(k) Assuming the retreat of continental glaciers took place about 10,000 years ago, calculate the rate at which lake level dropped if the change had been continuous.

_____

(l) If the change was episodic, suggest a way to estimate the relative amount of time associated with each "still-stand" of lake level. What assumptions must you make?

_____

_____

_____

FIGURE 14.6 Area just south of Lake Erie near Elyria, Ohio.

0   0.5   1 mile

0   0.5   1 km

Contour interval = 5 feet

FIGURE 14.7 **Mechanics of wave action offshore and near the shoreline.**

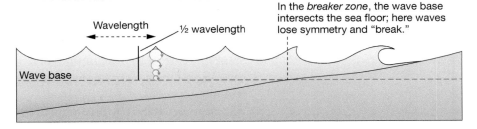

Within a deep-ocean wave, water molecules move in a circular path. The radius of the circle decreases with depth.

Wavelength

½ wavelength

In the *breaker zone*, the wave base intersects the sea floor; here waves lose symmetry and "break."

Wave base

14.3 Shoreline Erosion and Deposition

In this section, we will learn more about how a shoreline changes. Waves are the dominant agents of shoreline erosion and deposition. They erode coastal materials when they strike the shore and deposit loose materials to form beaches and other landforms. Waves also generate currents that parallel the shoreline and build landforms offshore. Wind is not only responsible for driving the waves; it also moves sediment directly in shoreline areas, producing coastal sand dunes. We will look first at the basics of how waves operate and then at how they produce shoreline landforms.

14.3.1 How Waves Form

Waves form by friction generated when wind blows across the surface of an ocean or lake. The symmetrical shape of waves offshore shows how the kinetic energy of the wind is transferred to the water. Offshore, water molecules move in circular paths, each molecule passing some energy on to those it contacts (**FIG. 14.7**). Loss of energy in these contacts limits the depth of wave action to approximately half of the wavelength, a depth referred to as the **wave base**.

When water is shallower than the wave base, as on the right in Figure 14.7, orbiting water molecules interfere with the sea floor or lake bottom, causing waves to lose symmetry and "break." The pileup of water increases the waves' kinetic energy, enhancing their ability to erode the shoreline.

FIGURE 14.8 shows the breaker zone associated with waves in California (Figure. 14.8a) and Hawaii (Fig. 14.8b). In both cases, the wind that generated the waves blew for thousands of miles uninterrupted by land or trees, which is the most favorable condition for wave formation. The arrow in Figure 14.8b shows where the waves have cut a notch in the lava cliffs of Kauai.

FIGURE 14.8 **Waves striking shorelines.**

(a) A breaker zone in California at low tide.

Wave-cut notch

(b) A breaker zone in Hawaii at high tide.

14.3 SHORELINE EROSION AND DEPOSITION   **347**

14.3.2 Wave Erosion and Deposition

A few basic principles explain how waves erode and deposit materials along shorelines and move sediment directly, forming landforms like barrier islands and spits.

- Shorelines are in a constant state of conflict between destructive wave erosion and the constructional processes of deposition, lava flows, and coral reef development.
- Waves are generated by the interaction between wind and the surface waters of oceans and large lakes.
- The kinetic energy of waves causes erosion and redeposition of *unconsolidated* sediment.
- Like streams and glaciers, waves use loose sediment to abrade the bases of solid bedrock cliffs. Waves move sediment back and forth across the tidal zone, abrading a flat wave-cut bench and carving wave-cut notches. When support of the base is undermined, the cliffs collapse by rockfall and slump.
- Waves then erode the rubble, exposing the base of the new cliffs, and the cycle repeats. In this way, shoreline cliffs gradually retreat inland. In tectonically more active coastal areas, there may be several uplifted benches; dating them enables geologists to estimate the rate of uplift.
- Wind also moves sediment by itself, forming coastal sand dunes.
- Shoreline currents redistribute sediment to produce barrier islands, spits, and other landforms.

14.3.3 Longshore Drift

In areas where there is an abundant supply of unconsolidated sediment, longshore currents move sand and silt parallel to the shoreline in a process called **longshore drift.** These currents are generated when waves strike the shoreline obliquely (i.e., not perpendicular to the shore). Each time a wave pushes onshore and then recedes, sand grains are moved onto the shore and then back toward the ocean. After many such zigzag cycles, sand grains gradually move along the beach—in what looks like a straight-line path to someone who hasn't been watching closely (**FIG. 14.9**).

FIGURE 14.9 Origin of longshore drift: Particle A eventually moves to point B by a complex zigzag path shown by the dashed lines. A-1: wave drives the grain up the beach in the direction that the wave is moving. 1-2: Water is pulled downslope to shoreline, carrying the particle with it; these processes are repeated (2-3-4-5-B) to transport the grain parallel to the shoreline.

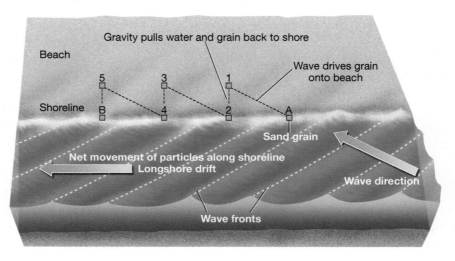

Name: _____   Section: _____

Course: _____   Date: _____

Examine the two shorelines below.

Wave-cut notch

(a) Indicate with arrows the direction in which the wind is blowing in each.

Two aspects of shoreline geometry affect the effectiveness of wave erosion: (1) Is the area exposed, projecting out into the ocean or is it an embayment, protected by flanking headlands? (2) Is the shoreline steep, allowing waves to crash onshore with full force or is it gentle, causing the waves to break offshore and lose some of their energy?

(b) Compare the shoreline geometry in the photographs above. In which would you expect wave erosion to be more effective? Explain.

_____

_____

_____

Similarly, oblique waves also generate currents just offshore that parallel the coastline. These currents are responsible for moving large volumes of sediment and for building such distinctive landforms discussed below, including familiar features like Coney Island and Cape Cod.

14.3.4 Erosional Features

Coastal erosion produces distinctive shoreline features (**FIG. 14.10**) and causes coastal landscapes to change in predictable ways. Coastal erosion is most rapid in places where the land extends out into the ocean, because this position allows waves to attack the land from nearly any direction. Conversely, coastal erosion is slowest in deep, low areas of coastal land called embayments where wave energy is diffused along a broad stretch of coastline.

Coastal erosion leads to two types of landforms to develop. The first group occurs along the shorelines: as waves drive loose sediment across shorelines underlain by bedrock, the sediment abrades a flat surface called a **wave-cut bench** and cuts into the base of bedrock cliffs to form a **wave-cut notch** (**FIG. 14.11**). Where the coastal cliffs are made of unconsolidated sediment, the waves eat into the

FIGURE 14.10 Erosional features of bedrock shorelines.

(a) A wave-cut notch along the Hawaiian coast.

(b) A wave-cut bench at the foot of the cliffs at Étretat, France.

(c) A sea arch on the coast of Hawaii.

cliff and use the sediment as added abrasives. Eventually, the notch undermines the cliff, causing slumping or rockfall, and the cliff face retreats away from the shoreline. Where humans have built homes on coastal cliffs, the result can be disastrous, particularly where the cliffs are made of unconsolidated coastal plain sediments or glacial deposits as along the Atlantic Coast (**FIG. 14.12**). Over long periods of time, wave-cut benches become wider as the coastal cliffs

FIGURE 14.11 Evidence for an emergent shoreline.

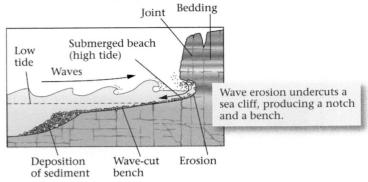

(a) Wave erosion undercuts a sea cliff, producing a notch and a bench.

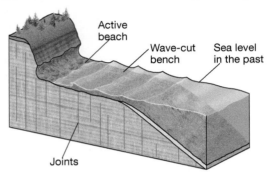

(b) Wave erosion produces a wave-cut bench along an emergent coast.

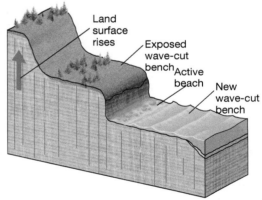

(c) As the land rises, the bench becomes a terrace, and a new wave-cut bench forms.

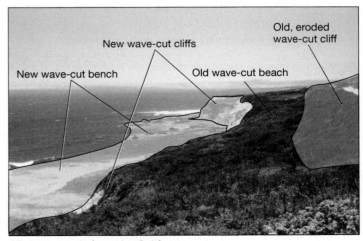

(d) An example from the California coast.

FIGURE 14.13 **Creation of a sea stack.**

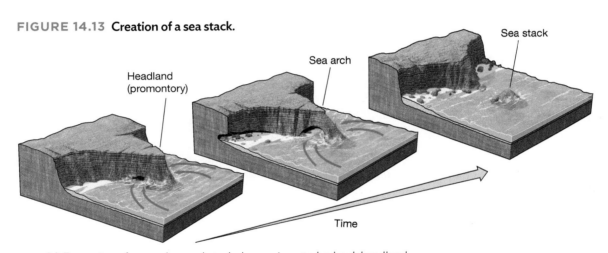

(a) Formation of sea arches and stacks by erosion at a bedrock headland.

retreat landward. In tectonically active areas, old wave-cut benches may be uplifted tens of feet above present sea level where a newer bench is being carved today. By dating the uplifted benches, geologists can estimate the amount of tectonic uplift.

The second group comprises sea arches and sea stacks: distinctive, often dramatic bedrock landforms found close to the current shoreline, a short distance from the shore. When a bedrock cliff retreats, it does not do so at the same rate in all places. Zones of weak bedrock may be eroded quickly, isolating stronger material and starting to cut into it as well. Eventually, a **sea arch**, named because of its natural arch appearance, forms. When further erosion removes the support for the arch, it will collapse and leave an isolated remnant of the bedrock called a **sea stack**

(b) Morro Rock in California, a classic sea stack.

(**FIG. 14.13a**). Morro Rock (**FIG. 14.13b**), off the coast of California, is a spectacularly beautiful sea stack. Sea stacks along a coastline mark the former position of the bedrock cliffs letting us measure the amount of cliff retreat.

Exercise 14.6 explored the factors of wave erosion and now Exercise 14.7 examines the products of wave erosion.

Name: _____   **Section:** _____

Course: _____   **Date:** _____

Refer to photos earlier in this chapter to answer the following questions.

(a) How did the large blocks in Figure 14.10a get into the surf zone? What is their eventual fate?

_____

_____

_____

(b) How did Morro Rock (Fig. 14.13b) become isolated from the bedrock shoreline?

_____

_____

_____

(c) What is the eventual fate of the sea arch in 14.10c?

_____

_____

_____

Examine the shoreline in **FIGURE 14.14**. Point Sur and False Sur are the same kind of feature and record a multistage development for this part of the California shoreline.

(d) Based on its size and steepness, is Point Sur made of a hard material like bedrock or a softer material like limestone? Explain.

_____

_____

_____

(e) Of what material or type of material is the area between Point Sur lighthouse and the California Sea Otter Game Refuge likely made of? Explain your reasoning.

_____

_____

_____

_____

(f) Suggest a sequence of events by which the Point Sur shoreline could have formed.

_____

_____

_____

_____

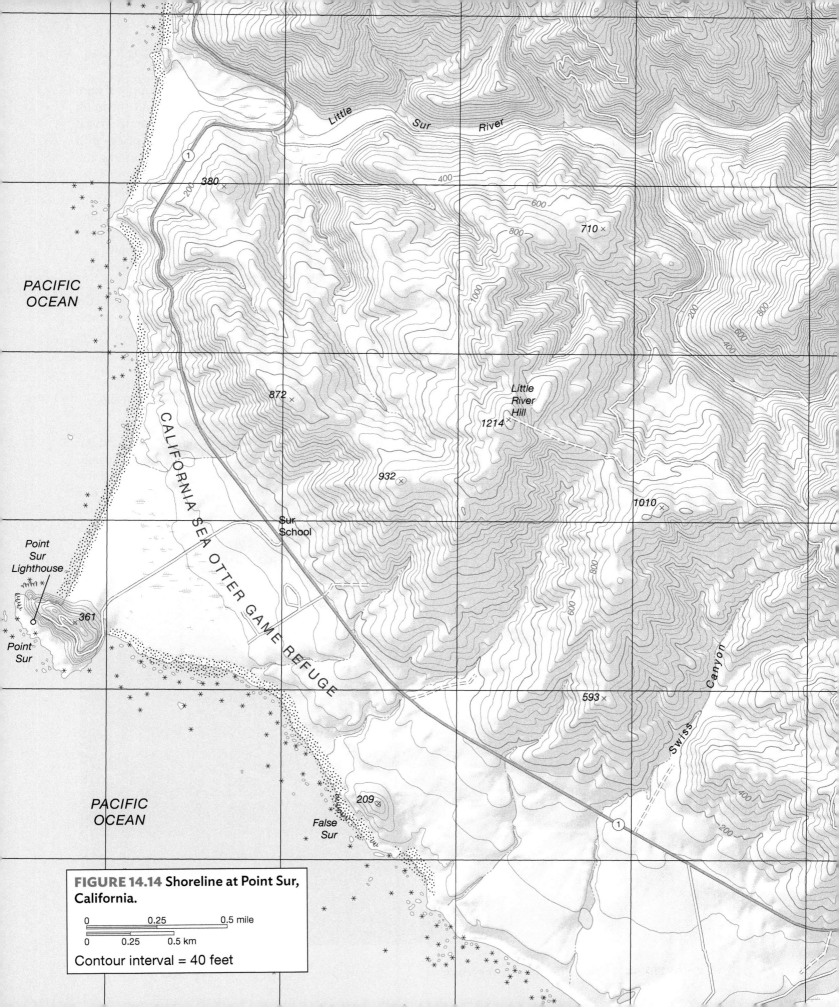

FIGURE 14.14 Shoreline at Point Sur, California.

Contour interval = 40 feet

14.3.5 Depositional Features

Prominent depositional features develop where there is an abundant supply of sand along shorelines. These range from continuous sand bars that extend for miles along the coast to small isolated beaches. The Gulf of Mexico and Atlantic coastal plains are underlain by easily eroded unconsolidated sediments, and places with familiar names display classic depositional features: Cape Cod, Cape Hatteras, the Outer Banks of North Carolina, the eastern Louisiana coast, Padre Island.

Common shoreline depositional features (**FIG. 14.15**) include the following:

- **Beaches** are the most common depositional features and consist of sand (or coarser sediment, coral and shell fragments, etc.—whatever is available).
- **Spits** are elongate sand bars attached at one end to the mainland. Some are straight, like those in Figure 14.15, but some are curved sharply and are called **hooks**.
- **Barrier islands** are elongate sand bars that lie offshore and are not connected to the mainland (e.g., the Outer Banks, Padre Island). Their name comes from the fact that they were barriers to early explorers, who had to search for inlets that would allow them to reach the shoreline.
- **Salt marshes/tidal marshes:** The area between a barrier island and the shoreline is typically a marshy wetland formed by sediment derived from the mainland. These areas are covered with vegetation tolerant to salt water; these plants are fully or partially submerged at high tide.

Sediment eroded from the mainland is deposited in bays between the shore and the barrier islands, forming marshy wetlands. These are important parts of the food chain, providing rich sources of nutrients for a wide range of aquatic organisms, and are important breeding areas for fish and the birds that feed on them. They are also part of our natural storm-protection system. If a storm surge manages to overflow the barrier island (as happened in Galveston, Texas, in 2008, for example), the wetlands act as a sponge, soaking up the water and lessening damage to the more densely inhabited mainland.

In Exercises 14.8 and 14.9, you will explore depositional evironments both in the present and the past.

FIGURE 14.15 Southwestern Long Island (NY) showing common shoreline depositional features. White areas on south shore of spits and barrier islands are *beaches*.

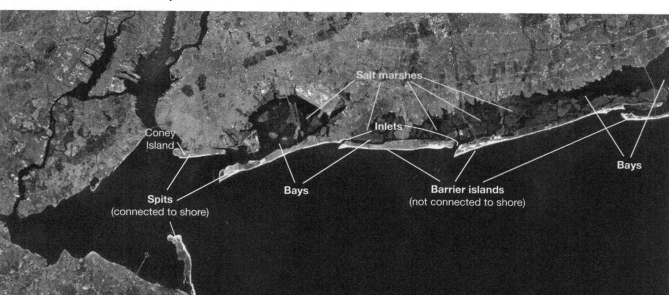

Name: _____　　**Section:** _____

Course: _____　　**Date:** _____

(a) Does the shoreline in **FIGURE 14.16** appear to be emergent or submergent? Explain.

_____

_____

(b) Identify and label the following depositional landforms on Figure 14.16: spit, bar, hook, barrier island, and beach.

(c) What evidence is there that sediment redistribution is taking place *landward* of the barrier island as well as on the barrier islands and spits that protect these areas?

_____

_____

(d) The rapid movement of sand by longshore drift could block access to the mainland by closing gaps in barrier islands and between spits. What steps can be taken to prevent futher erosion?

_____

_____

(e) Indicate the dominant direction of longshore drift. Explain your reasoning.

_____

_____

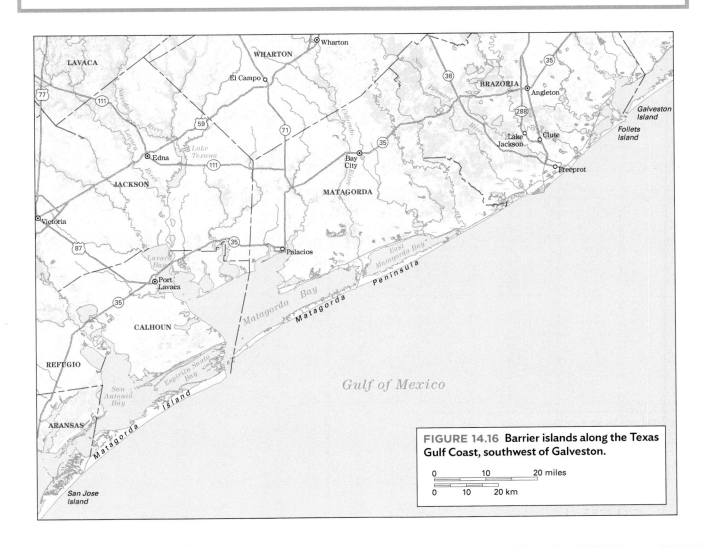

FIGURE 14.16 Barrier islands along the Texas Gulf Coast, southwest of Galveston.

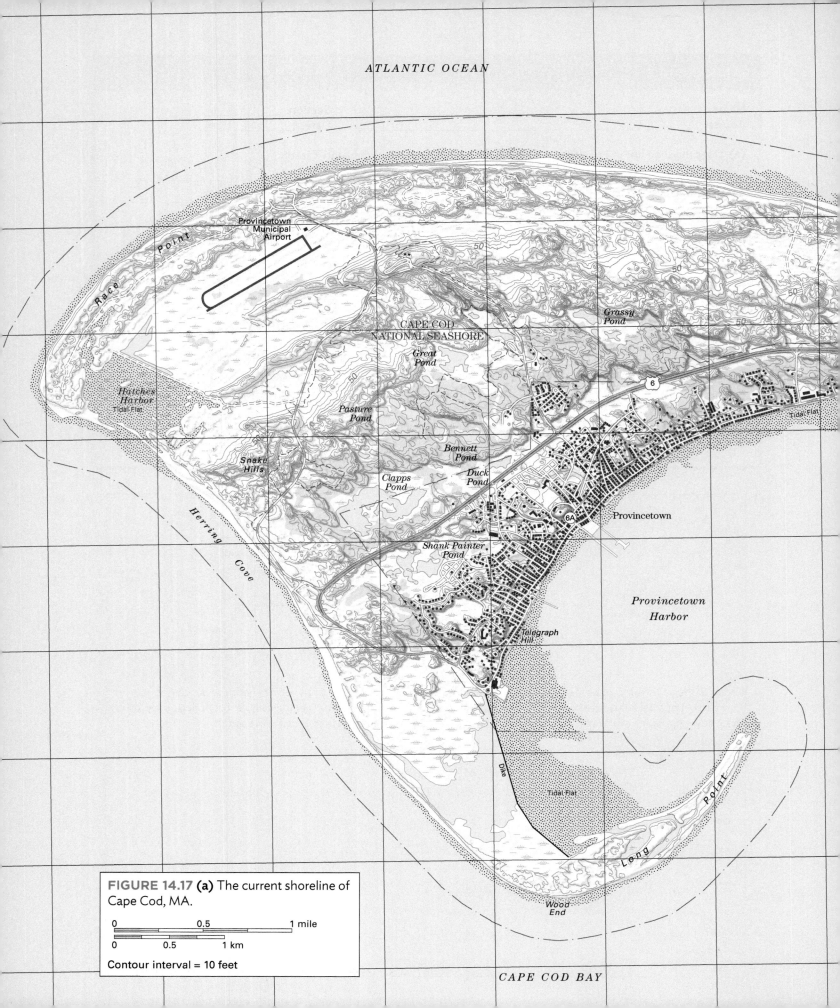

ATLANTIC OCEAN

Race Point

Provincetown
Municipal
Airport

CAPE COD
NATIONAL SEASHORE

50

Great
Pond

Grassy
Pond

50

50

50

Hatches
Harbor
Tidal Flat

50

6

Pasture
Pond

Tidal Flat

Snake
Hills

Bennett
Pond

Clapps
Pond

Duck
Pond

Herring

6A

Provincetown

Cove

Shank Painter
Pond

Telegraph
Hill

Provincetown
Harbor

Dike

Tidal Flat

Long

Point

Wood
End

CAPE COD BAY

FIGURE 14.17 (a) The current shoreline of
Cape Cod, MA.

0   0.5   1 mile

0   0.5   1 km

Contour interval = 10 feet

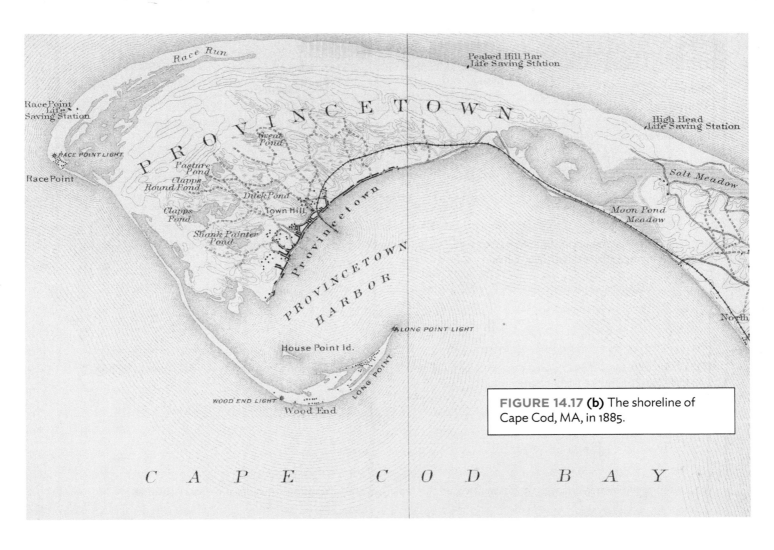

FIGURE 14.17 (b) The shoreline of Cape Cod, MA, in 1885.

Depositional Processes and Shoreline Landforms

Name: _____ Section: _____
Course: _____ Date: _____

FIGURES 14.17a–b are topographic maps of the northern end of Cape Cod made almost 100 years apart. As mentioned earlier, a terminal moraine here provides an abundant source of sand and gravel for shoreline processes. These two maps help illustrate how much change can occur along a coastline in a (geologically) short period. They also show how population pressures affect our use of limited, and therefore very valuable, shoreline space.

(a) What kind of landform is Long Point? _____

(b) Draw arrows on Figure 14.17a to indicate the direction of longshore currents in this area.

(c) Describe the *geologic* changes that have occurred in the century separating the compilation of these two maps.

_____

_____

_____

(continued)

Name: _____   Section: _____
Course: _____   Date: _____

(d) How have Cape Codders tried to prevent Provincetown Harbor from changing?

_____

_____

_____

(e) Based on what happened in the 98 years recorded by these two maps, which landforms might disappear? Which might change shape drastically? Explain your reasoning.

_____

_____

_____

(f) Which of these changes would be beneficial to people living or vacationing in Provincetown? Which would be negative? How might the latter be prevented?

_____

_____

_____

(g) Describe the *human* changes that have affected this area (e.g., transportation, housing, and other uses).

_____

_____

_____

14.4 Human Interaction and Interference with Shoreline Processes

People invest hundreds of thousands of dollars (or more) in shoreline homes and want to use those homes and the local beaches for a long time. But a storm can change a shoreline in just a few hours. The disconnect between what we want and how nature works has led us to use three expensive coastal management strategies: building seawalls to prevent wave erosion; renourishing eroded beach sand; and trapping sand moved by longshore drift with structures called *groynes*. These strategies work sometimes, but other times interfere with shoreline processes in such a way as to create new problems. We'll look first at the strategies, then at the problems.

14.4.1 Seawalls

To protect areas ravaged frequently by intense wave erosion, some communities choose to armor the shoreline with seawalls made of concrete, blocks of loose rock,

FIGURE 14.18 **Examples of sea wall construction.**

(a) A section of the Galveston, Texas seawall.

(b) Concrete blocks of a seawall.

or similar materials. These are designed to break the force of the waves and prevent further shoreline erosion. The 1900 hurricane that devastated Galveston, Texas, was a wake-up call for that community, and today the barrier island city is protected by an extensive seawall as shown in **FIGURE 14.18a.** Seawalls can be made with different designs and materials, like concrete as shown in **FIGURE 14.18b.**

14.4.2 Beach Nourishment

A single storm can wreak havoc along an unprotected beach, eroding vast amounts of sand as shown in **FIGURE 14.19a.** The most common remedy is to do in a short time what it would take nature decades to do: replace the beach (renourishment) by dredging sand from offshore, pumping it onto the beach, and spreading it out with bulldozers (**FIG. 14.19b**).

FIGURE 14.19 **Beach erosion and renourishment.**

(a) Effect of erosion along a sandy shore.

(b) Sand pumped from offshore areas to the beach is "redeposited" by bulldozers.

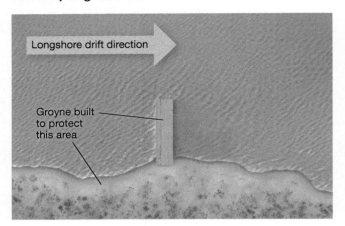
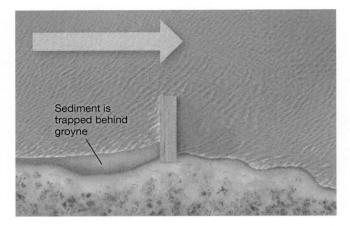

14.4.3 Groynes

Communities on barrier islands often use their knowledge of the longshore drift that built the islands to try to preserve their beaches. They build structures perpendicular to the shoreline in an attempt to trap moving sand and prevent its loss to downdrift areas (FIG. 14.20). These structures are called **groynes** (or commonly, groins).

14.4.4 Some Consequences of Human Interaction

Beach management practices sometimes backfire because the effects of building a seawall or groyne were not thought through fully. The most common problem is that while the shoreline is protected in one area, the seawall or groyne concentrates erosion in different areas, creating problems where there were none previously. For example, waves crashing against a seawall may remove the sand that accumulates naturally along the shoreline, doing exactly the opposite of what was intended. Or, as shown in FIGURE 14.21, sand trapped on the updrift side of a groyne is no longer available to replenish the beach naturally on the downdrift side, so the beach is preserved in one place but eroded in another. Exercise 14.10 gives you some experience recognizing these common problems.

FIGURE 14.21 Aerial view of shoreline showing potential negative effect of groyne construction.

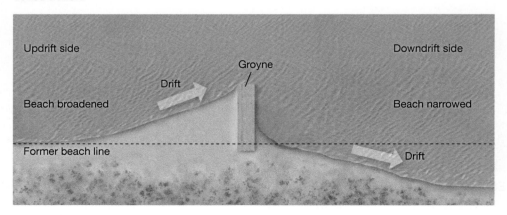

Name: _____   Section: _____

Course: _____   Date: _____

Examine the two photographs directly below showing seawalls built on the Pacific and Gulf coasts. The seawalls successfully prevented further shoreline retreat in both places but also had unanticipated negative results.

(a) What negative impacts do you recognize?

_____

_____

(b) The photograph below shows a groyne field and a seawall protecting one side of the hook at North Avenue Beach, Chicago, Illinois.

  i. Draw an arrow to indicate the direction of longshore drift

  ii. Describe the width of the beach in the areas between the groynes. Suggest an explanation for this pattern.

_____

_____

_____

(continued)

Name: _____ Section: _____
Course: _____ Date: _____

iii. The following photograph of Westhampton, New York, shows the direction of longshore drift. Note the series of groynes designed to protect the narrow barrier island. What problem do you recognize beyond the groynes (closer to the foreground)?

_____

_____

14.5 When Shorelines Become Dangerous

Residents of Thailand, Indonesia, Japan, the Gulf Coast from Florida to Texas, and the east coast from Florida to New York City need no reminder of the dangers of living along a shoreline. Hurricanes (typhoons in Asia) and tsunamis strike quickly and with force that overwhelms our coastal defenses. In contrast, the gradual rise of sea level is almost imperceptible but will eventually disrupt society more than any single catastrophic event. This section explores three ways in which shorelines become potential natural disasters.

14.5.1 Sea-Level Change

The slow rise of sea level is already causing problems worldwide that will worsen in the future. By 2100, moderate estimates project a further rise of about 6.5 feet (2 m), and in a few hundred years a rise of 26 feet. The highest point in the island nation of Maldives in the Indian Ocean is 8 feet above sea level, so the 350,000 Maldives citizens will be without a country within your lifetime. Exercise 14.12 will examine problems caused by sea-level rise.

14.5.2 Coastal Storms

When the normal force of wind is multiplied fivefold in winter "nor'easters" in New England or tenfold in hurricanes, wave-related processes are amplified catastrophically. Typical coastal storms come from a single direction and are easier to prepare for than hurricanes, whose wind velocities can be above 150 miles per hour and whose direction can shift rapidly.

Hurricanes and typhoons, their Pacific Ocean relatives, are enormous storm systems that develop when an atmospheric disturbance passes over warm ocean water (more than 80°F). The storm absorbs energy from the ocean water and forms a low-pressure system as hot air rises. Low-level winds flow toward the center of the system, with a swirling counterclockwise pattern caused by the Coriolis effect (FIG. 14.22).

Heat from the ocean adds energy and moisture, and water vapor condensing at high altitudes adds even more energy. If winds in the upper atmosphere are weak, they cannot prevent the storm from intensifying to hurricane levels (wind velocities greater than 74 miles per hour). While most wind associated with hurricanes is horizontal, winds near the center are a vertical downdraft of warm air that surrounds the eye, a generally clear and ominously calm sector of the storm. Most hurricanes are around 300 miles wide, including the eye, which is typically 20 to 40 miles across.

Hurricanes are pushed slowly by *steering currents* in the atmosphere, generally at 10 to 15 miles per hour. Winds throughout the lower atmosphere, ocean temperature, and interaction with landmasses can make it difficult to predict the path of a hurricane. Hurricanes weaken after making landfall because they are no longer nourished by the warm ocean water, but they may strengthen if they cross over water again. This happened to Katrina, which was only a category 1 hurricane when it hit Florida but grew to category 5 as it headed across the Gulf of Mexico toward New Orleans.

The hazards posed by hurricanes were demonstrated all too well by the effects of Katrina on New Orleans in 2005 and Sandy on New York City in 2013. Both cities were flooded and damaged by strong storm surge (FIG. 14.23a, b), but New York's vast underground infrastructure proved vulnerable in ways that New Orleans escaped.

A common misconception about coastal storms is that wind is the major hazard. Winds of 100 to 175 miles per hour are truly dangerous, but the storm surge, a wall of water driven onshore by the hurricane, is much more hazardous. Katrina's storm surge was estimated at 30 feet above normal sea level; it carried boats, houses, and other debris inland, causing widespread destruction and wiping out entire communities.

In addition to storm surge, coastal flooding typically results from heavy rain that accompanies hurricanes, sometimes as much as 15 inches. Rain from Katrina raised the level of Lake Pontchartrain, which breached the levees separating it from New Orleans (FIG. 14.23c), and storm surge inundated New York's network of subway and commuter tunnels (FIG. 14.23d). Salt water and electrical utilities should never mix—FIGURE 14.23e shows the result in the barrier island Breezy Point neighborhood of New York.

Problems related to a major storm last much longer than the storm itself. Floodwaters damage buildings, which must be inspected to guarantee their safety. Saltwater damage must be repaired, bacteria and mold disinfected, and sand deposited by storm surge removed. Downed trees block traffic, making it difficult to rescue isolated families and deliver emergency food and medicine. Water treatment plants overwhelmed by storm surge dump millions of gallons of sewage into the flood areas. Exposure to toxic materials in floodwaters, like gasoline from damaged gas stations and cars, is a long-term health problem. Exercise 14.11 examines how different communities might anticipate the strength and paths of hurricanes and some of the problems they cause.

FIGURE 14.22 Comparison of Hurricanes Katrina (a) and Sandy (b).

(a) Note the spiral form with a well-developed eye and swirling rain bands outlining the counterclockwise wind circulation pattern.

(b) Hurricane Sandy displayed the same spiral, counterclockwise wind circulation as Katrina, but its centre was less defined and, overall, had a larger ring of rain bands.

FIGURE 14.23 Damage caused by Hurricanes Katrina and Sandy.

(a) A neighborhood complex flattened by the storm surge in Biloxi, Mississippi.

(b) Storm surge hitting Manhattan.

(c) Approximately 80% of New Orleans was flooded when levees that protected the city from Lake Pontchartrain failed.

(d) New York's subway and highway tunnels were flooded, stranding many commuters. This station was lucky–some were completely filled, almost to street level.

(e) Contact between storm-surge saltwater and live electrical lines started fires that destroyed a large part of Breezy Point, New York.

Name: _____   Section: _____

Course: _____   Date: _____

Emergency planners must consider all the factors that determine how dangerous a storm will be: shoreline topography and composition, population density, and type of building construction as well as the strength and path of the storm. These conditions can vary widely over short distances and change rapidly if a storm changes direction.

Storm Path

The path of a hurricane determines whether an area is spared or severely damaged, as the path determines effective wind velocity at any point along the coast. The effective velocity of hurricane winds is a combination of the wind speed in the hurricane and that of the steering winds. In the figure below, Point A, in the direct path of the hurricane, will receive winds of 125 mph because the velocity of the steering winds adds to that of the hurricane itself.

(a) What will be the effective wind velocity of the hurricane at Point B? Explain.

_____

_____

_____

In general, the right side of a hurricane (the side that would be on your right if you were standing directly behind the hurricane) is the most dangerous because the full brunt of steering and wind hurricane velocities are there. The direction from which hurricane winds strike an area also depends on the precise storm path. Remembering that hurricane winds flow in a counterclockwise direction, answer the following questions referring to the figure below.

(b) As a hurricane passes, the direction of its winds shifts. Explain how a single storm could cause winds from opposite directions to affect an area.

_____

_____

_____

(c) The deep estuaries indicated by the arrows in the figure below are highly vulnerable to storm surge because their funnel shapes concentrate water to heights well above those of typical storm surge. Sketch the path that would cause the greatest storm surge into each estuary—the worst-case scenario—on the map below. Remembering Hurricane Katrina, makes the task easy for A, as it followed almost exactly the worst-case scenario.

Effect of storm path on effective wind velocity.

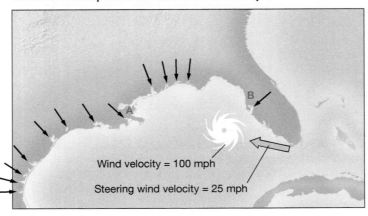

Wind velocity = 100 mph

Steering wind velocity = 25 mph

(continued)

Name: _____   Section: _____

Course: _____   Date: _____

(d) The following figure shows a hurricane in the area of the Bahama Islands. Using a colored pencil, sketch a hurricane path on the map that would cause the first winds from the hurricane to strike each of the following locations from the direction indicated:

- Location A from the south
- Location B from the north
- Location C from the east
- Location D from the north
- Location E from the west
- Location F from the east

Relationship between wind direction and hurricane path.

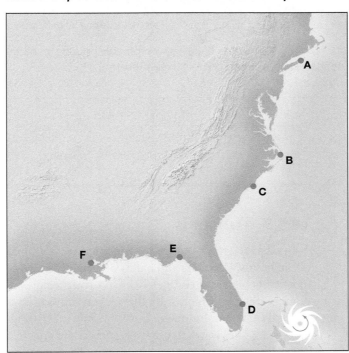

Landforms

Barrier islands and the wetlands behind them along shorelines are a natural line of defense against hurricane damage. The barrier islands break the force of the storm surge and the wetlands absorb water like a sponge, lessening inland flooding. Floridians are well aware of these phenomena.

(e) Compare the pictures of the east and west coasts of Florida on the following page. Which shoreline is more protected from a storm, Naples or Port. St. Lucie? Explain.

_____

_____

_____

(continued)

A tale of two coasts.

Naples on Florida's west coast.

Port St. Lucie on Florida's east coast.

(f) Developers often request rezoning so they can build highly profitable housing on barrier islands and fill in wetlands for shopping centers serving the new inhabitants. Why is this a problem?

_____

_____

_____

14.5.3 Tsunamis

Tsunamis are enormous waves generated by earthquakes or volcanic explosions in the ocean basins. Harmless and barely detectable in mid-ocean, they become walls of water tens of feet high when funneled into narrow coastal embayments. Tsunamis are discussed in more detail in Chapter 16; this section shows their effects on a single coastal city.

Earthquakes in Indonesia in 2004, Chile in 2010, and Japan in 2011 generated devastating tsunamis, waves that traveled across the Pacific Ocean at the speed of a jet plane and slammed into low-lying shorelines. Tsunami waves as high as 25–30 feet were reported from coastal cities in Japan. Television reports captured the awesome power of tsunamis, showing cars, large boats, and even small buildings being carried or smashed into pieces. FIGURE 14.24 captures some of that power, even without the live action.

Eight hours later and thousands of miles away, a tsunami generated by the Sendai earthquake hit Hawaii and, later still, the northwest coast of the United States. The waves were much lower, and damage was nothing compared with that in Japan.

Tsunamis travel at approximately 500 mph. At that rate, Japanese coastal cities 60–100 miles from the earthquake epicenter had only a few minutes warning—not nearly enough to evacuate to higher ground. That is why the damage was so severe and the loss of life so great, even though Japan is the world's leader in earthquake readiness.

Nations surrounding the Pacific Ocean's "Ring of Fire" have cooperated in forming a tsunami warning network so that some warning can be given to island and continental coastlines throughout the ocean. Sensors on strategically placed buoys can track the passage of a tsunami and relay that information to civil defense workers. FIGURE 14.25 shows estimated travel times for a tsunami generated by the Sendai earthquake.

FIGURE 14.24 Damage from tsunamis generated by the Sendai, Japan, earthquake (March 10 and 11, 2011).

(a) Tsunami slamming into Japanese coastline.

(b) Sendai, Japan, airport inundated by tsunami water and debris.

(c) Debris, including houses and a large ship, carried by the tsunami into the city center of Kesunnuma in northeastern Japan.

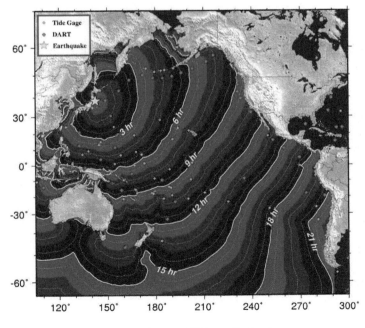

FIGURE 14.25 Tsunami tracking stations and estimated arrival times from the Sendai, Japan, earthquake. (DART = Deep-ocean Assessment and Reporting of Tsunamis sensors operated by NOAA.)

At 500 mph, some places will have little time to prepare, while others may have many hours. Note that the west coast of South America had nearly a full day to evacuate coastal areas, California and Oregon about 10 hours, and Honolulu about 8 hours. In Exercise 14.12, you will consider the risks of damage to different shorelines of the United States and make recommendations on how to reduce those risks.

Name: _____   **Section:** _____

Course: _____   **Date:** _____

? **What Do You Think**   Half of the population of the United
States lives within 50 miles (80 km) of a shoreline. Disasters caused by
recent tsunamis, hurricanes, and typhoons are making insurance companies
reexamine risks and reevaluate premiums for insurance along shorelines—or
consider if they should even offer insurance in some areas. They rely on geologists' expertise, and you have been contacted by a company for your advice
about whether there should be different policies and/or rates for the east and
gulf coasts of North America as compared with the west coast. *Your job is to
outline the factors that control potential damage to coastal properties in these two
regions.* Questions to consider:

   ■ Do the regions have the same risk of damage by tsunamis and hurricanes?

   ■ What factors determine the amount of potential damage in each of the regions?

   ■ How would continued global climate change affect risk? How far inland would a 5-foot
     sea-level rise shift the shoreline? A 25-foot rise?

   To help, six shoreline profiles have been provided, each ~5 miles long from either the Gulf of Mexico, or the Pacific or Atlantic coasts of the United States. On a separate sheet of paper, provide your
report and recommendations for each coast.

(continued)

Name: _____   Section: _____
Course: _____   Date: _____

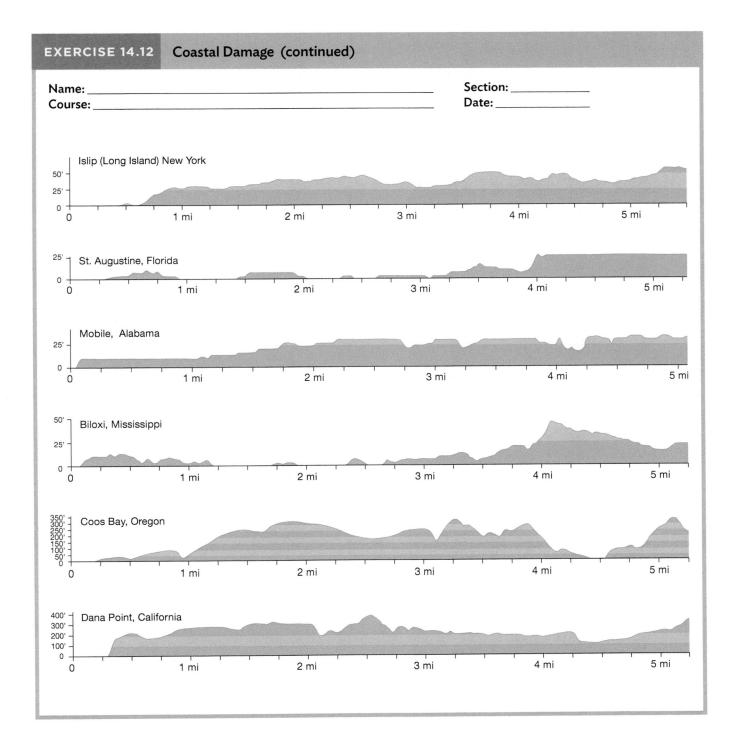

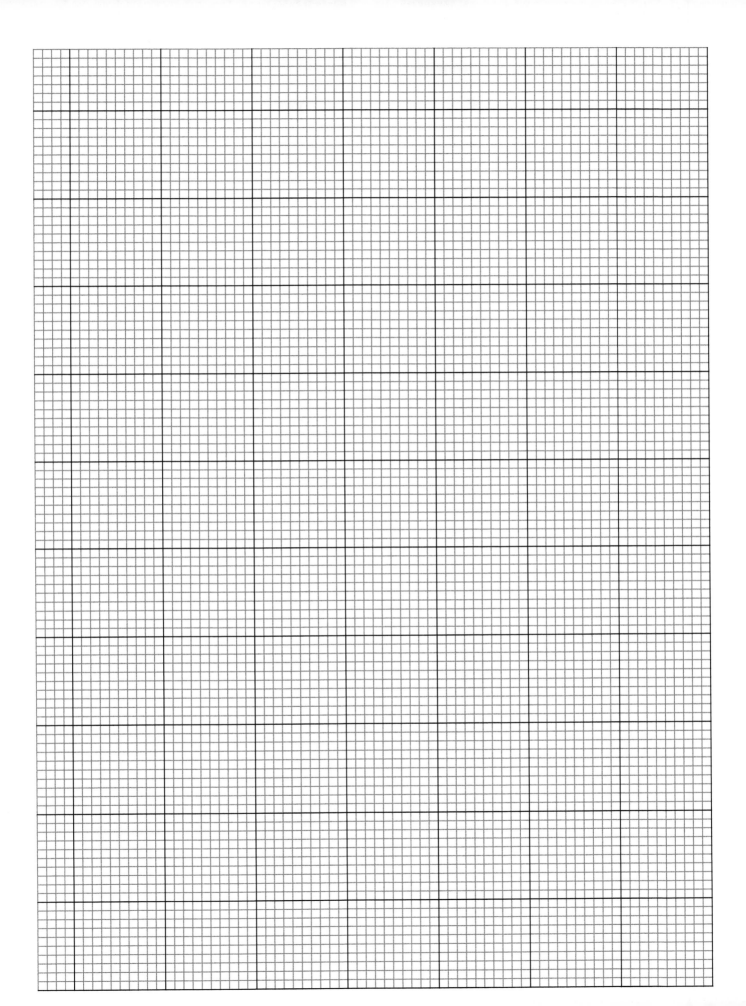

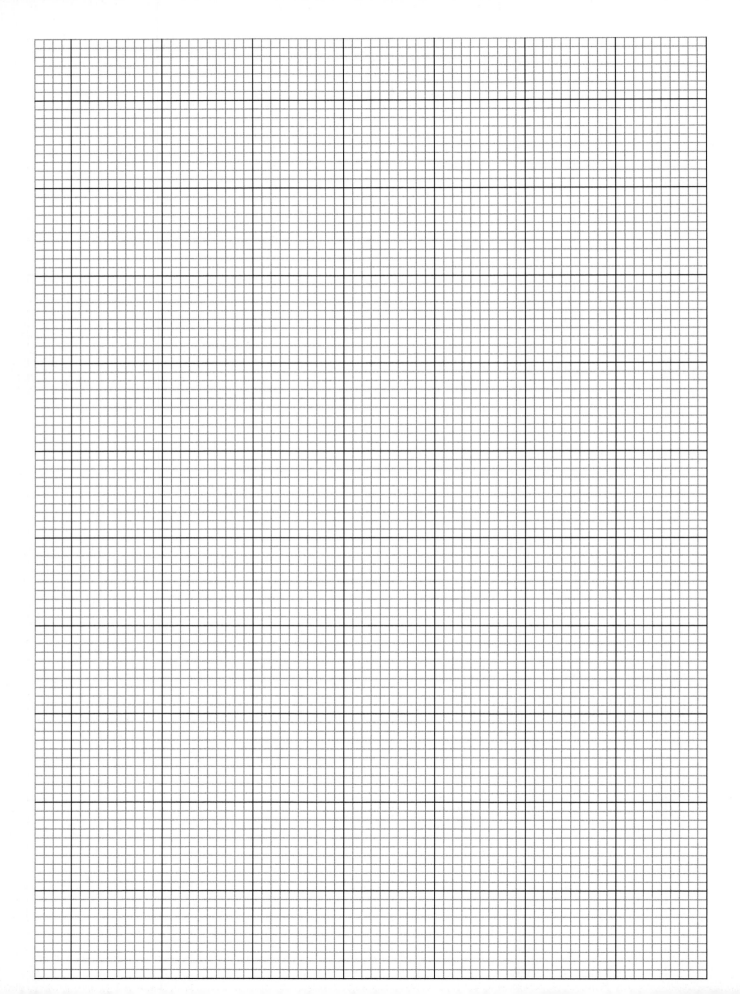

15

Interpreting Geologic Structures on Block Diagrams, Geologic Maps, and Cross Sections

Stress applied to rock produces deformation, such as the recumbent folds and thrust fault seen in this image of a coastal cliff in Cornwall, United Kingdom.

- Become familiar with common geologic structures such as folds and faults
- Visualize structures in three dimensions using block diagrams, maps, and cross sections
- Recognize the presence of folded and faulted rock from landscape features
- Interpret the geologic structure of an area from a geologic map
- Learn how to read a geologic map of a region

MATERIALS
NEEDED

- Colored pencils
- A fine-tipped black pen
- Tracing paper
- A pair of scissors and tape
- A protractor
- A straightedge

15.1 Introduction

The Earth is a dynamic place! Over time, lithosphere plates move relative to one another: at convergent boundaries, one plate sinks into the mantle beneath another; at rifts, a continental plate stretches and may break apart; at a mid-ocean ridge, two oceanic plates move away from each other; at a collision zone, continents press together; and at a transform boundary, two plates slip sideways past each other. All these processes generate stress that acts on the rocks in the crust. In familiar terms, *stress* refers to any of the following (**FIG. 15.1**): **pressure**, which is equal squeezing from all sides (Fig. 15.1a); **compression**, which is squeezing or squashing in a specific direction (indicated by the inward-pointing arrows in Fig. 15.1b); **tension**, which is stretching or pulling apart (indicated by the outward-pointing arrows in Fig. 15.1c); **shear**, which happens when one part of a material moves relative to another part in a direction parallel to the boundary between the parts (indicated by adjacent arrows pointing in opposite directions in Fig. 15.1d). Exercise 15.1 relates different types of stress to everyday processes.

The application of stress to rock produces **deformation**, which includes many phenomena, such as the displacement of rocks on sliding surfaces called **faults**, the bending or warping of layers to produce arch-like or trough-like shapes called **folds**, or the overall change in the shape of a rock body by thickening or thinning. Under certain conditions, a change in the shape of a rock body produces **foliation**, a fabric caused by the alignment of platy or elongate minerals.

The products of deformation, such as faults, folds, and foliations, are called **geologic structures**. Some geologic structures are very small and can be seen in their entirety within a single hand specimen. Typically, however, geologic structures in the Earth's crust are large enough that they affect the orientation and geometry of rock layers, which in turn may control the pattern of erosion and, therefore, the shape of the land surface.

Geologists represent the shapes and configurations of geologic structures in the crust with the aid of three kinds of diagrams. A **block diagram** is a three-dimensional representation of a region of the crust that depicts the configuration of structures on the ground (the map surface) as well as on one or two vertical slices

FIGURE 15.1 **Kinds of stress.**

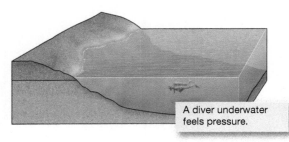

(a) Pressure.

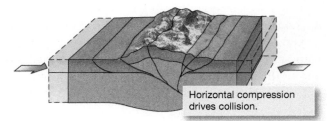

(b) Horizontal compression.

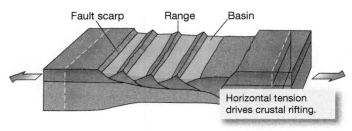

(c) Horizontal tension.

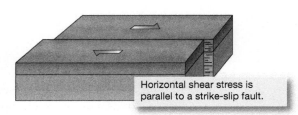

(d) Horizontal shear.

into the ground (cross-section surfaces). A **geologic map** represents the Earth's surface as it would appear looking straight down from above, showing the boundaries between rock units and where structures intersect the Earth's surface. A **cross section** represents the configuration of structures as seen in a vertical slice through the Earth. **FIGURE 15.2** shows how these different representations depict Sheep Mountain in Wyoming.

EXERCISE 15.1   **Picturing Stress**

Name: _____   Section: _____
Course: _____   Date: _____

For each of the phenomena described below, name the stress state involved.

(a) You spread frosting on a cake with a knife. The frosting starts out as a thick wad, then smears into a thin sheet.

_____

(b) You step on a filled balloon until the balloon flattens into a disk shape.

_____

(c) You pull a big rubber band between your fingers so that it becomes twice its original length.

_____

(d) A diver takes an empty plastic milk jug, with the lid screwed on tightly, down to the bottom of a lake. The jug collapses inward from all sides.

_____

The purpose of this chapter is to help you understand the various geometries of geologic structures and develop the ability to visualize structures and other geologic features by examining block diagrams, geologic maps, and cross sections. In addition, this chapter will help you to see how the distribution of rock units, as controlled by geologic structures, influences topography, as depicted on topographic maps and digital elevation maps (DEMs). Geologic structures can be very complex, and in this chapter we can only work with the simplest examples. Again, our main goal here is to help you develop the skill of visualizing geologic features in three dimensions.

15.2 Beginning with the Basics: Contacts and Attitude

15.2.1 Geologic Contacts and Geologic Formations

When you looked at Figure 15.2d, you saw patterns of lines. What do these lines represent? Each line is the trace of a **contact**, the boundary between two geologic units. In this context, a **trace** is simply the line representing the intersection of a planar feature with the plane of a map or cross section; a *unit* may be either a **stratigraphic**

FIGURE 15.2 Geology of Sheep Mountain in Wyoming.

(a) Oblique air photo.

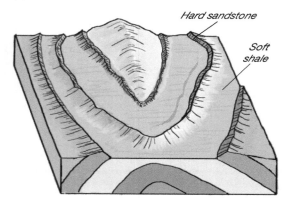

(b) Block diagram.

(c) Cross section.

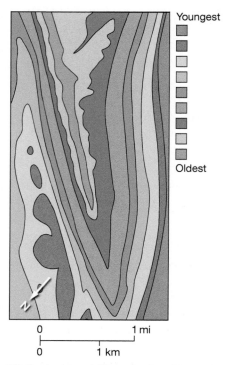

(d) Geologic map. The color bands represent rock units. The map is oriented to correspond with the photo in part (a).

formation (a sequence of sedimentary and/or volcanic layers that has a definable age and can be identified over a broad region), an igneous intrusion, or an interval of a specified type of metamorphic rock. Geologists recognize several types of contacts: (1) an **intrusive contact** is the boundary surface of an intrusive igneous body; (2) a **conformable contact** is the boundary between successive beds, sedimentary formations, or volcanic extrusions in a continuous stratigraphic sequence; (3) an **unconformable contact** (or **unconformity**) occurs where a period of erosion and/or deposition has interrupted deposition; and (4) a **fault contact** is where two units are juxtaposed across a fault. Throughout this chapter, you'll gain experience interpreting contacts, but to be sure you understand the definitions from the start, complete Exercise 15.2.

Name: _____   **Section:** _____

Course: _____   **Date:** _____

In the figure below, each arrow points to one of the four basic kinds of contacts. Add the labels.

Contacts.

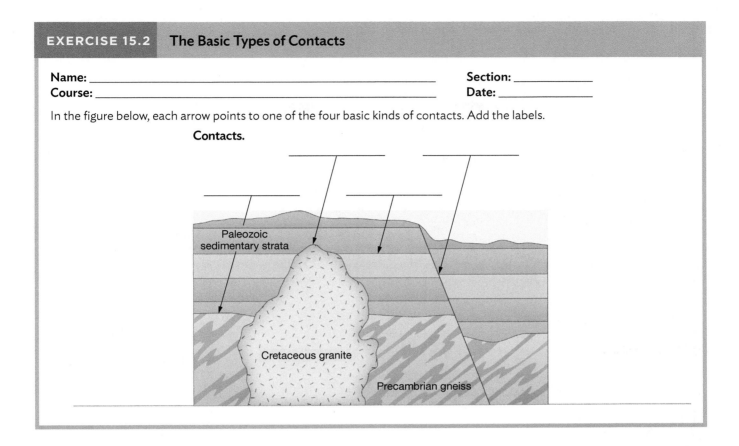

15.2.2 Describing the Orientation of Layers: Strike and Dip

You can efficiently convey information about the orientation, or **attitude**, of any planar geologic feature, such as a bed or a contact, by providing two numbers. The first number, called the **strike**, is the compass direction of a horizontal line drawn on the surface of the feature (**FIG. 15.3a**). You can think of the strike as the intersection between a horizontal surface (e.g., the flat surface of a lake) and the surface of the feature. We can give an approximate indication of strike by saying "the bed strikes northeast" or we can be very exact by saying "the bed has a strike of N 45° E," meaning that there is a 45° angle between the strike line and due north, as measured in a horizontal plane. The second number, called the **dip**, is the angle of tilt or the angle of slope of the bed, measured relative to a horizontal surface. A horizontal bed has a dip of 00°, and a vertical bed has a dip of 90°. A bed dipping 15° has a gentle dip, and a bed dipping 60° has a steep dip. The direction of dip is perpendicular to the direction of strike (**FIG. 15.3b, c**).

Because strike represents a line with two ends, a strike line actually trends in two directions: a strike line that trends north must also trend south; one that trends northwest must also trend southeast. How do we pick which direction a strike line trends? By convention, strike is read relative to north, so you will generally only see strikes described as angles east or west of north, or due north, east, or west (**FIG. 15.3d**). Thus, the beds on the left side of Figure 15.3A strike N 38°E or 38° east of north. Also by convention, beds that dip directly to the north are considered to strike west, while those that dip directly to the south strike east.

FIGURE 15.3 **Strike and dip show the orientation of planar structures.**

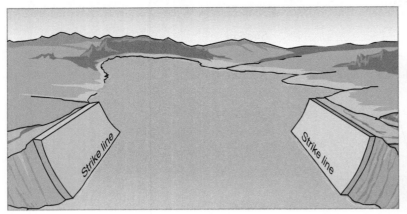

(a) A strike is the intersection of a horizontal plane with the bed surface. Strike lines for two sets of beds oriented in opposite directions are shown here.

(b) Strike line and dip direction shown for sloping beds at Turner Falls in Massachusetts.

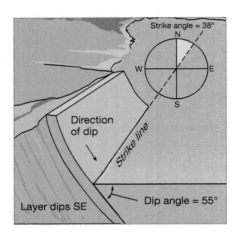

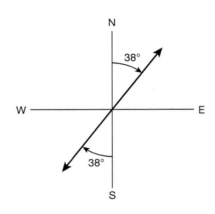

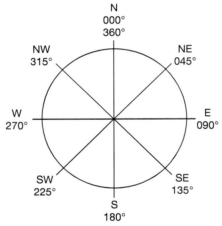

(c) This detail of the beds on the left side of (a) shows their strike and dip, which are used to describe the orientation, or attitude, of these beds.

(d) The strike line in (c) can be described as trending 38° northeast or 38°southwest. By convention, geologists will say the strike is N38°E.

(e) Strikes can also be specified by azimuths (compass angles between 000° and 360°). In azimuth notation, the strike line in (c) of N38°E is written as 038°.

When a strike is written as some angle relative to north, such as N 30° E, this is referred to as **quadrant notation**. However, geologists also use a shorthand notation for giving the strike and dip of a bed. We can also write the strike as a three-digit number, for we divide the compass dial into 360 degrees, or azimuths (**FIG. 15.3e**). A strike of 000° (or 360°) means the bed strikes due north; a strike of 045° means that the strike line trends 45° east of north (i.e., northeast); a strike of 090° is 90° east of north (i.e., due east); and a strike of 320° is 60° west of north. Writing strike as a three-digit number is referred to as **azimuth notation**. Because strike is measured relative to north, the allowable azimuth values are 000° to 090° for a northeast to east-trending strike line and 270° to 360° for a northwest to west-trending strike line. We write the dip as a two-digit number (an angle between 00° and 90°) followed by a general direction. Let's consider an example: if a bed has an attitude of 045°/60° NW, we mean that it strikes northeast and dips steeply northwest. A bed with an attitude of 053°/72° SE strikes *approximately* northeast and dips steeply to the southeast. Exercise 15.3 will give you some practice measuring strike and dip.

Name: _____   **Section:** _____

Course: _____   **Date:** _____

(a) Use a protractor to draw the indicated strike lines on each compass. Translate each azimuth into a direction (e.g., northeast).

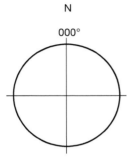 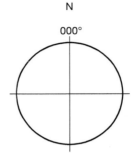

Strike: 060°   Strike: 340°   Strike: 090°

Direction: _____   Direction: _____   Direction: _____

(b) Use a protractor to measure the strikes below. Give the strike direction in both azimuth and quadrant notations, and describe the direction (e.g., northeast).

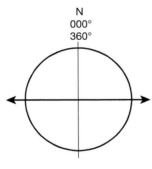 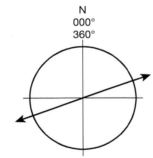 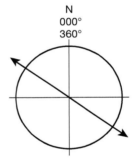

(Here the bed dips north.)

Azimuth: _____   Azimuth: _____   Azimuth: _____

Quadrant: _____   Quadrant: _____   Quadrant: _____

Direction: _____   Direction: _____   Direction: _____

(c) Use a protractor to measure the angle of dip for the two beds on the next page. The dashed lines indicate the level of the horizontal. The shaded surfaces are the surfaces of the beds. Using the strikes given and diagrams for each bed, indicate the rough direction of dip (e.g., west, northwest) for each bed. Remember, the direction of dip is perpendicular to the direction of strike.

(continued)

Name: _____   Section: _____

Course: _____   Date: _____

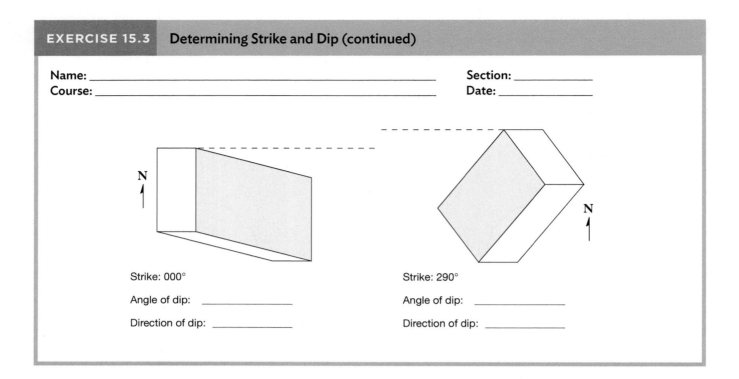

Strike: 000°

Angle of dip: _____

Direction of dip: _____

Strike: 290°

Angle of dip: _____

Direction of dip: _____

15.3 Working with Block Diagrams

We start our consideration of how to depict geologic features on a sheet of paper by considering block diagrams, which represent a three-dimensional chunk of Earth's crust and utilize the artist's concept of perspective (**FIG. 15.4a**). Typically, geologists draw blocks so that the top surface and two side surfaces are visible. The top is called the **map view**, and the side is a **cross-section view**. In the real world, the map-view surface would display the topography of the land surface, but for the sake of simplification, our drawings portray the top surface as a flat plane. In the following subsections, we introduce a variety of structures as they appear on block diagrams.

15.3.1 Block Diagrams of Flat-Lying and Dipping Strata

The magic of a block diagram is that it allows you to visualize rock units underground as well as at the surface. For example, **FIGURE 15.4b** shows three horizontal layers of strata. If the surface of the block is smooth and parallel to the layers, you can see only the top layer in the map view; the layers underground are visible only in the cross-section views. But if a canyon erodes into the strata, you can see the strata on the walls of the canyon, too (**FIG. 15.4c**).

Now, imagine what happens if the layers are tilted during deformation so that they have a dip. **FIGURE 15.4d** shows the result if the layers dip to the east. In the front cross-section face, we can see the dip. Because of the dip, the layers intersect the map-view surface, so the contacts between layers now appear as lines (the traces of the contacts) on the map-view surface. Note that, in this example, the beds strike due north, so their traces on the map surface trend due north. Also note that, in the case of tilted strata, the true dip angle appears in a cross-section face only if the face is oriented perpendicular to the strike. On the right-side face in Figure 15.4d, the beds look horizontal because the face is parallel to the strike. (On a randomly oriented cross-section face, the beds have a tilt somewhere between 0° and the true dip.) Practice drawing tilted strata in Exercise 15.4.

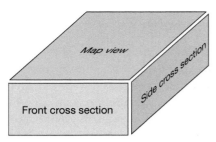

Map view

Side cross section

Front cross section

(a) Construction of a block diagram.

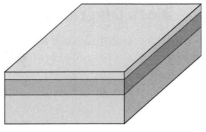

(b) A block diagram of three horizontal strata represented by different colors.

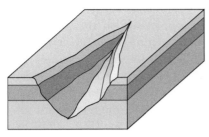

(c) A canyon cut into horizontal strata.

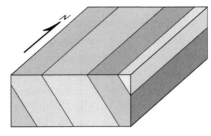

(d) A block diagram of east-dipping strata.

FIGURE 15.4 **Block diagrams.**

EXERCISE 15.4   **Portraying Tilted Strata on a Block Diagram**

Name: _____   Section: _____

Course: _____   Date: _____

(a) On the block diagram template below, sketch what a sequence of three layers would look like if their contacts had traces that trended north–south on the map view and dipped to the west at about 45°.

(b) On the block diagram template below, sketch what a sequence of three layers would look like if the traces had an east–west trend and dipped south at about 45°.

(c) On the block diagram template below, sketch what three layers would look like if the traces had a northeast–southwest trend and the layers dipped to the southeast at about 45°. (*Hint:* This is a bit trickier, because tilt appears in both cross-section faces.)

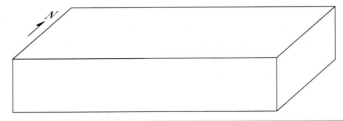

15.3.2 Block Diagrams of Simple Folds

When rocks are deformed and structures develop, the geometry of layers depicted on a block diagram become more complicated (**FIG. 15.5**). If deformation causes rock layers to bend and have a curve, we say that a **fold** has developed. Geologists distinguish between two general shapes of folds: an **anticline** is an arch-like fold whose layers dip away from the crest, whereas a **syncline** is a trough-like fold whose layers dip toward the base of the trough (Fig. 15.5a, b). Anticlines arch layers of rocks upward; synclines do the opposite—their strata bow *downward*. For the sake of discussion, the side of a fold is a **fold limb**, and the line that separates the two limbs (i.e., the line along which curvature is greatest) is the **fold hinge**. We can represent the hinge with a line and associated arrows on the map—the arrows point outward on an anticline and inward on a syncline. On a block diagram of the folds, we see several layers exposed (Fig. 15.5c). Note that the same set of layers appears on both sides of the hinge. (Exercise 15.5 allows you to discover that the age relations of layers, as seen on the map view, indicate whether a given fold is an anticline or syncline.) If the folded strata include a bed that is resistant to erosion, the bed may form topographic ridges at the ground surface (Fig. 15.5d). Note that the layers are repeated *symmetrically*, in mirror image across the fold hinges.

The hinge of a fold may be horizontal, producing a **nonplunging fold** (**FIG. 15.6a**), or it may have a tilt, or "plunge," producing a **plunging fold** (**FIG. 15.6b**); an arrowhead on the hinge line in Fig. 15.6 indicates the direction of plunge. Note that if the fold is nonplunging, the contacts are parallel to the hinge trace, whereas if the fold is plunging, the contacts curve around the hinge—this portion of a fold on the map surface is informally called the fold "nose." Note that anticlines plunge *toward* their noses, synclines *away from* their noses. Curving ridges may form if one or more of the beds that occur in the folded sequence are resistant to erosion.

In some situations, the hinge of a fold is itself curved, so that the plunge direction of a fold changes along its length. In the extreme, a fold can be as wide as it is long. In the case of down-warped beds, the result is a **basin**, a bowl-shaped structure; and in the case of up-warped beds, the result is a **dome**, shaped like an overturned bowl. Try Exercise 15.6 to see the differences between basins and domes.

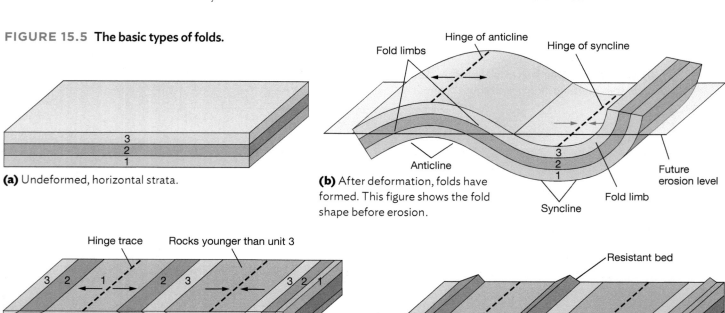

FIGURE 15.5 The basic types of folds.

(a) Undeformed, horizontal strata.

(b) After deformation, folds have formed. This figure shows the fold shape before erosion.

(c) After erosion, the map surface of the block exposes several different layers of strata.

(d) Topographic ridges may form if one of the beds of the folded strata is resistant to erosion.

FIGURE 15.6 Block diagrams showing the contrast between nonplunging and plunging folds.

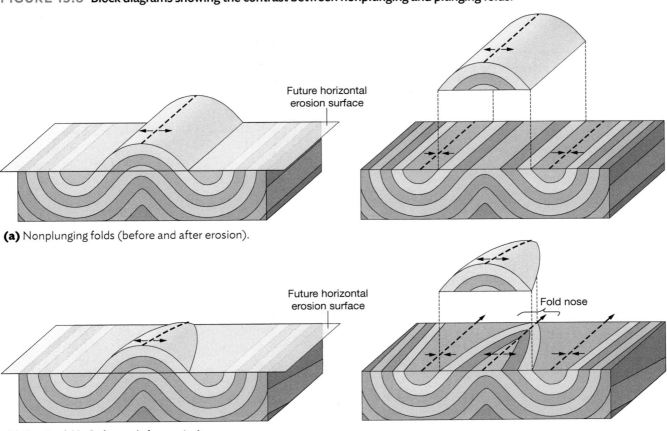

Future horizontal erosion surface

(a) Nonplunging folds (before and after erosion).

Future horizontal erosion surface

Fold nose

(b) Plunging folds (before and after erosion).

EXERCISE 15.5 | Age Relations of Folded Strata

Name: _____ **Section:** _____

Course: _____ **Date:** _____

Refer to the block diagram below. When erosion bevels the land surface, the map surface is like a horizontal slice through the fold. Keeping in mind that anticlines bow strata up and synclines bow them down, answer the following:

If resistant beds occur in the folded sequence, they form curving ridges.

(a) Are the strata along the hinge of the anticline younger or older than the strata on the exposed part of the limbs, as seen in the map-view surface? _____

(b) Are the strata along the hinge of the syncline younger or older than the strata on the exposed part of the limbs, as seen in the map-view surface? _____

Name: _____   Section: _____
Course: _____   Date: _____

(a) In the figure below, which of the following block diagrams illustrates a basin and which illustrates a dome? Add labels to the figure.

The difference between a basin and a dome.

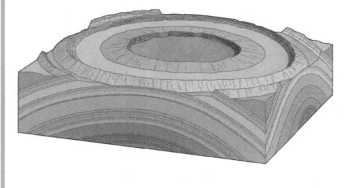
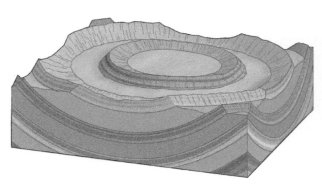

(b) Look at the distribution of strata in each of the blocks and circle the correct term in each statement.
   i. The center of a dome exposes (older/younger) strata relative to its outer edge.
   ii. The center of a basin exposes (older/younger) strata relative to its outer edge.

15.3.3 Block Diagrams of Faults

As we noted earlier, a fault is a surface on which one body of rock slides past another by an amount called the **fault displacement** (FIG. 15.7). Faults come in all sizes—some have displacements of millimeters or centimeters and are contained within a single layer of rock; others are larger and offset contacts between layers or between formations by many miles. Not all faults have the same dip—some faults are nearly vertical, whereas others dip at moderate or shallow angles. If the fault is not vertical, rock above the fault surface is the **hanging wall**, and rock below is the **footwall** (Fig. 15.7a).

Geologists distinguish among different kinds of faults based on the direction of displacement. **Strike-slip faults** tend to be nearly vertical, and the displacement on them is horizontal, parallel to the *strike* of the fault (Fig. 15.7b). On **dip-slip faults**, the displacement is parallel to the dip direction on the fault; if the hanging wall block moves up dip, it's a **reverse fault** (Fig. 15.7d), and if it moves down dip, it's a **normal fault** (Fig. 15.7c). If a reverse fault has a gentle dip (less than about 30°) or curves at depth to attain a gentle dip, then geologists generally refer to it as a **thrust fault** (Fig. 15.7e). Reverse and thrust faults form in response to compression, and normal faults form in response to tension.

You can recognize faulting, even if the fault surface itself is not visible (due to cover by soil or vegetation), if you find a boundary along which contacts terminate abruptly (FIG. 15.8). The configuration that you find depends on both the attitude of the fault and the attitude of the layers, as you will see in Exercise 15.7.

FIGURE 15.7 Hanging wall, footwall, and the classification of faults.

If you look across a strike-slip fault and the opposite side moved to your right, it's a right-lateral fault. If the opposite side moved to your left, it's a left-lateral fault.

This fault is left-lateral.

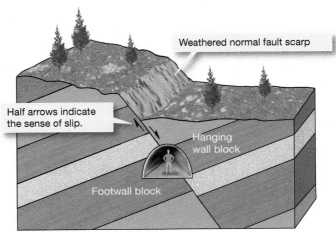

Weathered normal fault scarp

Half arrows indicate the sense of slip.

Hanging wall block

Footwall block

(a) The hanging wall is above the fault surface; the footwall is below.

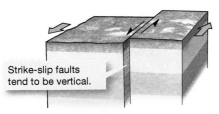

Strike-slip faults tend to be vertical.

(b) On a strike-slip fault, one block slides laterally past another, so no vertical displacement takes place.

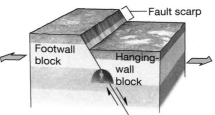

Fault scarp

Footwall block

Hanging-wall block

(c) Normal faults form during extension of the crust. The hanging wall moves down.

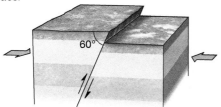

60°

(d) Reverse faults form during shortening of the crust. The hanging wall moves up and the fault is steep.

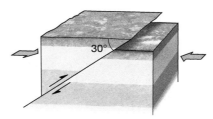

30°

(e) Thrust faults also form during shortening. The fault's slope is gentle (less than 30°).

EXERCISE 15.7 | Faulted Strata on a Block Diagram

Name: _____   **Section:** _____

Course: _____   **Date:** _____

The following questions refer to the figures on the next page.

(a) The block in (a) shows a vertical fault cutting across a nonplunging syncline. Complete the block diagram by adding arrows to show the sense of slip across the fault and by adding colored bands for the appropriate stratigraphic units in the blank areas. What type of fault is it? _____

(b) The block in (b) shows a dip-slip fault. Is this a normal or reverse fault? _____

(continued)

Name: _____   **Section:** _____

Course: _____   **Date:** _____

(c) As you walk from west to east across the map surface of (b), you cross layer 3 more than once. Explain how the faulting caused this.

_____

_____

(d) The red line on the front cross-section face of (b) represents a drill hole. Does the drill hole cut through the complete stratigraphic section, or do you see repetition or loss of section?

_____

_____

(a) Vertical fault.

(b) Dip-slip fault.

FIGURE 15.8 **Examples of the consequences of faulting on strata.**

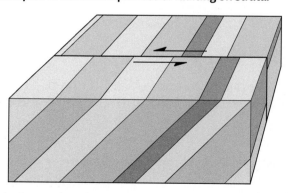

In this case, displacement on a strike-slip fault causes layers to terminate abruptly.

15.3.4 Block Diagrams of Unconformities

An **unconformity** is a contact that represents a period of nondeposition and/or erosion, as we noted earlier. Geologists recognize three different kinds: (1) at a **disconformity**, bedding above and below the unconformity is parallel, but there is a significant time gap between the age of the strata below and the age of the strata above; (2) at a **nonconformity**, strata are deposited on a "basement" of intrusive igneous and/or metamorphic rock; and (3) at an **angular unconformity**, the orientation of the beds above the unconformity is not the same as that below. Exercise 15.8 gives you a chance to distinguish among these three types. Unconformities will be examined in more detail in Chapter 17.

15.3.5 Block Diagrams of Igneous Intrusions

An igneous intrusion forms when molten rock (magma) pushes into or "intrudes" preexisting rock. Geologists distinguish between two general types of igneous intrusions. (1) **Tabular intrusions** have roughly parallel margins; these include wall-like intrusions called **dikes**, which cut across preexisting layering, and sheet-like intrusions called **sills**, which are parallel to layering. (2) **Plutons** are irregularly shaped, blob-shaped, or bulb-shaped intrusions. On a block diagram, you can generally distinguish among different types of intrusions based on their relationship with adjacent layering. To see how, try Exercise 15.9.

EXERCISE 15.8   **Interpreting Unconformities On a Block Diagram**

Name: _____   Section: _____
Course: _____   Date: _____

(a) In the space provided below each block in the figure that follows, indicate what type of unconformity is shown.

Block diagrams of unconformities.

Block 1: _____

Block 2: _____

Block 3: _____

Block 4: _____

(b) The sedimentary rocks in Block 2 were deposited as horizontal layers. What has happened to the layers? Was the unconformity originally horizontal or tilted? Explain.

_____

_____

(continued)

Name: _____   Section: _____
Course: _____   Date: _____

(c) In Block 3, in which direction are the post-unconformity strata dipping?

_____

(d) In Block 4, a gray area at the north edge of the block appears on the map surface. What geologic observation(s) could prove that the contact between the gray area and the sedimentary beds is an unconformity and not an intrusive contact?

_____

_____

_____

_____

EXERCISE 15.9   Interpreting Intrusions on a Block Diagram

Name: _____   Section: _____
Course: _____   Date: _____

(a) The following two blocks (on the next page) show sedimentary beds and intrusions. Match the type of intrusion to the appropriate letter on the block.

Pluton   Block 1: _____   Block 2: _____

Dike   Block 1: _____   Block 2: _____

Sill   Block 1: _____   Block 2: _____

(b) Using common sense to interpret cross-cutting relationships, list the sequence of intrusions for each block. If you can't determine an answer from the information shown, indicate so.

	Oldest	Middle	Youngest
Block 1:	_____	_____	_____
Block 2:	_____	_____	_____

(c) Analyses indicate the unlabeled intrusion in the front cross-section face of Block 2 is part of the same body as Intrusion A exposed on the top surface. Explain why you can't *see* the connection between the map-view exposure and the subsurface cross section on this block.

_____

_____

_____

(continued)

Name: _____ Section: _____

Course: _____ Date: _____

Blocks of igneous intrusions.

Block 1

Block 2

EXERCISE 15.10 | Completing Block Diagrams

Name: _____ Section: _____

Course: _____ Date: _____

Four cutout block diagrams are provided at the end of the book for additional practice and to help visualize structures in three dimensions. Cut and fold the diagrams as indicated, and use tape to hold the tabs together to make three-dimensional block diagrams.

(a) Complete the blank cross-section panels for Block 1, and describe the structure present. Does the block show horizontal or tilted strata? Folds? Faults?

_____

_____

_____

_____

(b) Complete the map view and blank cross-section views for Blocks 2 and 3. Compare and contrast the structures in these two blocks.

_____

_____

_____

_____

_____

(continued)

Name: _____   Section: _____

Course: _____   Date: _____

(c) Complete the map view and cross-section panels for Block 4. Be sure to add arrows showing the direction of slip. Describe the nature of the faulting. Is it dip-slip? If so, is it normal or reverse? Is it strike-slip? If so, is it left-lateral or right-lateral? Explain your reasoning.

_____

_____

_____

_____

15.4 Geologic Maps

15.4.1 Introducing Geologic Maps and Map Symbols

Now that you've become comfortable reading and interpreting block diagrams, we can focus more closely on how to interpret geology on the map-view surface. A map that shows the positions of contacts, the distribution of rock units, the orientation of layers, the position of faults and folds, and other geologic data is called a **geologic map** (FIG. 15.9a). Contacts between rock units are shown by lines (traces), and the units themselves are highlighted by patterns and/or colors and symbols that indicate their ages. The orientation of beds, faults, and foliations, as well as the position of fold hinges, can be represented by strike and dip symbols. The map's **explanation** (or *legend*) defines all the symbols, abbreviations, and colors on the map. FIGURE 15.9b, a geologic map of the Bull Creek quadrangle in Wyoming, illustrates the components of a geologic map. Note that all maps should have a scale, north arrow, and explanation.

FIGURE 15.9 Geologic maps.

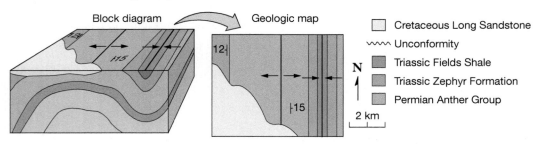

(a) A geologic map is the top surface of a block diagram. It shows the pattern of geologic units and structures as you would see them by looking straight down from above.

FIGURE 15.9 **Geologic maps (continued)**

M.L. Schroeder, 1976

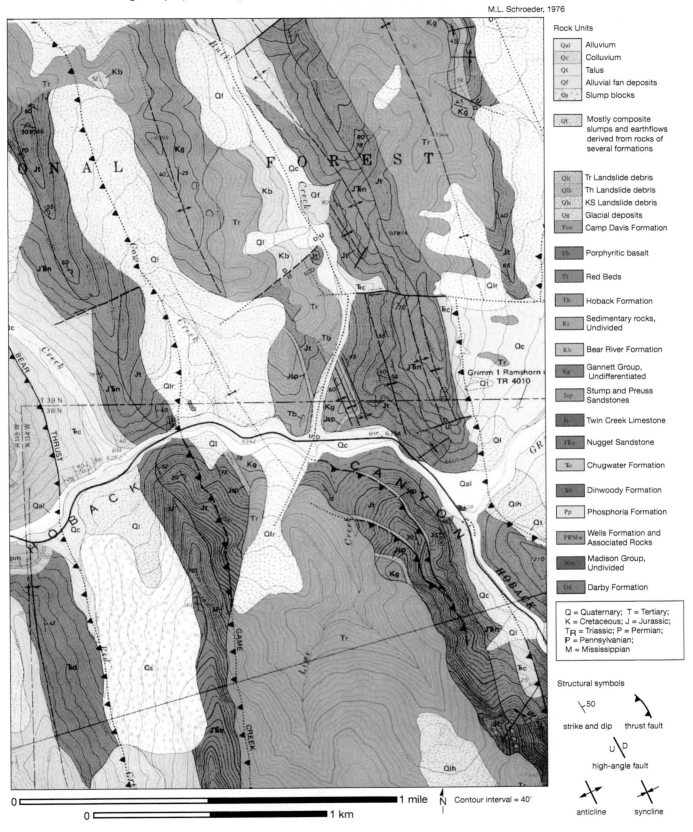

Rock Units

Qal	Alluvium
Qc	Colluvium
Qt	Talus
Qf	Alluvial fan deposits
Qs	Slump blocks

Qf — Mostly composite slumps and earthflows derived from rocks of several formations

Qlr	Tr Landslide debris
Qlh	Th Landslide debris
Qls	KS Landslide debris
Qg	Glacial deposits
Tcu	Camp Davis Formation

Tb	Porphyritic basalt
Tr	Red Beds
Th	Hoback Formation
Ks	Sedimentary rocks, Undivided
Kb	Bear River Formation
Kg	Gannett Group, Undifferentiated
Jsp	Stump and Preuss Sandstones
Jt	Twin Creek Limestone
JTRn	Nugget Sandstone
TRc	Chugwater Formation
TRd	Dinwoody Formation
Pp	Phosphoria Formation
PIPMw	Wells Formation and Associated Rocks
Mm	Madison Group, Undivided
Dd	Darby Formation

Q = Quaternary; T = Tertiary;
K = Cretaceous; J = Jurassic;
TR = Triassic; P = Permian;
IP = Pennsylvanian;
M = Mississippian

Structural symbols

⊢50
strike and dip   thrust fault

U|D
high-angle fault

anticline   syncline

0 ▬▬▬▬▬▬▬ 1 mile   N   Contour interval = 40'
0 ▬▬▬▬▬▬▬ 1 km

(b) Geologic map of the Bull Creek quadrangle, Teton and Sublette Counties, in Wyoming.

Let's begin our discussion of geologic maps by considering the various features that can be portrayed on these maps. (You will practice mapping features in Exercise 15.11.)

■ *Rock units:* Geologic maps show the different rock units in an area. These units may be bodies of intrusive igneous rock, layers of volcanic rock, sequences of sedimentary rocks, or complexes of metamorphic rock. The most common unit of sedimentary and/or volcanic rock is a stratigraphic formation, as noted earlier. These are commonly named for a place where it is well exposed. A formation may consist entirely of beds of a single rock type (e.g., the Bright Angel Shale consists only of shale) or it may contain beds of several different rock types (e.g., the Bowers Mountain Formation contains shale, sandstone, and rhyolite).

Typically, maps use patterns, shadings of gray, or colors to indicate the area in which a given unit occurs. On geologic maps produced in North America, an abbreviation for the map unit may also appear within the area occupied by the formation. This abbreviation generally has two parts: the first part represents the formation's age, in capital letters; the second part, in lowercase letters, represents the formation's name. For example, O indicates rocks of Ordovician age (Oce = Cape Elizabeth Formation, Osp = Spring Point Formation), and SO indicates Silurian or Ordovician age (SOb = Berwick Formation, SOe = Eliot Formation).

■ *Contacts:* Different kinds of contacts are generally shown with different types of lines. For example, a conformable or intrusive contact is a thin line, a fault contact is a thicker line, and an unconformity may be a slightly jagged or wavy line. In general, a visible contact is a solid line, whereas a covered contact (buried by sediment or vegetation) is a dashed line.

■ *Strike and dip:* On maps produced in North America, geologists use a symbol to represent the strike and dip of a layer. The symbol consists of a line segment drawn exactly parallel to the direction of strike and a short tick mark drawn perpendicular to the strike and pointing in the direction of dip (**FIG. 15.10a, b**). A number written next to the tick mark indicates the angle of dip. (It is not necessary to write a number indicating the strike angle because that is automatically represented by the map trend of the strike line.) Different symbols are used to represent bedding and foliation; in this book, we use only bedding symbols.

■ *Other structural symbols:* The explanation also includes symbols representing the traces of folds and faults. **FIGURE 15.10c** illustrates some of these symbols.

FIGURE 15.10 Indicating features on geologic maps.

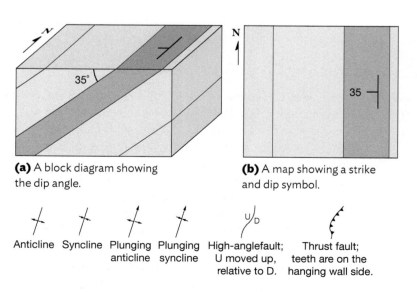

(a) A block diagram showing the dip angle.

(b) A map showing a strike and dip symbol.

Anticline   Syncline   Plunging anticline   Plunging syncline   High-anglefault; U moved up, relative to D.   Thrust fault; teeth are on the hanging wall side.

(c) Basic structural symbols used on geologic maps.

Name: _____   **Section:** _____

Course: _____   **Date:** _____

(a) On the blank map below of a region with no hills or valleys, draw the appropriate strike and dip symbol next to the appropriate point. To do this, you must use a protractor and measure the angle between the north direction (the side edge of the map) and the strike angle. Then, look at the direction of dip so that you put the dip tick on the correct side of the strike symbol. These points are on a contact between two formations:

A: 045°/30° SE

B: 280°/10° SW

C: 350°/25° W

(b) Based on the strike and dip symbols you show, draw a line representing the contact that passes through these points. Remember, the line needs to be parallel to the strike symbol.

_____

_____

(c) What is the structure shown by the structure symbols?

_____

_____

Blank map.

15.4.2 Constructing Cross Sections

We've seen that a cross section represents a vertical slice through the crust of the Earth. Thus, the sides of a block diagram are cross sections. If you start with a block diagram, you can construct the structure in the cross-section planes simply by drawing lines representing the contacts so that they connect to the contact traces in the map plane—the strike and dip data on the map tell you what angle the contact makes, relative to horizontal, and you use a protractor to draw the correct angle. If a fold occurs on the map surface, it generally also appears in the cross section.

So far, we've worked with data depicted on block diagrams. Now let's consider the more common challenge of producing a cross section from a geologic map. This takes a couple of extra steps—to see how to do it, refer to **FIGURE 15.11**.

On the left side of Figure 15.11a, you see a simple geologic map. The **line of section** (XX′) is the line on the map view along which you want to produce the cross section. The cross section is a vertical plane inserted into the ground along the line

FIGURE 15.11 Constructing a cross section.

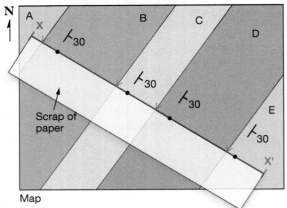

Map

Step 1: Mark data locations on the cross-section paper.

(a) Example with gently dipping beds.

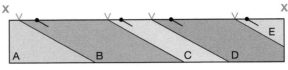

Step 2: Identify contact positions. Add dip marks at correct angles.

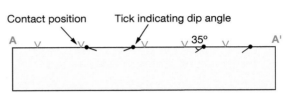

Step 3: Draw contacts so they obey location and dip data.

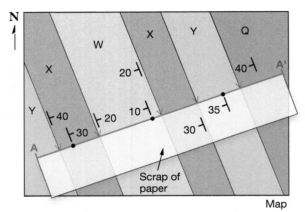

Map

Step 1: Mark data locations on the cross-section paper.

(b) Example with folded beds (syncline).

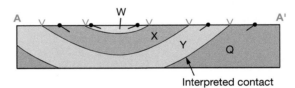

Step 2: Identify contact positions. Add dip marks at correct angles.

Step 3: Draw contacts so they obey location and dip data.

of section. Now, take a scrap of paper and align it with your line of section. Mark off the points where contacts cross the scrap of paper. Transfer these points to the cross-section frame on the right. Using a protractor, make a little tick mark indicating the dip of the contact; use the strike and dip symbol closest to each contact to provide this angle. Next, in the subsurface, sketch in lines that conform to the positions of the contacts and the dip angles (the contacts dip gently to the southeast). In Figure 15.11b, the contacts curve underground to define a syncline. Unless there is a reason to think otherwise, the layers should have constant thickness. Note that, because of this constraint, Layer Q in the second example appears in the lower left corner of the cross section; it would come to the surface to the west of the map area. Contrast your own cross sections in Exercise 15.12.

15.4.3 Basic Geologic Map Patterns

Geologic maps can get pretty complex, especially where structures are complicated or where topography is rugged. But, by applying what you have learned so far about block diagrams, you can start to interpret them. To make things simple, we begin with some very easy maps of areas that have no topography (i.e., the ground surface is flat), as in the block diagrams that you've worked with. Exercise 15.13 challenges you to look at a map and imagine the three-dimensional structure it represents. Also keep in mind that sedimentary and *extrusive* igneous rocks are commonly deposited in horizontal layers with the youngest layer at the top of the pile and the oldest at the bottom.

Name: _____   Section: _____
Course: _____   Date: _____

(a) The map surface of the block diagram in the figure below provides strikes and dips of the layers shown. From this information, show the layers with their proper angles in the front and side cross-section faces. Note that the strike of the layers is perpendicular to the front face of the block.

Block diagram with strikes and dips of the layers.

What kind of structure is shown? _____

(b) Complete the map view and cross-section views of the block diagrams below by showing a sequence of sedimentary rocks with the indicated orientations. Show at least three layers in each block, and plot the strike and dip symbol on the top surface.

Block A: 090°/40° S.

Block B: 000°/60° E.

(c) Complete the cross-section views of the block below.

Block diagram for creating cross-section views.

Earlier, we distinguished between nonplunging folds and plunging folds, in the context of discussing block diagrams. We can recognize these folds on geologic maps simply by the pattern of color bands representing formations—on a map, formation contacts of nonplunging folds trend parallel to the hinge trace, whereas those of plunging folds curve around the hinge trace so we can see the fold nose. Furthermore, we can distinguish between anticlines and synclines by the age relationships of the color bands—strata get progressively younger away from the hinge of an anticline and progressively older away from the hinge of a syncline. If the hinge isn't shown on the map, you can draw it in where the reversal of age takes place. See **FIGURE 15.12** for an example of a map and cross section of plunging folds.

FIGURE 15.12 Patterns of plunging folds.

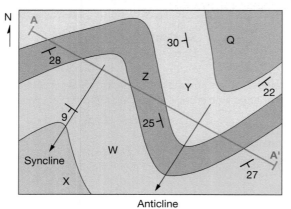

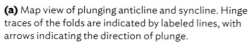

(a) Map view of plunging anticline and syncline. Hinge traces of the folds are indicated by labeled lines, with arrows indicating the direction of plunge.

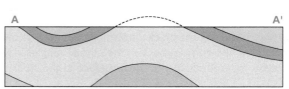

(b) Cross section of folds along the A–A' line.

Interpreting Simple Geologic Maps

Name: _____   Section: _____

Course: _____   Date: _____

For each of the following maps, identify the structure or geologic features portrayed. Does the map show a fault, fold, tilted strata, dike, pluton, unconformity, or some combination? To answer these questions, you may need to refer to the block diagrams presented earlier in the chapter. Remember—think in three dimensions! With a little practice, geologists learn to recognize the basic patterns quickly. *Note:* the geologic periods in the maps below in order from oldest to youngest are the Ordovician, Silurian, Devonian, Triassic, Jurassic, Cretaceous, and Tertiary.

Geologic maps.

Map A

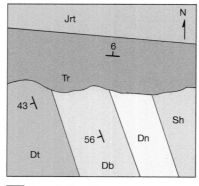

Jrt	Jurassic Tinta Fm.
Tr	Triassic Jones Sh.
Dt	Devonian Tella Fm.
Db	Devonian Bouser Fm.
Dn	Devonian Norfolk Sh.
Sh	Silurian Hallo Fm.

Map B

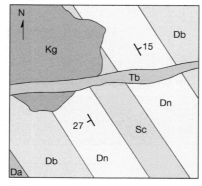

Tb	Tertiary basalt
Kg	Cretaceous granite
Da	Devonian Alsen Fm.
Db	Devonian Becraft Ls.
Dn	Devonian Norfolk Sh.
Sc	Silurian Cligfell Fm.

Map C

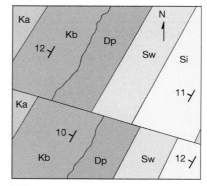

Ka	Cretaceous Altoona Fm.
Kb	Cretaceous Barrell Fm.
Dp	Devonian Potomoo Ls.
Sw	Silurian Wala Sh.
Si	Silurian Jack Fm.
Ot	Ordovician Trent Fm.

(a) Describe the geologic features of Map A.

    i. _____-aged strata are overlain at an unconformity by _____-aged strata. What type of unconformity is it? _____

    ii. The Triassic and Jurassic strata dip in a _____ direction at a _____ angle.

    iii. The Silurian and Devonian strata dip in a _____ direction at a _____ angle.

(continued)

Name: _____   Section: _____
Course: _____   Date: _____

(b) Describe the geologic features of Map B.

i. _____-aged strata are folded into a(n)_____. The hinge of the fold trends _____. Do the folded layers plunge? _____ Are the folded layers symmetrical? _____ If not, which side is steeper? _____

ii. A _____ intrudes the western portion of the folded layers (give age, rock, and type of the intrusion).

iii. A _____ intrudes both the folded layers and the intrusion described in (ii) (give age, rock, and type of the intrusion).

(c) Describe the geologic features of Map C.

i. A _____ trending fault cuts strata that strike in a _____ direction and dip to the _____.

ii. The fault is either a _____ fault or a dip-slip fault in which the _____ (N,S,E,W) block moved _____ relative to the _____ (N,S,E,W) block. Without seeing a cross section of the fault, it is not possible to determine if the fault is normal or _____.

iii. _____-aged strata are overlain at an unconformity by _____-aged strata. What type of unconformity is it?_____

(d) If you walk from left to right (west to east) along the southern edge of Map A, are you walking "up section" (i.e., into rocks of progressively younger age) or "down section" (i.e., into rocks of progressively older age)? _____

15.4.4 Geologic Maps with Contour Lines

When the map surface is not flat, geologic maps become even more challenging to interpret. That's because the trace of a contact that appears on a geologic map depends on both the slope angle and the slope direction of the land surface as well as the strike and dip of beds. We introduce only two simple situations here—the pattern of horizontal contacts and the pattern of vertical contacts. You'll address more complex situations in other geology courses. Work through Exercise 15.14 to see how these patterns appear on a map.

Name: _____   Section: _____
Course: _____   Date: _____

(a) Look at the block diagram and the geologic map on the next page. What is the relationship between a horizontal contact and a contour line—parallel, perpendicular, or oblique? Keeping in mind the definition of a contour line, explain why. Geologists refer to the arrangement of valleys on this map as a *dendritic pattern,* because it resembles the veins of a leaf. Dendritic drainage patterns tend to occur where the strata are horizontal.

_____

_____

_____

(continued)

Name: _____   Section: _____
Course: _____   Date: _____

(b) The gray stripe is a vertical basalt dike. Remember that when you are looking at a map, you are looking straight down from the sky. With this in mind, explain why the dike appears as a straight line on the map.

_____

_____

Map pattern of horizontal strata in a valley.

Dike
Contour
Contact
Stream

15.5 Structures Revealed in Landscapes

Unless you live in the Great Plains or along the Gulf Coast of the United States, you know that landscapes tend not to be as flat as the tops of the idealized block diagrams that we've worked with so far. In many cases, the distribution of rock units controls the details of the landscape, so erosion may cause structures to stand out in the landscape, especially in drier climates. For example, in regions of flat-lying strata, resistant rocks form cliffs, whereas nonresistant rocks form gentler slopes. Thus, a cliff exposing alternating resistant and nonresistant rocks develops a **stair-step profile**. Where strata are tilted, resistant rocks form topographic ridges, whereas nonresistant rock types tend to form valleys (**FIG. 15.13a**). Generally, the ridges are asymmetric—a dip slope parallel to the bedding forms on one side, and a scarp cutting across the bedding forms on the other. In the Appalachian Mountains of Pennsylvania, ridges trace out the shape of plunging folds (**FIG. 15.13b**). A region in which the structure of bedrock strongly influences topography is called a **structurally controlled landscape**, and you will see how this is manifested in Exercise 15.15.

FIGURE 15.13 **Structural control of topography.**

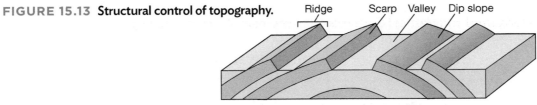

(a) A block diagram showing how resistant layers hold up ridges.

(b) A satellite photo of the Valley and Ridge Province of Pennsylvania (from *Google Earth*™).

EXERCISE 15.15	Interpreting Structurally Controlled Landscapes

Name: _____   **Section:** _____
Course: _____   **Date:** _____

The figure on the next page shows a region of central Pennsylvania (a) that includes the boundary between two different structural provinces (the Valley and Ridge Province to the southeast and the Plateau Province to the northwest). Enlargements of the two provinces are shown in parts (b) and (c) of the figures. Based on the general shape of the land surface, as indicated by the maps, answer the following:

(a) In which of the two provinces is the landscape structurally controlled?_____

(b) Compare the pattern of stream valleys in the Plateau Province with that depicted in the topography of the Valley and Ridge Province. Approximately what is the dip of the beds beneath the Plateau Province?_____

(c) In the Valley and Ridge Province, are the folds plunging or nonplunging? What is your evidence?_____

(continued)

Name: _____ Section: _____
Course: _____ Date: _____

(d) What is the overall trend of fold hinges in the portion of the Valley and Ridge Province depicted in the lower map?_____

(e) If fold hinges trend roughly perpendicular to the direction of compression, in what direction was the compressive "push" during the development of the folds in the Valley and Ridge Province? (Geologists have determined that these folds formed when Africa collided with eastern North America at the end of the Paleozoic Era.)_____

(a) Shaded relief of central Pennsylvania.

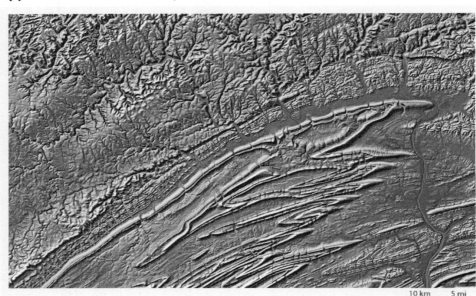

10 km   5 mi

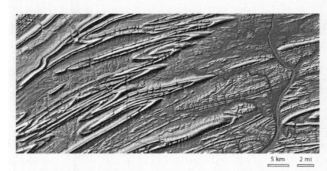

Location

5 km   2 mi

(b) Pennsylvania Valley and Ridge Province; the ridges are underlain by resistant sandstone layers.

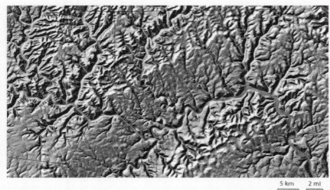

(c) Pennsylvania Plateau Province; the pattern of rivers and tributaries is called a dendritic drainage pattern.

5 km   2 mi

15.6 Reading Real Geologic Maps

15.6.1 Geologic Maps of Local Areas

You are now ready to apply what you've learned to interpreting the structure of selected areas of North America using excerpts from published geologic maps. Exercises 15.16 and 15.17 give you a sense of how to see "clues" in a map that help you to picture the three-dimensional configuration of rocks underground.

We finish this chapter by talking about how geologists make geologic maps in the first place. It isn't easy! Students who want to learn the skill generally attend a summer geology field camp, where they practice the art of mapping for several weeks and gradually develop an eye for identifying rock types, contacts, folds, and faults. Typically, in arid regions, not much soil forms, so bedrock may be abundantly exposed; in such areas, geologists may actually see contacts and can walk out the traces of contacts. Commonly, however, soil and vegetation cover much of the rocks, so outcrops are discontinuous and separated from one another by "covered intervals." In such cases, geologists must extrapolate contacts, using common sense and an understanding of geologic structures. Exercise 15.18 provides the opportunity for you to construct a map in an area where limited outcrop data are available. The map shown is called an outcrop map because individual outcrops of rock are outlined. To complete the map, you need to extrapolate contacts. In Exercise 15.19, you will use all of your skills to interpret the structural geology of a region and present your findings.

EXERCISE 15.16   **The Observation Peak Quadrangle of Wyoming**

Name: _____ Section: _____
Course: _____ Date: _____

Examine the geologic map of a portion of the Observation Peak quadrangle in Wyoming in **FIGURE 15.14**. This map area contains a number of interesting geologic features, some of which you can understand based on the work you have done earlier in this chapter. Each of the questions below refers to a specific feature on the map.

(a) In the northern part of the map, there is a large area of yellow (i.e., Quaternary deposits). What kind of contact forms the boundary between these deposits and older bedrock?_____

(b) The bright-red color represents igneous intrusions.

- What kind of intrusion is the larger round area?_____
- What kind of intrusions are the narrow bands? _____

(c) A thrust fault (a gently to moderately dipping reverse fault) is exposed in the southwest quarter of the map. The "teeth" of the thrust fault symbol lie on the hanging wall. In this locality, the fault dips about 40° in a westerly direction.

- Where Indian Creek crosses the fault, what rock unit is in the hanging wall, and what rock unit is in the footwall?_____
- Is the older rock in the hanging wall or in the footwall?_____
- Thinking about the movement direction on a thrust fault, does this make sense? (Explain your answer.)_____

(d) In the southeastern quarter of the map, you can see the trace of a fold.

- What type of fold is it?_____
- In which direction does it plunge?_____
- In the Ankareh Formation, what is the strike and dip of the strata on the western limb of the fold?_____

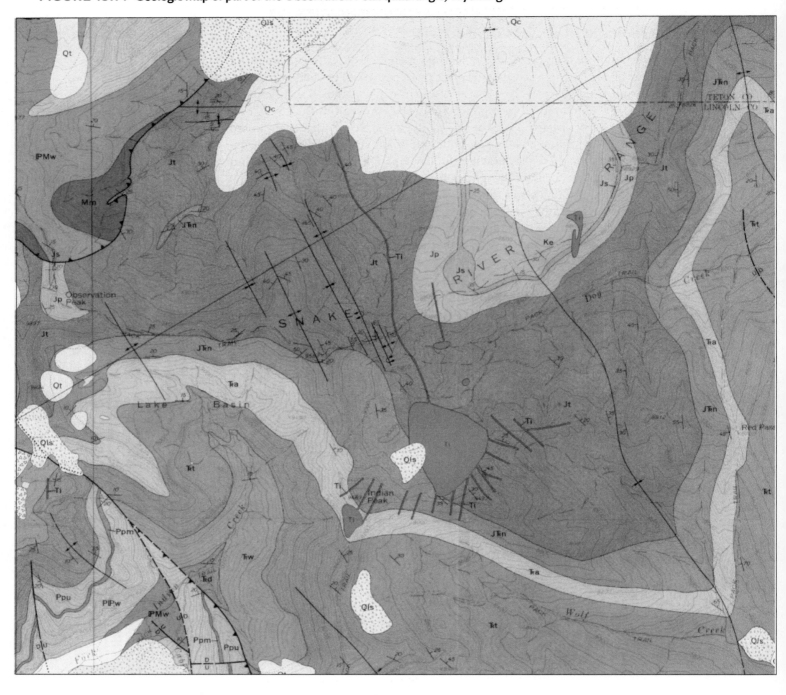

0   1 mile

0   1 km

contour interval = 40'

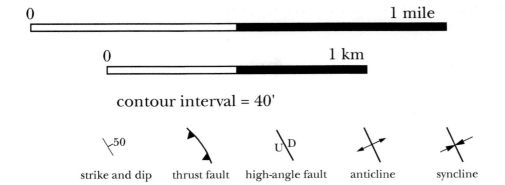

strike and dip   thrust fault   high-angle fault   anticline   syncline

Geologic Map of the
Observation Peak Quadrangle, Wyoming
by
Howard F. Albee
1973

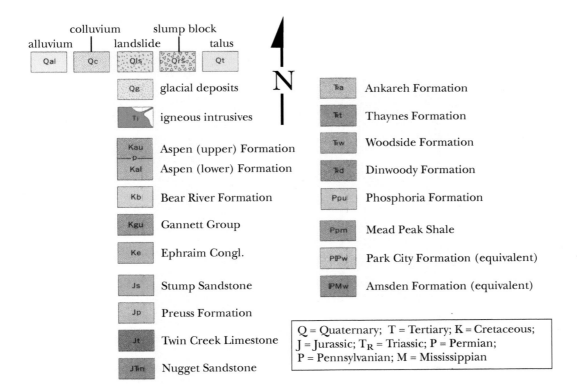

alluvium   colluvium   landslide   slump block   talus

Qal   Qc   Qls   Qrs   Qt

Qg   glacial deposits

Ti   igneous intrusives

Kau / Kal   Aspen (upper) Formation / Aspen (lower) Formation

Kb   Bear River Formation

Kgu   Gannett Group

Ke   Ephraim Congl.

Js   Stump Sandstone

Jp   Preuss Formation

Jt   Twin Creek Limestone

JTn   Nugget Sandstone

 Tra   Ankareh Formation

Trt   Thaynes Formation

Trw   Woodside Formation

Trd   Dinwoody Formation

Ppu   Phosphoria Formation

Ppm   Mead Peak Shale

PIPw   Park City Formation (equivalent)

IPMw   Amsden Formation (equivalent)

Q = Quaternary; T = Tertiary; K = Cretaceous;
J = Jurassic; T_R = Triassic; P = Permian;
P = Pennsylvanian; M = Mississippian

Name: _____   Section: _____

Course: _____   Date: _____

Examine the geologic map of part of the Grand Canyon area in Arizona (below). There is no legend because you don't have to know the specific ages of the units to answer the question.

In the lower right part of the map, what is the relative age of the bright-red rock layer compared to the pale-green layer? Note that the thin blue line running through the red layer represents the Colorado River, which flows through the bottom of the Grand Canyon. _____

Geologic map of part of the Grand Canyon.

Name: _____   **Section:** _____

Course: _____   **Date:** _____

The figure below is an outcrop map of an area showing several different rock layers and their attitudes. Using the structural information available on the map and the stratigraphic column, draw a geologic map that shows the contacts between the rock units present. Note that in a few outcrop areas, a contact is visible.

Completing an Outcrop Map
A geologist has just finished mapping a few square kilometers. She has drawn the approximate shapes of outcrops, has plotted strike and dip measurements, and has located contacts where they were exposed. Complete the map by extrapolating contacts across the covered areas and by adding appropriate symbols for folds, if they are present. When you have completed the map, describe the basic structure of the map area in words using the space provided here.

Structural Description: _____

_____

_____

_____

An outcrop map for structural interpretation.

Name: _____   Section: _____

Course: _____   Date: _____

?What Do You Think Knowledge of an area's deformation history helps avoid potentially calamitous situations, such as building a school directly on an active fault. Structural information can also pay off—big time—in our search for energy and mineral resources. For example, geologists have learned that oil and natural gas are often trapped in the crests of anticlines. Because it costs millions of dollars to drill an exploratory well, knowing where the anticlines are (or aren't) can mean the difference between a fortune and bankruptcy.

Imagine that a company has dug a shaft for an underground mine into a coal bed (gray layer in the figure below). The coal bed and all beds above and below it dip 10° W. A drill hole through the coal layer has provided the stratigraphic sequence and the thickness of the layers, as represented in the column on the left (drawn to scale). Mapping at the ground surface reveals two faults and the map traces of two distinctive beds. The miners have found that the coal layer terminates at the faults, as shown in the cross-section face. It is not economical to mine at a depth greater than the red line. Based on the data available, would you recommend the mining company buy the mineral rights beneath Region A (west of the western fault) or Region B (east of the eastern fault)? Complete the cross-section face to help you visualize the answer. Explain your decision on a separate piece of paper, or as a brief slide presentation.

Practical application problem.

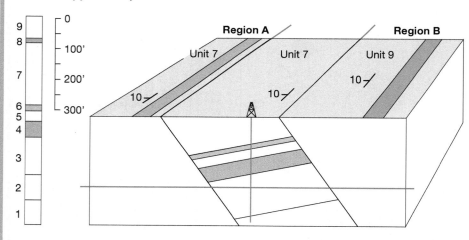

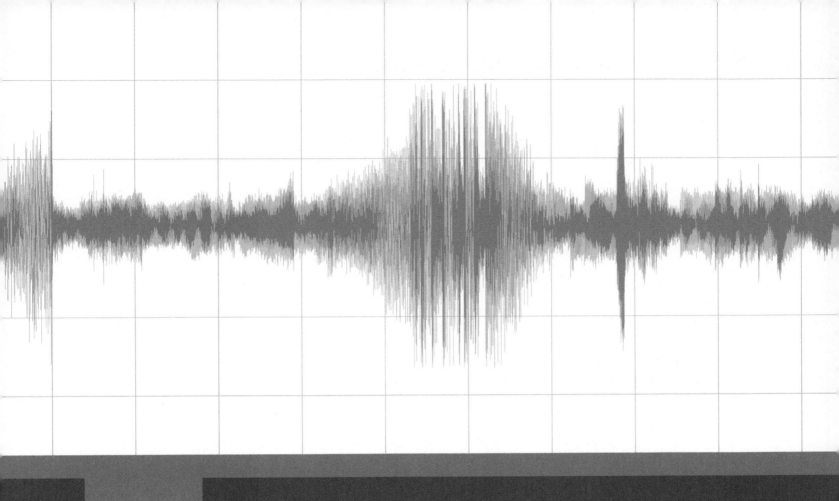

Earthquakes and Seismology

Earthquakes create different kinds of seismic waves that can be measured by a seismometer and that describe its strength and location.

- Understand how faulting causes the ground to move during earthquakes
- Recognize how earthquakes cause damage to buildings and other structures
- Learn how to locate an earthquake epicenter and determine its magnitude and when it occurred

MATERIALS NEEDED

- Sharp pencil
- Ruler with divisions in millimeters
- Architect's compass (or piece of string)

16.1 Introduction

Few things are as fearsome as a major earthquake. Unpredictable and enormously powerful, a great earthquake destroys more than buildings and other structures. It shakes our sense of safety and stability as it shakes the solid rock beneath our feet. But it is not just the shaking that is dangerous. Devastating tsunamis in 2004 and 2011 reminded us that oceanic earthquakes can ravage coastlines thousands of miles from the earthquake origin; landslides and mudslides triggered by earthquakes can engulf towns and villages; and the loss of water when rigid pipes break beneath city streets can cause health problems and make it difficult to fight fires.

In our attempt to understand earthquakes, we have developed tools that reveal Earth's internal structure, define the boundaries between tectonic plates, prove that the asthenosphere exists, and track the movement of plates as they are subducted into the mantle. In this chapter, we look at what an earthquake is and why it causes so much damage and learn how seismologists locate earthquakes and estimate the amount of energy they release. You will learn to read a seismogram and use it to locate an earthquake, determine when it happened, and measure its strength. First, let's review some basic facts about the causes and nature of earthquakes that are discussed in detail in your textbook.

16.2 Causes of Earthquakes: Seismic Waves

- Earthquakes occur when rocks in a fault zone break, releasing energy. The energy is brought to the surface by two kinds of seismic waves called **body waves** because they travel through the body of the Earth. It is this energy that causes the ground to shake initially.

- The point beneath the surface where the energy is released is called the **focus** (or hypocenter) of the earthquake. The point on the surface directly above the focus is called the **epicenter** (**FIG. 16.1**). In most cases, the epicenter, being closest to the focus, is the site of greatest ground motion and damage.

- There are two kinds of body waves, distinguished by how particles move as the wave passes through rocks: P-waves (primary waves) and S-waves (secondary waves). P-waves (**FIG. 16.2a**) are a seismic wave in which particles in rock vibrate back and

FIGURE 16.1 **The focus and epicenter of an earthquake.**

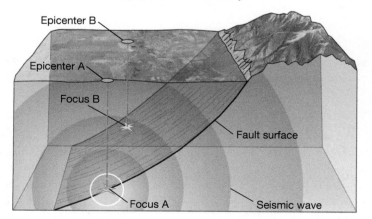

The focus is the point on the fault where slip begins. Seismic energy starts radiating from it. The epicenter is the point on the Earth's surface directly above the focus. Earthquake A just happened; earthquake B happened a while ago.

FIGURE 16.2 Different types of earthquake waves.

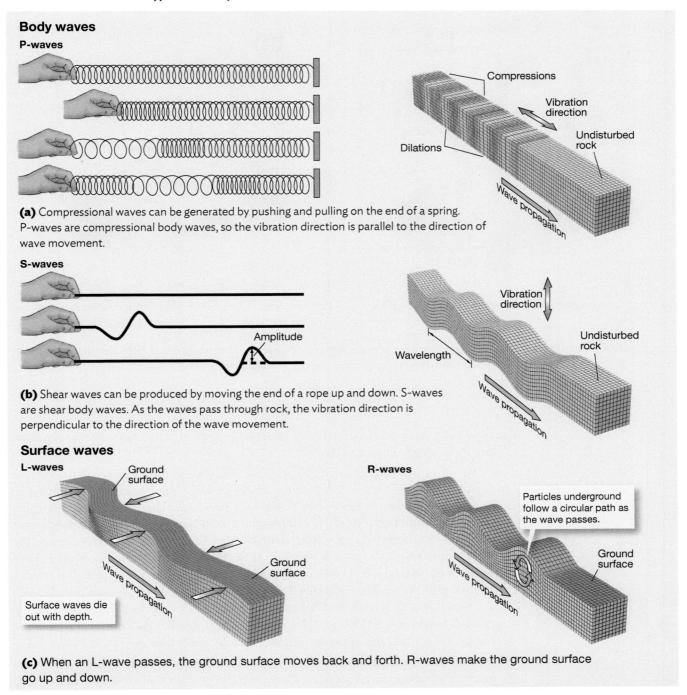

Body waves
P-waves

(a) Compressional waves can be generated by pushing and pulling on the end of a spring. P-waves are compressional body waves, so the vibration direction is parallel to the direction of wave movement.

Compressions

Vibration direction

Undisturbed rock

Dilations

Wave propagation

S-waves

Amplitude

(b) Shear waves can be produced by moving the end of a rope up and down. S-waves are shear body waves. As the waves pass through rock, the vibration direction is perpendicular to the direction of the wave movement.

Vibration direction

Undisturbed rock

Wavelength

Wave propagation

Surface waves
L-waves

Ground surface

Ground surface

Wave propagation

Surface waves die out with depth.

R-waves

Particles underground follow a circular path as the wave passes.

Ground surface

Wave propagation

(c) When an L-wave passes, the ground surface moves back and forth. R-waves make the ground surface go up and down.

forth (red arrow) *in the direction that the wave is traveling* (green arrow). This kind of wave is called a *longitudinal wave*. You can demonstrate this by stretching a Slinky on a table and pushing on one end while keeping the other end in place. As the "P-wave" passes through the Slinky, particles move as shown in Figure 16.2a. Instead of remaining equal distances apart, the coils bunch together in some places and move farther apart in others.

■ S-waves (**FIG. 16.2b**) are seismic waves in which the particle movement is ***perpendicular*** *to the direction in which the wave is traveling.* This kind of wave is called a *transverse wave.* You can demonstrate this by having two people hold the ends of a

FIGURE 16.3 Vertical and horizontal seismometers.

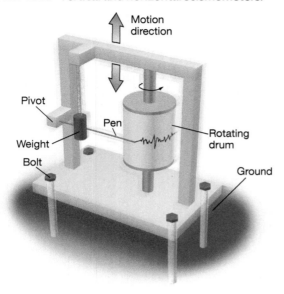

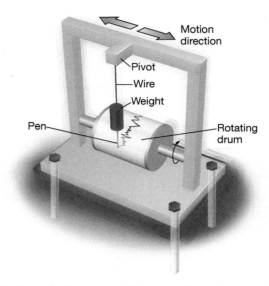

(a) Vertical seismometer: The pivot lets the pen record only vertical motion.

(b) Horizontal seismometer: The pivot allows the pen to record only horizontal motion.

As the ground vibrates, the inertia of the weight keeps the pen in position. The rotating drum moves, causing the pen to trace ground movement on the seismogram. Modern seismometers replace pen and pencil with digital recorders.

rope and asking one to whip the rope in an up-down motion. As the "S-wave" passes, the rope wriggles like a snake.

■ P-waves travel faster through rock than S-waves and therefore reach the surface first. When P- or S-waves reach the surface, some of their energy is converted to two **surface waves:** the **Love wave** (L-wave), a shear wave similar to S-waves in which particles vibrate horizontally, parallel to the ground surface, and the **Rayleigh wave** (R-wave), a unique wave in which particles move in a circular pattern opposite the direction in which the wave is traveling (**FIG. 16.2c**). Particle motion in shear Love waves is horizontal—you can model this with a rope as for the S-wave, but whip it horizontally rather than vertically. Particle motion in Rayleigh waves is circular, like the wheel of a bicycle as the bike moves. This analogy describes the rotational motion of the ground as the Rayleigh wave passes through but isn't perfect because the rotation is actually the opposite of how a bicycle wheel rotates.

■ Seismic waves are detected with instruments called **seismometers**. These are anchored in bedrock to measure the amount of ground movement associated with each type of wave. Seismic stations use separate seismometers to measure vertical and horizontal motion (**FIG. 16.3**). As the ground vibrates, the inertia of the weight keeps the pen in position. The rotating drum moves, causing the pen to trace ground movement on the seismogram. Modern seismometers replace pen and pencil with digital recorders. The printed or digital record of ground motion is a **seismogram**.

■ The strength of an earthquake is measured either by the Richter magnitude scale, based on the amount of ground motion and energy released, or by the Mercalli Intensity Scale, based on the amount of damage to structures.

Exercise 16.1 will help you to understand how seismic waves affect buildings and cause damage.

Name: _____ Section: _____
Course: _____ Date: _____

When P- and S-waves reach the surface, the ground vibrates and anything built on it is shaken in directions that depend on which wave is involved and the distance from the epicenter. The figure below shows the arrival of P-, S-, Love, and Rayleigh waves at a skyscraper.

Ground shaking caused by seismic waves

P-wave at epicenter   P-wave far from epicenter   S-wave at epicenter   S-wave far from epicenter   Love wave   Rayleigh wave

(a) Draw arrows to indicate how each of the buildings will move in response to the different types of waves.

(b) Why do the P- and S-waves at an earthquake epicenter make the ground shake differently from the ground in an area far from the epicenter?

_____

_____

_____

16.3 Locating Earthquakes

Locating earthquakes helps us to understand what causes them and to predict if an area will experience more in the future. Most earthquakes occur in linear belts caused by faulting at the three kinds of plate boundaries (**FIG. 16.4**) and are used to define those boundaries. But intraplate earthquakes also occur, and their causes are less well understood. How can we locate earthquake epicenters, especially when they are in remote areas? Seismologists triangulate epicenter locations by using sophisticated mathematical analysis of the arrival times of the different seismic waves from many seismic recording stations.

In this book, we use a much simpler method to locate an epicenter from only three seismic stations and determine precisely when the earthquake occurred. The basis for this method is the fact that the four types of seismic waves travel at different velocities. The same reasoning permits us to locate epicenters and determine the precise time of the faulting that causes individual earthquakes. Let's look at location first, then timing.

FIGURE 16.4 **Worldwide distribution of earthquake epicenters.** Most earthquakes occur in distinct belts along plate boundaries.

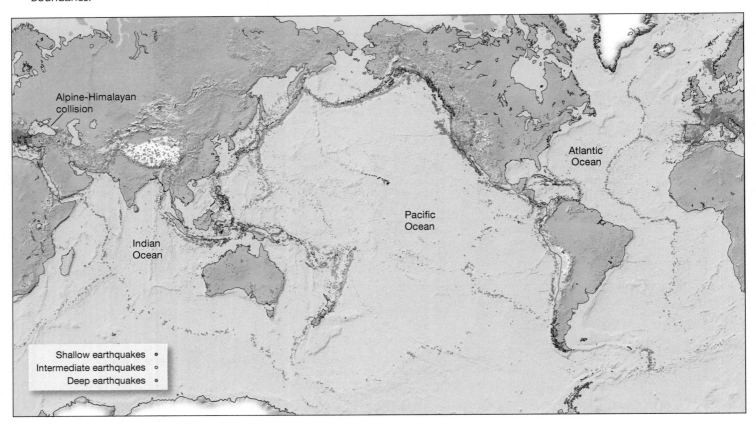

EXERCISE 16.2   **Locating Earthquake Epicenters**

Name: _____   Section: _____
Course: _____   Date: _____

This exercise leads you through the reasoning used to calculate the distance from a seismic station to an earthquake epicenter. But instead of two different seismic waves, let's see first how this works with two cars that start along a road at exactly the same time (see the figure on the next page). Both use cruise control set at 1 mile per minute (60 miles per hour), but the controls are not exactly the same. Car 1 covers each mile in exactly 60 seconds and Car 2 in 61 seconds. Because Car 1 arrives a second before Car 2 for each mile they travel, the delay between the arrival times of Car 1 and Car 2 increases at each mile marker.

To see how this works, complete the illustration on the next page:

(a) In each of the boxes to the right of Car 1 and Car 2, note the travel time (in seconds) needed to arrive at the different mileposts—the first one has been completed.

(b) In the boxes at the bottom of the figure, indicate the delay time between arrival of Car 1 and Car 2 at each milepost.

(continued)

Name: _____   Section: _____
Course: _____   Date: _____

The basis for locating earthquake epicenters based on the arrival times of different seismic waves.

| Car 1 travel-time | **60** | | | | | | |

Car 1
(1 mile in 60 seconds)

| Car 2 travel-time | **61** | | | | | | |

Car 2
(1 mile in 61 seconds)

—— 1 mile —— 2 miles —— 3 miles —— 4 miles —— 5 miles —— 6 miles —— 7 miles

| Delay time | **1** | | | | | | |

Of course, geologists don't know at first how far seismic waves traveled or when they were generated by an earthquake. But as with the cars in this exercise, geologists do know (1) the velocities of the different seismic waves; (2) that waves started at the same time (when the fault moved); and (3) the precise time when the different waves were recorded by seismometers. To figure out how far away an epicenter was and when the earthquake happened, we work backwards to derive the information.

You can see how this works by continuing to use the two imaginary cars instead of seismic waves and working backwards like a seismologist. Imagine you are looking out the window of a room waiting for Car 1 and Car 2 to drive by a streetlight outside your window. You don't know where they came from or what time they left, but you do know (1) their velocities (you have been told that Car 1 will arrive traveling at 1 mile in 60 seconds and Car 2 at 1 mile in 61 seconds); and (2) that they started at exactly the same time. As they drive by, you (3) record the precise delay between the times they passed the streetlight outside your window.

(c) Using that information, **how far** did the two cars travel if Car 2 passed the streetlight
  i.   25 seconds after Car 1? _____ miles
  ii. 45 seconds after Car 1? _____ miles

(d) Now determine the **precise time** that the cars started their trip (hour:minute:second) if Car 1 passed the streetlight at 12:25:00 and was
  i.   25 seconds before Car 2: ____:____:____
  ii. 45 seconds before Car 2: ____:____:____
  (**Hint:** Determine how far the cars traveled and then use the known velocity of Car 1 to estimate how much travel time it needed to go that distance.)

Now put the two pieces of reasoning together.

(e) If Car 1 arrives at precisely 1:45:22, followed by Car 2 at 1:46:37, how far did they travel? _____ miles

(f) At what precise time did they leave? ____:____:____

This simple exercise illustrates the reasoning used to determine the distance from a seismometer (the streetlight in this exercise) to an earthquake epicenter (the starting line of each car). But, in this exercise, you have been given the velocity of the cars. How do seismologists determine these measurements?

FIGURE 16.5 Travel-time curves show the relationship between distance traveled and relative seismic wave velocity.

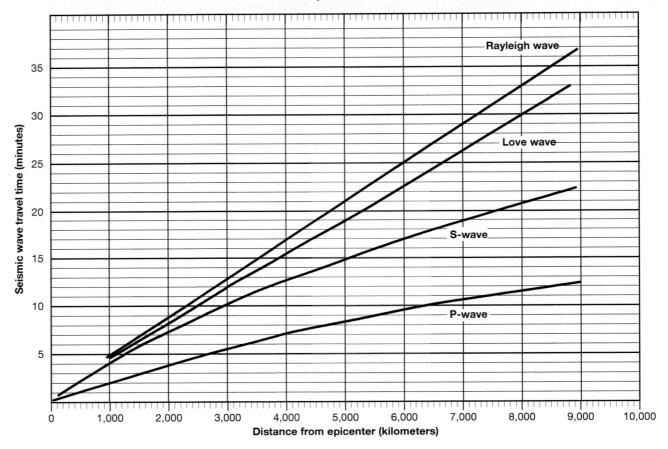

Seismologists have measured velocities of P-, S-, Love, and Rayleigh waves in different rock types and know that P-waves average approximately 6.3 kilometers per *second* at the surface and S-waves about 3.6 km/s. A graph of these speeds called a **travel-time diagram** is used to calculate the distance to an epicenter (**FIG. 16.5**). The black curves in Figure 16.5 show how much time it takes (vertical axis) the four types of seismic waves to travel the distances shown on the horizontal axis. To find the time it takes a P-wave to reach a point 4,000 km from an epicenter, find the intersection of the 4,000-km vertical line with the P-wave travel-time curve. Draw a horizontal line from the intersection to the time axis on the left and read the time required—7 minutes in this example. Exercise 16.3 provides practice in reading travel-time curves and then Exercise 16.4 takes you through the steps of how to locate an earthquake's epicenter.

EXERCISE 16.3	Reading a Travel-Time Curve

Name: _____   Section: _____
Course: _____   Date: _____

Refer to the travel-time curve in Figure 16.5.

(a) How long does it take a P-wave to travel 5,000 km? _____ minutes

(b) How long does it take an S-wave to travel 5,000 km? _____ minutes

(c) How long does it take a Love wave to travel 5,000 km? _____ minutes

(d) How long does it take a Rayleigh wave to travel 5,000 km? _____ minutes

Name: _____   **Section:** _____
Course: _____   **Date:** _____

Park the cars, and let's tackle an earthquake. Use the following series of steps to get all the information you need to identify the location of the earthquake and pinpoint when it occurred:

1. Identify the four different seismic waves on seismograms from three stations.

2. Determine the arrival times and measure the delays between different waves.

3. Use these data and the travel-time diagram to estimate each station's distance from the epicenter.

4. Use triangulation to locate the epicenter.

5. Determine the time of faulting with the travel-time diagram.

Step 1: Reading a Seismogram

Recognizing Types of Waves

You will need to know what P-, S-, Love, and Rayleigh waves look like on a seismogram in order to identify them correctly. Each seismic wave causes the ground to shake differently (Fig. 16.2), and this produces a different appearance on a seismogram. The differences are in wave amplitude (height) and frequency (the time between adjacent wave peaks). These differences are summarized in the figure below and will help you interpret the seismograms in the next part of this exercise.

This close-up of a seismogram shows the signals generated by different kinds of seismic waves.

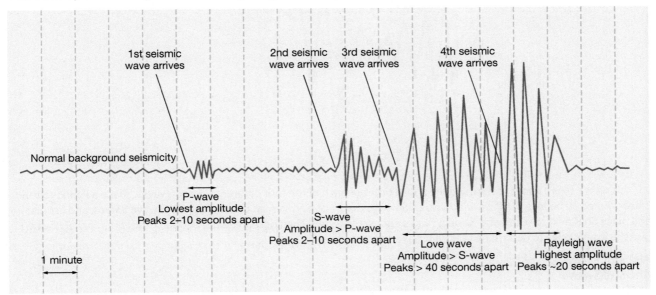

Now that you know what different types of waves look like on a seismogram, let's see how to measure their arrival times. The figure on the next page shows how waves look on a typical seismogram printout. The dashed vertical lines are time markers and are 1 minute apart. The waves reflect time moving forward from left to right on each row, and as a row ends, the time starts again on the left side of the next row below it (just like lines in a book). Seismic waves rarely arrive precisely on a minute marker, so you have to estimate the number of seconds before or after each minute. [*Note:* To avoid confusion involving time zones and changes to and from Daylight Savings Time, seismogram times are recorded in Greenwich Mean Time (GMT)].

(continued)

EXERCISE 16.4 Locating an Earthquake Epicenter and Determining When It Occurred (continued)

Name: ______________________________ **Section:** ____________
Course: ______________________________ **Date:** ____________

Recognizing seismic wave arrivals and measuring time on a seismogram.

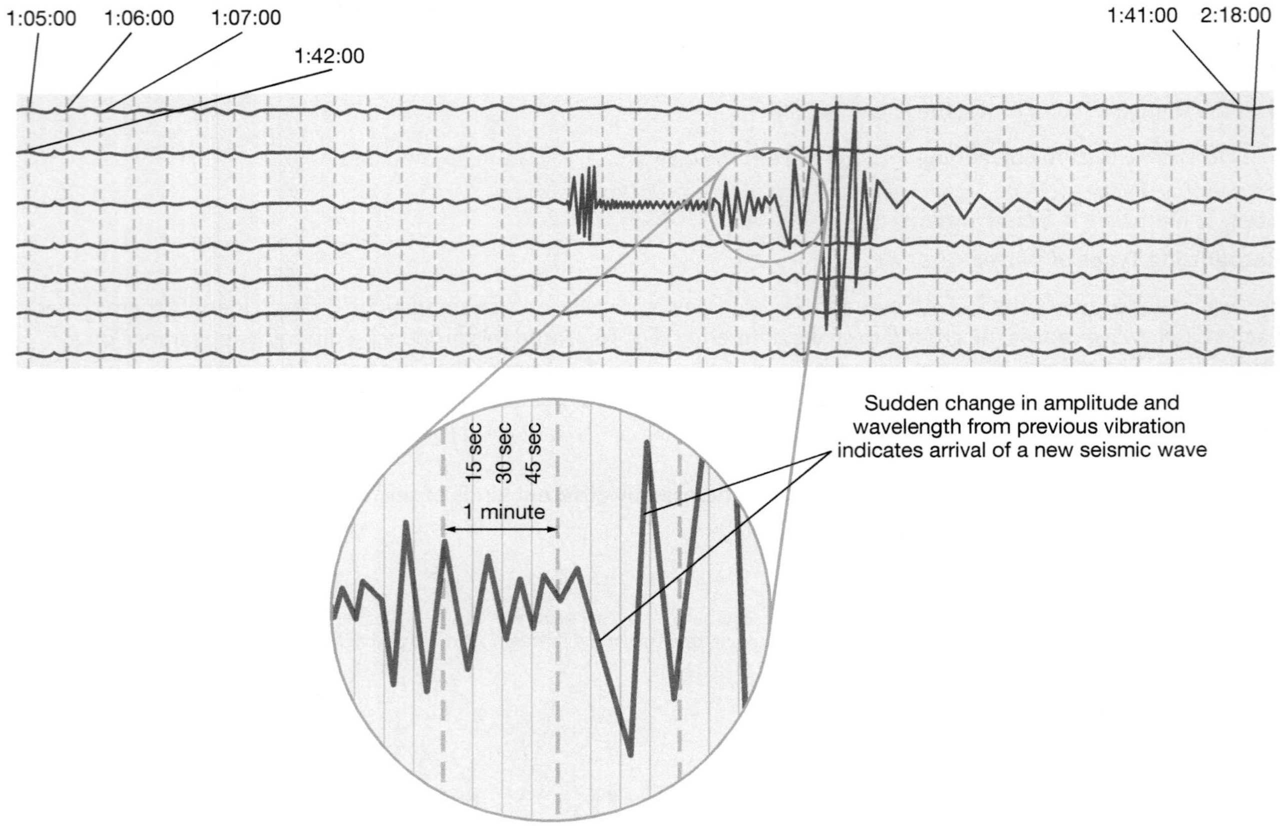

1:05:00
1:06:00
1:07:00
1:42:00
1:41:00
2:18:00
15 sec
30 sec
45 sec
1 minute
Sudden change in amplitude and wavelength from previous vibration indicates arrival of a new seismic wave

Using the figure above, determine the arrival times of each of the four different types of waves. Place a P next to the place where you believe the P wave arrives, an S where the S wave arrives, an L where the Love wave arrives, and estimate and place an R next to where the Rayleigh wave appears to arrive. Then determine the correct arrival time for each wave. Use the inset circles to determine precise times as necessary.

Arrival of P-wave _____ : _____ : _____
Arrival of S-wave _____ : _____ : _____
Arrival of Love wave _____ : _____ : _____
Estimated arrival of Rayleigh wave _____ : _____ : _____

Looking at the size of the amplitudes of the measurements on the seismograph, which wave types might cause the most damage in an earthquake? Explain. ____

____

____

(continued)

Name: _____   Section: _____

Course: _____   Date: _____

Step 2: Measuring the Delay between Arrival of Different Waves

The following figure shows seismograms from three stations. Identify each of the waves and record their arrival times in the table provided on the next page. Then calculate the times between arrivals by subtracting the P-wave arrival time from that of the S-wave, the S-wave from the Love wave, and the Love from the Rayleigh.

Seismograms for Exercise 16.4.

(a) Seattle, Washington

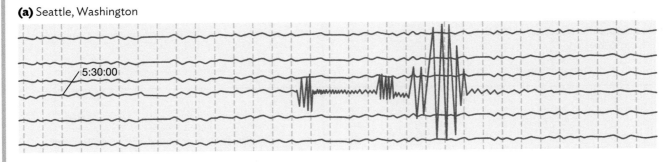

(b) Boston, Massachusetts

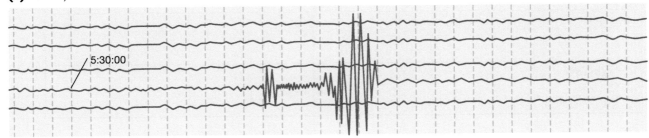

(c) Los Angeles, California

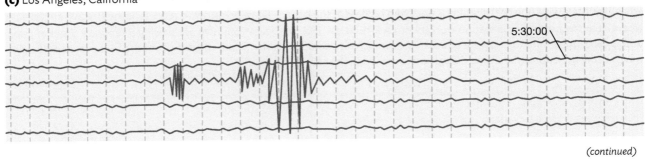

(continued)

EXERCISE 16.4 Locating an Earthquake Epicenter and Determining When It Occurred (continued)

Name: ______________________________ **Section:** __________

Course: ______________________________ **Date:** __________

Arrival times and delays between seismic waves.			
Seismic wave arrival times	**Seattle**	**Boston**	**Los Angeles**
P-Wave			
S-Wave			
Love Wave			
Rayleigh Wave			
Delays between seismic waves			
S–P			
Love–S			
Rayleigh–Love			

Step 3: Estimating Distance from the Epicenter to Each Station Using the Travel-Time Diagram

The next figure in this exercise shows how to use seismic wave delay data to locate the distance from each station to the epicenter. Start with one of the stations and then repeat for the others. Draw an arrow to represent the P-wave arrival anywhere near the bottom on a station worksheet (**APPENDIX 16.1**) or create your own scale using a separate sheet of paper. In this case, make sure to copy the scales in the worksheets *exactly*. Then indicate the arrivals of the S-, Love, and Rayleigh waves using the appropriate time delays you recorded in the table.

(continued)

Name: _____   Section: _____
Course: _____   Date: _____

Using a travel-time diagram to determine distance to an earthquake epicenter and time the earthquake occurred. Slide the station worksheet across the travel-time diagram until all four arrows coincide with the appropriate travel-time curves (possible positioned worksheet is shown in the figure below).

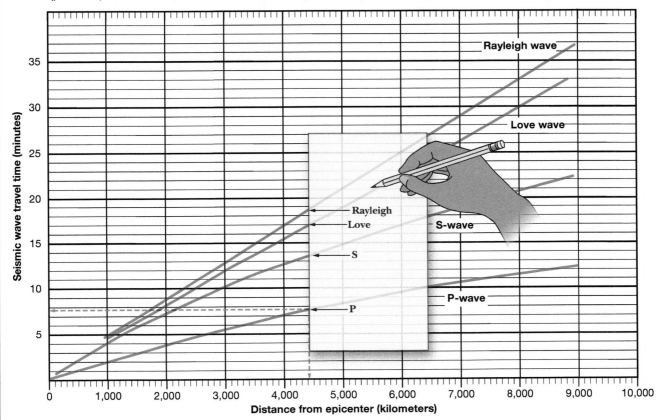

Draw a vertical line from the edge of the graph for that station to the horizontal distance scale in the figure above and read the distance from the epicenter. Repeat for the other two stations and record the data.
Distance to epicenter from Seattle: _____ km   Boston: _____ km   Los Angeles: _____ km

Step 4: Determining the Location of an Earthquake with Triangulation

It's one thing to know *how far* an epicenter is from a seismometer station, but quite a different thing to know exactly *where* it is. On the map of North America on the following page, seismologists from Nova Scotia's Cape Breton Island calculated that an earthquake occurred 4,000 km from their station. The epicenter must lie somewhere on a circle with a radius of 4,000 km centered on their station—but that could be in the Atlantic Ocean, Hudson Bay, Mexico's Yucatán Peninsula, or the front ranges of the Rocky Mountains.

(continued)

Name: _____   Section: _____

Course: _____   Date: _____

Locating an earthquake.

A second seismometer station in Caracas, Venezuela, estimates a distance of 6,000 km to the epicenter—somewhere on a circle with a radius of 6,000 km centered on Caracas. The two circles cross in two places, one in the Rockies, the other somewhere in the eastern Atlantic Ocean (outside the figure). The epicenter must be at one of these intersections, but both locations are equally possible. A third station is needed to settle the question, in this case pinpointing the epicenter in the front ranges of the Rocky Mountains. *Data from at least three seismic stations is needed to locate any epicenter, and the process is called* **triangulation**. The more stations used, the more accurate the location.

To locate the approximate epicenter (at last!), use an architect's compass or piece of string scaled to the appropriate distance for the figure. Draw an arc representing the distance for the first station and repeat the process for the other two stations as well. Review your work. Because of the tools you are using, your three arcs might not perfectly intersect, but they should be near each other. Draw a small circle with a 300 km diameter showing the area where you would expect to find the epicenter.

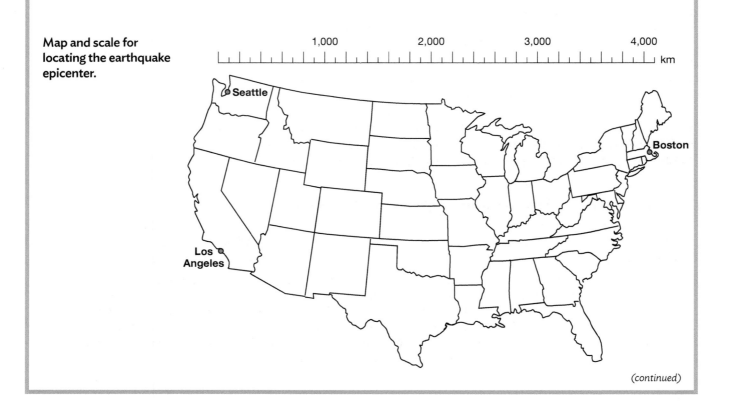

Map and scale for locating the earthquake epicenter.

(continued)

Name: _____   Section: _____

Course: _____   Date: _____

Step 5: Determining the Time When an Earthquake Occurred

When, exactly, did the earthquake occur at the epicenter? Align each data graph from Appendix 16.1 with the travel-time curves in Figure 16.5. For each, draw a horizontal line from the **P-wave intercept** on your graph to the time scale on the left side of the travel-time diagram, as shown by the green dashed arrow in the travel-time curve on page 419. Read directly how many minutes the P-wave took to travel to the station, using a millimeter ruler to estimate the number of seconds—in this case, 9 minutes 35 seconds.

     Subtract that amount of time from the P-wave arrival time in the table of this exercise to get the time when the earthquake occurred. Repeat for the other two stations—the answer should be the same for each.

     Time of the earthquake based on: Seattle _____ : _____ : ____   Boston _____ : _____ : _____

Los Angeles _____ : _____ : _____

16.4 Measuring the Strength of an Earthquake

The last piece of information we need is to determine the strength of the earthquake. There are two ways to describe the strength of an earthquake. The *Mercalli Intensity Scale* is based on the amount of damage sustained by buildings. But because damage to buildings can depend on factors unrelated to the energy released by an earthquake—such as the quality and nature of construction and type of ground beneath the buildings—this method is not very useful in our study of the Earth. In 1935, Charles Richter designed the first widely accepted method for estimating energy released in an earthquake—the Richter *magnitude scale*, which is based on the amount of energy released during faulting and calculated from the amount of actual bedrock motion. Each level of magnitude indicates an earthquake with ground motion *10 times greater* than the next lower level. Thus, a magnitude 4 earthquake has 10 times more ground motion than that of a magnitude 3 and one-tenth that of a magnitude 5.

We now know that Richter's method is accurate only for local, shallow-focus earthquakes. Modern estimates of earthquake strength use different methods involving body waves, surface waves, and a *moment magnitude* scale to calculate accurately the magnitude of shallow- and deep-focus, local and distant, and large and small earthquakes. They also depend on complex analyses of the rock type that broke in the fault, how much offset took place at the fault, and other factors that can't be determined from seismic records alone. In Exercise 16.5, we will use a simple graphical method to determine the magnitude of an earthquake.

Name: _____   Section: _____

Course: _____   Date: _____

In this simplified exercise, you will estimate m_b, the magnitude based on the amplitude of a body wave (P-wave). Because ground motion decreases the farther a seismic station is from an earthquake, distance from the epicenter must also be taken into account. This is done graphically (see next page). To determine m_b of the earthquake you measured in Exercise 16.4, mark the left-hand scale of the chart at the appropriate S-P delay for one of your stations to account for distance from the epicenter. Measure the maximum P-wave amplitude and mark it on the right-hand scale. Now draw a line connecting these two points. The value for m_b is where the line intersects the center magnitude scale.

(continued)

Name: _____   Section: _____

Course: _____   Date: _____

(a) What is m_b for an earthquake with exactly the same **P-wave amplitude** as the example in the figure below but with an S-P delay of 30 seconds? _____ 10 seconds? _____

(b) What is the relationship between wave amplitude, magnitude, and distance from the epicenter?

_____

_____

_____

(c) What is m_b for an earthquake with exactly the same **S-P delay time** as the example in the figure below but with a P-wave amplitude of 2 mm? _____ 100 mm? _____

(d) What is the magnitude of the earthquake based on the following data from three stations close to the epicenter determined in Exercise 16.4? Station A: P-S lag = 20 s, P-wave amplitude = 100 mm; Station B: P-S lag = 40 s; P-wave amplitude = 12 mm; Station C: P-S lag = 50 s, P-wave amplitude = 7 mm. _____

Note: The seismograms in Exercise 16.4 are artificial. If they were from a real earthquake, the values for m_b calculated from each should be nearly identical.

Determining the body wave magnitude of an earthquake.

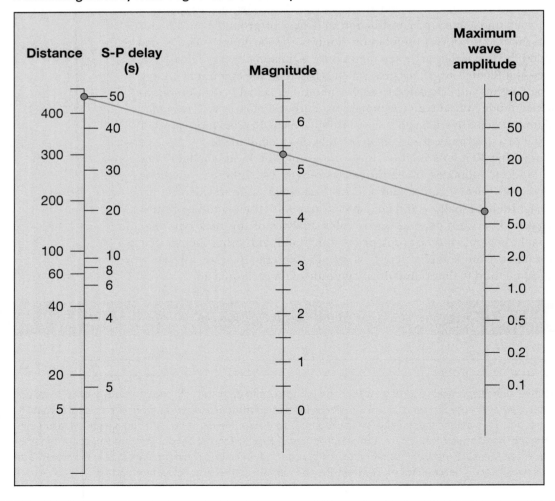

Name: _____   **Section:** _____

Course: _____   **Date:** _____

With the modern worldwide network of seismic stations, any earthquake epicenter can be located quickly and accurately. But what about earthquakes that took place *before* seismometers were invented? How can we define Earth's zones of seismic activity if we can't include earthquakes that occurred as (geologically) recently as 100 or 200 years ago? If there are records of damage associated with those events, geologists can estimate epicenter locations by making *isoseismal maps* based on the modified Mercalli Intensity Scale that show the geographic distribution of damage. First, historic reports of damage are analyzed for each location and given an approximate intensity value. These data are plotted on a map, and the map is contoured to show the variability of damage. Ideally, the epicenter is located within the area of greatest damage.

The figure below shows Mercalli intensity values for an 1872 earthquake that shook much of the Pacific Northwest. Contour the map to show areas of equal damage (isoseismal areas) and indicate with an x the location for the epicenter of this earthquake.

Modified Mercalli intensity values for the December 1872 Pacific Northwest earthquake.

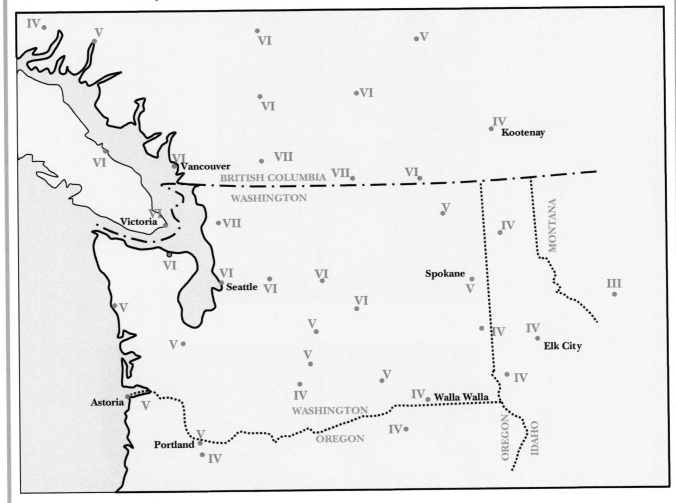

16.5 Predicting Earthquake Hazards: Liquefaction

One of the hazards associated with earthquakes is **liquefaction**, a process by which seismic vibration causes friction between sand grains in waterlogged sediment to be reduced so the sediment loses its ability to support overlying weight and flows like a liquid. At a small scale, this can be annoying (**FIG. 16.6a**); but on a larger scale, it can be catastrophic (**FIG. 16.6b**).

Liquefaction requires several key conditions: unconsolidated sediment, pores saturated or nearly saturated with water, and ground vibration. The sediment may be natural, such as rapidly deposited deltaic or other coastal sediments, or sandy fill used to create new land for shoreline development.

Landfill is increasingly used in crowded cities for new housing and business districts, but these could be severely damaged by liquefaction during an earthquake. Emergency planners must prepare for such an event, and they begin by identifying areas in which conditions for liquefaction are likely. The next exercise examines one such case.

FIGURE 16.6 **Results of liquefaction.**

(a) Upwelling liquefied sand in San Francisco broke through the sidewalk and curbs, causing minor disruption.

(b) Apartment houses in Niigata, Japan, rotated and sank when an earthquake caused liquefaction of the ground beneath them.

Name: _____   **Section:** _____

Course: _____   **Date:** _____

The figure below shows data from a study of liquefaction potential for San Francisco County. It separates areas where bedrock is exposed at the surface from those underlain by unconsolidated sediment and shows the depth to the water table in the sediment. Examine the map carefully to locate places where liquefaction has occurred in the past and for clues to why it happened in those locations.

(a) Briefly describe how the water table relates to past episodes and locations of liquefaction in San Francisco. Why does it seem important to study the water table when considering the possibility of liquefaction?

_____

_____

Liquefaction history in San Francisco related to depth to bedrock and water table height.

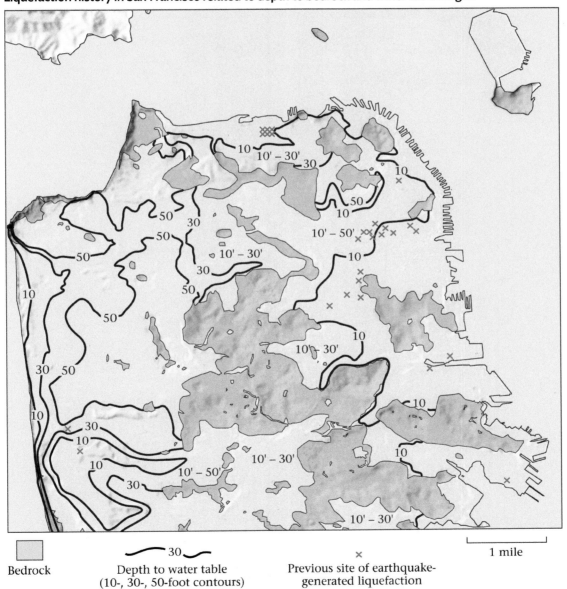

Bedrock

Depth to water table
(10-, 30-, 50-foot contours)

× Previous site of earthquake-
generated liquefaction

1 mile

(continued)

Name: _____   **Section:** _____

Course: _____   **Date:** _____

(b) Compare the sites of previous liquefaction events with the water table information in the previous map. What range of water table depths is associated with those events? _____ Shade areas of the previous page with a colored pencil to show where liquefaction is likely to take place in the future.

Topographic map of the San Francisco area, 1899.

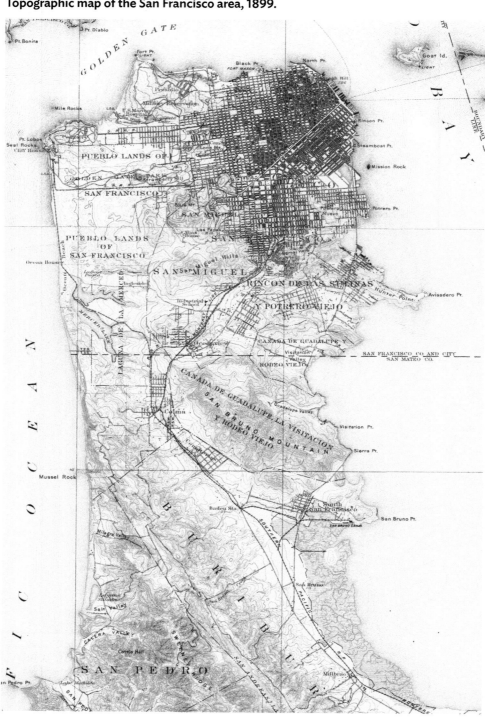

(continued)

Name: _____   Section: _____

Course: _____   Date: _____

(c) San Francisco grew dramatically between 1899 and 1999. To make room for the growing population and major new facilities, land was reclaimed from the sea, and these landfills are potential liquefaction sites. After comparing the map on the previous page with the satellite image that follows, color in areas on the photograph where there is a potential for liquefaction.

Satellite view of the San Francisco area, 1999.

(continued)

Name: _____   Section: _____

Course: _____   Date: _____

? **What do you think** If San Francisco is hit by another major earthquake, many roads will be blocked, and much of the relief effort will have to come by ship and plane. As adviser to the San Francisco disaster preparedness group, what might happen that could make supplies by ship and plane difficult to receive in San Francisco? On a separate piece of paper, write a memo to the City Council describing the steps that you would propose the city take in order to deal with these risks.

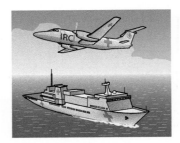

16.6 Tsunami!

The Japanese word *tsunami* is now familiar to the entire world because of the devastation caused by these waves along Indian Ocean shorelines in 2004 and more recently in Japan in 2011. A **tsunami** is a seismic shock wave transmitted through ocean water when the floor of the ocean is offset *vertically* during an earthquake. This displacement causes a series of shock waves to travel across the ocean at about 500 miles per hour—but if you were sitting in a small boat in the middle of the ocean, you wouldn't even know it passed beneath you. Unlike a typical wind-generated wave, a tsunami's wave height may be a foot or less; but its wavelength is thousands of feet.

These waves pose no danger in mid-ocean but can result in the worst coastal disasters when, like ordinary waves, they begin to "break" as they near land (see Figure 14.7). The word *tsunami* means "harbor wave," and it is in harbors and estuaries that the damage is magnified (**FIG. 16.7**). Tsunamis striking a relatively straight coastline distribute their energy along the entire shore. When the wave enters an embayment like a harbor or river mouth, the water is funneled into a narrow space and the wave can build to heights greater than 10 m (more than 33 feet) and cause unimaginable damage (see Fig. 14.24).

FIGURE 16.7 Concentration of tsunami energy along coastlines. Tsunami waves are concentrated into embayments, resulting in walls of water much higher than along straight coastal segments.

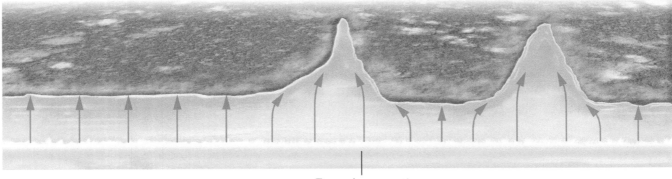

Tsunami wave crest

After watching dramatic images of tsunamis coming ashore near Sendai, Japan, some of our students asked how "just water" could cause so much damage. The amount of energy carried by a tsunami is truly unimaginable, but Exercise 16.8 offers a comparison that may help.

EXERCISE 16.8   **Why Is a Tsunami So Powerful?**

Name: _____   Section: _____
Course: _____   Date: _____

A cube of water 1 foot on a side (1 cubic foot, or 1 ft^3) weighs approximately 62 pounds. Imagine being hit by a 62-pound weight—it would certainly hurt.

(a) Now imagine a low wall of water 10 feet wide, 1 foot deep, and 1 foot high: it would weigh _____ lb.

(b) A wall of water 30 feet high (like the Sendai tsunami), 1 foot deep, and 10 feet wide would weigh _____ lb.

(c) A wall of water 30 feet high, 5,280 feet wide (a mile), and 1 foot deep would weigh _____ lb.

(d) To approximate a tsunami better: a wall of water 30 feet high, 5,280 feet wide, and "only" 2,640 feet deep would weigh _____ lb.

(e) One of the most powerful man-made objects is a modern railroad locomotive. A large locomotive weighs about 200 **tons** = 400,000 pounds. The impact of the conceptual tsunami in (d) above is equivalent to being hit by _____ locomotives.

This simple calculation should help you understand why "just water" can cause so much damage. And remember that a tsunami moves much faster than a locomotive.

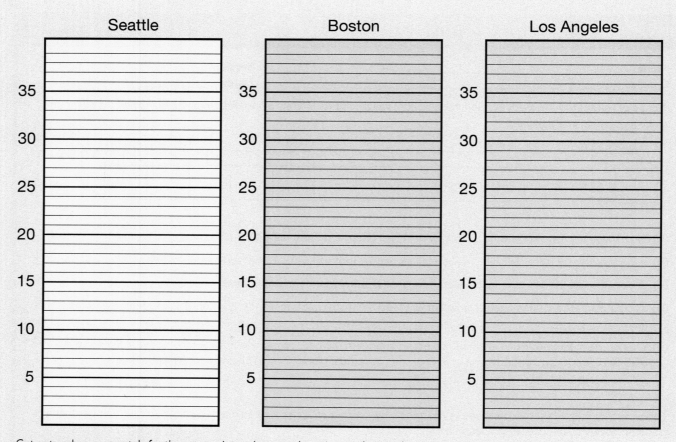

Seismic Analysis Worksheets

Cut out and use separately for the appropriate seismograph station on the travel-time curve on p. 414.

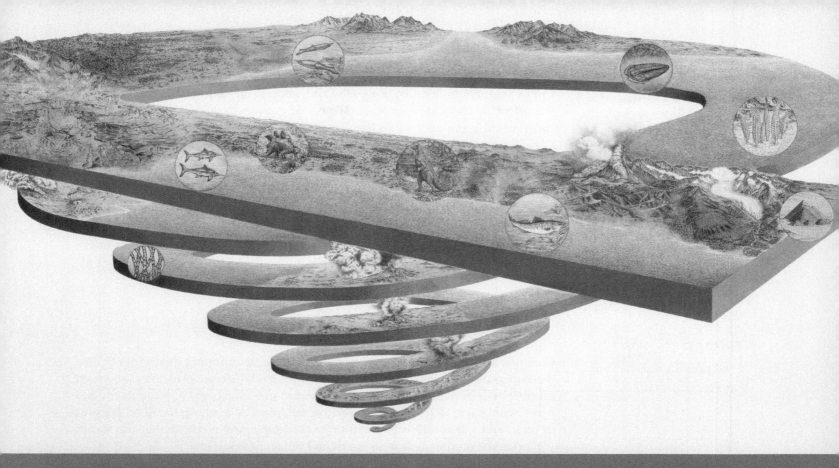

17

Interpreting Geologic History: What Happened, and When Did It Happen?

The Earth has an over 4.5 billion-year history and has undergone many changes, as depicted in this spiral timeline.

LEARNING OBJECTIVES

- Determine the relative ages of rocks and geologic processes and use these methods to interpret complex geological histories

- Learn how numerical (absolute) ages of rocks are calculated and apply them to dating geologic materials and events

- Understand how geologists piece together Earth history from widely separated areas

MATERIALS NEEDED

- Pen, pencils, calculator
- Drafter's compass

17.1 Introduction

You've learned to identify minerals, use mineralogy and texture to interpret the origin of rocks, deduce which agents of erosion have affected a given area, and recognize evidence of tectonic events. With these skills you can construct a three-dimensional picture of Earth, using topography and surface map patterns to infer underground relationships.

This chapter adds the fourth dimension—time: the ages of rocks and processes. Geologists ask two different questions about age: "Is a rock or process older or younger than another?" (their **relative** ages) and "Exactly how many years old are they?" (their **numerical** ages). We look first at how relative ages are determined, then at methods for calculating numerical age, and finally combine them to decipher geologic histories of varying complexity.

17.2 Physical Criteria for Determining Relative Age

Common sense is the most important resource for determining relative ages. Most reasoning used in relative age dating is intuitive, and the basic principles were used for hundreds of years before we could measure numerical ages. Geologists use two types of information to determine relative age: **physical methods** based on features in rocks and relationships between them, and **biological methods** that use fossils. We focus first on the physical methods and return to fossils later.

17.2.1 Principles of Original Horizontality and Superposition

The **principle of original horizontality** states that *most* sedimentary rocks are deposited in horizontal beds (there are exceptions, such as inclined sedimentation in alluvial fans, dunes, and deltas). Deposition as horizontal beds makes it easy to determine relative ages in a sequence of sedimentary beds *if the rocks are still in their original horizontal position*. In such cases, the oldest bed will be at the bottom of the sequence overlain by younger layers, with the youngest at the top.

This bit of common sense was first applied to sedimentary rocks by Nils Stensen (also known as Nicolaus Steno) almost 400 years ago and is called the **principle of superposition**. It cannot be used if rocks have been tilted or folded because, in some cases, the rocks may have been completely overturned so that the oldest is on top. In Exercise 17.1, you will look at an outcrop of rock and decide, like Steno, where the oldest and youngest layers are.

EXERCISE 17.1 **Relative Ages of Horizontal Rocks**

Name: _____   Section: _____

Course: _____   Date: _____

(a) The photograph on the next page shows sedimentary rocks in Painted Desert National Park. Assuming original horizontality, label the oldest and the youngest rocks. Where will the oldest rocks be in any sequence of undeformed, horizontal sedimentary rocks? Explain.

_____

_____

(continued)

Horizontal strata in Painted Desert National Park, Arizona.

(b) Would your answers be different if the rocks were volcanic ash deposits or lava flows? Explain.

_____

_____

17.2.2 Principle of Cross-Cutting Relationships

Superposition cannot be used if sedimentary rocks or lava flows have been tilted or folded from their original horizontal attitudes, nor for most metamorphic rocks and igneous rocks that weren't originally horizontal layers. The principle of cross-cutting relationships helps to determine the relative ages of such rocks: if one rock cuts across another, it must be younger than the rock that it cuts (**FIG. 17.1**).

FIGURE 17.1 Cross-bedded sandstones, Zion National Park, Utah. The person in the photograph is pointing to a contact that cuts across several inclined beds.

We use the term "cross-cutting" broadly, not just for features that physically cut others, but also for processes that have *affected* materials. For example, although the folding shown in photo (c) of Exercise 17.2 doesn't cut across the sedimentary layers, it certainly affected them and therefore had to have occurred after they were deposited. Contact metamorphism is another process that affects rocks without cutting across them. Thus, a lava flow bakes the rock or sediment that it flows upon.

EXERCISE 17.2 **Relative Ages in Cross-Cutting Situations**

Name: _____   Section: _____
Course: _____   Date: _____

Refer to Figure 17.1 to answer questions (a) and (b).

(a) Which is younger? The inclined beds in Figure 17.1 or the layer that cuts them?

_____

(b) Why can't the principle of superposition be used to determine the relative age of the rock layers in Figure 17.1?

_____

_____

This **principle of cross-cutting relationships** is useful for many types of geologic materials and processes, such as those shown in the photographs below. Refer to these photographs in order to answer the remaining questions of this Exercise.

Applying the principle of cross-cutting relationships.

(a) Dikes intruding granite of the Sierra Nevada batholith in Yosemite National Park, California.

(b) Vertical fault offsetting volcanic ash deposits in Kingman, Arizona.

(c) Folded sedimentary rocks on the island of Crete.

(continued)

Name: _____   Section: _____

Course: _____   Date: _____

(c) An intrusive igneous rock that cuts across other rock units as in photo (a) must be _____ than the units it cuts across. Using this principle, label the order of intrusion of the granite and dikes in the photos above.

(d) A fault, like in photo (b), must be _____ than the rocks it offsets. While you're at it, use the principle of original horizontality to label the oldest and youngest (horizontal) volcanic ash layers that the fault cuts.

(e) The process that folded the sedimentary rocks in photo (c) must be _____ than the rocks. Why can't you use the principle of original horizontality to determine the relative ages of the sedimentary layers in this photograph?

_____

_____

(f) Using your knowledge of the cross-cutting nature of contact metamorphism, how could you tell whether a basalt layer between two shale beds was a lava flow or a sill?

_____

_____

_____

_____

17.2.3 Principle of Inclusions

Pieces of one rock type are sometimes enclosed (included in) another rock. This is most common in clastic sedimentary rocks where fragments of older rocks are incorporated in conglomerates, breccias, and sandstones. It also happens where igneous rocks intrude an area and enclose pieces of the host rock. Inclusions of different rock types in an igneous rock are called **xenoliths** (from the Greek *xenos*, meaning stranger, and *lith*, meaning rock). The principle of inclusions states that such inclusions must have been there before the intrusion or before the sedimentary rock formed, and are therefore older than the rock that included them (**FIG. 17.2**).

FIGURE 17.2 Inclusions in igneous and sedimentary rocks.

(a) Gabbro inclusions in the Baring Granite in Maine.

(b) Fragments of rhyolite tuff in conglomerate from Maine.

Name: _____   Section: _____
Course: _____   Date: _____

(a) Which is older, the granite in Figure 17.2a or the xenoliths? Explain.

_____

_____

_____

_____

(b) Clasts in sedimentary rock must be _____ than the sedimentary rock in which they are included. Explain.

_____

_____

_____

_____

17.2.4 Sedimentary Structures

Some sedimentary structures indicate where the top or bottom of a bed was at the time it was deposited, so that it is possible to tell whether a bed is older or younger than another even if the rocks are vertical or completely overturned. These "top-and-bottom" features include cross-bedding, mud cracks, graded bedding, ripple marks, and impressions such as animal footprints. **FIGURE 17.3** illustrates some of the features that help determine the relative ages of sedimentary rocks.

Cross-bedding as we saw in Figure 17.1 is produced when grains are deposited by an air or water current. Inclined (cross-) beds truncated by overlying layers were used as an example of cross-cutting relationships, and in many cases the inclined layers cut older inclined layers as well.

FIGURE 17.3 Sedimentary "top-and-bottom" indicators of relative age.

 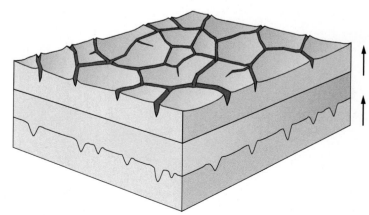

(a) Mud cracks: Mud cracks are widest at the top and narrow downward. The diagram at right is therefore right-side up, indicating that the bottom-most bed is older than the bed in the middle.

(b) Graded beds: The coarsest grains settle first and lie at the bottom of the bed. They are followed by progressively smaller grains, producing a size gradation. Arrows in the diagram at right show how a geologist would interpret the upright nature of the graded beds.

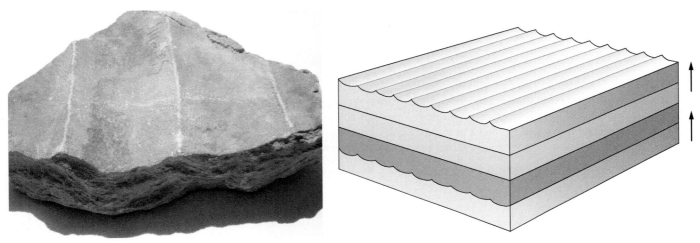

(c) Symmetrical ripple marks: The sharp points of the ripple marks point toward the top of the bed.

(d) Impressions: Features such as dinosaur footprints (left) and raindrop impressions (right) formed when something (here, a dinosaur and raindrops) sank into soft sediment.

Name: _____   Section: _____

Course: _____   Date: _____

(a) Sketch diagrams showing how the three sedimentary structures indicated below would appear in beds that had been turned upside down.

(i) Mud cracks   **(ii)** Graded beds   **(iii)** Symmetrical ripple marks

(b) Are the sedimentary features in Figure 17.3d right-side up or upside down as shown? Explain your reasoning.

_____

_____

_____

The figure below shows the value of sedimentary structures in relative age dating. A cliff face exposing horizontal rock (left side) might be incorrectly interpreted as undeformed horizontal strata without the top-and-bottom information that proves the layers have been folded and some must have been overturned. The right side of the figure shows what the geologist might have seen had the adjacent rocks not been eroded away or covered by glacial deposits.

(c) Number the layers, with 1 representing the oldest rock. Which is the youngest?

_____

_____

Reversals of top-and-bottom features reveal folding.

Legend:
~~~ Upright symmetrical ripple marks

888 Upright graded bedding

17.2.5 Unconformities: Evidence for a Gap in the Geologic Record

When rocks are deposited continuously in a basin without interruption by tectonic activity, uplift, or erosion, the result is a stack of parallel beds. Beds in a continuous sequence are said to be **conformable** because each conforms to, or has the same shape and orientation of, the others, as in the photograph of the Painted Desert that appears in Exercise 17.1.

Tilting, folding, and uplift leading to erosion interrupt this simple history and break the continuity of deposition. In these cases, younger layers are not parallel to the older folded or tilted beds, and erosion may remove large parts of the rock record, leaving a gap in an area's history. We may recognize that deposition was interrupted but can't always tell how long the interruption lasted or what happened during it. A contact indicating a gap in the geologic record is called an **unconformity** because the layer above it is not conformable with those below.

There are three kinds of unconformity (**FIG. 17.4**). A **disconformity** separates parallel beds when some older rocks below the disconformity were removed by erosion. A **nonconformity** is an erosion surface separating older igneous rocks from sedimentary rocks deposited after the pluton was eroded. When rocks above an unconformity cut across folded or tilted rocks below it, the contact is called an **angular unconformity**.

FIGURE 17.5 shows an angular unconformity in the Grand Canyon that separates two conformable sequences of sedimentary rock. Rocks above the unconformity are a horizontal sequence of sandstone, siltstone, and shale that is essentially undeformed and within which the principle of superposition can be applied. The sequence of sedimentary rock below the unconformity was originally horizontal but was tilted and eroded before the oldest overlying bed was deposited.

FIGURE 17.4 **The three kinds of unconformities and their formation.**

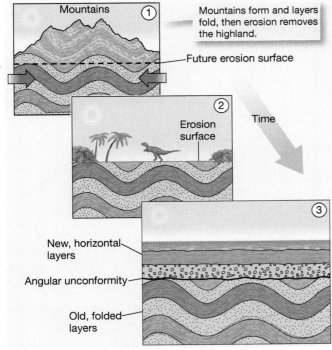

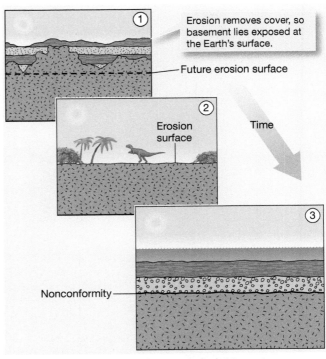

(a) An angular unconformity: (1) layers undergo folding; (2) erosion produces a flat surface; (3) sea level rises and new layers of sediment accumulate.

(b) A nonconformity: (1) a pluton intrudes; (2) erosion cuts down into the crystalline rock; (3) new sedimentary layers accumulate above the erosion surface.

FIGURE 17.4 The three kinds of unconformities and their formation. (continued)

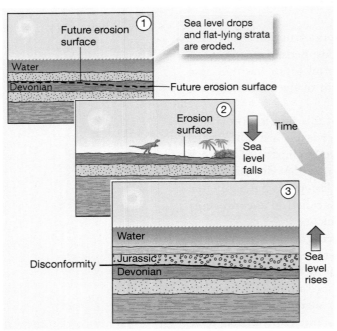

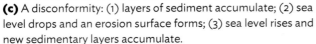

(d) This roadcut in Utah shows a sand-filled channel cut down into floodplain mud. The mud was exposed between floods, and a soil formed on it. When later buried, all the sediment turned into rock; the channel floor is an unconformity, and the ancient soil is a "paleosol." Note that the channel cut across the paleosol. The paleosol also represents an unconformity, a time during which deposition did not occur.

(c) A disconformity: (1) layers of sediment accumulate; (2) sea level drops and an erosion surface forms; (3) sea level rises and new sedimentary layers accumulate.

FIGURE 17.5 Angular unconformity in the Grand Canyon (highlighted by the red dashed line). The lower beds are tilted gently to the right and are separated by an angular unconformity from the horizontal beds that lie above them.

The only way to know how long it took for the tilting and erosion is to determine the ages of the youngest tilted rocks and of the oldest horizontal rock above the unconformity.

Applying Physical Principles of Relative Age Dating

Name: _____   Section: _____

Course: _____   Date: _____

In this exercise, you will apply the principles of relative age dating and your knowledge of geologic structures (Chapter 15) to interpret geologic histories of various degrees of complexity. Rock units in the four structural cross sections that follow are labeled with letters that have no meaning with respect to relative age (i.e., A can be older or younger than B). In all diagrams, sedimentary and metamorphic rocks are labeled with *uppercase* letters, igneous rocks with *lowercase* letters. Note that the rocks and some contacts are labeled but the *processes affecting those rocks* are not.

In the timeline on the right side of each cross section, arrange the materials in order from oldest (at the bottom— remember superposition) to youngest. Where an event has occurred (e.g., folding, tilting, erosion), draw an arrow to indicate the place in the sequence and label the event.

In many cases, you will have no doubt about the sequence of events, but in some there may be more than one possibility. In the space provided after each diagram, briefly explain why you ordered your choices the way you did.

Geologic cross section 1.

_____

_____

_____

_____

(continued)

Name: _____   Section: _____

Course: _____   Date: _____

Geologic cross section 2.

Geologic cross section 3.

(continued)

Name: _____   Section: _____
Course: _____   Date: _____

Geologic cross section 4.

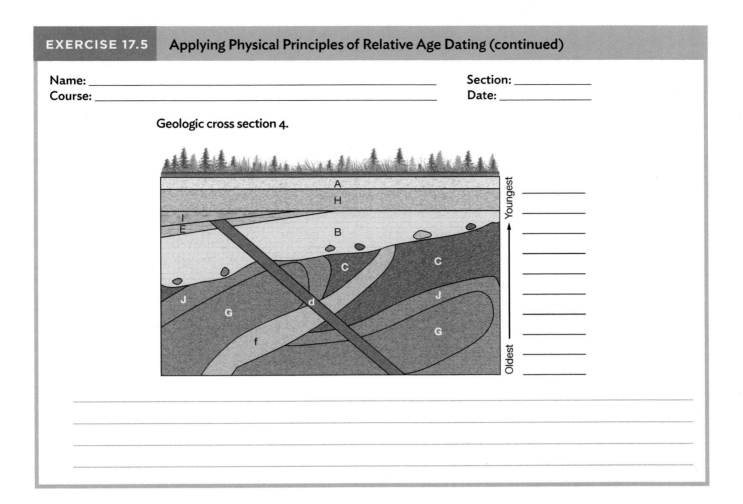

17.3 Biological Methods for Relative Age Dating and Correlation

In 1793, British canal builder and amateur naturalist William Smith noticed different fossils in the layers he was excavating. He discovered wherever he worked that some fossils were always found in rocks that lay above others, and he suggested that fossils could be used to tell the relative ages of the rocks.

17.3.1 Principle of Faunal and Floral Succession

Geologists confirmed Smith's hypothesis by showing that fossil animals (fauna) and plants (flora) throughout the world record an increasing complexity of life-forms from old rocks to young ones. This is the **principle of faunal and floral succession**. Not all fossils can be used to date rocks because some, like blue-green algae, have existed over most of geologic time and are not specific to a narrow time span.

Index fossils are remains of plants or animals that were distributed widely throughout the world but existed for only a short span of geologic time before becoming extinct. When we find an index fossil, we know that the rock in which it is found dates from that unique segment of time. This is like knowing that a Ford Edsel could only have been made in the three years between 1957 and 1960 or the Model A between 1903 and 1931. *Tyrannosaurus rex,* for example, lived only in the span of geologic time known as the Cretaceous Period; it should not have been in a Jurassic (an earlier time period) park.

17.3.2 The Geologic Time Scale

Determining the sequence of rock units by physical methods and using index fossils to place those units in their correct position in time resulted in the geologic time scale (**FIG. 17.6**). The chart divides geologic time into progressively smaller segments called eons, eras, periods, and epochs (not shown). Era names reveal the complexity of their life forms: Paleozoic, meaning *ancient* life; Mesozoic, meaning *middle* life; and Cenozoic, meaning *recent* life. The end of an era is marked by a major change in life-forms, such as an extinction in which most life-forms disappear and others fill their ecologic niches. For example, nearly 90% of fossil genera became extinct at the end of the Paleozoic Era, making room for the dinosaurs, and the extinction of the dinosaurs at the end of the Mesozoic Era made room for us mammals. Several period names come from areas where rocks of that particular age were best documented: Devonian from Devonshire in England; Permian from the Perm Basin in Russia; and the Mississippian and Pennsylvanian from U.S. states.

FIGURE 17.6 The geologic time scale.

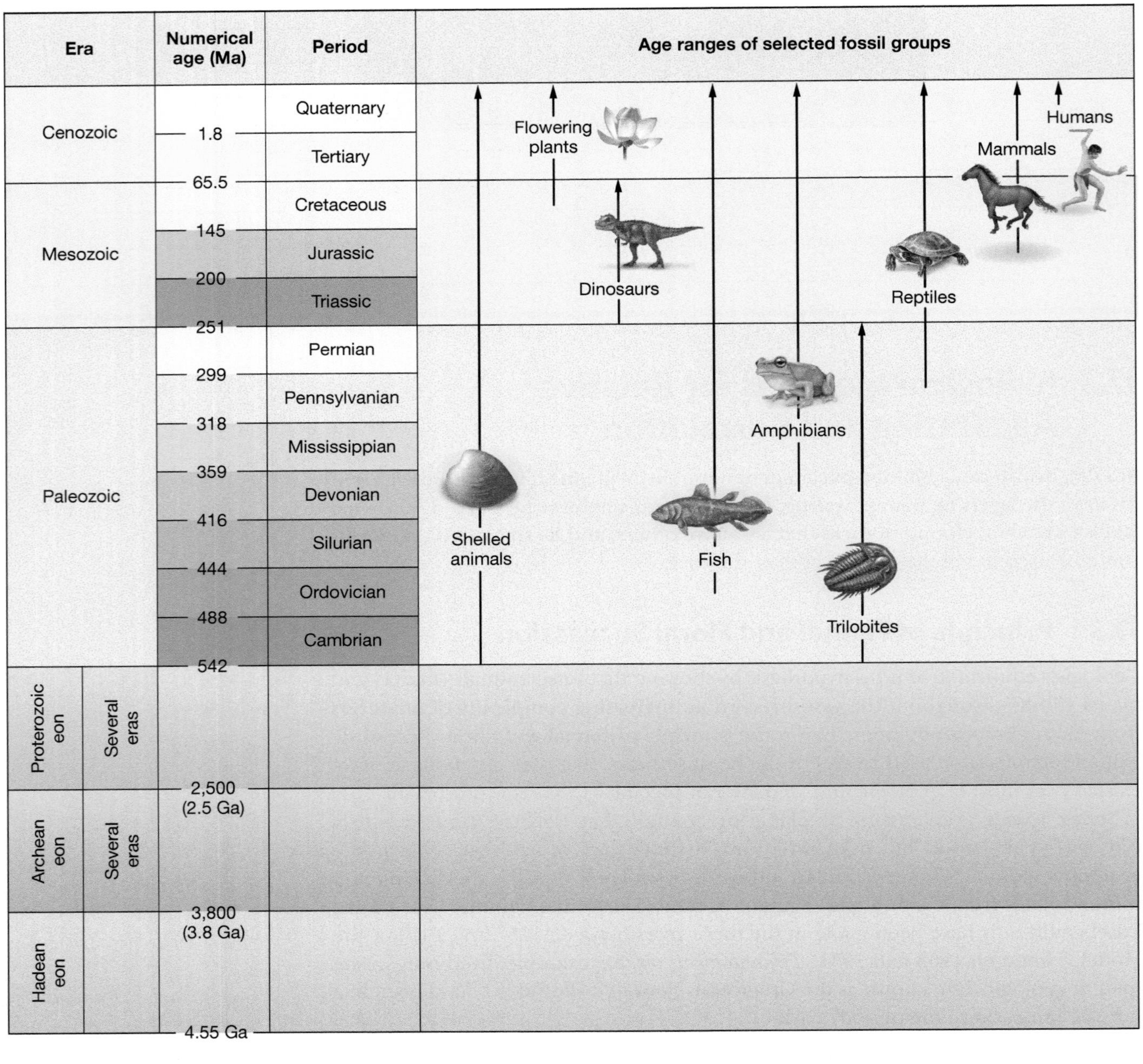

The geologic time scale was originally based entirely on *relative age* dating. We knew that Ordovician rocks and fossils were older than Silurian rocks and fossils, but had no way to tell *how much* older. The ability to calculate the numerical ages came nearly 100 years after the original time scale. Section 17.4 explores methods of numerical age dating.

17.3.3 Fossil Age Ranges

Some index fossil ages are very specific. The trilobites *Elrathia* and *Redlichia* lived only during the Middle and Early Cambrian, respectively. Others lived over a longer span, like *Cybele* (Ordovician and Silurian) and the brachiopod *Leptaena* (Middle Ordovician to Mississippian). But even index fossils with broad ranges can yield specific information if they occur with other index fossils whose overlap in time limits the possible age of the rock. This can be seen even in the broad fossil groups shown in Figure 17.6. Trilobite, fish, and reptile fossils each span several periods of geologic time, but if specimens of all three are found together, the rock that contains them could only have been formed during the Pennsylvanian or Permian.

EXERCISE 17.6 **Dating Rocks by Overlapping Fossil Range**

Name: _____   Section: _____
Course: _____   Date: _____

The following figures show (a) selected Paleozoic brachiopod species and (b) graphs their ranges within the geologic record.

(a) Selected brachiopod species.

(continued)

(a) Based on the overlaps in their ranges shown in the graph, what brachiopod fossil assemblage would indicate:

(i) a Permian age?

_____

(ii) a Silurian age?

_____

_____

(iii) an Ordovician age?

_____

_____

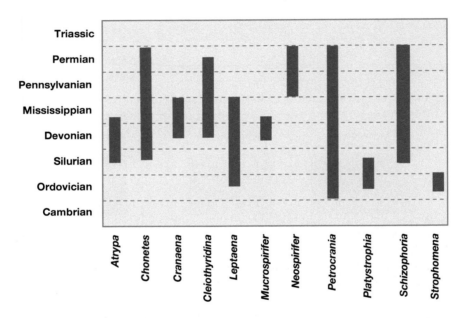

(b) Age ranges of brachiopod species.

(b) Now apply overlapping ranges to the first cross section in Exercise 17.5.

(i) If *Neospirifer* is found in Unit D, *Platystrophia* in F, and *Strophomena* in A, suggest an age for C. Explain your reasoning.

_____

_____

(ii) What is the extent of the gap in the geologic record represented by the angular unconformity below Layer D?

_____

_____

_____

(continued)

EXERCISE 17.6 **Dating Rocks by Overlapping Fossil Range (continued)**

Name: ______________________ Section: ____________
Course: ______________________ Date: ____________

(c) In the second cross section of Exercise 17.5, *Strophomena* is found in E, *Platystrophia* and *Petrocrania* in F, and *Petrocrania, Chonetes,* and *Neospirifer* in C.

(i) When were Units E, A, F, and I tilted? Explain.

____

____

____

(ii) What is the extent of the gap in the geologic record represented by the contact between C and the tilted rocks beneath it? Explain.

____

____

____

(iii) When in geologic time did the fault cutting Units K, C, I, F, A, and E occur? Explain.

____

____

____

17.4 Numerical Age Dating

The geologic time scale (Fig. 17.6) was used for relative age dating for about 100 years before numerical ages could be added. Numerical age dating is based on the fact that the nuclei of some atoms of elements found in minerals (**parent elements**) decay to form atoms of new elements (**daughter elements**) at a fixed rate *regardless of conditions.* This decay is called radioactivity and the atoms that decay are radioactive isotopes.

The decay "clock" begins when a mineral containing the parent element crystallizes during igneous and metamorphic processes. With time, the amount of the parent decreases and the amount of the daughter increases (**FIG. 17.7**). The amount of time the process takes depends on the *decay rates* of the different isotopes. The **half-life** is the amount of time it takes for half of the parent atoms in a mineral sample to decay to an equal number of daughter atoms (the center hourglass).

FIGURE 17.7 **Parent:daughter ratios during radioactive decay.**

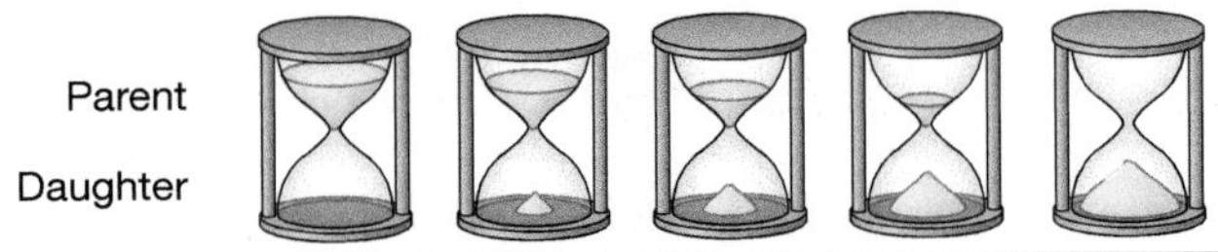

Percent parent	100	75	50	25	0
Percent daughter	0	25	50	75	100
Parent:daughter ratio	–	3:1	1:1	1:3	–

TABLE 17.1 Geologically important radioactive decay schemes.

Parent isotope	Daughter decay product	Half-life (years)	Useful dating range (years)	Dateable materials
^{147}Samarium	^{143}Neodymium	106 billion	>10,000,000	Garnets, micas
^{87}Rubidium	^{87}Strontium	48.8 billion	>10,000,000	Potassium-bearing minerals (mica, feldspar, hornblende)
^{238}Uranium	^{206}Lead	4.5 billion	>10,000,000	Uranium-bearing minerals (zircon, apatite, uraninite)
^{235}Uranium	^{207}Lead	713 million	>10,000,000	Uranium-bearing minerals (zircon, apatite, uraninite)
^{40}Potassium	^{40}Argon	1.3 billion	>10,000	Potassium-bearing minerals (mica, feldspar, hornblende)
^{14}Carbon	^{14}Nitrogen	5,730	100 to 70,000	Organic materials

TABLE 17.1 lists the isotopes used commonly in numerical age dating, their half-lives, and the minerals used in dating. In general, an isotope can date ages as old as ten of its half-lives; any older than that, and there wouldn't be enough parent atoms to measure accurately. Isotopes with short half-lives are therefore best used for relatively recent ages. Conversely, isotopes with very long half-lives, like ^{147}Samarium, decay so slowly that they can be used only to date very old rocks.

To calculate the numerical age of a rock, geologists crush it to separate minerals containing the desired isotope. A mass spectrometer determines the parent:daughter ratio and then a logarithmic equation is solved to calculate the age. Your calculation is easier: once you know the parent:daughter ratio, you can use TABLE 17.2 to calculate age through simple multiplication.

TABLE 17.2 Calculating the numerical age of a rock from decay scheme half-lives.

Percent of parent atoms remaining	Parent: daughter ratio	Number of half-lives elapsed	Multiply half-life by ___ to determine age	Percent of parent atoms remaining	Parent: daughter ratio	Number of half-lives elapsed	Multiply half-life by ___ to determine age
100	—	0	0	35.4	0.547	1½	1.500
98.9	89.90	1/64	0.016	25	0.333	2	2.000
97.9	46.62	1/32	0.031	12.5	0.143	3	3.000
95.8	22.81	1/16	0.062	6.2	0.066	4	4.000
91.7	11.05	1/8	0.125				
84.1	5.289	1/4	0.250				
70.7	2.413	1/2	0.500	0.05		11	Don't bother! There are too few parent atoms to measure accurately enough.
50	1.000	1	1.000	0.025		12	

Name: _____   Section: _____
Course: _____   Date: _____

(a) First, get practice calculating ages using Tables 17.1 and 17.2. How old is a rock if it contains:

    (i) a ^{235}uranium:^{207}lead ratio of 46.62? _____ years
    (ii) a ^{87}rubidium:^{87}strontium ratio of 89.9? _____ years
    (iii) 6.2% of its original ^{14}carbon? _____ years
    (iv) 97.9% of its original ^{40}potassium? _____ years

Now add more detail to the cross sections in Exercise 17.5.

(b) In the third cross section of Exercise 17.5, Dike E has zircon with a ^{235}uranium:^{207}lead ratio of 11.05; Dike A has zircon with a ^{238}uranium:^{206}lead ratio of 22.81; and Pluton F has hornblende with 84.1% of its parent ^{40}potassium.

    (i) How old is E? _____ A? _____ F? _____
    (ii) How old (in years and using period names) are Layers B, H, K, and J?

_____

_____

    (iii) When were these layers folded?

_____

_____

    (iv) When did the unconformity separating Layer I from the underlying rocks form?

_____

_____

    (v) How old are Layers I and D?

_____

_____

(c) In the fourth cross section of Exercise 17.5, Layer H has a thin volcanic ash bed at its base and zircon with a ^{235}uranium:^{207}lead ratio of 46.62; Layer D has zircon with a ^{235}uranium:^{207}lead ratio of 2.413; and Dike F has hornblende with 50% of its parent ^{40}potassium.

    (i) How old is H? _____ D? _____ F? _____
    (ii) When (in years and using period names) were Layers C, G, and J folded?

_____

_____

    (iii) How large a gap in the geologic record is represented by the unconformity below Layer B?

_____

_____

    (iv) How old is Layer I? _____
    (v) If Layer I contains the brachiopods *Neospirifer*, *Chonetes*, and *Schizophoria*, how does this help narrow its possible age?

_____

_____

    (vi) In that case, how large a gap in the geologic record is represented by the unconformity below Layer H?

_____

_____

17.5 Correlation: Fitting Pieces of the Puzzle Together

Imagine how difficult it would be for an alien geologist visiting Earth 200 million years from now to reconstruct today's geography. Plate tectonics could have moved some continents, split some and sutured others together; opened new oceans and shrunk or closed others. In what is now North America, there would be rock and fossil evidence of mangrove swamps; forests; grassy plains; large lakes and rivers; shoreline features; alpine glaciers and deserts; active volcanoes and other mountains. Numerical age dating would show rocks that today range from more than 3 billion to as little as 1 year old.

This is the challenge facing geologists today as we try to read the record of Earth history. There is no single place where all 4.6 billion years of Earth history are revealed—not even in the Grand Canyon. And at any one point in time, we can find evidence of all of the environments listed above—plus the deep marine and oceanic island settings. To work out a history for the entire planet, we first decipher the records of local areas and combine them into regional and larger-scale stories. This requires just about all of the skills you've learned during this course, from interpreting ancient environments and processes from the rocks they produce to deciphering the sequence of events and how long ago they occurred. Exercise 17.8 introduces you to the kind of reasoning used in combining information from two different areas into a regional picture.

EXERCISE 17.8 **Lithologic Correlation**

Name: _____   Section: _____

Course: _____   Date: _____

Five years ago, geologists determined the relative ages of rocks in two parts of the midcontinent, but the sequences were not the same (see the figure on the facing page). Unfortunately, similar rocks appear at several places in each section, making it difficult to know exactly which limestone, for example, in the western section correlates with a particular limestone in the east. It is better to compare *sequences* of units based on similar sequences of depositional environments rather than similarities in single rock units.

(a) Suggest correlations between layers of the two sequences by connecting the tops and bottoms of layers in the western section to those you believe are their matching layers in the eastern section. As in the real world, there may be more than one hypothesis, so explain your choice(s) and how you might further test them.

_____

_____

_____

(b) Do you think the environments indicated by the sedimentary rocks are the same in both the east and the west? Was deposition continuous (conformable) in both areas? Explain why or why not.

_____

_____

_____

_____

(continued)

Name: _____   Section: _____

Course: _____   Date: _____

Correlation of lithologic sequences.

Western sequence ◄——— 250 miles ———► Eastern sequence

During field mapping last year, trilobites were found in limestone units in both areas (see the figure on the next page). Paleontologists reported that these were identical index fossils from a narrow span of Middle Cambrian time.

(c) Using this additional information, draw lines indicating matching layers on the figure.

(d) Why does the presence of index fossils make correlation more accurate than correlation based on lithologic and sequence similarities alone?

_____

_____

_____

(continued)

Name: _____   Section: _____

Course: _____   Date: _____

Correlation assisted by index fossils.

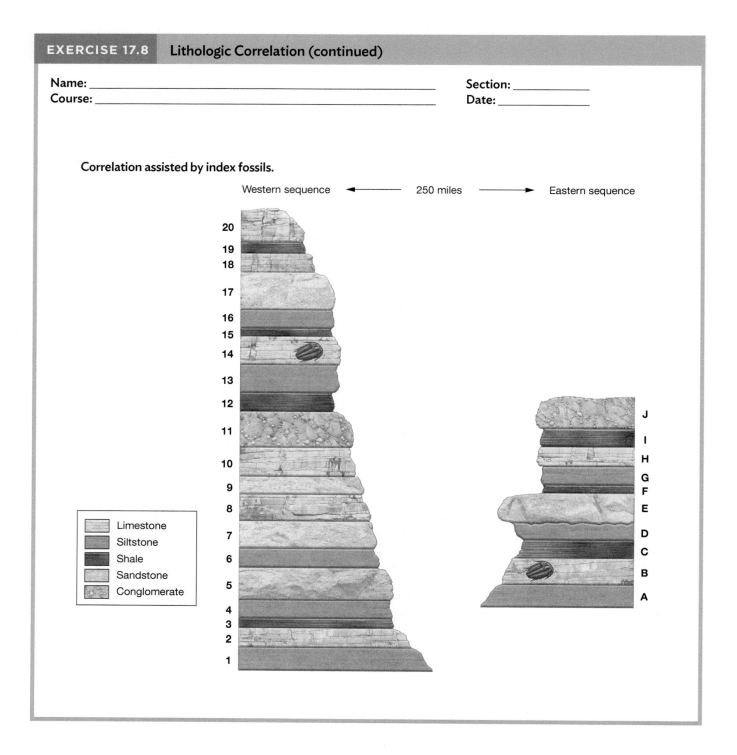

EXERCISE 17.9   Cretaceous Paleogeography of North America

Name: _____   Section: _____

Course: _____   Date: _____

After more than 200 years of study, geologists have gathered an enormous amount of data about the geologic history of North America. This exercise presents some of that data and asks **what do you think** the geography of the continent looked like toward the end of the Cretaceous Period, just before an event that led to extinction of most life-forms—including, most famously, the dinosaurs?

FIGURE 17.8 on the next page summarizes evidence from the distribution of sedimentary rocks that form in specific environments, like those you examined in Chapter 6; fossil and numerical age dating of sedimentary and igneous rocks; and interpretation of the folding, faulting, and metamorphic history of Cretaceous and older rocks. We saw earlier that index fossils are valuable for pinpointing the relative age of the rocks in which they are found. Here, we also use **facies fossils**, fossils of organisms that could only live in a narrowly restricted environment and therefore reveal the surface geography at the time they lived.

(a) On Figure 17.8, draw boundaries between the following North American geographic settings in the late Cretaceous Period:

- Continental interior
- Old, eroded mountain ranges
- Active tectonic zone
- Continental shoreline
- Shallow sea (continental shelf and parts of the continent flooded by shallow seas)
- Deep ocean

Evidence for these settings is described here. The facies fossils used as symbols on the map are, wherever possible, Cretaceous organisms.

? What Do You Think We all have impressions of what the Earth may have looked like during the cretaceous from watching movies and television. But using the evidence from Figure 17.8, describe on a separate sheet of paper what you think the United States and Canada looked like at that time, by region—north, south, central, and coastal areas. Then find your state or province and describe what you think it was like at that time, and suggest what you might want to explore to learn more.

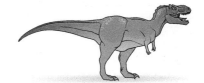

FIGURE 17.8 Map of North America today showing evidence for Cretaceous paleogeography.

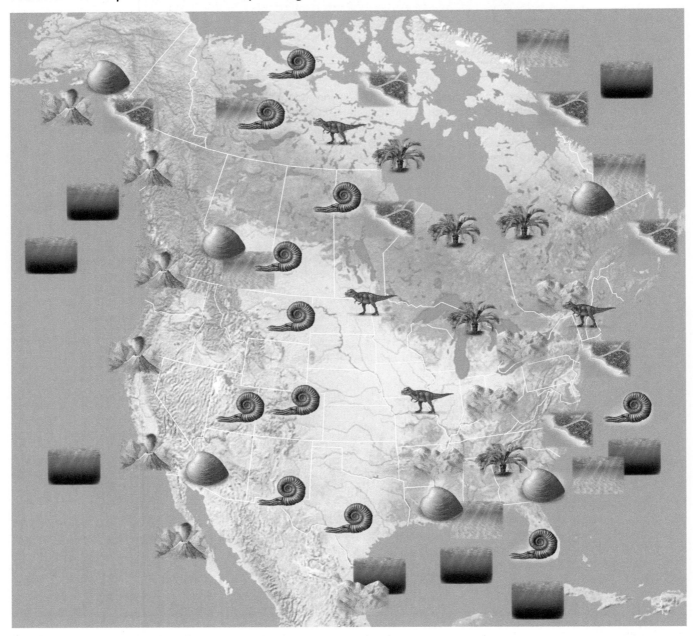

Continental Land Environments

Continental Interior	**Active Tectonic Zone**	**Old Mountains**	**Shorelines**
Terrestrial plants and animals	Volcanic arc rocks	Coarse clastic sedimentary rocks	Beach sandstones and coastal organisms

Marine Environments

Shallow Ocean	**Deep Ocean**
Shallow marine organisms and sedimentary rocks	Deep marine organisms and sedimentary rocks

CREDITS

Text Permission

Figure 11.18: Joanne Nova: Figure: "The 800 year lag – graphed," from Joannenova.com.au. Reprinted by permission of Joanne Nova.

Photos

Chapter 1

Page 1: Gary Crabbe/Aurora Photos; **p. 2**: Corey Templeton; **p. 7**: NASA; **p. 14 (left)**: G.R. Roberts, NSIL; **p. 14 (right)**: Belgian Federal Science Policy Office; **p. 18 (left)**: Dr. Stephen Hughes, Coastal Hydraulic Laboratories; **p. 18 (right)**: US Army Corps of Engineers/Steven Hughes; **p. 21 (both)**: Courtesy of Stephen Marshak; **p. 22 (left)**: Courtesy of Allan Ludman; **p. 22 (right)**: Courtesy of Stephen Marshak.

Chapter 2

Page 25: Buurserstraat386/Dreamstime.com; **p. 29**: NGDC/NOAA; **p. 36**: Unavco.org; **p. 38 (both)**: Marine Geoscience Data System/Natural Science Foundation; **p. 40**: NGDC/NOAA; **p. 50**: © Marie Tharp 1977/2003. Reproduced by permission of Marie Tharp Maps, LLC, 8 Edward Street, Sparkill, New York 10976.

Chapter 3

Page 55: Javier Trueba/MSF/Photo Researchers, Inc.; **p. 60 (top-left)**: Ross Frid/Visuals Unlimited, Inc.; **p. 60 (top-right)**: Mark Schneider/Visuals Unlimited, Inc.; **p. 60 (bottom-left)**: Ken Larsen/Smithsonian, National Museum of Natural History; **p. 60 (bottom-right)**: Mark Schneider/Visuals Unlimited, Inc.; **p. 61 (both)**: Courtesy of Allan Ludman; **p. 63 (top 4)**: Courtesy of Paul Brandes; **p. 63 (bottom-left)**: Richard P. Jacobs/JLM Visuals; **p. 63 (bottom-right)**: Scientifica/Visuals Unlimited, Inc.; **p. 64 (top-left)**: Courtesy of Stephen Marshak; **p. 64 (top-center)**: Mark Schneider/Visuals Unlimited, Inc.; **p. 64 (top-right)**: Courtesy of Allan Ludman; **p. 64 (bottom-left)**: 1995-1998 by Amethyst Galleries, Inc. http://mineral.galleries.com; **p. 64 (bottom-center)**: Mark Schneider/Visuals Unlimited, Inc.; **p. 64 (bottom-right)**: 1993 Jeff Scovil; **p. 65 (left)**: Scientifica/Visuals Unlimited, Inc.; **p. 65 (right)**: Biophoto Associates/Photo Researchers Inc.; **p. 66 (1)**: Scientifica/Visuals Unlimited, Inc.; **p. 66 (2-3)**: Courtesy of Paul Brandes; **p. 66 (4)**: Courtesy of Allan Ludman; **p. 66 (5)**: Courtesy of Paul Brandes.

Chapter 4

Page 85 (left): Rafael Laguillo/Dreamstime.com; **p. 85 (center)**: Dirk Wiersma/Science Source; **p. 85 (right)**: Les Palenik/Dreamstime.com; **p. 89 (top-left)**: Courtesy of Stephen Marshak; **p. 89 (top-right)**: Visualphotos.com; **p. 89 (center-left)**: Courtesy of Stephen Marshak; **p. 89 (center-right)**: Courtesy of Stephen Marshak; **p. 89 (bottom)**: Mark Schneider/Visuals Unlimited, Inc.; **p. 90 (top-left)**: Marli Bryant Miller, University of Oregon; **p. 90 (top-right)**: Michael C. Rygel; **p. 90 (bottom-left & right)**: Marli Bryant Miller, University of Oregon; **p. 91 (top-left & right)**: Courtesy of Stephen Marshak; **p. 91 (bottom-left)**: Rafael Laguillo/Dreamstime.com; **p. 91 (bottom-right)**: Courtesy of Allan Ludman; **p. 91 (bottom)**: Courtesy of Allan Ludman; **p. 104**: © Ron Chapple/Corbis.

Chapter 5

Page 105: Patricia Marroquin/Dreamstime.com; **p. 109 (left)**: Courtesy of Allan Ludman; **p. 109 (center)**: Albert Copley/Visuals Unlimited, Inc.; **p. 109 (right)**: Courtesy of Allan Ludman; **p. 111 (top-left)**: Courtesy of Allan Ludman; **p. 111 (top-right)**: Courtesy of Allan Ludman; **p. 111 (bottom-left)**: Courtesy of Stephen Marshak; **p. 111 (bottom-right)**: Marli Miller/Visuals Unlimited, Inc.; **p. 112**: Scientifica/Visuals Unlimited, Inc.; **p. 113 (left)**: Courtesy of Stephen Marshak; **p. 113 (right)**: Marli Bryant Miller, University of Oregon; **p. 114 (left)**: Courtesy of Allan Ludman; **p. 114 (top)**: Courtesy of Douglas W. Rankin; **p. 114 (bottom)**: Courtesy of Allan Ludman; **p. 115 (left to right)**: Courtesy of Allan Ludman; Albert Copley/Visuals Unlimited, Inc.; Courtesy of Allan Ludman; Courtesy of Allan Ludman; Courtesy of Stephen Marshak; Courtesy of Allan Ludman; Courtesy of Allan Ludman; **p. 121 (left)**: Marli Miller/Visuals Unlimited; **p. 121 (right)**: Courtesy of Allan Ludman; **p. 123**: Courtesy of Allan Ludman; Courtesy of Allan Ludman; **p. 127**: Alamy; **p. 128 (top-left)**: Wikimedia Commons; **p. 128 (top-right)**: Dr. Richard Roscoe/Visuals Unlimited, Inc.; **p. 128 (bottom-left)**: Dr. Richard Roscoe; **p. 128 (bottom-right)**: Shutterstock; **p. 129**: USGS.

Chapter 6

Page 135 Dreamstime.com; **p. 137 (top)**: R.Weller/Cochise College; **p. 137 (bottom)**: Joel Arem/Science Source; **p. 143(left)**: Marli Miller/Visuals Unlimited, Inc.; **p. 143 (right)**: © Kavring/Dreamstime.com; **p. 150 (left)**: Courtesy of Allan Ludman; **p. 150 (center)**: Courtesy of Allan Ludman; **p. 150 (right)**: Michael P. Gadomski/Science Source; **p. 151 (both)**: Courtesy of Allan Ludman; **p. 154 (top)**: Steven Kazlowski/Science Faction/Getty Images; **p. 154 (bottom)**: Glowimages/Corbis; **p. 155 (top)**: Courtesy of Allan Ludman; **p. 155 (bottom-left & right)**: Courtesy of Allan Ludman; **p. 156 (top-right)**: Stephen Marshak; **p. 156 (bottom-left)**: Dr. Marli Miller/Visuals Unlimited, Inc.; **p. 156 (bottom-right)**: Dr. Marli Miller/Visuals Unlimited, Inc.; **p. 157 (left)**: Courtesy of Stephen Marshak; **p. 157 (right)**: Omikron/Photo Researchers, Inc.; **p. 158 (top-left)**: Kandi Traxel/Dreamstime.com; **p. 158 (top-right)**: brachiopod: American Museum of Natural History; **p. 158 (bottom-left)**: Dr. John D. Cunningham/Visuals Unlimited, Inc.; **p. 158 (center-right)**: Imv/Dreamstime.com; **p. 158 (bottom-right)**: Bloopiers/Dreamstime.com; **p. 159 (top-left)**: American Museum of Natural History; **p. 159 (right)**: Xiao Bin Lin/Dreamstime.com; **p. 159 (bottom-left)**: Sam Pierson/Photo Researchers, Inc; **p. 160 (clockwise from top)**: Emma Marshak; Stephen Marshak; Marli Miller/Visuals Unlimited; Stephen Marshak; Stephen Marshak; Stephen Marshak; Yahn Arthus-Bertrand/Corbis; John S. Shelton; **p. 161 (left)**: Allan Ludman; **p. 161 (right)**: Stephen Marshak; **p. 162**: (Science Museum in Logroño). Photo by jynus, October 2005.

Chapter 7

Page 165: R.Weller/Cochise College; **p. 167 (top row)**: Ashley B. Staples, courtesy Appalachian State University; Scientifica/Visuals Unlimited, Inc.; **p. 167 (top-center row)**: Courtesy of Allan Ludman; **p. 167 (bottom-center row**: Courtesy of Allan Ludman; Biophoto Associates/Science Source; **p. 167 (bottom row)**: L.S. Stephanowicz/Visuals Unlimited; Biophoto Associates/Science Source; **p. 168 (top-left)**: Biophoto Associates;

An eruption of the Batu Tara Volcano in Indonesia spews glowing bombs of lava skyward. Volcanoes are an important component of the Earth System, serving to transfer rock and gas from our planet's interior to its surface. But, while beautiful to watch from a distance, the force of eruptions can threaten life and property.

CHAPTER 9

The Wrath of Vulcan: Volcanic Eruptions

Glowing waves rise and flow, burning all life on their way, and freeze into
black, crusty rock which adds to the height of the mountain and builds the land,
thereby adding another day to the geologic past. . . . I became a geologist forever,
by seeing with my own eyes: the Earth is alive!

—-Hans Cloos (geologist, 1886–1951), on seeing Mt. Vesuvius erupt

LEARNING OBJECTIVES

**By the end of this chapter, you
should understand . . .**

- how eruptions produce a great variety of materials, including lava, pyroclastic debris, and gases.

- that not all eruptions are alike–some yield streams of lava; others produce catastrophic explosions.

- why the type of an eruption reflects the character of lava, which in turn depends on geologic setting.

- how eruptions pose hazards to life and environment in many ways.

- that sometimes impending eruptions can be predicted.

- why eruptions may affect climate, evolution, and perhaps the future of civilizations.

9.1 Introduction

Every few hundred years, one of the hills on Vulcano, an island in the Mediterranean Sea off the western coast of Italy, rumbles and spews out molten rock, glassy cinders, and dense "smoke" (actually a mixture of various gases, fine ash, and very tiny liquid droplets). Ancient Romans thought that such eruptions happened when Vulcan, the god of fire, fueled his forges beneath the island to manufacture weapons for the other gods. Geologic study suggests instead that eruptions take place when hot magma, formed by melting inside the Earth, rises through the crust and emerges at the surface. No one believes the Roman myth anymore, but the island's name evolved into the English word **volcano**, which geologists use to designate either an erupting vent through which molten rock reaches the Earth's surface or an edifice (hill or mountain) built from the products of eruption.

On the main peninsula of Italy, not far from Vulcano, another volcano, Mt. Vesuvius, towers over the Bay of Naples. Nearly 2,000 years ago, a prosperous Roman resort and trading town named Pompeii sprawled at the foot of Vesuvius. One morning in 79 C.E., earthquakes signaled the mountain's awakening. At 1:00 P.M. on August 24, a ferociously turbulent, mottled cloud boiled up above Mt. Vesuvius's summit to a height of 27 km. The cloud soon drifted over Pompeii, turning day into night. Blocks and pellets of rock fell like hail, while fine ash and choking fumes enveloped the town (Fig. 9.1). People frantically rushed to escape, but for most it was too late. As the growing weight of falling volcanic debris began to crush buildings, a scalding, turbulent avalanche of ash mixed with pumice fragments surged down the flank of the volcano and

FIGURE 9.1 The eruption of Vesuvius buried Pompeii and nearby Herculaneum in 79 C.E.

(a) In this 1817 painting, the British artist J.M.W. Turner depicted the cataclysmic explosion.

(b) An artist's interpretation of the early phase of the eruption when roof-crushing debris rained on the town.

swept over Pompeii. When the next day dawned, the town and its neighbor, Herculaneum, had vanished beneath a 6-m-thick gray-black blanket of debris (Fig. 9.2a–d). This covering pro-tected the ruins of Pompeii and Herculaneum so well that when archaeologists started to excavate the towns 1,800 years later, they found artifacts and structures that gave an amazingly

FIGURE 9.2 The burial of Pompeii.

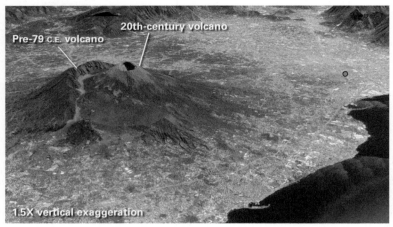

(a) As seen looking southeast from the air today, it's evident that Vesuvius was once much bigger. The red dot shows the location of Pompeii.

(b) Excavations exposed ruins of Pompeii with Vesuvius in the distance. The dashed line shows the volcano's profile prior to its eruption.

(c) Volcanic debris still buries much of Herculaneum.

(d) Streets and buildings of Pompeii are well preserved.

(e) Casts of people and animals convey the terror of that awful day.

complete picture of Roman daily life. In addition, they discovered odd-shaped open spaces in the debris covering Pompeii. Out of curiosity, they filled the spaces with plaster and then dug away the surrounding ash. The spaces turned out to be fossil casts of Pompeii's unfortunate inhabitants, contorted in agony or huddled in despair (Fig. 9.2e).

Clearly, volcanoes are unpredictable and dangerous. Volcanic activity can build a towering mountain, or it can blast one apart. The materials produced by this activity can provide the fertile soil and mineral deposits that enable a civilization to thrive, or they can provide a rain of destruction that can snuff one out. Because of the diversity and consequences of volcanic activity, this chapter sets out ambitious goals. We first build on Chapter 6 by looking more closely at the products of volcanic eruptions and at the basic characteristics of volcanoes. Then we consider the different kinds of volcanic eruptions on Earth and why they occur where they do. Finally, we review the hazards posed by volcanoes, the efforts made by geoscientists to predict eruptions and help minimize the damage they cause, and the possible influence of eruptions on climate and civilization.

9.2 The Products of Volcanic Eruptions

The drama of a volcanic eruption serves an important role in the Earth System because it transfers materials from inside the Earth to our planet's surface. Products of an eruption come in three forms—lava flows, pyroclastic debris, and gas. (Note that we use the term *lava flow* for both a molten, moving layer of lava and for the solid layer of rock that forms when the lava freezes.) We'll examine each of these products in turn.

Lava Flows

Sometimes lava races down the side of a volcano like a fast-moving, incandescent stream, sometimes it builds into a rubble-covered mound at a volcano's summit, and sometimes it oozes into blobs like a sticky but scalding paste. Clearly, not all lava behaves in the same way when it rises out of a volcano, so not all lava flows look the same. Why?

The character of a lava primarily reflects its **viscosity** (resistance to flow), and not all lavas have the same viscosity. Differences in viscosity depend on a variety of factors, including chemical composition, temperature, gas content, and crystal content. Silica content (the proportion of SiO_2, one of many chemicals making up lava) plays a particularly key role in controlling viscosity. Specifically, silica-poor (basaltic) lava is less viscous and thus flows farther than silica-rich (rhyolitic) lava (Fig. 9.3). That's because if silica is abundant in lava, silicon-oxygen

FIGURE 9.3 The characteristics of a lava flow depends on its viscosity.

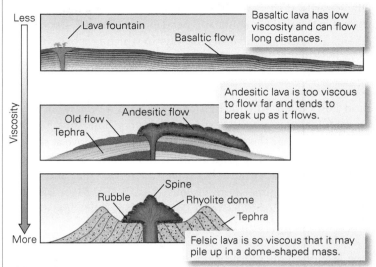

Basaltic lava has low viscosity and can flow long distances.

Andesitic lava is too viscous to flow far and tends to break up as it flows.

Felsic lava is so viscous that it may pile up in a dome-shaped mass.

(a) Three different kinds of flows.

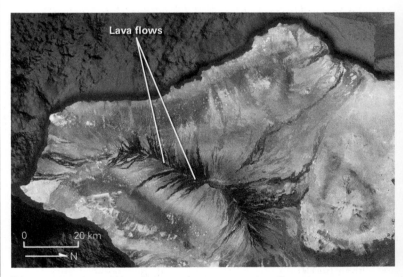

(b) A satellite view of Hawaii shows that numerous lava flows have come from fissures and vents on Kilauea.

(c) This rhyolite dome formed about 650 years ago, in Panum Crater, California. Tephra (cinders) accumulated around the vent.

tetrahedra link in strongly bonded chains or networks that can't move easily. If silica is not so abundant, tetrahedra form weaker bonds with relatively abundant metal ions, allowing faster movement. To illustrate the different ways in which lava behaves, we now examine flows of different compositions.

Basaltic Lava Flows Basaltic (mafic) lava has low viscosity and flows easily when it first emerges from a volcano because it contains relatively little silica and is very hot. Thus, on the steep slopes near the summit of a volcano, it can move at speeds of up 30 km per hour (Fig. 9.4a). The lava slows down to less-than-walking pace after it has traveled for a distance and starts to cool and become more viscous (Fig. 9.4b). Most basaltic flows measure less than a few kilometers long, but some extend as far as 600 km from the source.

How can basaltic lava travel large distances? Although all the lava of a flow moves when it first emerges from a volcano, rapid cooling causes the surface of the flow to harden after the flow has moved a short distance from the source. The solid crust serves as insulation, allowing the hot interior of the flow to remain liquid and continue to move. New molten lava injects between the original ground surface and the new solid crust—the addition of this lava effectively inflates the flow, jacking up the hardened crust and making the overall flow thicker. As time progresses, part of the flow's interior solidifies, so eventually molten lava moves only through a tunnel-like passageway, or **lava tube**, within the flow. The largest lava tubes may be tens of meters in diameter (Fig 9.4c). In some cases, they eventually drain and become empty tunnels (Fig. 9.4d).

The character of a basaltic lava flow's surface reflects the timing of freezing. Flows that have warm, pasty surfaces wrinkle into smooth, glassy, rope-like ridges (Fig. 9.4e)—geologists refer to such flows by its Hawaiian name, **pahoehoe** (pronounced pa-hoy-hoy). If the surface layer of the lava freezes, but then breaks up due to the continued movement of lava underneath, it becomes a jumble of sharp, angular fragments, creating a rubbly flow also known by a Hawaiian name, **a'a'** (pronounced ah-ah) (Fig. 9.4f). Footpaths made by people living in basaltic volcanic regions follow the smooth surface of pahoehoe flows rather than the rough, foot-slashing surface of a'a' flows.

During the final stages of cooling, lava flows contract because rock shrinks as it loses heat and may fracture into polygonal columns. This type of fracturing is called **columnar jointing** (Fig. 9.5a). Columnar jointing typically terminates in the rubble that occurs at the top and bottom of a flow.

Basaltic flows that erupt underwater look different from those that erupt on land because the lava cools so much more quickly in water. Because of rapid cooling, submarine basaltic lava can travel only a short distance before its surface freezes, producing a glass-encrusted blob, or "pillow" (Fig. 9.5b). The rind of a pillow momentarily stops the flow's advance, but soon the pressure of the lava squeezing into the pillow breaks the rind, and a new blob of lava squirts out, freezes, and produces another pillow. In some cases, successive pillows add to the end of previous ones, forming worm-like chains. Geologists refer to a lava flow consisting of a pile of such blobs as **pillow lava**.

Andesitic and Rhyolitic Lava Flows Because of its greater viscosity, andesitic lava cannot flow as easily as basaltic lava. When erupted, andesitic lava forms a mound above the vent. This mound advances slowly down the volcano's flank at only 1 to 5 m a day, becoming a lumpy flow with a bulbous snout. Typically, andesitic flows are less than a few kilometers long, though unusually hot flows may travel farther. Because the lava moves so slowly, the outside of the flow has time to solidify, so as it moves, the surface breaks up into angular blocks, and the whole flow looks like a jumble of rubble called *blocky lava*. On steep slopes, the blocks may tumble downhill, so the flow may evolve into a landslide of blocks.

Rhyolitic lava is the most viscous of all lavas because it has the highest silica concentration and the coolest temperature. Therefore, it tends to accumulate either above the vent in a bulbous mass called a *lava dome* (see Fig. 9.3c). Sometimes rhyolitic lava freezes while still in the vent and then pushes upward as a column-like *lava spire* or lava spine rising up to 100 m above the vent. Rhyolitic flows, where they do form, are rarely more than 1 to 2 km long and have broken and blocky surfaces.

Volcaniclastic Deposits

On a mild day in February 1943, as Dionisio Pulido prepared to sow the fertile soil of his field 330 km (200 miles) west of Mexico City, an earthquake jolted the ground, as it had dozens of times in the previous days. But this time, to Dionisio's amazement, the surface of his field visibly bulged upward by a few meters and then cracked. Ash and sulfurous fumes filled the air, and Dionisio fled. When he returned the following morning, his rich land lay buried beneath a 40-m-high mound of gray cinders—Dionisio had witnessed the birth of Paricutín, a new volcano. During the next several months, Paricutín erupted continuously, at times blasting clots of lava into the sky like fireworks. By the following year, it had become a steep-sided cone over 300 m high. Nine years later, when the volcano ceased all activity, its lava and debris covered 25 square km, and Dionisio's farm and those of his neighbors were gone.

Did you ever wonder . . .

if anyone has ever seen a brand-new volcano appear?

This description of Paricutín's eruption, and that of Vesuvius at the beginning of this chapter, emphasizes that volcanoes produce large quantities of fragmental material. Geologists

FIGURE 9.4 Features of basaltic lava flows. They have low viscosity and thus can flow long distances. Their surface and interior can be complex.

(a) A fast-moving flow coming from Mt. Etna, Sicily.

(b) A basaltic lava flow covers a highway in Hawaii.

A "skylight" into an active lava tube

(c) In a lava tube, still-molten lava flows beneath a crust of solid basalt.

An ancient lava tube in a road cut, Hawaii

(d) A drained lava tube exposed in a road cut on Hawaii.

"Ropes" of pahoehoe

0.5 m

(e) Pahoehoe from a recent lava flow in Hawaii. Note the coin for scale.

(f) The rubbly surface of an a'a' flow, Sunset Crater, Arizona.

FIGURE 9.5 Examples of structures within lava flows.

(a) Columnar jointing develops when the interior of a flow cools and cracks. Such jointing develops in dikes and sills. This example is Devils Postpile in California.

(b) Pillow basalt develops when lava erupts underwater. Later uplift may expose pillows above sea level, as in this Oregon outcrop.

use the term *volcaniclastic deposit*, in a general sense, for any accumulation of this material. Volcaniclastic deposits include **pyroclastic debris** (from the Greek *pyro*, meaning fire), which is specifically the debris forcefully ejected from a volcano during an eruption. Pyroclastic debris includes: fragments formed from lava ejected into the air while still molten, so they freeze in midair or soon after they land; fragments of all sizes ejected when an eruption blasts apart either recently solidified lava or pumice of the volcano's throat; or pre-existing volcanic rock surrounding the volcano's vent. But volcaniclastic deposits also include debris that tumbled down the flank of a volcano in landslide, or has mixed with water to form a muddy slurry, or has been carried and sorted by streams. Let's look at these components in more detail—you'll see that different types form in association with different kinds of eruptions.

Pyroclastic Debris from Basaltic Eruptions Basaltic lava rising in a volcano may contain dissolved volatiles, such as water. As such lava approaches the surface, the volatiles form bubbles, and in basaltic magma the bubbles can rise faster than the magma itself. When the bubbles reach the surface of the lava, they burst and eject clots and drops of molten lava upward to form dramatic fountains (Fig. 9.6a). To picture this process, think of the droplets that spray from a just-opened bottle of soda.

Geologists recognize several different types of fragments formed from frozen clots or drops of lava. Pea-sized fragments of glassy lava and scoria comprise a type of **lapilli**, from the Latin word for little stones; they are informally known as *cinders*. Rarely, flying droplets may trail thin strands of lava,

which freeze into filaments of glass known as *Pelé's hair*, after the Hawaiian goddess of volcanoes, and the droplets themselves freeze into tiny streamlined glassy beads known as *Pelé's tears*. Apple- to refrigerator-sized fragments, called **blocks** (Fig. 9.6b), may consist of already-solid volcanic rock, broken up during the eruption. Blocks tend to be angular and chunky. In some cases, however, blocks form from soft lava squirting out of the vent—such blocks, also known as **bombs**, have streamlined, polished surfaces (Fig. 9.6c).

Pyroclastic Debris from Andesitic or Rhyolitic Eruptions Andesitic or rhyolitic lava is more viscous than basalt and tends to be more gas rich. Eruptions of these lavas also tend to be explosive. Volcanic explosions can produce immense quantities of pyroclastic debris, much more than can come from a basaltic volcano (Fig. 9.7a). Debris ejected from explosive eruptions includes: **ash**, which consists of glassy particles less than 2 mm in diameter formed when frothy lava or recently formed pumice explosively breaks up during an eruption, or when pre-existing volcanic rock gets pulverized by the force of an explosion; *pumice lapilli*, which consists of angular pumice fragments; and *accretionary lapilli*, which consists of snowball-like lumps of ash formed when ash mixes with water in the air and then sticks together to form small balls (Fig. 9.7b–d).

Unconsolidated deposits of pyroclastic grains, regardless of size or composition, constitute **tephra** (Fig. 9.8a). Ash, or ash mixed with lapilli, becomes **tuff** when buried and transformed into coherent rock (Fig. 9.8b). In some cases the coherence forms during deposition, because grains are so hot that they

FIGURE 9.6 Examples of pyroclastic debris from a basaltic eruption on Hawaii.

(a) A fountain of basaltic lapilli spouts from a vent on Hawaii.

(b) Blocks and lapilli on the flank of a Hawaiian volcano.

(c) A bomb has a smooth, streaked surface.

FIGURE 9.7 Pyroclastic debris from andesitic or rhyolitic eruptions.

(a) Pyroclastic debris billowing from the 2008 eruption of Chaitén in Chile.

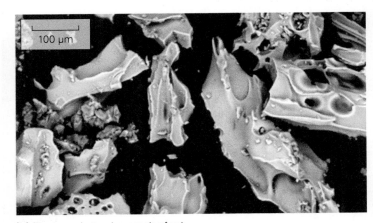

100 μm

(b) Electron photomicrograph of ash.

5 cm

(c) Pumice lapilli.

1 cm

(d) Accretionary lapilli.

FIGURE 9.8 Examples of volcaniclastic deposits (debris flows and lahars).

(a) Recent tephra on the flank of a volcano in Hawaii.

(b) A cliff of ~1 Ma tuff in New Mexico.

The landslide stripped away the forest.

(c) Water-soaked volcanic debris slid down the side of this volcano in Nicaragua.

Debris flow deposits

Stratified ash

Paleo-channel wall

(d) Deposits of a debris flow that accumulated about 35 Ma in Utah. Note that the debris flow filled a channel cut into finer, stratified ash.

(e) A lahar fills a river bed in New Zealand after an eruption in 2007.

(f) Deposits of a lahar from Mt. St. Helens, 20 years after its 1980 eruption, include logs ripped off hill slopes.

weld together. But more commonly, the coherence comes when the debris gets cemented together either by minerals precipitated from groundwater or by minerals that grow in the ash as it reacts with groundwater.

Other Volcaniclastic Deposits The nature and origin of debris produced during and after eruptions continue to be the subject of active research, for some of the deposits prove to be difficult to interpret. As we've noted, geologists use the term *volcaniclastic deposit* for any material that consists of volcanic igneous fragments, and they recognize three categories:

1. *Pyroclastic* deposits, as we have just seen, consist of fragments that ejected during an eruption, and they accumulate directly from the clouds of debris ejected into the sky or sent in avalanches down the flank of the volcano. The fragments in such deposits have not moved, subsequent to their original deposition.

2. *Volcani-sedimentary* deposits consist of volcanic material (lava and pyroclastic debris) that later moved downslope and was redeposited elsewhere, subsequent to accumulating after an eruption. Some of this material tumbles in landslides, breaking up to varying degrees as it moves. If volcanoes are covered with snow and ice or are drenched with rain, water mixes with debris to form a *volcanic debris flow* that moves downslope like wet concrete (Fig. 9.8c–f). Very wet, ash-rich debris flows down in a relatively fast-moving slurry called a **lahar**, which can reach speeds of 50 km per hour. Lahars tend to follow river channels and may travel for tens of kilometers away from the volcano. When debris flows and lahars stop moving, they yield a layer consisting of volcanic blocks suspended in ashy mud. Rivers may eventually sort and transport some volcanic sediment. Where this material accumulates, perhaps far downstream, it forms deposits of *volcanic sandstone* and/or volcanic conglomerate.

3. *Fragmental lava* deposits consist of debris produced when lava breaks up into angular clasts while flowing, without ever being ejected into the air.

As we've seen, fragmentation (or brecciation) happens when the inside of a lava flow continues to move after its surface has frozen—the crust breaks up due to the movement. But fragmentation may also happen when lava freezes very quickly and shatters upon erupting into water or ice. The resulting material, hyalocastite, consists of glassy fragments embedded in ash that has reacted with hot water.

Volcanic Gas

Most magma contains dissolved gases, including water (H_2O), carbon dioxide (CO_2), sulfur dioxide (SO_2), and hydrogen sulfide (H_2S). Generally, felsic lavas can contain more dissolved gas than mafic lavas—in fact, up to 9% by weight of a felsic magma consists of volatiles. As we've seen, these dissolved gases come out of solution when the magma approaches the Earth's surface. This process happens for two reasons, the first of which is that the ability of a liquid to hold dissolved gas decreases as the pressure acting on the liquid decreases. You see this phenomenon when you pop off the top of a carbonated beverage—the beverage was injected with CO_2 under pressure when it was bottled, and because popping the top decreases the pressure, bubbles form and give the beverage its sparkle. Second, gas comes out of solution as a side effect of crystallization. Gases can't fit easily into growing crystals, so they remain in the liquid magma, causing the concentration of gas in the liquid to increase until it exceeds the capacity of the liquid to keep it in solution. When this happens, gas bubbles form.

The sulfurous gases emitted by some volcanoes smell like rotten eggs. Incorporation of these gases dissolved in tiny water droplets yields corrosive sulfuric acid. This acid occurs in the form of an **aerosol**, meaning a haze of droplets, or solid particles, that are so small that they can remain suspended in air for a long time.

The fate of bubbles in magma depends on the viscosity of magma. For example, in low-viscosity mafic magma, gas bubbles can rise faster than the magma moves, and thus most reach the surface of the magma and enter the atmosphere before the lava does. Thus, some volcanoes may, for a while, produce large quantities of steam, without much lava (Fig. 9.9a). The last bubbles to form, however, remain as holes when the lava freezes around them. As we discussed in Chapter 6, these holes are called **vesicles** (Fig. 9.9b), and mafic rock in which more than 50% of the rock's volume consists of bubbles is called *scoria*. In high-viscosity felsic magmas, the gas has trouble escaping because bubbles can't push through the very sticky lava. When such magma reaches shallow depths, it effectively becomes a foam. As this foam approaches the Earth's surface, and the weight of overlying lava decreases, the gas expands so that in some cases bubbles may account for as much as 50% to 75% of the volume of the magma.

FIGURE 9.9 The gas component of volcanic eruptions.

(a) A volcano in Alaska erupting large quantities of steam.

(b) Gas bubbles frozen in lava produce vesicles, as in this block from Sunset Crater, Arizona.

Pumice forms when this material freezes—the thin films of melt between bubbles turn into glass. In some cases, pumice has such low density that it can float.

Take-Home Message

Volcanoes erupt lava, pyroclastic debris, and gas. The character of a lava flow—whether it has low viscosity and spreads over a large area or has high viscosity and builds a bulbous mound over the vent—depends largely on its silica content. Pyroclastic debris includes ash, lapilli, blocks, and bombs. Magma contains dissolved gas, which comes out of solution when the magma approaches the Earth's surface.

QUICK QUESTION: How can lava travel tens of kilometers or more from a volcanic vent without freezing?

9.3 Structure and Eruptive Style

Volcanic Architecture

As we saw in Chapter 6, melting in the upper mantle and lower crust produces magma, which rises into the upper crust. Typically, this magma accumulates underground in a **magma chamber**, a zone of open spaces and/or fractured rock that can contain a large quantity of magma and/or a mush of magma mixed with crystals. Some of the magma may solidify in the magma chamber and transform into intrusive igneous rock, but the rest rises along a pathway, or *conduit*, to the Earth's surface and erupts from an opening, or **vent**. The conduit may have the

shape of a chimney or may be a long crack called a **fissure** (Fig. 9.10). At times, vents at the top of chimney-shaped conduits erupt tall fountains of lava, whereas those along fissures erupt long curtains of lava.

Over time, new igneous rock (lava and/or pyroclastic debris) builds up around the vent to form a *volcanic edifice*. Eruptions that take place at the top of the edifice are called *summit eruptions*, whereas those that break through along the

FIGURE 9.10 Crater eruptions and fissure eruptions come from conduits of different shapes.

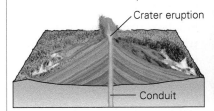

(a) At a crater eruption, lava spouts from a chimney-shaped conduit.

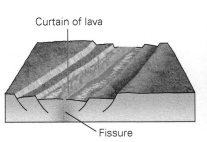

(b) At a fissure eruption, lava comes out in a curtain, along the length of a crack.

FIGURE 9.11 The formation of volcanic calderas.

(a) The crater of Santa Ana Volcano in El Salvador.

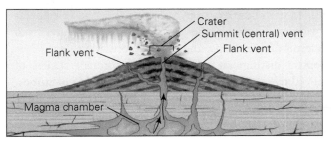

(b) As an eruption begins, the magma chamber inflates with magma. There can be a central vent and one or more flank vents.

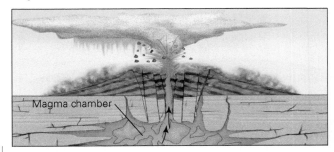

(c) During an eruption, the magma chamber drains, and the central portion of the volcano collapses downward.

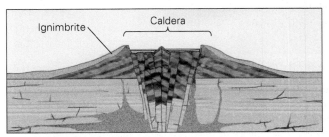

(d) The collapsed area becomes a caldera. Later, a new volcano may begin to grow within the caldera.

sides, or flanks, of the volcano are *flank eruptions*. In some cases, the vent lies at the floor of a circular depression called a **crater**, shaped like a bowl, up to 500 m across and 200 m deep (Fig. 9.11a). Craters form either because material accumulates around the vent during eruption or because the top part of the edifice collapses into the drained conduit when the eruption ceases.

During some major eruptions, a large portion of the volcanic edifice collapses into the drained magma chamber below, producing a **caldera**, a large circular depression up to thousands of meters across and up to several hundred meters deep (Fig. 9.11b–e). Typically, a caldera has steep walls and a fairly flat floor and may be

(e) This caldera in Oregon formed about 7,700 years ago. Afterward, it filled with water to become Crater Lake. Wizard Island, protruding from the lake, is a small volcano that grew on top of the caldera floor.

partially filled with new lava or pyroclastic debris. Some calderas fill with water and become lakes. Note that calderas differ from craters in terms of size, shape, and mode of formation.

Geologists distinguish among several different shapes of "subaerial" (above sea level) volcanic edifices. **Shield volcanoes**, broad, gentle domes, are so named because they resemble a soldier's shield lying on the ground. They form when the products of eruption have low viscosity and thus cannot pile up around the vent but rather spread out over large areas. The volcanoes of Hawaii, which produce layer upon layer of low-viscosity basaltic lava, are shield volcanoes (Fig. 9.12a), as are some volcanoes that erupt successive ignimbrites. **Cinder cones**, also known as *scoria cones*, consist of cone-shaped piles of basaltic lapilli and blocks, sometimes from a single eruption (Fig. 9.12b). **Stratovolcanoes**,

FIGURE 9.12 Different shapes of volcanoes.

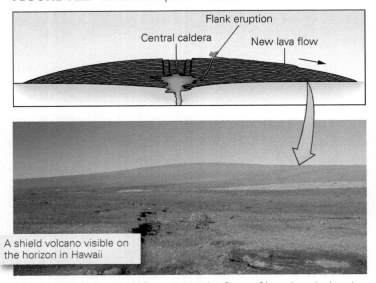

A shield volcano visible on the horizon in Hawaii

(a) A shield volcano, made from successive flows of low-viscosity basalt, has very gentle slopes.

(b) A cinder cone on the flank of a larger volcano in Arizona. The pile of cinders has assumed the angle of repose. A lava flow covers the land surface in the distance.

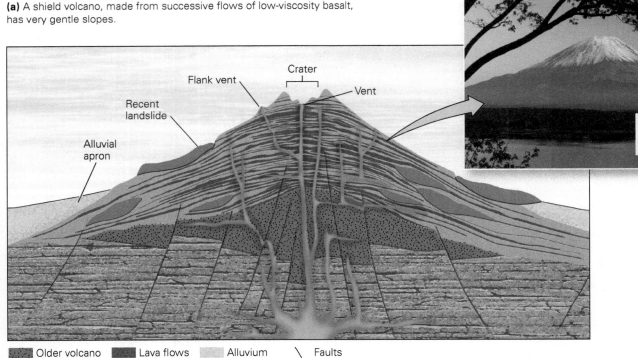

Mt. Fuji, a composite volcano in Japan, last erupted in 1707.

Older volcano	Lava flows	Alluvium	\ Faults
Pre-volcanic basement	Tephra	Landslides	Intrusives

(c) A composite volcano consists of layers of tephra and lava. Volcanic debris flows and ash avalanches modify slopes and contribute to the development of a classic cone-like shape.

also known as *composite volcanoes*, are large (up to 3 km high) and cone-shaped, generally with steeper slopes near the summit, and consist of interleaved contrasting layers (hence the prefix *strato–*) of lava, tephra, and volcaniclastic debris (Fig. 9.12c). Their shape, exemplified by Japan's Mt. Fuji, serves as the classic image that most people have of a volcano.

Let's look at the nature of stratovolcanoes a little more closely. Their edifices build from the products of many eruptions over an extended period of time. Not all eruptions produce the same kind of material. Specifically, eruptions producing pyroclastic debris produce layers of tephra, eruptions of andesite produce blocky flows that breakup into bouldery landslides on the volcano's slopes, and eruptions of low-viscosity lava produce flows that cascade down the flanks of the volcano. Lava flows resist erosion and thus armor the underlying tephra, preventing it from being washed away. Over time, the volcano builds into a symmetrical cone. But, for many reasons, this shape doesn't last indefinitely. For example, large landslides carry masses of rock down the slopes and build broad aprons around the base of the volcano. Heavy rains or spring snow melt can trigger debris flows, which transport volcaniclastic sediment out to alluvial fans surrounding the volcano. Finally, explosive eruptions can blast away a large portion of the volcano's edifice.

The hills or mountains resulting from volcanism come in a great range of sizes (Fig. 9.13). Shield volcanoes tend to be the largest, followed by stratovolcanoes. Cinder cones tend to be relatively small and are often found on the flanks of larger volcanoes.

The Concept of Eruptive Style: Will It Flow or Will It Blow?

Kilauea, a volcano on Hawaii, produces rivers of lava that cascade down the volcano's flanks. Mt. St. Helens, a volcano near the Washington-Oregon border, exploded catastrophically in 1980 and blanketed the surrounding countryside with tephra. Clearly, different volcanoes erupt differently and, as we've noted, successive eruptions from the same stratovolcano may differ markedly in character from one another. Geologists refer to the character of an eruption as **eruptive style**. Below we describe several distinct eruptive styles and explore why the differences occur (see **Geology at a Glance**, pp. 286–287).

Effusive Eruptions

The term *effusive* comes from the Latin word *effundere*, to pour out, and indeed that's what happens during an **effusive eruption**—lava pours out from a vent or fissure. This lava may fill a *lava lake* around the crater and/or spill down the side of the mountain in a sheet or in a channelized flow (Fig. 9.14a, b). Geologists refer to small- to moderate-sized effusive eruptions as *Hawaiian eruptions*, because they are common on Hawaii. Successive eruptions build layer upon layer of basalt (Fig. 9.14c).

Effusive eruptions occur where the magma feeding the volcano is hot and mafic and therefore has low viscosity. Pressure, applied to the magma chamber by the weight of overlying rock, squeezes magma upward and out of the vent; in some cases, the pressure is great enough to drive the magma up into a *lava fountain* spewing out of the vent (see Fig. 9.10a). As we have seen, when the magma rises, gas comes out of solution and forms bubbles. The presence of bubbles decreases the overall density and viscosity of the magma, allowing it to rise faster. If the conduit through which the magma rises narrows in the throat of the volcano, the velocity of the rising magma increases even more, much like the velocity of water coming out of a hose increases if you pinch the end of the hose. Such pinching of conduits may play a role in producing very high magma fountains spurting up to 500 m into the air above the vent.

Explosive Eruptions

Volcanoes that forcefully emit significant quantities of pyroclastic debris are called **explosive eruptions**. Geologists recognize a variety of different types based on the size of the explosion and the products of the explosion, as we now see.

FIGURE 9.13 These profiles emphasize that volcanoes come in different sizes. Large shield volcanoes, like those on Hawaii, are many times larger than cinder cones.

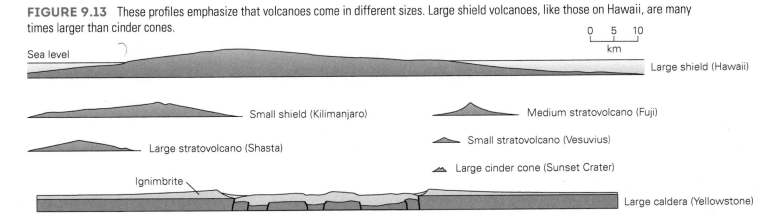

Volcanoes

Beneath a volcano, magma rises to fill a pervasively cracked region of crust and forms a magma chamber. Some of the magma erupts at a surface vent. Once molten rock has erupted at the surface, it is called lava. Some lava spills down the side of the volcano in lava flows. Some fountains out of a vent to form scoria fragments that pile up in a cone around the vent. Eruptions may eject larger chunks as blocks or bombs. The nature of eruptions depends on the viscosity of the lava, which in turn depends on lava composition. Volcanic explosions blast up a cloud of ash and lapilli, and may pulverize pre-existing

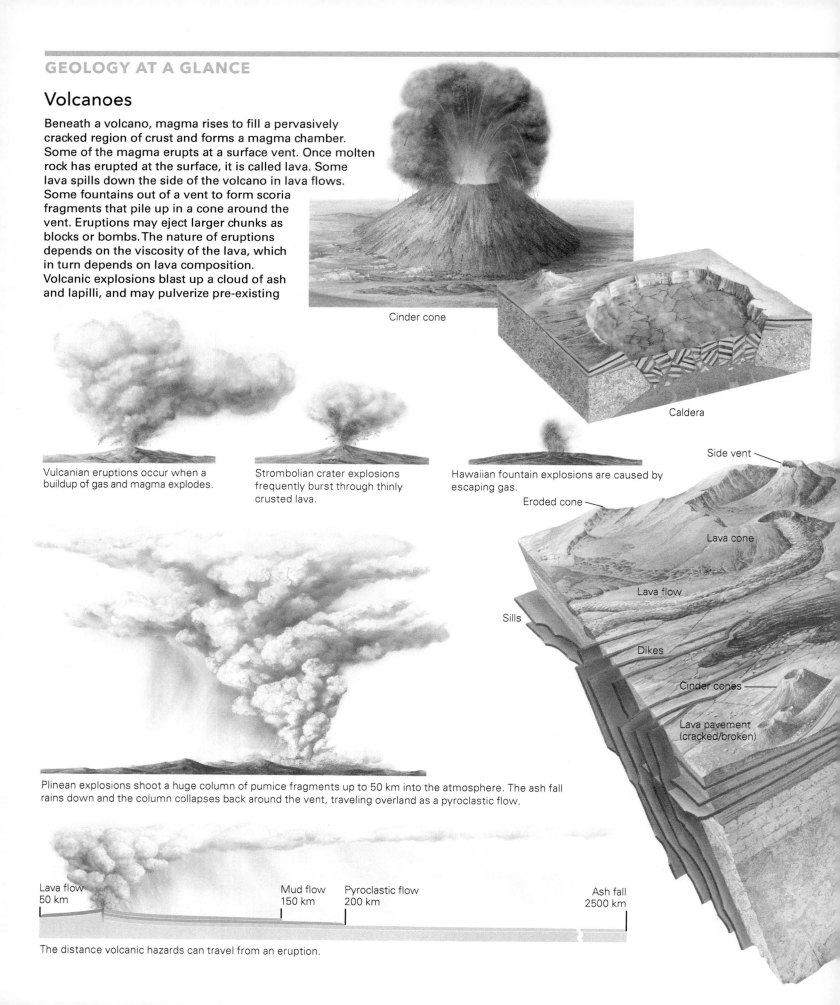

Cinder cone

Caldera

Vulcanian eruptions occur when a buildup of gas and magma explodes.

Strombolian crater explosions frequently burst through thinly crusted lava.

Hawaiian fountain explosions are caused by escaping gas.

Side vent

Eroded cone

Lava cone

Lava flow

Sills

Dikes

Cinder cones

Lava pavement (cracked/broken)

Plinean explosions shoot a huge column of pumice fragments up to 50 km into the atmosphere. The ash fall rains down and the column collapses back around the vent, traveling overland as a pyroclastic flow.

Lava flow
50 km

Mud flow
150 km

Pyroclastic flow
200 km

Ash fall
2500 km

The distance volcanic hazards can travel from an eruption.

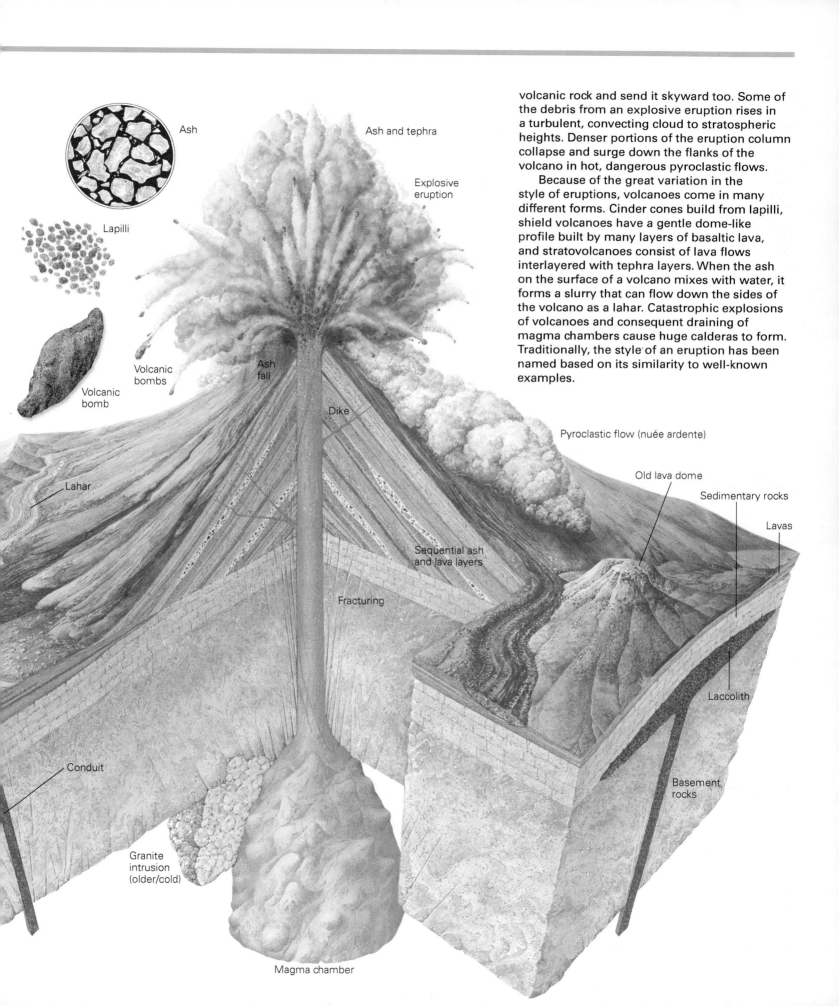

volcanic rock and send it skyward too. Some of the debris from an explosive eruption rises in a turbulent, convecting cloud to stratospheric heights. Denser portions of the eruption column collapse and surge down the flanks of the volcano in hot, dangerous pyroclastic flows.

Because of the great variation in the style of eruptions, volcanoes come in many different forms. Cinder cones build from lapilli, shield volcanoes have a gentle dome-like profile built by many layers of basaltic lava, and stratovolcanoes consist of lava flows interlayered with tephra layers. When the ash on the surface of a volcano mixes with water, it forms a slurry that can flow down the sides of the volcano as a lahar. Catastrophic explosions of volcanoes and consequent draining of magma chambers cause huge calderas to form. Traditionally, the style of an eruption has been named based on its similarity to well-known examples.

Ash

Lapilli

Volcanic bombs

Volcanic bomb

Ash and tephra

Explosive eruption

Ash fall

Dike

Pyroclastic flow (nuée ardente)

Old lava dome

Sedimentary rocks

Lavas

Lahar

Sequential ash and lava layers

Fracturing

Conduit

Laccolith

Basement rocks

Granite intrusion (older/cold)

Magma chamber

FIGURE 9.14 The effects of effusive eruptions.

(a) A 1986 effusive eruption on Hawaii.

(b) A lava lake in the caldera of Kilauea, Hawaii.

(c) Layer upon layer of basaltic lava flows, exposed on the wall of a caldera in Hawaii.

The Diversity of Explosive Types Ancient Romans referred to the island of Stromboli as "the lighthouse of the Mediterranean" because it has erupted about every 10 to 20 minutes through recorded history, and the red-hot clots that it ejects trace out glowing arcs of light in the night sky. Occasionally, Stromboli also produces basaltic lava flows, but most of the material it erupts comes out in the form of scoria lapilli and blocks, which build into a cone around the vent (Fig. 9.15a). (Not surprisingly, geologists refer to eruptions that produce a fountain of basaltic lapilli as a *Strombolian eruption*, regardless of where it occurs.) Somewhat larger explosive eruptions emit both a fountain of lava and a dense plume of pyroclastic debris (Fig. 9.15b). (Such events are *Vulcanian eruptions*, named for the island of Vulcano.)

In some explosive eruptions, much of the pressure driving the eruption comes from the sudden heating of water by magma so that it flashes to steam and expands very rapidly. The expanding steam can rip up pre-existing rock from the conduit of the volcano and can send it skyward. In *phreatic eruptions*, groundwater (possibly from melting snow or heavy rain) interacts with the magma and the eruption blasts steam, ash, and coarser blocks skyward, but little if any lava appears at the surface. When the vent lies in relatively shallow seawater—heating the water produces prodigious amounts of steam that billow out of the sea, along with fountains of wet ash (Fig. 9.15c). (Such eruptions are called *Surtseyan eruptions*, for the island of Surtsey off the coast of Iceland.) If seawater suddenly gains access via cracks to a large magma chamber, the resulting flash to steam may blast the entire volcano apart in a huge explosion.

Plinean Eruptions Really huge explosive eruptions of stratovolcanoes are known as *Plinean eruptions*, named for the Roman scholar, Pliny the Younger, who observed and described the eruption of Vesuvius. Plinean eruptions (Fig. 9.15d) can eject many cubic kilometers of material into the atmosphere and may destroy a substantial part of the stratovolcano's edifice itself. In fact, the explosion can completely change the profile of the volcano such that it no longer has a cone-like shape (Box 9.1).

Plinean eruptions take place when andesitic and rhyolitic magmas rising in a volcano contain very large quantities of gas. As we've seen, when this gas comes out of solution, it forms so many bubbles that they comprise most of the magma's volume. Because of their high silica content, andesitic and rhyolitic magmas are so viscous that the gas bubbles cannot rise through the magma and escape as the gassy magma rises. The pressure within the trapped bubbles becomes much greater than in the air above the volcano, and only the thin bubble walls keep the gas from bursting free. Eventually, as the rising froth shears against the walls of the conduit, the walls of the bubbles do stretch and break, and when this happens the bubble walls shatter into dust-sized pieces of ash,

FIGURE 9.15 Examples of explosive eruptive styles. No two eruptions are exactly alike.

(a) A large Strombolian eruption on Mt. Etna, Sicily.

(b) A lava fountain in the plume during an eruption of Mt. Etna.

(c) A Surtseyan eruption of a subsea volcano near Tonga.

(d) The Plinean eruption of Mt. Pinatubo in the Philippines.

and these surround the pumice lapilli (larger chunks that still contain both bubbles and bubble walls). Suddenly the very hot gas that had been held in by bubble walls is released and it expands violently, producing immense pressure that pushes surrounding debris upward. If the pressure cracks the lava dome capping the vent, the mixture of fragments and gas burst out of the volcano's vent at very high velocity (over 300 km per hour), like a giant shotgun blast. The sudden release of this material decreases the pressure on magma deeper in the conduit, allowing bubbles in the deeper magma to expand and shatter, so more and more pyroclastic debris erupts until the magma chamber drains. The ejected debris forms a huge **eruption column**.

Geologists recognize several distinct regions within a Plinean eruptive column (**Fig. 9.16a**). The blast from an explosive eruption can propel debris upward for hundreds of meters to a couple of kilometers and forms the lower part, or *gas-thrust region*, of the eruption column. But the eruption column of huge eruptions is much taller than the gas-thrust region. That's because the mixture of hot ash, hot volcanic gas, and air is lighter than cooler air around it and thus, like a hot-air balloon, is buoyant. The debris continues to rise as a turbulent, billowing cloud or *convective plume*. At stratospheric heights, 10 to 50 km high, the convective plume spreads out into a broad *ash umbrella*—the mushroom head of an overall mushroom cloud (**Fig. 9.16b**). The formation of an umbrella occurs where the plume has cooled enough so that it is no longer buoyant.

Debris from the convective cloud and ash umbrella of a huge volcanic explosion falls from the air, like hail and snow, and blankets the countryside near the volcano. Strong winds of the

BOX 9.1   CONSIDER THIS . . .

Volcanic Explosions to Remember

A volcanic explosion generates an enduring image of destruction, for an explosion can rip a volcano apart and devastate the surrounding region. To compare volcanic explosions, geologists sometimes use the **volcanic explosivity index** (VEI), a logarithmic scale on which the largest known eruption has been assigned a VEI of 8; larger ones could conceivably take place. This index takes into account the volume of debris ejected, the height of the eruptive column, and an estimate of the energy released during the explosion. The historic record shows that there have been about 100 eruptions with VEIs in the range of 4 to 6 since 1800 C.E., and the largest-observed eruption in recorded history (Tambora, in 1815) ranks as a 7. The geologic record shows that "mega-colossal" explosions with a VEI of 8 have taken place during the past few million years. One of these formed the caldera of Yellowstone National Park, Wyoming, about 600,000 years ago (**Fig. Bx9.1a**). To get a sense of the

consequences of a volcanic explosion, let's look at three notable examples.

Mt. St. Helens, a snow-crested stratovolcano in the Cascade Mountains of northwestern United States, had not erupted since 1857. However, geologic evidence suggested that the mountain had a violent past, punctuated by many explosive eruptions. On March 20, 1980, an earthquake announced that the volcano was awakening. A week later, a crater 80 m in diameter burst open at the summit and began emitting gas and pyroclastic debris. Geologists who set up monitoring stations to observe the volcano noted that its north side was beginning to bulge markedly, suggesting that the volcano was filling with magma and was expanding like a balloon. Their concern that an eruption was imminent led local authorities to evacuate people in the area.

The climactic eruption came suddenly. At 8:32 A.M. on May 18, a geologist, David Johnston, monitoring the volcano from a distance

of 10 km, shouted over his two-way radio, "Vancouver, Vancouver, this is it!" An earthquake had triggered a huge landslide that caused 3 cubic km of the volcano's weakened north side to slide away. The sudden landslide released pressure on the magma inside the volcano, causing a sudden and violent expansion of gases that blasted through the side of the volcano (**Fig. Bx9.1b**). Rock, steam, and ash screamed north at the speed of sound and flattened a forest and everything in it over an area of 600 square km (**Fig. Bx9.1c**). Tragically, Johnston, along with 60 others, vanished forever. Seconds after the sideways blast, a vertical column carried about 540 million tons of ash (about 1 cubic km) 25 km into the sky, where the jet stream carried it away; the ash was able to circle the globe. In towns near the volcano, a blizzard of ash choked roads and buried fields. Water-saturated ash formed viscous slurries, or lahars, that flooded river valleys, carrying away everything in their path. When the eruption was finally over, the once

FIGURE Bx9.1 Examples of explosive eruptions.

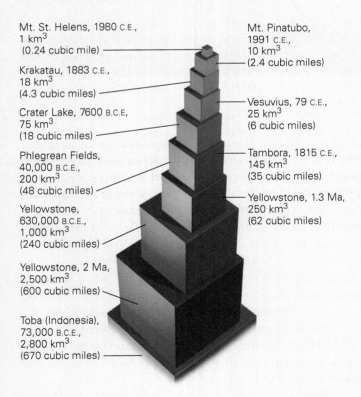

Mt. St. Helens, 1980 C.E.,
1 km³
(0.24 cubic mile)

Krakatau, 1883 C.E.,
18 km³
(4.3 cubic miles)

Crater Lake, 7600 B.C.E,
75 km³
(18 cubic miles)

Phlegrean Fields,
40,000 B.C.E.,
200 km³
(48 cubic miles)

Yellowstone,
630,000 B.C.E.,
1,000 km³
(240 cubic miles)

Yellowstone, 2 Ma,
2,500 km³
(600 cubic miles)

Toba (Indonesia),
73,000 B.C.E.,
2,800 km³
(670 cubic miles)

Mt. Pinatubo,
1991 C.E.,
10 km³
(2.4 cubic miles)

Vesuvius, 79 C.E.,
25 km³
(6 cubic miles)

Tambora, 1815 C.E.,
145 km³
(35 cubic miles)

Yellowstone, 1.3 Ma,
250 km³
(62 cubic miles)

(a) The relative amounts of pyroclastic debris (in cubic km) ejected during major explosive eruptions.

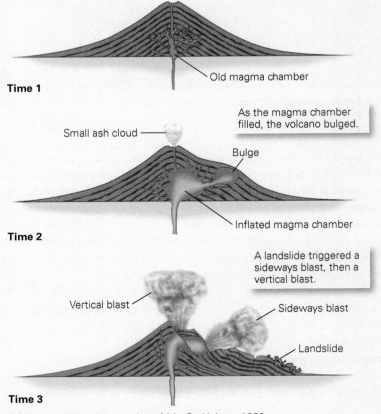

Time 1

Old magma chamber

As the magma chamber filled, the volcano bulged.

Small ash cloud

Bulge

Inflated magma chamber

Time 2

A landslide triggered a sideways blast, then a vertical blast.

Vertical blast

Sideways blast

Landslide

Time 3

(b) Stages during the eruption of Mt. St. Helens, 1980.

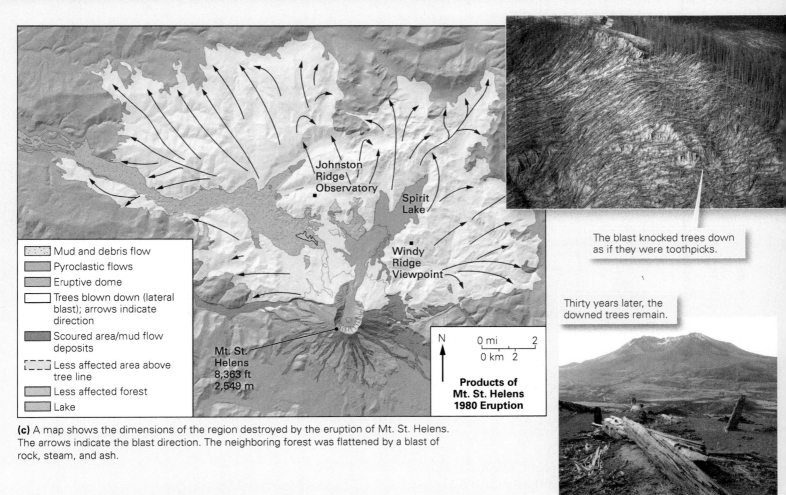

The blast knocked trees down as if they were toothpicks.

Thirty years later, the downed trees remain.

(c) A map shows the dimensions of the region destroyed by the eruption of Mt. St. Helens. The arrows indicate the blast direction. The neighboring forest was flattened by a blast of rock, steam, and ash.

Map legend:
- Mud and debris flow
- Pyroclastic flows
- Eruptive dome
- Trees blown down (lateral blast); arrows indicate direction
- Scoured area/mud flow deposits
- Less affected area above tree line
- Less affected forest
- Lake

Johnston Ridge Observatory

Spirit Lake

Windy Ridge Viewpoint

Mt. St. Helens 8,363 ft 2,549 m

N

0 mi 2
0 km 2

Products of Mt. St. Helens 1980 Eruption

cone-shaped peak of Mt. St. Helens had disappeared—the summit now lay 440 m lower, and the once snow-covered mountain was a gray mound with a large gouge in one side. The volcano came alive again in 2004, but it did not explode.

The death toll due to the 1902 explosion of Mt. Pelée, on the Caribbean island of Martinique, was much higher. On the morning of May 8, the 100-m-high rhyolite spire stuck in the conduit of the volcano suddenly disintegrated. The immense gas pressure that had been building beneath the obstruction was suddenly released, and in the same way champagne bursts out of a bottle when the cork is pulled, a cloud of ash and pumice lapilli spewed out of Mt. Pelée. Collapse of the ash column formed a pyroclastic flow—at a temperature of 200°C to 450°C—that swept down Pelée's flank. This flow rode on a cushion of air and reached speeds of up to 300 km per hour before slamming into the busy port town of St. Pierre. Within moments, the town's buildings were flattened and its 28,000 inhabitants were dead of incineration or asphyxiation. Only two people survived—one was a prisoner who was protected by the stout walls of his underground cell.

An even greater explosion happened in 1883. Krakatau, a volcano between Indonesia and Sumatra, had grown to become a 9-km-long island rising 800 m (2,600 feet) above the sea. On May 20, the island began to erupt with a series of large explosions, yielding ash that settled as far as 500 km away. Smaller explosions continued through June and July, and steam and ash rose from the island, forming a huge black cloud that rained ash into the surrounding straits. Ships sailing by couldn't see where they were going, and their crews had to shovel ash off the decks. Krakatau's demise came at 10 A.M. on August 27, perhaps when the volcano cracked and the magma chamber suddenly flooded with seawater. The resulting blast, 5,000 times greater than the Hiroshima atomic bomb

explosion, could be heard as far as 4,800 km away, and subaudible sound traveled around the globe seven times. Giant sea waves pushed out by the explosion slammed into nearby coastal towns, killing over 36,000 people. Near the volcano, a layer of ash up to 40 m thick accumulated. When the air finally cleared, Krakatau was gone, replaced by a submarine caldera some 300 m deep (**Fig. Bx9.1d**). All told, the eruption shot 20 cubic km of rock into the sky. Some ash reached elevations of 27 km. Because of this ash, people around the world could view spectacular sunsets during the next several years.

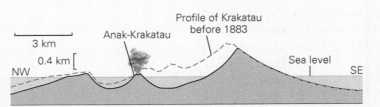

Profile of Krakatau before 1883

Anak-Krakatau

3 km

0.4 km

NW

Sea level

SE

(d) Profile of Krakatau before and after the eruption. Note that a new volcano (Anak-Krakatau) has formed.

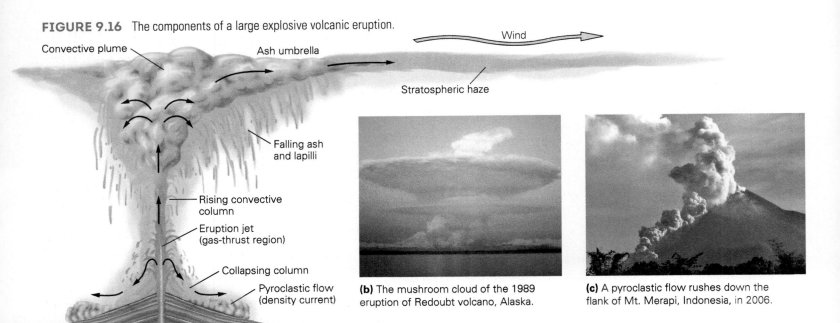

FIGURE 9.16 The components of a large explosive volcanic eruption.

Convective plume

Ash umbrella

Wind

Stratospheric haze

Falling ash and lapilli

Rising convective column

Eruption jet (gas-thrust region)

Collapsing column

Pyroclastic flow (density current)

(b) The mushroom cloud of the 1989 eruption of Redoubt volcano, Alaska.

(c) A pyroclastic flow rushes down the flank of Mt. Merapi, Indonesia, in 2006.

(a) A large explosive eruptive cloud (Plinean-type) contains several components.

jet stream may waft substantial amounts of ash in the umbrella great distances—hundreds or even thousands of kilometers—away from the volcano. In some cases, gravity can cause heavier debris at the top of the gas-thrust region to collapse downward, forming a mixture of air, hot ash, and pumice lapilli that rushes down the side of a volcano in a scalding avalanche. This surge of air and debris stays relatively close to the ground because it is denser than the clear air above (**Fig. 9.16c**). Such avalanches of hot ash are known as **pyroclastic flows** (or as pyroclastic density currents, by analogy to underwater turbidity currents). In older literature, a pyroclastic flow was called a *nuée ardente*, French for glowing cloud. Tuff formed from ash and/or pumice lapilli that fell like snow from the sky is called *air-fall tuff*, whereas a sheet of tuff that formed from a pyroclastic flow is an **ignimbrite**. Ash and pumice lapilli in an ignimbrite is sometimes so hot that it welds together to form a hard mass.

Supervolcanoes In recent years, geologists have realized that some volcanic explosions of the geologic past dwarf any that have been observed during human history (see Box 9.1). Such incomprehensibly huge volcanoes have come to be known informally as **supervolcanoes**, and they can produce hundreds to a few thousand cubic kilometers of pyroclastic debris. After the eruption, a huge caldera forms as the land collapses into the drained magma chamber (see Fig. 9.11). Eruptions that occurred hundreds of thousands of years ago in the area that is now Yellowstone Park serve as an example—in the aftermath of one of these explosions, a caldera 72 km across formed!

Take-Home Message

At a volcano, lava rises from a magma chamber and erupts from chimney-like conduits or from crack-like fissures. During effusive eruptions, low-viscosity basalt lava flows build low, dome-like shield volcanoes. Fountaining basalt spatters to build tephra cones. Volcanoes erupting underwater produce huge bursts of steam and clots of muddy ash. Successive, alternating eruptions of felsic or intermediate pyroclastic debris and lava build stratovolcanoes, and drainage of lava beneath the surface or explosions produce calderas. Immense explosions of supervolcanoes produce giant calderas.

QUICK QUESTION: How can you distinguish between a volcanic caldera and a meteorite crater?

9.4 Geologic Settings of Volcanism

Different styles of volcanism occur at different locations on Earth. Most eruptions occur along plate boundaries, but major eruptions also occur at hot spots and in rifts (**Fig. 9.17a**). We'll now look at the settings in which eruptions occur, in the context of plate tectonics theory, and see why different kinds of volcanoes form in different settings.

Mid-Ocean Ridge Submarine Eruptions

Products of mid-ocean ridge volcanism cover 70% of our planet's surface. We don't generally see this volcanic activity, however, because the ocean hides most of it beneath a blanket of water. Mid-ocean ridge volcanoes, which develop along fissures parallel to the ridge axis, are not all continuously active. Each one turns on and off in a time scale measured in tens to hundreds of years. They erupt basalt, formed when hot mantle rock rises from great depth to shallow depths beneath the ridge and undergoes decompression melting (see Chapter 6). This basalt, because it cools so quickly underwater, forms pillow-lava mounds or aprons. The pillow basalts commonly occur in association with hyaloclastites. Water that heats up as it circulates through the crust near the magma chamber bursts out of hydrothermal (hot-water) vents along these mounds, producing black smokers (see Chapter 4).

Volcanic Arcs at Convergent Boundaries

Most of the subaerial volcanoes on Earth lie along convergent-plate boundaries (subduction zones). The volcanoes form when volatiles rise from the rock of the subducting plate into the overlying hot asthenosphere, causing flux melting in the asthenosphere. The resulting magma then rises and eventually erupts along the edge of the overriding plate. Some of these volcanoes grow on oceanic crust and become volcanic island arcs, such as the Marianas of the western Pacific and the Aleutians of the northern Pacific (Fig. 9.17b). Others grow on continental crust, building continental volcanic arcs such as the Cascade volcanic chain of Washington and Oregon or the Andes chain of South America. Typically, individual volcanoes in volcanic arcs lie about 50 to 100 km apart. Subduction zones border over 60% of the Pacific Ocean, creating a 20,000-km-long chain of volcanoes known as the *Ring of Fire.*

In island arcs, where magma rises from the mantle through oceanic crust, volcanoes initially primarily produce basalt, formed by partial melting of the mantle. This lava builds an edifice of pillows and hyaloclastites that eventually rises above the sea level. During its initial appearance above sea level, the eruption produces blasts of steam and ash. When the vent rises entirely above sea level, a shield of basalt starts to grow. Processes such as fractional crystallization and assimilation (see Chapter 6) may eventually yield andesitic lava, so the volcano can evolve into a stratovolcano.

In continental arcs, some basalt rises to the surface, but andesitic and rhyolitic eruptions are more common because more of the magma undergoes fractional crystallization and assimilation within the crust, and in addition, heat transfer partially melts some of the continental crust and produces felsic magma (see Chapter 6). Because many different kinds of magma form at volcanic arcs, these volcanoes sometimes have effusive eruptions and sometimes pyroclastic eruptions, and build stratovolcanoes, which occasionally explode. Examples include the elegant symmetrical cone of Mt. Fuji (see Fig. 9.12c) and the blasted-apart hulk of Mt. St. Helens (see Box 9.1).

Volcanism of Continental Rifts

The igneous activity of rifts happens because thinning of the continental lithosphere allows the underlying asthenosphere to rise to shallower depths, where it undergoes decompression and partially melts to produce basaltic magma. Some of this magma rises straight to the surface and erupts as basalt, but some gets trapped at the base or within the continental crust and undergoes fractional crystallization and/or assimilates surrounding crust to produce intermediate or felsic magmas. Trapped magma can also partially melt continental crust through heat transfer, producing rhyolitic magma.

Because of the diversity of magmas that can form beneath rifts, rifts can host both basaltic fissure eruptions, in which curtains of lava fountain up or linear chains of cinder cones develop, and explosive rhyolitic volcanoes. Thus, you may find both large basalt flows and immense sheets of rhyolites in rifts. In some locations, eruptions build stratovolcanoes such as Mt. Kilimanjaro in Africa.

Oceanic Hot-Spot Volcanism

Oceanic hot-spot volcanoes form where asthenosphere undergoes decompression melting and produces voluminous amounts of basaltic magma. Most oceanic hot-spot volcanoes, such as the ones that produced Hawaii, occur in the interior of plates, away from plate boundaries. A few, such as the ones that produced Iceland, sit astride a mid-ocean ridge. Most geologists favor the hypothesis that hot-spot volcanoes lie above mantle plumes, localized upwellings from the deep mantle, but some argue for alternative interpretations.

When a hot-spot volcano first forms on oceanic lithosphere, basaltic magma erupts at the surface of the seafloor. At first, such submarine eruptions yield a mound of pillow lava and hyaloclastite. With time, the volcano grows up above the sea surface and becomes an island. After the volcano emerges from the sea, the basalt lava that erupts no longer freezes so quickly and thus flows as a thin sheet over a great distance. Thousands of thin basalt flows pile up, layer upon layer, to build a broad, dome-shaped shield volcano with gentle slopes (Fig. 9.18). As the volcano grows, portions of it can't resist the pull of gravity and slip seaward, creating large submarine slumps.

The big island of Hawaii, the tallest oceanic hot-spot volcano on Earth today, currently consists of five shield volcanoes, each built around a different vent. The island now

FIGURE 9.17 Volcanoes of the world.

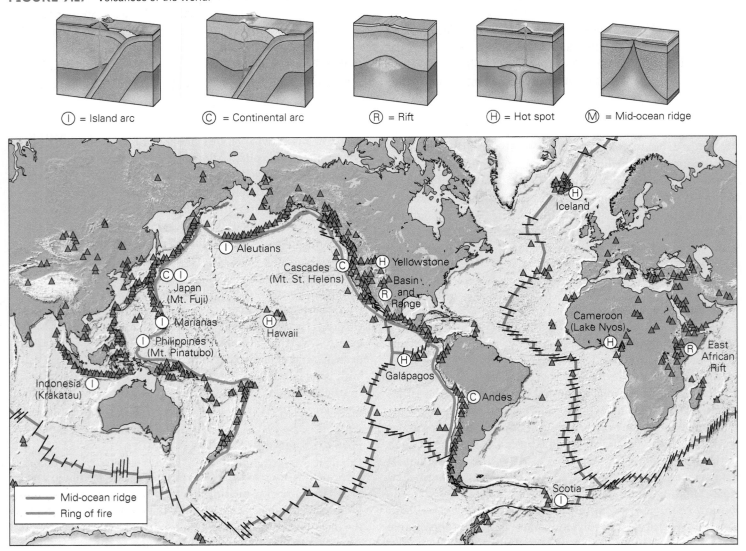

Ⓘ = Island arc   Ⓒ = Continental arc   Ⓡ = Rift   Ⓗ = Hot spot   Ⓜ = Mid-ocean ridge

(a) A map showing the distribution of volcanoes around the world and the basic geologic settings in which volcanoes form, in the context of plate tectonics theory.

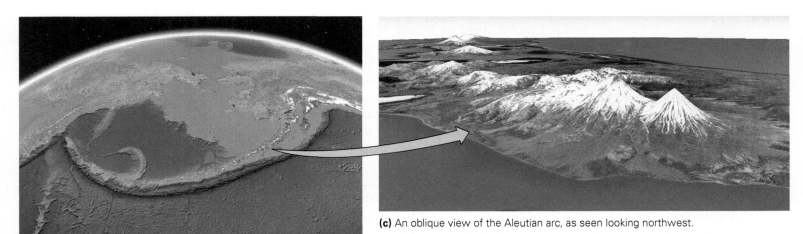

(b) The Aleutian Arc forms the northern edge of the Pacific Plate. It displays a distinct curvature.

(c) An oblique view of the Aleutian arc, as seen looking northwest.

FIGURE 9.18 The interior of an oceanic hot-spot volcano is complicated. Initially, eruption produces pillow basalts. When the volcano emerges above sea level, it becomes a shield volcano. The margins of the island frequently undergo slumping, and the weight of the volcano pushes down the surface of the lithosphere. The Hawaiian Islands exemplify this architecture.

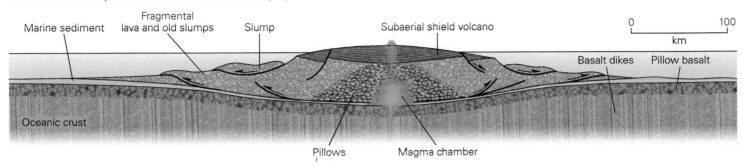

towers over 9 km above the adjacent ocean floor (about 4.2 km above sea level), the greatest relief from base to top of any mountain on Earth—by comparison, Mt. Everest rises 8.85 km above the plains of India. Calderas up to 3 km wide have formed at the summit. Vast sheets of basaltic lava extrude from chimney-shaped conduits and fissures, both at the summit and on the flanks of the volcanoes (see Fig. 9.3b).

Iceland also formed over a hot spot, one that lies beneath the Mid-Atlantic Ridge—the presence of this hot spot means that far more lava erupted here than beneath other places along the ridge. As a result, Iceland sits on a broad oceanic plateau. Because Iceland straddles a divergent-plate boundary, it is being stretched apart, with faults forming as a consequence. Indeed, the central part of the island is a narrow rift, in which the youngest volcanic rocks of the island have erupted (Fig. 9.19). This rift is the trace of the Mid-Atlantic Ridge. Faulting cracks the crust and so provides a conduit to a magma chamber. Thus, eruptions on Iceland tend to begin as fissure eruptions, spewing curtains of lava. Eventually, the curtains die out and are replaced by more localized eruptions that form linear chains of cinder cones.

Not all volcanic activity on Iceland occurs subaerially. Some eruptions take place under glaciers. During 1996, for example, an eruption at the base of a 600-m-thick glacier melted the ice and produced a column of steam that rose several kilo-

meters into the air. Meltwater accumulated under the ice for six days, until it burst through the edge of the glacier and became a flood (called a *jökulhlaup*, in Icelandic) that lasted two days and destroyed roads, bridges, and telephone lines. The 2010 eruption of the Eyjafjallajokull Volcano caused similar problems, and was also disruptive in other ways, as we will see.

Some of Iceland's volcanic activity occurs off the coast. Such activity produced the island of Surtsey. The birth of Surtsey was heralded by huge quantities of steam bubbling up from the ocean. Eventually, steam pressure explosively ejected ash as high as 5 km into the atmosphere. Surtsey finally emerged from the sea on November 14, 1963, building up a cone of ash and lapilli that rose almost 200 m above sea level in just three months. Waves could easily have eroded the cinder cone away, but the island has survived because lava erupted from the vent and flowed over the cinders, effectively encasing them in an armor-like blanket of solid rock.

Continental Hot-Spot Volcanism

Yellowstone National Park lies at the northeast end of a string of calderas, known as the Yellowstone hot-spot track, whose remnants crop out in the Snake River Plain of Idaho (Fig. 9.20a). The oldest of these calderas, at the southwest end of the track, erupted 16 million years ago (Ma). Recent studies have found evidence of a mantle plume beneath Yellowstone, adding support to the hypothesis that the Yellowstone hot-spot track formed as the North American plate moved over a plume.

Ongoing activity beneath Yellowstone has yielded fascinating landforms, volcanic rock deposits, and geysers. Eruptions at the Yellowstone hot spot differ from those in Hawaii in an important way: unlike Hawaii, the Yellowstone hot spot erupts both basaltic lava and rhyolitic pyroclastic debris. This happens because heat transfer from the rising basaltic magma partially melts the continental crust to produce felsic magma.

FIGURE 9.19 Iceland, a hot spot on the Mid-Atlantic Ridge.

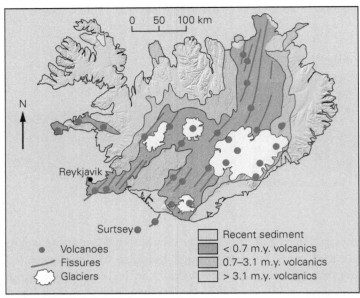

(a) A geologic map of Iceland shows how the youngest volcanoes occur in the central rift, effectively the on-land portion of the Mid-Atlantic Ridge.

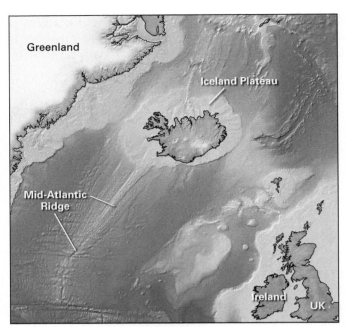

(b) A bathymetric map shows that Iceland sits atop a huge plateau straddling the Mid-Atlantic Ridge. Light blue is shallower water; dark blue is deeper.

(c) A rift cutting through basalt, on Iceland.

About 630,000 years ago (0.63 Ma), immense pyroclastic flows and convective clouds of ash and pumice lapilli blasted out of the Yellowstone region. Close to the eruption, numerous ignimbrites built up, and ash and lapilli from the giant cloud sifted down over the United States as far east as the Mississippi River (Fig. 9.20b). The 0.63-Ma eruption produced an immense caldera, up to 72 km across, that overlaps earlier calderas (Fig. 9.20c). When the debris settled, it blanketed an area of 2,500 square km with tuffs that, in the park, reached a thickness of 400 m—Yellowstone was a supervolcano! The park's name reflects the brilliant color of volcaniclastic debris exposures in the park's canyons (Fig. 9.20d). Eruptive activity, producing basalt and rhyolite lavas

and more pyroclastic debris, continued until about 70,000 years ago. Magma remains in the crust beneath the park today. It's the energy radiating from this magma that heats the water filling hot springs and spurting out of geysers.

Flood-Basalt Eruptions

In several locations around the world, huge sheets of low-viscosity lava erupted and spread out in vast sheets. Geologists refer to the lava of these sheets as **flood basalt** (Fig. 9.21a). Over time, many successive eruptions of flood basalt can build up a broad *basalt plateau*. What causes flood-basalt eruptions? A popular hypothesis suggests that flood basalts form when a mantle plume starts to rise beneath a region that is undergoing rifting (Fig. 6.27a). As the plume reaches the base of the lithosphere, it has a bulbous head containing a large amount of partially molten rock. Stretching and thinning of the overlying lithosphere results in further decompression of the plume head and causes even more melt to form. The melt intrudes along fissures that form in the rift and erupts spectacularly at the surface. Once the plume head no longer exists, the volume of eruption decreases, and "normal" hot-spot volcanism (with less magma production) takes place.

The aggregate volume of rock in a basalt plateau may be so great (over 175,000 km^3) that geologists also refer to the region as a **large igneous province** (LIP; see Fig. 6.26). (The term has also been used for regions of immense rhyo-

FIGURE 9.20 Hot-spot volcanic activity in Yellowstone National Park.

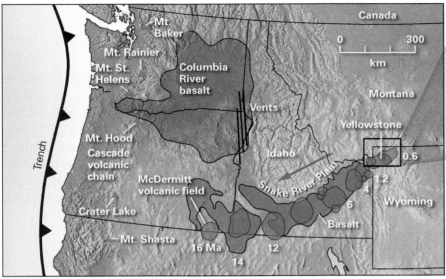

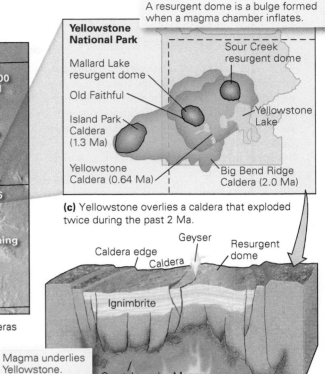

A resurgent dome is a bulge formed when a magma chamber inflates.

(c) Yellowstone overlies a caldera that exploded twice during the past 2 Ma.

(a) Yellowstone lies at the end of a continental hot-spot track. Progressively older calderas follow the Snake River Plain. The blue arrow indicates plate motion.

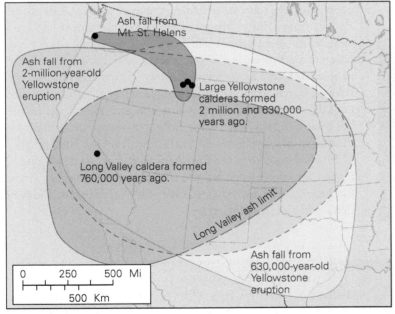

(b) The ash produced by explosions of the Yellowstone calderas covered vast areas—much more than Mt. St. Helens.

(d) Felsic tuffs form the colorful walls of Yellowstone Canyon.

lite eruption, such as the Yellowstone region.) An example of a LIP, the Columbia River Plateau, occurs in Washington and Oregon (see Fig. 6.27b). The basalt here, which erupted around 15 million years ago, reaches a thickness of 3.5 km. Geologists have identified about 300 individual flows in the Columbia River Plateau. Lava in some of these flows traveled great distances—up to 600 km—from its source. Eventually, basalt covered an area of 220,000 km². Even larger

flood-basalt provinces occur in eastern Siberia (an occurrence known as the Siberian traps; Fig. 9.21b), the Deccan Plateau of India, the Paraná region of Brazil, and the Karoo Plateau of South Africa.

Take-Home Message

Most volcanic activity takes place on plate boundaries, but some occurs at hot spots. The style of eruption depends on the setting. The sea hides divergent-boundary volcanoes, which erupt pillow basalt. Volcanic arcs rise above sea level and may produce stratovolcanoes. Oceanic hot spots produce shield volcanoes. Continental hot spots and rifts produce both effusive and explosive eruptions.

QUICK QUESTION: How does a volcano formed in a continental island arc differ from one formed at an oceanic hot spot?

FIGURE 9.21 According to one hypothesis, flood basalts erupt when the head of a plume reaches the base of rifting lithosphere.

(a) Flood-basalt layers exposed on the wall of a canyon in Idaho.

9.5 Beware: Volcanoes Are Hazards!

Like earthquakes, volcanoes are natural hazards that have the potential to cause great destruction to humanity. According to one estimate, volcanic eruptions in the last 2,000 years have caused about a quarter of a million deaths. Considering the rapid expansion of cities, far more people live in dangerous proximity to volcanoes today than ever before, so if anything, the hazard posed by volcanoes has gotten worse—imagine if a large explosion were to occur next to a major city today. Let's now look at the different kinds of threats posed by volcanic eruptions.

Hazards due to Eruptive Materials

Threat of Flows When you think of an eruption, perhaps the first threat that comes to mind is the lava that flows from a volcano. Indeed, lava is a threat to real estate, and on many occasions, lava has overwhelmed towns (Fig. 9.22a–d). Basaltic lava from effusive eruptions is the greatest threat because it can spread over a broad area. In Hawaii, recent lava flows have covered roads, housing developments, and vehicles. Although people have time to get out of the way of such flows, they might have to watch helplessly from a distance as an advancing flow engulfs their homes. Even before the lava even touches it, a building will burst into flame from the intense heat. The most disastrous lava flow in recent times came from the 2002 eruption of Mt. Nyiragongo in the East African Rift. Lava flows traveled almost 50 km and flooded the streets in the Congolese city of Goma, encasing them with a 2-m-thick layer of basalt. The flows destroyed almost half the city.

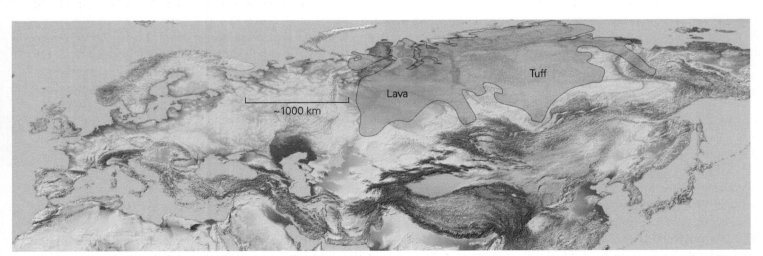

(b) An area the size of Europe was covered by flood basalts (the "Siberian traps") and associated tuffs in Siberia. The time of the eruption, about 250 Ma, coincides with the end of the Paleozoic, when there was mass extinction. The map shows the maximum extent of the volcanic rock before erosion.

Pyroclastic flows can move extremely fast (100 to 300 km per hour) and are so hot (500° to 1,000°C) that they represent a profound hazard to humans and the environment (Fig. 9.22e, f). Even relatively small examples, such as the flow that struck St. Pierre on Martinique, can flatten towns and devastate fields even though they leave only a few centimeters of ash and lapilli behind. People caught in the direct path of such flows may be incinerated, and even those protected from the ash itself may die from inhaling toxic, superhot gases.

Threat of Falling Ash and Lapilli During a pyroclastic eruption, large quantities of ash and lapilli erupt into the air, later to fall back to the ground (Fig. 9.22g). Close to the volcano, pumice and lapilli tumble out of the sky and can accumulate to form a blanket up to several meters thick. The mass, especially when saturated with rainwater, causes roofs and power lines to collapse. Winds can carry fine ash over a broad region. In the Philippines, for example, a typhoon spread heavy air-fall ash from the 1991 eruption of Mt. Pinatubo so that it covered a 4,000-square-km area. An ash fall buries crops, coats the leaves of trees, and may spread toxic chemicals that poison the soil. Ash also insidiously infiltrates machinery, causing moving parts to wear out.

Threat to Aircraft Fine ash from an eruption can also present a hazard to airplanes. Like a sandblaster, the sharp, angular shards of ash abrade turbine blades, greatly reducing engine efficiency. The ash, along with sulfuric acid formed from the volcanic gas, scores windows and damages the fuselage. Also, when heated inside a jet engine, the ash melts, creating a liquid that coats interior parts of the engine and freezes to glass, coating temperature sensors, which falsely indicate that the engines are overheating so they automatically shut down.

Encounters between airliners and volcanic plumes have led to terrifying incidents. In 1982, a British Airways 747 flew through the ash cloud above a volcano in Java. The windshield turned opaque and all four engines failed. For 13 minutes, the plane silently glided earthward, dropping from 11.5 km (37,000 ft). The pilot frantically tried to restart the engines to no avail and prepared to ditch at sea. Finally, at 3.7 km (12,000 ft), the engines had cooled sufficiently and suddenly roared back to life and the plane headed to Jakarta for an emergency landing. There, without functioning instruments, the pilot squinted out an open side window to see the runway and brought the plane safely to a halt with only his toes touching the pedals. A similar event happened between a KLM 747 and the eruptive cloud of Redoubt Volcano in Alaska in 1989.

Because of the lessons learned from such incidents, the 2010 eruption of the Eyjafjallajokull Volcano in Iceland had a profound impact on air traffic. All told, the eruption sent about 0.25 cubic km of pyroclastic material up into the air. The jet stream, a high-altitude current of rapidly moving air, was passing over Iceland at the time of the eruption and thus dispersed the ash throughout European air space. Because of concern that this ash could damage planes, officials shut down almost all air traffic across Europe for six days. The closure directly cost airlines $200 million/day, disrupted travel plans for countless passengers, and halted shipment of everything from electronic goods to flowers, thus impacting economies worldwide.

Other Hazards Related to Eruptions

Threat of the Blast Most exploding volcanoes direct their fury upward. But some, like Mt. St. Helens, explode sideways. The forcefully ejected gas and ash, like the blast of a bomb, flattens everything in its path. In the case of Mt. St. Helens, the region around the volcano had been a beautiful pine forest. But after the eruption, the once-towering trees, stripped of bark and needles, lay flattened onto the hill slopes, all pointing in the direction away from the blast (see Box 9.1).

Threat of Landslides Eruptions commonly trigger large landslides along a volcano's flanks. The debris, composed of ash and solidified lava that erupted earlier, can move quite fast (250 km per hour) and far. During the eruption of Mt. St. Helens, 8 billion tons of debris took off down the mountainside, careened over a 360-m-high ridge, and tumbled down a river valley, until the last of it finally came to rest over 20 km from the volcano.

Threat of Lahars When volcanic ash and other debris mix with water, the result is a lahar, an ashy slurry that resembles wet concrete. A lahar can move downslope at speeds of over 50 km per hour. Because lahars are denser and more viscous than clear water, they pack more force than clear water and literally carry away everything in their path. The lahars of Mt. St. Helens traveled along existing drainages for more than 40 km from the volcano. When they had passed, they left a gray and barren wake of mud, boulders, broken bridges, and crumpled houses, as if a giant knife had scraped across the landscape. The lahars generated during the 1991 eruption of Pinatubo in the Philippines were even more devastating, for the eruption was bigger and coincided with the drenching rains of a typhoon.

Lahars may develop in regions where snow and ice cover an erupting volcano, for the eruption melts the snow and ice, thereby creating a supply of water. Perhaps the most destructive lahar of recent times accompanied the eruption of the snow-crested Nevado del Ruiz in Colombia on the night of November 13, 1985. The lahar surged down a valley like a 40-m-high wave, hitting the sleeping town of Armero, 60 km from the volcano. Ninety percent of the buildings in the town vanished, replaced by a 5-m-thick layer of mud, which now entombs the bodies of 25,000 people (Fig. 9.22h).

FIGURE 9.22 Hazards due to lava and ash from volcanic eruptions.

Lava Flows

(a) A lava flow reaches a house in Hawaii and sets it on fire.

(b) Lava from Mt. Etna threatens a town and olive grove in Sicily.

(c) Residents rescue household goods after a lava flow filled the streets of Goma, along the East African Rift.

(d) This empty school bus was engulfed by lava in Hawaii.

Pyroclastic Debris

(e) A pyroclastic flow from the 1991 eruption of Mt. Pinatubo chases a fleeing vehicle.

(f) A blizzard of ash fell from the cloud erupted by Mt. Pinatubo in the Philippines.

(g) Lapilli falls from an eruption in Iceland.

(h) A lahar submerges farmland in Colombia.

Threat of Earthquakes Earthquakes accompany almost all major volcanic eruptions, for the movement of magma breaks rocks underground. Such earthquakes may trigger landslides on the volcano's flanks and can cause nearby buildings to collapse and dams to rupture, even before the eruption itself begins.

Threat of Tsunamis Where explosive eruptions occur in an island arc, the blast and the underwater collapse of a caldera can generate huge sea waves, or tsunamis, tens of meters high. Most of the 36,000 deaths attributed to the 1883 eruption of Krakatau were not due to ash or lava but rather to tsunamis that slammed into nearby coastal towns. Tsunamis may also be generated by huge submarine landslides that occur when part of a volcanic island suddenly slumps into the sea.

Threat of Gas We have already seen that volcanoes erupt not only solid material but also large quantities of gases such as water vapor, carbon dioxide, sulfur dioxide, and hydrogen sulfide. Usually the gas eruption accompanies the lava and ash eruption, with the gas contributing only a minor part of the calamity. For example, sulfur gases, mixing with moisture, produce sulfuric acid aerosols that can cause respiratory problems in people who live downwind. But occasionally the gas alone snuffs out life in its path without causing any other damage. Such an event occurred in 1986 near Lake Nyos in western Africa.

Lake Nyos is a small but deep lake filling the crater of an active volcano in Cameroon. Though only 1 km across, the lake reaches a depth of over 200 m. Because of its depth, the cool bottom water of the lake does not mix with warm surface water. Carbon-dioxide gas slowly bubbles out of cracks in the floor of the crater and dissolves in the cool bottom water, eventually saturating the water with CO_2. On August 21, 1986, perhaps because a landslide or wind disturbed the water, the water within the lake overturned and the saturated bottom water rose to the surface (Fig. 9.23a, b). As it rose, the pressure

FIGURE 9.23 The CO_2 gas disaster, Lake Nyos, Cameroon.

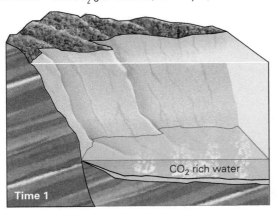
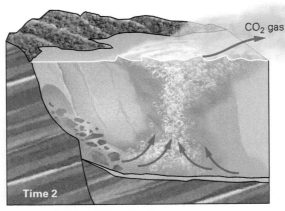

(a) CO_2 dissolved in the colder bottom water (purple). When a landslide or wind disturbed the water, it rose and the CO_2 came out of solution and, in gas form, flowed out of the crater.

(b) Lake Nyos, after the disaster. The crater lake has been discolored by turbulence.

(c) The CO_2 suffocated cattle on the slopes below the volcano.

acting on the water decreased, the CO_2 came out of solution, and the lake suddenly expelled a forceful froth of CO_2 bubbles. Because it is denser than air, this invisible gas flowed down the flank of the volcano and spread out over the countryside for a distance of about 23 km before dispersing. Although not toxic, carbon dioxide cannot provide oxygen for metabolism or oxidation. When the gas cloud engulfed the village of Nyos, it quietly put out cooking fires and suffocated the sleeping inhabitants. The next morning, the landscape looked exactly as it had the day before, except for the lifeless bodies of 1,742 people and about 6,000 head of cattle (Fig. 9.23c).

Take-Home Message

Volcanoes can be dangerous! The lava flows, pyroclastic debris, explosions, mudflows (lahars), landslides, earthquakes, and tsunamis that can be produced during eruptions can destroy cities and farmland. Ash that enters the air can be a hazard for air travel.

QUICK QUESTION: Why can a lahar do so much more damage than an equivalent-sized flood of clear water?

9.6 Protection from Vulcan's Wrath

Volcanic eruptions are a natural hazard of extreme danger. Can anything be done to protect lives and property from this danger? The answer is yes. Below we first examine the evidence that geologists use to determine whether a volcano has the potential to erupt, and then we consider the suite of observations that may allow geologists to predict the timing of an impending eruption.

Active, Dormant, and Extinct Volcanoes

Geologists refer to volcanoes that are erupting, have erupted recently, or are likely to erupt soon as **active volcanoes** and distinguish them from **dormant volcanoes**, which have not erupted for hundreds to thousands of years but may erupt again in the future. Volcanoes that were active in the geologic past but have shut off entirely and will never erupt again because the geologic cause of volcanism no longer exists are called **extinct**

volcanoes. As examples, geologists consider Hawaii's Kilauea to be active, for it currently is erupting and has erupted frequently during recorded history. In contrast, Mt. Rainier in the Cascades last erupted centuries to millennia ago, but since subduction continues along the western edge of Oregon and Washington, the volcano could erupt in the future, and so it is considered dormant. Devils Tower, in eastern Wyoming, is the remnant of a shallow igneous intrusion, formed beneath a volcano and subsequently exposed by erosion (Fig. 9.24). This was a volcanic region at the time the magma of Devils Tower intruded, tens of millions of years ago. Volcanism will not happen again where the geologic causes for volcanism no longer exist, so we can say that volcanism in the Devils Tower area is extinct. Similarly, when the volcanoes that built the island of Kauai lay over the Hawaiian hot spot, they were active, but now that the island has moved off, its volcanoes have become extinct.

How do you determine whether a volcano is active, dormant, or extinct? One way is to examine the historical record. Another is to determine the age of erupted rocks and to search for evidence that the volcano still lies within a tectonically active area. Finally, you can examine the landscape character of the volcano. Specifically, the shape (shield, stratovolcano, or cinder cone) of an erupting volcano depends primarily on the eruptive style, because at an erupting volcano, the process of construction happens faster than the process of erosion. Once a volcano stops erupting, erosion attacks. The rate at which erosion destroys a volcano depends on whether it's composed of pyroclastic debris or lava. Cinder cones and ash piles can wash away quickly.

FIGURE 9.24 Devils Tower, Wyoming formed as an intrusion into sedimentary rocks beneath a volcano. It solidified hundreds of meters below the surface of the Earth and has been exposed by erosion. Cooling produced spectacular columnar joints.

The vertical lines are columnar joints.

In contrast, composite or shield volcanoes, which have been armor-plated by lava flows, can withstand the attack of water and ice for quite some time. In the end, however, erosion wins out, and you can distinguish a dormant volcano from an active volcano by the extent to which river or glacial valleys have been carved into its flanks (Fig. 9.25). In some cases, the softer exterior of a volcano completely erodes away, leaving behind the plug of harder frozen magma that once lay within or beneath the volcano, as well as the network of dikes that radiate from this plug. You can see good examples of such landforms at Shiprock, New Mexico (see Fig. 6.13).

Predicting Eruptions

Predicting the time of an eruption decades or even years in advance is impossible. The only way to constrain a long-term prediction is to determine the recurrence interval (the average time between eruptions). Geologists determine recurrence intervals by determining the age of erupted layers comprising the volcano's edifice. For example, Mt. Fuji has erupted about 65 times in the last 10,000 years. So its eruptive recurrence interval is about 150 years. Note that a recurrence interval does not indicate periodicity—some of Fuji's eruptions were decades apart while others were centuries apart. The recurrence interval just gives a sense of the probability, and surprises happen.

> **Did you ever wonder . . .**
>
> if a volcano could erupt beneath London, England?

Unlike earthquakes, volcanic eruptions can (in general) be predicted. The 2014 eruption of Mt. Ontake in Japan, however, serves as a rare exception. The microseismicity, hinting that magma was rising in the throat of the volcano, did not start until an hour before a significant eruption of gas and ash. Sadly, the ash covered and killed about 30 hikers who had climbed the volcano to enjoy the Fall foliage. Some volcanoes send out distinct warning signals announcing that an eruption may take place very soon, for as magma squeezes into the magma chamber, it causes a number of changes that geologists can measure.

- *Earthquake activity:* Movement of magma generates vibrations in the Earth. When magma flows into a volcano, rocks surrounding the magma chamber crack, and blocks slip with respect to each other. Such cracking and shifting cause earthquakes. Thus, in the days or weeks preceding an eruption, the region between 1 and 7 km beneath a volcano becomes seismically active.
- *Changes in heat flow:* The presence of hot magma increases the local heat flow, the amount of heat passing up through rock. In some cases, the increase in the heat flow melts snow or ice on the volcano, triggering floods and lahars even before an eruption occurs.

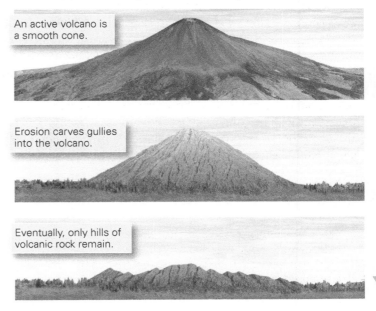

FIGURE 9.25 The shape of a volcano changes as it is eroded.

An active volcano is a smooth cone.

Erosion carves gullies into the volcano.

Eventually, only hills of volcanic rock remain.

Time

- *Changes in shape:* As magma fills the magma chamber inside a volcano, it pushes outward and can cause the surface of the volcano to bulge; the same effect happens when you blow into a balloon. Geologists now use laser sighting, accurate tiltmeters, surveys using global positioning systems, and a technique called satellite interferometry (InSAR, which uses radar beams emitted by satellites to measure elevation changes) to detect modification of a volcano's shape due to the rise of magma (Fig. 9.26a).
- *Increases in gas and steam emission:* Even though magma remains below the surface, gases bubbling out of the magma, or steam formed by the heating of groundwater by the volcano, percolate upward through cracks in the Earth and rise from the volcanic vent. So an increase in the volume of gas emission, or the birth of new hot springs, may indicate that magma has entered the ground below (Fig. 9.26b).

Mitigating Volcanic Hazards

Danger Assessment Maps Let's say that a given active volcano has the potential to erupt in the near future. What can we do to prevent the loss of life and property? Since we can't prevent the eruption, the first and most effective precaution is to define the regions that can be directly affected by the eruption—to compile a **volcanic-hazard assessment map** (Fig. 9.27). These maps delineate areas that lie in the path of potential lava flows, lahars, or pyroclastic flows. River valleys originating on the flanks of a volcano are particularly dangerous places to be because lahars may flow down them.

Before the 1991 eruption of Mt. Pinatubo in the Philippines, geologists had defined areas potentially in the path of

FIGURE 9.26 Measuring the activity of volcanoes.

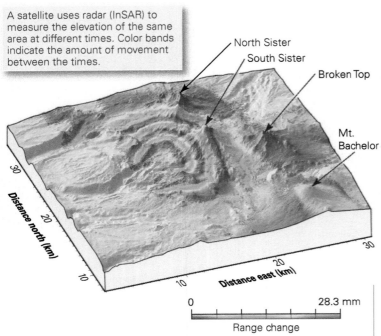

A satellite uses radar (InSAR) to measure the elevation of the same area at different times. Color bands indicate the amount of movement between the times.

North Sister
South Sister
Broken Top
Mt. Bachelor

Distance north (km)
Distance east (km)

0   28.3 mm
Range change

(a) An InSAR map of the Three Sisters Wilderness in Oregon. Satellites can map and detect movement of the ground surface over time.

(b) Geologists can detect changes in gas composition.

pyroclastic flows and had predicted which river valleys were likely hosts for lahars. Although the predicted pyroclastic-flow paths proved to be accurate, the region actually affected by lahars was much greater. Nevertheless, many lives were saved by evacuating people in areas thought to be under threat.

Volcano Monitoring and Evacuation Because geologists can determine when magma has moved into the magma chamber of a volcano, government agencies now send monitoring teams to a volcano at the first sign of activity. These teams set up instruments to record earthquakes, measure the heat flow, determine changes in the volcano's shape, and analyze emissions. If an eruption seems imminent, they may issue a warning and call for area residents to evacuate.

Unfortunately, because of the uncertainty of prediction, the decision about whether or not to evacuate is a hard one. In the case of Mt. St. Helens in 1980, hundreds of lives were saved by timely evacuation, but in the case of Mt. Pelée in 1902, thousands of lives were lost because warning signs were ignored. In the Philippines, evacuation of people from the danger area around Mt. Pinatubo, over many years, succeeded in saving thousands of lives, so the prediction was a success. In 1976, however, there was a fierce debate over the need for an evacuation around a volcano on Guadeloupe, in the French West Indies. Eventually, the population of a threatened town was evacuated, but as months passed, the volcano did not erupt. Instead, tempers did, and anger at the cost of the evacuation translated into lawsuits; the prediction was not a success.

Diverting Flows Sometimes people have used direct force to change the direction of a flow or even to stop it. For example, during a 1669 eruption of Mt. Etna, an active volcano on the Italian island of Sicily, basaltic lava formed a glowing orange river that began to spill down the side of the mountain. When the flow approached the town of Catania, 16 km from

FIGURE 9.27 A volcanic-hazard assessment map for Mt. Rainier, Washington, showing the regions that might be affected by flows and lahars.

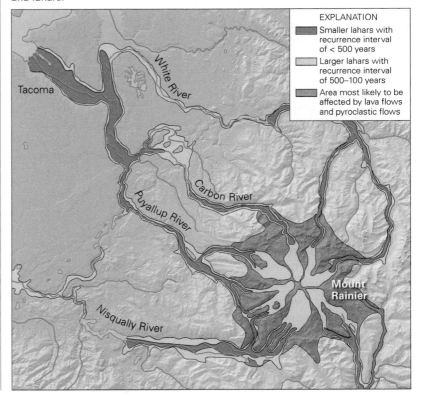

EXPLANATION
- Smaller lahars with recurrence interval of < 500 years
- Larger lahars with recurrence interval of 500–100 years
- Area most likely to be affected by lava flows and pyroclastic flows

Tacoma
White River
Carbon River
Puyallup River
Nisqually River
Mount Rainier

FIGURE 9.28 Efforts to divert lava flows away from inhabited locations.

(a) Workers spray the lava flow to solidify it and use a bulldozer to build an embankment to divert it on the flanks of Mt. Etna.

(b) Firefighters pumping 6 million cubic meters of water on a lava flow, in an effort to freeze it and stop it.

the summit, 50 townspeople protected by wet cowhides boldly hacked through the chilled side of the flow to create an opening through which the lava could exit. They hoped thereby to cut off the supply of lava feeding the end of the flow, near their homes. Their strategy worked, and the flow began to ooze through the new hole in its side. Unfortunately, the diverted flow began to move toward the neighboring town of Paterno. Five hundred men of Paterno then chased away the Catanians so that the hole would not be kept open, and eventually the flow once again headed toward Catania, burying part of the town.

More recently, people use high explosives to blast breaches in the flanks of flows and use bulldozers to build dams and channels to divert flows. Major efforts to divert flows from a 1983 eruption of Mt. Etna, and again in 1992, were successful (Fig. 9.28a). Inhabitants of Iceland used a particularly creative approach in 1973 to stop a flow before it overran a town—they sprayed cold seawater onto the flow to freeze it in its tracks (Fig. 9.28b). The flow did stop short of the town, but whether this was a consequence of the cold shower it received remains unknown.

> **Did you ever wonder...**
>
> whether people could redirect a lava flow?

Take-Home Message

Volcanoes don't erupt continuously and don't last forever, so we can distinguish among active, dormant, and extinct volcanoes. Once a volcano ceases to erupt, erosion destroys its eruptive shape. Geologists can provide near-term predictions of eruptions so that people can take precautions.

QUICK QUESTION: Using the Web, discover how many times Vesuvius has erupted since 79 C.E. and calculate its recurrence interval. Is it wise to continue building housing on its flanks?

9.7 Effect of Volcanoes on Climate and Civilization

Can Eruptions Affect Climate?

In 1783, Benjamin Franklin was living in Europe, serving as the American ambassador to France. The summer of that year seemed to be unusually cool and hazy. Franklin, who was an accomplished scientist as well as a statesman, couldn't resist seeking an explanation for this phenomenon and learned that in June of 1783 a huge volcanic eruption had taken place in Iceland. He wondered if the "smoke" from the eruption had prevented sunlight from reaching the Earth, thus causing the cooler temperatures. Franklin reported this idea at a meeting, and by doing so, he may well have been the first scientist ever to suggest a link between eruptions and climate.

Franklin's idea seemed to be confirmed in 1815, when Mt. Tambora in Indonesia exploded. Tambora's explosion ejected over 100 cubic km of ash and pumice into the air (compared with 1 cubic km from Mt. St. Helens). Ten thousand people were killed by the eruption and the associated tsunami. Another 82,000 died of starvation. The sky became so hazy that stars dimmed by a full magnitude. Temperatures dipped so low in the northern hemisphere that 1816 became known as "the year without a summer." The unusual weather of that year inspired artists and writers. For example, memories of fabulous sunsets and the hazy glow of the sky inspired the luminous and atmospheric quality that made the landscape paintings of the English artist J. M. W. Turner so famous (see Fig. 9.1a), and Byron's 1816 poem "Darkness" contains the gloomy lines "The bright Sun was extinguish'd, and the stars / Did wander darkling in the eternal space . . . / Morn came and went—and came, and brought no day." Two years later, Mary Shelley, trapped indoors by bad weather, wrote Frankenstein, with its numerous scenes of gloom and doom.

Geoscientists have witnessed other examples of eruption-triggered coolness more recently. In the months following the 1883 eruption of Krakatau and the 1991 eruption of Pinatubo, global temperatures noticeably dipped. Classical literature provides more evidence of the volcanic impact on climate. For example, Plutarch wrote around 100 c.e., "there was . . . after Caesar's murder . . . the obscuration of the Sun's rays. For during all the year its orb rose pale and without radiance . . . and the fruits, imperfect and half ripe, withered away." Similar conditions appear to have occurred in China the same year, as described in records from the Han dynasty, and may have been a consequence of volcanic eruption.

To study the effect of volcanic activity on climate even further in the past, geologists have studied ice from the glaciers of Greenland and Antarctica. Glacial ice has layers, each of which represents the snow that fell in a single year. Some layers contain concentrations of sulfuric acid, formed when sulfur dioxide from volcanic gas dissolves in the water from which snow forms. These layers indicate years in which major eruptions occurred. Years in which ice contains acid correspond to years during which the thinness of tree rings elsewhere in the world indicates a cool growing season.

How can a volcanic eruption create these cooling effects? As a result of a large explosive eruption, fine ash and sulfuric-acid aerosols enter the stratosphere. It takes only about two weeks for the ash and aerosols to circle the planet (**Fig. 9.29**),

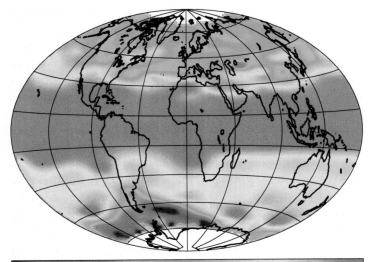

FIGURE 9.29 A map showing the global concentration of aerosols two months after the Mt. Pinatubo eruption in 1991.

Low concentration   High concentration

and they stay suspended in the stratosphere for many months to years because they float above the weather and do not get washed away by rainfall. The resulting haze causes cooler average temperatures because it reflects and/or scatters incoming visible solar radiation during the day but not the infrared radiation that rises from the Earth's surface at night. Thus, it keeps energy from reaching the Earth, but unlike greenhouse gases (such as CO_2), it does not prevent heat from escaping. A Krakatau-scale eruption can lead to a drop in global average temperature of 0.3° to 1°C. According to some calculations, a series of large eruptions over a short period of time could cause a global average temperature drop of 6°C. The temperature dip seems to last up to a few years.

Some researchers are currently exploring the possibility that the eruption of LIPs may have longer-lasting effects, perhaps changing climate so much that species go extinct. The apparent coincidence of the eruption of the Siberian traps with the extinctions that define the end of the Paleozoic may be an example.

Volcanoes and Civilization

Not all volcanic activity is bad. Over time, volcanic activity has played a major role in making the Earth a habitable planet. Eruptions and underlying igneous intrusions produced the rock making up the Earth's crust, and gases emitted by volcanoes provided the raw materials from which the atmosphere and oceans formed. The black smokers surrounding vents along mid-ocean ridges may have served as a birthplace for life, and volcanic islands in the oceans have hosted isolated populations whose evolution adds to the diversity of life on the planet. Volcanic activity continues to bring nutrients (potassium, sulfur, calcium, and phosphorus) from Earth's interior to the surface and to provide fertile soils that nurture plant growth. And in more recent times, people have exploited the mineral and energy resources generated by volcanic eruptions. Thus, volcanoes and people have lived in close association since the first human-like ancestors walked the Earth 3 million years ago. In fact, one of the earliest relics of human ancestors consists of footprints fossilized in a volcanic ash layer in East Africa.

But as we have seen, volcanic eruptions also pose a hazard. Eruptions may even lead to the demise of civilizations. The history of the Minoan people, who inhabited several islands in the eastern Mediterranean during the Bronze Age, illustrates this possibility. Beginning around 3000 b.c.e., the Minoans built elaborate cities and prospered. Then their civilization waned and disappeared (**Fig. 9.30a**). Geologists have discovered that the disappearance of the Minoans came within 150 years of a series of explosive eruptions of the Santorini Volcano in the first half of the 17th century b.c.e. Remnants of

(a) The ruins of palaces left by the Minoans.

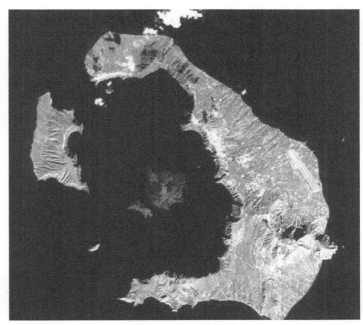

(b) From space, we can see the 11-km-wide caldera, all that is left of Santorini.

(c) The inner wall of the caldera reveals the typical geology of a stratovolcano; we see both lava and tuff layers.

the volcano now constitute Thera, one of the islands of Greece (Fig. 9.30b). After a huge eruption, the center of the volcano collapsed into the sea, leaving only a steep-walled caldera (Fig. 9.30c). Archaeologists speculate that pyroclastic debris from the eruptions periodically darkened the sky, burying Minoan settlements and destroying crops. In addition, related earthquakes crumbled homes, and tsunamis generated by the eruptions damaged Minoan seaports. Perhaps the Minoans took these calamities as a sign of the gods' displeasure, became demoralized, and left the region. Or perhaps trade was disrupted, and bad times led to political unrest. Eventually the Mycenaeans moved in, bringing the culture that evolved into that of classical Greece. The Minoans, though, were not completely forgotten. Plato, in his dialogues, refers to a lost city, home of an advanced civilization that bore many similarities to that of the Minoans. According to Plato, this city, which he named Atlantis, disappeared beneath the waves of the sea. Per-

haps this legend evolved from the true history of the Minoans, as modified by Egyptian scholars who passed it on to Plato.

Numerous cultures living along the Pacific Ring of Fire have evolved religious practices that are based on volcanic activity—no surprise, considering the awesome might of a volcanic eruption in comparison with the power of humans. In some cultures, this reverence took the form of sacrifice in hopes of preventing an eruption that could destroy villages and bury food supplies. In traditional Hawaiian culture, Pelé, goddess of the volcano, created all the major landforms of the Hawaiian Islands. She gouged out the craters that top the volcanoes, her fits and moods bring about the eruptions, and her tears are the smooth, glassy lapilli ejected from the lava fountains.

The largest eruption to have happened in the last million years of Earth's history took place at the Toba Volcano in Indonesia about 73,000 years ago. The explosion put out huge quantities of ash, some of which was nearly white and covered much of southern Asia like a snowfall. In addition, the eruption injected a huge dose of aerosols into the atmosphere. The aerosols and ash diminished the solar radiation reaching the Earth, and the white ash on the ground reflected some of the radiation that did reach the planet back into space. The resulting cooling event may have cooled the atmosphere for a decade, possibly as long as 1,000 years. The duration of the cooling may have been sufficient to cause species of organisms to go extinct. Anthropologists have speculated that the event killed off all but 3,000 to 10,000 humans on Earth. Genetic studies suggest that a bottleneck in evolution occurred about the same time as the Toba eruption, in that all modern humans are descended from a single ancestor who lived about that time. If so, then the Toba eruption could have significantly impacted human evolution.

The observed effect of volcanic eruptions on the climate provides a model with which to predict the consequences of a nuclear war. Researchers have speculated that so much dust and gas would be blown into the sky in the mushroom clouds of nuclear explosions that a "nuclear winter" would ensue.

Take-Home Message

The ash, gases, and aerosols produced by explosive eruptions can be blown around the globe. This material can cause significant global cooling. Climatic effects, as well as other consequences of eruptions, may have impacted human evolution and civilization.

QUICK QUESTION: Not all eruptions of equivalent size (defined by the volume of material erupted) trigger equivalent amounts of global cooling. Why? (*Hint:* Think about eruptive style.)

FIGURE 9.31 Volcanism on other planets and moons in the Solar System.

(a) Maria of the Moon were seas of basaltic lava.

(b) A volcano rises above the plains of Venus.

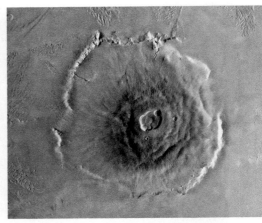

(c) Olympus Mons rises 27 km above the surface of Mars. It's the largest volcano in our Solar System.

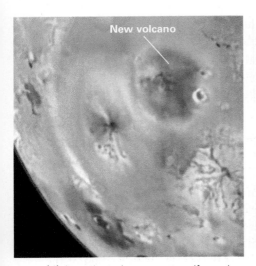

(d) An active volcano erupts sulfur on Io, a moon of Jupiter.

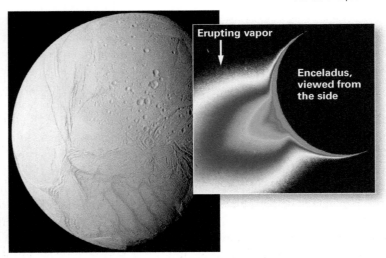

(e) Large cracks at the southern end of Enceladus, a moon of Saturn, erupt water vapor.

9.8 Volcanoes on Other Planets

We conclude this chapter by looking beyond the Earth, for our planet is not the only one in the Solar System to have hosted volcanic eruptions. We can see the effects of volcanic activity on our nearest neighbor, the Moon, just by looking up on a clear night. The broad darker areas of the Moon, the **maria** (singular *mare*, after the Latin word for sea), consist of flood basalts that erupted more than 3 billion years ago (Fig. 9.31a). Geologists propose that the flood basalts formed when huge meteors collided with the Moon, blasting out giant craters. Crater formation decreased the pressure in the Moon's mantle so that it underwent partial melting, producing basaltic magma that rose to the surface and filled the craters.

On Venus, about 22,000 volcanic edifices have been identified. Some of these even have calderas at their crests (Fig. 9.31b). Though no volcanoes currently erupt on Mars, the planet's surface displays a record of a spectacular volcanic past. The largest known mountain in the Solar System, Olympus Mons (Fig. 9.31c), is an extinct shield volcano on Mars. The base of Olympus Mons is 600 km across, and its peak rises 27 km above the surrounding plains.

Active volcanism currently occurs on Io, one of the many moons of Jupiter. Cameras in the *Galileo* spacecraft have recorded these volcanoes in the act of spraying plumes of sulfur gas into space (Fig. 9.31d) and have tracked immense, moving basaltic lava flows. Different colors of erupted material make the surface of this moon resemble a pizza. Researchers have proposed that the volcanic activity is due to tides: the gravitational pull exerted by Jupiter and by other moons alternately stretches and then squeezes Io, generating sufficient friction to keep Io's mantle hot. Geologists have also detected eruptions from moons of Saturn (Fig. 9.31e).

> **Did you ever wonder...**
>
> if the Earth is the only planet with volcanoes?

> ## Take-Home Message
>
> Space exploration reveals that volcanism occurs not only on Earth but has also left its mark on other terrestrial planets and on the moons of giant planets. Satellites have detected active eruptions on moons of Jupiter and Saturn.
>
> **QUICK QUESTION:** Since most volcanic activity on Earth is a result of plate tectonics, what does the lack of volcanic activity on the Moon tell us about whether or not plate tectonics happens on the Moon?

CHAPTER SUMMARY

- Volcanoes are vents at which molten rock (lava), pyroclastic debris, gas, and aerosols erupt at the Earth's surface. A hill, mountain, crater, or caldera depression created by volcanism is also called a volcano.
- The characteristics of a lava flow depend on its viscosity, which in turn depends on its temperature and composition.
- Basaltic lava can flow great distances. Pahoehoe flows have smooth, ropy surfaces, whereas a'a' flows have rough, rubbly surfaces. Andesitic and rhyolitic lava flows tend to pile into mounds at the vent.
- Pyroclastic debris includes powder-sized ash, marble-sized lapilli, and apple- to refrigerator-sized blocks and bombs. Some falls from the air, whereas other debris forms incandescent pyroclastic flows (density currents) that rush away from the volcano.

- Eruptions may occur at a volcano's summit or from fissures on its flanks. The summit of an erupting volcano may collapse to form a bowl-shaped depression called a caldera.
- A volcano's shape depends on the type of eruption. Shield volcanoes are broad, gentle rises. Cinder cones are steep-sided, symmetrical hills composed of tephra. Composite volcanoes (stratovolcanoes) can become quite large and consist of alternating layers of pyroclastic debris and lava.
- The type of eruption depends on several factors, including the lava's viscosity and gas content. Effusive eruptions produce only flows of lava, whereas explosive eruptions produce clouds and flows of pyroclastic debris.
- Different kinds of volcanoes form in different geologic settings as defined by plate tectonics theory.
- Volcanic eruptions pose many hazards: lava flows overrun roads and towns, ash falls blanket the landscape, pyroclastic

flows incinerate towns and fields, landslides and lahars bury the land surface, earthquakes topple structures and rupture dams, tsunamis wash away coastal towns, and invisible gases suffocate people and animals.

- Eruptions can be predicted by earthquake activity, changes in heat flow, changes in shape of the volcano, and the emission of gas and steam.

- We can minimize the consequences of an eruption by avoiding construction in danger zones and by drawing up evacuation plans.
- Immense flood basalts cover portions of the Moon. The largest known volcano, Olympus Mons, towers over the surface of Mars. Satellites have documented evidence for eruptions on moons of Jupiter and Saturn.

GUIDE TERMS

a'a' (p. 276)
aerosol (p. 281)
active volcano (p. 302)
ash (p. 278)
block (p. 278)
bomb (p. 278)
caldera (p. 283)
cinder cone (p. 284)
columnar jointing (p. 276)
crater (p. 283)
dormant volcano (p. 302)

effusive eruption (p. 285)
eruption column (p. 289)
eruptive style (p. 285)
explosive eruption (p. 285)
extinct volcano (p. 302)
fissure (p. 282)
flood basalt (p. 296)
ignimbrite (p. 292)
lahar (p. 281)
lapilli (p. 278)

large igneous province (LIP) (p. 296)
lava tube (p. 276)
magma chamber (p. 282)
mare (p. 309)
pahoehoe (p. 276)
pillow lava (p. 276)
pyroclastic debris (p. 278)
pyroclastic flow (p. 292)
shield volcano (p. 284)
stratovolcano (p. 284)

supervolcano (p. 292)
tephra (p. 278)
tuff (p. 278)
vent (p. 282)
vesicle (p. 281)
viscosity (p. 275)
volcanic explosivity index (VEI) (p. 290)
volcanic-hazard assessment map (p. 303)
volcano (p. 273)

REVIEW QUESTIONS

1. Describe the three different kinds of material that can erupt from a volcano.
2. Describe the differences between a pyroclastic flow and a lahar.
3. Describe the differences among shield volcanoes, stratovolcanoes, and cinder cones. How are these differences explained by the composition of their lavas and other factors?
4. Why do some volcanic eruptions consist mostly of lava flows, whereas others are explosive and do not produce flows?

5. Describe the activity in the mantle that leads to hot-spot eruptions.
6. How do continental-rift eruptions form flood basalts?
7. Contrast an island volcanic arc with a continental volcanic arc. What is a hot-spot volcano?
8. Identify some of the major volcanic hazards, and explain how they develop.
9. How do geologists predict volcanic eruptions?
10. Explain how steps can be taken to protect people from the effects of eruptions.

ON FURTHER THOUGHT

11. The Long Valley Caldera, near the Sierra Nevada range, exploded about 700,000 years ago and produced a huge ignimbrite (a lapilli tuff deposited from vast pyroclastic density currents) called the Bishop Tuff. About 30 km to the northwest lies Mono Lake (see photo), with an island in the middle and a string of craters extending south from its south shore. Hot springs and tufa deposits can be found along the lake. You can see the lake on *Google Earth*™ at Lat 37° 59′ 56.58″ N Long 119° 2′ 18.20″ W. Explain the origin of Mono Lake. Do you think that it represents a volcanic hazard?

12. Mt. Fuji is a 3.6-km-high stratovolcano in Japan formed as a consequence of subduction (see photo below). With *Google Earth*™ you can reach the volcano at Lat 35° 21′ 46.72″ N Long 138° 43′ 49.38″ E. It contains volcanic rocks with a range of compositions, including some andesitic rocks. Why do andesites erupt at Mt. Fuji? Very little andesite occurs on the Marianas Islands, which are also subduction-related volcanoes. Why?

13. The city of Albuquerque lies along the Rio Grande in New Mexico. Within the valley, numerous volcanic features crop out. Using *Google Earth*™, you can fly to Albuquerque and then along the river to find many examples. Many of the volcanoes are basaltic, but in places you will see huge caldera remnants. In fact, the city of Los Alamos lies atop thick ignimbrites. What causes the volcanism in the Rio Grande Valley, and why are there different kinds of volcanism? Look at the photo of the volcanic cluster (see photo below). These occur north of Santa Fe, at Lat 36° 45′ 27.51″ N Long 105° 47′ 24.85″ W—use *Google Earth*™ to get a closer view. Judging from the character of these volcanoes, would you say they are active? Why? How would you evaluate the volcanic hazard of this region? (*Hint:* Use the Web to find a map of seismicity for the Rio Grande Valley region, and think about its implications.)

smartw⚙rk

smartwork.wwnorton.com

This chapter's Smartwork features:

- Art exercise on lava flows and viscosity.
- Simulation exercises on basin and range formation and sedimentation.
- Composite volcano labeling activity.

GEOTOURS

This chapter's GeoTour exercise (E) features:

- Shield volcanoes
- Composite cone volcanoes
- Cinder cone volcanoes

Another View Left: the ash cloud from the 2011 eruption of a volcano in the Puyehue-Cordón Caulle chain of Chile. The ash circled the globe within two weeks, disrupting air traffic throughout the southern hemisphere. Right: A large ash plume with lava erupting from the Eyjafjallajokull Volcano in Iceland, April 2010. The ash cloud from the eruption grounded air traffic around the world.

This fossil of a fish was carefully exposed by removing the overlying layer of rock. Fine details of the fish's bones and fins have been preserved for millions of years, allowing us to see a species that no longer exists.

Memories of Past Life: Fossils and Evolution

LEARNING OBJECTIVES

By the end of this interlude, you should understand . . .

- what a fossil is and how fossils form.
- why relatively few organisms become fossils.
- how to recognize some of the more common fossils.
- how the study of fossils contributes to an understanding of life evolution.

E.1 The Discovery of Fossils

If you look closely at outcrops of sedimentary strata or of air-fall tuff, you might occasionally find features that resemble shells, bones, leaves, or footprints, either on the surfaces of layers or within the rock itself (**Fig. E.1a–c**). Especially impressive examples were displayed in ancient Greek temples as trophies, "dragon" (dinosaur) bones were used in traditional Chinese medicine, and mythical creatures such as griffins and the Native American thunderbird may have been inspired by skeletons embedded in rock. The origin of these features mystified early thinkers. Some thought that they had somehow grown underground, in already solid rock. Today such **fossils**—from the Latin word *fossilis*, which means dug up—are considered to be the remnants or traces of ancient living organisms that were buried with the material from which the rock formed and were preserved after lithification. Surprisingly, this interpretation, though proposed by the Greek historian Herodotus in 450 B.C.E. and revived by Leonardo da Vinci in 1500 C.E., did not become widely accepted until the 1669 publication of a book in which a Danish physician named Nicolas Steno (1638–86) argued that components of organisms could be incorporated in rock without losing their distinctive shape. A British contemporary of Steno, Robert Hooke (1635–1703), emphasized that fossils provide insight into the nature of life that existed earlier in Earth history, because most fossils represent *extinct species*, meaning species that lived in the past but can no longer be found alive today. The concept of extinction remained controversial until Georges Cuvier (1769–1832), a French zoologist, carefully demonstrated that the skeletons and teeth of fossil organisms differ from those of any modern ones. Cuvier was also the first to classify fossils using the same systematic approach that biologists had developed for classifying modern organisms. Subsequently, **paleontologists**, researchers who study fossils, collected vast numbers of fossil specimens, which they named, classified, and cataloged. Museums accumulated extensive collections of fossils, which, in turn, could be used as a basis for comparison in the analysis of new discoveries (Fig. E.1d). Thus, the 19th century saw **paleontology**, the study of fossils, ripen into a science.

Paleontology went beyond being merely an exercise in description when William Smith, a British engineer who supervised canal construction in England during the 1830s, noted that fossil species in the lower layers of strata differ from those in the higher layers within a sequence of sedimentary rocks. Smith eventually realized that sequences of strata, in fact, contain a predictable succession of fossils, from base to top and that a given fossil species can only be found in a specific interval of the strata. His discovery made it possible for geologists to use fossils as a basis for determining the age of one interval of sedimentary strata relative to another. Fossils, therefore, have become an indispensable tool for studying geologic history and for documenting the evolution of life.

How do fossils form? Where can we find them? What can they tell us about how life has changed over Earth's history? To address these questions, this interlude provides a brief overview

FIGURE E.1 Examples of fossils and fossil collections.

(a) Fossil shells in 400-Ma sandstone. (Ma means "million-year old.")

(b) Fossil leaves in 300-Ma shale.

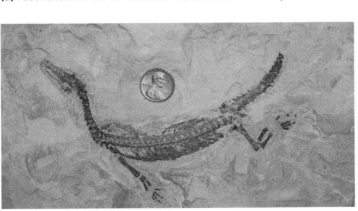

(c) Fossil skeleton in 200-Ma sandstone.

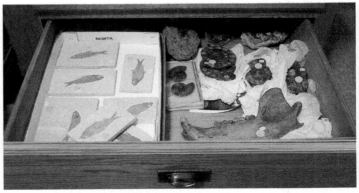

(d) A drawer of fossil specimens in a museum.

of fossils. We'll use the background provided here in the discussion of geologic time and Earth history covered by the next two chapters.

E.2 Fossilization

What Kinds of Rocks Contain Fossils?

Fossils form when organisms die and become buried by sediment or air-fall ash, or when organisms travel over or through these materials and leave imprints or debris. The vast majority of fossils occur in sedimentary rocks, though some important examples have been found in volcanic tuffs (Fig. E.2). Fossils cannot survive the recrystallization, new mineral growth, and shearing that accompany all but the lowest grades of metamorphism and thus do not occur in metamorphic rocks. Similarly, fossils cannot be found in intrusive igneous rocks because organisms do not live in intrusive environments and could not survive in igneous heat. And, with one exception, they are not found in lava flows or hot pyroclastic flows because they would be incinerated before the material solidified into rock. (The exception is where very low-viscosity basaltic lava flows around tree trunks or other organisms and freezes into rock before the organisms have completely burned up—the space left in the lava, where the organism once stood is, effectively, a fossil.)

Forming Fossils

Paleontologists refer to the process of forming a fossil as **fossilization**. To see how a fossil develops, let's consider an example (Fig. E.3a). Imagine an elderly dinosaur searching for food along the muddy shore of a lake on a scalding summer day in the geologic past. The hungry dinosaur succumbs to the heat and collapses dead into the mud. Soon after, scavengers strip the skeleton of meat and scatter the bones. But before the bones have had time to weather away, it rains heavily and streams draining nearby hills dump silty water into the lake, so the lake level rises and submerges the carcass with that water. After the storm, silt settles out of the quiet water and buries the bones along with the dinosaur's footprints. More sediment from succeeding floods buries the bones and prints still deeper, permanently protecting them from being destroyed by currents or by burrowing organisms. Much later, sea level rises and a thick sequence of marine sediment accumulates over the beds of mud and silt until, eventually, the sediment containing the bones and footprints becomes so deeply buried that it turns into sedimentary rock—the silt turns into siltstone and mud turns into shale. The dinosaur's footprints remain outlined by the contact between the siltstone and shale while its bones reside within the siltstone. Over time, minerals precipitating

from groundwater replace some of the chemicals constituting the bones, until the bones themselves become rock-like. The buried bones and footprints are now fossils.

How do fossils end up back at the Earth's surface, where they can be found? As time passes, the region containing the dinosaur-fossil-bearing beds stops subsiding and starts to undergo uplift. Erosion gradually strips away overlying strata until rocks containing the bones and footprints become exposed in an outcrop. If a team of paleontologists observes the fossils protruding from the outcrop, they may undertake an excavation, taking care to avoid breaking the specimens (Fig. E.3b). If they're lucky, they can uncover enough bones to reconstruct a skeleton so that the dinosaur can rise again, though this time in a museum (Fig. E.3c).

FIGURE E.2 The famous fossil footprints at a site called Laetoli, in Olduvai Gorge, Tanzania. They were left when an adult and child of a human ancestor, *Australopithecus*, walked on two feet over ash that had recently been erupted by a nearby volcano. The ash had been dampened by rain when a second ash eruption buried it and thereby preserved the footprints.

FIGURE E.3 From a living organism to a museum display.

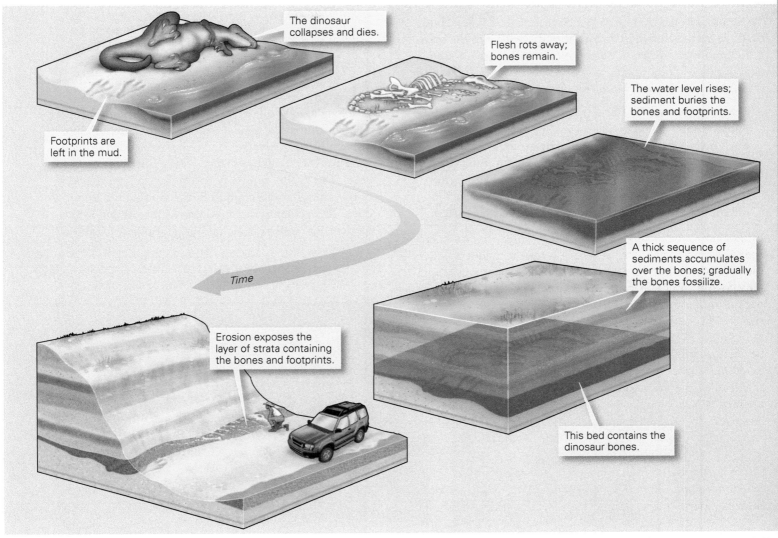

The dinosaur collapses and dies.

Footprints are left in the mud.

Flesh rots away; bones remain.

The water level rises; sediment buries the bones and footprints.

A thick sequence of sediments accumulates over the bones; gradually the bones fossilize.

Time

Erosion exposes the layer of strata containing the bones and footprints.

This bed contains the dinosaur bones.

(a) The stages in fossilization of a dinosaur.

(b) A paleontologist collecting specimens.

(c) A display of dinosaur fossils (or plaster casts of fossils) in a museum.

Paleontologists may also quarry out slabs of rock containing footprints. In recent years, bidding wars have made some fossil finds extremely valuable. For example, a skeleton of a *Tyrannosaurus rex*, a 67-million-year-old dinosaur, sold at auction in 1997 for $7.6 million. The specimen, named Sue, after its discoverer, now stands in the Field Museum of Chicago.

The Many Different Kinds of Fossils

The dinosaur bones that we've just discussed are a type of **body fossil**, derived by fossilization of the body, or part of the body, of an organism. In detail, paleontologists distinguish among many kinds of body fossils, according to the specific way in which the fossil formed. Here are some examples:

- *Frozen or dried fossils:* In a few environments, whole bodies of organisms, including flesh and skin, may be preserved. Such body fossils are fairly young, by geologic standards—their ages can be measured in thousands, not millions, of years. Examples include woolly mammoths that became incorporated in the permafrost (permanently frozen ground) of Siberia (Fig. E.4a) and the desiccated (dried out) carcasses of creatures that died in desert caves.

- *Fossils preserved in tar or amber:* Small pools of oil locally accumulate at the Earth's surface in places where cracks provide a conduit through which the oil can seep upward from underground. Once at the surface, volatile components of the oil evaporate, and bacteria degrade what remains, leaving behind sticky tar. At the La Brea Tar Pits in Los Angeles, California, tar accumulated in a swampy area long ago. While grazing, drinking, or hunting at the swamp, animals became mired in the tar and sank into it. Tar acts as a preservative, and bones embedded in the La Brea Tar Pits have survived in great shape for over 40,000 years (Fig. E.4b). Similarly, insects landing on the bark of trees may become trapped in the sap that the trees produce. This golden syrup envelops the insects and over time hardens into **amber**, which if buried, can last for at least

FIGURE E.4 Examples of different kinds of fossils.

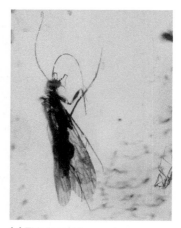

(a) This 1-m long baby mammoth, found in Siberia, died 37,000 years ago.

(b) A fossil skeleton of a 2-m-high giant ground sloth from the La Brea Tar Pits in California.

(c) This insect became embedded in amber about 200 million years ago.

(d) Fossil shells, the "hard parts" of invertebrates.

(e) The carbonized impressions of fern fronds in a shale.

(f) Petrified wood from Arizona. It is so hard that it remains after the rock that surrounded it has eroded away.

200 million years (Fig. E.4c). Amber that contains insect fossils has become popular as jewelry.

- *Preserved hard parts:* Paleontologists refer to the bones (internal skeletons) of vertebrate animals and the shells (external skeletons) of invertebrate animals informally as hard parts. Bones and shells are hard because they consist of durable minerals, such as calcite or silica. In some cases, the original minerals of a bone or shell may survive in a rock long after the rock lithifies. More commonly, the minerals of the hard parts recrystallize during diagenesis of sedimentary rock (see Chapter 7). But even when this happens, the shape of the bone or shell can be preserved as a fossil (Fig. E.4d).

- *Molds and casts:* As sediment compacts around the hard parts of an organism, it conforms to their shape. If the hard parts later dissolve away, the shape may still remain as an indentation called a **mold** (see Fig. E.1a)—sculptors use the same word to refer to the receptacle into which they pour bronze or plaster. The sediment that fills the mold forms a **cast** (see Fig. E.4d), which also depicts the shape of the hard part. Molds and casts can appear as indentations or protrusions from bedding surfaces, respectively, and since they are a relict of an organism's body, they are considered to be a type of body fossil.

- *Carbonized impressions of bodies:* Impressions are simply flattened molds or casts created when soft or semi-soft organisms (such as leaves, insects, shell-less invertebrates, sponges, feathers, or jellyfish) get pressed between layers of sediment. Chemical reactions eventually remove most of the organic material, leaving only a thin film of carbon on the surface of the impression (Fig. E.4e).

- *Permineralized fossils:* **Permineralization** refers to the process by which minerals precipitate in porous material, such as wood or bone, underground. The ions from which the minerals grow come from groundwater solutions that slowly seeped into the pores. **Petrified wood**, an example of a permineralized fossil, forms when volcanic ash buries a forest. Groundwater passing through the ash dissolves silica and carries it into the wood, where the silica replaces cell interiors. Eventually, the wood completely transforms into hard chert. (The word *petrified* literally means turned to stone.) During the process, the cell walls of the wood transform into organic films that survive permineralization, so the fine detail of the wood's cell structure and bark can be seen in a petrified log (Fig. E.4f). The color of petrified logs come from impurities such as iron or carbon in the chert.

Not all visible fossils are body fossils. Paleontologists refer to a fossilized feature formed by the action of an organism as a **trace fossil**. In detail, we can distinguish among several types of trace fossils, including the following:

- *Footprints:* We've already noted that organisms may leave distinctive footprints in the mud. These can be buried and preserved in rock (Fig. E.5a, b). Paleontologists can study assemblages of fossil footprints to determine how organisms moved and even how they interacted with one another.

- *Burrows:* These are sediment-filled holes or tunnels left behind when an organism digs its way through sediment at or below the surface. Sediment within the burrow may have a slightly different texture or permeability than surrounding unburrowed sediment and thus remain visible in rock.

- *Feeding marks:* These form when an organism disrupts the surface of a sedimentary bed in order to eat organisms that live in the sediment (Fig. E.5c).

FIGURE E.5 Examples of trace fossils.

(a) Molds of dinosaur footprints. These push down into the top of a bed.

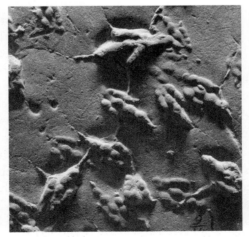

(b) Casts of dinosaur footprints. These protrude from the base of a bed.

(c) Feeding traces on the surface of a bed of sandstone in Ireland.

- *Coprolites:* Organisms leave behind excrement that has passed through their digestive track. This material, when buried and fossilized by the same processes that lead to fossilization of the organism itself, becomes fossils called *coprolites.*

Some fossils are not visible, but instead are chemical. These **chemical fossils**, which can be studied only with laboratory instruments, include:

- *Molecular fossils (biomarkers):* The life activity of an organism produces organic chemicals. When the organism dies and becomes buried in sediment, these organic chemicals tend to break up. In some cases, specific segments of the chemicals may be durable enough to undergo lithification of sediment. Such distinctive, durable molecular segments are called molecular fossils, or **biomarkers**.
- *Distinctive isotope ratios:* An *isotope ratio* refers to the relative proportion of a lighter isotope to a heavier isotope of the same element. (Recall that lighter and heavier isotopes have the same atomic number, but the lighter one has a smaller atomic weight than does the heavier one.) The life activity of organisms tends to utilize lighter isotopes slightly more than heavier ones, so the isotopic ratio found in strata deposited at the time the organisms lived differs from that found in strata when they didn't. For example, photosynthesis preferentially uses ^{12}C instead of ^{13}C, so enrichment of ^{12}C in strata serves as fossil evidence for the appearance of photosynthetic organisms. Isotope ratios are a type of trace fossil, because they are a consequence of the organisms' life activity.

We've seen how paleontologists describe a body fossil based on how the fossil formed. It's also useful to distinguish among different fossils on the basis of the fossil's size. Paleontologists, therefore, distinguish between **macrofossils**, which are ones that are large enough to be seen with the naked eye, and **microfossils**, which can be seen only with a microscope. Microfossils include the remnants of plankton, algae, bacteria, and pollen (Fig. E.6).

Fossil Preservation

Not all living organisms become fossils when they die. In fact, only a small percentage do, for it takes special circumstances to produce a fossil and allow it to survive. Examples of conditions that have an effect on the degree to which a recognizable fossil can be preserved include the following.

- *How fast burial takes place:* If an organism dies in a depositional environment where sediment can accumulate rapidly, it may be buried before it has time to rot, oxidize, or be eaten and thus has a better chance of being preserved. Organisms that lie exposed for a long time before burial will be less likely to be preserved.

FIGURE E.6 Examples of fossil plankton shells. Because of their size, geologists refer to these as microfossils or nanofossils.

- *The energy of the depositional setting:* Specimen preservation will be better for organisms deposited along with sediment in quiet water, a so-called low-energy environment, for the fossils remain intact as they are buried. In high-energy environments, where there are strong currents or waves, organisms tumble about, break up, and are dispersed as fragments before being buried.
- *The presence of hard parts:* Organisms without durable hard parts (shells or bones) usually don't get fossilized, for soft flesh decays long before hard parts do under most depositional conditions. For this reason, there are more examples of bivalves (a class of organisms, including clams and oysters, with strong shells) in the fossil record than there are of jellyfish (which have no shells) or spiders (which have very fragile shells).
- *Oxygen content of the depositional environment:* A dead squirrel by the side of the road won't become a fossil. As time passes, birds, dogs, or other scavengers may come along and eat the carcass. And if that doesn't happen, maggots, bacteria, and fungi infest the carcass and gradually digest it. Flesh that has not been eaten or does not rot can oxidize (react with oxygen), a reaction that breaks down organic chemicals. The remaining skeleton weathers in air and turns to dust. Thus, before roadkill can become incorporated in sediment, it has vanished. If, however, a carcass settles into an oxygen-poor environment (*anoxic conditions*), such as occurs in a stagnant lagoon, oxidation reactions happen slowly, scavenging organisms aren't abundant, and bacterial metabolism takes place very slowly. In such environments, the organism won't rot away before it has a chance to be buried and preserved, so the likelihood that the organism becomes fossilized increases.

By carefully studying modern organisms and by taking into account the concepts we've just described, paleontologists can provide rough estimates of the **preservation potential** of organisms, meaning the likelihood that an organism will be buried and eventually transformed into a fossil. For example, in a typical modern-day shallow-marine environment, such as the mud-and-sand sea floor close to a beach, about 30% of the organisms have sturdy shells and thus a high preservation potential, 40% have fragile shells and a low preservation potential, and the remaining 30% have no hard parts at all and are not likely to be fossilized except in special circumstances. Of the 30% with sturdy shells, though, few happen to die in a depositional setting where they are buried fast enough and actually *do* become fossilized. Thus, fossilization is the exception rather than the rule.

Extraordinary Fossils: A Special Window to the Past

Although, as we've just seen, only hard parts survive in most fossilization environments, paleontologists have discovered a few special locations where relics of soft parts have as well; such fossils are known as **extraordinary fossils**. Extraordinary fossils include insects preserved in amber and frozen or desiccated organisms. The category also includes fossils that settled on the anoxic floor of quiet-water lakes or lagoons or the deep ocean. In these settings, the soft parts have disappeared but not before leaving distinct carbonized impressions.

One of the most famous sources of extraordinary fossils occurs in a small quarry near Messel, Germany. By carefully prying apart thin beds in the quarry, paleontologists have been able to extract extraordinary fossils of 49-million-year-old mammals, birds, fish, and amphibians that died in a shallow-water lake (Fig. E.7a). Bird fossils from the quarry include the delicate imprints of feathers, bat fossils come complete with impressions of ears and wings, and other mammal fossils have an aura of carbonized fur. In southern Germany, exposures of the Solnhofen Limestone, an approximately 150-million-year-old rock made of calcite mud deposited in a stagnant lagoon, contain extraordinary fossils of about 600 species, including *Archaeopteryx*, one of the earliest birds (Fig. E.7b). And exposures of the Burgess Shale in the Canadian Rockies of British Columbia have yielded a plentitude of fossils showing what shell-less invertebrates that inhabited the sea floor about 510 million years ago looked like (Fig. E.7c, d). Significantly, the *Burgess Shale fauna* is so strange—for example, it includes organisms with circular jaws—that it has been hard to determine how these organisms are related to present-day ones.

In a few cases, extraordinary fossils include actual tissue, a discovery that has led to a research race to find the oldest preserved DNA. (**DNA**, deoxyribonucleic acid, is the complex molecule, shaped like a double helix, that contains the code that guides the growth and development of an organism. Individual components of this code are called *genes*.) Paleontologists have isolated small segments of DNA from amber-encased insects that are over 40 million years old. The amounts are not enough, however, to clone extinct species, as suggested by the popular 1993 film *Jurassic Park*.

E.3 Taxonomy and Identification

Since the days of Georges Cuvier, the classification of fossils has followed the same principles that Carolus Linnaeus, a Swedish biologist, developed in the 18th century for the classification of living organisms. The study of how to classify organisms is now referred to as **taxonomy**.

Linnaeus's scheme for taxonomy has a hierarchy of divisions. First, all life is divided into three *domains*, named Archaea, Bacteria, and Eukarya. The domains differ from one another based on fundamental characteristics of the genes in their DNA. **Archaea** include a vast array of tiny single-celled microorganisms that grow not only in the mild environments of oceans, soils, and wetlands but also in the harsh environments of hot springs, black smokers, salt lakes, very acidic sediments, and saline groundwater (Fig. E.8a). Organisms that can survive in harsh environments are known as *extremophiles*; many extremophiles do not need light or air but rather live off the energy stored in the chemical bonds of minerals. **Bacteria** are also tiny single-celled organisms, species of which inhabit almost all livable environments on Earth (Fig. E.8b). Visually, it may be difficult to distinguish bacteria from archaea, but on a genetic level they are profoundly different. Nevertheless, both archaea and bacteria are **prokarya**, meaning that their cells do not contain a nucleus (a distinct membrane-surrounded region of a cell containing all the cell's DNA). In this regard, archaea and bacteria differ from **eukarya**, organisms whose cells do contain a nucleus. Taxonomists divide the Eukarya domain into several kingdoms.

- *Protista:* various unicellular and simple multicellular organisms
- *Fungi:* mushrooms and yeast
- *Plantae:* trees, grasses, and ferns
- *Animalia:* sponges, corals, snails, dinosaurs, ants, and people

Each kingdom consists of one or more phyla. A phylum, in turn, includes several classes, a class includes several orders, an order

FIGURE E.7 Extraordinary fossils. These fossils are particularly well preserved.

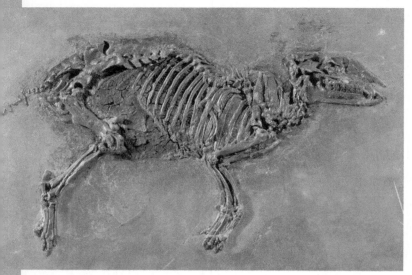

(a) A 50-million-year-old mammal fossil was chiseled from oil shale near Messel, Germany. It still contains the remains of skin.

(b) *Archaeopteryx* from the 150-million-year-old Solnhofen Limestone of Germany. The imprints of feathers are clearly visible.

(c) The Burgess Shale of the Canadian Rockies contains unique Cambrian arthropods, such as Marella, shown here.

(d) An artist's reconstruction of a Cambrian ecosystem. The paintings are based on Burgess Shale fossils.

includes several families, a family includes several genera, and a genus includes one or more species (Fig. E.9). Kingdoms, therefore, represent the broadest category of eukarya, and species represent the narrowest.

Keeping in mind the concepts of taxonomy, you'll find that there's nothing magical about identifying fossils. Typically, you can recognize common fossils in the field by examining their *morphology* (form or shape). If the fossil is well preserved and has distinctive features, the process can be straightforward so even beginners can distinguish the major groups of fossils from one another on sight. But if fossils are broken into fragments

and parts are missing, or if the fossil shares many characteristics with many different species, identification can be challenging. In many cases classification of a given organism has remained controversial.

Many fossil organisms resemble modern organisms, and this similarity provides a starting point for classification. For example, to identify a fossil, paleontologists look at the nature of the skeleton (is it internal or external?); the symmetry of the organism (is it bilaterally symmetric, like a mammal, so that one side is a mirror image of the other, or does it have fivefold symmetry like a starfish?); the design of the shell (in the case of

FIGURE E.8 The simplest forms of life.

(a) Archaea cells.

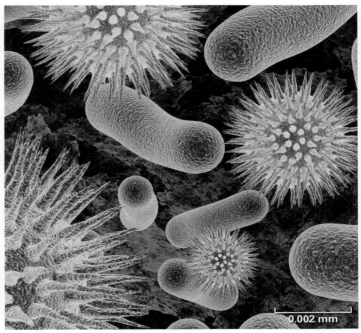

(b) Bacteria cells.

invertebrates); and the design of the jaws, teeth, or feet (in the case of vertebrates). A fossil mammal looks like a mammal and not a fish, and a fossil clam (class Bivalvia) looks like a clam and not a snail (class Gastropoda). Similarly, a fossil organism with a spiral shell that does not contain internal chambers is a member of the class Gastropoda (the snails), whereas an organism with a chambered, spiral shell is a member of the class Cephalopoda (Fig. E.10a). At taxonomic levels below class, identification may involve focusing on details, such as the number of ridges on the surface of the shell.

Paleontologists have found countless species of fossils that resemble living organisms only at the level of orders or even higher. For example, a group of extinct organisms called trilobites have no close living relatives (Fig. E.10b). But they were clearly segmented invertebrate animals, and as such, they resemble arthropods such as insects and crustaceans. Thus, they are considered to be a distinct class of the phylum Arthropoda. In the case of fossils that contain preserved DNA, paleontologists may someday be able to determine relationships among organisms more accurately by specifying the percentages of shared genes within the DNA.

Figure E.11 provides simplified sketches of some of the common types of invertebrate fossils. With this figure, you should be able to identify many of the fossils you'll find in a typical bed of limestone. Some of the notable characteristics of these fossils include the following.

- *Trilobites:* These have a segmented shell that is divided lengthwise into three parts. They are a type of arthropod.
- *Gastropods (snails):* Most fossil specimens of gastropods have a spiral shell that does not contain internal chambers.
- *Bivalves (clams and oysters):* These have a shell that can be divided into two similar halves. The plane of symmetry is parallel to the plane of the shell.
- *Brachiopods (lamp shells):* The top and bottom parts of these shells have different shapes, and the plane of symmetry is perpendicular to the plane of the shell. Examples typically have ridges radiating out from the hinge.
- *Bryozoans:* These are colonial animals. Their fossils resemble a screen-like grid of cells. Each cell is the shell of a single animal.
- *Crinoids (sea lilies):* These organisms look like a flower but actually are animals. They have a stalk consisting of numerous circular plates stacked one on top of the other.
- *Graptolites:* These look like tiny saw blades. They are remnants of colonial animals that floated in the sea.
- *Cephalopods:* These include ammonites, with a spiral shell, and nautiloids, with a straight shell. Their shells contain internal chambers and have ridged surfaces. These organisms were squid-like.
- *Corals:* These include colonial organisms that form distinctive mounds or columns in tropical reefs. Paleozoic examples include solitary examples with a cone-like shell.

FIGURE E.9 The taxonomic subdivisions. The center column shows how the names apply to human beings.

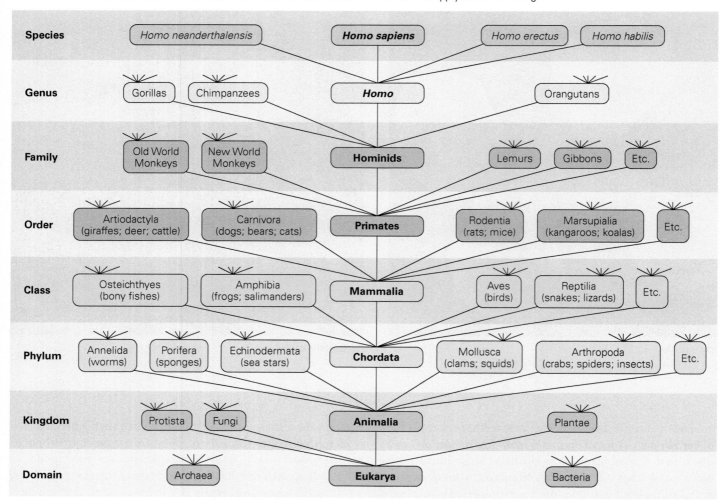

E.4 The Fossil Record

A Brief History of Life

Based on laboratory experiments conducted in the 1950s, researchers speculated that reactions in concentrated "soups" of chemicals that formed when seawater evaporated in shallow, coastal pools led to the formation of the earliest protein-like organic chemicals (proto-life). More recent studies suggest, instead, that such reactions took place in warm groundwater beneath the Earth's surface or at hydrothermal vents (black smokers) on the sea floor. Presently, researchers are paying particular attention to the hydrothermal vent environment as the cradle of life. Vent chimneys are hollow and have walls through which fluids can pass, so the walls resemble membranes that separate different chemical environments and across which weak electrical currents develop. In this environment, chemical reactions do yield protein-like chemicals. While these chemicals are non-biotic, researchers speculate that they could at some point have developed into the building blocks of life.

While the nature of proto-life remains a mystery, the study of fossils in the oldest-known sedimentary rocks has started to provide an image of early life. Specifically, archaea and bacteria fossils appear in rocks as old as about 3.7 billion years. For the first billion years or so of life history, cells of these organisms were the only types of life on Earth. Then, at about 2.5 Ga (billion years ago), organisms of the Protista kingdom first appeared. Early multicellular organisms, shell-less invertebrates of the animal kingdom, and fungi came into existence at perhaps 1.0 to 1.5 Ga. Complex multicellular organisms began

FIGURE E.10 Examples of fossil classification.

(a) Examples of ammonites, a type of cephalopod. The inset shows segmentation inside a shell.

(b) Examples of trilobites. Note that each specimen has three parts (hence the prefix *tri-*).

to populate marine environments by about 635 Ma (million years ago), and the first shelly fauna can be found in rocks as old as 542 Ma. The great variety of shelly invertebrate classes whose descendants are alive today appeared during the next 20 million years or so, a relatively short period of time compared to the age of the Earth. Paleontologists refer to this event as the **Cambrian explosion**, after the geologic time interval in which it occurred. Within each class, life "radiated" (diversified) into different orders. Eventually, during the next few

FIGURE E.11 Common types of invertebrate fossils.

Trilobite   Gastropod   Bivalve

Brachiopod   Bryozoan

Crinoid

Graptolite   Ammonite   Coral

hundred million years, fish, land plants, amphibians, reptiles, and finally birds and mammals appeared successively.

Researchers have been working hard to understand *phylogeny* (evolutionary relationships) among organisms, using both the morphology of organisms and, more recently, the study of genetic material. We can portray ideas about which groups radiated from which ancestors in a chart called the tree of life, or, more formally, the **phylogenetic tree** (Fig. E.12). Study of DNA is now enabling researchers to understand relationships between molecular processes and evolutionary change.

Is the Fossil Record Complete?

By some estimates, more than 250,000 species of fossils have been collected and identified to date, by thousands of investigators and collectors working on all continents over the past two centuries. These fossils define the framework of life's evolution. But the record is far from complete—known fossils cannot account for every intermediate step in the evolution of every organism. As many as 8.7 million eukaryotic species may

FIGURE E.12 Phylogenetic trees.

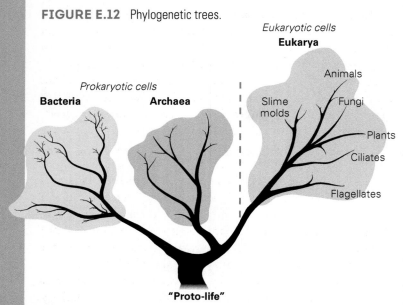

(a) The "tree of life" symbolically illustrates relations among different domains of organisms on Earth. Archaea and bacteria are both prokaryotes and don't have nuclei. All other life forms are eukaryotes because they have cells with a nucleus.

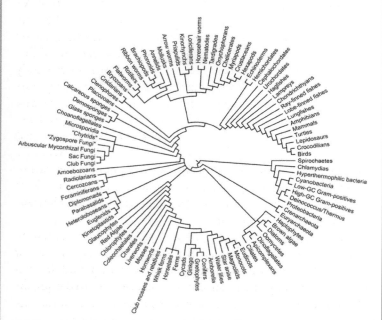

(b) Example of a phylogenetic tree in biology. The position of each branch is based on the study of DNA.

be living on Earth today, and over the billions of years that life has existed there may have been 5 billion to 50 billion species of life in the three domains. Clearly, known fossils represent at most a very tiny percentage of these species. Why is the record so incomplete?

First, despite all the fossil-collecting efforts of the past two centuries, paleontologists have not even come close to sampling every cubic centimeter of exposed sedimentary rock on Earth, much less the vast volumes of sedimentary rock that remain below the surface. Just as biologists have not yet identified every living species of insect, paleontologists have not yet identified every species of fossil. New species and even genera of fossils continue to be discovered every year.

Second, not all organisms are represented in the rock record because not all organisms have a high preservation potential. As noted earlier, fossilization occurs only under special conditions, and thus only a minuscule fraction of the organisms that have lived on Earth have left a fossil record. There may be few, if any, fossils of a vast number of extinct species, so we have no way of knowing what they looked like or even that they ever existed.

Finally, as we will learn in Chapter 12, the sequence of sedimentary strata that exists on Earth does not account for every minute of time since the formation of our planet. Sediments accumulate only in environments where conditions are appropriate for deposition and not for erosion—sediments do not accumulate, for example, on the dry great plains or on mountain peaks, but they do accumulate in the sea and in the floodplains and deltas of rivers. Because Earth's climate changes through time and because the sea level rises and falls, certain locations on continents are sometimes sites of deposition and sometimes aren't, and on occasion they may become sites of erosion. Therefore, strata only accumulate episodically.

In sum, a rock sequence provides an incomplete record of Earth history, organisms have a low probability of being preserved, and paleontologists have found only a small percentage of the fossils preserved in rock. So the incompleteness of the fossil record comes as no surprise.

E.5 Evolution and Extinction

Darwin's Grand Idea

As a young man in England in the early 19th century, Charles Darwin had been unable to settle on a career but had developed a strong interest in natural history. Therefore, he jumped at the opportunity to serve as a naturalist aboard HMS *Beagle* on an around-the-world surveying cruise. During the five years of the cruise, from 1831 to 1836, Darwin made detailed observations of plants, animals, and geology in the field and amassed an immense specimen collection from South America, Australia, and Africa. Just before Darwin departed on the voyage, a friend gave him a copy of the first geology textbook, Charles Lyell's 1830 publication *Principles of Geology*, which argued in favor of James Hutton's proposal that the Earth had a long history and that geologic time extended much farther into the past than did human civilization.

A visit to the Galápagos Islands, off the coast of Peru, led to a turning point in Darwin's thinking during the voyage. The naturalist was most impressed with the variability of Galápagos finches. He marveled not only at the fact that different varieties of the bird occurred on different islands but at how each variety had adapted to utilize a particular food supply. With Lyell's writings in mind, Darwin developed a hypothesis that the finches had begun as a single species that later branched into several different species when populations of the birds became isolated on different islands. This can happen because offspring can differ from their parents and new traits can be transferred to succeeding generations. If enough change accumulates over many generations, the living population ends up being so different from its distant ancestors that the population can be classified as a new species. During the course of evolution, old species vanish and new species appear. The accumulation of changes may eventually yield a population that is so different from its ancestors that taxonomists consider it to be a new genus. Greater accumulations of differences resulted in new classes, orders, or even phyla earlier in Earth's history. Change in a population over a succession of generations, due to the transfer of inheritable characteristics, is the process of **evolution**.

Darwin and his contemporary, Alfred Russel Wallace, not only proposed that evolution took place but also came up with an explanation for why it occurs. The crux of their explanation is simply this: A population of organisms cannot increase in number forever because it is limited by competition for scarce resources in the environment. In nature, only organisms capable of survival can pass on their characteristics to the next generation. In each new generation, some individuals have characteristics that make them more fit, whereas some have characteristics that make them less fit. The fitter organisms are more likely to survive long enough to produce offspring. Thus, the beneficial characteristics that they possess get passed on to the next generation. Darwin called this process **natural selection**, because it occurs on its own in nature. According to Darwin, when natural selection takes place over long periods of time, it eventually produces new organisms that differ so significantly from their distant ancestors that the new organisms can be considered to constitute a new species. If environmental conditions change, or if competitors enter the environment, species that do not evolve and become better adapted to survive eventually die off and become extinct.

Darwin's view of evolution has been successfully supported by many observations and so far has not been definitively disproven by any observation or experiment. Also, it can be used to make testable predictions. Thus, scientists now refer to Darwin's idea as the **theory of evolution by natural selection** (often abbreviated "the theory of evolution"; see Box P.1 in the Prelude for the definition of a theory).

In the century and a half since Darwin published his work, *genetics* (the study of genes) has developed and provided insight into how evolution works. Progress began in the late 19th century when an Austrian monk, Gregor Mendel, studied peas in the garden of his monastery and showed that genetic mutations led to new traits that could be passed on to offspring. Traits that make an organism less likely to survive are not passed on, either because the organism dies before it has offspring or because the offspring themselves cannot survive, but traits that make an organism better suited to survival are passed on to succeeding generations. With the discovery of DNA in 1953, biologists began to understand the molecular nature of genes and mutations, and thus of evolution. And with the genome projects of the 21st century, which define the detailed architecture of DNA molecules for a given species, it is now possible to pinpoint the exact arrangement of genes responsible for specific traits.

The theory of evolution by natural selection provides a conceptual framework in which to understand paleontology. By studying fossils in sequences of strata, paleontologists have observed progressive changes in species through time, and they can document that some species have died out and others have appeared during Earth history. But because of the incompleteness of the fossil record, many questions remain as to the rates at which evolution takes place during the course of geologic time. As a result, different researchers have suggested different concepts of rates. For example, Cuvier, back in the early 19th century, thought that extinction happened primarily during catastrophes, such as giant floods, and that a whole new assemblage of life took over the earth after each catastrophe—Cuvier's view came to be known as **catastrophism**. In contrast, James Hutton and his followers, such as Lyell and Darwin, assumed that evolution happened at a constant, slow rate—their view came to be called **gradualism**. (Gradualism reflects a strict interpretation of a broader idea, called uniformitarianism, which we'll discuss in Chapter 12.)

More recently, researchers have suggested that evolution takes place in fits and starts: evolution occurs very slowly for quite a while, and then during a relatively short period, it takes place very rapidly. This concept is called **punctuated equilibrium**. Factors that could cause sudden accelerations in the rate of evolution include (1) a sudden *mass-extinction event* during which many organisms disappear, leaving ecological niches open for new species to colonize; (2) a relatively rapid change in the Earth's climate that puts stress on organisms—new species that can survive the new climate survive, whereas those that can't become extinct; (3) formation of new environments, as may happen when rifting splits apart a continent and generates a new ocean with new coastlines; and (4) the isolation of a breeding population. The punctuated evolution concept takes into account that sudden events leading to widespread extinction do take place during Earth's history but that evolution can happen steadily during time intervals between these events.

Regardless of the process of evolution, the survivability of different kinds of organisms is not all the same. Some populations are very durable in that they survive as an identifiable genus or even species for long intervals of geologic time (10s to 100s of million years). But others appear and then disappear within a relatively short interval of geologic time (less than a few million years).

Extinction: When Species Vanish

As we've noted, **extinction** occurs when the last members of a species die, so there are no parents to pass on their genetic traits to offspring. Some species become extinct as a population evolves into new species, whereas other species just vanish, leaving no hereditary offspring. These days, we take for granted that species become extinct because a great number have, unfortunately, vanished from the Earth during human history. Before the 1770s, however, few geologists thought that extinction occurred; they thought fossils that didn't resemble known species must have living relatives somewhere on the planet. Considering that large parts of the Earth remained unexplored, this idea wasn't so far-fetched. However, by the end of the 18th century, in light of Cuvier's work and the completion of the map of the Earth by explorers, it became clear that fossil organisms did not have modern-day counterparts. The bones of mastodons and woolly mammoths, for example, were too different from those of elephants to be of the same species, but the animals were too big to hide. Twentieth-century studies concluded that many different phenomena can contribute to extinction. Some of the geologic factors that may cause extinction include the following.

- *Global climate change:* At times, the Earth's mean temperature has been significantly colder than today's, whereas at other times it has been much warmer. Because of a change in climate, an individual species may lose its habitat, and if it cannot adapt to the new habitat or migrate to stay with its old one, the species will disappear.
- *Tectonic activity:* Tectonic activity causes both vertical movement of the crust over broad regions and changes in sea-floor spreading rates. These phenomena can modify the distribution and area of habitats. Species that cannot adapt die off.
- *Asteroid or comet impact:* Many geologists have concluded that impacts of large meteorites with the Earth have been catastrophic for life. A large impact would send dust and debris into the atmosphere that could blot out the Sun and plunge the Earth into darkness and cold (see Chapter 23). Such a change, though relatively short lived, could interrupt the food chain.
- *Voluminous volcanic eruption:* Several times during Earth history, incredible quantities of lava have spilled out on the surface and/or incredible volumes of ash and gas have spewed into the air. These eruptions, perhaps due to the rise of superplumes in the mantle, were accompanied by the release of enough greenhouse gas into the atmosphere to alter the climate.
- *The appearance of a new predator or competitor:* Some extinctions may happen simply because a new predator appears on the scene and kills individuals of a given species at a faster rate than new individuals can be born. (For example, when humans first arrived in North America, they killed off most species of giant mammals.) Similarly, if a more efficient competitor appears, the competitor steals an ecological niche from the weaker species, whose members can't obtain enough food and thus die off.

Some extinctions happen over long time intervals, when the replacement rate of a population simply becomes lower than the mortality rate, but others happen suddenly, when a cataclysmic event leads to the rapid extermination of many organisms. For example, in 1870 the population of passenger pigeons in North America exceeded 3 billion. Due to widespread hunting by people, the population dropped rapidly during the next two decades and the last representative of the species died in 1914.

Of note, paleontologists have found that the number of different genera of fossils, a representation of **biodiversity** (the overall variation of life), changes over time and has abruptly decreased at specific times during Earth history. A worldwide abrupt decrease in the number of fossil genera is called a **mass-extinction event**. At least five major mass-extinction events have happened during the past half-billion years (**Fig. E.13**).

FIGURE E.13 This graph shows how the diversity of life has changed with time. Sudden drops indicate periods when mass extinctions occurred.

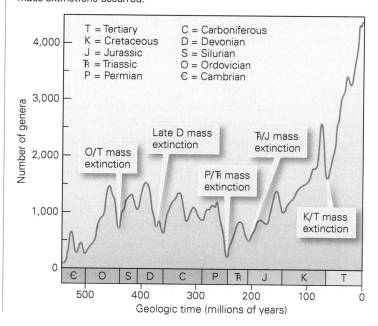

These events define the boundaries between some of the major intervals into which geologists divide time. For example, a major extinction event marks the end of the Cretaceous Period, 65 Ma. During this event, all dinosaur species (with the exception of their modified descendants, the birds) vanished, along with most marine invertebrate species. A huge extinction event also brought the Permian to a close. Significantly, the rate at which species have been disappearing during the past few centuries has been so rapid that some researchers and writers refer to our present time as the *sixth extinction*.

INTERLUDE SUMMARY

- Fossils are records of past life on Earth. Shapes of materials derived from the body of an organism are body fossil, whereas imprints due to the activity of an organism are trace fossils.
- Fossilization involves several steps, and not all organisms have the same likelihood of being preserved. Those with hard parts have a higher preservation potential, while organisms with soft parts can only be preserved under special circumstances.
- Some fossils are molds or casts of hard parts; some form when minerals replace organic materials. Chemical fossils are remnants of molecules formed by living organisms.

- Taxonomy classifies organisms into subdivisions, from domains down to species. Generally, fossils are classified based on morphology of the fossil or organism. It's fairly easy to recognize classes of common fossil organisms.
- The fossil record is incomplete, yet paleontologists can track the evolution of many organisms and can define the "tree of life." Whether evolution happens gradually, or in fits and starts, remains unclear.
- Extinction can happen for many reasons. During mass extinction events, huge numbers of species go extinct all at once and, therefore, biodiversity is decreased.

GUIDE TERMS

amber (p. 422)
archaea (p. 425)
bacteria (p. 425)
biodiversity (p. 432)
biomarker (p. 424)
body fossil (p. 422)
Cambrian explosion (p. 429)
cast (p. 423)
catastrophism (p. 431)

chemical fossil (p. 424)
DNA (p. 425)
eukarya (p. 425)
evolution (p. 431)
extinction (p. 432)
extraordinary fossil (p. 425)
fossil (p. 419)
fossilization (p. 420)
gradualism (p. 431)

macrofossil (p. 424)
mass-extinction event (p. 432)
microfossil (p. 424)
mold (p. 423)
natural selection (p. 431)
paleontologist (p. 419)
paleontology (p. 419)
permineralization (p. 423)
petrified wood (p. 423)

phylogenetic tree (p. 429)
preservation potential (p. 425)
prokarya (p. 425)
punctuated equilibrium (p. 431)
taxonomy (p. 425)
theory of evolution by natural selection (p. 431)
trace fossil (p. 423)

REVIEW QUESTIONS

1. What is a fossil, and how can fossils form?
2. Do fossil bones and shells always have the same chemical composition as do modern ones? Explain your answer.
3. What is meant by the "preservation potential" of an organism?
4. Explain the basis for classifying fossils.

5. What is the theory of evolution by natural selection, and how does the study of fossils provide evidence that can test its validity?
6. What are the alternative ideas that paleontologists have had concerning the rate of evolution over geologic time.
7. What is a mass-extinction event, and what phenomena might cause such an event?

The view from an airplane window of the Colorado Plateau region in Arizona and Utah reveals layer upon layer of strata deposited long ago and now exposed by erosion. These layers preserve a record of the Earth's very long history.

CHAPTER 12

Deep Time: How Old Is Old?

If the Eiffel Tower were now representing the world's age, the skin of paint on the pinnacle-knob at its summit would represent man's share of that age; and anybody would perceive that that skin was what the tower was built for. I reckon they would, I dunno.

—Mark Twain (1835–1910)

12.1 Introduction

In May of 1869, a one-armed Civil War veteran named John Wesley Powell set out with a team of nine geologists and scouts to explore the previously unmapped expanse of the Grand Canyon, the greatest gorge on Earth. Though Powell and his companions battled fearsome rapids and the pangs of starvation, most managed to emerge from the mouth of the canyon three months later (**Fig. 12.1**). During their voyage, seemingly insurmountable walls of rock both imprisoned and amazed the explorers and led them to pose important questions about the Earth and its history, questions that even casual tourists to the canyon ponder today: Did the Colorado River sculpt this marvel, and if so, how long did it take? When did the rocks making up the walls of the canyon form? Was there a time before the colorful layers accumulated? Such questions pertain to **geologic time**, the span of time since the Earth's formation.

In this chapter, we first learn the geologic principles that allowed geologists to develop the concept of geologic time and thus to create a frame of reference for describing the *relative age* of rocks, fossils, structures, and landscapes. This information

sets the stage for discussing the *geologic column*, the chart that geologists use to divide time into intervals. Then we describe how geologists can obtain a rock's *numerical age* (its age in years), by a procedure called *isotopic dating* (also known as *radiometric dating*). Isotopic dating permitted the establishment of the *geologic time scale*, which provides numerical ages for intervals on the geologic column. With the concept of geologic time in mind, a hike down a trail into the Grand Canyon becomes a trip into what some authors have called *deep time*. Humans are obsessed with time (**Box 12.1**), so the geologic discovery that our planet's history extends billions of years into the past changed humanity's perception of its place in the Universe as profoundly as did the astronomical discovery that the limit of space extends billions of light years beyond the edge of our Solar System.

FIGURE 12.1 Woodcut illustration of the "noonday rest in Marble Canyon," from J. W. Powell's *The Exploration of the Colorado River and Its Canyons* (1895). "We pass many side canyons today that are dark, gloomy passages back into the heart of the rocks."

BOX 12.1 CONSIDER THIS . . .

Time: A Human Obsession

When you plan your daily schedule, you have to know not only where you need to be but when you need to be there. Because time assumes such significance in human consciousness today, we have developed elaborate tools to measure it and formal scales to record it. We use a *second* as the basic unit of time measurement. What exactly is a second? From 1900 to 1968, we defined the second as 1/31,556,925.9747 of the year 1900, but now we define it as the duration of time that it takes for a cesium atom to change back and forth between two energy states 9,192,631,770 times. This change is measured with a device called an atomic clock, which is accurate to about 1 second per 30 million years. We sum 60 seconds into 1 minute, 60 minutes into 1 hour, and 24 hours into 1 day, about the time it takes for Earth to spin once on its axis.

In the pre-industrial era, each locality kept its own time, setting noon as the moment when the Sun reached the highest point in the sky. But with the advent of train travel and telegraphs, people needed to calibrate schedules from place to place. So in 1883, countries around the globe agreed to divide the world into 15°-wide bands of longitude called time zones—in each time zone, all clocks keep the same standard time. The times in each zone are set in relation to Greenwich mean time (GMT), the time at the astronomical observatory in Greenwich, England. Today the world standard for time is determined by a group of about 200 atomic clocks that together define Coordinated Universal Time (abbreviated as UTC, based on the French *Temps universel coordonné*). UTC is the basis for the global positioning system (GPS), used for precise navigation. The time that appears on your cell phone is UTC.

12.2 The Concept of Geologic Time

Setting the Stage for Studying the Past

Until relatively recently, people in most cultures believed that geologic time began about the same time that human history began and that our planet has been virtually unchanged since its birth. With this concept in mind, an Irish archbishop named James Ussher (1581–1656) tallied successions of lineages and reigns described in the Old and New Testaments to determine the age of the Earth and, in 1654, stated his conclusion: the birth of the Earth took place on October 23, 4004 B.C.E.

Not long after Ussher had implied that, in effect, the Earth has existed for only about 250 human generations (6,000 years), Nicolas Steno (1638–86) proposed an idea that established the foundation for a very different approach to thinking about geologic time. Steno was serving as a physician in a nobleman's court in Florence, Italy, when he realized that unusual triangular-shaped rocks, known as *tongue stones* by the local people who had chiseled them out of nearby outcrops, resembled the teeth of sharks (**Fig. 12.2**). He speculated that the tongue stones were not the tongues of dragons, as the locals thought, but rather were shark teeth that had been buried with sediment and seashells on the seafloor and that the sediment and teeth together had later transformed into rocks that were uplifted above sea level when the mountains formed. Steno eventually concluded that the presence of shark teeth, along with other **fossils** (remnants of ancient life preserved in rock; see Interlude E) of marine organisms in rocks now exposed in mountains, implied that the Earth could change over time. This realization set the stage for the founding of the science of geology, by James Hutton, a century later.

Hutton (1726–97), a Scottish gentleman farmer and doctor, lived during the Age of Enlightenment when, sparked by the discovery of physical laws by Sir Isaac Newton, scientists

FIGURE 12.2 A fossilized shark's tooth. Before Steno explained the origin of such fossils, they were thought to be dragons' tongues.

began to seek natural rather than supernatural explanations for features of the world around them. While wandering in the highlands of Scotland, a region where rocks are well exposed, Hutton noted that many features (such as ripple marks and cross beds) found in sedimentary rock types resembled features he could see forming today in modern depositional environments. These observations led Hutton to propose that the formation of rocks and landscapes, in general, were a consequence of processes that he could see happening today.

Hutton's idea, discussed in his 1785 book called *The Theory of the Earth*, came to be known as the principle of **uniformitarianism**. According to this principle, physical processes we observe today also operated in the past at roughly the same rates, and these processes were responsible for the formation of geologic features that we now see in outcrops. More concisely, the principle can be stated as "the present is the key to the past." Because the rates of most geologic processes taking place today are so slow, Hutton deduced that the development of individual geologic features takes a very long time. Further, he deduced that not all features formed at the same time, so the Earth has a history that includes a succession of slow events, and thus that the Earth existed for a long time before human history began. In fact, he speculated that we could see "no vestige of a beginning, nor prospect of an end."

Hutton was not a particularly clear writer, and it took the efforts of subsequent geologists to clarify the implications of the principle of uniformitarianism and to publicize them. Once this had been accomplished, geologists around the world began to apply their growing understanding of geologic processes to define and interpret geologic events of the Earth's past.

Relative versus Numerical Age

Like historians, geologists strive to establish both the sequence of events that created an array of geologic features—such as rocks, structures, and landscapes—and, when possible, the date on which each event happened (Fig. 12.3). We specify the age of one feature with respect to another in a sequence as its **relative age** and

the age of a feature given in years as its **numerical age** (or, in older literature, its *absolute age*). Recall that we can abbreviate numeral ages by using the units Ka, for thousands of years, Ma for millions of years, and Ga for billions of years; *K* stands for kilo-, *M* for mega-, and *G* for giga-. Geologists learned how to determine relative age long before they could determine numerical age, so we will look next at the principles leading to relative-age determination next.

Take-Home Message

The principle of uniformitarianism ("the present is the key to the past") implies that the Earth must be very old, for geologic processes happen slowly, and that we can interpret events in Earth's history. Geologists distinguish between relative age (is one event older or younger than another?) and numerical age (how many years ago did an event happen?).

QUICK QUESTION: What observations led Hutton to propose uniformitarianism?

FIGURE 12.3 The difference between relative and numerical age.

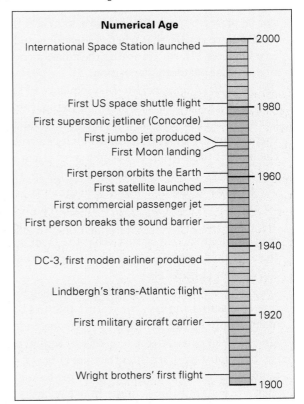

(a) The relative ages of important moments in aviation and space flight.

(b) The numerical ages of these same events. Clearly this chart provides more information, for it displays the dates of the events and indicates the amount of time between the events.

12.3 Geologic Principles Used for Defining Relative Age

Building from the work of Steno, Hutton, and others, the British geologist Charles Lyell (1797–1875) laid out a set of formal, usable geologic principles in the first modern textbook of geology (*Principles of Geology*, published between 1830 and 1833). These principles, defined below, continue to provide the basic framework within which geologists read the record of Earth history and determine relative ages.

- *The principle of uniformitarianism*: As noted earlier, physical processes we observe operating today also operated in the past, at roughly comparable rates (**Fig. 12.4a, b**); in other words, the present is the key to the past.
- *The principle of original horizontality*: Sediments on Earth settle out of fluids in a gravitational field, and the surfaces on which sediments accumulate (such as a floodplain or the bed of a lake or sea) are fairly flat. Therefore, layers of sediment when originally deposited are fairly horizontal (**Fig. 12.4c**). If sediments collect on a steep slope, they typically slide downslope before lithification and so will not be preserved as sedimentary rocks. With this principle in mind, we realize that when we see folds and tilted beds (see Chapter 11), we are seeing the consequences of deformation that postdates deposition.
- *The principle of superposition:* In a sequence of sedimentary rock layers, each layer must be younger than the one below, for a layer of sediment cannot accumulate unless there is already a substrate on which it can collect. Thus, the layer at the bottom of a sequence of strata is the oldest, and the layer at the top is the youngest (**Fig. 12.4d**).
- *The principle of lateral continuity:* Sediments generally accumulate in continuous sheets within a given region. Thus, if today you find a sedimentary layer cut by a canyon, then you can assume that the layer once spanned the area that was later eroded by the river that formed the canyon (**Fig. 12.4e**).
- *The principle of cross-cutting relations:* If one geologic feature cuts across another, the feature that has been cut is older. Applying this principle, we can conclude that if an igneous dike cuts across a sequence of sedimentary beds, the beds must be older than the dike (**Fig. 12.4f**), and if a fault cuts across and displaces layers of sedimentary rock, then the fault must be younger than the layers. In contrast, if a layer of sediment buries a fault, the sediment must be younger than the fault.

- *The principle of baked contacts:* During the formation of an igneous intrusion, hot magma injects into cooler rock. As a consequence, heat from the intrusion "bakes" (metamorphoses) surrounding rocks. Thus, rock that has been baked by an intrusion must be older than the intrusion (see **Fig. 12.4f**). Note that since an intrusion loses heat to its surroundings at its margins, the margin of an intrusion cools more rapidly. A fine-grained chilled margin occurs within the younger intrusion (**Fig. 12.4g**).
- *The principle of inclusions:* This principle states that an "inclusion" (a fragment of one rock incorporated in another) is always older than the rock that contains it. Thus, a layer of younger sediment deposited on older rock may contain inclusions (clasts) of the older rock, whereas a younger intrusion into an older wall rock may contain inclusions (xenoliths) of the wall rock. Note that we can use this concept to distinguish sills from lava flows (**Fig. 12.4h**).

Geologists apply the above geologic principles to determine the relative ages of rocks, structures, and other geologic features at a given location. We can then go further by interpreting the development of each feature to be the consequence of a specific "geologic event." Examples of geologic events include deposition of sedimentary beds, erosion of the land surface, intrusion or extrusion of igneous rocks, deformation (folding and/or faulting), and episodes of metamorphism. The succession of events, in order of relative age, that have produced the rock, structure, and landscape of a region is called the *geologic history* of the region.

To see how to work out the geologic history of an area, let's work through an example (**Fig. 12.5a**). The principle of superposition requires that the oldest sedimentary layer of the figure is Bed 1 while the youngest is Bed 7, and the principle of original horizontality means that folding postdates deposition of beds. The principles of cross-cutting relations, inclusions, and baked contacts allow us to determine the relative ages of the intrusions and faults relative to the beds and to each other. Thus, in this example, we can propose the following geologic history for this region (**Fig. 12.5b**): deposition of the sedimentary sequence in order from Beds 1 to 7, intrusion of the sill, folding of the sedimentary beds and the sill, intrusion of the granite pluton, faulting, intrusion of the dike, erosion to form the present-day land surface.

Adding Fossils to the Story: Fossil Succession

As Britain entered the industrial revolution in the late 18th and early 19th centuries, new factories demanded coal to fire their steam engines. Various companies decided to build a network of canals to transport coal and iron, and hired an

FIGURE 12.4 Major geological principles used for determining relative ages.

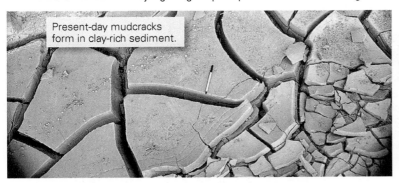

Present-day mudcracks form in clay-rich sediment.

Ancient mudcracks in solid rock

(a) Uniformitarianism: The processes that formed cracks in the dried-up mud puddle on the left also formed the mudcracks preserved in the ancient, solid rock on the right. We can see these ancient mudcracks because erosion removed the adjacent bed.

Present-day volcanism produces molten lava.

Layers of basalt formed during volcanic activity.

(b) Uniformitarianism (cont.): We can observe lava flows forming today, so we can infer that solid lava flows represent the products of volcanic eruptions in the past.

Modern sediment, exposed at low tide, on the coast of France.

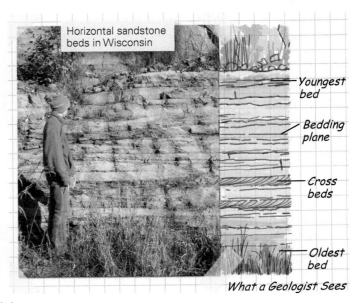

Horizontal sandstone beds in Wisconsin

Youngest bed

Bedding plane

Cross beds

Oldest bed

What a Geologist Sees

(c) Original horizontality: Gravity causes sediments to accumulate in horizontal sheets.

FIGURE 12.4 (continued)

Time 1   Time 2   Time 3

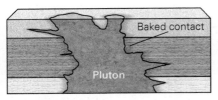

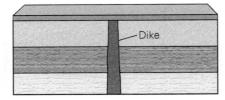

Youngest

Oldest

(d) Superposition: In a sequence of strata, the oldest bed is on the bottom, and the youngest on top. Pouring sand into a glass illustrates this point.

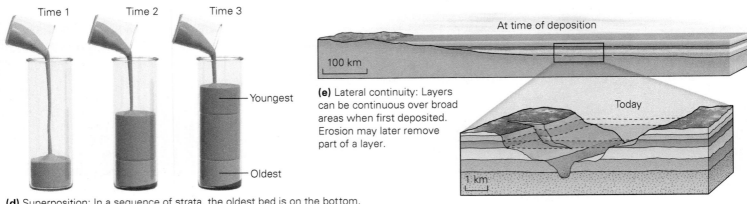

At time of deposition

100 km

(e) Lateral continuity: Layers can be continuous over broad areas when first deposited. Erosion may later remove part of a layer.

Today

1 km

Baked contact

Pluton

Dike

(f) By the principle of cross-cutting relations, the pluton is younger than the beds it cuts across (a baked contact—metamorphic aureole—forms in the strata next to the pluton), and the dike is younger than the beds it cuts across. The sediment layer that buries the dike is younger than the dike.

Chilled margin   *Dike interior*   *Chilled margin*

Contact   *Contact*

Older dike   Older dike

Younger dike

What a Geologist Sees

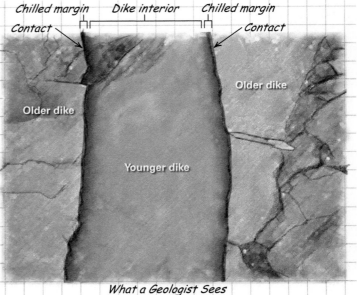

(g) Chilled margins can be used to determine age relationships. In this outcrop in California, a younger dike intrudes an older one. The younger dike is finer-grained and darker where it cooled faster at the contact with the older one.

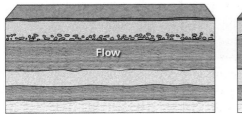

Flow

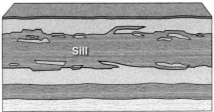

Sill

(h) By the principle of inclusions, the pebbles of basalt in a conglomerate must be older than the conglomerate and xenoliths of sandstone must be older than the basalt containing them.

FIGURE 12.5 Interpreting the geologic history of a region, using geologic principles as a guide.

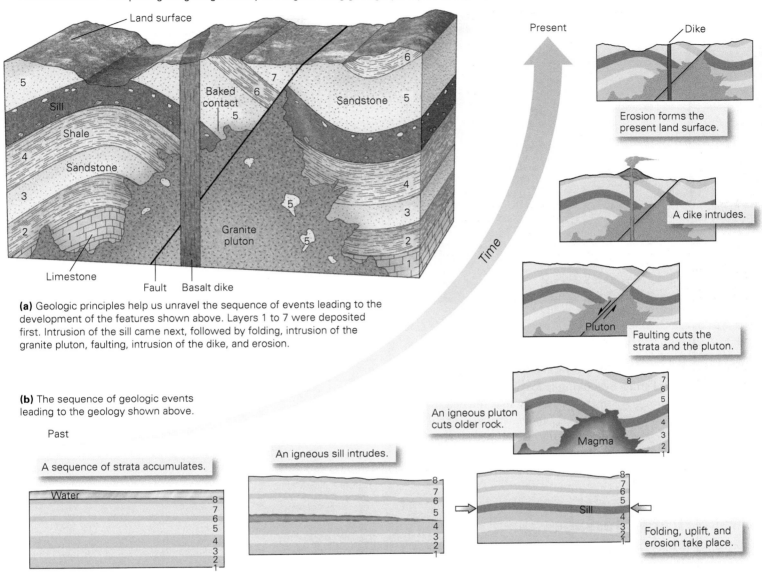

(a) Geologic principles help us unravel the sequence of events leading to the development of the features shown above. Layers 1 to 7 were deposited first. Intrusion of the sill came next, followed by folding, intrusion of the granite pluton, faulting, intrusion of the dike, and erosion.

(b) The sequence of geologic events leading to the geology shown above.

Past

A sequence of strata accumulates.

An igneous sill intrudes.

An igneous pluton cuts older rock.

Faulting cuts the strata and the pluton.

A dike intrudes.

Erosion forms the present land surface.

Folding, uplift, and erosion take place.

engineer named William Smith (1769–1839) to survey the excavations. Canal digging provided fresh exposures of bedrock, which previously had been covered by vegetation. Smith learned to recognize distinctive layers of sedimentary rock and to identify the **fossil assemblage**—the group of fossil species—that they contained (**Fig. 12.6**). As we noted in Interlude E, he also realized that a particular fossil assemblage can be found only in a limited interval of strata and not in beds above or below this interval. Thus, once a fossil species disappears at a horizon in a sequence of strata, it never reappears higher in the sequence. In other words, "extinction is forever." Smith's observation has been repeated at thousands of locations around the world and has been codified as the *principle of fossil succession.*

To see how this principle works, examine **Figure 12.7**, which depicts a sequence of strata. Bed 1 at the base contains fossil species A, Bed 2 contains A and B, Bed 3 contains B and C, Bed 4 contains C, and so on. From these data, we can define the *range* of specific fossils in the sequence, meaning the interval in the sequence in which the fossils occur. Note that the sequence contains a definable succession of fossils (A, B, C, D, E, F), that the range in which a particular species occurs may overlap with the range of other species, and that once a species vanishes, it does not reappear higher in the sequence. Some species can be found over a broad region, but existed only for a short interval of geologic time, and thus can be diagnostic of a precise time interval in rocks at many different locations. The fossils of such species are called **index fossils.**

FIGURE 12.6 A close-up photo of a bedding surface showing many fossils. The ring-shaped ones are pieces of crinoid stems.

FIGURE 12.7 The principle of fossil succession.

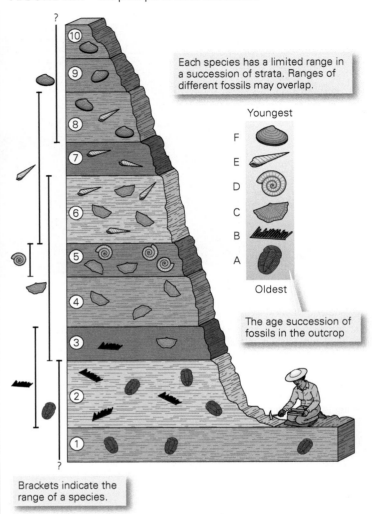

Each species has a limited range in a succession of strata. Ranges of different fossils may overlap.

Youngest

F
E
D
C
B
A

Oldest

The age succession of fossils in the outcrop

Brackets indicate the range of a species.

Because of the principle of fossil succession, we can define the relative ages of strata by looking at fossils. For example, if we find a bed containing Fossil A, we can say that the bed is older than a bed containing, say, Fossil F. Geologists have now determined the relative ages of over 200,000 fossil species. Recognition of the principle of fossil successions provides the geologic underpinnings for the theory of evolution (see Interlude E).

Take-Home Message

Geologic principles (including uniformitarianism, superposition, cross-cutting relations, and fossil succession) provide the basis for determining the relative ages of rocks and other geologic features. By working out relative ages, we can reconstruct the geologic history of a region.

QUICK QUESTION: If a fault forms a fault scarp, what is the relative age of the fault and the landscape surface?

12.4 Unconformities: Gaps in the Record

James Hutton used a boat to explore the seaside of Scotland, because shore cliffs provided great exposures of rock, stripped of soil and shrubbery. He was particularly puzzled by an outcrop he found at Siccar Point on the east coast. Here he saw a sequence of strata consisting of red sandstone and conglomerate that rested on a distinctly different sequence, one that consisted of gray sandstone and shale (**Fig. 12.8a**). Further, the beds of gray sandstone and shale have a nearly vertical dip (slope), whereas the beds of red sandstone and conglomerate have a dip of less than 15°—the gently dipping layers seemed to lie across the truncated ends of the vertical layers, like a handkerchief resting on a row of books. (See Box 11.1 for the definition of *dip*.) Perhaps as Hutton sat and stared at this odd geometric relationship, the tide came in and deposited a new layer of sand on top of the rocky shore. With the principle of uniformitarianism in mind, Hutton suddenly realized the significance of the outcrop—the gray sandstone–shale sequence had been deposited, turned into rock, tilted, and truncated by erosion before the red sandstone–conglomerate beds had been deposited. Thus, the surface between the gray and red rock sequences represented a time interval during which new strata

FIGURE 12.8 Examples of unconformities, as visible in outcrops.

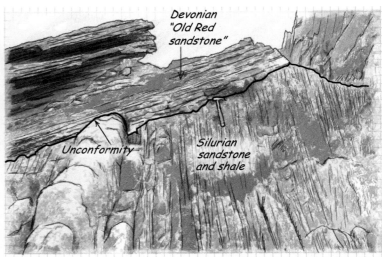

What a Geologist Sees

(a) James Hutton found this unconformity along the east coast of Scotland. He deduced that the layers above were deposited long after the beds below had been tilted. Geologists have since determined that strata above are about 80 million years younger than strata below.

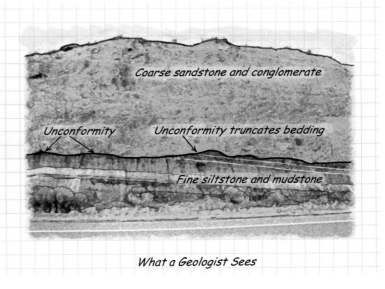

What a Geologist Sees

(b) A roadcut in Utah reveals an unconformity between a coarse sandstone and conglomerate above and a fine siltstone and mudstone below. Note that the irregularities along this unconformity locally truncate bedding of the siltstone and mudstone.

had not been deposited at Siccar Point and the older strata had been eroded away. Hutton realized that Siccar Point exposed the record of a long and complex saga of geologic history.

We now refer to a boundary surface between two units, which represents a period of nondeposition and possibly erosion, as an **unconformity** (Fig. 12.8b). The gap in the geologic record that an unconformity represents is called a *hiatus*. Geologists recognize three main types of unconformities.

- *Angular unconformity:* An **angular unconformity** represents an erosional surface that cuts across previously tilted or folded underlying layers, such that the orientation of layers below an unconformity differs from that of the layers above (Fig. 12.9a)—Siccar Point, shown in Figure 12.8a, exposes an angular unconformity. Angular unconformities form where rocks were deformed before being exposed at the Earth's surface.

FIGURE 12.9 The three kinds of unconformities and their formation.

Time →

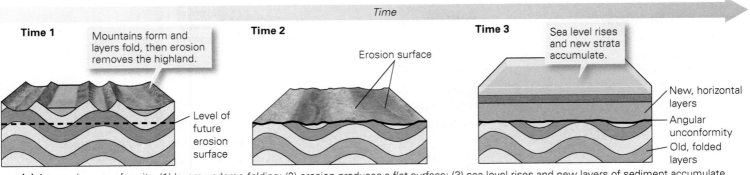

Time 1 — Mountains form and layers fold, then erosion removes the highland. / Level of future erosion surface

Time 2 — Erosion surface

Time 3 — Sea level rises and new strata accumulate. / New, horizontal layers / Angular unconformity / Old, folded layers

(a) An angular unconformity: (1) layers undergo folding; (2) erosion produces a flat surface; (3) sea level rises and new layers of sediment accumulate.

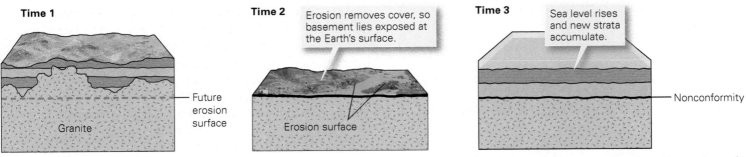

Time 1 — Granite / Future erosion surface

Time 2 — Erosion removes cover, so basement lies exposed at the Earth's surface. / Erosion surface

Time 3 — Sea level rises and new strata accumulate. / Nonconformity

(b) A nonconformity: (1) a pluton intrudes; (2) erosion cuts down into the crystalline rock; (3) new sedimentary layers accumulate above the erosion surface.

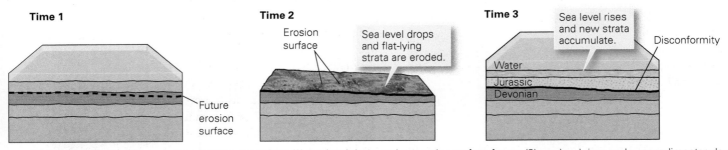

Time 1 — Future erosion surface

Time 2 — Erosion surface / Sea level drops and flat-lying strata are eroded.

Time 3 — Sea level rises and new strata accumulate. / Disconformity / Water / Jurassic / Devonian

(c) A disconformity: (1) layers of sediment accumulate; (2) sea level drops and an erosion surface forms; (3) sea level rises and new sedimentary layers accumulate.

- *Nonconformity:* A **nonconformity** is a type of unconformity at which sedimentary rocks overlie older intrusive igneous rocks and/or metamorphic rocks (**Fig. 12.9b**). The igneous or metamorphic rocks underwent cooling, uplift, and erosion prior to becoming the substrate or "basement" on which the "cover" of new sediments accumulated.
- *Disconformity:* Imagine that a sequence of sedimentary beds has been deposited beneath a shallow sea. Then sea level drops, exposing the beds for some time. During this time, no new sediment accumulates, and some of the pre-existing sediment gets eroded away. Later, sea level rises, and a new sequence of sediment accumulates over the old. The boundary between the two sequences is a **disconformity** (**Fig. 12.9c**). Even though the beds above

and below the disconformity are parallel, the boundary between them represents an interruption in deposition. The unconformity in the outcrop shown in Figure 12.8b is a disconformity.

The succession of strata at a particular location provides a record of Earth history there. But because of unconformities, the record preserved in the rock layers is incomplete. It's as if geologic history were being chronicled by a video recorder that turns on only intermittently—when it's on (= times of deposition), the

> **Did you ever wonder . . .**
>
> if the strata of the Grand Canyon represent all of Earth's history?

rock record accumulates, but when it's off (= times of non-deposition and possibly erosion), an unconformity develops. Because of unconformities, no single location on Earth contains a complete record of Earth history.

How can you recognize an unconformity in the field? At angular unconformities, the strata above have a different dip than the strata below, and at nonconformities, the juxtaposition of cover over basement serves as a clue. Disconformities may be hard to recognize since beds above and below are parallel. A disconformity may be indicated by a gap in the fossil succession and/or by the presence of a surface of erosion and weathering. If the surface was exposed at the Earth's surface for a while, a pebbly layer of debris might occur just above it, and/or a *paleosol* (a remnant of a soil horizon that has been lithified) may be visible just below it (**Fig. 12.10**).

Take-Home Message

Unconformities represent time intervals of nondeposition and possibly erosion. Strata above and below an unconformity may be parallel, so a gap in the fossil record or evidence of erosion represents the unconformity. In cases where rock below the unconformity was folded or tilted before deposition of strata above, an angular discordance marks the unconformity. Some unconformities juxtapose strata above with basement below.

QUICK QUESTION: Is there any one place on the surface of the Earth where the exposed stratigraphic succession represents all of geologic time? Explain.

FIGURE 12.10 This road cut in Utah shows a sand-filled channel cut down into floodplain mud. The mud was exposed between floods, and a soil formed on it. When later buried, all the sediment turned into rock; the channel floor is now an unconformity, and the ancient soil is now a paleosol. Note that the channel cut across the paleosol. The paleosol also represents an unconformity, a time during which deposition did not occur.

Channel (unconformity surface)

Paleosol horizon

12.5 Stratigraphic Formations and Their Correlation

The Concept of a Formation

When William Smith first began to explore the strata exposed along the newly dug canals of England, he realized that distinctive sets of beds, with distinctive assemblages of fossils, could be found at many locations. Smith, and the generations of geologists that have followed, now routinely divide thick successions of strata into recognizable units, called stratigraphic formations, which others can recognize and identify. Formally defined, a **stratigraphic formation** (formation, for short) is an interval of strata composed of a specific rock type or group of rock types that together can be traced over a fairly broad region. A formation represents the products of deposition during a definable interval of time. The boundary surface between two formations is a type of **geologic contact**, or contact, for short. (Fault surfaces, unconformities, and the boundary between an igneous intrusion and its wall rock are also types of contacts.)

Geologists summarize information about the sequence of sedimentary strata at a location by drawing a **stratigraphic column**. Typically, stratigraphic columns are constructed to scale so that the relative thicknesses of beds or formations portrayed on the column are in proportion to the thicknesses of these units in outcrop. Geologists may represent the relative resistance to erosion of beds (or formations) by making the right side of the column irregular to symbolize the way the units might erode on a cliff face—units that stick out further are more resistant.

Let's see how the concept of a stratigraphic formation and of a stratigraphic column applies to the Grand Canyon. The walls of the canyon look striped because they expose a variety of rock types that differ in color and in resistance to erosion. Geologists identify major

contrasts distinguishing one interval of strata from another and use them as a basis for dividing the strata into formations, each of which may consist of many beds (Fig. 12.11). Note that some formations consist of beds of a single rock type, whereas others include interlayered beds of two or more rock types. Also, not all formations have the same thickness. Commonly, geologists name a formation after a locality where it was first identified or first studied. For example, the Schoharie Formation was first defined based on exposures in Schoharie Creek of eastern New York. If relevant, geologists can depict unconformities in the section by a wavy line. If a formation consists of only one rock type, we may incorporate that rock type in the name (such as the Kaibab Limestone), but if a formation contains more than one rock type, we use the word formation in the name (such as the Toroweap Formation). Note that in the formal name of a formation, all words are capitalized. Several adjacent formations in a succession may be lumped together as a **stratigraphic group** (or simply a group).

Correlating Strata

How does the stratigraphy of a sedimentary succession exposed at one locality relate to that exposed at another? Stated another way, can we determine the relative age of strata at one location to that of strata at another? The answer is yes. Geologists determine such relations by a process called **stratigraphic correlation** (correlation, for short). Geologists use two approaches for correlating intervals of strata.

When correlating formations among nearby regions, we can simply look for similarities in successions of rock type. We call this method *lithologic correlation*. For example, the sequence of strata on the southern rim of the Grand Canyon clearly correlates with the sequence on the northern rim, because they contain the same rock types in the same order. In some cases, a sequence contains a key bed, or **marker bed**, which is a particularly unique layer that provides a definitive basis for correlation.

Lithologic correlation doesn't necessarily work over broad areas because the depositional setting and the source of sediments can change from location to location. Therefore, beds deposited at one location during a given time interval may look quite different from the beds deposited at another location during the same time interval. To correlate rock units over *broad* areas, we must rely on fossils to define the relative ages of sedimentary units. We call this method *fossil correlation*. If fossils of the same relative age occur at both locations, we can say that the strata at the two locations correlate. Note that the fossils in correlative units are not necessarily the same species—they won't be if the depositional environments are different—but they lived during the same time interval. Fossil correlation can allow geologists to determine whether or not beds of the same rock type at different locations represent the same formation.

As an example, imagine that the Santuit Sandstone and Oswaldo Sandstone look the same but are of different ages (Fig. 12.12). In Location A, the units are separated by the Milo Limestone, but at Location C the units are in direct contact. At first glance, the combination of the two units at Location C may look like a single unit. But a sharp-eyed geologist, looking at the strata closely, will find that the fossils are of significantly different age and will depict the contact between the two units by an unconformity.

Let's now apply correlation principles to the challenge of determining the relative ages of formations exposed in the Grand Canyon to those exposed in the mountains near Las Vegas, Nevada, 150 km to the west (Fig. 12.13a). Near Las Vegas, we find a sequence of sedimentary rocks that includes a limestone formation called the Monte Cristo Limestone. The Monte Cristo Limestone contains fossils of the same relative age as those of the Redwall Limestone of the Grand Canyon, but the Monte Cristo Limestone is much thicker than the Redwall Limestone. Because the formations contain fossils of the same relative age, we conclude that they were deposited during the same time interval, and thus we say that they correlate with one another. Note also that not only are the units thicker in the Las Vegas area than in the Grand Canyon area, but there are more of them. Thus, the contact beneath the Grand Canyon's Redwall Limestone is an unconformity.

Why does the stratigraphy of Las Vegas differ from that of the Grand Canyon? During part of the time when thick sediments were accumulating near Las Vegas, no sediments accumulated near the Grand Canyon because the region of Las Vegas lay below sea level, whereas the region of the Grand Canyon was dry land. Geologists studying this contrast concluded that in the geologic past the location of Las Vegas was part of a passive-margin basin that sank (subsided) rapidly and remained submerged below the sea almost continuously; the Grand Canyon column, on the other hand, accumulated on the crust of a craton that episodically emerged above sea level (Fig. 12.13b).

Geologic Maps

Once William Smith succeeded in correlating stratigraphic formations throughout central England, he faced the challenge of communicating his ideas to others. One way would be to create a table that compared stratigraphic columns from different locations. But since Smith was a surveyor and worked with maps, it occurred to him that he could outline and color in areas on a map to represent areas in which strata of a given relative age occurred. He did this using the data he had collected, and in 1815 he produced the first modern geologic map. In general, a **geologic map** portrays the spatial distribution of rock units at the Earth's surface.

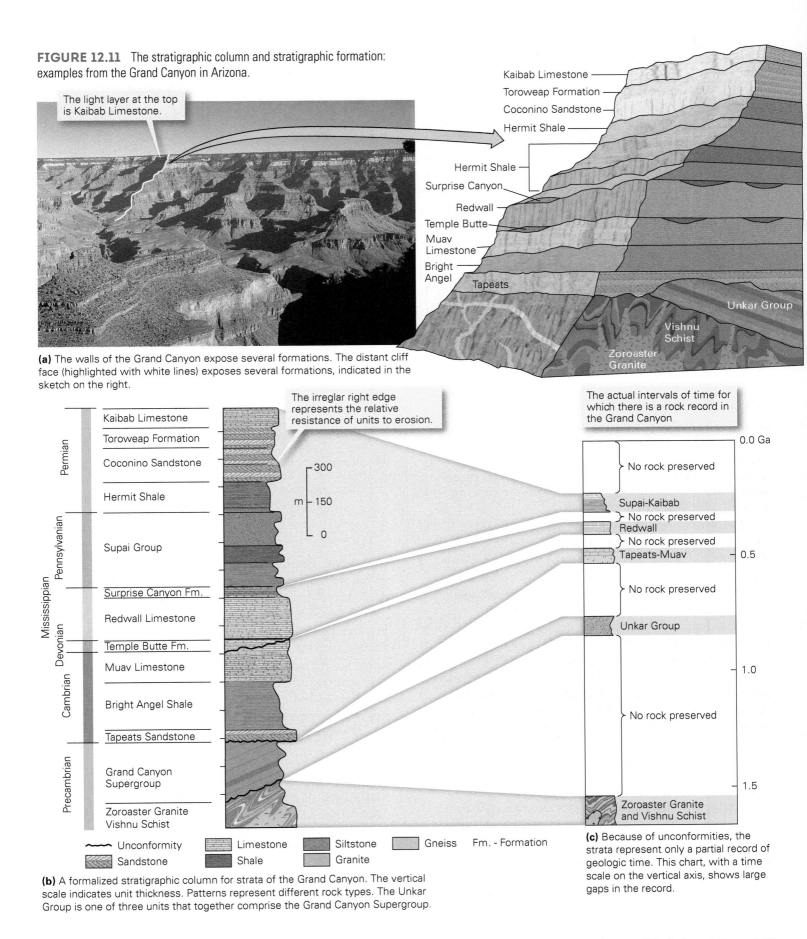

FIGURE 12.11 The stratigraphic column and stratigraphic formation: examples from the Grand Canyon in Arizona.

The light layer at the top is Kaibab Limestone.

Kaibab Limestone
Toroweap Formation
Coconino Sandstone
Hermit Shale

Hermit Shale
Surprise Canyon
Redwall
Temple Butte
Muav Limestone
Bright Angel
Tapeats

Unkar Group
Vishnu Schist
Zoroaster Granite

(a) The walls of the Grand Canyon expose several formations. The distant cliff face (highlighted with white lines) exposes several formations, indicated in the sketch on the right.

The irreglar right edge represents the relative resistance of units to erosion.

Permian
Kaibab Limestone
Toroweap Formation
Coconino Sandstone
Hermit Shale

Pennsylvanian
Supai Group

Mississippian
Surprise Canyon Fm.
Redwall Limestone

Devonian
Temple Butte Fm.
Muav Limestone

Cambrian
Bright Angel Shale
Tapeats Sandstone

Precambrian
Grand Canyon Supergroup
Zoroaster Granite
Vishnu Schist

300
m — 150
0

The actual intervals of time for which there is a rock record in the Grand Canyon

0.0 Ga
No rock preserved
Supai-Kaibab
No rock preserved
Redwall
No rock preserved
Tapeats-Muav — 0.5
No rock preserved
Unkar Group
1.0
No rock preserved
1.5
Zoroaster Granite and Vishnu Schist

Unconformity
Sandstone
Limestone
Shale
Siltstone
Granite
Gneiss   Fm. - Formation

(b) A formalized stratigraphic column for strata of the Grand Canyon. The vertical scale indicates unit thickness. Patterns represent different rock types. The Unkar Group is one of three units that together comprise the Grand Canyon Supergroup.

(c) Because of unconformities, the strata represent only a partial record of geologic time. This chart, with a time scale on the vertical axis, shows large gaps in the record.

FIGURE 12.12 The principles of correlation.

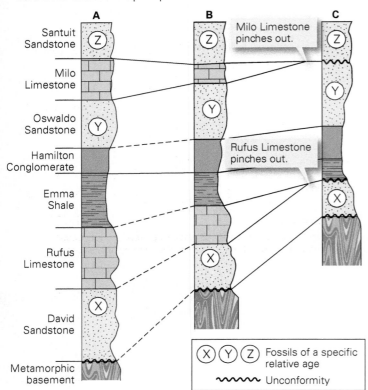

(a) Stratigraphic columns can be correlated by matching rock types (lithologic correlation). The Hamilton Conglomerate is a marker horizon. Because some strata pinch out, Column C contains unconformities. Fossil correlation indicates that the youngest beds in C are Santuit Sandstone.

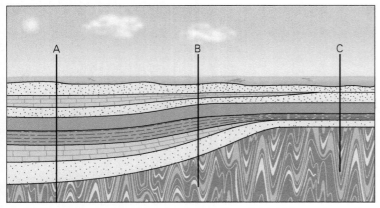

(b) At the time of deposition, locations A, B, and C (which correlate with the columns in part a) were in different parts of a basin. The basin floor was subsiding fastest at A.

Significantly, the pattern displayed on a geologic map can provide insight into the presence and orientation of geologic structures in the map area (Fig. 12.14a–c). With experience, a geologist can interpret the pattern of contacts and distribution of formations on a map and can recognize folds, faults, and unconformities. For example, if mountain building has warped the strata in a region into an anticline (see Chapter 11),

FIGURE 12.13 An application of correlation to relate strata near Las Vegas to strata in the Grand Canyon.

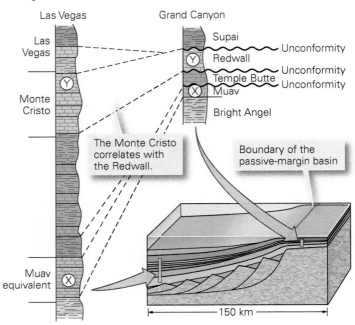

(a) The section between fossils of age X and fossils of age Y is much thicker near Las Vegas than in the Grand Canyon. The edge of a passive-margin basin lay between the two localities at the time of deposition.

(b) A passive-margin basin forms over crust that has stretched and thinned.

the same succession of strata will appear on both limbs of the fold but with opposite dip directions—one limb will look like the mirror reflection of the other, with the oldest strata cropping out along the hinge. Contacts on a geologic map appear as lines. Geologists use a variety of symbols to depict folds, faults, and the strike-and-dip of layers (see Box 11.1). Using computer technology, it's now possible to plot geologic contacts on *digital elevation maps* that portray the ground surface in three dimensions (Fig. 12.14d). *Geologic cross sections* indicate the relationships of underground geologic contacts and structures on the plane of a vertical slice.

Take-Home Message

A stratigraphic formation is a recognizable sequence of beds that can be mapped across a broad region. Geologists correlate formations regionally on the basis of rock type and fossil content, and they portray the configuration of formations in a region on a geologic map.

QUICK QUESTION: What will a syncline look like on a geologic map?

FIGURE 12.14 A geologic map depicts the distribution of rock units and structures.

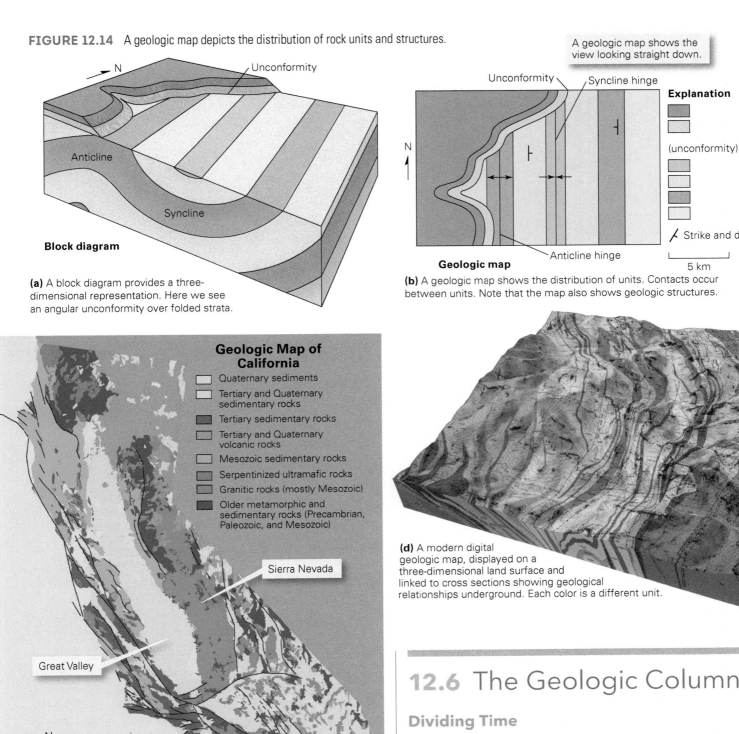

Block diagram

(a) A block diagram provides a three-dimensional representation. Here we see an angular unconformity over folded strata.

A geologic map shows the view looking straight down.

Unconformity · Syncline hinge

Explanation

(unconformity)

Anticline hinge

Geologic map

5 km

Strike and dip

(b) A geologic map shows the distribution of units. Contacts occur between units. Note that the map also shows geologic structures.

Geologic Map of California

- Quaternary sediments
- Tertiary and Quaternary sedimentary rocks
- Tertiary sedimentary rocks
- Tertiary and Quaternary volcanic rocks
- Mesozoic sedimentary rocks
- Serpentinized ultramafic rocks
- Granitic rocks (mostly Mesozoic)
- Older metamorphic and sedimentary rocks (Precambrian, Paleozoic, and Mesozoic)

Sierra Nevada

Great Valley

0   100 mi
0   100 km

(c) A geologic map of California indicates that the state is underlain by many different rock units. Granite underlies the Sierras, and Quaternary sediments underlie the Great Valley. The black lines are fault traces.

(d) A modern digital geologic map, displayed on a three-dimensional land surface and linked to cross sections showing geological relationships underground. Each color is a different unit.

12.6 The Geologic Column

Dividing Time

As stated earlier, no one locality on Earth provides a complete record of our planet's history, because stratigraphic columns can contain unconformities. But by correlating strata from locality to locality at millions of places around the world, geologists have pieced together a composite stratigraphic column, called the **geologic column**, that represents the entirety of Earth history (Fig. 12.15). The column is divided into segments, each of which represents a specific interval of time. The largest subdivisions break Earth history into the Hadean, Archean,

FIGURE 12.15 Global correlation of strata led to the development of the geologic column. (Not to scale.)

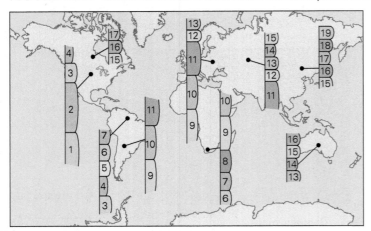

(a) Each of these small columns represents the stratigraphy at a given location. By correlating these columns, geologists determined their relative ages, filled in the gaps in the record, and produced the geologic column.

Eon	Era	Period	Epoch
Phanerozoic	Cenozoic	Quaternary	Holocene
			Pleistocene
		Neogene	Pliocene
		Tertiary	Miocene
			Oligocene
		Paleogene	Eocene
			Paleocene
	Mesozoic	Cretaceous	
		Jurassic	
		Triassic	
	Paleozoic	Permian	
		Carboniferous	Pennsylvanian
			Mississippian
		Devonian	
		Silurian	
		Ordovician	
		Cambrian	
Precambrian	Proterozoic		
	Archean		

(Column numbering at left, top to bottom: 19, 18, 17, 16, 15, 14, 13, 12, 11, 10, 9, 8, 7, 6, 5, 4, 3, 2, 1)

(b) By correlation, the strata from localities around the world were stacked in a chart representing geologic time to create the geologic column. Geologists assigned names to time intervals, but since the column was built without knowledge of numerical ages, it does not depict the duration of these intervals. Subdivisions of eons in the Precambrian are not shown. The Hadean is not shown because rocks do not preserve a record of it.

Proterozoic, and Phanerozoic **Eons**—the first three of these, together, constitute the **Precambrian**. (Note that Hadean rocks don't exist, so they are not shown in Figure 12.5.) In the names of the two youngest eons, the suffix –*zoic* means life, so Phanerozoic means visible life, and Proterozoic means first life. These names can be a bit confusing, though, because decades after the eons had been named, geologists discovered that the earliest life, cells of bacteria and archaea, actually appeared during the Archean Eon. Eons, in turn, can be subdivided into **eras**. The Phanerozoic Eon, for example includes, in order from oldest to youngest, the Paleozoic (ancient life), Meso-zoic (middle life), and Cenozoic (recent life) Eras. We further divide each era into **periods** and each period into **epochs**.

Where do the names of the periods come from? They refer either to localities where a fairly complete stratigraphic column representing that time interval was first identified (e.g., rocks representing the Devonian Period crop out near Devon, Eng-land) or to a characteristic of the time (rocks from the Carbon-iferous Period contain a lot of coal). The terminology was not set up in a planned fashion that would make it easy to learn. Instead, time divisions and their naming were established hap-hazardly in the years between 1760 and 1845, when geologists first began to refine their understanding of geologic history and fossil succession. Also, because the divisions were defined before numerical ages could be determined, they are all of dif-ferent durations.

Life Evolution in the Context of the Geologic Column

The succession of fossils preserved in strata of the geologic col-umn defines the course of life's evolution throughout Earth

history (**Fig. 12.16**). Simple bacteria and archaea appeared during the Archean Eon, but complex shell-less invertebrates did not evolve until the late Proterozoic. The appearance of invertebrates with shells defines the Precambrian-Cambrian boundary. During the Cambrian, there was a sudden diversi-fication in life, with many new families appearing over a rela-tively short interval—this event is called the **Cambrian explo-sion** (see Interlude E; **Fig. 12.17**).

Progressively more complex organisms populated the Earth during the Paleozoic. For example, the first fish swam in Ordovician seas, land plants started to spread over the continents during the Silurian, and amphibians appeared during the Devonian. (Note that prior to the Silurian, the land surface was completely unvegetated and would have been a stark, dusty desert, even at the equator.) Though

FIGURE 12.16 Life evolution in the context of the geologic column. The Earth formed at the beginning of the Hadean Eon.

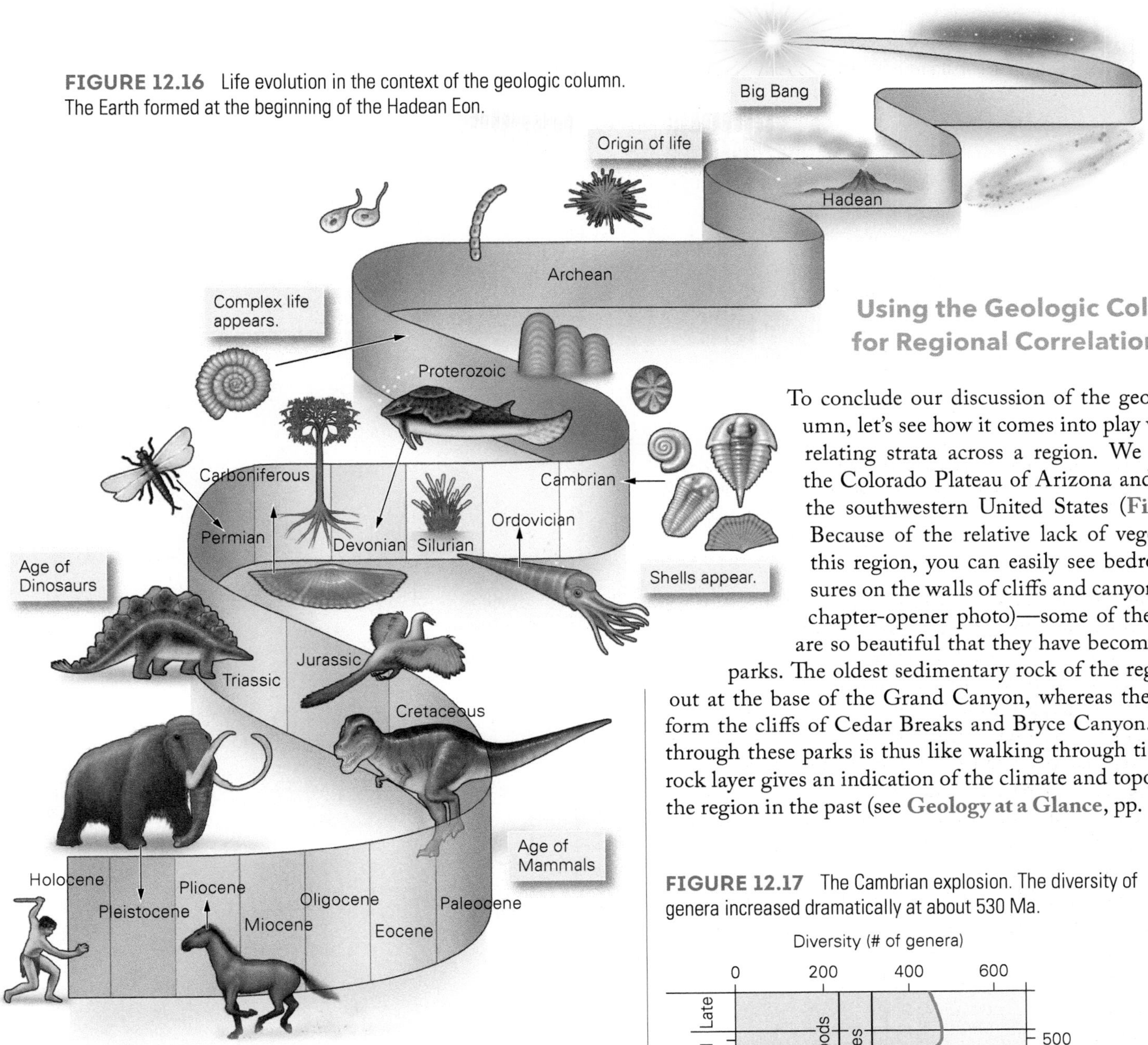

Big Bang
Origin of life
Hadean
Archean
Complex life appears.
Proterozoic
Cambrian
Shells appear.
Ordovician
Silurian
Devonian
Carboniferous
Permian
Age of Dinosaurs
Triassic
Jurassic
Cretaceous
Age of Mammals
Paleocene
Eocene
Oligocene
Miocene
Pliocene
Pleistocene
Holocene

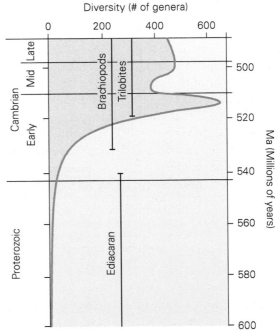

reptiles appeared during the Pennsylvanian Period, the first dinosaurs did not stomp across the land until the Triassic. Dinosaurs continued to inhabit the Earth until their sudden extinction at the end of the Cretaceous Period. For this reason, geologists refer to the Mesozoic Era as the *Age of Dinosaurs.* Small mammals appeared during the Triassic Period, but the diversification (development of many different species) of mammals to fill a wide range of ecological niches did not happen until the beginning of the Cenozoic Era, so geologists call the Cenozoic the *Age of Mammals.* Birds also appeared during the Mesozoic—specifically, at the beginning of the Cretaceous Period—but underwent great diversification in the Cenozoic Era.

Using the Geologic Column for Regional Correlation

To conclude our discussion of the geologic column, let's see how it comes into play when correlating strata across a region. We return to the Colorado Plateau of Arizona and Utah, in the southwestern United States (**Fig. 12.18**). Because of the relative lack of vegetation in this region, you can easily see bedrock exposures on the walls of cliffs and canyons (see the chapter-opener photo)—some of these locales are so beautiful that they have become national parks. The oldest sedimentary rock of the region crops out at the base of the Grand Canyon, whereas the youngest form the cliffs of Cedar Breaks and Bryce Canyon. Walking through these parks is thus like walking through time—each rock layer gives an indication of the climate and topography of the region in the past (see **Geology at a Glance**, pp. 454–455).

FIGURE 12.17 The Cambrian explosion. The diversity of genera increased dramatically at about 530 Ma.

Diversity (# of genera)
0
200
400
600
Late
Mid
Early
Cambrian
Proterozoic
Brachiopods
Trilobites
Ediacaran
500
520
540
560
580
600
Ma (Millions of years)

FIGURE 12.18 Correlation of strata among the national parks of Arizona and Utah.

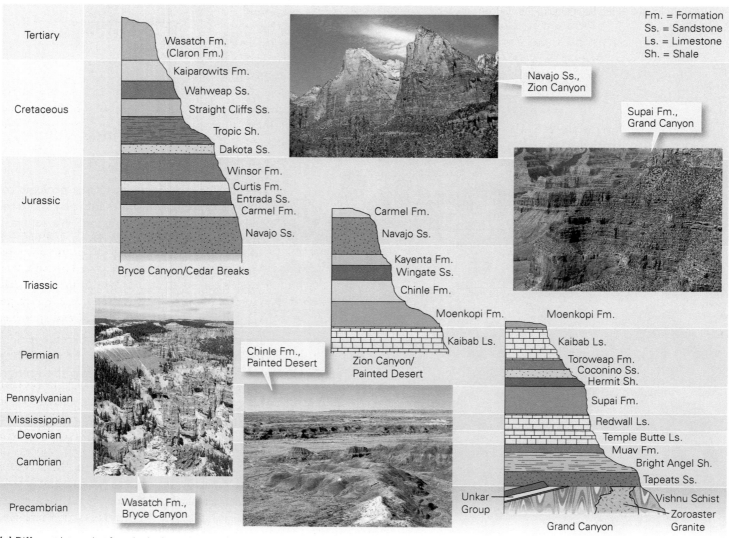

Fm. = Formation
Ss. = Sandstone
Ls. = Limestone
Sh. = Shale

(a) Different intervals of geologic time are represented by the strata of different parks.

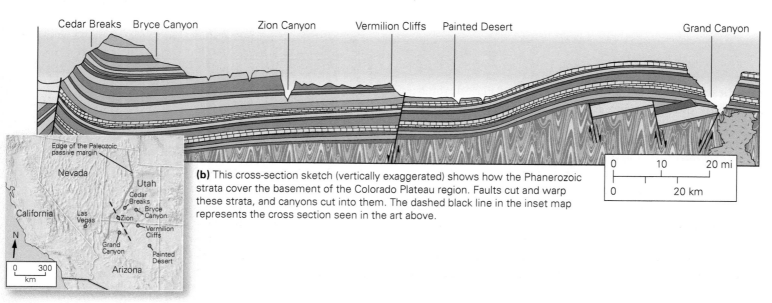

(b) This cross-section sketch (vertically exaggerated) shows how the Phanerozoic strata cover the basement of the Colorado Plateau region. Faults cut and warp these strata, and canyons cut into them. The dashed black line in the inset map represents the cross section seen in the art above.

For example, when the Precambrian metamorphic and igneous rocks exposed in the inner gorge of the Grand Canyon first formed, the region was a high mountain range, perhaps as dramatic as the Himalayas today. When the fossiliferous beds of the Kaibab Limestone at the rim of the canyon first developed, the region was a Bahama-like carbonate reef and platform, bathed in a warm, shallow sea. And when the rocks making up the towering red cliffs of sandstone in Zion Canyon were deposited, the region was a Sahara-like desert, blanketed with huge sand dunes.

Take-Home Message

Correlation of stratigraphic sequences from around the world led to the production of a chart, the geologic column, that represents the entirety of Earth history. The column, developed using only relative-age relations, is subdivided into eons, eras, periods, and epochs.

QUICK QUESTION: What feature of living organisms appeared at the Precambrian/Cambrian boundary?

12.7 How Do We Determine Numerical Ages?

Geologists since the days of Hutton could determine the relative ages of geologic events, but they had no way to specify *numerical ages* (called absolute ages in older literature), meaning the age in years of an event. Thus, they could not define a timeline for Earth history or determine the duration of events. This situation changed with the discovery of radioactivity. Simply put, a **radioactive element** is one that decays so that its atoms transform into atoms of another element at a constant rate. The rate can be measured in the lab and can be specified in years. In the 1950s, geologists first developed techniques for using measurements of radioactive elements to calculate the ages of rocks. Geologists originally referred to this process of determining the numerical age of rocks as *radiometric dating*; more recently, it has come to be known as **isotopic dating**. We refer to the overall determination and interpretation of numerical ages as **geochronology**. The technique of isotopic dating has been vastly improved over the years. We begin our discussion of this technique by first learning more about radioactive decay.

Radioactive Decay

As we've noted earlier, different versions of an element, called **isotopes** of the element, have the same atomic number but a different atomic weight (see Box 1.3). To see how this terminology applies, let's consider two isotopes of uranium. All uranium atoms have 92 protons, but the uranium-238 isotope (abbreviated ^{238}U) has an atomic weight of 238 and thus has 146 neutrons, whereas the ^{235}U isotope has an atomic weight of 235 and thus has 143 neutrons. Some elements have only one isotope, which is stable in that all atoms of the element could last until the end of the Universe—unless they become fuel for the nuclear reactions in stars. But many elements have two or more isotopes. Of these, some are *stable*, but some are not. The *unstable* isotopes, by definition, are called *radioactive isotopes*. Unstable in this context means that the isotopes undergo a change called *radioactive decay*, which converts them into a different element. Radioactive decay can take place by a variety of reactions, but regardless of the details, all these reactions change the atomic number of the nucleus and, therefore, the identity of the element. We refer to the isotope that undergoes decay as the *parent isotope* and the decay product as the *daughter isotope*.

Physicists cannot specify how long an individual radioactive isotope will survive before it decays, but they can measure how long it takes for half of a group of parent isotopes to decay. This time is called the **half-life** of the isotope. **Figure 12.19** can help you visualize the concept of a half-life. Imagine a crystal containing 16 radioactive parent isotopes. (Note that in a real crystal, the number of atoms would be immensely larger.) After one half-life, 8 isotopes have decayed, so the crystal now contains 8 parent and 8 daughter isotopes. After a second half-life, 4 of the remaining parent isotopes have decayed, so the crystal contains 4 parent and 12 daughter isotopes. And after a third half-life, 2 more parent isotopes have decayed, so the crystal contains 2 parent and 14 daughter isotopes. For a given decay reaction, the half-life is a constant, measured in years.

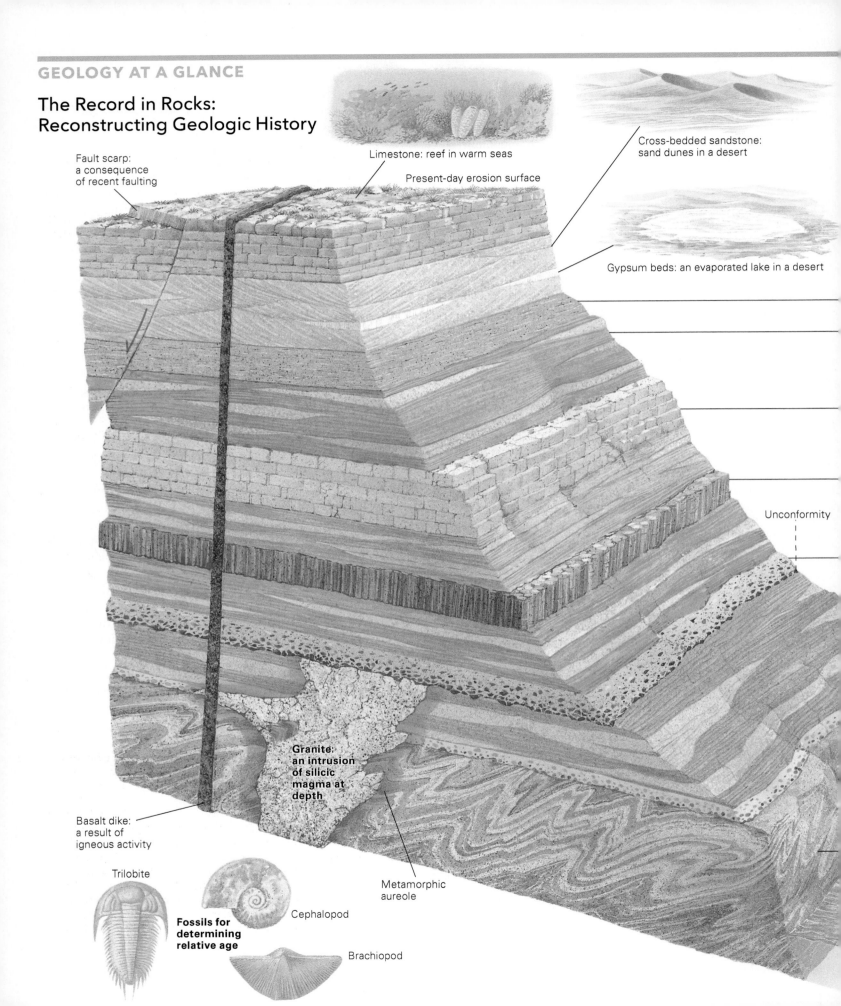

The Record in Rocks: Reconstructing Geologic History

Fault scarp: a consequence of recent faulting

Limestone: reef in warm seas

Present-day erosion surface

Cross-bedded sandstone: sand dunes in a desert

Gypsum beds: an evaporated lake in a desert

Unconformity

Granite: an intrusion of silicic magma at depth

Basalt dike: a result of igneous activity

Metamorphic aureole

Trilobite

Fossils for determining relative age

Cephalopod

Brachiopod

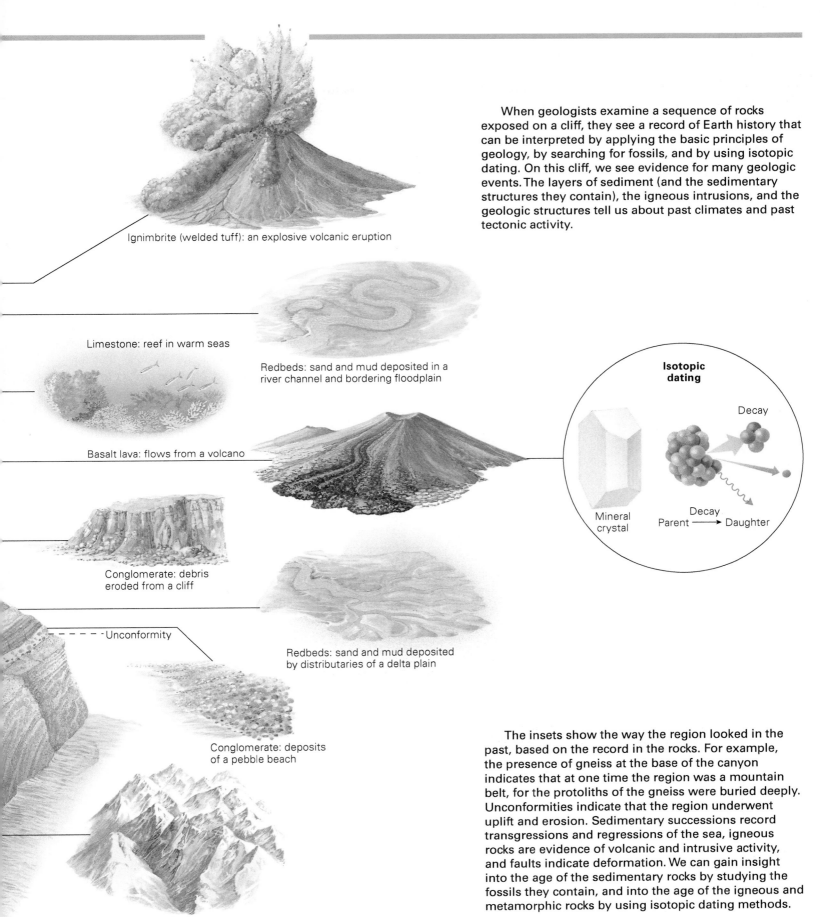

When geologists examine a sequence of rocks exposed on a cliff, they see a record of Earth history that can be interpreted by applying the basic principles of geology, by searching for fossils, and by using isotopic dating. On this cliff, we see evidence for many geologic events. The layers of sediment (and the sedimentary structures they contain), the igneous intrusions, and the geologic structures tell us about past climates and past tectonic activity.

Ignimbrite (welded tuff): an explosive volcanic eruption

Limestone: reef in warm seas

Redbeds: sand and mud deposited in a river channel and bordering floodplain

Isotopic dating

Decay

Mineral crystal

Decay
Parent ⟶ Daughter

Basalt lava: flows from a volcano

Conglomerate: debris eroded from a cliff

Redbeds: sand and mud deposited by distributaries of a delta plain

Unconformity

Conglomerate: deposits of a pebble beach

The insets show the way the region looked in the past, based on the record in the rocks. For example, the presence of gneiss at the base of the canyon indicates that at one time the region was a mountain belt, for the protoliths of the gneiss were buried deeply. Unconformities indicate that the region underwent uplift and erosion. Sedimentary successions record transgressions and regressions of the sea, igneous rocks are evidence of volcanic and intrusive activity, and faults indicate deformation. We can gain insight into the age of the sedimentary rocks by studying the fossils they contain, and into the age of the igneous and metamorphic rocks by using isotopic dating methods.

Gneiss: metamorphism at depth beneath a mountain belt

FIGURE 12.19 The concept of a half-life, in the context of radiaoctive decay.

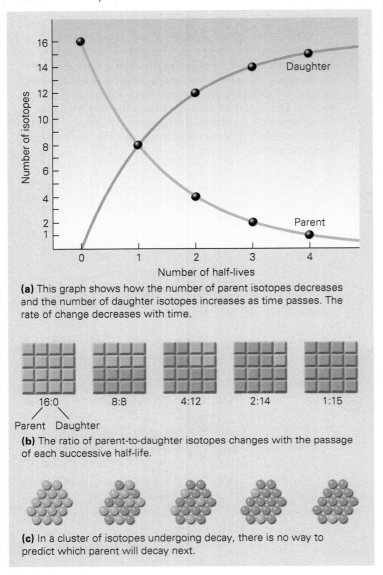

(a) This graph shows how the number of parent isotopes decreases and the number of daughter isotopes increases as time passes. The rate of change decreases with time.

16:0 8:8 4:12 2:14 1:15

Parent Daughter

(b) The ratio of parent-to-daughter isotopes changes with the passage of each successive half-life.

(c) In a cluster of isotopes undergoing decay, there is no way to predict which parent will decay next.

Isotopic Dating Technique

Since radioactive decay proceeds at a known rate, like the ticktock of a clock, it provides a basis for telling time. In other words, because an element's half-life is a constant, we can calculate the age of a mineral by measuring the ratio of parent to daughter isotopes in the mineral. How do geologists actually obtain an isotopic date? First, we must find the right kind of elements to work with. Although there are many different pairs of parent and daughter isotopes among the known radioactive elements, only a few have long enough half-lives and occur in sufficient abundance in minerals to be useful for isotopic dating—we list some of the elements that are particularly useful for isotopic dating in **Table 12.1**. Each radioactive element has its own half-life. Note that *carbon dating* is not used for dating rocks because appropriate carbon isotopes only occur in organisms and have a very short half-life (**Box 12.2**). Second, we must identify the right kind of minerals to work with. Not all minerals contain radioactive elements, but fortunately some common minerals do. Now we can set to work using the following steps.

- *Collecting the rocks:* Geologists collect unweathered rocks for dating, for the chemical reactions that happen during weathering may remove parent or daughter isotopes. If, for example, weathering allows daughter elements to escape, then the isotopic clock becomes inaccurate.
- *Separating the minerals:* Once a good sample of fresh rock has been collected, the sample is crushed and the appropriate minerals are separated from the debris.
- *Extracting parent and daughter isotopes:* To separate out the parent and daughter isotopes from minerals, geologists use several techniques, including dissolving the minerals in acid or evaporating portions of them with a laser. This stage must take place in a *clean lab*, a special facility with ultra-filtered air and water, to avoid contaminating the samples with stray isotopes.

TABLE 12.1 Isotopes Used in the Isotopic Dating of Rocks

Parent → Daughter	Half-Life (years)	Minerals Containing the Isotopes
^{147}Sm → ^{143}Nd	106 billion	Garnets, micas
^{87}Rb → ^{87}Sr	48.8 billion	Potassium-bearing minerals (mica, feldspar, hornblende)
^{238}U → ^{206}Pb	4.5 billion	Uranium-bearing minerals (zircon)
^{40}K → ^{40}Ar	1.3 billion	Potassium-bearing minerals (mica, feldspar, hornblende)
^{235}U → ^{207}Pb	713 million	Uranium-bearing minerals (zircon)

Sm = samarium, Nd = neodymium, Rb = rubidium, Sr = strontium, U = uranium, Pb = lead, K = potassium, Ar = argon.

Carbon-14 Dating

Many people who have heard of carbon-14 (^{14}C) dating assume that it can be used to define the numerical age of rocks. But this is not the case. Rather, ^{14}C dating tells us the ages of organic materials—such as wood, cotton fibers, charcoal, flesh, bones, and shells—that contain carbon originally extracted from the atmosphere by photosynthesis. ^{14}C, a radioactive isotope of carbon, forms naturally in the atmosphere when cosmic rays (charged particles from space) bombard atmospheric nitrogen-14 (^{14}N) atoms. When plants consume carbon dioxide during photosynthesis, or when animals consume plants, they ingest a tiny amount of ^{14}C along with ^{12}C, the more common isotope of carbon. After an organism dies and can no longer exchange carbon with the atmosphere, the ^{14}C in its body begins to decay back to ^{14}N. Thus, the ratio of ^{14}C to ^{12}C changes at a rate determined by the half-life of ^{14}C.

We can use ^{14}C dating to determine the age of prehistoric fire pits or of organic debris in sediment. ^{14}C has a short half-life—only 5,730 years. Thus, the method cannot be used to date anything older than about 70,000 years, for after that time essentially no ^{14}C remains in the material. But this range makes it a useful tool for geologists studying sediments of the last ice age and for archaeologists studying ancient cultures or prehistoric peoples. Again, since rocks do not contain organic carbon, and may be significantly older than 70,000 years, we cannot determine the age of rocks by using the ^{14}C dating method.

- *Analyzing the parent-daughter ratio*: Geologists pass the isotopes through a mass spectrometer, a sophisticated instrument that uses a strong magnet to separate isotopes from one another according to their respective weights (**Fig. 12.20**). The instrument can count the number of atoms of specific isotopes separately.

At the end of the laboratory process, geologists can define the ratio of parent-to-daughter isotopes in a mineral and from this ratio determine the age of the mineral. Needless to say, the description of the procedure here has been simplified—in reality, obtaining an isotopic date requires complex calculations and can be time-consuming and expensive.

What Does an Isotopic Date Mean?

At high temperatures, atoms in a crystal lattice vibrate so rapidly that chemical bonds break and reattach relatively easily. As a consequence, isotopes escape from or move into crystals, so parent-daughter ratios are meaningless. Because isotopic dating is based on the parent-daughter ratio, the "isotopic clock" starts only when crystals become cool enough for isotopes to be locked into the lattice. The temperature below which isotopes are no longer free to move is called the **closure temperature** of a mineral. When we specify an isotopic date for a rock, we are defining the time at which a specific mineral in the rock cooled below its closure temperature.

With the concept of closure temperature in mind, we can interpret the meaning of isotopic dates. In the case of igneous rocks, isotopic dating of minerals with high closure temperature (e.g., >650°C) tells you when a magma or lava cooled to form a solid, cool igneous rock. In the case of metamorphic rocks, an isotopic date from minerals with high closure temperature tells you when a rock cooled from a metamorphic temperature (e.g., >450°C) above the closure temperature to a temperature below. Not all minerals have the same closure temperature, so different minerals in a rock that cools very slowly will yield different dates.

In recent years, geologists have started to carry out dating using isotopic systems that have very low closure temperatures (as low as 75°C). Dating these low-closure temperature minerals constrains the time of exhumation, meaning the

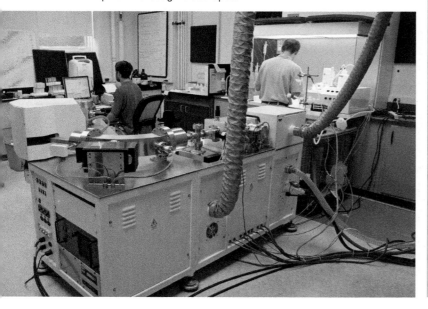

FIGURE 12.20 In an isotopic dating laboratory, samples are analyzed using a mass spectrometer. This instrument measures the ratio of parent-to-daughter isotopes.

time at which uplift and erosion led to the return of a rock that was once, say, 20 km below the surface back to within a few kilometers of the surface.

Can we isotopically date a clastic sedimentary rock directly? No. If we date minerals in a sedimentary rock, we're determining only when these minerals first crystallized as part of an igneous or metamorphic rock, not the time when the minerals were deposited as sediment nor the time when the sediment lithified to form a sedimentary rock. For example, if we date the feldspar grains contained within a granite pebble in a conglomerate, we're dating the time the granite cooled below feldspar's closure temperature, not the time the pebble was deposited by a stream.

The age of mineral grains in sediment, however, can be useful. In recent years, geologists have used *detrital geochronology*, determination of the ages of detrital (clastic) grains, to learn the age of the rocks in the sediment's source region and thus determine where the sediment came from. Such ages also put an upper limit on the age of the sedimentary rock, for according to the principle of inclusions, the sedimentary rock must be younger than the grains it contains.

Other Methods of Determining Numerical Age

Isotopic dating is not the only means of constraining the age of a geological material or of events that have happened on Earth. Let's consider a few additional techniques.

Counting Changes of Season The changes in seasons affect a wide variety of phenomena, including the following.

- *The growth rate of trees:* Trees grow seasonally, with different growth rates in different seasons. These variations produce alternating dense (dark) and less-dense (light) bands, for growth rate affects cell size which, in turn, affects wood density.
- *The organic productivity of lakes and seas:* During the winter, less light reaches the Earth, water temperatures decrease, and the supply of nutrients decreases. Therefore, more organic material will be deposited in summer than in winter. So alternations between organic-rich and organic-poor sediment indicate the seasons.
- *The growth rate of chemically precipitated sedimentary rocks:* Factors that control precipitation rates, such as the rate of groundwater flow and temperature, change seasonally in some locations. Such changes may form distinct bands in chemical sedimentary rocks such as travertine.
- *The growth rate of shell-secreting organisms:* Organisms grow and produce new shell material on a seasonal basis. Such variations can produce ridges in shells of mollusks and alternating dark and light bands in the heads of coral colonies.
- *The layering in glaciers:* During the snowy season, more snow falls relative to dust than during the dry season, so annual snowfall includes a dusty layer and a clean layer. These contrasts are preserved as visible banding in ice.

As a consequence of these seasonal changes, **growth bands** develop in trees, travertine deposits, and shelly organisms, and *rhythmic layering* develops in sedimentary accumulations and glacier ice (**Fig. 12.21a–c**). By counting bands or layers, geologists can determine how long an organism survived and how long a sedimentary accumulation took to form. If rings or layers have developed right up to the present, we can count backward and determine how long ago they began to form.

Dendrochronologists, scientists who study and date **tree rings**, the growth bands in trees, have found that not only do such rings count time, but they also preserve a record of the changing climate, for during warm, rainy years, trees grow faster than they do during drought years. In fact, climate variations over time yield distinctive patterns of tree rings, much like the bar codes on products in supermarkets. By correlating the older rings of a still-living tree with the youngest rings measured in a log from a dead tree, by using these patterns, it's possible to extend the record of tree rings back before living trees started to grow. For example, the oldest living trees, bristlecone pines, are almost 4,000 years old—by correlating the older rings of these trees with rings in preserved logs, dendrochronologists have extended the tree-ring record back for many thousands of years more (**Fig. 12.21d**).

Glacier ice also preserves a valuable record of past climate, for the ratio of different oxygen isotopes in the water molecules making up the ice reflects the global temperature at the time the snow fell to create the ice, as we'll discuss further in Chapter 22. Ice cores drilled through the thick Greenland ice cap contain a continuous record of climate in polar latitudes back through 750,000 years. Geologists are racing to sample the record of past climate recorded in glaciers on mountain peaks in temperate and equatorial regions before the glaciers melt away entirely.

Magnetostratigraphy As we discussed in Chapter 3, the polarity of Earth's magnetic field flips every now and then through geological time. Geologists have determined when the reversals took place and have constructed a reference column showing the succession of reversals through time (**Fig. 12.22**). By comparing the pattern of the reversals in a sequence of strata with the pattern of reversals in a reference column, a study known as *magnetostratigraphy*, geologists can determine the age of the sequence.

Fission-Track Dating In certain minerals, the ejection of an atomic particle during the decay of a radioactive isotope damages the nearby crystal, creating a line called a **fission track**. This track resembles the line of crushed grass left behind when you ride a bike across a lawn. As time passes, more atoms undergo fission, so the number of fission tracks in

FIGURE 12.21 Using layering and rings as a basis for dating.

(a) Dust settling during the summer highlights boundaries between snow layers, now turned to ice in this Oregon glacier.

(b) The ridges in this giant clamshell from the Red Sea form during successive seasons of growth.

(c) Each ring in this slice of wood represents the growth of one year. The width of each ring depends on the temperature and rainfall during growth. Patterns of rings are like bar codes—the pattern in a living tree can be correlated with the pattern in a dead tree, which can be correlated with the pattern in an ancient, buried tree. Such correlation extends the tree-ring record back in time.

the crystal increases (**Fig. 12.23**). Therefore, the number of fission tracks in a given volume of a crystal represents the age of the crystal. Geologists have been able to measure the rate at which fission tracks are produced and thus can determine the age of a mineral grain by counting the fission tracks within it. The closure temperature for fission tracks is fairly low, so fission-track dating is used primarily to help constrain rates of exhumation.

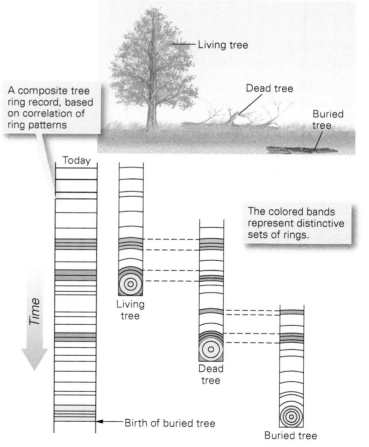

(d) Dendrochronology is based on the correlation of tree rings. Each of the columns in the diagram represents a core drilled out of a tree. Distinctive clusters of closely spaced rings indicate dry seasons. By correlation, researchers extend the climate record back in time before the oldest living tree started to grow.

FIGURE 12.22 Magnetostratigraphy involves comparing the sequence of polarity reversals in strata with the sequence of polarity reversals in a global reference column to determine the age of the strata.

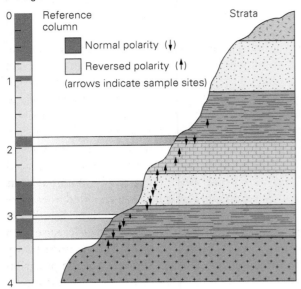

FIGURE 12.23 The method of fission-track dating.

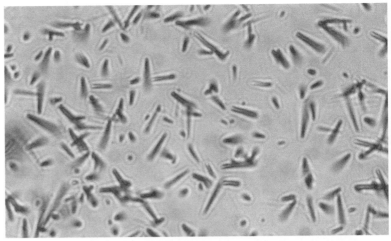

(a) This high-magnification photomicrograph shows fission tracks in a crystal. When formed, each track is only a few atoms wide. Treating the sample with acid enlarges the tracks so they are visible.

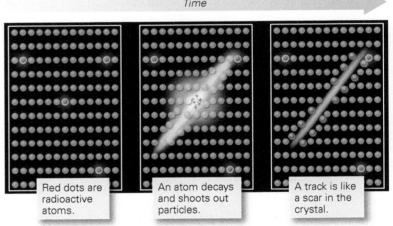

Time

Red dots are radioactive atoms.

An atom decays and shoots out particles.

A track is like a scar in the crystal.

(b) A fission track forms when a radioactive atom decays and blasts out particles that disrupt the crystal structure in a narrow band.

Take-Home Message

Isotopic dating specifies numerical ages in years. To obtain an isotopic date, we measure the ratio of parent radioactive isotopes to stable daughter products in a mineral. A date for a mineral gives the time at which the mineral cooled below a closure temperature. Using this method, we can date the time an igneous rock solidifies, a metamorphic rock cools, or a body of rock is exhumed. We cannot isotopically date sedimentary rock directly. Counting growth bands or seasonal layers can constrain ages of younger materials.

QUICK QUESTION: How can we date changes in climate during the past few hundred thousand years?

12.8 Numerical Ages and Geologic Time

Dating Sedimentary Rocks

The mind grows giddy gazing so far back into the abyss of time.
—John Playfair (British geologist; 1747–1819)

We have seen that isotopic dating can be used to date the time when igneous rocks formed and when rocks metamorphosed but not when sedimentary rocks were deposited. So how do we determine the numerical age of a sedimentary rock? We must answer this question if we want to add numerical ages to the geologic column—remember, the column was originally constructed by studying only the relative ages of fossil-bearing sedimentary rocks and did not specify dates.

Geologists obtain dates for sedimentary rocks by studying cross-cutting relationships between sedimentary rocks and datable igneous or metamorphic rocks. For example, if we find a sequence of sedimentary strata deposited unconformably on a datable granite, the strata must be younger than the granite. If a datable basalt dike cuts the strata, the strata must be older than the dike. And if a datable volcanic ash buried the strata, then the strata must be older than the ash.

Let's see how cross-cutting relations can help us constrain the numerical age of an imaginary bed of sandstone that contains fossilized dinosaur bones (Fig. 12.24). Geologists assign the beds to the Cretaceous Period by correlating the bones with fossils in known Cretaceous strata from elsewhere. Field study shows that the sandstone was deposited unconformably over an eroded pluton consisting of granite that has a numerical age, determined by uranium-lead (U-Pb) dating, of 125 Ma. Further study shows that a basalt dike whose numerical age, based on potassium-argon (K-Ar) dating, is 80 Ma, cuts across the bed. These measurements mean that this Cretaceous sandstone bed was deposited sometime between 125 Ma and 80 Ma. Note that the data provide an age range, not an exact age. Thus, from this observation we can only conclude that the Cretaceous Period includes, but is not limited to, the time interval of 125 to 80 Ma.

The Geologic Time Scale

Geologists have searched the world for localities where they can recognize cross-cutting relations between datable igneous rocks and sedimentary rocks or for layers of datable volcanic rocks interbedded with sedimentary rocks. By isotopically dating the igneous rocks, they have provided numerical ages for the boundaries between all geologic periods. For example, a compilation of many studies from around the world has led to a refinement of the numerical ages assigned to the Cretaceous Period—currently, the beginning of the Cretaceous has been placed at 145 Ma and the end at 66 Ma. (With this information in hand, we can say that the bed in Figure 12.24 was deposited during the middle part of the Cretaceous, not at the beginning or end.)

Because numerical ages depend on the documentation of datable cross-cutting relations, discovery of new data can require changes in the numerical ages assigned to period boundaries. (That's why we prefer the term *numerical age* to *absolute age*.) For example, around 1995, new dates on rhyolite ash layers above and below the Cambrian/Precambrian boundary showed that this boundary occurred closer to an age of 542 Ma—previous, less-definitive studies had placed the boundary at 570 Ma. More recently, the boundary has been moved to 541 Ma. Also, because repeated measurements of the same sample might yield slightly different results, a given numerical age is not perfectly "precise." To be technically accurate, a reported age has an uncertainty (plus or minus) value attached, which indicates the precision of the measurement. For example, researchers would report the start of the Cambrian as 541 ± 1 Ma. (We are leaving off precision specifications in this book for the sake of simplicity.) Note that the terms *precision* and *accuracy* have different meanings in scientific discussion. *Precision* refers to the uncertainty of a result that reflects the repeatability of a measurement. *Accuracy* refers to the closeness of the result to the real or true value.

The chart in Figure 12.25 gives the numerical ages of periods and eras in the geologic column, as reported by the International Commission on Stratigraphy in 2013. We refer to such a chart, on which intervals of the geologic column have been assigned numerical ages, as the **geologic time scale**. Because of the numerical constraints provided by the geologic time scale, when we say that the first dinosaurs appeared during the Triassic Period, we are implying that dinosaurs appeared after 252 Ma. (The oldest dinosaur fossil known actually comes from strata that are 240 to 245 Ma.)

What Is the Age of the Earth?

During the 18th and 19th centuries, before the discovery of isotopic dating, scientists came up with a great variety of clever solutions to the question, "How old is the Earth?" All of these have since been proven wrong. Lord William Kelvin, a 19th-century physicist renowned for his discoveries in thermodynamics, made the most influential scientific estimate of the Earth's age of his time. Kelvin calculated how long it would take for the Earth to cool down from a temperature as hot as the Sun's and concluded (in 1862) that our planet is about 20 million years old.

FIGURE 12.24 The Cretaceous sandstone bed was deposited on the granite, so it must be younger than 125 Ma. The dike cuts the bed, so the bed must be older than 80 Ma. Thus, the Cretaceous bed was deposited between 125 and 80 Ma. The Paleocene sandstone was unconformably deposited over the dike and lies beneath a 50-million-year-old layer of ash. Therefore, it must have been deposited between 80 and 50 Ma.

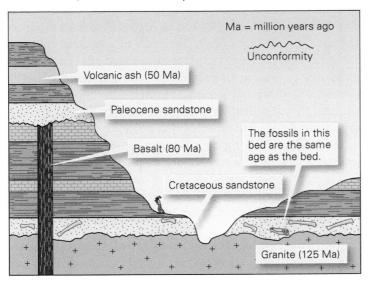

Ma = million years ago

Unconformity

Volcanic ash (50 Ma)

Paleocene sandstone

Basalt (80 Ma)

The fossils in this bed are the same age as the bed.

Cretaceous sandstone

Granite (125 Ma)

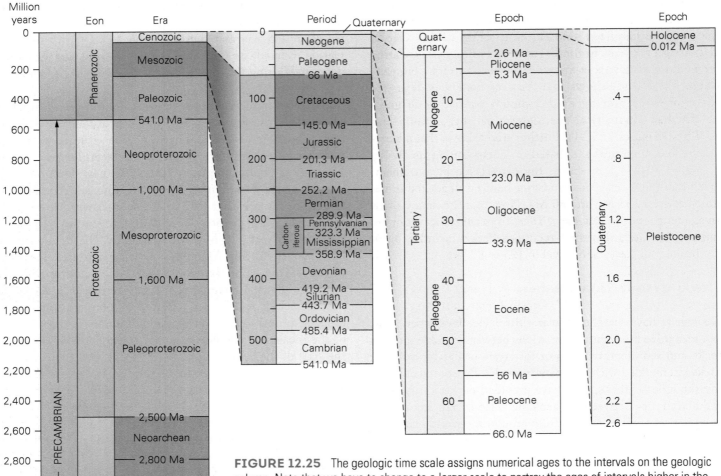

FIGURE 12.25 The geologic time scale assigns numerical ages to the intervals on the geologic column. Note that we have to change to a larger scale to portray the ages of intervals higher in the column, because these are shorter subdivisions. This time scale utilizes numbers favored by the International Commission on Stratigraphy.

Kelvin's estimate contrasted with those being promoted by followers of Hutton, Lyell, and Darwin, who argued that if the concepts of uniformitarianism and evolution were correct, the Earth must be much older. They held that physical processes that shape the Earth and form its rocks, as well as the process of natural selection that yields the diversity of species, all take a very long time. Geologists and physicists continued to debate the age issue for many years. The route to a solution appeared in 1896, when Henri Becquerel announced the discovery of radioactivity. Geologists immediately realized that the Earth's interior was producing some heat from the decay of radioactive material. This realization uncovered the key flaw in Kelvin's argument: Kelvin had assumed that no new heat was produced after the Earth first formed. Because radioactivity constantly generates new heat in the Earth, the planet has cooled down much more slowly than Kelvin had calculated and could be much older. The discovery of radioactivity not only invalidated Kelvin's estimate of the Earth's age, it also led to the development of isotopic dating.

Since the 1950s, geologists have scoured the planet to identify its oldest rocks. Samples from several localities (Wyoming,

Canada, Greenland, and China) have yielded dates as old as 4.03 Ga (Fig. 12.26). Individual clastic grains of the mineral zircon have yielded dates of up to 4.4 Ga, indicating that by 4.4 Ga solid crust existed, at least for a while. Isotopic dating of Moon rocks yields dates of up to 4.50 Ga, and dates on the meteorites thought to reflect the most primitive solids of the Solar System have yielded ages as old as 4.57 Ga. Geologists consider 4.57 Ga meteorites to be fragments of very early, undifferentiated planetesimals. Meteorites from the oldest differentiated planetesimals (ones that had separated into a core and mantle) are slightly younger, and these ages are taken to be the same as the age of the Earth itself. Based on these ages, therefore, researchers estimate that the Earth itself formed at 4.54 Ga.

Did you ever wonder . . .

how old the Earth's oldest rock is?

Why don't we find whole rocks with ages between 4.03 and 4.54 Ga in the Earth's crust? Geologists have come up with several ideas to explain the lack of extremely old rocks. One idea comes from calculations defining how the temperature of this planet's interior has changed over time. These calculations indicate that during the first half-billion years of its existence, the Earth might have been so hot that rocks in the crust remained above the closure temperature for minerals, and isotopic clocks could not start "ticking." More recent studies, looking at isotope ratios in the oldest (4.4 Ga)

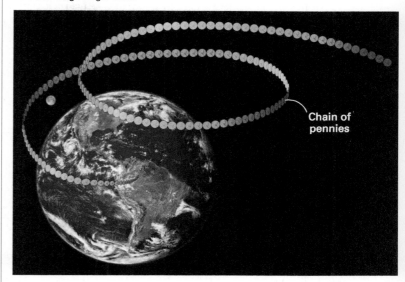

FIGURE 12.27 We can use the analogy of distance to represent the duration of geologic time.

Chain of pennies

zircons, suggest that the Earth had cooled sufficiently to host oceans of water within only a couple of hundred million years of its formation. So an alternative view is that intense bombardment of the Earth by meteorites just prior to 4.03 Ga destroyed or remelted any crust that existed and vaporized the earliest oceans. As noted earlier, geologists have named the time interval between the birth of the Earth and the origin of the oldest isotopically dated rock as the Hadean Eon, to emphasize that conditions at the surface, at times, resembled literary images of Hades.

Picturing Geologic Time

The number 4.57 billion is so staggeringly large that we can't really begin to comprehend it. If you lined up this many pennies in a row, they would make an 87,400-km-long line that would wrap around the Earth's equator more than twice (Fig. 12.27). Notably, at the scale of our penny chain, human history is only about 100 city blocks long.

Another way to grasp the immensity of geologic time is to equate the entire 4.57 billion years to a single calendar year. On this scale, the oldest rocks preserved on Earth date from early February, the first archaea appear in the sea on February 21, the first shelly invertebrates burrowed through the mud on October 25, and the first amphibians crawled onto the land about November 20. On December 7, the continents coalesce into the supercontinent of Pangaea. The first mammals and birds appear about December 15, along with the dinosaurs, and the Age of Dinosaurs ends on December 25. The last week of December

FIGURE 12.26 An outcrop of the Acasta Gneiss, in Canada, showing rocks of different ages. The oldest have yielded isotopic ages of 4.03 Ga.

represents the last 66 million years of Earth history, including the entire Age of Mammals. The first human-like ancestor appears on December 31 at 3 P.M., and our species, *Homo sapiens*, shows up an hour before midnight. The last ice age ends a minute before midnight, and all of recorded human history takes place in the last 30 seconds. To put it another way, human history occupies the last 0.0001% of Earth history. The Earth is so old that there has been more than enough time for the rocks, mountains, and life forms of Earth to have formed and evolved.

Take-Home Message

Numerical dates for sedimentary rocks come from isotopic dating of cross-cutting datable rocks. Such work led to the geologic time scale, which assigns dates to periods. The oldest rock of Earth's crust is about 4.0 Ga. Dating of meteorites indicates the Earth is 4.54 Ga.

QUICK QUESTION: Why don't all periods on the geologic time column have the same duration in years?

CHAPTER SUMMARY

- Geologic time refers to the time span since the Earth's formation.
- Relative age specifies whether one geologic feature is older or younger than another; numerical age provides the age of a geologic feature in years.
- Using such principles as uniformitarianism, original horizontality, superposition, and cross-cutting relations, we can construct the geologic history of a region.
- The principle of fossil succession states that the assemblage of fossils in strata changes from base to top of a sequence. Once a species becomes extinct, it never reappears.
- Strata are not necessarily deposited continuously at a location. An interval of nondeposition and/or erosion is called an unconformity. Geologists recognize three kinds: angular unconformity, nonconformity, and disconformity.
- A stratigraphic column shows the succession of strata in a region. The process of determining the relationship between strata at one location and strata at another is called correlation.
- A given succession of strata that can be traced over a fairly broad region is called a stratigraphic formation. A geologic map shows the distribution of formations.

- A composite chart that represents the entirety of geologic time is the geologic column. The column's largest subdivisions, each of which represents a specific interval of time, are eons. Eons are subdivided into eras, eras into periods, and periods into epochs.
- The numerical age of rocks can be determined by isotopic (radiometric) dating. This is because radioactive elements decay at a rate characterized by a known half-life.
- The isotopic date of a mineral specifies the time at which the mineral cooled below a closure temperature. We can use isotopic dating to determine when an igneous rock solidified and when a metamorphic rock cooled from high temperatures. To date sedimentary strata, we must examine cross-cutting relations among dated igneous or metamorphic rock and the strata.
- Other methods for dating materials include counting growth rings in trees and seasonal layers in glaciers.
- From the isotopic dating of meteors and Moon rocks, geologists conclude that the Earth formed about 4.54 billion years ago. Our species, *Homo sapiens*, has been around for only a tiny fraction of geologic time.

GUIDE TERMS

angular unconformity (p. 443)

Cambrian explosion (p. 450)

closure temperature (p. 457)

disconformity (p. 444)

eon (p. 450)

epoch (p. 450)

era (p. 450)

fission track (p. 458)

fossil (p. 436)

fossil assemblage (p. 441)

geochronology (p. 453)

geologic column (p. 449)

geologic contact (p. 445)

geologic map (p. 446)

geologic time (p. 435)

geologic time scale (p. 461)

growth bands (p. 458)

half-life (p. 453)

index fossil (p. 441)

isotope (p. 453)

isotopic dating (p. 453)

marker bed (p. 446)

nonconformity (p. 443)

numerical age (p. 437)

period (p. 450)

Precambrian (p. 450)

radioactive element (p. 453)

relative age (p. 437)

stratigraphic column (p. 445)

stratigraphic correlation (p. 446)

stratigraphic formation (p. 445)

stratigraphic group (p. 446)

tree rings (p. 458)

unconformity (p. 443)

uniformitarianism (p. 437)

REVIEW QUESTIONS

1. Contrast numerical age with relative age.
2. Describe the principles that allow us to determine the relative ages of geologic events.
3. How does the principle of fossil succession allow determination of relative ages?
4. How does an unconformity develop? Describe the three kinds of unconformities.
5. Describe two different methods of correlating rock units. How was correlation used to develop the geologic column? What is a stratigraphic formation?
6. What does the process of radioactive decay entail?
7. How do geologists obtain an isotopic date? What does the age of an igneous rock mean? What does the age of a metamorphic rock mean?
8. Why can't we date sedimentary rocks directly? How do we assign numerical ages to intervals on the geologic column, to produce a geologic time scale?
9. How are growth rings and ice layering useful in determining the ages of geologic events?
10. What is the age of the oldest rocks on Earth? What is the current estimate of the numerical age of the Earth? Why is there a difference?

ON FURTHER THOUGHT

11. Imagine an outcrop exposing a succession of alternating sandstone and conglomerate beds. A geologist studying the outcrop notes the following.

    • The sandstone beds contain fragments of land plants, but the fragments are too small to permit identification of species.
    • A layer of volcanic ash overlies the sandstone bed. Isotopic dating indicates that this ash is 300 Ma.
    • A paleosol occurs at the base of the ash layer.

    • A basalt dike, dated at 100 Ma, cuts both the ash and the sandstone-conglomerate sequence.
    • Pebbles of granite in the conglomerate yield radiometric dates of 400 Ma.

    On the basis of these observations, how old is the sandstone and conglomerate? (Specify both the numerical age range and the period or periods of the geologic column during which it formed.) If the igneous rocks were not present, could you still specify the maximum or minimum ages of the sedimentary beds? Explain.

12. Examine the photograph and the "What a Geologist Sees" interpretation of an outcrop in eastern New York state below. Write a brief geologic history that explains the relationships displayed in this outcrop. The strata directly above the unconformity are Late Silurian (Rondout Formation), whereas the strata below the unconformity are Middle Ordovician (Austin Glen Formation).

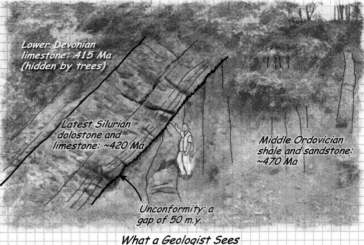

Lower Devonian limestone: 415 Ma (hidden by trees)

Latest Silurian dolostone and limestone: ~420 Ma

Middle Ordovician shale and sandstone: ~470 Ma

Unconformity: a gap of 50 m.y.

What a Geologist Sees

13. Examine the photograph and the "What a Geologist Sees" interpretation of an outcrop in Missouri below. Note that the strata thin close to the unconformity. Write a brief geologic history that explains the relationships displayed in this outcrop. The strata above the unconformity are of the Cambrian-age Lamotte Sandstone.

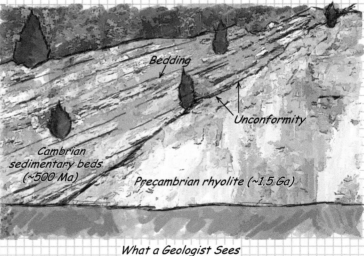

Bedding

Unconformity

Cambrian sedimentary beds (~500 Ma)

Precambrian rhyolite (~1.5 Ga)

What a Geologist Sees

smartwork   smartwork.wwnorton.com

This chapter's Smartwork features:

- Art-based problems on uncomformities.
- What A Geologist Sees exercises on strata of the Grand Canyon.
- Geologic time labeling activity.

GEOTOURS

This chapter's GeoTour exercise (J) features:

- Relative age dating and unconformities
- Stratigraphic formations in southern Utah
- Rock layers and monoclines, Circle Cliffs, Utah

The presence of these fossiliferous limestone beds in Illinois tell us that the middle of North America was once covered by a shallow sea. The dip of the strata tells us that long after the sediment turned to rock, tectonics deformed this part of the continent. Much later, uplift and erosion exposed the rock. Clearly, the Earth has a history!

CHAPTER 13

A Biography of Earth

> [T]he man who should know the true history of the bit of chalk which every carpenter carries about in his breeches pocket, though ignorant of all other history, is likely, if he will think his knowledge out to its ultimate results, to have a truer and therefore a better conception of this wonderful universe and of man's relation to it than the most learned student who [has] deep-read the records of humanity [but is] ignorant of those of nature.
>
> —*Thomas Henry Huxley, from* On a Piece of Chalk *(1868)*

LEARNING OBJECTIVES

By the end of this chapter, you should understand . . .

- how many geologic clues indicate that Earth changes over time, so the Earth has a history.
- that the earliest crust and oceans may date to 4.4 Ga but were destroyed by bombardment.
- that oceans and life have existed continuously since at least 3.8 Ga, but that the atmosphere began to accumulate oxygen at only about 2.5 Ga.
- when supercontinents formed and then rifted apart during Earth history.
- that the fossil record indicates that early life consisted of archaea and bacteria; after oxygen levels increased, complex multicellular life became possible, and after shells evolved, organisms diversified.
- that due to sea-level rise and fall, continental interiors sometimes hosted shallow seas.
- when and why mountain belts formed in the past.

13.1 Introduction

In 1868, a well-known British scientist, Thomas Henry Huxley, presented a public lecture on geology to an audience in Norwich, England. Seeking a way to convey his fascination with Earth history to people with no geologic background, he focused his audience's attention on the piece of chalk he had been writing with (see the epigraph above). And what a tale the chalk has to tell! Chalk, a type of limestone, consists of microscopic marine algae shells and shrimp feces. The specific chalk that Huxley held came from beds deposited in Cretaceous time (the name Cretaceous, in fact, derives from the Latin word for chalk). These beds now form the white cliffs bordering the shore of England (**Fig. 13.1**). Geologists in Huxley's day knew of similar chalk beds in outcrops throughout much of Europe and had discovered that the chalk contains not only plankton shells but also fossils of bizarre swimming reptiles, fish, and invertebrates—species absent in the seas of today. Clearly, when the chalk was deposited, warm seas holding unfamiliar creatures covered some of what is dry land today.

Clues in his humble piece of chalk allowed Huxley to demonstrate to his audience that the landscape features and living inhabitants of the Earth in the past differ markedly from those today and thus that the Earth has a history. Geologic research of the past few centuries has led to the conclusion that physical and biological components of the Earth System have interacted pervasively during this long history, in ways that have transformed a formerly barren, crater-pocked surface into countless environments and landscapes supporting a diversity of life.

In this chapter, we offer a concise geologic biography of our planet, from its birth 4.54 billion years ago to the present. We illustrate how continents came into existence and have waltzed across the globe ever since. We also describe mountain-building events, changes in Earth's climate and sea level through time, and the evolution of life. To simplify the discussion, remember that we use the following abbreviations: Ga for billion years ago, Ma for million years ago, and Ka for thousand years ago.

13.2 Methods for Studying the Past

When historians outline human history, they describe daily life, wars, economics, governments, leaders, inventions, and explorations. When geologists outline Earth history, they describe the changes of depositional environments, mountain-building events (orogenies), past climates, the rise and fall in sea level, life evolution, the past configuration of plate boundaries and continents, and changes in the composition of the atmosphere and oceans. Historians collect data by reading written accounts, examining relics and monuments, and for more recent events, listening to recordings or watching videos. Geologists collect data by examining rocks, geologic structures, and fossils and, for more recent events, by studying sediments, ice cores, and tree rings.

Figuring out Earth's past hasn't been an easy task for geologists. The record that we can see isn't complete, because the materials that hold the record of the past don't form continuously through time and many important clues have been eroded away and/or covered by younger rocks. Also, it can be very challenging to obtain and interpret accurate isotopic ages of old rocks. Nevertheless, enough of the record exists to outline major geologic events of the past. Following are a few examples of how geologists use observational data to study Earth history.

- *Identifying ancient orogens:* We identify present-day orogens (mountain belts) by finding regions of high, rugged peaks. However, since it takes as little as 50 million years to erode a mountain range entirely away, we cannot identify orogens of the past simply by studying topography. Rather, we look for the rock record that orogeny leaves behind. Orogeny causes igneous activity, deformation, and metamorphism. Thus, a belt of crust containing these features represents an ancient orogen (**Fig. 13.2**). We can determine the age of an orogeny by isotopically dating the metamorphic and igneous rocks that crop out in the orogen. Orogeny also leads to the development of unconformities, for uplift exposes rocks to erosion. It also leads to the formation of sedimentary basins in which the detritus, produced by erosion of mountains, accumulates. These basins, which border the orogen, develop because the weight of the orogen pushes the lithosphere's surface down, forming a depression that traps sediment.

- *Recognizing the growth of continents:* Not all continental crust formed at the same time. To determine how a continent grew, geologists find the ages of different regions of the crust by using isotopic dating techniques. They can figure out not only when rocks originally formed from magmas rising out of the mantle but also when the rocks were metamorphosed during a subsequent orogeny. The identities of the rock types making up the crust indicate the tectonic environment in which the crust formed.

- *Recognizing past depositional environments:* The environment at a particular location changes through time. To learn about these changes, we study successions of sedimentary rocks, for depositional environment controls both the type of sediment accumulating at a location and the type of organisms that live there.

- *Recognizing past changes in relative sea level:* We can determine when sea level has gone up or down by looking for changes in the depositional environment. For example, a marine limestone above an alluvial-fan conglomerate indicates a rise in sea level.

- *Recognizing positions of continents in the past:* To help us find out where a continent was located in the past, we have three sources of information. First, apparent polar-wander paths give us a sense of continental movement (see Chapter 3; **Fig. 13.3a**). Second, marine magnetic anomalies

FIGURE 13.1 Horizontal chalk beds exposed along the coast of southern England, formed from layers of deep-sea sediment. The thin, dark beds, between white chalk layers, consist of chert. The chalk erodes easily, so the pebbles on the beach all consist of chert.

Bedding

Person

FIGURE 13.2 Evidence of mountain building in the past. Even after the topography of a mountain belt has eroded away, a record of mountain building remains; deformed and metamorphosed rock defines a distinct belt.

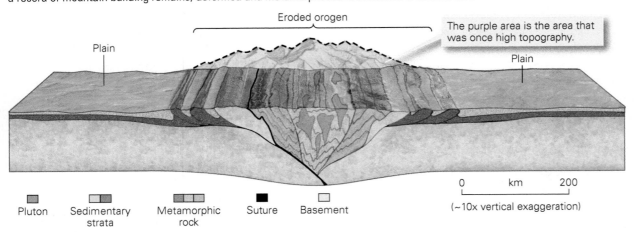

Eroded orogen

The purple area is the area that was once high topography.

Plain

Plain

0   km   200
(~10x vertical exaggeration)

Pluton   Sedimentary strata   Metamorphic rock   Suture   Basement

define changes in the ocean basin width between continents over time (Fig. 13.3b). Third, comparison of rocks and/or fossils from different continents permits correlations that indicate whether continents were adjacent.

- *Recognizing past climates:* We can gain insight into past climates by looking at fossils and rock types that formed at given latitudes. For example, if organisms requiring semitropical conditions lived near the poles during a given time period, then the atmosphere overall must have been warmer. Geologists have also learned how to use the ratios of certain isotopes in fossil shells as an indication of past temperatures.
- *Recognizing life evolution:* Progressive changes in the assemblage of fossils in a sequence of strata represent changes in the assemblage of organisms inhabiting Earth through time and thus characterize life's evolution.

As you read the following sections describing specific events in Earth's history, try to think about how geologists used the tools that we've just described to identify and characterize the event.

Take-Home Message

We can reconstruct geologic history from a variety of clues. Outcrops of deformed and metamorphosed rocks indicate where mountain belts once existed, the character and distribution of sedimentary strata provide clues to the timing of sea-level rise and fall and to the nature of past environments, study of paleomagnetism and correlation of rock units allows researchers to constrain the past positions of continents relative to one another, and the fossil record provides a window into the evolution of life.

QUICK QUESTION: How can you determine the numerical age of an ancient orogen?

13.3 The Hadean and Before

Formation of the Earth, Revisited

The current scientific interpretation of the Solar System's formation places the beginning of the process at about 4.570 Ga, when a supernova explosion sent shock waves, as well as atoms of heavier elements, into a nebula within our region of the Milky Way Galaxy. (Note: We're adding an extra decimal to the ages in our discussion here, so as to distinguish among events that happened fairly soon after one another. The ages given have a precision of about ± 0.003 Ga, but their accuracy remains a subject of research.) Perhaps stimulated by the shock waves, this nebula collapsed rapidly to form the Sun, which ignited around 4.567 Ga.

According to the nebular theory of Solar System formation that we discussed in Chapter 1, during the next million years a protoplanetary disc formed, and dust and ice condensed in the disc. Based on the isotopic dating of meteorites, thought to be remnants of the earliest planetesimals, the planetesimals soon began to grow and between 4.560 and 4.540, several had grown into sizable protoplanets by sweeping in material from their orbit. Once they got large enough and hot enough, protoplanets underwent **differentiation**, during which iron within the body began to melt and gravity pulled the iron down to the center of the planet where it accumulated to form the core. Core formation left behind a mantle composed of ultramafic rock. (Recall that the heat leading to differentiation came from the compression of matter into a dense ball, the transfer of kinetic energy of colliding

FIGURE 13.3 Paleomagnetic tools that geologists used to determine the past positions of the continents.

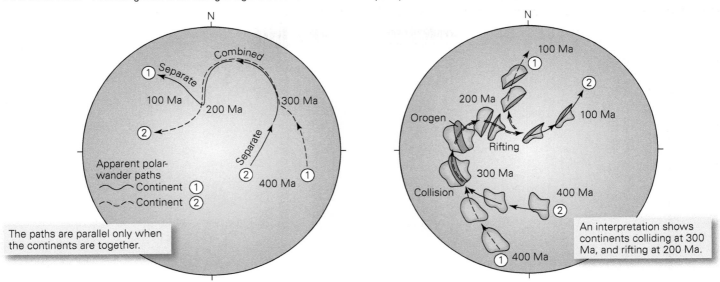

(a) Comparison of the apparent polar-wander paths for two continents indicates when they moved together and when they moved separately.

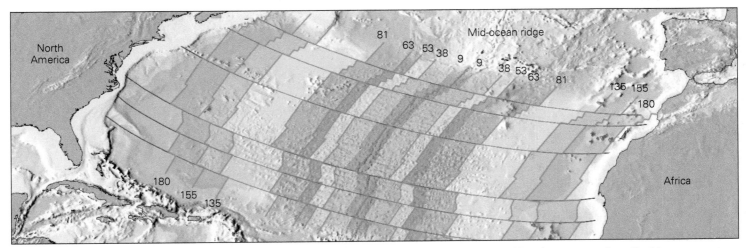

(b) Marine magnetic anomalies indicate how the distance between continents separated by a mid-ocean ridge changes over time. On this map, the age of anomaly boundaries is indicated in Ma.

objects into thermal energy, and the production of heat by decay of relatively abundant radioactive elements.) By about 4.540 Ga, the largest protoplanets had differentiated, as indicated by isotopic ages of meteorites thought to be remnants of differentiated planetesimals, and had swept their orbits clear of debris, thus attaining the status of "planet" (see Chapter 1). In the context of this scenario, geologists use 4.540 Ga as the birth date of the Earth.

Events of the Hadean

The newborn Earth started to cool and stabilize, but it didn't remain unscathed for long. At about 4.533, it cataclysmically collided with a protoplanet named *Theia*. This event blasted much of the Earth's mantle into orbit and may have added new material from the colliding object into the Earth's remaining mantle and core. The orbiting debris quickly coalesced into the Moon, which, at the time of its formation, was only 20,000 km from the Earth—by comparison, the Moon is 384,000 km from Earth today, and it continues to move farther away at about 3.8 cm per year.

In the wake of Moon formation, the Earth was so hot that much of its surface was probably an ocean of seething magma (**Fig. 13.4a**). But temperature rapidly diminished as heat radiated into space and the supply of new heat from radioactive decay diminished (because elements with short half-lives had

(a) At a very early stage, during or after differentiation, the surface might have been largely molten. The loss of heat to space would allow patches of solid ultramafic solid crust to form. Meteorite impacts could have then destroyed the crust.

(b) When Earth's surface fell below the boiling point of water, water from the atmosphere rained onto the surface, submerging it with early oceans.

decayed). Rafts of solid rock formed on the surface of the magma ocean, but most of these eventually sank and remelted to be recycled into new rocks. In addition, rapid outgassing took place, meaning that volatile (gassy) elements or compounds originally incorporated in mantle minerals were released and erupted at the Earth's surface, along with lava. These gases accumulated to constitute a toxic atmosphere consisting mostly of water (H_2O), methane (CH_4), ammonia (NH_3), hydrogen (H_2), nitrogen (N_2), carbon dioxide (CO_2), and sulfur dioxide (SO_2). Some researchers speculate that gases from comets colliding with Earth may have contributed additional gases to the early atmosphere.

By about 4.4 Ga, the Earth might have become cool enough for a solid crust and even liquid water to exist at its surface (**Fig. 13.4b**). The evidence for this statement comes from grains of a durable mineral called zircon, which has been extracted from much younger sandstone beds exposed in Western Australia. The zircons, which yield isotopic ages of 4.4 Ga, formed originally in an igneous rock, indicating the Earth was cool enough for rock to solidify. Further, isotopic ratios of oxygen in the zircon indicate that it possibly was altered by interaction with surface water, hinting at the presence of early oceans. What did the Earth's surface look like at this time? An observer from space probably would have found small, barren landmasses spotted with volcanoes poking up above an acidic sea. But both land and sea would have been obscured by murky, dense (H_2O-, CO_2-, and SO_2-rich) air.

Take-Home Message

The Earth formed not long after the birth of the Sun. It differentiated and swept its orbit clear of debris by about 4.54 Ga, a date taken as the birth of the Earth. Very little record remains of the first half-billion years of Earth history. During the Hadean (4.57–3.85 Ga), the Earth differentiated and the Moon formed. A rock record of this eon doesn't exist because our planet's surface may have been partially molten and rapidly recycled by remelting.

QUICK QUESTION: When might the earliest liquid water on the Earth have accumulated? What's the evidence?

13.4 The Archean Eon: Birth of Continents and Life

The Transition from Planet Formation to Planet Evolution

Though mineral grains as old as 4.4 Ga exist, most rocks are younger than 3.85 Ga. What destroyed most, if not all, of the pre-3.85-Ga rock (and any oceans, if they existed) of the Earth? The answer may come from studies of cratering on the Moon. These studies suggest that the Moon—and, therefore, all inner planets of the Solar System—underwent a period of intense meteorite bombardment, called the *late heavy bombardment*, between about 4.0 and 3.85 Ga. Researchers speculate that this event would have pulverized and/or melted almost all crust that had existed on Earth at the time and would have destroyed the existing atmosphere and ocean. Only after the bombardment ceased could longer-lasting crust, atmosphere, and oceans begin to form. In addition to bombardment, convective movements involving mantle and crust may have continuously recycled crust—in effect, soon after an area of crust formed, it might have been subducted and remelted.

The discovery of 3.85-Ga marine sedimentary rocks in Greenland suggests that the appearance or reappearance of land, sea, and an atmosphere happened at about 3.85 Ga. The end of the Hadean was once placed at 3.85 Ga, the time at which the late heavy bombardment ceased, and the rock record becomes fairly complete. Now geologists consider the end of the Hadean to be at 4.0 Ga, essentially the age of the oldest-known rock and thus the time at which planet formation processes had ceased and the record of the rocks begins. The next eon of Earth history is the **Archean**, from the Greek words *arkhaios* meaning ancient and *arche* meaning beginning.

Land Appears

With the advent of the Archean, the Earth's crust was cool and stable enough for isotopic clocks to start ticking; the rate of crustal recycling decreased, and marine strata started to be preserved. Thus, the Earth of the Archean clearly had land and sea, a situation that has persisted ever since. Geologists still argue about whether plate tectonics in the form that occurs today operated in the early part of the Archean Eon. Most researchers picture an early Archean Earth with rapidly moving small plates, numerous volcanic island arcs, and abundant hot-spot volcanoes—the rates of plate-tectonic processes may have been faster in the Archean than they are today because the Earth's interior was hotter (due to the availability of more radioactive atoms and to leftover heat from planet formation). Others propose that early Archean lithosphere was too warm and buoyant to subduct and that plate tectonics could not have operated until the later part of the Archean; these authors argue that plume-related volcanism was the main source of new crust until the late Archean. Regardless of which model ultimately proves more correct, it is clear that the Archean was a time during which significant volumes of new continental crust came into existence.

What processes produced continental crust? According to one model, early crust formed from mafic igneous rocks that originally extruded or intruded at convergent plate boundaries and/or at hot-spot volcanoes. When the arcs and oceanic plateaus collided with one another, they sutured together to form larger, relatively buoyant blocks that remained at the Earth's surface.

The development of convergent-plate boundaries along the margins of these blocks, and of rifts and hot-spot volcanoes within the blocks, led to production of flood basalts. Partial melting of basaltic crust, perhaps at or near its base, yielded felsic and intermediate magmas, which rose and solidified in the upper crust or were extruded at the surface. Thus, with time, continents differentiated into a more mafic lower crust and a more felsic upper crust. As collisions continued, the blocks coalesced into still larger *protocontinents* (**Fig. 13.5**), which slowly cooled and became stronger. As a result of these processes, the first long-lived blocks of durable continental crust came into existence between 3.2 and 2.7 Ga, and by the end of the Archean Eon about 80% of the Earth's continental area had formed (**Fig. 13.6**). Since that time, relatively little "juvenile" (newly extracted from the mantle) rock has formed. Most rock that is younger than about 2.7 Ga is "recycled" in the sense that it either has gone through various stages of the rock cycle in the crust (see Interlude C) or it has been carried back into the mantle where it subsequently became incorporated in new magma.

A clear stratigraphic record of marine sediment deposition has been preserved in remnants of Archean crust, indicating that oceans filled in the Archean and have existed ever since. Permanent oceans could survive only after the Earth's surface had cooled below the boiling point of water. Prior to that time, gaseous H_2O saturated the atmosphere—in fact, prior to ocean formation, H_2O and CO_2 were the dominant gases of the atmosphere. Once the oceans formed, however, the atmosphere lost most of its H_2O. And once liquid water existed, substantial amounts of atmospheric CO_2 dissolved into it. Thus, the Archean saw the atmosphere transform from a foggy mixture of H_2O and CO_2 into a transparent gas dominantly composed of N_2 gas. Since N_2 is inert, meaning it doesn't chemically react with or dissolve in other materials, it was left behind and became the major component of the atmosphere.

Archean cratons contain five principal rock types: *gneiss*, relicts of Archean metamorphism in collisional zones; *greenstone*, metamorphosed relicts of ocean crust trapped between colliding blocks of continental crust, as well of basalts that had filled early continental rifts, basalts produced at hot spots, and basaltic volcanoes of island arcs; *granite*, formed from magmas generated by the partial melting of the crust in continental volcanic arcs or above hot spots; *graywacke*, a mixture of sand and clay eroded from the volcanic areas and dumped into the ocean; and *chert*, formed by the precipitation of silica in the deep sea. Archean shallow-water sediments are rare, either because continents were so small that depositional environments in which such sediments could accumulate didn't exist or because any that were present have eroded away.

Once land areas had formed, rivers flowed over their stark, unvegetated surfaces. Geologists reached this conclusion because sedimentary beds from this time contain clastic grains

FIGURE 13.5 A model for crust formation during the Archean Eon.

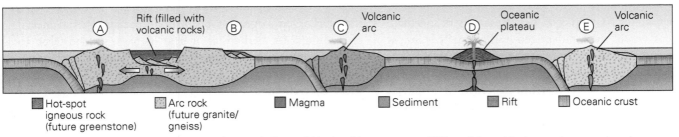

(a) In the Archean, island arcs and hot-spot volcanoes built small blocks of buoyant crust. Rifting of these blocks may have produced flood basalts, and erosion of the blocks produced sediment. (Not to scale.)

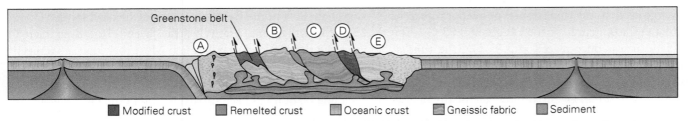

(b) Buoyant blocks collided and sutured together, forming protocontinents. Melting at depth produced granite. Eventually, regions of crust cooled, stabilized, and became cratons. (Not to scale.)

(c) An exposure of Archean rock in the Upper Peninsula of Michigan. This rock, migmatite, was once buried so deeply that it started to melt.

that were clearly rounded by transport in liquid water. Salts that weathered out of rock and were transported to the sea by rivers made the oceans salty.

The First Life

Clearly, the Archean Eon saw many firsts in Earth history. Not only did the first continents appear during the Archean but probably also the first life. Geologists use three sources of evidence to identify early life.

- *Chemical (molecular) fossils, or biomarkers:* These are durable chemicals that represent pieces of larger molecules produced by the metabolism of living organisms.

- *Isotopic signatures:* By analyzing the ratio of ^{12}C to ^{13}C in carbon-rich sediment, geologists can determine if the sediment once contained the bodies of organisms because organisms preferentially incorporate ^{12}C.

- *Fossil forms:* Given appropriate depositional conditions, fossils of bacteria or archaea cells can be preserved in rock. However, identification of such fossil forms remains controversial—similar shapes can result from inorganic crystal growth.

The search for the earliest evidence of life continues to make headlines in the popular media (**Box 13.1**). Most geologists currently conclude that life has existed on Earth since at least 3.5 Ga, and perhaps since 3.8 Ga, for rocks of this age contain isotopic signatures of organisms. The oldest undisputed body fossils of bacteria and archaea occur in 3.2-Ga

FIGURE 13.6 As time progressed, the area of the Earth covered by continental crust increased. Most crust had formed by the beginning of the Proterozoic.

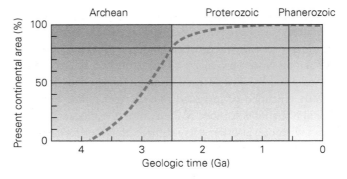

rocks (Fig. 13.7a)—shapes resembling such organisms occur in rocks as old as 3.4 to 3.5 Ga, but their identity remains less certain. Some rocks of this age contain **stromatolites**, distinctive mounds of sediment, some of which were produced by mats of cyanobacteria. Such stromatolites form because cyanobacteria secrete a mucus-like substance to which sediment settling from water sticks. As the mat gets buried, new cyanobacteria colonize the top of the sediment, building a mound upward (Fig. 13.7b); modern examples locally occur in shallow, tropical waters (Fig. 13.7c). Biomarkers in Archean sediments indicate that photosynthetic organisms appeared by 2.7 Ga.

By the end of the Archean, and perhaps as early as 3.5 Ga, organisms similar to cyanobacteria evolved the ability to carry out photosynthesis and moved into shallower, well-lit water. Though these organisms produced oxygen, very little of it accumulated in the atmosphere, for it was either dissolved in the sea or absorbed by weathering reactions with rocks. Thus, though the composition of the Earth's atmosphere at the end of the Archean differed significantly from that of the atmosphere that existed at the start of the Hadean, it was still unbreathable. It probably consisted mostly of about 75% N_2 gas and 25% CO_2 gas, with only traces of oxygen.

As the Archean Eon came to a close, the first continents had formed, and life colonized not only the depths of the sea but also the shallow-marine realm. Plate tectonics had commenced, continental drift was taking place, collisional mountain belts were forming, and erosion was occurring. Oxygen was beginning to enter the air but had not yet accumulated in any significant quantity—the air would not be breathable. The stage was set for another major change in the Earth System.

Take-Home Message

The Archean (4.0–2.5 Ga) began with the late heavy bombardment, during which almost all crust was destroyed. A solid crust, reformed by cooling of the mantle's skin, appeared soon after, and by 3.8 Ga, oceans formed and have existed ever since. Plate-tectonic-like activity probably began in the Archean; there were also huge mantle plumes. During this eon, the first continental crust formed from colliding volcanic arcs and hot-spot volcanoes, the atmosphere changed, and life appeared. By the end of the eon, the first continents existed.

QUICK QUESTION: What kinds of rock form the blocks of Archean crust that remain today?

FIGURE 13.7 Archean life forms.

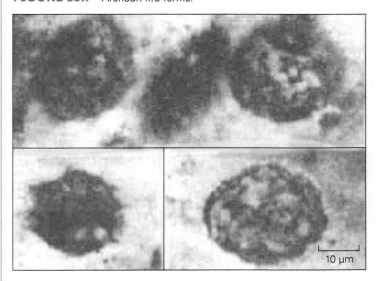

(a) These shapes in 3.2-Ga chert from South America are thought to be fossil bacteria or archaea.

(b) This weathered outcrop of 1.85-Ga dolostone near Marquette, Michigan, reveals the layer-like structure of stromatolites. The delicate ridges represent the fossilized remnants of bacterial mats. Similar stromatolites also occur in exposures of Archean rocks.

(c) Modern stromatolites in Sharks Bay, Western Australia.

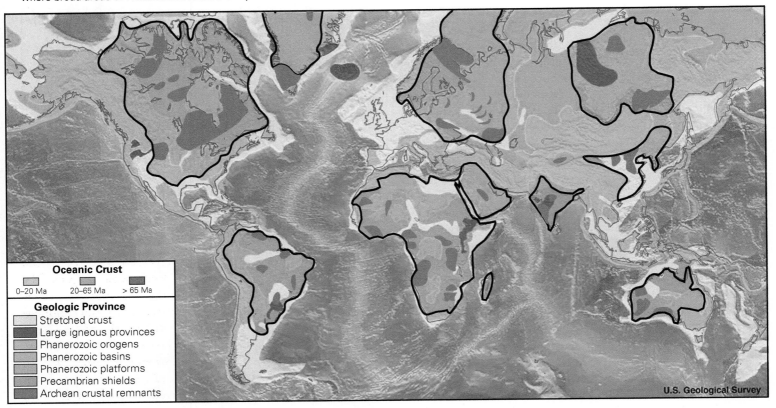

Oceanic Crust
0–20 Ma   20–65 Ma   > 65 Ma

Geologic Province
Stretched crust
Large igneous provinces
Phanerozoic orogens
Phanerozoic basins
Phanerozoic platforms
Precambrian shields
Archean crustal remnants

U.S. Geological Survey

13.5 The Proterzoic Eon: The Earth in Transition

Continued Growth of Continents

The **Proterozoic Eon** (from the Greek meaning earlier life) spans roughly 2 billion years, from about 2.5 Ga to the beginning of the Cambrian Period at 541 Ma—thus, it encompasses almost half of Earth's history. During Proterozoic time, Earth's surface environment changed from being an unfamiliar world of small, fast-moving plates, small continents, and an oxygen-free atmosphere, to the more familiar world of mostly large, slow-moving plates, large continents, and an oxygenated atmosphere.

First, let's look at changes to the continents. New continental crust continued to form during the Proterozoic Eon but at progressively slower rates, and by the middle of the eon over 90% of the Earth's continental crust had formed. In addition, collisions between Archean continental blocks, and between these blocks and volcanic island arcs or hot-spot volcanoes, gradually assembled larger continents. Size matters when it comes to the geologic behavior of continents, for the interior of

a larger continent can be isolated from heating by subduction-related igneous activity that happened along its margins. Such interior regions, therefore, slowly cool and strengthen until they become rigid and durable. The resulting region of cold, relatively stable continental crust, as we have seen, is called a **craton**. All cratons that exist today had formed by about 1 Ga (Fig. 13.8), meaning that the crust of cratons ranges from 3.85 Ga to about 1 Ga. Thus, cratons are the old, long-lived parts of continents.

To understand the character of a craton, let's examine North America's craton a bit more closely. We see that it consists of two regions (Fig. 13.9). Throughout the **shield**, outcrops expose Precambrian "basement," which consists of igneous and metamorphic rocks older than about 1 Ga. The landscape of the shield tends to have fairly low relief—there are small hills and valleys but no dramatic mountain ranges. Most of North America's shield lies in Canada, so geologists refer to it as the Canadian Shield. Throughout the **cratonic platform**, which surrounds the shield and also underlies Hudson Bay, a blanket or "cover" of Paleozoic or Mesozoic strata overlies the Precambrian basement. In the eastern platform of North America, Paleozoic strata are the youngest bedrock, whereas in the western platform most of the Paleozoic strata are covered

BOX 13.1 CONSIDER THIS . . .

Where Was the Cradle of Life?

What specific environment on the Archean Earth served as the cradle of life? Laboratory experiments conducted in the 1950s led many researchers to think that life began in warm pools of surface water, beneath a methane- and ammonia-rich atmosphere streaked by bolts of lightning (see Interlude E). The only problem with this hypothesis is that more recent evidence suggests that the early atmosphere consisted mostly of CO_2 and N_2, with relatively little methane and ammonia. Thus, some researchers suggest instead that submarine hot-water vents, so-called black smokers, served as the hosts of the first organisms. These vents emit clouds of ion-charged solutions from which sulfide minerals precipitate and build chimneys. The chimney's are hollow, and their surfaces act like membranes in keeping two chemically distinct environments separate. This differ-ence creates a weak electric charge, perhaps providing energy for "proto-life" molecules, molecules that have structures that resemble proteins of living organisms, to start developing. The earliest life in the Archean Eon may well have been thermophilic (heat-loving) bacteria or archaea that originated at deep-sea hydrothermal vents and dined on pyrite at dark depths in the ocean alongside these vents.

---

by Mesozoic and Cenozoic strata derived from sediments eroded from mountains to the west.

By using isotopic dating on samples from both outcrops and drill holes, geologists have been able to subdivide the Precambrian basement of North America's craton into distinct provinces, each of which has been given a name (Fig. 13.10). It appears that the Canadian Shield consists of several Archean crustal blocks sutured together by Proterozoic orogens. The basement of the cratonic platform in the United States, in contrast, grew when a series of volcanic island arcs and continental slivers accreted, or attached, to the margin of the Canadian Shield between 1.8 and 1.6 Ga—these accreted belts are known as the Yavapai and Mazatzal Provinces, respectively. In the Midwest, granite plutons intruded much of this accreted region, and rhyolite ash flows covered it, due to widespread felsic igneous activity between 1.5 and 1.3 Ga.

Successive collisions ultimately brought together most continental crust on Earth into a single supercontinent, named **Rodinia**, by around 1 Ga. The last major collision during the formation of Rodinia was the **Grenville orogeny**. The resulting Grenville orogen was likely as huge as the present-day Himalayas. If you look at a popular (though not universally accepted) reconstruction of Rodinia, you can identify the crustal provinces that would eventually become the familiar continents of today (Fig. 13.11a). Several studies suggest that sometime between 800 and 600 Ma, Rodinia effectively turned inside out in that Antarctica, India, and Australia broke away from western North America and later collided with the future South America, possibly forming a short-lived supercontinent that some geologists refer to as *Pannotia* (Fig. 13.11b).

Life Becomes More Complex

The map of the Earth clearly changed radically during the Proterozoic. But that's not all that changed—fossil evidence suggests that this eon also saw important steps in the evolution of life. When the Proterozoic began, most life was *pro-karyotic*, meaning that it consisted of single-celled organisms (archaea and bacteria) without a nucleus. Studies of chemical fossils (biomarkers; see Interlude E) hint that *eukaryotic* life, consisting of cells that have nuclei, originated as early as 2.7

FIGURE 13.9 On this map of North America, we see four different geologic provinces: shield areas, where Precambrian rocks of the craton crop out; platform areas, where Phanerozoic sedimentary rocks have buried Precambrian rocks. Phanerozoic orogenic belts composed of rocks deformed during the past half-billion years, and the coastal plain, which is underlain by Cretaceous and Cenozoic strata.

Craton
- Mesozoic cover
- Paleozoic cover
- Shield

Shield

Shield

Western platform

CRATON

USA Rocky Mountains

Cordillera

Colorado Plateau

Eastern platform

Appalachians

Coastal Plain

Ouachitas

Orogens
- Phanerozoic orogens
- Platform strata within Rocky Mts.

FIGURE 13.10 The North American craton consists of a collage of different belts and blocks stitched together during collisional and accretionary orogenies of Precambrian time.

Explanation

G = Grenville; M = Mazatal; Y = Yavapai;

P = Penokean; THO = Trans-Hudson orogen;

WY = Wyoming; WT = Wopmay; T = Thelon;

S = Superior; M = Mojave; RH = Rae and Hearn;

SL = Slave

— Edge of the craton

— Pre-1.8 and post-1.8 Ga crust boundary

☐ Proterozeroic rifts of various ages

☐ Grenville orogen (1.3 – 1.0 Ga)

⊞ Granite-rhyolite province (1.5 – 1.3 Ga)

☐ Mazatzal accreted crust (1.7 – 1.6 Ga)

☐ Yavapai accreted crust (1.8 – 1.7 Ga)

☐ Proterozoic collisional orogens (1.9 – 1.8 Ga)

☐ Proterozoic accreted crust (2.0 – 1.8 Ga)

☐ Archean provinces (> 2.5 Ga)

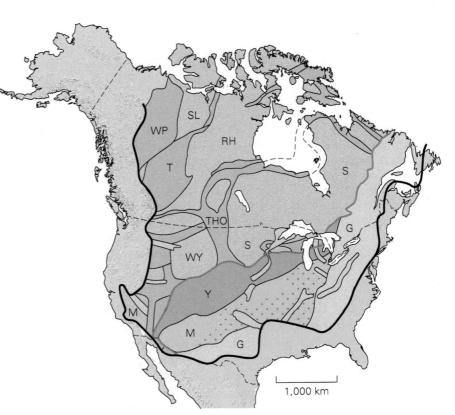

FIGURE 13.11 Supercontinents in the late Precambrian.

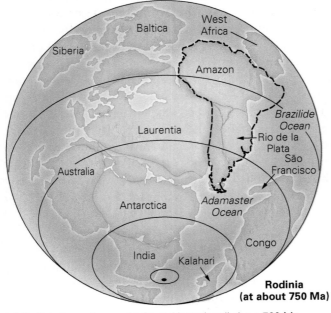

**Rodinia
(at about 750 Ma)**

(a) Rodinia formed around 1 Ga and lasted until about 700 Ma. North America and Greenland together comprise Laurentia.

**Pannotia
(at about 570 Ma)**

(b) According to one model, by 570 Ma Rodinia had broken apart; continents that once lay to the west of Laurentia ended up to the east of Africa. The resulting supercontinent, Pannotia, broke up soon after it formed.

Ga, but the first body fossils of eukaryotic organism appear in 2.1 Ga rocks, and abundant body fossils of eukaryotic organisms can be found only in rocks younger than about 1.5 Ga. Thus, the proliferation of eukaryotic life, the foundation from which complex organisms eventually evolved, took place during the Proterozoic.

The last half-billion years of the Proterozoic Eon saw the remarkable transition from simple organisms into complex ones. Ciliate protozoans (single-celled organisms coated with fibers that give them mobility) appear at about 750 Ma. A great leap forward in complexity of organisms occurred during the next 150 million years of the eon, for sediments deposited perhaps as early as 620 Ma and certainly by 565 Ma contain several types of multicellular animals that together constitute the **Ediacaran fauna**, named for a region in southern Australia where fossils of these organisms were first found. Ediacaran species survived into the beginning of the Cambrian before becoming extinct. Their fossil forms suggest that some of these invertebrate organisms resembled jellyfish, while others resembled worms (**Fig. 13.12a**).

FIGURE 13.12 Major changes in the Earth System during the Proterozoic Eon.

(a) *Dicksonia*, a fossil of the Ediacaran fauna. These complex, soft-bodied marine organisms appeared in the late Proterozoic.

(b) An outcrop of BIF in the Iron Ranges of Michigan's Upper Peninsula. The red stripes are jasper (red chert) and the gray stripes are hematite. The rock was folded during a mountain-building event long after deposition. The hammer indicates scale.

Strata contain large clasts surrounded by mudstone, for glaciers can carry clasts of all sizes.

Bedding

(c) Layers of Proterozoic glacial till crop out in Africa, indicating that low-latitude landmasses were glaciated during the Proterozoic.

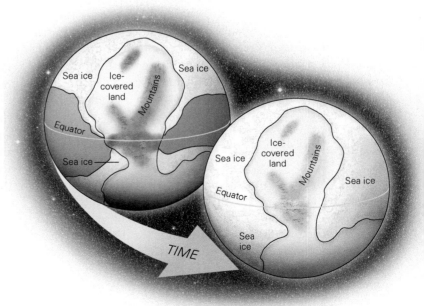

(d) This planet may have frozen over completely to form "snowball Earth." Glaciers first grew on land, and eventually the sea surface froze over.

The evolution of life played a key role in the evolution of Earth's atmosphere. Before life appeared, there was hardly any free oxygen (O_2) in the atmosphere. With the appearance of photosynthetic organisms, oxygen began to enter the atmosphere. But it was not until about 2.4 Ga that the concentration of oxygen in the atmosphere increased dramatically. This event, called the **great oxygenation event**, happened when the land and sea were no longer able to react with, absorb, or dissolve all the oxygen produced by organisms, so the oxygen began to accumulate as a gas in air.

One of the important consequences of this change is that the oceans became oxidizing environments (meaning that they contained atoms, such as oxygen, that could transfer electrons to other atoms). Iron atoms, in particular, can pick up electrons and thus become *oxidized*. Oxidized iron is not soluble in water, so when the oceans became oxidizing, they could no longer contain large quantities of dissolved iron. Between 2.4 Ga and 1.8 Ga, as the atmosphere became oxidizing, huge amounts of iron settled out of the ocean to form colorful sedimentary beds known as banded iron formation (BIF). *BIF* consists of alternating layers, or bands, of iron oxide minerals (hematite or magnetite) and jasper (red chert) (**Fig. 13.12b**). Though BIF did form in the Archean, most of the world's BIF, humanity's primary source of iron for making steel, accumulated between 2.4 and 1.8 Ga, implying that the transition to an oxygenated atmosphere was complete by about 1.8 Ga. Other geological evidence reinforces this idea, as described in **Box 13.2**.

The great oxygenation event profoundly influenced the evolution of life in the Earth System. Life could become more complex because oxygen-dependent (aerobic) metabolism can produce energy much more efficiently than can oxygen-free (anaerobic) metabolism—eating sulfide minerals may sustain an archaea cell, but it can't keep a multicellular organism alive. Addition of oxygen to the atmosphere also made the land surface habitable, because some oxygen in the air reacted to produce ozone (O_3) molecules, which absorb deadly ultraviolet radiation from the Sun and prevent it from reaching the surface.

Snowball Earth

Study of Proterozoic strata indicates that radical climate shifts took place near the end of the Proterozoic Eon. Specifically, researchers have found accumulations of glacial sediments in late Proterozoic stratigraphic sequences worldwide. What's strange about the occurrence of these sediments is that they occur even in regions that were located at the equator at the time they were deposited (**Fig. 13.12c**). This observation implies that the entire planet was cold enough at the end of

the Proterozoic for glaciers to grow at all latitudes. Geologists still are debating the character and history of these global ice ages (see Chapter 22), but in one model, glaciers covered all land, and the entire ocean surface froze. The ice-covered globe that our planet may have become at the end of the Proterozoic has come to be known as **snowball Earth** (**Fig. 13.12d**).

Did you ever wonder . . .

if the oceans have ever frozen over entirely?

The shell of ice covering snowball Earth would have cut off the oceans from the atmosphere, and many life forms died off. Earth might have remained a snowball forever were it not for volcanic CO_2. The icy sheath covering the oceans prevented atmospheric CO_2 from dissolving in seawater, but it did not prevent volcanic activity from continuing to add CO_2 to the atmosphere. CO_2 is a greenhouse gas, meaning that it traps heat in the atmosphere much as glass panes trap heat in a greenhouse (see Chapter 23), so as the CO_2 concentration increased, Earth warmed up and eventually the glaciers melted. Life may have survived snowball Earth conditions only near submarine black smokers and near hot springs. When the ice vanished, life rapidly expanded into new environments, where new species, such as those of the Ediacaran fauna, evolved.

Transition to the Phanerozoic Eon

As the Proterozoic came to a close, Earth's climate warmed and rifting broke apart the late Proterozoic supercontinent. As continents drifted apart, life evolved and diversified to occupy the many new environments that formed. Over a relatively short period of time, shells appeared and the fossil record became much more complete. This event defines the end of the Proterozoic Eon, and therefore of the Precambrian, and the start of the Phanerozoic Eon. Of note, geologists recognized the significance of this event long before they could assign it a numerical age (currently 541 Ma).

The **Phanerozoic Eon** (Greek for visible life) encompasses the last 541 million years of Earth history. Its name reflects the appearance of diverse organisms with hard shells or skeletons that became the well-preserved fossils you can find easily in sedimentary rock outcrops. The Phanerozoic Eon consists of three eras—the Paleozoic (Greek for ancient life), the Mesozoic (middle life), and the Cenozoic (recent life). Geologists have divided the Mesozoic and Cenozoic each into three periods and the Paleozoic into six periods. In the sections that follow, we consider changes in the map of our planet's surface (its *paleogeography*), as manifested by the distribution of continents, seas, and mountain belts, as well as life evolution that happened during the three eras.

BOX 13.2   CONSIDER THIS . . .

The Evolution of Atmospheric Oxygen

Without oxygen, the great variety of life that exists on Earth could not survive. Presently, the atmosphere contains 21% oxygen, but this has not always been the case. Throughout most of the Archean Eon and into the beginning of the Proterozoic Eon, the atmosphere contained less than 1% oxygen. Several lines of evidence lead geologists to conclude that a transformation from an oxygen-poor to an oxygen-rich atmosphere occurred during the great oxygenation event, a period lasting from about 2.4 to about 1.8 Ga, the early part of the Proterozoic.

As noted earlier, one line of evidence comes from studying the deposition of BIFs, a process that could only have happened in an oxygenated environment. Another line of evidence comes from examining clastic grains in sandstones. In sediments deposited before 1.8 Ga, well-formed pyrite (iron sulfide) occurs as clasts in sediment. This could only be pos-

sible if the atmosphere before 1.8 Ga contained very little oxygen, for in an oxygen-rich atmosphere, pyrite rapidly undergoes chemical weathering (oxidation) and doesn't survive long enough at the Earth's surface to become a sedimentary clast. A third line of evidence comes from studying the age of *redbeds*, clastic sedimentary rocks colored by the presence of bright red hematite (iron oxide). Redbeds form when oxygen-rich groundwater flows through sediment during lithification, and such rocks appear in the geologic record only after 1.8 Ga.

Oxygen concentration in the atmosphere has changed considerably over Earth's history. As we have noted, it constituted less than 1% of the atmosphere during the Archean. By 1.8 Ga, after the great oxygenation event, it had risen to about 3% and stayed at roughly that level until about 0.6 Ga (**Fig. Bx13.2**). Then, because all the materials on land and in the

sea that could absorb oxygen had become *saturated* and could hold no more O_2, atmospheric concentrations gradually grew, reaching about 12% at the end of the Proterozoic. The proportion grew substantially when photosynthetic organisms began to prosper on land, and it has oscillated between 35% and 15% during the past half-billion years. Oxygen concentration has remained at 21% since about 25 Ma. Keeping in mind that atmospheric oxygen comes from photosynthetic organisms, geologists suggest that increases reflect proliferation of photosynthetic life (such as land-based plants) and that decreases reflect mass-extinction events. The concentration of O_2 can't get higher than about 35%, because if it did, land plants would become explosively combustible, since oxygen feeds fire, and so much vegetation would burn that the amount of photosynthesis would decrease until oxygen levels decreased.

FIGURE Bx13.2   The change in the proportion of oxygen content in the atmosphere over time. Oxygen level remained low until the end of the Protoerozoic.

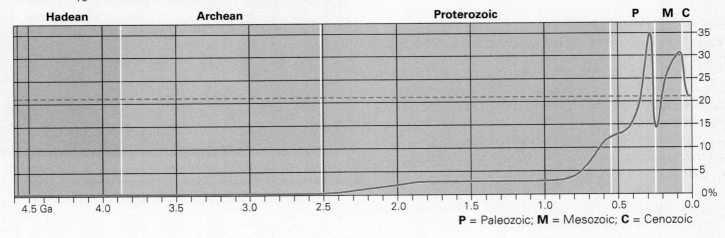

P = Paleozoic; **M** = Mesozoic; **C** = Cenozoic

Take-Home Message

During the Proterozoic (2.5–0.54 Ga), cratons formed and then sutured together to form continents and, eventually, supercontinents. The atmosphere began to accumulate significant oxygen, and the chemical behavior of the seas changed. Near the end of the eon, the Earth may have been completely ice covered. When the eon ended, the climate warmed, supercontinents rifted apart, and multicellular organisms appeared.

QUICK QUESTION: What evidence suggests that oxygen began to accumulate in the air during the Proterozoic?

FIGURE 13.13 Land and sea in the early Paleozoic Era.

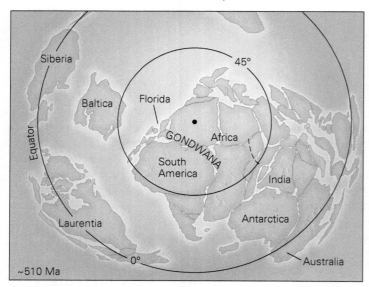

(a) The distribution of continents in the Cambrian Period (510 Ma), as viewed looking down on the South Pole.

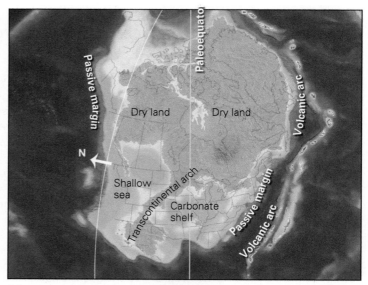

(b) A paleogeographic map of North America shows the regions of dry land and shallow sea in the Late Cambrian Period.

13.6 The Paleozoic Era: Continents Reassemble, and Life Gets Complex

The Early Paleozoic Era (Cambrian-Ordovician Periods, 541-444 Ma)

Paleogeography At the beginning of the Paleozoic Era, Pannotia broke up, yielding smaller continents, including **Laurentia** (composed of North America and Greenland), **Gondwana** (South America, Africa, Antarctica, India, and Australia), Baltica (Europe), and Siberia (**Fig.13.13a**). New passive-margin basins formed along the edges of these new continents.

Sea level rose and fell significantly multiple times during part of the early Paleozoic. At times of high sea level, transgression took place and vast areas of continental interiors became shallow seas, known as *epicontinental seas* (**Fig. 13.13b**). These regions are now cratonic platforms. In many places, water depths in epicontinental seas reached only a few meters, creating a well-lit marine environment in which life abounded, so deposition in these seas yielded layers of fossiliferous sediment. When sea level dropped, regression took place and unconformities formed. Thus, the craton was covered by unconformity-bounded sequences of sediment—the layer cake of strata in the Grand Canyon formed from such sediment (**Box 13.3**).

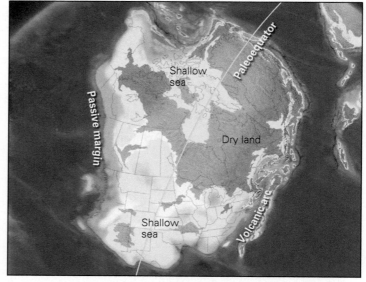

(c) During the Middle Ordovician Period, shallow seas covered much of North America. A volcanic arc formed off the east coast.

The geologically peaceful world of the early Paleozoic Era in Laurentia abruptly came to a close in the Middle Ordovician Period, for at this time its eastern margin rammed into a volcanic island arc and other crustal fragments. The resulting collision, called the *Taconic orogeny*, deformed and metamorphosed strata of the continent's margin and produced a mountain range in what is now the eastern part of the Appalachians (**Fig. 13.13c**).

Life Evolution The fossil record indicates that soon after the Cambrian began, life underwent remarkable diversification. This event, which paleontologists refer to as the **Cambrian**

explosion, took several million years (see Interlude E). What caused this event? No one can say for sure, but considering that it occurred roughly at the time a supercontinent broke up, it may have had something to do with the production of new ecological niches and the isolation of populations that resulted when small continents formed and drifted apart.

The first animals to appear in the Cambrian Period had simple tube- or cone-shaped shells, but soon thereafter the shells became more complex. Shells may have evolved as a means of protection against predation by organisms such as conodonts, small, eel-like organisms with hard parts that resemble teeth. By the end of the Cambrian, trilobites were grazing the seafloor. Trilobites shared the environment with mollusks, brachiopods, nautiloids, gastropods, graptolites, and echinoderms (Fig. 13.14; see Interlude E). Thus, a complex food chain arose, which included plankton, bottom feeders, and at the top, predators. Many of the organisms crawled over or swam around reefs composed of mounds of sponges with mineral skeletons. The Ordovician Period saw the first crinoids and the first vertebrate animals, jawless fish.

Although the sea teemed with organisms during the early Paleozoic Era, there were no land organisms for most of this time, so the land surface was a stark landscape of rock and sediment, subjected to rapid erosion rates. Our earliest record of primitive land plants and green algae comes from the Late Ordovician Period, but these plants were very small and occurred only along bodies of water. As we mentioned earlier, the invasion of the land could begin only when there was enough ozone in the atmosphere to protect the land surface from UV radiation. At the end of the Ordovician, mass extinction took place, perhaps because of a brief ice age and associated sea-level lowering of the time.

The Middle Paleozoic Era (Silurian-Devonian Periods, 444-359 Ma)

Paleogeography As the world entered the Silurian Period, the start of the middle Paleozoic, global climate warmed (leading to so-called greenhouse conditions), sea level rose, and the continents flooded once again. In some places, where water in the epicontinental seas was clear and could exchange with water from the oceans, huge reef complexes grew, forming a layer of fossiliferous limestone on the continents. Also, several orogenies took place, yielding new mountain belts during the middle Paleozoic Era. For example, collisions on the eastern side of Laurentia during Silurian and Devonian time produced the *Caledonian orogen* (affecting eastern Greenland, western Scandinavia, and Scotland) and the *Acadian orogen* in the region that is now the Appalachians (Fig. 13.15a).

Throughout much of the middle Paleozoic, the western margin of North America continued to be a passive-margin basin. But finally, in the Late Devonian, the quiet environment of the basin ceased, possibly because of a collision with an island arc. This event, known as the *Antler orogeny*, was the first of many orogenies to affect the western margin of the continent. The Caledonian, Acadian, and Antler orogenies all shed deltas of sediment onto the continents—these deposits formed thick successions of redbeds, such as those visible today in the Catskill Mountains (Fig. 13.15b, c).

Life Evolution During the middle Paleozoic Era, new species of trilobites, gastropods, crinoids, and bivalves appeared in the sea, replacing species that had disappeared during the mass extinction at the end of the Ordovician Period. On land, vascular plants with woody tissues, seeds, and veins (for transporting water and food) rooted for the first time. With the evolution of veins and wood, plants could grow much larger, and by the Late Devonian Period the land surface hosted swampy forests with tree-sized relatives of club mosses and ferns. Also at this time, spiders, scorpions, insects, and crustaceans began to exploit both dry-land and freshwater habitats, and jawed fish, including sharks and bony fish, began to cruise the oceans. Finally, at the very end of the Devonian Period, the first amphibians crawled out onto land and inhaled air with lungs (Fig. 13.15d).

The Late Paleozoic Era (Carboniferous-Permian Periods, 359-251 Ma)

Paleogeography The climate cooled significantly in the late Paleozoic (leading to so-called icehouse conditions). Seas

FIGURE 13.14 A museum diorama illustrates what early Paleozoic marine organisms may have looked like.

FIGURE 13.15 Paleogeography and fossils of Silurian and Devonian time.

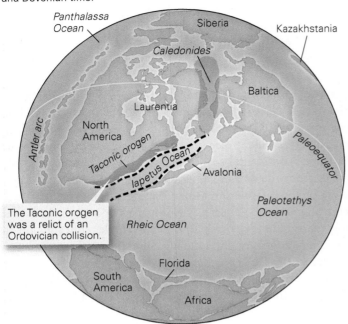

(a) During the Silurian and Devonian Periods, Laurentia collided with Baltica, Avalonia, and South America in succession, as oceans in between were consumed. The Antler arc formed off the west coast.

The Taconic orogen was a relict of an Ordovician collision.

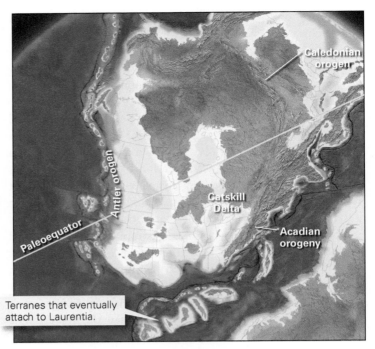

Terranes that eventually attach to Laurentia.

(b) During the Devonian Period, the Acadian orogeny shed sediments into a shallow sea to form the Catskill Delta on the east coast of Laurentia. The Antler orogeny shed sediments in the west.

(c) A road cut exposing Devonian redbeds (sandstone and shale) in New York.

~ 20 cm

(d) A Late Devonian fossil skeleton of *Tiktaalik*; this lobe-finned fish was one of the first animals to walk on land.

gradually retreated from the continents, so that during the Carboniferous Period, regions that had hosted the limestone-forming reefs of epicontinental seas now became coastal areas and river deltas in which sand, shale, and organic debris accumulated. In fact, during the Carboniferous Period, Laurentia lay near the equator, so it enjoyed tropical and semitropical conditions that favored lush growth in swamps. This growth left thick piles of plant debris that transformed into coal after burial. Much of Gondwana and Siberia, in contrast, lay at high latitudes and, by the Permian Period, had become covered by ice sheets.

The late Paleozoic Era also saw a succession of continental collisions, culminating in the formation of a single supercontinent, Pangaea (Fig. 13.16a). The largest collision occurred during Carboniferous and Permian time, when Gondwana rammed into Laurentia and Baltica, causing the *Alleghanian orogeny* of North America (Fig. 13.16b). During this event, the final stage in the development of the Appalachians, eastern North America rammed against northwestern Africa, and what is now the Gulf Coast region of North America squashed against the northern margin of South America. A vast mountain belt grew, in which deformation generated huge faults and folds. We now see the eroded remnants of rocks deformed during this event in the Appalachian and Ouachita Mountains of North America. By the end of the collisions, nearly all land on Earth had

FIGURE 13.16 Paleogeography at the end of the Paleozoic Era.

Approximate area of part (b)

(a) At the end of the Paleozoic, almost all land had combined into a single supercontinent called Pangaea.

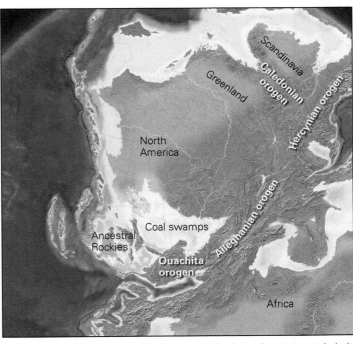

(b) During the Alleghanian and Hercynian orogenies, a huge mountain belt formed. The Caledonian orogeny had formed earlier. Coal swamps bordered interior seas, and the Ancestral Rockies rose.

combined into the giant supercontinent, Pangaea, so named by Alfred Wegener who, more than a century ago, first proposed its existence. Imagine how different the world would be if you could walk from the middle of North America to the middle of Africa or Asia.

Along the continental side of the Alleghanian orogen, a wide band of deformation called the **Appalachian fold-thrust belt** formed. In this province, a distinctive style of deformation, called *thin-skinned deformation*, took place. In a thin-skinned fold-thrust belt, an array or system of thrust faults cuts across what was originally a layer cake of sedimentary strata (Fig. 13.17). Movement on the faults displaces the strata and results in the formation of large folds. At depth, the thrust faults merge with a near-horizontal sliding surface, called a detachment, that lies just above the Precambrian basement. The adjective *thin-skinned* highlights the fact that the thrust faults do not cut into the basement but occur only in the overlying cover or "skin" of sedimentary strata.

Stresses generated during the Alleghanian orogeny were so strong that pre-existing faults in the continental crust clear across North America became active again. The movement produced *basement uplifts* (local high areas, cored by Precambrian metamorphic and igneous rocks) and sediment-filled basins in the Midwest and in the region of the present-day Rocky Mountains (Colorado, New Mexico, and Wyoming).

Geologists refer to the late Paleozoic basement uplifts of the Rocky Mountain region as the **Ancestral Rockies**.

The assembly of Pangaea involved a number of other collisions around the world as well. Notably, Africa collided with southern Europe during the *Hercynian orogeny*. Also, a rift or small ocean in Russia closed, leading to the uplift of the Ural Mountains, and parts of China along with other fragments of Asia attached to southern Siberia.

Life Evolution The fossil record indicates that during the late Paleozoic Era, plants and animals continued to evolve toward more familiar forms. In coal swamps, fixed-wing insects such as huge dragonflies flew through a tangle of ferns, club mosses, and scouring rushes, and by the end of the Carboniferous Period insects such as the cockroach, with foldable wings, appeared (Fig. 13.18). Forests containing gymnosperms ("naked seed" plants, such as conifers) and cycads (trees with a palm-like stalk peaked by a fan of fern-like fronds) became widespread in the Permian Period. Amphibians and, later, reptiles populated the land. The appearance of reptiles marked the evolution of a radically new component in animal reproduction: eggs with a protective shell. By producing such eggs, reptiles could reproduce without returning to the water and thus could populate previously uninhabitable environments on land.

BOX 13.3 CONSIDER THIS . . .

Stratigraphic Sequences and Sea-Level Change

As we have seen in this chapter, there have been intervals in geologic history when the interior of North America was submerged beneath a shallow sea and times when it was high and dry. This observation implies that sea level, relative to the surface of the continent, rises and falls through geologic time. When the continental surface was dry and exposed to the atmosphere, weathering and erosion ground away at previously deposited rock and, as a result, created a continent-wide unconformity. In the early 1960s, an American stratigrapher named Larry Sloss introduced the term **stratigraphic sequence** to refer to the strata deposited on the continent during periods when continents were submerged. Such sequences are bounded above and below by regional unconformities.

We can picture the deposition of an *idealized* sequence as follows. As the starting condition, much of the surface of a continent lies above sea level, and an unconformity develops. Then, as a transgression takes place, the shoreline migrates inland and the continent's interior progressively floods. Thus, the pre-existing unconformity gets progressively buried, and the bottom layers of the newly deposited sequence simplistically tend to be older near the margin of the continent than toward the interior.

During transgression, the depositional environment at a location changes as the sea deepens. Thus, the base of a sequence consists of terrestrial strata (river alluvium). This sediment is buried by nearshore sediment, then by deeper-water sediment (**Fig. Bx13.3a**). Eventually, nearly the entire width

of the continent, with the exception of highlands and mountain belts, lies below sea level. As regression proceeds, the interior of the continent is exposed first and then the margins. (In detail, the location and behavior of individual sedimentary basins influences

the local positions of shorelines.) So a new unconformity forms first in the interior and then later along the margins. Many shorter-duration transgressions and regressions may happen during a single long-duration rise or fall.

FIGURE Bx13.3 The rise and fall of sea level and its manifestation in the stratigraphic record.

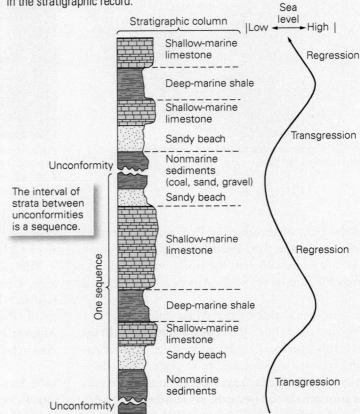

(a) Different types of strata are deposited as sea level rises and falls. Unconformities develop when sea level is low.

The late Paleozoic Era came to a close with two major mass-extinction events, during which over 95% of marine species disappeared. Why these particular events occurred remains a subject of debate. According to one hypothesis, the terminal **Permian mass extinction** occurred as a result of an episode of extraordinary volcanic activity in the region that is now Siberia—basalt sheets extruded during the event are known as the Siberian traps. Eruptions could have clouded the atmosphere, acidified the oceans, and disrupted the food chain. Another hypothesis relates the mass extinction to a huge meteorite impact.

Take-Home Message

Life diversified radically at the beginning of the Paleozoic. During the Paleozoic, life moved onto land, and by the end of it, reptiles roamed through forests of trees. Shallow seas transgressed and regressed over the continents, building a layer cake of Paleozoic strata, and a series of collisions produced orogens. At the end of the eon, collisions led to the assembly of Pangaea.

QUICK QUESTION: What event, indicated by the fossil record, marks the end of the Paleozoic?

Sloss recognized six major stratigraphic sequences in North America, and he named each after a nation of Native Americans (**Fig. Bx13.3b**). Each sequence represents deposition during an interval of time lasting tens of millions of years. The transgressions and regressions could have been caused by global (eustatic) sea-level change, or they could reflect mountain-building processes, or they could reflect the subsidence or uplift of continents.

In more recent decades, studies of strata along continental passive margins have provided an even more detailed record of sequences, because there is less erosion in these regions.

Taken together, this information may provide insight into the history of the global rise and fall of sea level, though this interpretation remains controversial (**Fig. Bx13.3c**). Some sea-level changes may reflect changes in

seafloor-spreading rates and thus in the volume of mid-ocean ridges; some may reflect hot-spot activity; some may reflect variations in Earth's climate that caused the formation or melting of ice sheets; others may represent changes in areas of continents accompanying continental collisions; and still others may reflect the warping of continental surfaces as a result of mountain building.

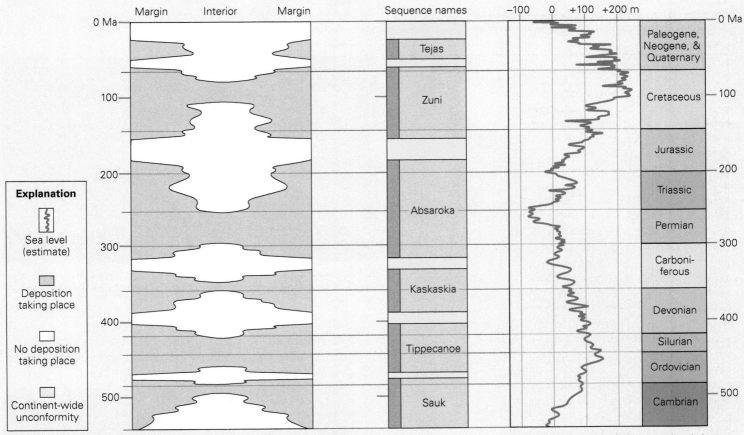

(b) Stratigraphic sequences of North America, as named by Sloss (1962). Symbolically, the chart on the left shows that, overall, continental margins were sites of deposition while the interior was not. At times, the whole continent was a not a site of deposition—the resulting continent-wide unconformities separate the sequences, as shown by the chart in the middle.

(c) An interpretation of global sea-level change, based on analysis of stratigraphy in passive-margin basins. The interpretation remains controversial. (0 = present day)

13.7 The Mesozoic Era: When Dinosaurs Ruled

The Early and Middle Mesozoic Era (Triassic-Jurassic Periods, 251-145 Ma)

Paleogeography Pangaea existed for about 100 million years, until the Late Triassic. Then rifts developed and the supercontinent began to break apart, and by the end of the

Jurassic Period, the Mid-Atlantic Ridge formed, the North Atlantic Ocean and Gulf of Mexico started to grow, and North America split away from Europe and Africa (**Fig. 13.19a**). During the early stages of its formation, the North Atlantic was narrow and shallow, and evaporation made its water so salty that thick evaporite deposits accumulated along its margins. These evaporites now lie buried beneath the younger strata in the passive-margin basins that rim the North Atlantic—they are particularly thick beneath along the Gulf Coast region of the United States.

The Earth, overall, had a warm climate during the Triassic and Early Jurassic. But during the Late Jurassic and Early

FIGURE 13.17 Features of the Appalachian Mountains in the eastern United States.

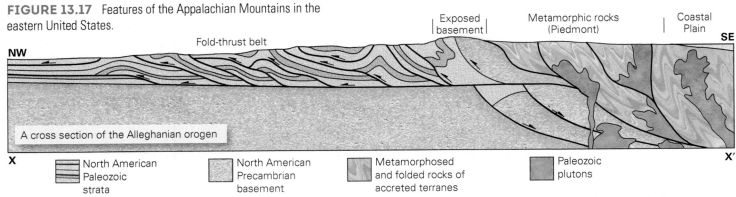

A cross section of the Alleghanian orogen

Legend:
- North American Paleozoic strata
- North American Precambrian basement
- Metamorphosed and folded rocks of accreted terranes
- Paleozoic plutons

(a) In the fold-thrust belt, strata have been pushed westward and were folded and faulted. The Blue Ridge exposes a slice of Precambrian basement. Metamorphic and plutonic rocks underlie the Piedmont. Cross section location is shown in (b).

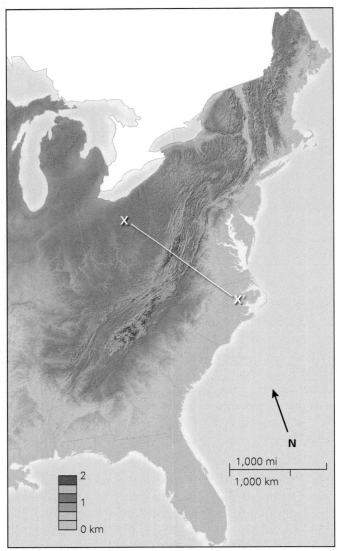

(b) The eroded remnants of the Appalachian orogeny stand out in the eastern United States. The white line shows the approximate cross-section position.

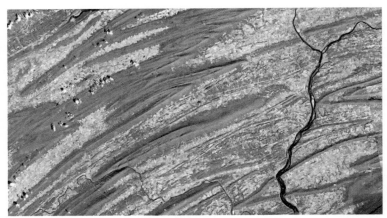

(c) Folds stand out in this satellite image of the Pennsylvania Valley and Ridge. Resistant sandstone layers form the ridges. The field of view is 80 km wide.

FIGURE 13.18 A museum diorama of a Carboniferous coal swamp includes a giant dragonfly with a wingspan of about 1 m. The inset photo gives a sense of its size relative to a human.

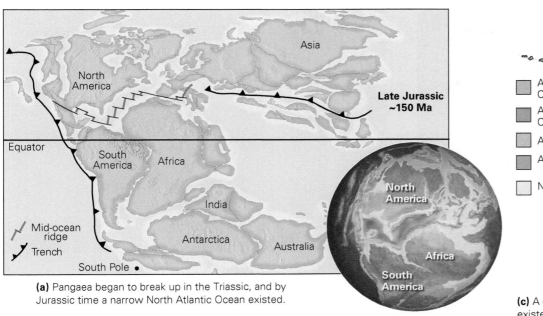

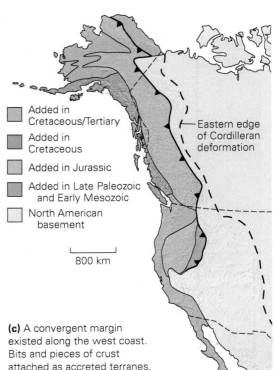

Late Jurassic
~150 Ma

Equator

Mid-ocean
ridge

Trench

South Pole

(a) Pangaea began to break up in the Triassic, and by Jurassic time a narrow North Atlantic Ocean existed.

Added in Cretaceous/Tertiary

Added in Cretaceous

Added in Jurassic

Added in Late Paleozoic and Early Mesozoic

North American basement

Eastern edge of Cordilleran deformation

800 km

(c) A convergent margin existed along the west coast. Bits and pieces of crust attached as accreted terranes.

(b) During the Jurassic, immense sand dunes blanketed the southwestern United States. Sandstone beds in Zion Park are the relicts of these dunes.

Cretaceous, the climate cooled. Large areas of North America's interior were nonmarine environments in which thick deposits of red sandstones and shales, now exposed in the spectacular cliffs of Zion National Park, were deposited (Fig. 13.19b). Then, as the Middle Jurassic Period began, sea level began to rise until eventually a shallow sea submerged much of what is now the Rocky Mountain region of the western United States.

On the western margin of North America, convergent-margin tectonics became the order of the day. Beginning with Late Permian and continuing through Mesozoic time, subduction generated volcanic island arcs and caused them, along with microcontinents and oceanic plateaus (the product of hot-spot volcanism), to collide with North America. Thus,

North America grew in land area by the "accretion" (addition) of crustal fragments onto its western margin (Fig. 13.19c). Because these fragments consist of crust that formed elsewhere, not originally on or adjacent to the continent, geologists refer to them as **exotic terranes**. At the end of the Jurassic, subduction of Pacific Ocean floor beneath North America began, an event that produced a major continental volcanic arc, the Sierran arc. This arc continued to erupt through the Cretaceous—we'll learn more about it later in this chapter.

Life Evolution During the early Mesozoic Era, a variety of new plant and animal species appeared, filling the ecological niches left vacant by the Late Permian mass extinction. Reptiles, such as plesiosaurs, begin to swim in the oceans (Fig. 13.20a), and new kinds of corals became the predominant reef builders. On land, gymnosperms and reptiles diversified, and the Earth saw its first turtles and flying reptiles (such as pterodactyls; Fig. 13.20b). And at the end of the Triassic Period, the first true dinosaurs evolved. Dinosaurs differed from other reptiles in that their legs were positioned under their bodies rather than off to the sides, and they were possibly warm-blooded. By the end of the Jurassic Period, gigantic sauropod dinosaurs (weighing up to 100 tons), along with other familiar beasts such as stegosaurus, thundered across the landscape (Fig. 13.20c), and the

Did you ever wonder . . .

when the dinosaurs lived?

FIGURE 13.20 Reptiles take to the land and sea.

(a) Plesiosaurs were swimming reptiles that had flippers instead of legs.

(b) There were many species of pterodactyl, some of which had wing spans up to 11 m. The name means "winged finger."

(c) During the Jurassic, giant dinosaurs roamed the land. This painting shows several species.

first feathered birds, such as archaeopteryx, took to the skies. The earliest ancestors of mammals appeared at the end of the Triassic Period, in the form of small, rat-like creatures.

The Late Mesozoic Era (Cretaceous Period, 145–65 Ma)

Paleogeography During the Cretaceous Period, several more *exotic* arcs accreted along the west coast (Fig. 13.21a). Also, the Earth's climate continued to shift to warmer greenhouse conditions, and sea level rose significantly, reaching levels that had not been attained for the previous 200 million years. Great shallow seas flooded most of the continents. In fact, during the latter part of the Cretaceous Period, a shark could have swum from the Gulf of Mexico to the Arctic Ocean in the Western Interior Seaway or, similarly, across much of western Europe (Fig. 13.21b).

In western North America, the *Sierran arc*, a large continental volcanic arc that was initiated at the end of the Jurassic Period, continued to be active. This arc resembled the present-day Andean arc of western South America. Though the volcanoes of the Sierran arc have long since eroded away, we can see their roots in the form of the plutons that now constitute the granitic batholith of the Sierra Nevada range. A thick accretionary prism, formed from sediments and debris scraped off the subducting oceanic plate, piled up to the west of the Sierran arc and now crops out in the Coast Ranges of California. Compressional stresses along the western North American convergent boundary activated large thrust faults east of the arc, an event geologists refer to as the **Sevier orogeny**. This orogeny produced a thin-skinned fold-thrust belt whose remnants you can see today in the Canadian Rockies and in western Wyoming (Fig. 13.21c).

FIGURE 13.21 Cretaceous paleogeography.

Convergent boundary   Thrust fault   Volcanic arc

(a) In Early Cretaceous, several exotic island arcs collided with western North America.

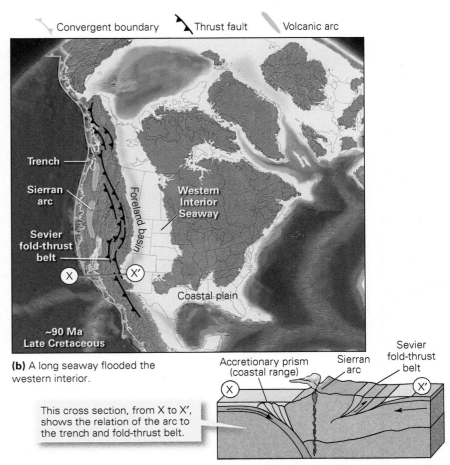

(b) A long seaway flooded the western interior.

This cross section, from X to X', shows the relation of the arc to the trench and fold-thrust belt.

(c) In Late Cretaceous, a continental volcanic arc formed. A fold-thrust belt formed to the east, as did a transcontinental seaway.

The weight of the fold-thrust belt helped push the surface of the continent down, forming a wide foreland basin that filled with sediment (see Chapter 7). The depth of the basin may have been enhanced by the downward pull of the subducting plate beneath it. This foreland basin constituted the western part of the Western Interior Seaway.

The breakup of Pangaea continued through the Cretaceous Period, with the opening of the South Atlantic Ocean and the separation of South America and Africa from Antarctica and Australia. India broke away from Gondwana and headed rapidly northward toward Asia (Fig. 13.22a, b). Along the continental margins of the newly formed Mesozoic oceans, large passive-margin basins developed, which filled with great thicknesses of sediments. The passive-margin basin sediment along the Gulf Coast of the United States, eventually accumulated a wedge of sediment that's over 15 km thick.

At the end of the Cretaceous Period, continued compression along the convergent boundary of western North America caused deformation to sweep eastwards (Fig. 13.22c). Slip occurred on the large reverse faults in the region of Wyoming,

Colorado, eastern Utah, and northern Arizona. In contrast to the faults of fold-thrust belts, these faults penetrated deep into the Precambrian basement rocks of the continent and thus movement on them generated **basement uplifts** (Fig. 13.22d) by bringing basement rocks in the hanging-wall block up and over Paleozoic strata in the footwall. In the process, layers of Paleozoic strata overlying the uplifting basement warped over the fault to form large *monoclines*, folds whose shape resembles the drape of a carpet over a step. This event, which happened during the **Laramide orogeny**, formed the structure of the present Rocky Mountains in the United States (Fig. 13.23a). Some geologists have suggested that the contrast in the location of faulting between the Sevier and Laramide orogenies may reflect contrasts in the dip of the subducting plate. During the Laramide orogeny, the subducting plate entered the mantle at a shallower angle and therefore scraped along and applied stress to the base of the continent farther inland. The change in subduction angle may have been due to the presence of an oceanic plateau, a region of thicker oceanic crust, in the downgoing slab. Significantly, this change in dip angle did not occur

FIGURE 13.22 Paleogeography in Late Cretaceous through Eocene time.

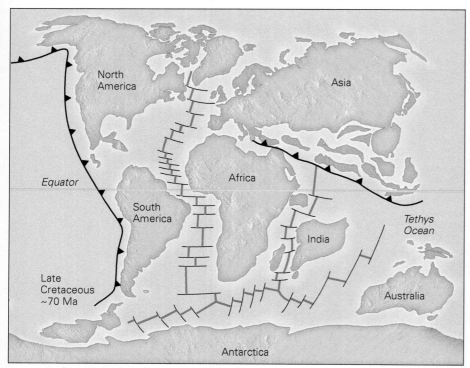

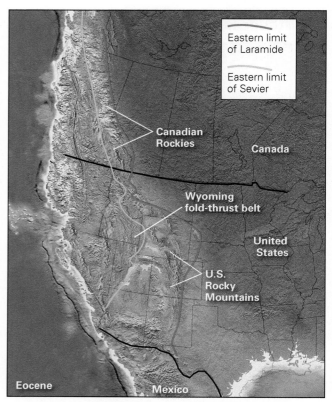

(a) By the Late Cretaceous Period, the Atlantic Ocean had formed, and India was moving rapidly northward to eventually collide with Asia.

(c) During the Laramide orogeny, deformation shifted eastward in the United States, moving from the Sevier belt to the Rocky Mountains, and the style of deformation changed.

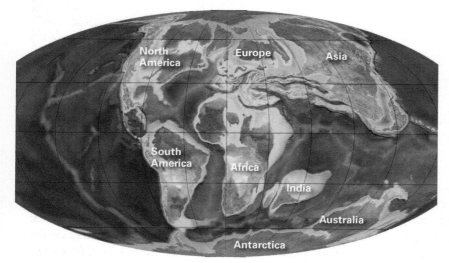

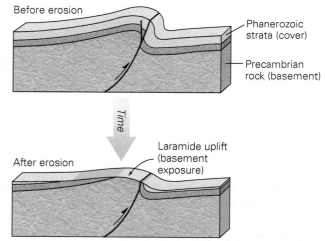

(b) In this Late Cretaceous paleogeographic reconstruction, southern Europe and Asia are beginning to form from a collage of many crustal blocks.

(d) The Laramide orogeny produced "basement-cored uplifts." In these, faults lifted up blocks of basement, causing the overlying strata to bend into a stair-step-like fold.

in Canada, so during the Laramide orogeny, the Canadian Rockies simply continued to grow eastward as a thin-skinned fold-thrust belt (**Fig. 13.23b**).

Geologists have determined that seafloor-spreading rates may have been as much as three times faster during the Cretaceous than they are today. As a result, more of the oceanic crust was younger and warmer than it is today, and since young seafloor lies at a shallower depth than does older seafloor (due to isostasy; see Chapter 11), Cretaceous mid-ocean ridges occupied more volume than they do today. Also during the Cretaceous, huge submarine plateaus formed from basalts erupted at hot-spot volcanoes. The existence of these plateaus implies that particularly active mantle plumes, or **superplumes**, reached the base of the lithosphere. Melting at the top of such plumes

FIGURE 13.23 Examples of mountains formed during the Laramide orogeny.

Unconformity between basement and cover had erosion not taken place

Exposed Precambrian basement

Dipping strata

(a) An air photo of the Wind River Mountains in Wyoming, showing the basement that has been uplifted. The fault is on the left (southwest) side of the range.

(b) The Laramide portion of the Canadian Rocky Mountains consists of thrust sheets containing dipping strata.

produced immense quantities of magma, which erupted and built up the plateaus. Growth of submarine plateaus also displaced seawater. The combination of having broader mid-ocean ridges and large oceanic plateaus, by displacing seawater, may have caused the sea-level rise that happened during the Cretaceous. During this time, the sea submerged what is now the coastal plain of eastern and southern United States, and submerged much of England and Europe, creating the setting in which the chalk deposits we mentioned at the beginning of the chapter could accumulate.

Notably, volcanism associated with extra-rapid seafloor spreading, as well as with submarine plateau growth, likely released large quantities of CO_2, a greenhouse gas, into the atmosphere. Geologists hypothesize that this increased atmospheric CO_2 concentration led to a global rise in atmospheric temperature. Rising temperatures would cause seawater to expand and polar ice sheets to melt, both phenomena that would make sea level go up even more. Considering all the phenomena that caused sea level to rise during the Cretaceous, it's no surprise that the continents flooded and that large epicontinental seas formed during this era.

Life Evolution In the seas of the late Mesozoic world, modern fish appeared and became dominant. In contrast with earlier fish, new fish had short jaws, rounded scales, symmetrical tails, and specialized fins. Huge swimming reptiles and gigantic turtles (with shells up to 4 m across) preyed on the fish. On land, cycads largely vanished, and angiosperms (flowering plants), including hardwood trees, began to compete successfully with conifers for dominance of the forest. Dinosaurs reached their peak of success

FIGURE 13.24 The Cretaceous-Tertiary (K-T) impact. The event caused a mass extinction.

(a) An artist's image of the 13-km-wide object as it hit.

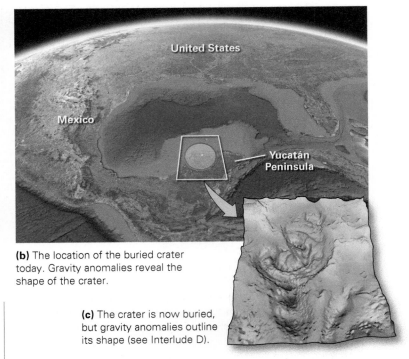

(b) The location of the buried crater today. Gravity anomalies reveal the shape of the crater.

(c) The crater is now buried, but gravity anomalies outline its shape (see Interlude D).

at this time, inhabiting almost all environments on Earth. Social herds of grazing dinosaurs roamed the plains, preyed on by the fearsome *Tyrannosaurus rex* (a Cretaceous, not a Jurassic, dinosaur, despite what Hollywood says!). Pterosaurs, with wingspans of up to 11 m, soared overhead, and birds began to diversify. Mammals also diversified and developed larger brains and more specialized teeth, but for the most part they remained small and rat-like.

The "K-T Boundary Event" Geologists first recognized the K-T boundary (K stands for Cretaceous and T for Tertiary, an older term for Cenozoic time before the Quaternary) from 18th-century studies that identified an abrupt global change in fossil assemblages. Until the 1980s, most geologists assumed the faunal turnover took millions of years. But modern dating techniques indicate that this change happened almost instantaneously and that it signaled a sudden mass extinction of most species on Earth. The dinosaurs, rulers of the planet for over 150 million years, simply vanished, along with 90% of some plankton species in the ocean and up to 75% of plant species. What catastrophe could cause such a sudden and extensive mass extinction? From data collected in the 1970s and 1980s, most geologists have concluded that the Cretaceous Period came to a close, at least in part, as a result of the impact of a 13-km-wide meteorite at the site of the present-day Yucatán Peninsula in Mexico (**Fig. 13.24a, b**).

The discoveries leading up to this conclusion provide fascinating insight into how science works. The story began when Walter Alvarez, a geologist studying strata in Italy, noted that a thin layer of clay interrupted the deposition of deep-sea limestone precisely at the K-T boundary. Cretaceous plankton shells constituted the limestone below the clay layer, whereas Cenozoic plankton shells made up the limestone just above the clay. Apparently, for a short interval of time at the

K-T boundary, all the plankton died, so only clay settled out of the sea. When Alvarez, his father, Luis (a physicist), and other colleagues analyzed the clay, they learned that it contained *iridium*, a very heavy element found only in extraterrestrial objects. Soon geologists were finding similar iridium-bearing clay layers at the K-T boundary all over the world. Further study showed that the clay layer contained other unusual materials, such as tiny glass spheres (formed from the flash freezing of molten rock), wood ash, and shocked quartz (grains of quartz that had been subjected to intense pressure). Only an immense impact could explain all these features. The glass spherules formed when melt sprayed in the air from the impact site, the iridium came from fragments of the colliding object, and the shocked quartz grains were produced and scattered by the force of the impact. The wood ash resulted when forests were set ablaze at the time—this conceivably happened because the impact ejected super-hot debris at such high velocity that the debris almost went into orbit and could reach forests worldwide. The impact also generated 2-km-high tsunamis that inundated the shores of continents and generated a blast of super-hot air.

Researchers suggest that the impact caused unfathomable destruction because the dust, ash, and aerosols that it produced lofted into the atmosphere and transformed the air into a murky haze that reflected incoming sunlight. As a result, photosynthesis became difficult, so all but the hardiest plants died, and winter-like cold might have lasted all year, perhaps for years. Finally, sulfur-bearing aerosols could have combined with water to produce acid rain, acidifying the ocean and land. These conditions could have broken the food chain and, therefore, could have triggered extinctions.

Geologists suggest that the meteorite responsible for the K-T boundary event landed on the northwestern coast of the Yucatán Peninsula, because beneath the reefs and sediments of this tropical realm lies a 100-km-wide by 16-km-deep scar called the Chicxulub crater (Fig. 13.24c). A layer of glass spherules up to 1 m thick occurs at the K-T boundary in strata near the site. And radiometric dating indicates that igneous melts in the crater formed at the time of the K-T boundary event. The discovery of this event has led geologists to speculate that other such collisions may have punctuated the path of life evolution throughout Earth history and has led to modern-day efforts to track asteroids that pass close to the Earth.

Take-Home Message

The Mesozoic began with the breakup of Pangaea and the formation of the Atlantic. A convergent-plate boundary formed along the west coast of North America, yielding the Sierran arc and eventually leading to the uplift of the Rocky Mountains. Dinosaurs ruled the planet and modern forests appeared. A huge meteorite impact marks the K-T boundary event, the end of the era—it may have caused the extinction of the dinosaurs.

QUICK QUESTION: Did all of today's continents break off of Pangaea at the same time?

13.8 The Cenozoic Era: The Modern World Comes to Be

Paleogeography Plate tectonics doesn't stop, so during the last 66 million years the map of the Earth has continued to change, gradually producing the configuration of continents we see today. The final stages of the Pangaea breakup separated Australia from Antarctica and Greenland from North America and formed the North Sea between Britain and continental Europe. The Atlantic Ocean continued to grow because of seafloor spreading on the Mid-Atlantic Ridge, and thus the Americas moved relatively westward, away from Europe and Africa. Meanwhile, the continents that once constituted Gondwana drifted northward as the intervening ocean was consumed by subduction. Several volcanic island arcs and microcontinents started colliding with Asia beginning around 50 to 60 million years ago, and then about 40 Ma India collided. The overall result of this protracted period of collisional

tectonics uplifted the Himalayas and the Tibetan Plateau. Meanwhile, Africa along with some volcanic island arcs and microcontinents collided with Europe to produce the Alps of southern Europe and the Zagros Mountains of Iran. Finally, collision between Australia and New Guinea led to orogeny in Papua New Guinea. Thus, collisions of the former Gondwana continents with the southern margins of Europe and Asia resulted in the formation of the largest orogenic belt on Earth today, the **Alpine-Himalayan chain** (Fig. 13.25).

As the Americas moved westward, convergent-plate boundaries evolved along their western margins. In South America, convergent-boundary activity built the Andes, which remains an active orogen to the present day. In North America, convergent-boundary activity continued without interruption until about 40 Ma (the Eocene Epoch) yielding, as we have seen, the Laramide orogeny. Then the Farallon-Pacific ridge reached the continental margin, and the configuration of plates along the western shore of North America began to evolve. By 25 Ma, a transform boundary had replaced part of the convergent boundary in the western part of the continent (Fig. 13.26). Where this happened, volcanism and compression ceased in western North America, and strike-slip faulting took over. This led to the formation of the San Andreas fault system in California, and the Queen Charlotte fault system off the west coast of Canada. Along the San Andreas and Queen Charlotte faults today, the Pacific Plate moves northward with respect to North America at a rate of about 6 cm per year. In the western United States, convergent-boundary tectonics continues only in Washington, Oregon, and northern California, where subduction of the Juan de Fuca Plate generates the volcanism of the Cascade volcanic chain. At depth beneath North America, the subducted plate peeled off the base of North America and began to sink deeper into the mantle.

As compression associated with convergent tectonics ceased in the western United States south of the Cascades, the region began to undergo extension in a roughly east-west direction. The result was the formation of the **Basin and Range Province**, a broad continental rift. Continued extension in this rift, over the past 20

SEE FOR YOURSELF . . .

Basin and Range rift, Utah

LATITUDE
39°15'1.83"N

LONGITUDE
114°38'32.10"W

Look down from 250 km (~155 mi).

In this region of the Cenozoic Basin and Range rift, darker bands are fault-block mountains, whereas lighter areas are sediment-filled basins. White areas are evaporates, from dried-up lakes.

FIGURE 13.25 The two main active continental orogenic systems on the Earth today. The Alpine-Himalayan system formed when Africa, India, and Australia collided with Asia (inset). The Cordilleran and Andean systems reflect the consequences of convergent-boundary tectonism along the eastern Pacific Ocean.

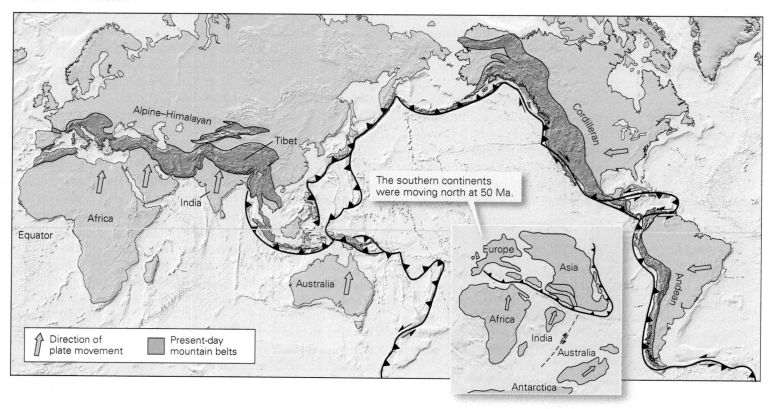

FIGURE 13.26 The western margin changed from a convergent-plate boundary into a transform-plate boundary after subduction of the Farallon Ridge. Then the San Andreas fault developed. To the east, the Basin and Range rift was developed.

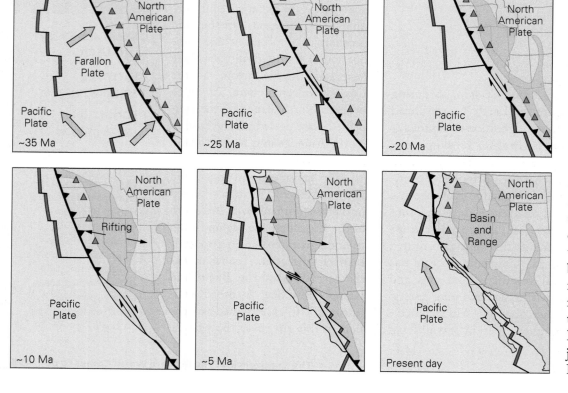

Ma, has caused the region to stretch to twice its original width (**Fig. 13.27**). The Basin and Range Province's name reflects its topography—the province contains long, narrow mountain ranges separated from each other by flat, sediment-filled basins. This topography formed when the crust of the region was broken up by normal faults (see Chapter 11). Blocks of crust above these faults slipped down and tilted, producing narrow, wedge-shaped depressions. The upward protruding crests of the tilted blocks form the ranges. The depressions between the ranges rapidly filled with sediment eroded from the ranges and became the basins. The Basin and Range Province terminates just north of the Snake River Plain, the track of the hot spot

FIGURE 13.27 The Basin and Range Province is a rift. Its opening caused rotation of the Sierra Nevada. The opening of the Rio Grande Rift caused rotation of the Colorado Plateau, which is an unrifted block of cratonic crust. The inset shows a cross section along the red line.

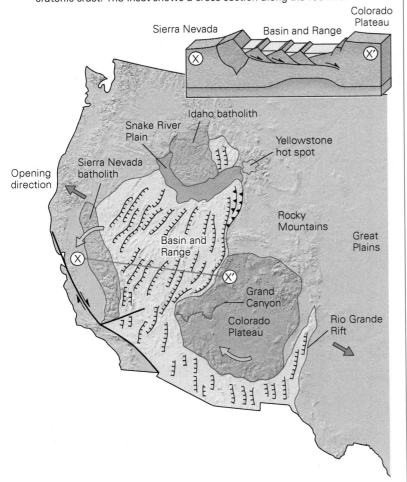

this name is no longer "official" but remains widely used.) The Quaternary begins at 2.6 Ma and continues to the present. Between 2.6 Ma and 12 Ka, an interval of time called the Pleistocene Epoch, continental glaciers expanded and retreated across northern continents at least 20 times, an event known as the **Pleistocene Ice Age** (Fig. 13.28). During each *glaciation*, the time intervals when the glaciers grew, sea level fell so much that the continental shelf became exposed to air, and at times a **land bridge** formed across the Bering Strait, west of Alaska. Animals and people migrated across this bridge from Asia into North America. A partial land bridge also formed from Southeast Asia to Australia, making human migration to Australia easier. Erosion and deposition by the glaciers created much of the landscape we see today in northern temperate regions. During *interglacials*, intervals of time when glaciers retreated, the land bridges and broad areas of continental shelves were submerged again. About 12,000 years ago, the climate warmed, and we entered the interglacial time interval we are still experiencing today (see Chapter 22). This most recent interval of time is the **Holocene Epoch**.

Life Evolution Within a few million years of the K-T boundary catastrophe, plant life recovered, and forests of both angiosperms and gymnosperms reappeared. The grasses, which first appeared in the Cretaceous, spread across the plains in temperate and subtropical climates by the middle of the Cenozoic Era, transforming them into vast grasslands. The dinosaurs, except

FIGURE 13.28 The maximum advance of the Pleistocene ice sheet in North America.

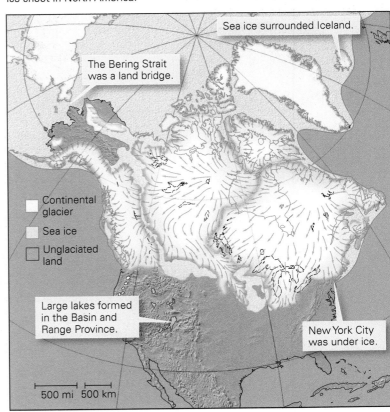

that now lies beneath Yellowstone National Park. As North America drifts westward, volcanic calderas have formed along the Snake River Plain; Yellowstone National Park straddles the most recent caldera (see Chapter 9).

Recall that during the Cretaceous Period, the world experienced greenhouse conditions and sea level rose so that extensive areas of continents were submerged. During the Cenozoic Era, however, the global climate rapidly shifted to icehouse (cooler) conditions, and by the early Oligocene Epoch Antarctic glaciers reappeared for the first time since the Triassic. The climate continued to grow colder through the Late Miocene Epoch, leading to the formation of grasslands in temperate climates. In the Pliocene, when the Isthmus of Panama formed, land separated the Atlantic completely from the Pacific, and the configuration of oceanic currents changed. The change in currents, in turn, may have decreased the transport of oceanic heat to polar regions and may have triggered the formation of the sea ice that covered the Arctic Ocean.

The Cenozoic consists of three periods—the Paleogene, the Neogene, and the Quaternary. (Until recently, the Paleogene and Neogene together comprised the Tertiary Period;

The Earth has a History

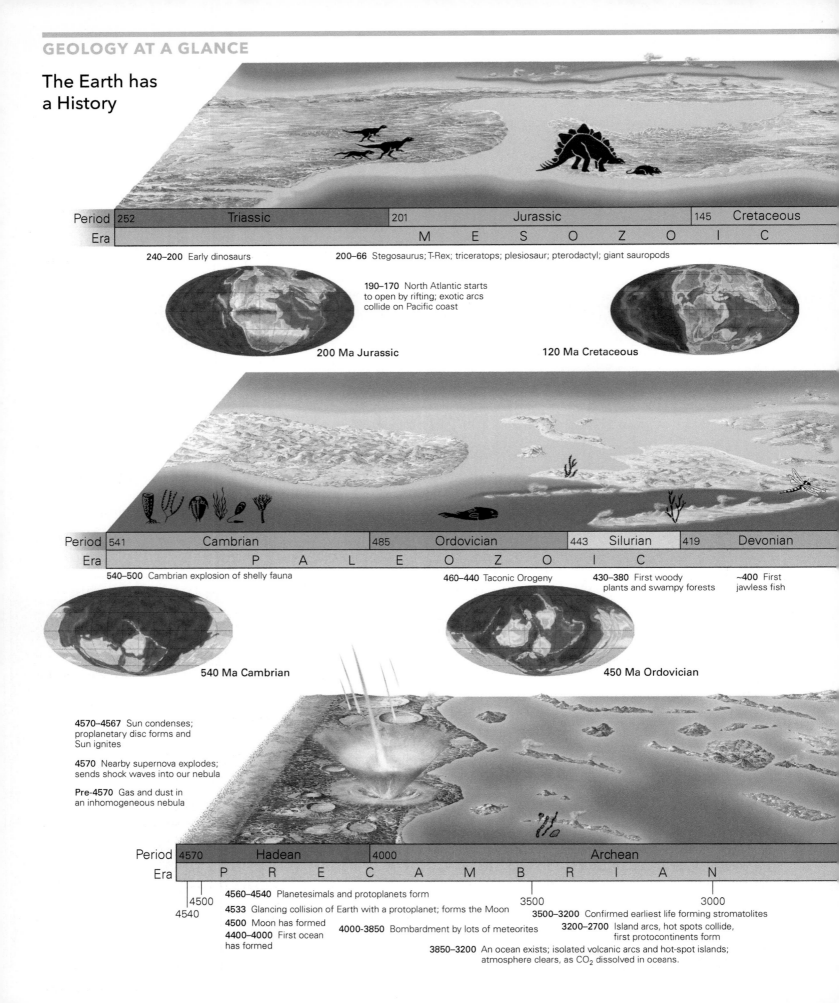

Period	252	Triassic		201	Jurassic		145	Cretaceous
Era			M E S O Z O I C					

240–200 Early dinosaurs

200–66 Stegosaurus; T-Rex; triceratops; plesiosaur; pterodactyl; giant sauropods

190–170 North Atlantic starts to open by rifting; exotic arcs collide on Pacific coast

200 Ma Jurassic

120 Ma Cretaceous

Period	541	Cambrian		485	Ordovician		443	Silurian	419	Devonian
Era			P A L E O Z O I C							

540–500 Cambrian explosion of shelly fauna

460–440 Taconic Orogeny

430–380 First woody plants and swampy forests

~400 First jawless fish

540 Ma Cambrian

450 Ma Ordovician

4570–4567 Sun condenses; proplanetary disc forms and Sun ignites

4570 Nearby supernova explodes; sends shock waves into our nebula

Pre-4570 Gas and dust in an inhomogeneous nebula

Period	4570	Hadean	4000	Archean
Era		P R E C A M B R I A N		

4540
4500
4560–4540 Planetesimals and protoplanets form

4533 Glancing collision of Earth with a protoplanet; forms the Moon

4500 Moon has formed
4400–4000 First ocean has formed

4000-3850 Bombardment by lots of meteorites

3500
3000

3500–3200 Confirmed earliest life forming stromatolites

3200–2700 Island arcs, hot spots collide, first protocontinents form

3850–3200 An ocean exists; isolated volcanic arcs and hot-spot islands; atmosphere clears, as CO_2 dissolved in oceans.

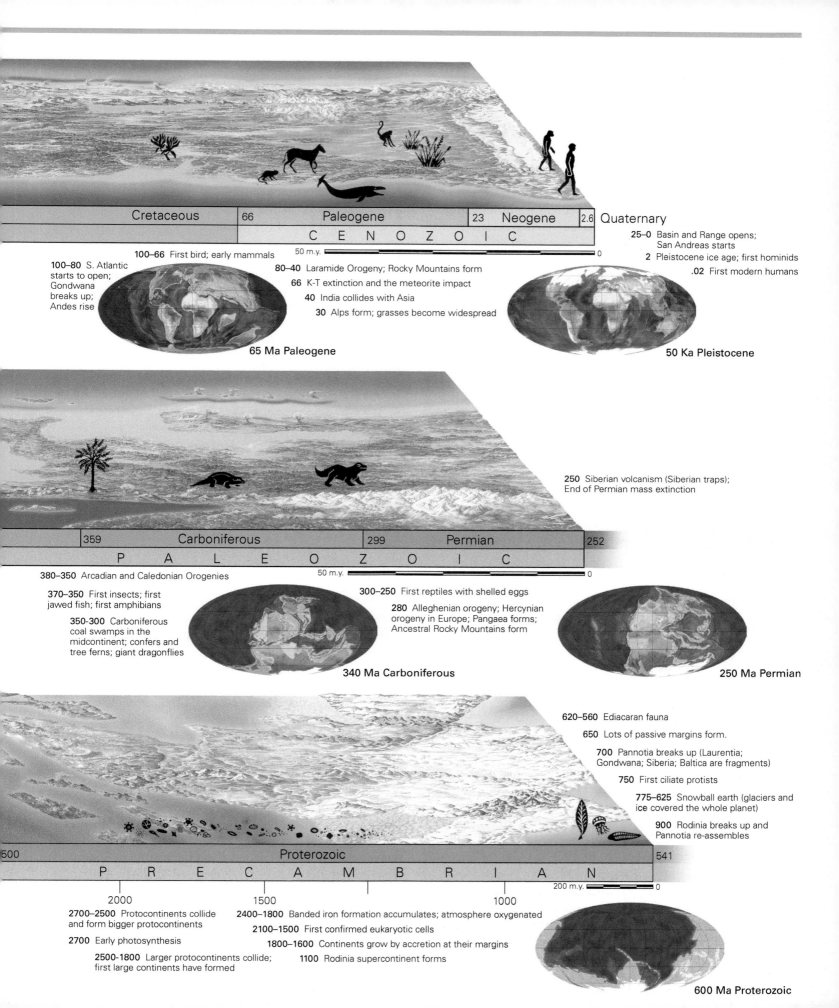

Cretaceous	66	Paleogene	23	Neogene	2.6	Quaternary

C E N O Z O I C

50 m.y.　0

100–66 First bird; early mammals

100–80 S. Atlantic starts to open; Gondwana breaks up; Andes rise

80–40 Laramide Orogeny; Rocky Mountains form

66 K-T extinction and the meteorite impact

40 India collides with Asia

30 Alps form; grasses become widespread

25–0 Basin and Range opens; San Andreas starts

2 Pleistocene ice age; first hominids

.02 First modern humans

65 Ma Paleogene

50 Ka Pleistocene

	359	Carboniferous	299	Permian	252

P A L E O Z O I C

50 m.y.　0

250 Siberian volcanism (Siberian traps); End of Permian mass extinction

380–350 Arcadian and Caledonian Orogenies

370–350 First insects; first jawed fish; first amphibians

350–300 Carboniferous coal swamps in the midcontinent; confers and tree ferns; giant dragonflies

300–250 First reptiles with shelled eggs

280 Alleghenian orogeny; Hercynian orogeny in Europe; Pangaea forms; Ancestral Rocky Mountains form

340 Ma Carboniferous

250 Ma Permian

620–560 Ediacaran fauna

650 Lots of passive margins form.

700 Pannotia breaks up (Laurentia; Gondwana; Siberia; Baltica are fragments)

750 First ciliate protists

775–625 Snowball earth (glaciers and ice covered the whole planet)

900 Rodinia breaks up and Pannotia re-assembles

2500	Proterozoic	541

P R E C A M B R I A N

200 m.y.　0

2000　1500　1000

2700–2500 Protocontinents collide and form bigger protocontinents

2700 Early photosynthesis

2500-1800 Larger protocontinents collide; first large continents have formed

2400–1800 Banded iron formation accumulates; atmosphere oxygenated

2100–1500 First confirmed eukaryotic cells

1800–1600 Continents grow by accretion at their margins

1100 Rodinia supercontinent forms

600 Ma Proterozoic

for their distant relatives, the birds, were gone for good, and mammals rapidly diversified to fill the ecological niches that dinosaurs left vacant. In fact, most of the modern groups of mammals that exist today originated at the beginning of the Cenozoic Era, giving this time the nickname *Age of Mammals*. During the latter part of the era, particularly huge mammals appeared—including mammoths, mastodons, giant beavers, giant bears, and giant sloths—but these became extinct during the past 10,000 years, perhaps because of hunting by humans.

It was during the Cenozoic that our own ancestors first appeared. The fossil record indicates that ape-like primates diversified during the Miocene Epoch, about 20 Ma, and the first human-like primates appeared about 4 Ma. The first members of the human genus, *Homo*, have been found in 2.4 Ma strata. Evidence from studies in Africa indicates that *Homo erectus*, an ancestor capable of making stone axes, appeared about 1.6 Ma, and the line leading to *Homo sapiens* (our species) diverged from *Homo neanderthalensis* (Neanderthal man) about 500 Ka years ago. The first modern people appeared 200 Ka years ago, sharing the planet with two other species of the genus *Homo*, the Neanderthals and the Denisovans. But the last Neanderthals and Denisovans died off 25,000 years ago, leaving *Homo sapiens* as the only human species on Earth.

As summarized in **Geology at a Glance** (pp. 498–499), Earth's history reflects the complex consequences of plate interactions, sea-level changes, atmospheric changes, life evolution, and even meteorite impact. In the past few millennia, humans have had a huge effect on the planet, causing changes significant enough to be obvious in the geologic record of the future. In fact, geologists now informally refer to the more recent portion of the Holocene, specifically, the time during which human activities have had a major impact on the Earth System, as the **Anthropocene**. Different researchers assign different start dates to the Anthropocene—some place the start at the beginning of the industrial revolution, a few centuries ago, whereas others place its start at the beginning of widespread agriculture, a few millennia ago. We'll pick up the thread of this story in Chapter 23, where we discuss ideas of how the Earth System may change in the future.

Take-Home Message

During the Cenozoic, the mountain belts of today rose, and modern plate boundaries became established. After the K-T mass extinction, mammals diversified. During the Pleistocene, glaciers covered large areas of continents, and humans appeared.

QUICK QUESTION: What interval of time does the Anthropocene refer to?

CHAPTER SUMMARY

- Earth formed about 4.54 billion years ago. For part of the first 600 million years, the Hadean Eon, the planet was so hot that its surface was a magma ocean.
- The Archean Eon began about 4.00 Ga, when the oldest rock that remains formed. Continental crust, assembled out of volcanic arcs and hot-spot volcanoes that were too buoyant to subduct, grew during the Archean. The atmosphere contained little oxygen, but the first life forms—bacteria and archaea—appeared.
- In the Proterozoic Eon, which began at 2.5 Ga, Archean cratons collided and were sutured together along orogenic belts, forming large Proterozoic cratons. Photosynthesis by organisms added oxygen to the atmosphere. By the end of the Proterozoic, complex shell-less marine invertebrates populated the planet. Most continental crust accumulated to form a supercontinent called Rodinia at 1 Ga.
- At the beginning of the Paleozoic Era, rifting yielded several separate continents. Sea level rose and fell a number of times, creating sequences of strata in continental interiors. Continents began to collide and coalesce again, leading to orogenies and, by the end of the era, to another supercontinent, Pangaea. Early Paleozoic evolution produced many invertebrates with shells, and jawless fish. Land plants and

- insects appeared in the middle Paleozoic. And, by the end of the eon, there were land reptiles and gymnosperm trees.
- In the Mesozoic Era, Pangaea broke apart and the Atlantic Ocean formed. Convergent-boundary tectonics dominated along the western margin of North America. Dinosaurs appeared in Late Triassic time and became prominent land animals through the Mesozoic Era. During the Cretaceous Period, sea level was very high, and the continents flooded. Angiosperms appeared at this time, along with modern fish. A huge mass-extinction event, which wiped out the dinosaurs, occurred at the end of the Cretaceous Period, probably because of the impact of a large meteorite.
- In the Cenozoic Era, continental fragments of Pangaea collided again. The collision of Africa and India with Asia and Europe formed the Alpine-Himalayan orogen. Convergent tectonics has persisted along the margin of South America, creating the Andes, but ceased in North America when the San Andreas fault formed. Rifting in the western United States during the Cenozoic Era produced the Basin and Range Province. Various kinds of mammals filled niches left vacant, and the human genus, *Homo*, appeared and evolved throughout the radically shifting climate and ice ages of the Pleistocene Epoch.

KEY TERMS

Alpine-Himalayan chain (p. 495)

Ancestral Rockies (p. 485)

Anthropocene (p. 498)

Appalachian fold-thrust belt (p. 485)

Archean Eon (p. 473)

basement uplifts (p. 491)

Basin and Range Province (p. 495)

Cambrian explosion (pp. 482–83)

craton (p. 476)

cratonic platform (p. 476)

differentiation (p. 470)

Ediacaran fauna (p. 479)

exotic terrane (p. 489)

Gondwana (p. 482)

great oxygenation event (p. 480)

Grenville orogeny (p. 477)

Holocene Epoch (p. 497)

land bridge (p. 497)

Laramide orogeny (p. 491)

Laurentia (p. 482)

Permian mass extinction (p. 486)

Phanerozoic Eon (p. 480)

Pleistocene Ice Age (p. 497)

Proterozoic Eon (p. 476)

Rodinia (p. 477)

Sevier orogeny (p. 490)

shield (p. 476)

snowball Earth (p. 480)

stratigraphic sequence (p. 486)

stromatolite (p. 475)

superplume (p. 492)

REVIEW QUESTIONS

1. Why are there no whole rocks on Earth that yield isotopic dates older than 4 billion years?

2. Describe the condition of the crust, atmosphere, and oceans during the Hadean Eon.

3. How did the atmosphere and tectonic conditions change during the Proterozoic Eon?

4. What evidence do we have that the Earth nearly froze over twice during the Proterozoic Eon?

5. How did the Cambrian explosion of life change the nature of the living world?

6. How did the Alleghanian and Ancestral Rockies orogenies affect North America?

7. What are the major types of organisms that appeared during the Paleozoic?

8. Describe the plate-tectonic conditions that led to the formation of the Sierran arc and the Sevier thrust belt. What happened during the Laramide orogeny?

9. What life forms appeared during the Mesozoic?

10. What may have caused the flooding of the continents during the Cretaceous Period?

11. What could have caused the K-T extinctions?

12. What continents formed as a result of the breakup of Pangaea?

13. What caused the Himalayas and the Alps to form?

14. What major tectonic provinces formed in the western United States during the Cenozoic?

15. What major climatic and biologic events happened during the Pleistocene?

ON FURTHER THOUGHT

16. During intervals of the Paleozoic, large areas of continents were submerged by shallow seas. Using *Google Earth*™, tour North America from space. Do any present-day regions within North America consist of continental crust that was submerged by seawater? What about regions offshore? (Hint: Look at the region just east of Florida.)

17. Geologists have concluded that 80% to 90% of Earth's continental crust had formed by 2.5 Ga. But if you look at a geological map of the world, you find that only about 10% of the Earth's continental crustal surface is labeled "Precambrian." Why?

 smartwork.wwnorton.com

This chapter's Smartwork features:

• Ranking activity on time intervals in Earth's history.
• Cretaceous paleogeography labeling exercise.
• Video question on landslide hazards.

GEOTOURS

This chapter's GeoTour exercise (K) features:

• Paleography of the Earth

PART V

EARTH RESOURCES

The earliest humans were hunter-gatherers and needed only food and water to survive. But then people discovered that fires made food easier to eat and campsites more comfortable, weapons made hunting more successful, shelters made daily life more pleasant, and farming made food supplies more reliable—and humanity's needs expanded. Specifically, people began to require energy resources (sources of heat and/or power) and mineral resources (materials from which metals and other chemicals can be derived). In a general sense, we use the term resource for any item that can be employed for a useful purpose. Modern society requires resources obtained directly from the Earth System in order to survive and prosper. Think about it . . . metals, oil, plastics, wallboard, brick, coal, pottery, cement, uranium, and more all come from the Earth's crust. To appreciate the value and cost of such Earth resources, it's important to know how they

form, where they can be found, how they're extracted, whether or not they're sustainable, and how their use can impact the environment. In Chapter 14, we focus on the energy resources that come from the Earth. These include fossil fuels (oil and coal) as well as nuclear fuel and moving water. Chapter 15 focuses on nonenergy resources, particularly the mineral deposits from which we obtain metals.

An exposed fracture surface reveals a weathered coating of malachite, a beautiful green mineral sometimes used for jewelry. Malachite is also a copper ore mineral, meaning that its crystals contain a significant proportion of copper atoms. The copper we use for wires and coins comes from this and other ore minerals. The Earth provides many of the resources essential to society.

These lumps of coal, piled near a coal mine in Indiana, formed from vegetation that accumu-lated in swamps of central North America about 310 Ma and was then buried deeply where it transformed into rock. Burning one of the larger chunks would light a lightbulb for a day.

CHAPTER 14

Squeezing Power from a Stone: Energy Resources

To keep a lamp burning, we have to keep putting oil in it.

—Mother Teresa (Nobel Peace Prize winner, 1910–1997)

14.1 Introduction

The extreme chill of an arctic midwinter doesn't stop a wolf from stalking its prey. The wolf's legs move through the snow, its heart pumps, its lungs inhale and exhale, and its body radiates heat—all these activities require energy. **Energy**, as defined by a physicist, is the capacity to do work, to cause a change in a physical or biological system. This means that energy can raise the temperature of a material, can drive chemical reactions, can cause an object to move or change shape, can generate light and/or magnetism, or can change the state of a material (from solid to liquid or gas). A wolf's energy comes from the metabolism of sugar, protein, and carbohydrates in its body. These chemicals, in turn, come from the food the wolf catches and eats—thus, we can think of mice, rabbits, and deer as an **energy resource**, a source of materials that yield energy, for a wolf.

Early humans, like wolves, could supply their energy needs entirely from their food, so they could survive by hunting and gathering. But when people discovered how to use fire, tools, and weapons, their need for energy resources began to exceed that of other animals. Before the advent of civilization, wood and dried dung could supply humanity's energy resource needs—these materials could serve as **fuel**, an energy resource in a usable and transportable form (Fig. 14.1a). As people began to congregate in towns, however, they began to use energy for agriculture and transportation. At first, animal power, wind, and flowing water met society's additional energy demand, but as populations grew, and new industries such as iron smelting emerged, energy resource needs began to outpace the supplies available at the Earth's surface. In fact, to feed the smelting industry, 17th-century woodcutters devastated European forests (Fig. 14.1b). The industrial revolution could

FIGURE 14.1 Nongeologic sources of energy dominated in the past.

(a) Women collecting dung to burn for cooking in India (ca. 1977).

(b) A painting of an ironworks in Norway from 1800 by John Edy (1760–1820).

not begin unless new fuel supplies could be found, and society turned to coal, the fossilized remains of woody plants, to meet the demand. Coal could be transported easily and contains about 1.7 times more energy per kilo than wood, so coal kept 18th-century cooking and heating stoves hot, and it powered the steam engines of factories and trains around the industrializing world.

Since the industrial revolution, society's hunger for energy has increased unabated (Fig. 14.2). In the United States today, for example, an average city dweller uses more than 110 times the amount of energy that a prehistoric hunter did. Most energy for human consumption in the industrial world now comes from oil, natural gas, and coal, but we still use wind and flowing water. In the last half century we've added nuclear energy, geothermal energy, and solar energy to the list of energy resources, and there has been growing interest in expanding the use of biofuels from plant crops. In 2007, the world's energy picture changed significantly when efforts to extract natural gas from shale began to burgeon, and natural gas has now started to substitute for other fuels. But use of energy brings with it myriad challenges to society—the distribution of supplies can spark discord among nations, production and consumption both can have undesirable consequences for the environment and climate, and issues concerning long-term sustainability of resources remain incompletely answered.

Why does a geology book include a chapter devoted to energy resources? Because most of these resources originate in geologic materials or are the result of geologic processes. Thus, to understand the source and limitations of energy resources and to find new resources, we must understand their geological context and geological consequences. (That's why the energy industry employs tens of thousands of geologists.) To help you to understand the geology of energy, this chapter begins by surveying the various types of energy resources on Earth. Then we focus on *fossil fuels* (oil, gas, and coal), which are combustible materials derived from organisms that lived in the past. The chapter continues with a survey of other energy resources and concludes by outlining the dilemmas that society faces as conventional energy resources begin to run out and products of energy consumption enter our environment.

FIGURE 14.2 The proportion of different sources of energy that people use has change over time, and the amount of energy used almost continuously increases.

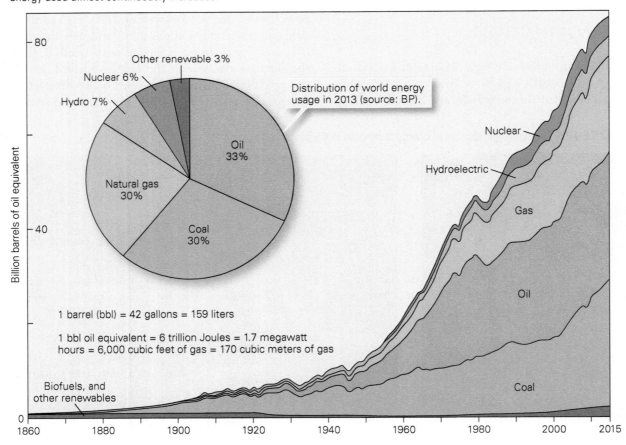

14.2 Sources of Energy in the Earth System

What comes to mind when someone asks you to name an energy resource? Perhaps you think about the gasoline that fills the tanks of cars, or the mounds of coal piled outside of a power plant, or the flowing stream that turns a water-wheel. Alternatively, you may think of windmills or arrays of solar panels, because they are appearing on the landscape with increasing frequency. Let's step back and consider where the energy in these energy resources comes from in the first place (Fig. 14.3):

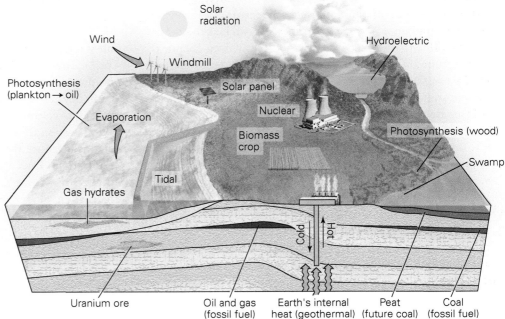

FIGURE 14.3 The diverse sources of energy on Earth. Surface sources are, ultimately, driven by heat from the Sun. Subsurface sources include fossil fuels, heat rising from hot rocks at depth, and radioactive minerals.

- *Energy directly from the Sun:* Solar energy, resulting from nuclear fusion reactions in the Sun, bathes the Earth's surface. It may be converted directly into electricity, using solar-energy panels, or it may be used to heat water in tanks.
- *Energy directly from gravity:* The gravitational attraction of the Moon, and to a lesser extent the Sun, causes ocean *tides*, the daily up-and-down movement of the sea surface. The flow of water in and out of channels during tidal changes can drive turbines.
- *Energy involving both solar energy and gravity:* Solar radiation heats the air, which becomes buoyant and rises. As this happens, gravity causes cooler air to sink. The resulting air movement, *wind*, powers sails and windmills. Solar energy also evaporates water, which enters the atmosphere. When the water condenses, it rains and falls on the land, where it accumulates in streams that flow downhill in response to gravity. This moving water powers water-wheels and turbines.
- *Energy via photosynthesis:* Algae and green plants absorb some of the solar energy that reaches the Earth's surface. Their green color comes from a pigment called *chlorophyll*. With the aid of chlorophyll, plants produce sugar through a chemical reaction called *photosynthesis*. In chemist's shorthand, we can write the reaction in this way:

$$6CO_2 + 12H_2O + Light \rightarrow 6O_2 + C_6H_{12}O_6 + 6H_2O$$

carbon dioxide   water   oxygen   sugar   water

Plants use the sugar produced by photosynthesis to manufacture more complex chemicals, or they metabolize it directly to provide themselves with energy. Burning plant matter in a fire releases potential energy stored in the chemical bonds of organic chemicals. During burning, the organic molecules react with oxygen and break apart to produce carbon dioxide, water, and carbon (soot):

$$\underset{\text{molecules}}{\text{plant}} + O_2 \xrightarrow{\text{burning}} CO_2 + H_2O + C + \underset{\text{gases}}{\text{other}} + \underset{\text{energy}}{\text{heat}}$$

The flames you see in fire consist of glowing gases released and heated by this reaction.

People have burned wood to produce energy for centuries. More recently, plant material (*biomass*) from corn, sugar cane, switchgrass, and algae has been used to produce ethanol, a flammable alcohol.

- *Energy from fossil fuels*: Oil, natural gas, and coal come from organisms that lived long ago and thus store solar energy that reached the Earth long ago. We refer to these substances as **fossil fuels,** to emphasize that they were derived from ancient organisms, the remains of which have been preserved in rocks over geologic time.

Did you ever wonder . . .

what the "fossils" are in fossil fuel?

- *Energy from chemical reactions:* A number of inorganic chemicals can burn to produce light and energy. The energy results from "exothermic" (heat-producing) chemical reactions. A dynamite explosion is an extreme example of such energy production. Recently, researchers have been studying electrochemical devices, such as hydrogen fuel cells, that produce electricity directly from chemical reactions.
- *Energy from nuclear fission:* Atoms of radioactive elements can split into smaller pieces, a process called *nuclear fission* (see Box 1.3). During fission, a tiny amount of mass transforms into a large amount of energy, called *nuclear energy*. This type of energy runs nuclear power plants and nuclear submarines.
- *Energy from Earth's internal heat:* Some of Earth's internal energy dates from the birth of the planet, while some is produced by radioactive decay in minerals. This internal energy heats water underground. The resulting hot water, when transformed to steam, provides *geothermal energy* that can drive turbines or heat buildings.

Take-Home Message

Energy comes from several sources—solar radiation, gravity, chemical reactions, radioactive decay, and the Earth's internal heat. Solar radiation and gravity together drive wind and water movement. Products of living organisms can be preserved in rocks as fossil fuels.

QUICK QUESTION: What kinds of energy sources are available on the Moon?

14.3 Introducing Hydrocarbon Resources

What Are Oil and Gas?

For reasons of economics and convenience, industrialized societies today rely primarily on familiar products derived from oil (such as gasoline, jet fuel, kerosene, and diesel) and various kinds of natural gas (such as methane and propane) for their energy needs. Why are these fuels so popular? They have a relatively high **energy density**, meaning that they contain a relatively large amount of energy per unit of weight. For example, 1 g of oil provides twice as much energy as 1 g of coal and about 500 times more energy than a battery of comparable weight provides. So an airplane can cross an ocean on a tank of jet fuel but wouldn't even be able to get off the ground if it had to run on batteries. Chemically, both oil and natural gas are

hydrocarbons, because they consist of chain-like or ring-like molecules made of carbon and hydrogen atoms. For example, bottled gas (propane) has the chemical formula C_3H_9. Hydrocarbons are a type of organic chemical, so-named because similar carbon-based chemicals make up living organisms.

Some hydrocarbons are gaseous and invisible, some resemble watery liquids, some appear syrupy, and some are solid (**Fig. 14.4**). The *viscosity* (ability to flow) and the *volatility* (ability to evaporate) of a hydrocarbon product depend on the size of its component molecules. Products composed of short chains tend to be less viscous (they can flow more easily) and more volatile (they evaporate more easily) than products composed of long chains, because the long chains tend to tangle and bond with each other. Thus, at room temperature short-chain molecules occur in gaseous form (such as cooking gas, which is 95% methane), moderate-length-chain molecules occur in liquid

FIGURE 14.4 The diversity of hydrocarbon products in order of increasing viscosity.

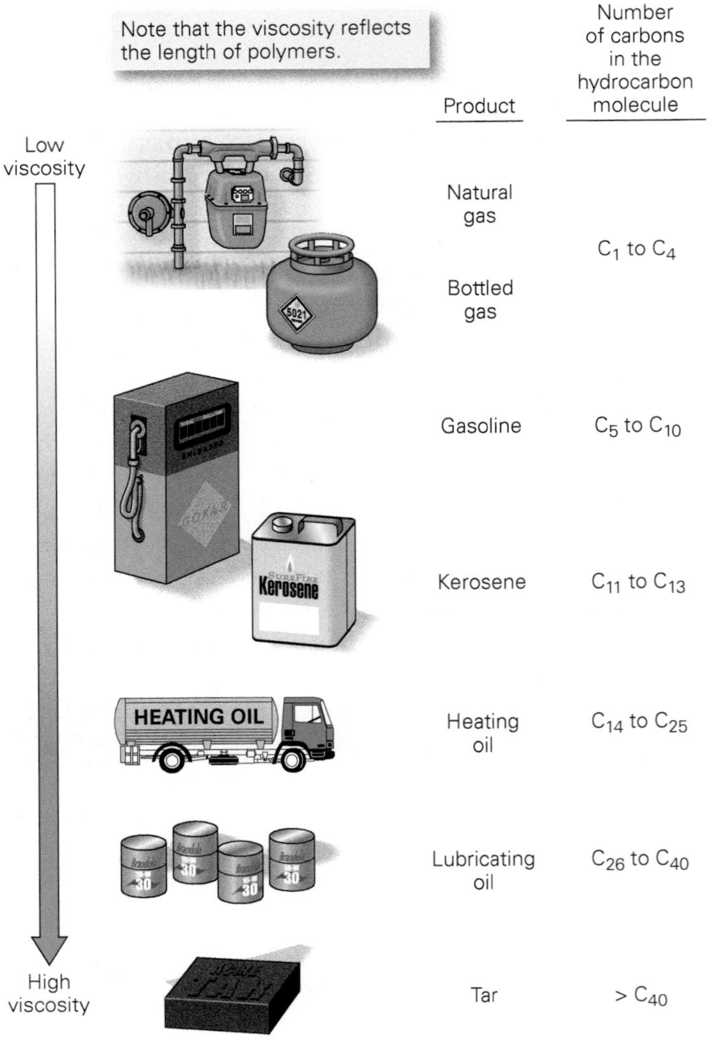

Note that the viscosity reflects the length of polymers.

	Product	Number of carbons in the hydrocarbon molecule
Low viscosity	Natural gas	
	Bottled gas	C_1 to C_4
	Gasoline	C_5 to C_{10}
	Kerosene	C_{11} to C_{13}
	Heating oil	C_{14} to C_{25}
	Lubricating oil	C_{26} to C_{40}
High viscosity	Tar	$> C_{40}$

FIGURE 14.5 The Iraqi army set fire to 700 oil wells in Kuwait in 1991, a tragic display of the energy locked in fossil fuels underground.

form (such as gasoline and oil), and long-chain molecules occur in solid form (tar).

Why can we use hydrocarbons as fuel? Simply because hydrocarbons, like wood, burn, meaning they react with oxygen to form carbon dioxide, water, and heat. As an example, we can describe the burning of gasoline by the following reaction:

$$2C_8H_{18} + 25O_2 \rightarrow 16CO_2 + 18H_2O + \text{heat and light}$$

During such reactions, potential energy stored in the chemical bonds of the hydrocarbon molecules converts into heat and light (Fig. 14.5). This energy can be used to run engines or to transform water into the steam that drives generators in a power plant.

Hydrocarbon Generation in Source Rocks

Popular media often incorrectly imply that oil and gas are derived from buried trees or the carcasses of dinosaurs. In fact, the hydrocarbon molecules form from organic chemicals, such as fatty molecules called lipids, that were once in plankton. *Plankton* is made up of very tiny floating organisms including single-celled and very small multicellular plants (algae) as well as protists and microscopic animals. Typically, most planktonic organisms range in size from 0.02 to 2.0 mm in diameter. Note that it is the organic cells of plankton that can transform into hydrocarbons, not the mineral shells.

When the organisms die, they sink to the floor of the lake or sea that they lived in, and if the water is relatively "quiet" (nonflowing), they accumulate (Fig. 14.6). In most locations, relatively little organic matter settles out of the water column, because most plankton gets consumed by organisms higher in the food chain. But if surface waters are nutrient-rich and receive a lot of sunlight, plankton blooms and a significant amount can settle out. Commonly, the seafloor or lake-floor hosts an oxygen-rich environment populated by scavengers

FIGURE 14.6 The formation of oil. The process begins when organic debris settles with sediment. As burial depth increases, heat and pressure transform the sediment into black shale in which organic matter becomes kerogen. At appropriate temperatures, kerogen becomes oil, which then seeps upward.

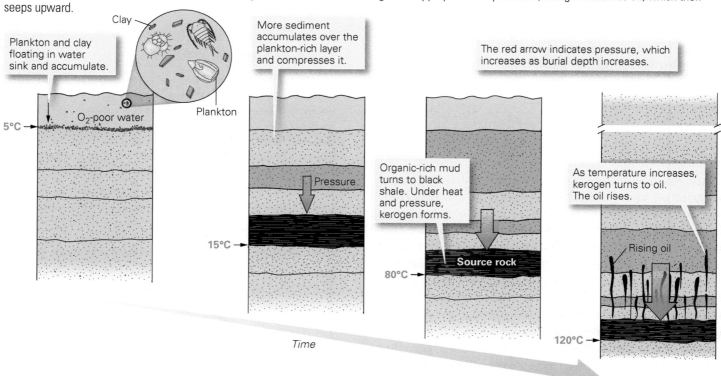

and microbes. As a result, dead plankton cells are consumed, decay, or oxidize before being buried. So, the organic matter in their cells transforms into CH_4 or CO_2 that bubbles away. But in oxygen-poor waters, the organic material can survive long enough to mix with clay and form an organic-rich, muddy ooze, which can then become buried by still more sediment so that it becomes preserved. Eventually, pressure from the weight of overlying sediment squeezes out the water, and the ooze becomes compacted and lithified to become black *organic shale*. (Shale that does not contain organic matter, in contrast, tends to be gray, tan, or red.) Organic shale contains the raw materials from which hydrocarbons form, so we refer to it as a **source rock**.

If organic shale is buried deeply enough (2 to 4 km), it becomes warmer, since temperature increases with depth in the Earth. Chemical reactions that take place in warm source rocks slowly transform the organic material in the shale into a variety of large waxy molecules that together comprise **kerogen**. Shale containing more than 25% to 75% kerogen is called **oil shale**. If oil shale warms to temperatures of greater than about 90°, kerogen molecules break into smaller oil and natural gas molecules, a process known as **hydrocarbon generation**. At temperatures over about 160°, any remaining oil breaks down to form natural gas. And at temperatures over 225°, organic matter loses all its hydrogen and transforms into graphite (pure carbon). Thus, oil itself forms only in a relatively narrow range of temperatures, called the **oil window** (Fig. 14.7). For regions with a geothermal gradient of 25°C/km, the oil window lies at depths of 3.5 to 6.5 km. Since gas survives to a higher temperature, the gas window extends down to 9 km, so the gas window is larger. If the geothermal gradient is low (15°C/km), oil can survive down to depths of about 11 km and gas down to 15 km. This means that, at most, hydrocarbons exist only in the topmost third of the crust.

Conventional vs. Unconventional Hydrocarbon Reserves

Oil and gas do not occur in all rocks at all locations. A known supply of oil and gas held underground is a **hydrocarbon reserve**—if the reserve consists dominantly of oil, it's usually called an *oil reserve* and if it consists predominantly of gas, it's a *gas reserve*. Some hydrocarbon reserves contain both oil and gas. Until relatively recently, oil companies could only economically obtain supplies of hydrocarbons that could be pumped from the ground relatively easily, meaning that the underground hydrocarbons could flow through the rock containing them to the drillhole. We refer to such hydrocarbon reserves as **conventional reserves**. In recent years, the rising price of hydrocarbons, as well as improvements in technology, have made it possible to obtain supplies that previously were

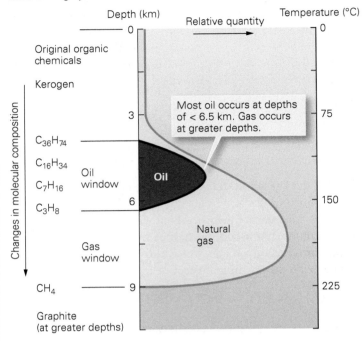

FIGURE 14.7 The "oil window" indicates subsurface conditions in which oil can form and survive. Deeper down, oil breaks down to form gas. At greater depth, metamorphism transforms organic material to graphite.

not easy to pump out simply by drilling a hole into the hydrocarbon-bearing rock. These hard-to-get supplies are known as **unconventional reserves**. The ability to access unconventional reserves has led to major changes in the energy industry.

Take-Home Message

Oil and gas are hydrocarbons derived from the remains of plankton buried with clay in an organic ooze. Burial transforms ooze into source rock, a black shale containing kerogen. If the rock is subjected to appropriate temperatures, organics transform into oil and gas. Hydrocarbon reserves are accumulations of oil and/or gas underground.

QUICK QUESTION: What is the difference between a conventional and unconventional reserve?

14.4 Conventional Hydrocarbon Systems

We've just noted that the hydrocarbons of a conventional reserve can be easily pumped out of the ground. The development of such a reserve requires a specific association of materials, conditions, and time. Geologists refer to this association as a **conventional hydrocarbon system** (Fig. 14.8). We already discussed the first two components of the system, namely the formation of a source rock of organic shale and the existence of thermal conditions that transform the kerogen in the shale into smaller hydrocarbon molecules. Let's now look at the remaining components, the migration of oil into a reservoir rock that lies within a configuration of rocks called an oil trap.

Reservoir Rocks and Hydrocarbon Migration

The clay flakes of an oil shale fit together tightly and thus prevent kerogen and any hydrocarbons forming within the rock or from moving easily through the rock. Therefore, you can't simply drill a hole into a source rock and pump out oil—the oil won't flow into the well fast enough to make the process cost efficient. To extract oil or gas from a conventional reserve, energy companies instead drill into **reservoir rocks**, rocks that contain, or could contain, accessible oil or gas. By "accessible," we mean oil or gas that can flow through rock and be sucked into a well fairly easily by pumping.

> **Did you ever wonder ...**
>
> whether there are actually lakes or pools of oil underground?

To be a reservoir rock, a body of rock must have space in which the oil or gas can reside and must have channels through which the oil or gas can move. The space can be in the form of openings, or **pores**, between clastic grains (which exist because the grains didn't fit together tightly and because cement didn't fill all the spaces during cementation) or in the form of cracks and fractures that developed after the rock formed. In some cases, groundwater passing through rock dissolves minerals and creates new pores. **Porosity** refers to the amount of open space in a rock. Not all rocks have the same porosity (Fig. 14.9). For example, shale typically has a low porosity (less than 10%), whereas poorly cemented sandstone has a high porosity (up to 35%). That means that about a third of a block of porous sandstone actually consists of open space. The oil or gas in a reservoir rock occurs in the pores (just as water fills the holes in a sponge) so it is distributed through the rock—it does not occur in open pools underground. **Permeability** refers to the degree to which pore spaces connect to one another. In a permeable rock, the pores and cracks are linked, so a fluid is able to flow slowly through the rock, following a tortuous pathway. Note that even if a rock has high porosity, it is not

necessarily permeable (see Fig. 14.9), for if the pores aren't connected fluid can't move from one to another.

Keeping the concepts of porosity and permeability in mind, we can see that a poorly cemented sandstone makes a good reservoir rock because it is both porous and permeable. A highly fractured rock can be porous and permeable, even if there is no pore space between individual grains. A limestone can be permeable if groundwater has dissolved the surfaces of cracks in the rock. The greater the porosity, the greater

FIGURE 14.8 Stages of a conventional hydrocarbon system.

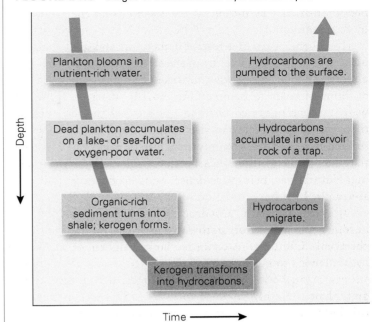

FIGURE 14.9 Porosity and permeability in sedimentary rocks. Rocks with high porosity and high permeability make the best reservoir rocks.

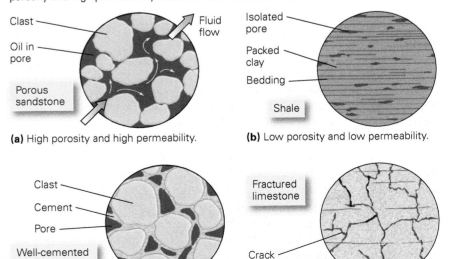

(a) High porosity and high permeability.

(b) Low porosity and low permeability.

(c) High porosity and low permeability.

(d) Low porosity and high permeability.

the capacity of a reservoir rock to hold oil, and the greater the rock's permeability, the easier it is for the oil to be extracted.

To fill the pores of a reservoir rock, oil and gas must first **migrate** (move) from the source rock into a reservoir rock, a process that takes thousands to millions of years to happen (Fig. 14.10). Why do hydrocarbons migrate? Oil and gas are less dense than water, so they try to rise toward the Earth's surface to get above groundwater, just as salad oil rises above the vinegar in a bottle of salad dressing. Natural gas, being less dense, ends up floating above oil. In other words, buoyancy drives oil and gas upward. Typically, a hydrocarbon system must have a good **migration pathway**, such as a set of permeable fractures, in order for large volumes of hydrocarbons to move.

Traps and Seals

The existence of reservoir rock alone does not create a conventional reserve, because if hydrocarbons can flow into a reservoir rock, they can also flow out. If oil or gas escape from the reservoir rock and ultimately reach the Earth's surface, where they can leak away at a **oil seep** or *gas seep* (Fig. 14.11), there will be none left underground to extract. Thus, for an oil reserve to exist, oil and gas must be held underground in the reservoir rock by means of a geologic configuration called a **trap**.

An oil or gas trap has two components. First, a **seal rock**, a relatively impermeable rock such as shale, salt, or unfractured limestone, must lie above the reservoir rock and stop the hydrocarbons from rising further. Second, the seal and reservoir rock bodies must be arranged in a geometry that collects the hydrocarbons in a restricted area. Geologists recognize several types of hydrocarbon trap geometries, four of which are described in Box 14.1.

Note that when we talk about trapping hydrocarbons underground, we are talking about a temporary process in the context of geologic time. Oil and gas may be trapped for millions to over a hundred million years, but eventually they may manage to pass through a seal rock because no rock is absolutely impermeable—most rocks contain joints that can provide permeability. Also, in some cases, microbes eat hydrocarbons in the subsurface. Thus innumerable oil reserves that existed in the past have vanished, and the oil fields we find today, if left alone, may disappear millions of years in the future.

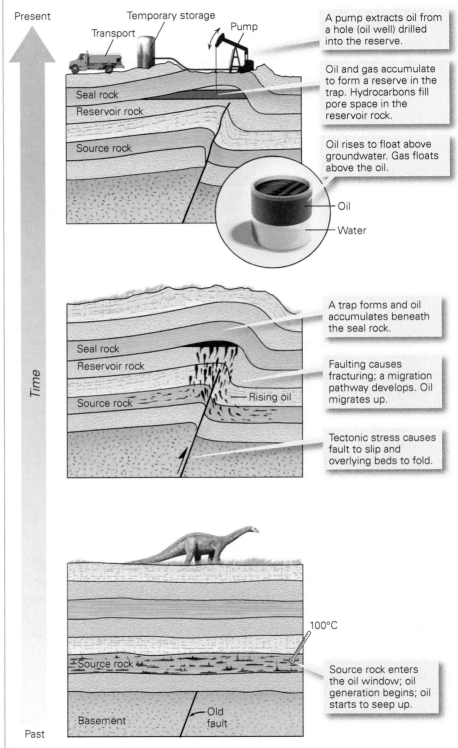

FIGURE 14.10 Initially, oil resides in the source rock. Because it is buoyant relative to groundwater, the oil migrates into the overlying reservoir rock. The oil accumulates beneath a seal rock in a trap.

Present

Transport — Temporary storage — Pump

Seal rock
Reservoir rock
Source rock

A pump extracts oil from a hole (oil well) drilled into the reserve.

Oil and gas accumulate to form a reserve in the trap. Hydrocarbons fill pore space in the reservoir rock.

Oil rises to float above groundwater. Gas floats above the oil.

Oil
Water

Time

Seal rock
Reservoir rock
Source rock — Rising oil

A trap forms and oil accumulates beneath the seal rock.

Faulting causes fracturing; a migration pathway develops. Oil migrates up.

Tectonic stress causes fault to slip and overlying beds to fold.

100°C
Source rock
Basement — Old fault

Source rock enters the oil window; oil generation begins; oil starts to seep up.

Past

FIGURE 14.11 Examples of hydrocarbon seeps at the Earth's surface.

(a) The La Brea tar pit is an oil seep that now forms the centerpiece of a small park in Los Angeles, California.

(b) The Darvasa gas crater (known as the "door to hell") in Turkmenistan formed in 1971 when a drilling rig tapped into a cavern filled with natural gas. Engineers lit a fire hoping to burn off the gas, but it's above a seep, so the fire has burned ever since.

Birth of the Conventional Oil Industry

People have used oil since the dawn of civilization—as a cement, as a waterproof sealant, and even as a preservative to embalm mummies. In the United States, during the first half of the 19th century, "rock oil" (later called petroleum, from the Latin words *petra*, meaning rock, and *oleum*, meaning oil), collected at seeps, was used to grease wagon axles and to make patent medicines. But such oil was rare and expensive. In 1854, George Bissell, a New York lawyer, realized that oil might have broader uses, particularly as fuel for lamps, to replace increasingly scarce whale oil. Bissell and a group of investors hired Edwin Drake, a colorful character who had drifted among many professions, to find a way to drill for oil in rocks beneath a hill near Titusville, Pennsylvania, where oily films floated on the water of springs. Using the phony title "Colonel" to add respectability to his name, Drake hired drillers and obtained a steam-powered drill. Work was slow and the investors became discouraged, but the very day that Drake received a letter ordering him to stop drilling, his drillers discovered that the hole, which had reached a depth of 21.2 m, had filled with oil. They set up a pump, and on August 27, 1859, for the first time in history, pumped oil out of the ground. No one had given much thought to the question of how to store the oil, so workers dumped it into empty whisky barrels. (These days, a **barrel of oil [bbl]** has become a standard unit of measurement: 1 bbl = 42 gallons = 159 liters. Oil may also be sold by weight: 1 metric ton (1 tonne) of oil = 6.5 barrels.)

Within a few years, thousands of oil wells had been drilled in many states, and by the turn of the 20th century, civilization had begun its addiction to oil. Initially, most oil went into the production of kerosene for lamps. Later, when electricity took over from kerosene as the primary source for illumination, gasoline derived from oil became the fuel of choice for the newly invented automobile. Oil was also used to fuel electric power plants. In its early years, the oil industry was in perpetual chaos. When "wildcatters" discovered a new oil field, there would be a short-lived boom during which the price of oil could drop to pennies a barrel. In the midst of this chaos, John D. Rockefeller established the Standard Oil Company, which monopolized the production, transport, and marketing of oil. In 1911, the Supreme Court broke Standard Oil down into several companies (including Exxon, Chevron, Mobil, Sohio, Amoco, Arco, Conoco, and Marathon), some of which have recombined in recent decades. Oil became a global industry governed by the complex interplay of politics, profits, supply, and demand.

The Modern Search for Oil

Wildcatters discovered the earliest *oil fields*, the land area above an oil-filled trap, either by blind luck or by searching for surface seeps. But in the 20th century, when most known seeps had been drilled and blind luck became too risky, oil companies realized that finding new oil fields would require systematic exploration. The modern-day search for oil is a complex, sometimes dangerous, and often exciting endeavor with many steps.

Source rocks are always sedimentary, as are most reservoir and seal rocks, so geologists begin exploration by looking for a region containing appropriate sedimentary rocks. Then they compile a geologic map of the area, showing the distribution of rock units. From this information, it may be possible to construct a preliminary cross section depicting the geometry of the sedimentary layers underground as they would appear on an imaginary vertical slice through the Earth.

BOX 14.1   CONSIDER THIS . . .

Types of Oil and Gas Traps

Geologists who work for oil companies spend much of their time trying to identify underground traps. No two traps are exactly alike, but we can classify most into the following four categories.

- *Anticline trap:* In some places, sedimentary beds are not horizontal, as they are when originally deposited, but have been bent by the forces involved in mountain building. These bends, as we have seen, are called folds. An anticline is a type of fold with an arch-like shape (**Fig. Bx14.1a**). If the layers in the anticline include a source rock overlain by a reservoir rock that is overlain by a seal rock, then we have the recipe for an oil reserve. The oil and gas rise from the source rock, enter the reservoir rock, and are trapped in the crest of the anticline.

- *Fault trap:* If the slip on a fault crushes and grinds the adjacent rock to make an impermeable layer along the fault, then oil and gas may migrate upward along bedding in the reservoir rock until they stop at the fault surface (**Fig. Bx14.1b**). A fault trap may also develop if the slip juxtaposes a seal rock against a reservoir rock.

- *Salt-dome trap:* In some sedimentary basins, the sequence of strata contains a thick layer of salt, deposited when the basin was first formed and seawater covering the basin was shallow and very salty. Sandstone, shale, and limestone overlie the salt. The salt layer is not as dense as sandstone, limestone, or shale, so it is buoyant and tends to rise up slowly through the overlying strata. Once the salt starts to rise, the weight of surrounding strata squeezes the salt out of the salt layer and up into a growing, bulbous *salt dome*. As the dome rises, it bends up the adjacent layers of sedimentary rock. Oil and gas in reservoir rock layers migrate upward until they are trapped against the boundary of the salt dome, for salt is impermeable (**Fig. Bx14.1c**).

- *Stratigraphic trap:* In a stratigraphic trap, a tilted reservoir rock bed "pinches out" (thins and disappears up-dip) between two impermeable layers. Oil and gas migrating upward along the bed accumulate at the pinch-out (**Fig. Bx14.1d**).

FIGURE Bx14.1 Examples of oil traps. A trap is a configuration of a seal rock over a reservoir rock in a geometry that keeps the oil underground.

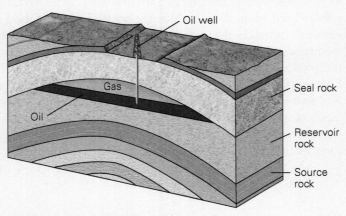

(a) Anticline trap. Oil and gas rise to the crest of the fold.

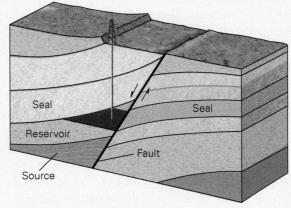

(b) Fault trap. Oil and gas collect in tilted strata adjacent to the fault.

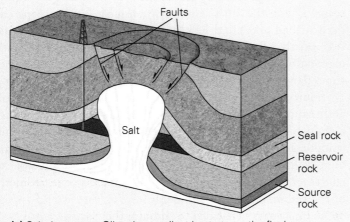

(c) Salt-dome trap. Oil and gas collect in strata on the flanks of the dome, beneath salt.

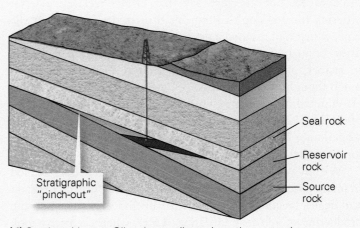

(d) Stratigraphic trap. Oil and gas collect where the reservoir layer pinches out.

To add detail to the cross section, explorationists obtain a **seismic-reflection profile** of the region. On land, this is done by using a special vibrating truck or by setting off dynamite explosions that send seismic waves into the ground (Fig. 14.12a; see Interlude D). The seismic waves reflect off contacts between rock layers, just as sonar waves sent out by a submarine reflect off the bottom of the sea. Reflected seismic waves then return to the ground surface, where sensitive seismometers (geophones) stuck into the ground record their arrival. A computer measures the time between the generation of a seismic wave and its return and, based on this information, defines the depth to the contacts at which the wave reflected (Fig. 14.12b). To explore for oil in sedimentary layers below the sea floor, the exploration company uses an "air gun" dragged behind a ship to send pulses of compressed air into the water (Fig. 14.12c). The pulses carry enough energy to produce seismic waves in the strata beneath the water. Reflected signals are received by geophones dragged behind the ship. Using the data collected by geophones, computer programs construct an image of the configuration of underground rock layers and, in some cases, can even detect reserves of oil or gas. Technological advances now enable geologists to create 3-D seismic-reflection data blocks of the subsurface both under land and underwater (Fig. 14.12d). Such blocks are expensive—just one may cost millions of dollars to create.

Drilling and Refining

If geologic studies identify a trap, as well as good source rocks and reservoir rocks, and a likelihood that strata have been heated into the oil or gas window, then geologists make a recommendation to drill. They do not make such recommendations lightly, as drilling a deep well may cost tens of millions of dollars. If management accepts the geologists' recommendation, drillers go to work.

These days, drillers use rotary drills to grind a hole down through rock. A rotary drill consists of a pipe tipped by a rotating bit, a bulb of metal studded with hard metal prongs (Fig. 14.13a). As the bit rotates, it scratches and gouges and

FIGURE 14.12 Using seismic-reflection profiling to describe the character of underground beds and help locate reservoirs.

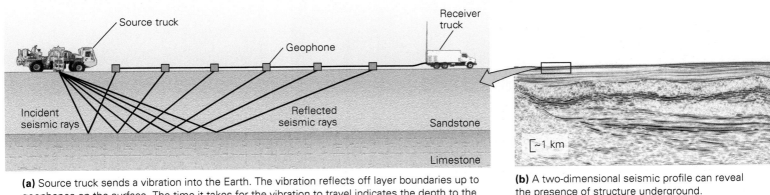

(a) Source truck sends a vibration into the Earth. The vibration reflects off layer boundaries up to geophones on the surface. The time it takes for the vibration to travel indicates the depth to the reflector.

(b) A two-dimensional seismic profile can reveal the presence of structure underground.

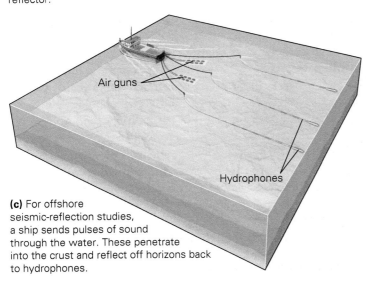

(c) For offshore seismic-reflection studies, a ship sends pulses of sound through the water. These penetrate into the crust and reflect off horizons back to hydrophones.

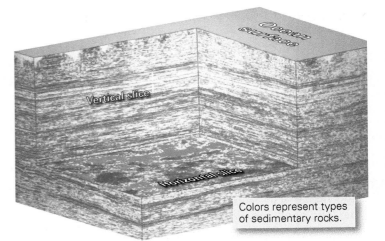

(d) Modern techniques produce three-dimensional "blocks" of data, so geologists can study both vertical and horizontal slices through the subsurface.

Oil Field near Lamesa, Texas

LATITUDE
32°33'18.42"N

LONGITUDE
101°46'55.39"W

Looking down from 8 km up (~5 mi).

This view shows a grid of farm fields, 1.6 km (1 mi) wide, within which small roads lead to patches of dirt. Each patch hosts (or hosted) a pump for extracting oil. These wells are tapping an oil reserve in Permian strata in Texas.

FIGURE 14.13 Drilling rigs and oil pumps.

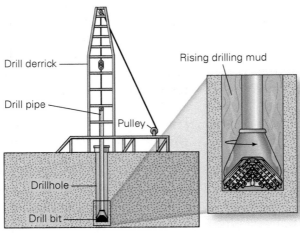

(a) An on-shore drilling rig. The inset shows a close-up of the drill bit. Drilling mud carries the cuttings up and out of the hole.

(b) The Lakeview gusher, in California, spilled 9 million bbl in 1910.

(c) An aerial view of an oil field with many, closely-spaced wells.

(d) An off-shore drilling rig. The derrick is constructed on top of a platform. The flare burns off gas.

turns the rock it contacts into powder and chips. Drillers pump **drilling mud**, a slurry of water mixed with clay and other materials, down the center of the pipe. The mud flows down, past a propeller that rotates the drill bit, and then squirts out of holes at the end of the bit. The extruded mud cools the bit head, which otherwise would heat up due to friction as it grinds against rock, then flows up the hole on the outside of the drill pipe. As it rises, the mud carries *rock cuttings* (fragments of rock that were broken up by the drill bit) up and out of the hole. Mud also serves another very important purpose—its weight counters the natural pressure of the oil and gas in underground reservoir rocks. By doing so, it prevents hydrocarbons from entering the hole until drilling stops and the hole has been "completed." Completing a hole involves removing the drill pipe, inserting a casing of steel pipe, filling the space between the casing and the walls of the drillhole with concrete, and capping the hole. Were it not for the mud, the natural pressure in the reservoir rock would drive oil and/or gas into the hole. And if the pressure were great enough, the hydrocarbons

would rush up the hole and spurt out of the ground as a *gusher* or *blowout* (Fig. 14.13b). Gushers and blowouts can be disastrous, because they spill oil onto the land and, in some cases, ignite into an inferno.

Early drilling methods could produce only vertical drillholes, because it wasn't just the drill bit that turned during drilling, but rather the whole drill pipe from the surface down, as well as the drill bit. Thus, an oil field might contain many closely spaced wells (Fig. 14.13c). But as technology advanced, and the drill bit became the only part to rotate, engineers developed methods that allow drillers to control the path of the drill bit so the hole can curve and become inclined at an angle from vertical or can even be horizontal. Such **directional drilling** has become so precise that a driller, by using a joystick to steer the bit and by watching output from sensors that specify the exact location of the bit in three-dimensional space, can hit an underground target that is only several centimeters wide from a distance of a few kilometers. Drillers can even bend a hole and guide it to stay within a horizontal bed for several kilometers.

Drillers must use derricks (towers) to hoist the heavy drill pipe. To drill in an offshore hydrocarbon reserve, one that occurs in strata beneath the continental shelf, the derrick must be constructed on an *offshore-drilling facility* (Fig. 14.13d). These may be built on huge towers rising from the seafloor or on giant submerged pontoons. Using directional drilling, it's possible to reach multiple targets from the same platform. On completion of a hole, workers remove the drilling rig and set up a pump. Some pumps resemble a bird pecking for grain; their heads move up and down to pull up oil that has seeped out of pores in the reservoir rock into the drillhole (Fig. 14.14a).

You may be surprised to learn that simple pumping gets only about 30% of the oil in a reservoir rock out of the ground. Thus oil companies use *secondary recovery techniques* to coax out more oil (as much as 20% more). For example, a company may drive oil toward a drillhole by forcing steam into holes in the ground nearby—the steam heats the oil in the ground, making it less viscous, and pushes it along. In some cases, drillers create artificial fractures in rock around the hole by pumping a high-pressure water and chemical mixture into a portion of the hole. This process, called **hydrofracturing** (*hydraulic fracturing* or simply *fracking*), creates new fractures and opens up pre-existing ones—the fractures provide easy routes for the oil to follow from the rock to the well. We'll discuss hydrofracturing in more detail later in this chapter.

Once extracted directly from the ground, "crude oil" flows first into storage tanks and then into a pipeline or tanker, which transports it to a refinery (Fig. 14.14b–d). At a refinery, workers distill crude oil into several separate components by first heating it to a temperature of about 400°C and then by pumping it into a vertical pipe called a *distillation column* (Fig. 14.14e). Lighter molecules rise to the top of the column, while heavier molecules stay at the bottom. Outlets at different levels in the column allow removal of molecules of different sizes—tar comes out the bottom, oil above that, gasoline above that, and propane from the top. The heat may also "crack" larger molecules to make smaller ones. Chemical factories buy the largest molecules left at the bottom and transform them into plastics.

Where Do Conventional Reserves of Oil Occur?

Conventional reserves are not randomly distributed around the Earth. Currently, countries bordering the Persian Gulf contain the world's largest reserves in 25 *supergiant fields* (Fig. 14.15a). In fact, this region has almost 60% of the world's conventional reserves, whereas the United States, the largest consumer of oil, has only a few percent of the total.

What determines where conventional reserves occur? To start with, a region must have been in an environment where plankton could grow well, so that sediments being deposited in the region are rich in organic content. Much of the region that is now the Middle East was situated in tropical areas between latitude 20° S and 20° N between the Jurassic (135 million years ago [Ma]) and the Late Cretaceous (66 Ma), where biological productivity was high (Fig. 14.15b). So sediments deposited at that time were rich in organic matter. Thick successions of porous sandstone buried the source rocks of the Middle East, and crustal compression due to the collision between Africa and Asia folded the strata to produce excellent traps.

The Middle East is not the only source of conventional oil (see Fig. 14.15a). Reserves also occur in sedimentary basins formed along passive continental margins, such as the Gulf Coast of the United States and the Atlantic coasts of Africa and Brazil, as well as in the intracratonic and foreland basins on continents (see Chapter 7).

Take-Home Message

Conventional hydrocarbon reserves are ones in which oil has migrated from a source rock into a porous and permeable reservoir rock, situated within an oil trap, so that the oil or gas can be pumped fairly easily. The first oil drilling took place in 1859. Modern methods for finding, drilling, producing, and refining oil are very complex and expensive.

QUICK QUESTION: Where do most of the conventional oil reserves in the world occur today?

14.5 Unconventional Hydrocarbon Reserves

In an **unconventional hydrocarbon reserve**, the material (rock or sediment) contains significant quantities of hydrocarbons, but either the material does not have adequate permeability or the hydrocarbons themselves are too viscous to flow. Thus, the hydrocarbons cannot be extracted simply by drilling into the material and pumping. Extraction of unconventional hydrocarbons was not possible until engineers developed new technologies and the price per barrel of hydrocarbons became high enough for the extraction to be profitable. These conditions were met 10 to 15 years ago, and since then efforts to extract hydrocarbons from, specifically, shale gas and tar sand have grown at a very rapid rate, and now such reserves provide a significant portion of the global energy. Let's examine the geologic context of these reserves.

FIGURE 14.14 Pumping, transporting, and refining oil.

(a) When drilling is complete, the derrick is replaced by a pump, which sucks oil out of the ground. This design is called a pumpjack.

The head of the pump goes up and down.

Storage tanks

Hole

(d) Distilling columns of an oil refinery transform crude oil into gasoline and other hydrocarbon products.

(b) This oil supertanker is 330 meters long and can carry 300,000 metric tons. When the ship is loaded, the red painted area is almost completely underwater.

(c) The Trans-Alaska Pipeline transports oil from fields on the Arctic coast to a tanker port on the southern coast of Alaska.

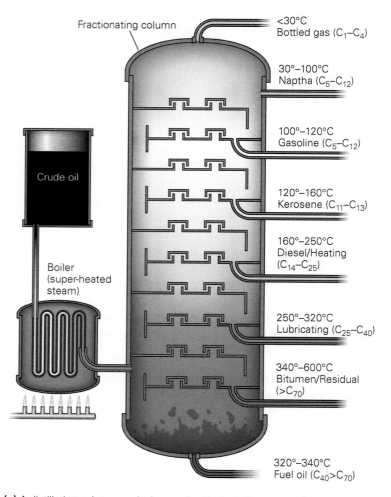

Fractionating column

<30°C
Bottled gas (C_1–C_4)

30°–100°C
Naptha (C_5–C_{12})

100°–120°C
Gasoline (C_5–C_{12})

120°–160°C
Kerosene (C_{11}–C_{13})

160°–250°C
Diesel/Heating (C_{14}–C_{25})

250°–320°C
Lubricating (C_{25}–C_{40})

340°–600°C
Bitumen/Residual (>C_{70})

320°–340°C
Fuel oil (C_{40}>C_{70})

Crude oil

Boiler (super-heated steam)

(e) A distillation column works by gravity. Heated oil separates into bubbles of lighter hydrocarbons and droplets of heavier ones. Heavier ones sink and light ones rise.

FIGURE 14.15 The distribution of oil reserves around the world.

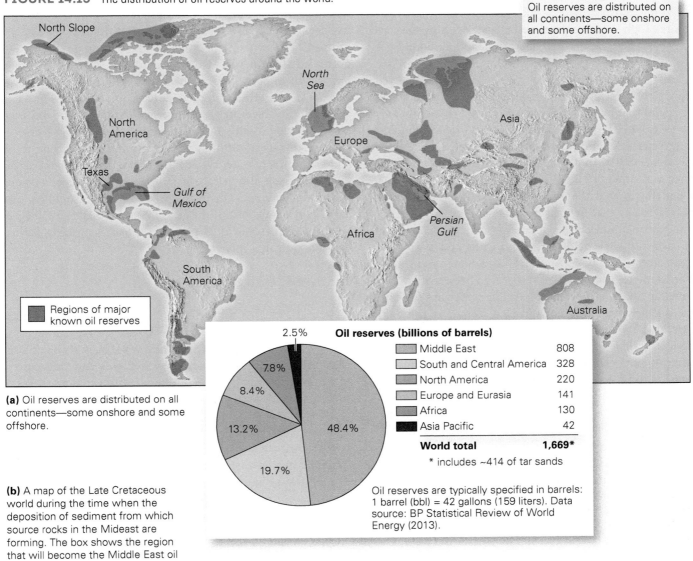

Oil reserves are distributed on all continents—some onshore and some offshore.

(a) Oil reserves are distributed on all continents—some onshore and some offshore.

Oil reserves (billions of barrels)	
Middle East	808
South and Central America	328
North America	220
Europe and Eurasia	141
Africa	130
Asia Pacific	42
World total	**1,669***

* includes ~414 of tar sands

Oil reserves are typically specified in barrels: 1 barrel (bbl) = 42 gallons (159 liters). Data source: BP Statistical Review of World Energy (2013).

Pie chart values: 48.4%, 19.7%, 13.2%, 8.4%, 7.8%, 2.5%

(b) A map of the Late Cretaceous world during the time when the deposition of sediment from which source rocks in the Mideast are forming. The box shows the region that will become the Middle East oil fields of today. Note that the region lay in the warm subtropics in which marine plankton could thrive.

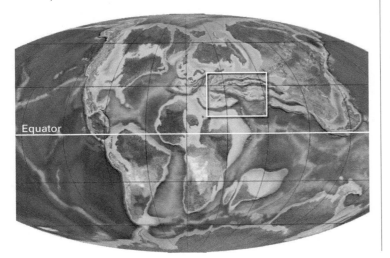

Shale Gas

As we've seen, natural gas consists of volatile short-chain hydrocarbon molecules (methane, ethane, propane, and butane). Gas burns more cleanly than oil, in that combustion of gas produces only carbon dioxide and water, while the burning of oil not only produces carbon dioxide and water but also complex organic pollutants. Thus, natural gas has long been a preferred fuel for home cooking and heating. And when the cost of natural gas decreased, many electrical generating stations were converted to burn natural gas. It can also be used to fuel cars and trucks if the vehicles have been appropriately modified.

If gas is the main hydrocarbon of a conventional reserve, it may be economical to extract and transport the gas. Gas often occurs in association with oil, or in place of oil, in conventional reserves. In many of these reserves, the volume of gas is too small to be economically produced because gas must be compressed for transport, which takes energy, and transportation requires high-pressure pipelines or special ships that are expensive to operate. So oil-field operators commonly vent gas from a pipe and burn it as a flare where it enters the air (see Fig. 14.13d).

Huge quantities of natural gas remain in source rocks (organic shale) that have been heated to the gas window. This resource is called **shale gas**. Until recently, this gas could not be extracted economically by pumping because of shale's very low permeability. In 2008, Terry Engelder of Penn State University and others pointed out that previous reports had greatly underestimated the amount of shale gas available in sedimentary basins that lie near populated areas (Fig. 14.16). The combination of increased gas-volume estimates and of the ability to access the gas by directional drilling and hydrofracturing has led to a "gas boom" in the United States and worldwide. For example, thousands of wells have been drilled into the Marcellus Shale, a Devonian formation that lies beneath portions of Pennsylvania, Ohio, and New York, and the Bakken Shale of the Williston basin in North Dakota and adjacent states. The shale gas beds are not that thick, and in these basins they do not occur in conventional traps. But because of directional drilling, a single well can follow a bed horizontally for many kilometers, and several wells can be drilled from the same platform. And because of hydrofracturing, the permeability of the rock can be increased. The gas flows into the drillhole and up to the ground under its own pressure.

Energy companies have spent billions of dollars to lease the right to obtain gas from large areas of the region, and some local landowners have become millionaires overnight. Thousands of people have obtained jobs working for energy companies as well as in the towns that house the workers. So much shale gas has been extracted in recent years that it has led some power companies to switch their generators to natural gas, and it has decreased the amount of overseas oil that the United States has had to import. The boom remains controversial, though, because of lingering questions about the amount of gas that can really be recovered and because of environmental concerns associated with hydrofracturing (Box 14.2). Not only are residents worried that chemicals in hydrofracturing fluids may contaminate water supplies, but there are also worries that fracturing may also release gas into sources of groundwater. (Natural gas does occur in the groundwater of some regions, but it's not always clear if the gas entered the water from new or enlarged fractures or if its presence reflects long-term natural seepage from shale beds.)

Tar Sands (Oil Sands)

In several locations around the world, most notably Alberta (in western Canada) and Venezuela, vast reserves of very viscous, tar-like *heavy oil* exist. This heavy oil, known also as bitumen, has the consistency of gooey molasses and thus cannot be pumped directly from the ground. It fills the pore spaces of sand or of poorly cemented sandstone, constituting up to 12% of the sediment or rock volume. Sand or sandstone containing high concentrations of bitumen is known as **tar sand** or *oil sand*.

The hydrocarbon system that leads to the generation of tar sands begins with the production and burial of a source rock in a large sedimentary basin. When subjected to temperatures of the oil window, the source rock yields oil and gas, which migrate into sandstone layers and then up the dip of tilted layers to the edge of the basin, where they become caught in stratigraphic traps (see Box 14.1). Initially, these hydrocarbons have relatively low viscosity, so in the geologic past they could have been pumped easily. But over time, microbes attacked the oil reserve underground, digested lighter, smaller hydrocarbon molecules, and left behind only the larger molecules, whose presence makes the remaining oil so viscous. Geologists refer to such a transformation process as *biodegradation*. Generation of tar sand by biodegradation is yet another example of the interaction between physical and biological components of the Earth System.

FIGURE 14.16 Map of basins with assessed shale oil and shale gas formations, as of May 2013.

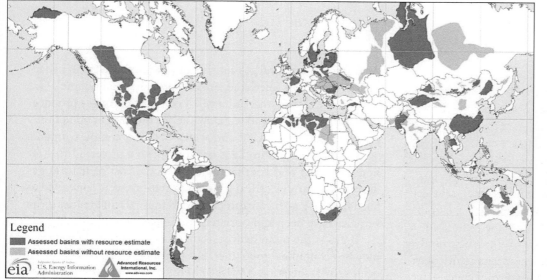

Legend
- Assessed basins with resource estimate
- Assessed basins without resource estimate

eia U.S. Energy Information Administration

Advanced Resources International, Inc.
www.adv-res.com

Production of usable oil from tar sand is difficult and expensive but not impossible. It takes about two tons of tar sand, and a lot of energy, to produce one barrel of oil. Oil companies mine near-surface deposits in vast open-pit mines and then heat the tar sand in a furnace to extract the oil (Fig. 14.17a). Producers then crack the heavy oil molecules to produce smaller, more usable molecules. Trucks dump the drained sand back into the mine pit. To extract oil from deeper deposits of tar sand, oil companies drill wells and pump steam or solvents down into the sand to liquefy the oil enough so that it can be pumped out.

Oil Shale

Vast reserves of organic shale have not been subjected to temperatures of the oil window, or if they were, they did not stay within the oil window long enough to complete the transformation to oil. Such rock still contains a high proportion of kerogen. Shale that contains at least 15 to 30% kerogen is called **oil shale**. Oil shale is not the same as coal because the organic matter within it exists in the form of waxy hydrocarbon molecules, not as elemental carbon.

Lumps of oil shale can be burned directly and thus have been used as a fuel since ancient times (Fig. 14.17b). In the 1850s, researchers developed techniques to produce liquid oil from oil shale. The process involves heating the oil shale to a temperature of 500°C; at this temperature, the shale decomposes and the kerogen transforms into liquid hydrocarbon and gas. Large supplies of oil shale occur in Estonia, Scotland, China, and Russia, and in the Green River basin of Wyoming in the United States. As is the case with tar sand, production of oil from oil shale is possible but very expensive. In addition to the expense of mining and environmental reclamation, producers must pay for the energy needed to heat the shale. It takes about 40% of the energy yielded by a volume of oil shale to produce the oil itself.

Gas Hydrate

Gas hydrate is a chemical compound consisting of methane (CH_4) molecules surrounded by a cage-like arrangement of water molecules. An accumulation of gas hydrate occurs as a whitish solid that resembles ordinary water ice (Fig. 14.17c). Gas hydrate forms when anaerobic bacteria (bacteria that live in the absence of oxygen) eat organic matter, such as dead plankton that have been incorporated into sediments of the seafloor. When the bacteria digest organic matter, they produce methane as a by-product, and the methane bubbles into the cold seawater that fills pore spaces in sediments. Under pressures found at depth in the ocean, the methane dissolves in the pore water and produces gas-hydrate molecules—the

FIGURE 14.17 Examples of alternative hydrocarbon sources.

(a) An open-pit mine in Canada for digging up tar sand. Trucks haul the sand to a plant where it is heated so hydrocarbons can be extracted.

(b) Oil shale can be set ablaze.

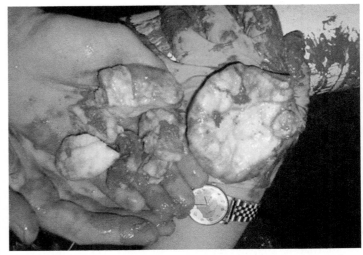

(c) Gas hydrate samples (white material) dug up from the muddy sea floor.

BOX 14.2   CONSIDER THIS . . .

Hydrofracturing (*Fracking*)

Hydrofracturing (*hydraulic fracturing* or *fracking*), a technology first utilized in the 1950s, has been in the news quite a bit in recent years, where it's commonly referred to as *fracking*. Drillers use the technique to open and propagate existing joints in rocks at depth as well as to generate new cracks in the rock. These fractures provide a permeability pathway through which hydrocarbons can flow to reach a drill hole and be extracted. Originally, hydrofracturing was used in conventional vertical wells as a means to enhance secondary recovery. Today it is also being widely used in horizontal wells following gas shale beds (**Fig Bx14.2a, b**). What is hydrofracturing, how does it work, and what risks are potentially involved in its use?

To hydraulically fracture a hole, drillers start by sealing off a length of a well with *packers*, which are simply inflatable balloons that when filled with high-pressure fluid press tightly against the wall of the hole (**Fig Bx14.2c**). Then the drillers insert a pipe through one of the packers into the sealed-off section of the well and pump *fracking fluid* into this section under high pressure. When the pressure generated by the fluid within the sealed section becomes great enough, it forces open existing joints that intersect the hole and may cause these joints to lengthen at their tip (**Fig Bx14.2d**). The process may also generate new cracks in the rock adjacent to the hole. The area affected by hydrofracturing can extend tens of meters out from the drillhole. Once fracturing has been completed, drillers pump out the fluid and

complete the hole. Hydrocarbons then flow along the fractures into the drillhole and up to the surface, where drillers capture it and compress it for transport (**Fig Bx14.2e**). The volume of fluid used to hydrofracture a section of hole is roughly equivalent to the volume in an Olympic swimming pool—usually several sections of a hole may be subjected to hydrofracturing, so the process is repeated several times in the hole.

What's in fracking fluid? A typical example consists of about 95% water, 9.5% quartz sand, and 0.5% other chemicals. The sand is necessary because it props the holes open once the fluid has been removed—without the sand, the cracks opened by hydrofracturing would close up tightly under the pressure applied by surrounding rock, and thus could not serve as permeability pathways. The 0.5% portion of fracking fluid that is not water or sand is a mixture of many chemicals, including oils that make the fluid more slippery so it can inject farther into the rock; acid, which dissolves cement between grains and increases porosity; detergent, which lowers the surface tension of water so it doesn't stick to grains; guar gum to make the fluid more viscous so that it can carry more sand; antifreeze to prevent scale buildup; and biocides, which prevent the growth of bacteria that could clog pores. Hydrofracturing requires a lot of equipment and materials, so at a drilling site where it's taking place, there will be lots of trucks carrying water, sand, and other chemicals as well as trucks carrying portable pumps and

giant mixing vats. The drill site may also have holding tanks or retaining ponds for storing fluid that has been removed from the ground once hydrofracturing has been finished.

Concerns about hydrofracturing have become the subject of intense public debate. The most common concern is that fracking fluid can contaminate drinking water underground. To understand the nature of this risk, it's necessary to understand how groundwater changes with depth. As we'll discuss further in Chapter 19, *groundwater* is water that fills or saturates pores and cracks in rock or sediment underground, beneath a surface called the *water table*—above the water table, pores and cracks contain some air. Typically, groundwater in the upper several hundred to a few thousand meters can be fresh and drinkable, but below that depth groundwater tends to be saline (**Fig Bx14.2f**). If the section of the hole subjected to hydrofracturing lies deeper than the saline boundary, the fluids from the section probably won't mix with drinkable groundwater, for they are denser than groundwater and thus are not buoyant. Leakage from the portion of the vertical hole above the saline boundary, however, can be problematic, so it is important that this portion of the hole be cased and sealed thoroughly before fracking fluid is pumped in. Leakage at the surface, from tanks or holding ponds, or from transporting trucks is also of concern—to avoid contamination, handling the fluids at the surface must be very carefully monitored.

---

reaction can occur in water as shallow as 90 m in colder, polar water but not until depths of about 300 m in warmer, equatorial water. Exploration tests suggest that gas hydrate occurs as layers interbedded with sediment and/or as a cement holding together the sediment at depths of between 90 and 900 m beneath the seafloor. Geologists estimate that an immense amount of methane lies trapped in gas-hydrate layers. In fact, worldwide there may be more organic carbon stored in gas hydrate than in all other reservoirs combined! So far, however, techniques for safely recovering gas hydrate from the seafloor have not been devised.

Take-Home Message

Gas shale, tar sand, and oil shale are unconventional reserves, because it is difficult and expensive to extract hydrocarbons from them. Development of new technologies, however, has made extraction feasible. In particular, directional drilling and hydrofracturing has led to a huge increase in production of shale gas.

QUICK QUESTION: How can usable fuels be obtained from oil shale and tar sand?

FIGURE Bx14.2 Directional drilling and hydrofracturing. New technologies have led to economic production of shale gas.

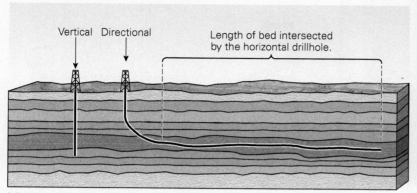

(a) Directional drilling permits the drillhole to follow a relatively thin bed for many kilometers, so the amount of shale gas accessed can be large. A vertical hole intersects the gas shale for only a short distance.

(b) A drilling site. The trucks and the holding pond are used during hydrofracturing. Many holes can be drilled from this site, like spokes of a wheel.

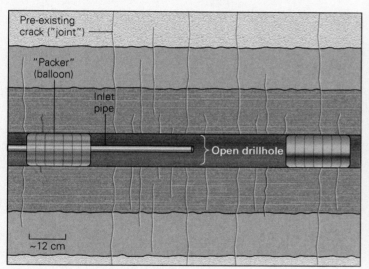

(c) The first step in hydrofracturing. After the hole has been drilled, packers seal off a portion, and a pipe is inserted through one of the packers.

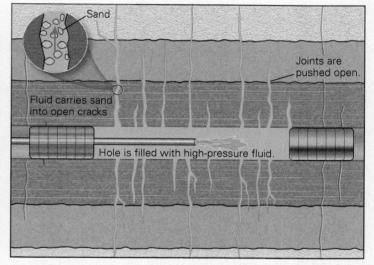

(d) High-pressure fluid is pumped into the segment of hole. The pressure pushes open cracks and forms new ones. Sand injected with the fluid keeps the cracks from closing.

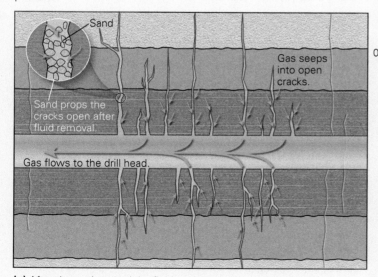

(e) After the packers and the fluid are removed, gas can seep into the pipe and flow to the drill head.

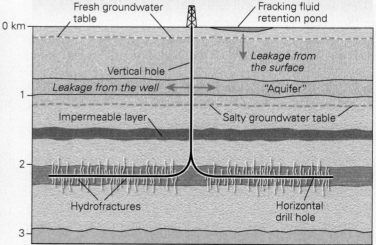

(f) Potential for the contamination of groundwater by hydrofracturing.

FIGURE 14.18 The formation of coal. Coal forms when plant debris becomes deeply buried.

(a) A museum diorama depicting a Carboniferous coal swamp.

(b) If there is a transgression, peat formed in the coal swamp can be buried and preserved.

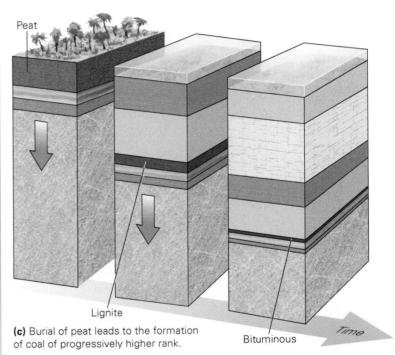

(c) Burial of peat leads to the formation of coal of progressively higher rank.

14.6 Coal: Energy from the Swamps of the Past

Coal, a black, brittle, sedimentary rock that burns, consists of elemental carbon mixed with minor amounts of organic chemicals, quartz, and clay. Typically, the carbon atoms in coal have bonded together, forming large, complicated molecules called coal *macerals*. Like oil and gas, coal is a fossil fuel because it stores solar energy that reached Earth long ago. But coal does not have the same composition or origin as oil or gas—coal contains carbon, not hydrocarbons—and in contrast to oil, coal forms from plant material (wood, stems, leaves), not plankton. Coal commonly occurs in beds, called *coal seams*, that may be centimeters to meters thick and may be traceable over very large regions.

Significant coal deposits could not form until vascular land plants appeared on Earth in the late Silurian Period, about 420 million years ago. The most extensive deposits of coal in the world occur in Carboniferous-age strata (359 to 299 Ma). In fact, geologists coined the name *Carboniferous* because strata representing this interval of the geologic column contain so much coal. Not all coal reserves, however, are Carboniferous—during the Cretaceous (145 to 66 Ma), large areas of freshwater coal swamps developed in Wyoming and adjacent states.

The Formation of Coal

The development of broad, continuous coal seams requires the accumulation of a substantial amount of vegetation in an *anoxic* (oxygen-poor) *environment*. Such accumulations can develop during times when the climate becomes very wet and warm, as happened in the Carboniferous, when large areas of continents

lay in equatorial latitudes, and in the Cretaceous, when superplumes dumped large quantities of greenhouse gases into the atmosphere. Wet climates cause the water table to rise until broad plains become saturated with water, and lower areas become submerged by shallow water. If it's warm, vegetation flourishes, so such wet regions become **coal swamps**, broad lowlands that resemble the wetlands and rainforests of modern tropical to semitropical regions (Fig. 14.18a). In the stagnant water of the swamp, oxygen from the air doesn't mix into the water, and microorganisms completely consume any oxygen that had been dissolved in the water, so the water becomes anoxic. Thus, vegetation that dies and falls into the water doesn't rot entirely away but rather gets buried by more dead vegetation until a compacted and partially decayed layer of organic matter, called **peat**, accumulates. The peat may be buried by fluvial (river) deposits, or if sea level then rises, and a transgression takes place (see Chapter 7), layers of marine sediments—such as sand, mud, or carbonate debris—bury and preserve the peat. If buried deeply enough, the succession of sediment turns into sedimentary strata, with the coal occurring as a sedimentary bed (Fig. 14.18b).

How do the remains of plants transform into coal? As we've seen, the first step involves the formation of peat, which contains about 50% carbon. (Notably, peat itself serves as a fuel in many parts of the world, where thick deposits formed from moss and grasses in bogs during the last several thousand years. This peat can easily be cut out of the ground and, once dried, burns.) To transform peat into coal, the peat must be buried to a depth of 4 to 10 km by overlying sediment. Such deep burial can happen where the surface of the continent gradually sinks, creating a sedimentary basin (see Chapter 7). At depth in the pile, the weight of overlying sediment compacts the peat and squeezes out any remaining water. Then, because temperature increases with depth in the Earth, deeply buried peat gradually heats up. Heat accelerates chemical reactions that gradually destroy plant fiber and release molecules such as H_2O, CO_2, CH_4, and N_2. These gases seep out of the reacting peat layer, leaving behind a residue concentrated with carbon. Once the proportion of carbon in the residue exceeds about 60%, the deposit formally becomes coal. With further burial and higher temperatures, chemical reactions yield progressively higher concentrations of carbon (Fig. 14.18c).

The Classification of Coal

Geologists classify coal according to the concentration of carbon, which in turn reflects the temperature to which the coal has been subjected underground. At temperatures of less than 100°C, coal is a soft, dark brown material called *lignite*. At higher temperatures (100° to 200°C), lignite transforms into dull, black *bituminous coal*. At still higher temperatures (200° to 300°C), bituminous coal transforms into shiny, black *anthracite* (also called hard coal). The progressive transformation of peat to anthracite, which occurs as the coal layer is buried more deeply and becomes warmer, reflects the completeness of chemical reactions that remove hydrogen, oxygen, and nitrogen atoms from the organic chemicals of the peat and leave behind carbon (Fig. 14.18c). Thus, lignite contains only about 60% carbon, bituminous about 70%, and anthracite about 90%. As the carbon content of coal increases, we say the **coal rank** increases—lignite is low-rank coal, bituminous is intermediate-rank coal, and anthracite is high-rank coal.

The burning of coal is a chemical reaction: $C + O_2 \rightarrow CO_2$. Therefore, the different ranks of coal produce different amounts of energy when burned. Anthracite contains more carbon per kilogram than lignite contains, so it produces more energy when burned. Specifically, burning a kilogram of anthracite yields about five times as much energy as burning a kilogram of peat.

Notably, the temperatures necessary to form anthracite develop only on the borders of mountain belts. Here mountain-building processes can push thick sheets of rock up along thrust faults and over the coal-bearing sediment, so the sediment ends up at depths of 8 to 10 km, where temperatures reach 300°C. In addition, mountain uplift drives very hot groundwater from great depth up through the coal and can cause its rank to increase. Metamorphism in the interiors of mountain belts leads to the expulsion of all elements except carbon from organic layers, and the remaining carbon atoms rearrange to form graphite, the gray mineral used to make pencils. Thus, coal cannot be found in metamorphic rocks.

Finding, Mining, and Using Coal

Because the vegetation that eventually becomes coal was initially deposited in a sequence of sediment, coal occurs as sedimentary beds (seams, in mining parlance) interlayered with other sedimentary rocks (Fig. 14.19). To find coal, geologists search for sequences of strata that were deposited in tropical to semitropical shallow-marine to terrestrial environments—the environments in which a swamp could exist. The sedimentary strata of continents contain huge quantities of discovered coal, or **coal reserves**. For example, economic seams (beds of coal 1 to 3 m thick, thick enough to be worth mining) of Cretaceous age occur in the U.S. and Canadian Rocky Mountain region, while economic seams of Carboniferous age are found throughout the midwestern United States. Coal is found widely in Europe, Asia, and Australia (Fig. 14.20a, b).

FIGURE 14.19 An example of coal beds interlayered with beds of sandstone and shale.

FIGURE 14.20 The distribution of coal, and its consumption.

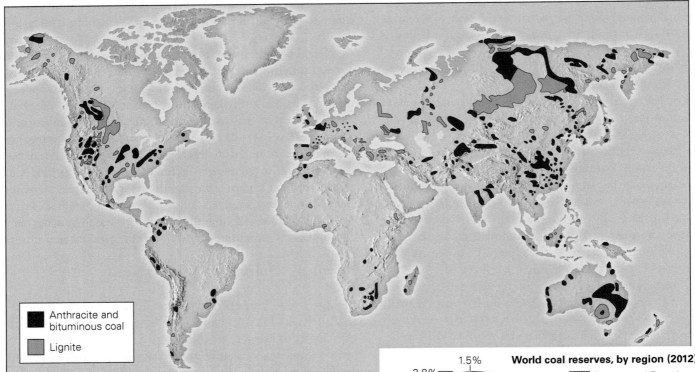

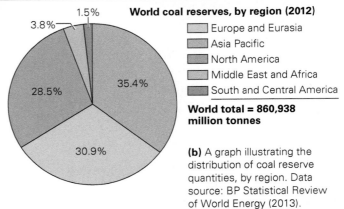

World coal reserves, by region (2012)

- Europe and Eurasia
- Asia Pacific
- North America
- Middle East and Africa
- South and Central America

1.5%
3.8%
35.4%
28.5%
30.9%

World total = 860,938 million tonnes

(b) A graph illustrating the distribution of coal reserve quantities, by region. Data source: BP Statistical Review of World Energy (2013).

(a) A map showing global distribution of coal reserves. Most coal accumulated in continental interior basins.

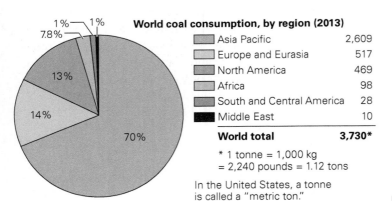

World coal consumption, by region (2013)

Asia Pacific	2,609
Europe and Eurasia	517
North America	469
Africa	98
South and Central America	28
Middle East	10
World total	**3,730***

1%
1%
7.8%
13%
14%
70%

* 1 tonne = 1,000 kg = 2,240 pounds = 1.12 tons

In the United States, a tonne is called a "metric ton."

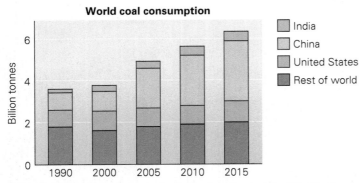

World coal consumption

- India
- China
- United States
- Rest of world

c) Coal consumption varies greatly and is changing rapidly. Growth of consumption in China has more than tripled in the last 25 years. Data source: U.S. Energy Information Administration (EIA).

The United States was the largest consumer of coal until about 1986, when China's rate of consumption surpassed that of the United States. China's consumption has tripled since 2005, reflecting the country's rapid industrialization—in 2012, China burned 55% of the coal mined, the United States about 12%, India about 8%, and the rest of the world about 25% (Fig. 14.20c). All told, society is now consuming about 8 billion tons of coal a year, about 70% of which fuels electricity-generating stations. In fact, coal currently provides about 21% of the world's energy supply.

The way in which companies mine coal depends on the depth of the coal seam. If the coal seam lies within about 100 m of the ground surface, *strip mining* proves to be most economical. In strip mines, miners use a giant shovel, called a dragline, to scrape off soil and layers of sedimentary rock above the coal seam (Fig. 14.21a). Draglines are so big that the shovel could swallow a two-car garage without a trace. Once the dragline has exposed the seam, smaller machinery scrapes out the coal and dumps it into trucks or onto a conveyor belt where it is carried to storage piles (Fig. 14.21b, c). Before modern environmental awareness took hold, strip mining left huge scars on the landscape. Without topsoil, the rubble and exposed rock of the mining operation remained barren of vegetation. Coal beds that formed from coastal swamps tend to contain pyrite (FeS), which weathers when exposed to air and water to form sulfuric acid; sulfuric acid contributes to making the soil unsuitable for growth. In many contemporary mines, however, the dragline operator separates out and preserves soil. Then, when the coal has been scraped out, the operator fills the hole with the rock that had been stripped to expose the coal and covers the rock back up with the saved soil, on which grass or trees may eventually grow. Within years to decades, the former mine site can become a pasture or a forest. In hilly areas, however, miners may use a practice called *mountaintop removal*, during which they blast off the top of the mountain and dump the debris into adjacent valleys. This practice disrupts the landscape permanently.

Deep coal can be obtained only by *underground mining*. To develop an underground mine, miners dig a shaft down to the depth of the coal seam and then create a maze of tunnels, using huge grinding machines that chew their way into the coal (Fig. 14.21d). Depending on circumstances, miners either leave columns of coal behind to hold up the mine roof, or they let the mined area collapse, so the ground level above sinks once mining is finished.

Underground coal mining can be very dangerous not only because the sedimentary rocks forming the roof of the mine are

FIGURE 14.21 Coal can be mined in strip mines or in underground mines.

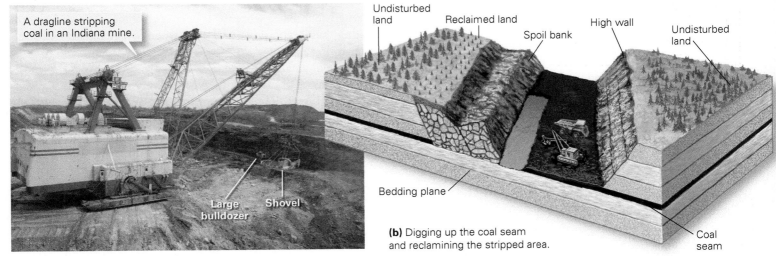

(a) A dragline stripping overburden.

(b) Digging up the coal seam and reclaiming the stripped area.

(c) Piles of recently mined coal.

(d) Underground coal mining.

weak and can collapse but also because methane gas released by continuing chemical reactions in coal can accumulate in the mine, leading to the danger of a small spark triggering a deadly mine explosion. Unless they breathe through filters, underground miners also risk contracting black lung disease from the inhalation of coal dust. The dust particles wedge into tiny cavities of the lungs and gradually cut off the oxygen supply or cause pneumonia.

Gas from Coal

Coal-Bed Methane
As we've noted, the natural process by which coal forms underground yields methane, a type of natural gas. Over time, some of the gas escapes to the atmosphere, but vast amounts remain within the coal in pores or bonded to coal molecules. Such **coal-bed methane**, trapped in strata too deep to be reached by mining, is an energy resource that has become a target for extraction in many regions of the world.

Obtaining coal-bed methane from deep layers of strata involves drilling rather than mining. Drillers penetrate a coal bed with a hole and then start pumping out groundwater. As a result of pumping out water, the pressure in the vicinity of the drillhole decreases relative to the surrounding bed. Methane bubbles into the hole and then up to the ground surface, where condensers compress it into tanks for storage. Disposal of the water produced by coal-bed methane extraction can be a major problem. If the water is pure, it can be used for irrigation, but in deep coal beds the water may be saline and thus cannot be used for crops. Producers either pump this water back underground or evaporate it in large ponds, so that they can extract and collect the salt.

Coal Gasification.
Traditional burning of coal produces clouds of smoke containing *fly ash* (solid residue left after the carbon in coal has been burned) and noxious gases (including sulfur dioxide, SO_2, which forms because coal contains sulfur-bearing minerals such as pyrite). Today smoke can be partially cleaned by expensive scrubbers, but pollution remains a major problem—the abundance of coal-burning plants in China has played a major role in producing the country's air pollution. Alternatively, solid coal can be transformed into various gases, as well as solid by-products, before burning. The gases burn relatively cleanly. The process of producing relatively clean-burning gases from solid coal is called **coal gasification**; the process was invented in the late 18th and early 19th centuries and was used extensively to produce fuels during World War II.

Coal gasification involves the following steps. First, pulverized coal is placed in a large container. Then a mixture of steam and oxygen passes through the coal at high pressure. As a result, the coal heats up to a high temperature but does not ignite. Under these conditions, chemical reactions break down and oxidize the molecules in coal to produce hydrogen (H_2) and other gases such as carbon monoxide (CO), H_2O,

and CO_2. Solid ash, as well as sulfur and mercury, concentrate at the bottom of the container and can be removed before the gases are burned so that the contaminants do not go up the chimney and into the atmosphere. The CO gas and H_2 gas can then be combined, through a chemical reaction, to produce hydrocarbons. Alternatively, the CO gas can react with water to produce more H_2 (plus CO_2). Of note, the hydrogen can be concentrated to produce fuel cells (which we will discuss later).

Underground Coal-Bed Fires

Coal will burn not only in furnaces but also in surface and subsurface mines as long as the fire has access to oxygen. Coal mining of the past two centuries has exposed much more coal to the air and has provided many more opportunities for fires to begin. Once started, such a *coal-bed fire* progresses underground by sucking in oxygen from joints and pore spaces in surrounding rock. The fires may be difficult or impossible to extinguish because they are inaccessible. Some fires begin as a result of lightning strikes, some from spontaneous combustion (when coal reacts with air, it heats up), some in the aftermath of methane explosions, and some when people intentionally set trash fires in mines.

Major coal-bed fires can be truly disastrous. The most notorious of these fires in North America began as a result of trash burning in a mine near the town of Centralia, Pennsylvania (**Fig. 14.22a**). For the past 50 years, the fire has progressed underground, eventually burning coal seams beneath the town itself. The fire produces toxic fumes that rise through the ground and make the overlying landscape uninhabitable, and it also causes the land surface to collapse and sink. Eventually, inhabitants had to abandon many neighborhoods of the town. Much longer-lived fires occur elsewhere—one in Australia may have been burning for a few thousand years. Satellite imagery, by highlighting warm spots on the ground surface, indicates that thousands of coal-bed fires are currently burning. Many of the fires occur in northern China—recent estimates suggest that 200 million tons of coal burn in China every year, an amount equal to approximately 20% of the annual national production of coal in China (**Fig. 14.22b**).

Take-Home Message

Coal forms from the accumulations of plant material over time in anoxic coal swamps. When buried deeply, this organic material undergoes reactions that concentrate carbon. Higher-rank coal contains more carbon. Coal occurs as beds, called seams, in sedimentary successions and must be mined underground or in open pits.

QUICK QUESTION: Why do underground coal fires start, and why are they so hard to stop?

FIGURE 14.22   Coal mine fires—long-lived disasters.

(a) A coal-bed fire beneath Centralia, Pennsylvania, produces noxious gas and has forced the evacuation of many homes.

(b) A burning coal bed in China, exposed in a mine wall, glows red.

14.7 Nuclear Power

How Does a Nuclear Power Plant Work?

So far we have looked at fuels, such as oil, gas, and coal, that release energy when they undergo *chemical burning*. During such burning, a chemical reaction between the fuel and oxygen releases the potential energy stored in the chemical bonds of the fuel. The energy that drives a nuclear power plant comes from a totally different process—*nuclear fission*, the breaking of the nuclear bonds that hold protons and neutrons together in the nucleus. Fission splits an atom into smaller pieces, and during this process, a small amount of mass transforms into thermal and electromagnetic energy, as Einstein characterized in his famous equation, $E = mc^2$ (where E is energy, m is mass, and c is the speed of light).

A **nuclear reactor**, the heart of the plant, commonly lies within a containment building made of reinforced concrete (Fig. 14.23). The reactor contains nuclear fuel, consisting of pellets of concentrated uranium oxide or a comparable radio-active material that is packed into metal tubes called *fuel rods*. Fission occurs when a speeding neutron strikes a radioactive isotope, causing it to split. For example, radioactive uranium-235 (^{235}U) splits into barium-141 (^{141}Ba) and krypton-92 (^{92}Kr) plus three neutrons. The neutrons released during the fission of one atom strike other atoms, thereby triggering more fission in a self-perpetuating process called a **chain reaction**, which overall produces lots of energy, including heat. Pipes carry water close to the heat-generating fuel rods, and the heat transforms the water into high-pressure steam. The pipes then carry this steam to a turbine, where it rotates fan blades—the rotation drives a dynamo that generates electricity. Eventually the steam goes into cooling towers, where it condenses back into water that can be reused in the plant or returned to the environment.

Compared with fossil fuels, the energy density of enriched uranium is vast—1 g of reactor fuel contains almost 80,000 times as much energy as 1 g of gasoline, and yields no air pollution or greenhouse gases. Thus, nuclear power plants could produce a large proportion of global energy supply. But they don't, at present, because of societies' concerns about handling nuclear fuel and nuclear waste.

The Geology of Uranium

Where does uranium come from? The Earth's radioactive elements, including uranium, probably developed during the explosion of a supernova that happened before the existence of our Solar System. Uranium atoms from this explosion became part of the nebula out of which the Earth formed and thus were incorporated into the planet. Large atoms like uranium don't fit well into the crystal structure of minerals, so when melts form, they preferentially enter the melt and rise with the melt. Eventually, uranium atoms were carried into the upper crust by rising granitic magma.

Even though granite contains uranium, it does not contain very much. But nature has a way of concentrating uranium. Hot water circulating through a pluton after intrusion dissolves the uranium and precipitates it as the mineral pitchblende (UO_2) in veins. Uranium may be further concentrated once plutons, and the associated uranium-rich veins, weather and erode at the ground surface. Sand derived from a weathered pluton washes down a stream, and as it does so, uranium-rich grains stay behind because they are so heavy relative to quartz and feldspar grains. The world's richest uranium deposits, in fact, occur in ancient streambed gravels. Uranium deposits may also form when groundwater percolates through uranium-rich

FIGURE 14.23 Producing electricity at a nuclear power plant.

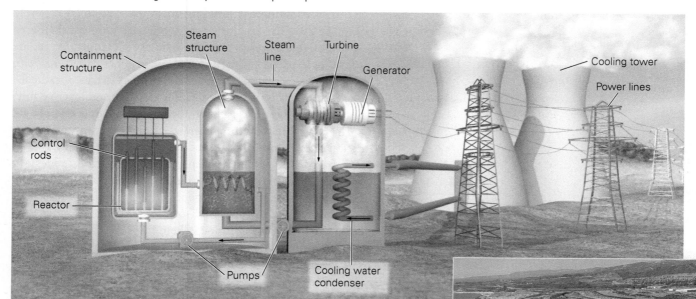

Containment structure · Control rods · Reactor · Steam structure · Steam line · Turbine · Generator · Pumps · Cooling water condenser · Cooling tower · Power lines

(a) In a nuclear power plant, a reactor heats water, which produces high-pressure steam. The steam drives a turbine that in turn drives a generator to produce electricity. A condenser transforms the steam back into water.

(b) This nuclear power plant in California has two reactors, each in its own containment building.

sedimentary rocks, for the uranium dissolves in the water and moves with the water to another location where the chemical environment is different, causing new uranium-bearing minerals to precipitate out of solution and fill the pores of the host sedimentary rock.

You can't just mine uranium and put it into a reactor. That's because ^{235}U, the isotope of uranium that serves as the most common fuel for conventional nuclear power plants, accounts for only about 0.7% of naturally occurring uranium—most uranium consists of ^{238}U. Thus, to make a fuel suitable for use in a power plant, the ^{235}U concentration in a mass of natural uranium must be increased by a factor of 2 or 3, an expensive process called *uranium enrichment*.

Challenges of Using Nuclear Power

Maintaining safety at nuclear power plants requires hard work. In conventional reactors, operators must ensure that circulating water constantly cools the nuclear fuel, and the rate of nuclear fission must be regulated by the insertion of *control rods*, made of materials that absorb neutrons and thus decrease the number of collisions between neutrons and radioactive atoms. Without control rods, the number of neutrons dashing around in the nuclear fuel would progressively increase, causing the rate of fission and accompanying heat production to increase. Eventually, the fuel would become so hot that it would melt. Such

a **meltdown** might cause a steam explosion, or it could generate such high temperatures that water molecules break to form hydrogen gas and oxygen gas, a mixture that can be very explosive. If the explosion is large enough, it could breach the containment building and scatter radioactive debris into the air. Note that a meltdown is not the same as an atomic bomb explosion. An atomic bomb explosion can only occur if there is a sufficient "critical mass" (quantity) of highly enriched uranium (90% ^{235}U), in which fission reactions happen so quickly that the fuel itself explodes. (By comparison, "reactor-grade" uranium is only 3% to 4% ^{235}U.)

Did you ever wonder...

whether a nuclear power plant could explode like an atomic bomb?

The first nuclear power plant designed to generate electricity for the public became operational in 1954. Today, about 435 nuclear power plants are in operation, and about 70 are under construction. Over the past 60 years, there have been three significant accidents. The first occurred in 1979 at the Three Mile Island plant in Pennsylvania, when a stuck valve allowed coolant water to escape, causing the reactor to overheat. Eventually, some of that radioactive coolant leaked out into the environment, but contamination due to the leak was limited. The next, and much more serious nuclear accident occurred at the power plant in Chernobyl, Ukraine, in April 1986, while engineers were conducting a test. The fuel pile became too hot, triggering a hydrogen explosion that ruptured the roof of the containment building and spread fragments of the reactor and its fuel around the plant grounds, and within six weeks, 20 people had died from radiation sickness. In addition, some of the radioactive material entered the atmosphere and dispersed over eastern Europe and Scandinavia, but no one yet knows whether this fallout affected the health of exposed populations. The reactor has been entombed in concrete, and the surrounding region has remained closed. In 2011, a disaster second only to Chernobyl in terms of the amount of radiation released, occurred at the multireactor Fukushima power plant along the east coast of northern Japan. This disaster occurred when the catastrophic tsunami that followed the magnitude 9.0 Tōhoku earthquake knocked out both the power lines providing electricity to pumps that circulated cooling water and the backup diesel generators (see Chapter 10). As a result, some of the reactors overheated, and they suffered partial meltdowns and hydrogen gas explosions. Long-term health effects are not known.

One of the biggest challenges to the nuclear industry pertains to the storage of **nuclear waste**, the radioactive material produced in a nuclear plant. It includes spent fuel, which contains radioactive elements, as well as water and equipment that have come in contact with radioactive materials. Radioactive elements emit gamma rays and X-rays, which can damage living organisms and cause cancer. Some radioactive material decays quickly (in decades to centuries), but some remains dangerous for thousands of years or more. Nuclear waste cannot just be stashed in a warehouse or buried in a town landfill. Some of the waste is hot enough that it needs to be cooled with water. Even cooler waste has the potential to leak radioactive elements into municipal water supplies or nearby lakes or streams. Ideally, waste should be sealed in containers that will last for thousands of years (the time needed for the short-lived radioactive atoms to undergo decay) and stored in a place where it will not come in contact with the environment. Finding an appropriate place is not easy, and so far, experts disagree about which is the best way to dispose of nuclear waste. For some years the U.S. government favored storing waste at Yucca Mountain in the Nevada desert, but this is no longer likely and most nuclear waste remains on the site of the power plant that produced it.

Take-Home Message

Controlled fission in reactors produces nuclear power. The fuel consists of uranium or other elements obtained by mining. Reactors run the risk of meltdown but cannot explode like an atomic bomb. They also yield radioactive waste, which is difficult to store.

QUICK QUESTION: What is the difference between a meltdown in a reactor and the explosion of an atomic bomb?

14.8 Other Energy Sources

Geothermal Energy

As the name suggests, **geothermal energy** comes from heat in the Earth's crust. We can distinguish between high-temperature geothermal energy, which is used for producing heat and electricity at a commercial scale, and low-temperature geothermal energy (also known as *ambient geothermal energy*), which is used for warming and cooling the water of an individual household.

High-temperature geothermal energy exists because the crust becomes progressively hotter with increasing depth, at a rate defined by the geothermal gradient. In active volcanic areas, the increase happens so fast that a temperature of 100°C or more can be attained within only several hundred meters of the Earth's surface. Thus, at relatively shallow depths, bedrock, and any groundwater contained in bedrock, is at or near the boiling point of water. Power companies can use this geothermal energy in many ways. For example, in some places, they simply pump hot groundwater through pipes to heat houses or spas directly. If the groundwater is hot enough, it turns to steam when it rises to the Earth's surface and decompresses. This steam can drive

Geothermal Powerplant, New Zealand

LATITUDE
38°37'34.84"S

LONGITUDE
176°6'18.82"E

Zoom to 2 km (1.2 mi) and look straight down.

You're seeing a geothermal powerplant along the Waikato River in New Zealand. If you fly SSW, you cross Lake Taupo, a caldera marking the site of the world's largest eruption of the last 5,000 years. Further south is Mt. Tongariro, a stratovolcano that has erupted over 70 times in the last two centuries.

turbines and generate electricity (Fig. 14.24). In Iceland and New Zealand, which sit astride volcanic areas, geothermal energy provides a substantial portion of electricity needs. But on a global basis, the impact is much smaller.

Ambient geothermal energy takes advantage of the fact that below a depth of a few meters, the ground temperatures remain nearly constant all year (at about the average annual temperature of the air above). By installing pipes in the ground, typically down to a depth of 5 m, home owners can cool the water used in their house during the summer, and can heat the water used in their house in the winter, before running it through a powered cooling system or heating system, respectively. This decreases the amount of energy needed to heat or cool the water and lower costs.

Biofuels

In recent years, farmers have begun to produce rapidly growing crops specifically for the purpose of producing biomass for fuel production. The resulting liquids are called **biofuels**. The most commonly used biofuel is ethanol, a type of alcohol, which can substitute for gasoline in car engines. The process of producing ethanol from corn includes the following steps: First, producers grind corn into a fine powder, mix it with water, and cook it to produce a mash of starch. Then they add an enzyme to the mash, which converts the mash into sugar. The sugar, when mixed with yeast, ferments. Fermentation produces ethanol and CO_2. Finally, the fermented mash is distilled to concentrate the ethanol. While corn is the main source of ethanol in North America, ethanol in Brazil is produced directly, without fermentation, from sugar extracted from sugarcane.

Researchers have also begun to develop processes that yield ethanol from cellulose, permitting perennial grasses and the stalks of other plants to become a source of liquid fuel, or from algae, which naturally produces fatty chemicals (lipids) from which hydrocarbons can be produced. Such processes could help make ethanol a renewable energy source. And recent technologies have also led to the commercial production of *biodiesel*, a fuel produced by chemical modification of fats and vegetable oils. Biodiesel can be mixed with petroleum-derived diesel to run trucks and buses.

Hydroelectric and Wind Power

For millennia, people have used flowing water and air to produce energy. In fact, many towns were established next to rivers, where streams could rotate the waterwheels that powered mills and factories. And in agricultural areas, farmers used windmills to pump water for irrigation. In the past century, engineers have begun to employ the same basic technology to drive generators that produce electricity. Energy derived from flowing fluids is clean, or "green" in the sense that its production does not release chemical or radioactive pollutants, and is renewable in that its production does not consume limited resources. But its use does impact the environment.

In a modern hydroelectric power plant, the potential energy of water is converted into kinetic energy as the water flows from a higher elevation to a lower elevation. The flowing water turns turbine blades placed in a pipe, and the turbine drives an electrical generator. Most hydroelectric plants rely on water from a reservoir held back by a dam. The largest of these is the Three Gorges Dam on the Yangtze River in China

(Fig. 14.25a). Dam construction increases the available potential energy of the water because the water level in a filled reservoir is higher than the level of the valley floor that the dam spans. Hydroelectric energy is clean, and reservoirs may have the added benefit of providing flood control, irrigation water, and recreational opportunities. But the construction of dams and reservoirs may bring unwanted changes to a region, so the benefits of their construction must be weighed against potential harm. Damming a river may flood a spectacular canyon, eliminate exciting rapids, or destroy an ecosystem. Further, reservoirs trap sediment and nutrients, thus disrupting the supply of these materials to downstream floodplains or deltas, a process that may adversely affect agriculture.

Not all hydroelectric power generation utilizes flowing river water—engineers have been developing new means to tap **tidal power** (the daily rise and fall of the sea; see Chapter 18). One approach involves building a dam, called a *tidal barrage*, across the entrance to a bay or estuary (the flooded mouth of a river) in which there are large tides. When the tide rises, water spills into the enclosed area through openings in the dam. When the tide outside drops, water flows back to the sea via a pipe that carries it through a power-generating turbine (Fig. 14.25b). More recently, engineers have developed technologies to place huge fan blades underwater in nearshore regions where tidal currents naturally flow; the blades slowly turn in the current and run generators.

When you think of wind energy, you may picture a classic Dutch windmill driving a water pump. Modern efforts to harness the wind are on a much larger scale. To produce wind-generated electricity, engineers identify regions, either onshore or just offshore, with steady breezes. In these regions, they build wind farms that consist of numerous towers, each of which holds a wind turbine, a giant fan blade that turns even in a gentle breeze (Fig. 14.25c). Some towers are on the

FIGURE 14.25 Hydroelectric and tidal power.

(a) Gravity causes water held back by the Three Gorges Dam to flow through turbines and generate electricity.

(c) A wind farm in southwestern England. The towers are about 50 m high.

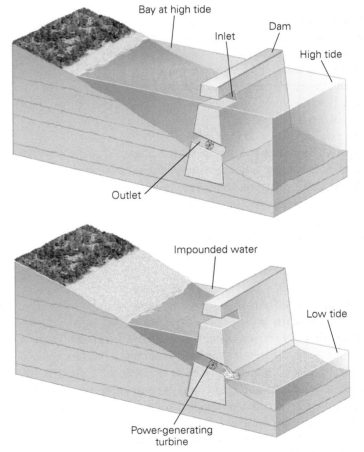

(b) To produce tidal power, a dam traps seawater at high tide; the water can flow through a turbine at low tide.

FIGURE 14.26 Solar energy and fuel cells.

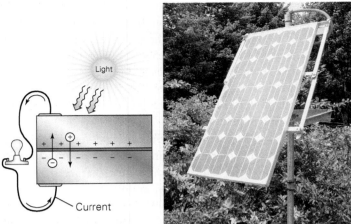

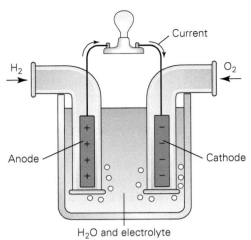

(a) A photovoltaic cell produces electricity directly from solar radiation.

(b) A hydrogen fuel cell.

order of 100 m (300 ft) tall, with fan blades that are over 40 m (120 ft) long. Large wind farms can host hundreds of towers. Wind energy produces no pollutants, but as with any type of energy source, wind power has some drawbacks. Cluttering the horizon with towers may spoil a beautiful view, and the constant loud hum of the towers can disturb nearby residents. The towers may also be a hazard to migrating birds, and offshore towers may interfere with marine life.

Solar Energy

The Sun drenches the Earth with energy in quantities that dwarf the amounts stored in fossil fuels. Were it possible to harness this energy directly, humanity would have a reliable and totally clean solution for powering modern technology. But using solar energy is not quite so simple because converting light into heat remains quite inefficient.

Let's consider two options for producing solar energy. The first option is a *solar collector*, a device that collects energy to produce heat. One class of solar collectors includes mirrors or lenses that focus light striking a broad area into a smaller area. On a small scale, such devices can be used for cooking; on a large scale, they can produce steam to drive turbines. Another class of solar collectors consists of a black surface placed beneath a glass plate. The black surface absorbs light that has passed through the glass plate and heats up, and the glass does not let the heat escape. When a consumer runs water between the glass and the black surface, the water heats up.

Photovoltaic cells (solar cells), the second option, convert light energy directly into electricity (**Fig. 14.26a**). Most photovoltaic cells consist of two wafers of silicon pressed together. One wafer also contains atoms of arsenic, and the other wafer includes atoms of boron. When light strikes the cell, arsenic atoms release electrons that flow over to the boron atoms. If a

wire loop connects the back side of one wafer to the back side of the other, this phenomenon produces an electrical current. The production costs of solar cells have decreased substantially in recent years, and thus their use has increased substantially.

Fuel Cells

In a fuel cell, chemical reactions produce electricity directly. Let's consider a *hydrogen fuel cell*. Hydrogen gas flows through a tube across an anode (a strip of platinum) that has been placed in a water solution containing an electrolyte (a substance that enables the solution to conduct electricity). At the same time, a stream of oxygen gas flows onto a separate platinum cathode that has also been placed into the solution. A wire connects the anode and the cathode to provide an electrical circuit (**Fig. 14.26b**). In this configuration, hydrogen reacts with oxygen to produce water and electricity. Fuel cells are efficient and clean. Their limitation lies in the need for a design that will protect the cells from damage by impact and that will enable them to store hydrogen, an explosive gas, in a safe way. Also, it takes a significant amount of energy from other sources to produce the hydrogen used in fuel cells.

Take-Home Message

A variety of alternative energy resources are now under development. Biomass can be transformed into burnable alcohol and biodiesel. Geothermal energy utilizes groundwater that has been warmed by heat from Earth's interior. Flowing water (in rivers or tides), flowing air, solar panels, and fuel cells can also produce energy.

QUICK QUESTION: Is there any way that home owners can use heat stored in the Earth on their property to lower their energy costs?

14.9 Energy Choices, Energy Problems

The Age of Oil and the Oil Crunch

Energy usage in industrialized countries grew with dizzying speed through the mid-20th century, and during this time people came to rely increasingly on oil (see Fig. 14.2). Oil remains the single largest source of energy globally, accounting for about 33% of global energy consumption. The United States, European Union, and Japan combined used more oil than the rest of the world until about 2006. Then consumption in these industrialized nations leveled off and started to decrease, while usage in the rest of the world has increased as countries in Asia and South America industrialize. According to statistics published in 2013, the Asia-Pacific region uses about 33% of global energy, North America as a whole now uses about 26%, Europe and Eurasia together use about 21%, and Africa uses only 4%. The United States still uses more oil per capita (about 22 bbl/year) than any country except Saudi Arabia—by comparison, per capita use of oil in China is about 3 bbl/year.

During the latter half of the 20th century, conventional oil supplies within the borders of industrialized countries could no longer match the demand, and these countries began to import more oil than they produced themselves. Through the 1960s, oil prices remained low (about $1.80 a barrel), so this was not a problem (Fig. 14.27a). In 1973, however, a complex tangle of politics and war led the Organization of Petroleum Exporting Countries (OPEC) to limit its oil exports. In the United States, fear of an oil shortage turned to panic, and motorists began lining up at gas stations, in many cases waiting for hours to fill their tanks. The price of oil rose to $18 a barrel, and newspaper headlines proclaimed, "Energy Crisis!" Governments in industrialized countries instituted new rules to encourage oil conservation. During the last two decades of the 20th century, the oil market stabilized, though political events occasionally led to price jumps and short-term shortages. Since 2004, oil prices rose overall, passing the $147/bbl mark in 2008. During the Great Recession of 2008, the price then collapsed, but in recent years, it has hovered around $100/bbl.

Will a day come when shortages of conventional oil arise not because of an embargo or limitations on refining capacity, but because there is no more oil to produce? Already, evidence suggests that the rate of new discoveries can no longer keep up with the rate of consumption, so society is tapping into reserves faster than reserves are increasing (Fig. 14.27b). To address such a question, we must keep in mind the distinction between renewable and nonrenewable energy resources (see Geology at a Glance, pp. 536–537). We can call a particular resource renewable if nature can replace it within a short time relative to a human life span (in months or, at most, decades), whereas a resource is nonrenewable if nature takes a very long time (hundreds to perhaps millions of years) to replenish it. Oil is a nonrenewable resource in that the rate at which humans consume it far exceeds the rate at which nature replenishes it, so we will inevitably run out of oil. The question is, when?

Historians in the future may refer to our time as the Oil Age because so much of our economy depends on oil. How

FIGURE 14.27 Price, discovery, and consumption of oil.

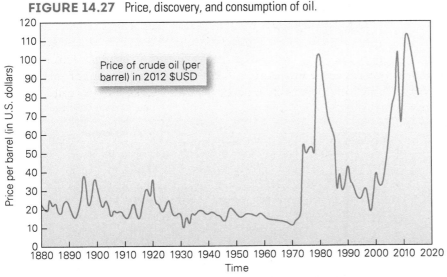

(a) The price of oil held fairly steady for almost 100 years. Starting in 1970, it has risen and fallen dramatically. Data source: BP Statistical Review of World Energy (2013).

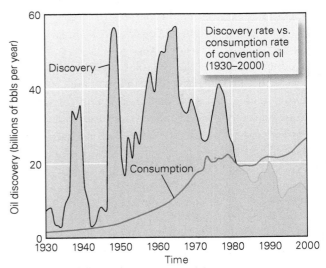

(b) Despite short-term dips, consumption of oil has continued to grow, but the rate of new discovery has not. Data source: ExxonMobil; consumption based on data from EIA.

Power from the Earth

Water, Wind, and Tides

The hydrologic cycle carries water over land. Water flows back toward the sea.

Forming and Mining Coal

Plants in coastal swamps and forests die, become buried, and transform into coal.

Coal at shallow depths can be accessed by strip mines.

Forming and Finding Oil

Plankton, algae, and clay settle to the floor of quiet water in a lake or sea. Eventually, the organic sediment becomes buried deeply and becomes a source rock. Chemical reactions yield oil, which percolates upward.

Tectonic processes form oil traps. Oil accumulates in reservoir rock within the trap; a seal rock keeps the oil underground.

Regardless of whether an oil reserve is under land or under sea, modern drilling technology can reach it and pump it.

Exploration for oil utilizes seismic-reflection profiling, which can reveal the configuration of layers underground.

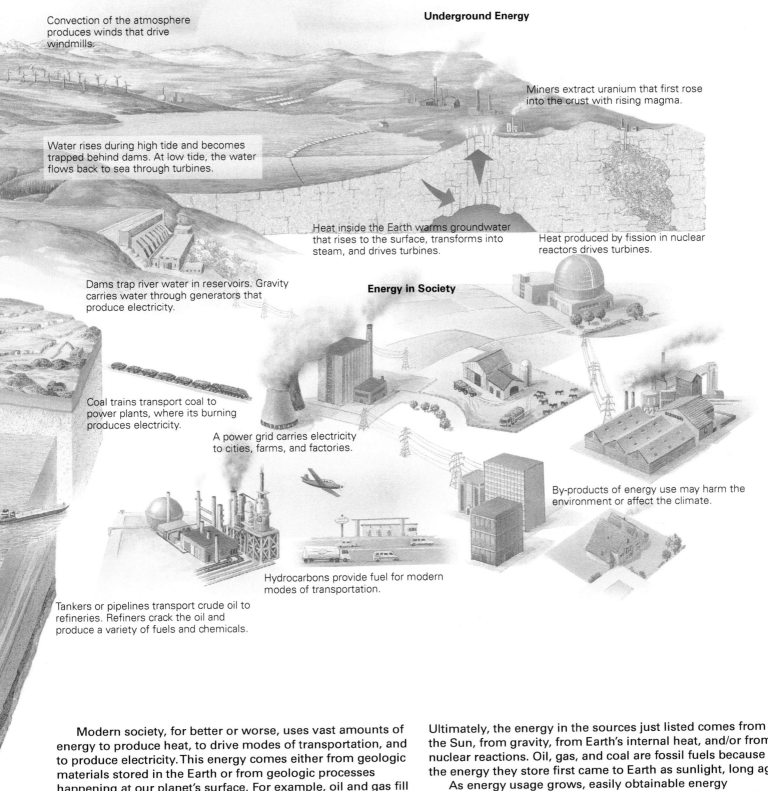

Convection of the atmosphere produces winds that drive windmills.

Underground Energy

Miners extract uranium that first rose into the crust with rising magma.

Water rises during high tide and becomes trapped behind dams. At low tide, the water flows back to sea through turbines.

Heat inside the Earth warms groundwater that rises to the surface, transforms into steam, and drives turbines.

Heat produced by fission in nuclear reactors drives turbines.

Dams trap river water in reservoirs. Gravity carries water through generators that produce electricity.

Energy in Society

Coal trains transport coal to power plants, where its burning produces electricity.

A power grid carries electricity to cities, farms, and factories.

By-products of energy use may harm the environment or affect the climate.

Hydrocarbons provide fuel for modern modes of transportation.

Tankers or pipelines transport crude oil to refineries. Refiners crack the oil and produce a variety of fuels and chemicals.

Modern society, for better or worse, uses vast amounts of energy to produce heat, to drive modes of transportation, and to produce electricity. This energy comes either from geologic materials stored in the Earth or from geologic processes happening at our planet's surface. For example, oil and gas fill the pores of reservoir rocks at depth below the surface, coal occurs in sedimentary beds, and uranium concentrates in ore deposits. A hydroelectric power plant taps into the hydrologic cycle, windmills operate because of atmospheric convection, and geothermal energy comes from hot groundwater.

Ultimately, the energy in the sources just listed comes from the Sun, from gravity, from Earth's internal heat, and/or from nuclear reactions. Oil, gas, and coal are fossil fuels because the energy they store first came to Earth as sunlight, long ago.

As energy usage grows, easily obtainable energy resources dwindle, the environment can be degraded, and the composition of the atmosphere changes. The pattern of energy use that forms the backbone of society today may have to change radically in the not-so-distant future if we wish to avoid a decline in living standards.

long will the Oil Age last? A reliable answer to this question is hard to come by, because there is not total agreement on the numbers that go into the calculation, especially as the use of unconventional reserves increases, so estimates vary widely. Geologists estimate that we've already used a substantial proportion of our conventional reserves, but that there are still about 1,250 billion barrels of proven conventional oil reserves, meaning reserves that have been documented and are still in the ground. Optimistically, there may be an additional 2,000 billion barrels of unproven conventional reserves, meaning oil that has not yet been found but might exist. Thus, the world possibly holds between 1,250 and 3,350 billion barrels of conventional oil. Presently, humanity consumes oil at a rate of about 33 billion barrels per year. At this rate, conventional oil supplies will last until sometime between 2050 and 2150.

Did you ever wonder...

how much longer the world's oil supply will last?

Some geologists argue that the beginning of the end of the Oil Age has begun, because the rate of consumption now exceeds the rate of discovery, and in many regions the rate of production has already started to decrease. The peak of production for a given reserve is called **Hubbert's Peak**, after the geologist who first emphasized that the production of reserves must decline because oil is a nonrenewable resource (Fig. 14.28a). Hubbert's Peak for the United States appears to have been passed in the 1970s. Some researchers argue that the global peak may occur between 2012 and 2015, but this number remains uncertain. Conservation approaches, such as increasing the gas mileage of cars and increasing the amount of insulation in buildings, could stretch out supplies and make them last decades longer.

Of course, the picture of oil reserves changes significantly if unconventional reserves are included in estimates. Currently, there are an estimated 414 billion barrels of proven unconventional oil reserves, and there may be more than a trillion additional barrels of unconventional reserves yet to be discovered. But wide disagreement remains concerning whether it's fair to include all of these reserves in estimates of hydrocarbon supplies because a significant proportion would be so difficult and expensive to access that they may never really be an economical energy source.

Even the combination of conventional and unconventional oil reserves means that at current rates of consumption supplies can last for only another 200 years, so the Oil Age will last a total of about 350 years. On a timeline representing the 4,000 years since the construction of the Egyptian pyramids, this looks like a very short blip. We may indeed be living during a unique interval of human history.

Can Other Fossil Fuels Replace Oil?

As true limits to the conventional oil supply approach, societies are looking first at relatively abundant supplies of other fossil fuels, namely natural gas and coal, as sources of energy (Fig. 14.28b). Proven global reserves of natural gas are about 187 trillion cubic meters, which would provide approximately

FIGURE 14.28 Hubbert's Peak and the future of energy.

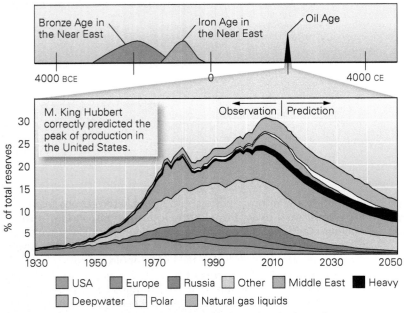

(a) A plot of production vs. time suggests that some time in the early 21st century, the production of oil globally will start to decrease.

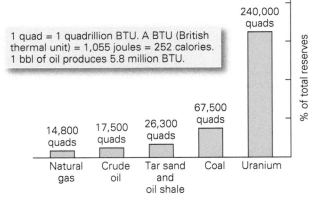

(b) Estimated nonrenewable energy resources on Earth.

the same amount of energy as about 1.2 trillion bbl. Tapping into this gas supply requires expensive technologies for extraction and transport, but given the current price of oil, it has become economical not only to produce conventional gas but also to produce shale gas. In the United States, production of shale gas has increased from less than 33 billion cubic meters per year in 2006 to 306 billion cubic meters per year in 2013. This change has significantly altered the dependence of the United States on imported oil. Similarly, worldwide coal reserves are estimated to be about 850 trillion tons, which contains approximately the same amount of energy as 11 trillion bbl. But the stated number for coal reserves does not distinguish clearly between accessible coal, which can be mined, and inaccessible coal, which is too deep to be mined.

Environmental Issues of Fossil Fuel Use

Environmental concerns about energy resources begin right at the source. Oil drilling requires substantial equipment, the use of which can damage the land. And as demonstrated by the 2010 Gulf of Mexico offshore well blowout, oil drilling can lead to tragic loss of life and disastrous marine oil spills (Box 14.3). Oil spills from pipelines or trucks sink into the subsurface and contaminate groundwater, and oil spills from ships and tankers create slicks that spread over the sea surface and foul the shoreline (Fig. 14.29). Coal and uranium mining also scar the land and can lead to the production of **acid mine runoff**, a dilute solution of sulfuric acid that forms when sulfur-bearing minerals such as pyrite (FeS_2) in mines react with rainwater. The runoff enters streams and kills fish and plants. Collapse of underground coal mines may cause the ground surface to sink.

Numerous air-pollution issues also arise from the burning of fossil fuels, which sends soot, carbon monoxide, sulfur dioxide, nitrous oxide, and unburned hydrocarbons into the air. Coal, for example, commonly contains sulfur, primarily in the form of pyrite, which enters the air as sulfur dioxide (SO_2) when coal is burned. This gas combines with rainwater to form dilute sulfuric acid (H_2SO_4), or **acid rain**. For this reason, many countries now regulate the amount of sulfur that coal can contain when it is burned.

But even if pollutants can be decreased, the burning of fossil fuels still releases carbon dioxide (CO_2) into the atmosphere. CO_2 is important because it is a **greenhouse gas,** meaning that it traps heat in the Earth's atmosphere much like glass traps heat in a greenhouse (see Chapter 23). A global increase of CO_2 will lead to a global increase in atmospheric temperature (global warming), which in turn may alter the distribution of climatic belts and lead to a rise in sea level, among many other effects. Because of concern about CO_2 production, research efforts are under way to replace fossil fuels with biofuels derived from perennial plants, for these biofuels are "carbon neutral" in that, since plants absorb CO_2 as they grow, the CO_2 added to the air by burning fuels derived from plants will be absorbed by the growth of new plants. There are also efforts to develop techniques to capture CO_2 at power plants, liquefy it, and pump it into reservoir rocks deep underground. This process is called *carbon sequestration*. We'll learn more about this issue in Chapter 23.

Alternatives to Hydrocarbons

Can nuclear power or hydroelectric power replace oil? Vast supplies of uranium, the fuel of traditional nuclear plants, remain

FIGURE 14.29 Marine oil spills. These can come from drilling rigs, or from tankers.

(a) An oil tanker leaking oil on the sea surface.

(b) Oil spills can contaminate the shore and can be very difficult to clean.

BOX 14.3 CONSIDER THIS . . .

Offshore Drilling and the Deepwater Horizon Disaster

A substantial proportion of the world's oil reserves reside in the sedimentary basins that underlie the continental shelves of passive continental margins. To access such reserves, oil companies build offshore drilling platforms. Such drilling requires complex technology. In water less than 600 m (2,000 ft) deep, companies position fixed platforms on towers resting on the seafloor. In deeper water, semi-submersible platforms float on huge submerged pontoons (Fig. Bx14.3a). With these, oil companies can now access fields lying beneath 3 km (10,000 ft) of water.

North America's largest offshore fields occur in the passive-margin basin that fringes the coast of the Gulf of Mexico (Fig. Bx14.3b). This basin started forming in Jurassic time, subsequent to the breakup of Pangaea, and its floor has been slowly sinking ever since. Up to 15 to 20 km (9 to 12 miles) of sediment (mud, salt, sand, marine shells) fill the basin. Some of the mud was rich in organic matter; when buried deeply, this converted to hydrocarbons that now fill pores of reservoir rocks in salt-dome traps and stratigraphic traps. More than 3,500 platforms operate in the Gulf at present, together yielding up to 1.7 million bbl/day.

During both onshore and offshore exploration, drillers worry about the possibility of a **blowout.** A blowout happens when the pressure within a hydrocarbon reserve penetrated by a well exceeds the pressure that drillers had planned for, causing the hydrocarbons (oil and/or gas) to rush up the well in an uncontrolled manner and burst out of the well at the surface in an oil gusher or gas plume, which can explode and burn if ignited. Blowouts are rare because although fluids below the ground are under great pressure due to the weight of overlying material, engineers always fill the hole with drilling mud (a mixture of water, clay, and other chemicals) with a density greater than that of clear water. The weight of drilling mud can counter the pressure of underground hydrocarbons and hold the fluids underground. But if drillers encounter a bed in which pressures are unexpectedly high, or if they remove the mud before the walls of the well have been sealed with a casing (a pipe, cemented in place by concrete, that lines the hole), a blowout may happen.

A catastrophic blowout occurred on April 20, 2010, when drillers on the Deepwater Horizon, a huge semi-submersible platform leased by BP, were completing a 5.5-km-long (18,000 ft) hole in 1.5-km-deep (5,000 ft) water south of Louisiana. Due to a series of errors, the casing was not sufficiently strong when workers began to replace the drilling mud with clear water. Thus, the high-pressure, gassy oil in the reservoir that the well had punctured rushed up the drill hole. A backup safety device called a blowout preventer failed, so the gassy oil reached the platform and sprayed 100 m (328 ft) into the sky. Sparks from electronic gear triggered an explosion, and the platform became a fountain of flame and smoke that killed 11 workers. An armada of fireboats could not douse the conflagration (Fig. Bx14.3c), and after 36 hours the still-burning platform tipped over and sank.

Robot submersibles sent to the seafloor to investigate found that the twisted mess of bent and ruptured pipes at the well head was billowing oil and gas (Fig. Bx14.3d). Estimates as to the amount of hydrocarbons released vary wildly, but most data suggest that on the order of 50,000 to 62,000 bbl/day of hydrocarbons entered the Gulf's water from the well. (By comparison, natural oil seeps at many localities around the Gulf together yield about 1,000 to 4,000 bbl/day.) Stopping this underwater gusher proved to be an immense challenge, and initial efforts to block the well or to put a containment dome over the well head failed. It was not until July 15, almost three months after the blowout, that the flow was finally stopped, and it was not until September 19 that a new relief well intersected the blown well and provided a conduit to pump concrete down to block the original well permanently.

All told, about 4.2 million bbl of hydrocarbons contaminated the Gulf from the Deepwater Horizon blowout. The more volatile components of the spill evaporated, but enough liquid hydrocarbons remained to form a slick that, at times, covered an area of over 100,000 sq km (Fig. Bx14.3e). Thousands of people labored to contain the damage—floating booms were set up to contain the oil, skimmer ships traversed the slick to suck up oil, sandbag barriers were placed along the coast from Louisiana to Florida to keep the oil out of wetlands and beaches. Also, planes spread chemical dispersants on the floating oil to break it into tiny particles. In the near term, the spill was devastating to wetlands, wildlife, and the fishing and tourism industries. Over the longer term, natural processes—microbes that eat the oil droplets—will conquer the spill.

untapped. Further, nuclear engineers have designed alternative plants, powered by breeder reactors, that essentially produce new fuel. But many people view nuclear plants with concern because of issues pertaining to radiation, accidents, terrorism, and waste storage, and these concerns have slowed the industry. A substantial increase in hydroelectric power production is not likely, as most major rivers have already been dammed, and industrialized countries have little appetite for taming any more. Similarly, the growth of geothermal-energy output seems limited. Coal supplies are fairly abundant, but burning large quantities of coal contributes to air pollution and adds greenhouse gases to the atmosphere.

Because of the potential problems that might result from relying more on coal, hydroelectric, and nuclear energy, researchers have been increasingly exploring clean energy options. One possibility is solar power, and the cost of solar power is steadily decreasing. Similarly, we can turn to wind power for relatively small-scale energy production. Because

FIGURE Bx14.3 Offshore drilling and the Deepwater Horizon disaster.

(a) The Deepwater Horizon oil-drilling platform as it appeared in the Gulf of Mexico in July of 2009.

(c) Fireboats dousing the burning rig before the rig sank.

(b) Drilling on the Gulf Coast margin. Most drill sites are on the continental shelf, and more recently deeper water sites have been explored. The roughness of the slope to the abyssal plain is due to salt domes. Each yellow dot is a drilling platform. The location of the Deepwater Horizon platform is indicated by the larger, white dot.

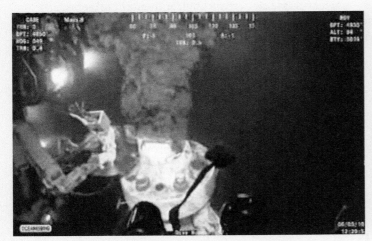

(d) A plume of oil billows into the water from the well head, as viewed by underwater cameras.

(e) A satellite image showing the oil slick in the Gulf of Mexico, southeast of the Mississippi Delta.

sunlight reaching the Earth changes during the day and with the amount of overcast, and because wind speed varies, solar power and wind power can't provide the steady supply of energy that the present-day *energy grid* (the interconnected network of power lines and transformers that distribute energy around the country) requires. This problem might someday be overcome with "smart grids," which can accommodate for rapid fluctuations in energy input. Fusion power may be possible some day, but physicists and engineers have not yet figured out a way to harness it. Clearly, society will be facing difficult choices in the not-so-distant future about where to obtain energy, and we will need to invest in the research required to discover new alternatives.

Take-Home Message

Oil is a nonrenewable resource and conventional supplies may run out in less than a century—we live in the Oil Age, which may, when it ends, have lasted less than 350 years. Unconventional hydrocarbon supplies may last longer, but use of fossil fuel has environmental consequences.

QUICK QUESTION: What is "Hubbert's Peak," and when was it reached in the United States?

CHAPTER SUMMARY

- Energy resources come in a variety of forms: energy directly from the Sun; energy from tides, flowing water, or wind; energy stored by photosynthesis (either in contemporary plants or in fossil fuels); energy from inorganic chemical reactions; energy from nuclear fission; and geothermal energy.

- Oil and gas are hydrocarbons, a type of organic chemical. The viscosity and volatility of a hydrocarbon depend on the length of its molecules.

- Oil and gas originally develop from the dead bodies of plankton and algae, which settle out in a quiet-water, oxygen-poor depositional environment and form black organic shale. Later, chemical reactions at elevated temperatures convert the dead plankton into kerogen and then oil.

- For a conventional oil reserve to be usable, oil must migrate from a source rock into a porous and permeable rock called a reservoir rock. Unless the reservoir rock is overlain by an impermeable seal rock, the oil will escape to the ground surface. The subsurface configuration of strata that ensures the entrapment of oil in a good reservoir rock is called an oil trap.

- Substantial volumes of hydrocarbons also exist in unconventional reserves, such as tar sand, oil shale, and gas hydrate.

- For coal to form, abundant plant debris must be deposited in an oxygen-poor environment so that it does not completely decompose. Compaction near the ground surface creates peat, which, when buried deeply and heated, transforms into coal. Coal has a high concentration of carbon.

- Geologists rank coal based on the amount of carbon it contains: lignite (low rank), bituminous (medium rank), and anthracite (high rank).

- Coal occurs in beds, interlayered with other sedimentary rocks. Coal beds can be mined by either strip mining or underground mining.

- Coal-bed methane and coal gasification provide additional sources of energy.

- Nuclear power plants generate energy by using the heat released from the nuclear fission of radioactive elements. The heat turns water into steam, and the steam drives turbines.

- Some economic uranium deposits occur as veins in igneous rock bodies; some are found in sedimentary beds.

- Nuclear reactors must be carefully controlled to avoid overheating or meltdown. The disposal of radioactive nuclear waste can create environmental problems.

- Geothermal energy uses Earth's internal heat to transform groundwater into steam that drives turbines; hydroelectric power uses the potential energy of water; and solar energy uses solar cells to convert sunlight to electricity.

- We now live in the Oil Age, but oil supplies may last only for another century or two. Natural gas may become an increasingly important energy supply in the near future.

- Most energy resources have environmental consequences. Oil spills pollute the landscape and sea, and the sulfur associated with some fuel deposits causes acid mine runoff. The burning of coal can produce acid rain, and the burning of coal and hydrocarbons produces smog and can contribute to global warming.

GUIDE TERMS

acid mine runoff (p. 539)

acid rain (p. 539)

barrel of oil (bbl) (p. 513)

biofuel (p. 532)

blowout (p. 540)

chain reaction (p. 529)

coal (p. 524)

coal-bed methane (p. 528)

coal gasification (p. 526)

coal rank (p. 525)

coal reserve (p. 525)

coal swamp (p. 524)

conventional hydrocarbon system (p. 511)

conventional reserve (p. 510)

directional drilling (p. 516)

drilling mud (p. 516)

energy (p. 505)

energy density (p. 508)

energy resource (p. 505)

fossil fuel (p. 507)

fuel (p. 503)

gas hydrate (p. 521)

geothermal energy (p. 531)

greenhouse gas (p. 539)

Hubbert's Peak (p. 538)

hydrocarbon (p. 508)

hydrocarbon generation (p. 510)

hydrocarbon reserve (p. 510)

hydrofracturing (pp. 517, 522)

kerogen (p. 510)

meltdown (p. 530)

migrate (p. 512)

migration pathway (p. 512)

nuclear reactor (p. 529)

nuclear waste (p. 531)

oil seep (p. 512)

oil shale (pp. 510, 521)

oil window (p. 510)

peat (p. 525)

permeability (p. 511)

photovoltaic cell (p. 534)

pore (p. 511)

porosity (p. 511)

reservoir rock (p. 511)

seal rock (p. 512)

seismic-reflection profile (p. 515)

shale gas (p. 520)

source rock (p. 510)

tar sand (p. 520)

tidal power (p. 533)

trap (p. 512)

unconventional hydrocarbon reserve (p. 517)

REVIEW QUESTIONS

1. What are the fundamental sources of energy?
2. How does the length of a hydrocarbon chain affect its viscosity and volatility?
3. What is the source of the organic material in oil?
4. What is the oil window, and what happens to oil at temperatures higher than the oil window?
5. How is organic matter trapped and transformed to yield an oil reserve?
6. What are the different kinds of oil traps?
7. What are tar sand and oil shale, and how can oil be extracted from them?
8. What are gas hydrates, and where do they occur?
9. How do porosity and permeability affect the oil-bearing potential of a rock?
10. Where is most of the world's oil found? At present rates of consumption, how long will oil supplies last?
11. How is coal formed, and what class of rock is coal considered to be?
12. What conditions cause coal to transform in rank from peat to anthracite?
13. What are some of the environmental drawbacks of mining and burning coal?
14. What is coal-bed methane, and how is it extracted?
15. Describe the nuclear reactions in a nuclear reactor and the means that engineers use to control reaction rates.
16. Where does uranium form in the Earth's crust? Where does it usually accumulate in minable quantities?
17. What are some of the drawbacks of nuclear energy?
18. Discuss the pros and cons of alternative energy sources.
19. What is geothermal energy? What limits its use?
20. What is the difference between renewable and nonrenewable resources?
21. What are the major environmental consequences of producing and burning fossil fuels?
22. What is the likely future of hydrocarbon production and use in the 21st century?

ON FURTHER THOUGHT

23. Much of the oil production in the United States takes place at offshore platforms along the coast of the Gulf of Mexico. Consider the geologic setting of the Gulf Coast, in the context of the theory of plate tectonics, and explain why an immensely thick sequence of sediment accumulated in this region and why so many salt-dome traps formed.

24. Ethanol can potentially be used as an alternative to petroleum as a liquid fuel. Ethanol can be produced by processing corn, sugarcane, or certain perennial grasses (e.g., switchgrass or Miscanthus). What factors should be considered in determining which of these crops would be the most appropriate for use as a source of ethanol in North America?

 **smartwork** smartwork.wwnorton.com

This chapter's Smartwork features:

- Labeling exercise on types of oil traps.
- Animation problem on oil formation and trapping.
- Activities on formation and types of coal.

GEOTOURS

This chapter's GeoTour exercise (L) features:

- Hydrocarbon resources
- Coal resources
- Other energy resources

Another View   Solar-panel arrays are beginning to carpet the landscape in sunny regions. This example (the Beneixama photovoltaic power plant in Spain) generates 20 megawatts of electricity at peak production and covers 500,000 m² (= 0.5 km², or 123 acres). By comparison, a typical nuclear power plant produces 1,000 megawatts of electricity (enough for a city of 1.2 million). A solar array large enough to produce as much electricity as a nuclear power plant would have to cover an area of about 25 square km.

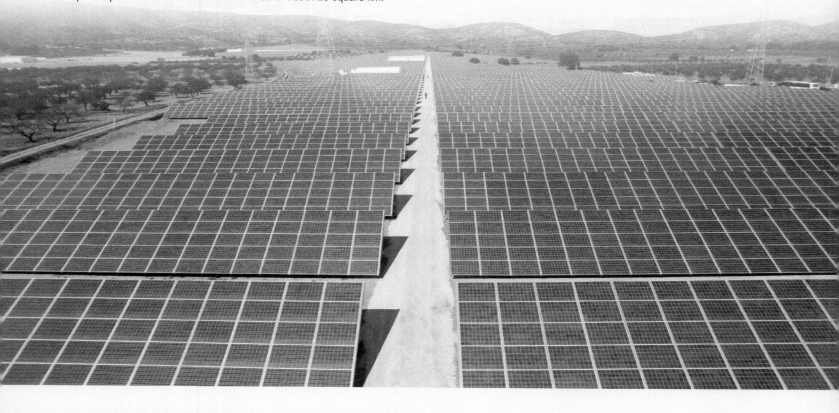

An 2010 earthquake triggered a landslide on a rain-soaked hillslope in Taiwan. The debris buried a highway. Where there are slopes, unstable ground can develop and become a natural hazard.

CHAPTER 16

Unsafe Ground: Landslides and Other Mass Movements

> Gravity is a habit that is hard to shake off.
>
> —*Terry Pratchett (British author)*

LEARNING OBJECTIVES

By the end of this chapter, you should understand . . .

- the characteristics and consequences of different types of mass movements.
- factors that determine whether a slope is stable or unstable.
- the events that can trigger a mass-movement event.
- why some regions are more susceptible to mass movements than are others.
- how landslide hazards can be evaluated and, in some cases, prevented.

16.1 Introduction

It was Sunday, May 31, 1970, a market day, and thousands of people had crammed into the Andean town of Yungay, Peru, to shop. Suddenly they felt the jolt of an earthquake that was strong enough to topple some masonry houses. But worse was yet to come. Shocks from the earthquake also caused an 800-m-wide ice slab to break off the end of a glacier at the top of Nevado Huascarán, a nearby 6.6-km-high mountain peak. Gravity instantly pulled the ice slab down the mountain's steep slopes. As it tumbled down over 3.7 km, the ice disintegrated into a chaotic avalanche of chunks traveling at speeds of over 300 km per hour. Near the base of the mountain, most of the avalanche channeled into a valley and thickened into a moving layer as high as a ten-story building, ripping up rocks and soil along the way. Friction transformed the ice into water, which when mixed with rock and dust created 50 million cubic meters of a muddy slurry viscous enough to buoy along boulders larger than houses. This mass, sometimes riding on a compressed air cushion that allowed it to pass by without disturbing the grass below, traveled over 14.5 km in less than 4 minutes.

On rounding a curve near the mouth of the valley, part of the mass shot up the sides and flew over the ridge between the valley and Yungay. As the town's inhabitants and visitors stumbled out of earthquake-damaged buildings, they heard a deafening roar and looked up to see a churning mud cloud descending on them. Moments later, the town was completely buried under several meters of mud and rock—only the top of the church and a few palm trees remained visible to show where Yungay once lay (Fig. 16.1). Over 18,000 people are forever entombed beneath the resulting debris layer. Today the site is a grassy meadow, spotted with memorials left by mourning relatives.

Could the Yungay tragedy have been prevented? Perhaps. A few years earlier, climbers had recognized the instability of glacial ice on Nevado Huascarán, and Peruvian newspapers had published a warning, but alas, no one took notice. In the aftermath of the event, geologists discovered that

FIGURE 16.1 The May 1970 Yungay landslide disaster in Peru.

(a) Before the landslide, the town of Yungay perched on a hill near the ice-covered mountain Nevado Huascarán.

(b) The landslide completely buried the town beneath debris. A landslide scar is visible on the mountain in the distance.

Yungay had been built on ancient layers of debris from past calamities. Peru subsequently prevented new construction in the danger zone.

People often assume that the ground beneath them is *terra firma*, a solid foundation on which they can build their lives. But the catastrophe at Yungay says otherwise. The **substrate** (material below the surface) underlying sloping regions of the Earth's surface—regardless of whether it consists of rock or *regolith* (loose, sediment, debris, and soil)—is inherently "unstable" in the sense that under the relentless pull of gravity it will eventually move downslope. Geologists refer to the downslope transport of rock, regolith, snow, and ice as **mass movement**, or *mass wasting*. Like earthquakes, volcanic eruptions, storms, and floods, mass movements are a type of **natural hazard**, meaning a dangerous aspect of the environment that can cause damage to life and property. Unfortunately, mass movement becomes more of a threat every year because as the world's population grows, cities expand into areas of unsafe ground. In addition to representing a hazard that we must address, mass movement also plays a critical role in the rock cycle, for it serves as the first step in the transportation of sediment. And it plays a critical role in the evolution of landscapes in that it modifies the shapes of slopes.

In this chapter, we look at the types, causes, and consequences of mass movement and the precautions society can take to protect people and property from its dangers. You might want to consider this information when selecting a site for your home or when voting on land-use propositions for your community.

16.2 Types of Mass Movement

In general discussion, most people refer to any mass movement of rock and/or regolith down a slope as a **landslide**. Geologists and engineers, however, find it useful to distinguish among different kinds of mass movements based on four features: (1) the type of material involved (rock or regolith); (2) the velocity of movement (slow, intermediate, or fast); (3) the character of the moving mass (coherent or chaotic; wet or dry); and (4) the environment in which the movement takes place (subaerial or submarine). Similarly, most people think of an **avalanche** as a mass movement of snow—geologists and engineers, however, apply the term more broadly to include any mass movement that moves like a turbulent cloud.

Why bother classifying mass movements? We make these distinctions because different types of mass movements have different consequences and therefore represent different kinds of hazard—by characterizing mass movements more completely,

we can better prepare for them. Below we examine mass movements that occur on land, roughly in order from slow to very fast. We then briefly introduce submarine mass movements.

Creep and Solifluction

Creep (also known as *soil creep*) refers to the slow, gradual downslope movement of regolith on a slope. Creep happens when regolith alternately expands and contracts in response to freezing and thawing or wetting and drying. During freezing or wetting, the regolith expands and its particles move outward, perpendicular to the slope. During the thawing or drying, the regolith contracts and gravity makes the particles sink vertically and thus migrate downslope slightly (**Fig. 16.2a, b**). You can't see creep by staring at a hillslope because it occurs too slowly, but over a period of years, creep causes trees, fences, gravestones, walls, and foundations built on a hillside to tilt downslope. Notably, trees that continue to grow after they have been tilted display a pronounced curvature at their base (**Fig. 16.2c**).

In Arctic or high-elevation regions, regolith freezes solid to great depth during the winter. In the brief summer thaw, only the uppermost 1 to 3 m of the ground thaws. Since meltwater cannot sink into the underlying *permafrost* (permanently frozen ground), the melted layer becomes soggy and weak and slowly flows downslope in overlapping sheets. Geologists refer to this kind of creep, characteristic of cold, treeless tundra regions, as **solifluction** (**Fig. 16.2d**).

Rock Glaciers

Slow mass movement also takes place in a **rock glacier**, a body made of rock fragments embedded in a matrix of ice (**Fig. 16.2e**). Rock glaciers differ from more familiar ice-dominated glaciers in terms of the proportion of rock fragments to ice—in a rock glacier, most of the volume consists of rock, whereas in an ice-dominated glacier, most of the volume consists of ice. In effect, rock glaciers are breccias cemented by ice. Since ice is weak, the combined mass of rock and ice in a rock glacier can slowly flow downslope, as does the relatively pure ice of an ice-dominated glacier.

Rock glaciers form in two ways. First, they develop where snow or rain percolates down into a pile of rock debris that has accumulated above permafrost at the base of a cliff. This water can't infiltrate the frozen ground below the debris pile, so it freezes to form ice in the pores between clasts within the debris pile. Second, rock glaciers develop where an ice-dominated glacier already containing abundant rock debris begins to melt. As melting progresses, the proportion of rock to ice in the glacier increases, and if enough melting takes place, the glacier eventually contains more rock than ice.

FIGURE 16.2 The process and consequences of slow mass movements (creep and solifluction).

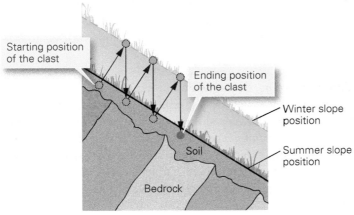

(a) Creep due to freezing and thawing: The clast rises perpendicular to the ground during freezing and sinks vertically during thawing. After 3 years, it migrates to the position shown.

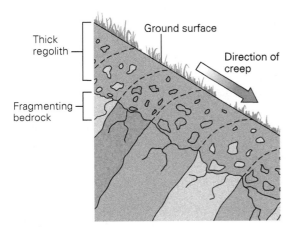

(b) As rock layers weather and break up, the resulting debris creeps downslope.

(c) Soil creep causes walls to bend and crack, building foundations to sink, trees to bend, and power poles and gravestones to tilt.

(d) Solifluction on a hillslope in the tundra.

(e) A rock glacier in Alaska. Note how the flow of the ice below wrinkles the rock layer on the glacier's surface.

Slumps

Near the Pacific Palisades, along the coast of southern California, Highway 1 runs between the beach and a 120-m-high cliff. On March 31, 1958, a gash developed about 200 m inland of the cliff's edge, and a semicoherent mass of sediment and rock began to move downslope. Four days later, when the movement finally stopped, a 1-km-long stretch of the coastal highway had been buried—it took weeks for bulldozers to make this stretch passable again. A similar event happened in northern New York State during the summer of 2011 when, after weeks of drenching rains, a 1.5-km-wide portion of a slope began to move down and out into the floor of Keene Valley. The mass moved at only centimeters to tens of centimeters per day, but even at this slow rate the accumulated displacement destroyed several expensive homes. In places, the boundary between the moving mass and the unmoving land upslope evolved into a 5-m-high escarpment.

Geologists refer to such relatively slow-moving mass-movement events, during which moving rock and/or regolith does not disintegrate into a jumble of debris but rather stays somewhat coherent, as a **slump**, and they refer to the moving mass itself as a *slump block* (Fig. 16.3). A slump block slides down a **failure surface**—some failure surfaces are planar, but commonly they curve and resemble a spoon lying concave side up. Geologists refer to the exposed upslope edge of a

FIGURE 16.3 The process of slumping on a hillslope. Note the scarps that form at the head of the slump.

(a) A head scarp on the hillslope.

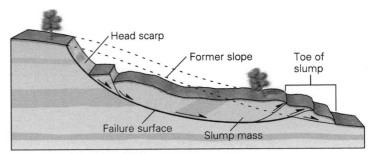

(b) Cross section of a slump.

(c) Slumping dumped sediment into this river in Costa Rica.

(d) A slump beginning to form along a highway in Utah.

failure surface as the **head scarp** and the downslope end of a slump block as the block's "toe." The upslope and downslope ends of a slump block may break into a series of discrete slices, each separated from its neighbor by a small sliding surface. On a hillslope, slices of the toe can move up and over the pre-existing land surface to form curving ridges. If the toe ends up on a beach or river bank, moving water eventually erodes it away. Slumps come in all sizes, from only a few meters across to tens of kilometers across. They move at speeds from millimeters per day to tens of meters per minute. Structures (such as houses, patios, and swimming pools) built on slump blocks or across the head scarp crack and fall apart, whereas those build at the toe may be knocked over or buried.

Mudflows, Debris Flows, and Lahars

Rio de Janeiro, Brazil, originally occupied only the flatlands bordering beautiful crescent beaches that had formed between steep hills. But in recent decades, the city's population has grown so much that in many places densely populated communities of makeshift shacks have been built on steep slopes. These communities, many of which have no storm drains, were built on the thick regolith that resulted from long-term weathering of bedrock in Brazil's tropical climate. Particularly heavy rains can saturate the regolith, transforming it into a viscous slurry of mud, resembling wet concrete, that flows downslope. The communities built on the regolith can disappear overnight, replaced by a muddle of mud and debris. And at the base of the cliffs, the flowing mud may knock over and bury buildings of all sizes. In unpopulated areas of Brazil, similar mass movements rip away forests (Fig. 16.4a, b). Geologists refer to a moving slurry of mud as a **mudflow**, or *mudslide*, and a slurry consisting of a mixture of mud mixed with larger, pebble- to boulder-sized fragments as a **debris flow**, or *debris slide* (Fig. 16.4c; Box 16.1).

Mudflows are not just phenomena of tropical regions—any slope underlain by poorly consolidated material can give way in a mudflow or debris flow during or following a heavy rain, and if people live nearby, the

FIGURE 16.4 Examples of mudflows and lahars.

(a) A 2011 mudslide destroyed a high-rise building at the base of the hill.

(b) Mudslides of 2011 stripped away forests on hillslopes in Brazil.

(c) A recent debris flow in Utah. Note the chaotic mixture of rock chunks and mud.

BOX 16.1 CONSIDER THIS . . .

What Goes Up Must Come Down

Along the shore of California, as waves slowly cut into the land to produce low, flat areas called *wave-cut benches* (see Chapter 18), tectonic motions of this active plate boundary are constantly at work. As a result, the land surface slowly rises such that former wave-cut benches become small plateaus, or terraces. One such terrace lies at an elevation of 180 m above sea level, about 500 m east of the present-day beach at La Conchita. While the surface of the terrace is flat, the west face of this terrace has become a cliff-like

bluff (**Fig. Bx16.1a**). Relatively little vegetation covers the bluff or the terrace above, so rain infiltrates into the ground, sinks down, and saturates clay and debris on the terrace and its bluff, making the material very weak. Every now and then, the weight of surface material causes the bluff to give way, and a mass of mud and debris flows downslope at rates of up to 10 m per second.

If the region of La Conchita were uninhabited, such mass wasting would just be part of the natural process of landscape

evolution—gravity brings down land that had been raised by tectonic activity. But when downslope movements take place in La Conchita, it makes headlines because on the modern wave-cut bench between the shore and the base of the bluff developers built a community housing 350 people. In 1995, a mud and debris flow overwhelmed 9 houses at the base of the bluff. An even more devastating flow happened in 2005, burying 13 houses, damaging 23, and killing 10 people (**Fig. Bx16.1b, c**).

FIGURE Bx16.1 The 2005 La Conchita mudslide along the coast of California.

(a) A housing development was built in a narrow strip between the beach and steep cliffs.

(b) During heavy rains, the slope gave way and heavy mud flowed down, burying houses and taking several lives.

(c) Rescuers at the toe of the mudslide.

FIGURE 16.5 The Oso, Washington, mudslide of 2014.

(a) The slide surged over the river, damming it temporarily, and tragically buried a small community on the opposite bank.

(b) The mudslide happened in an area where previous slides had taken place. The mountain slope was being undercut by the river.

movement has tragic consequences. In March 2014, near Oso, Washington, in the temperate northwest, a forested hillslope bordering a river gave way and within a few minutes buried a 2.5-sq-km (1-sq-mile) area of the river valley below with mud and wet sand (Fig. 16.5).

The speed at which material moves in a debris flow or mud flow depends on the slope angle and on the water content. Flows move faster if they contain more water so they are less viscous, and if they move on steeper slopes. On a gentle slope, drier mudflows move like molasses, but on a steep slope, very wet mud may move at over 100 km per hour. Because mud and debris flows have greater viscosity than clear water, they can carry large rock chunks as well as houses and cars. They typically follow channels downslope and at the base of the slope will spread out into a broad lobe.

Particularly devastating mudflows spill down the river valleys bordering volcanoes. These mudflows, known as **lahars**, form when volcanic ash from an ongoing or previous eruption mixes with water from the snow and ice that melts in a volcano's heat or from heavy rains (Fig. 16.6; see Chapter 9). A lahar occurred on November 13, 1985, in the Andes Mountains in Colombia. That night, a major eruption melted a volcano's thick snowcap, creating hot water that mixed with ash. A scalding lahar rushed down river valleys and swept over the nearby town of Armero while most inhabitants were asleep. Of the 25,000 residents, 20,000 perished.

FIGURE 16.6 Lahars develop when volcanic ash mixes with water from rain or melting snow and ice.

(a) A lahar that rushed down the side of Mt. St. Helens, Washington.

(b) Lahars can overrun populated areas far from the volcano.

Rockslides and Debris Slides

In the early 1960s, engineers built a huge new dam across a river on the northern side of Monte Toc in the Italian Alps to create a reservoir for generating electricity. This dam, the Vaiont Dam, was an engineering marvel, a concrete wall rising 260 m (as high as an 85-story skyscraper) above the valley floor (Fig. 16.7a). Unfortunately, the dam's builders did not appreciate the hazard posed by nearby Monte Toc. The side of Monte Toc facing the reservoir was underlain by a succession of limestone beds overlying a horizon of weak shale. These beds dipped parallel to the surface of the mountain and curved under the reservoir. As the reservoir filled, the flank of the mountain cracked, shook, and rumbled. Local residents began to call Monte Toc *la montagna che cammina* (the mountain that walks).

After several days of rain, Monte Toc began to rumble so much that on October 9, 1963, engineers lowered the water level in the reservoir. They thought the wet ground might slump a little into the reservoir, with minor consequences, so no one ordered the evacuation of the town of Longarone, a few kilometers down the valley below the dam. Unfortunately, the engineers underestimated the problem. At 10:30 that evening, a huge chunk of Monte Toc—600 million tons of rock—detached from the mountain and slid downslope along the weak shale horizon into the reservoir. Some debris rocketed up the opposite wall of the valley to a height of 260 m above the original reservoir level (Fig. 16.7b). The displaced water of the reservoir spilled over the top of the dam and rushed down into the valley below. When the flood had passed, nothing of Longarone and its 1,500 inhabitants remained. Though the dam itself still stands, it holds back only debris and has never provided any electricity.

Geologists refer to such a sudden movement of rock and debris down a nonvertical slope as a **rockslide** if the mass consists only of rock or as a **debris slide** if it consists mostly of regolith. Once a slide has taken place, it leaves a scar on the slope and forms a debris pile at the base of the slope. Slides happen when bedrock and/or regolith detaches from a slope, slips rapidly downhill on a failure surface, and breaks up into a chaotic jumble. Slides are more likely to occur where a weak layer of rock or sediment at depth below the ground parallels the land surface. (At the Vaiont Dam, the plane of weakness that would become the failure surface was a weak shale bed.) Slides may move at speeds of up to 300 km per hour—they are particularly fast when a cushion of air gets trapped beneath, in which case there is virtually no friction between the slide and its substrate, and the mass moves like a hovercraft. Rock and debris slides sometimes have enough momentum to climb the opposite side of the valley into which they fall. Slides, like slumps, come at a variety of scales. Most are small, involving blocks up to a few meters across. Some, such as the Vaiont slide, are large enough to cause a catastrophe.

Avalanches

In the winter of 1999, an unusual weather system passed over the Austrian Alps. First it snowed. Then the temperature warmed and the snow began to melt. But then the weather turned cold again, and the melted snow froze into a hard, icy crust. This cold snap ushered in a blizzard that blanketed the ice crust with tens of centimeters (1 to 2 ft) of new snow. With the frozen snow layer underneath acting as a failure surface, 200,000 tons of new snow began to slide down the mountain. As it accelerated, the mass transformed into a **snow avalanche**, a chaotic jumble of snow surging downslope. At the bottom of the slope, the avalanche overran a ski resort, crushing and carrying away buildings, cars, and trees and killing more than 30 people. It took searchers and their specially trained dogs many days to find buried survivors and victims under the 5- to 20-m-thick pile of snow that the avalanche deposited (Fig. 16.8a).

Snow avalanches display a variety of behaviors, depending on both the temperature of the snow and on the steepness of the slope down which the snow moves. Specifically, *wet-snow avalanches*, which involve snow that has started to melt and thus contains some liquid water, behave like a viscous slurry in that they hug the slope as they move and entrain relatively little air. Wet-snow avalanches generally travel at speeds of less than 30 km per hour and can pick up rock debris and vegetation along their path. *Dry-snow avalanches* contain cold, powdery snow that on tumbling down a steep slope disintegrates into a turbulent, air-rich cloud that rushes along at hurricane speeds of up to 250 km per hour (Fig. 16.8b). Both wet-snow and dry-snow avalanches can become powerful enough to flatten forests in their paths (Fig. 16.8c).

What triggers snow avalanches? Some happen when a *cornice*, a large drift of snow that builds up on the lee side of a windy mountain summit, suddenly gives way and falls onto slopes below where it knocks free additional snow. Others happen when a broad slab of snow on a moderate slope detaches

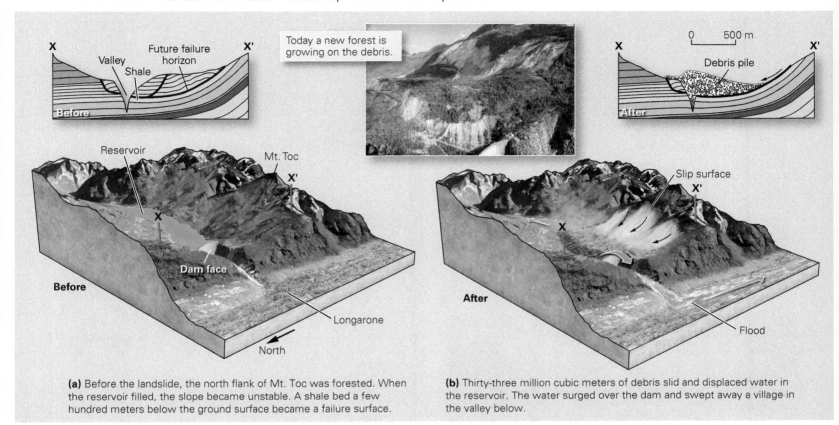

(a) Before the landslide, the north flank of Mt. Toc was forested. When the reservoir filled, the slope became unstable. A shale bed a few hundred meters below the ground surface became a failure surface.

(b) Thirty-three million cubic meters of debris slid and displaced water in the reservoir. The water surged over the dam and swept away a village in the valley below.

from its substrate along an icy failure surface. Avalanches tend to affect the same localities year after year, because of the characteristics of snow buildup and because of the occurrence of *avalanche chutes*, shallow valleys running down the slope that channel the tumbling snow. To protect populated areas downslope of known avalanche chutes, experts may use special explosives to trigger small, controlled avalanches before the snow piles deep enough to become a dangerous hazard.

As we've noted, geologists commonly use the word *avalanche* in a broader sense for any mass movement during which the solid fragments are suspended in so much fluid (air or water) that the flowing mixture behaves like a turbulent cloud. Thus, a *debris avalanche* contains rock fragments and regolith mixed with air, and a *submarine avalanche* consists of sediment suspended in water. Avalanches of all types flow downslope because the mixture of solid and fluid in an avalanche is denser than the surrounding pure fluid—for this reason, geologists refer to various kinds of avalanches as *density currents*.

Rockfalls and Debris Falls

Rockfalls and debris falls, as their names suggest, occur when a mass free-falls from a cliff (Fig. 16.9a, b). Commonly, rockfalls happen when a body of rock separates from a cliff face along

a *joint*, a natural crack in rock across which a block of rock no longer connects to bedrock (see Chapter 11). Some joints are vertical, so after the rock fall, a new vertical cliff forms. Others, called exfoliation joints, are parallel to the hillslope. Most rockfalls involve only a few blocks detaching from a cliff face and dropping downslope. But some falls dislodge immense quantities of rock. In September 1881, a 600-m-high crag of slate, undermined by quarrying, suddenly collapsed onto the town of Elm in a valley of the Swiss Alps. Over 10 million cubic meters of rock fell to the valley floor, burying Elm and its 115 inhabitants to a depth of 10 to 20 m.

Friction and collision with other rocks may bring some blocks that have fallen to a halt before they reach the bottom of the slope; these blocks pile up to form a **talus**, a sloping apron or fan of rocks along the base of the cliff (Fig. 16.9c). Debris that has fallen a long way can reach speeds of 300 km per hour and may have so much momentum that it keeps moving as an avalanche-like cloud of fragments mixed with air when it reaches the base of a cliff. Large, fast rockfalls push the air in front of them, creating a blast of hurricane-like wind. For example, the wind in front of a 1996 rockfall in Yosemite National Park flattened over 2,000 trees.

Rockfalls happen fairly frequently along steep highway road cuts, leading to the posting of "falling-rock zone" signs

FIGURE 16.8 Examples of avalanches.

(a) Aftermath of a 1999 avalanche in the Austrian Alps. Masses of snow buried several homes.

(b) Avalanche chutes down the side of a mountain in the Canadian Rockies. Recent avalanches have flattened trees.

(c) A dry-snow avalanche in Alaska is a turbulent cloud.

Did you ever wonder . . .

why earthquakes don't occur everywhere?

(Fig. 16.9d). Such rockfalls take place because highway cuts are, effectively, new cliffs. In some cases, construction of the road cut weakens the material underlying the road cut, allowing frost wedging and root wedging to more easily break it free.

Submarine Mass Movements

So far, we've focused on mass movements that occur subaerially, for these are the ones we can see and are affected by most.

But mass wasting also happens underwater. The sedimentary record contains abundant evidence of submarine mass movements, because after they take place they tend to be buried by younger sediments and are preserved.

Geologists distinguish three types of submarine mass movements, according to whether the mass remains coherent or disintegrates as it moves (Fig. 16.10). In **submarine slumps**, semicoherent blocks slip downslope on weak detachments—the layers constituting the blocks become contorted as they move, like a tablecloth that slides off a table. In **submarine debris flows**, the moving mass breaks apart to form a slurry containing larger clasts (pebbles to boulders) suspended in a mud matrix. And in **turbidity currents**, sediment disperses in water to create a turbulent cloud of suspended sediment that rushes downslope as an avalanche. Turbidity currents commonly flow down submarine canyons—their movement, in fact, erodes the seafloor so it contributes to the formation of the canyon. When the turbidity current starts to slow, its entrained sediment settles out in a sequence, with coarser grains at the base and finer grains at the top. The resulting deposits, therefore, consist of

FIGURE 16.9 Examples of rockfalls.

(a) Successive rockfalls have littered the base of this sandstone cliff with boulders. Note the talus at the base of the cliff.

(c) A boulder apron in the Canadian Rockies; boulders fall from the high cliffs and accumulate in the apron.

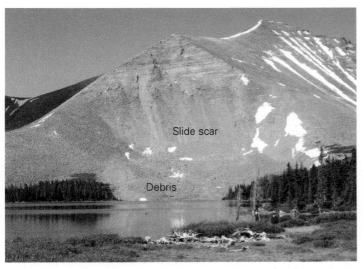

Slide scar

Debris

(b) A rockslide buried the forest bordering a lake in the Uinta Mountains, Utah. Fresh rock exposed by the slide has a lighter color.

(d) A rockfall along a highway in Vermont. Note that the blocks separated from the wall along joints.

graded beds (see Chapter 7)—typically, the deposits accumulate in a fan at the mouth of a submarine canyon.

In recent years, geologists have used satellites as well as ship-board *side-scan sonar* (sonar that analyzes a 60-km-wide swath of the seafloor, instead of just a line, as it moves) to map out the extent of submarine landslides (**Fig. 16.11a**). The shapes of slumps and landslide deposits stand out on the resulting new generation of high-resolution bathymetric maps. Geologists have found that submarine slopes bordering both hot-spot volcanoes and active plate boundaries are scalloped by immense slumps, because tectonic activity jars these areas with earthquakes that set masses of material in motion. For example, slumps up to 200 km long and 100 km wide have substantially modified the flanks of the Hawaiian Islands (**Fig. 16.11b**). Some

of the slumping events even carried away large chunks of the subaerial parts of the islands—in fact, the steep portions of the islands' coasts are the head scarps of huge slumps. Studies suggest that huge slumping events off Hawaii happen, on average, about once every 100,000 years. Significantly, passive-margin coasts are not immune to slumping, and immense slumps have been mapped along the coasts of the Atlantic Ocean.

Since a submarine slump can develop fairly quickly, and since its movement can displace a large area of the seafloor, it can trigger a tsunami. A submarine slump set in motion by a 1998 earthquake in Papua New Guinea generated a tsunami that devastated a 40-km-long stretch of coast and killed 2,100 people. A prehistoric tsunami triggered by a slump off the coast of Norway left its trace all around the North Sea (**Box 16.2**).

FIGURE 16.10 Submarine mass movements.

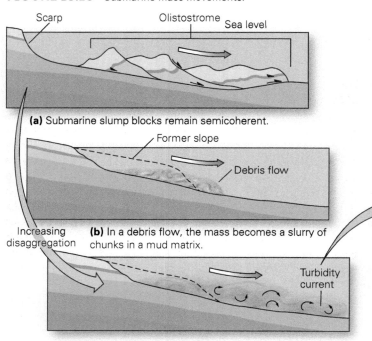

(a) Submarine slump blocks remain semicoherent.

(b) In a debris flow, the mass becomes a slurry of chunks in a mud matrix.

Increasing disaggregation

A laboratory model of a turbidity current. The cloud consists of fine clay suspended in water.

(c) A turbidity current is a cloud of sediment suspended in water; it flows near the seafloor because it is denser than clear water.

FIGURE 16.11 Examples of huge submarine slumps and debris flows.

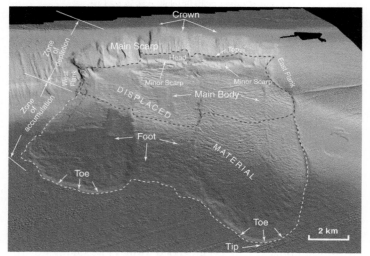

(a) A digital bathymetric map of a slip along the coast of California. The parts of the slump are labeled.

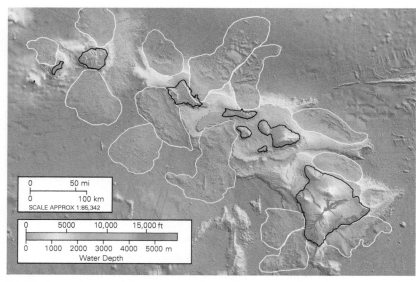

(b) A bathymetric map of the area around Hawaii shows several huge slumps, shaded in tan.

Take-Home Message

Mass movements differ from one another based on speed and character. Creep, slumping, and solifluction are slow. Mudflows and debris flows move faster, and avalanches and rockfalls move the fastest. Movements occur on land and underwater.

QUICK QUESTION: In what way is a snow avalanche like a turbidity current?

16.3 Why Do Mass Movements Occur?

We've seen that mass movements travel at a range of different velocities, from slow (creep) to faster (slumps, mud and debris flows, and rock and debris slides) to fastest (snow avalanches and rock and debris falls; see **Geology at a Glance**, pp. 602–603).

BOX 16.2 CONSIDER THIS . . .

The Storegga Slide and North Sea Tsunamis

The Firth of Forth, a long inlet of the North Sea, forms the waterfront of Edinburgh, Scotland. At its western end, it merges with a broad plain in which mud and peat have been accumulating since the last ice age. Around 1865, geologists investigating this sediment discovered an unusual layer of sand containing bashed seashells, marine plankton, and torn-up fragments of substrate. This sand layer lies sandwiched between mud layers at an elevation of up to 4 m above the high-tide limit and 80 km inland from the shore. How could the sand layer have been deposited? The mystery baffled geologists for many decades. During this time, layers of shelly sand, similar to the one found in Scotland, were discovered at many other localities along both sides of the North Sea (**Fig. Bx16.2**). In some cases, the layer occurred 20 m above the high-tide limit. Geologists studying the coast also found locations where coastal cliffs appeared to have been eroded by wave action at elevations well out of reach of normal storm waves.

While land-based geologists puzzled about these unusual sand beds and coastal erosional features, marine geologists investigating the continental shelf off the western coast of Norway discovered a region of very irregular sea floor underlain with a jumble of chaotic blocks, some of which are 10 km by 30 km across and 200 m thick. When mapped out, they indicate that a 290-km-long sector of the continental shelf had collapsed in a series of submarine slides that together involve about 5,580 cubic km of debris—the overall feature is called the Storegga Slide.

Further studies show that the Storegga Slide formed during three movement events: one occurred 30,000 years ago, the second about 7,950 years ago, and the third about 6,000 years ago. Now the pieces of the puzzle were in place. Immense submarine slides displace enough ocean water to create tsunamis. The wave produced by the second Storegga Slide may coincide with the disappearance of Stone Age tribes along the North Sea coast, suggesting that the tribes were effectively washed away.

If such a calamity happened in the past, could it happen again, with submarine-slide-generated tsunamis inundating coastal cities with large populations? Geologists now realize that submarine landslides can trigger tsunamis every bit as devastating as earthquake- and volcano-generated tsunamis. A slide in 1929 along the coast of Newfoundland, for example, not only created a turbidity current that broke the trans-Atlantic telephone cable but also generated tsunamis that washed away houses and boats along the coast of Newfoundland at elevations of up to 27 m above sea level. With a bit of looking, geologists have found huge boulders flung by tsunamis onto the land, layers of sand and gravel deposited well above the high-tide limit, and erosional features high up on shoreline cliffs along many coastal areas, even in areas (such as the Bahamas and southeastern Australia) far from seismic or volcanic regions. And submarine mapping shows that many large slumps occur all along continental shelves.

FIGURE Bx16.2 Map of the North Sea region showing the location of sites (red dots) where marine sand layers occur significantly above the high-tide limit. These were caused by tsunamis generated by movement of the Storegga Slide. The map shows the estimated position of the tsunamis at 2 hours, 4 hours, and 6 hours.

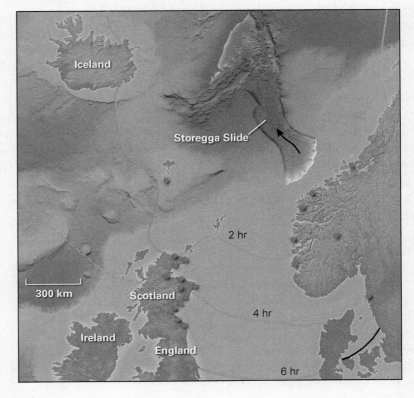

The velocity depends on the steepness of the slope and the water or air content of the mass. Why do mass movements take place? The stage must be set by the following phenomena: (1) fracturing and weathering of the substrate, which weakens the substrate so it cannot hold up against the pull of gravity; (2) the development of relief, which provides slopes down which masses move; and (3) an event that sets mass in motion. Let's look at these phenomena more closely.

Weakening the Substrate: Fragmentation and Weathering

If the Earth's surface were covered by completely unfractured rock, mass movements would be of little concern, for intact rock has great strength and could form stalwart mountain faces that would not tumble. But, in reality, the rock of the Earth's upper crust has been fractured by jointing and faulting and has undergone chemical weathering. Also, in many locations long-term weathering and/ or deposition has covered bedrock with regolith (sediment or soil). Regolith and fractured rock are much weaker than intact rock and can indeed collapse in response to gravitational pull (Fig. 16.12). Thus jointing, faulting, and weathering ultimately make mass movements possible.

Why are regolith and fractured rocks weaker than intact bedrock?

The answer comes from looking at the strength of the attachments holding materials together. A mass of intact bedrock is relatively strong because the chemical bonds within its interlocking grains, or within the cements between grains, can't be broken easily. Weathered rock tends to be weaker, because strong bonds between the original grains of the rock have been replaced by weaker bonds between weathering products, such as clays and iron oxides. Regolith is relatively weak because the grains are held together only by friction (caused by roughness along the contact between two grains), electrostatic attraction (the weak force that develops between clay flakes because the surfaces of the flakes are charged), and/or the surface tension of water (the weak force caused by the attraction of water molecules to one another). All of these forces combined are weaker than chemical bonds holding together the atoms in the minerals of intact rock. To picture this contrast, think how much easier it is to bust up a sand castle (whose strength comes primarily from the surface tension of water films on the sand grains) than it is to bust up a granite sculpture of a castle.

Slope Stability

Mass movements do not take place on all slopes, and even on slopes where such movements are possible, they occur only occasionally. Geologists distinguish between *stable slopes*, on which sliding is unlikely, and *unstable slopes*, on which sliding will likely happen. When material starts moving on an unstable slope, we say that **slope failure** has occurred. Whether a slope fails or not depends on the balance between two forces—the *downslope force*, caused by gravity, and the *resistance force*, which inhibits sliding. If the downslope force exceeds the resistance force, the slope fails and mass movement results.

Let's examine the battle between downslope forces and resistance forces more closely by imagining a block sitting on a slope. We can represent the gravitational attraction between the

FIGURE 16.13 Forces that trigger downslope movement.

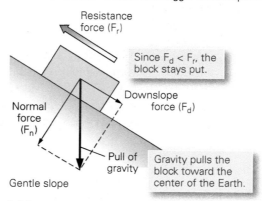

(a) Gravity can be divided into a normal force and a downslope force. If the resistance force, caused by friction, is greater than the downslope force, the block does not move.

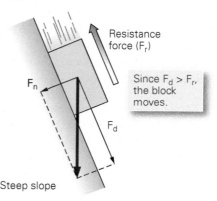

(b) If the slope angle increases, the downslope force due to gravity increases. If the downslope force becomes greater than the resistance force, the block starts to move.

block and the Earth by an arrow (a vector) that points straight down, toward the Earth's center of gravity. This arrow can be separated into two components—the downslope force parallel to the slope and the normal force perpendicular to the slope. Note that for a given mass the magnitude of the downslope force increases as the slope angle increases, so downslope forces are greater on steeper slopes. We can symbolize the resistance force by an arrow pointing uphill. (As we have seen, resistance force comes from chemical bonds, electrostatic attraction, friction, and surface tension.) If the downslope force is larger than the resistance force, then the block moves—otherwise, it stays in place (Fig. 16.13).

Because of resistance force, granular debris tends to pile up to produce the steepest slope it can without collapsing. The angle of this slope is called the **angle of repose**, and for most dry, unconsolidated materials (such as dry sand) it generally has a value of between 30° and 37°. The angle depends partly on the shape and size of grains, which determine the amount of friction across grain boundaries. For example, steeper angles of repose (up to 45°) characterize talus slopes composed of large, irregularly shaped grains (Fig. 16.14).

In many locations, the resistance force is less than might be expected because a weak surface exists at some depth below ground level. If downslope movement begins on the weak surface, the weak surface becomes a failure surface. Geologists recognize several different kinds of weak surfaces that are likely to become failure surfaces (Fig. 16.15). These include wet clay layers; wet, unconsolidated sand layers; joints; weak bedding planes, such as shale beds or evaporite beds; and metamorphic foliation planes.

Weak surfaces that dip parallel to the land surface slope are particularly likely to become failure surfaces. An example of such failure occurred in Madison Canyon, southwestern Montana, on August 17, 1959. That day, shock waves from a strong earthquake jarred the region. Metamorphic rock with a strong foliation formed the bedrock of the canyon's southern wall. When the ground vibrated, rock detached along a foliation plane and tumbled downslope. Unfortunately, 28 campers lay sleeping on the valley floor. They were probably awakened by the hurricane-like winds blasting in front of the moving mass but seconds later were buried under 45 m of rubble.

FIGURE 16.14 The angle of repose is the steepest slope that a pile of unconsolidated sediment can have and remain stable. The angle depends on the shape and size of grains.

FIGURE 16.15 Different kinds of weak surfaces can become failure surfaces.

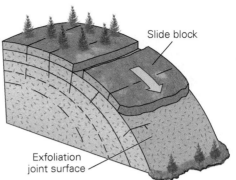

(a) Exfoliation joints form parallel to slope surfaces in granite and become failure surfaces.

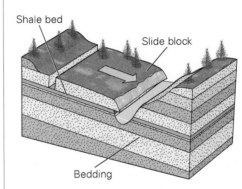

(b) In sedimentary rocks, bedding planes (particularly in weak shale) become failure surfaces.

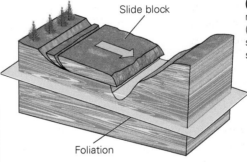

(c) In metamorphic rock, foliation planes (particularly in mica-rich schist) become failure surfaces.

Fingers on the Trigger: What Causes Slope Failure?

What triggers an individual mass-wasting event? In other words, what causes the balance of forces to change so that the downslope force exceeds the resistance force and a slope suddenly fails? Here we look at various phenomena—natural and human-made—that trigger slope failure.

Shocks, Vibrations, and Liquefaction Earthquake tremors, storms, the passing of large trucks, or blasting in construction sites may cause a mass that was on the verge of moving actually to start moving. For example, an earthquake-triggered slide dumped debris into southeastern Alaska's Lituya Bay in 1958. The debris displaced the water in the bay,

Mass Movement

In Earth's gravity field, what goes up must come down—sometimes with disastrous consequences. Rock and regolith are not infinitely strong, so every now and then slopes or cliffs give way in response to gravity, and materials slide, tumble, or career downslope. This downslope movement, called mass movement, or mass wasting, is the first step in the process of erosion and sediment formation.

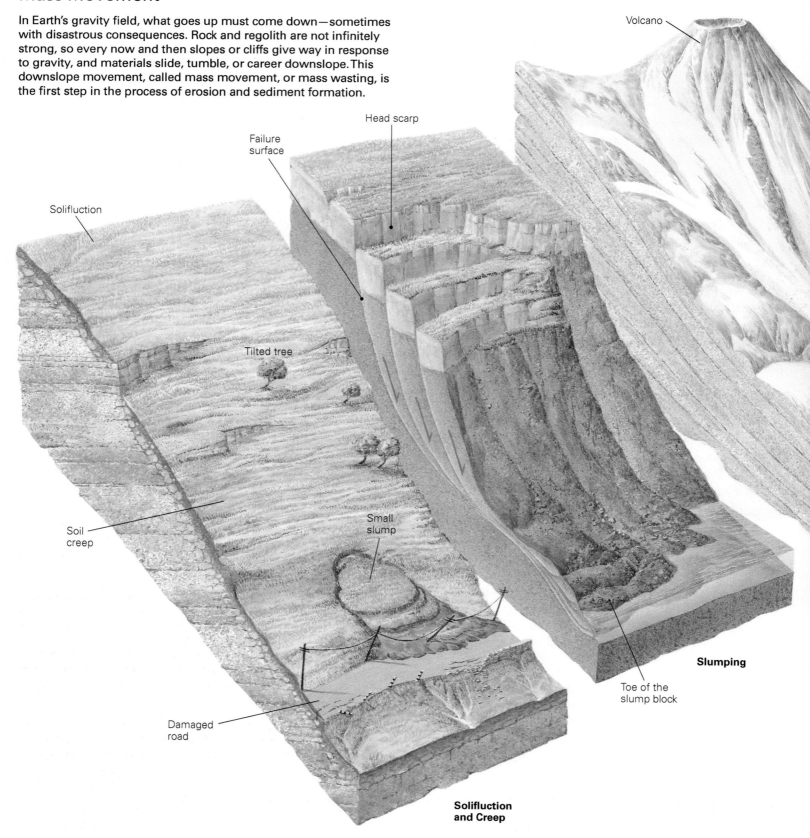

Volcano

Head scarp

Failure surface

Solifluction

Tilted tree

Soil creep

Small slump

Damaged road

Slumping

Toe of the slump block

Solifluction and Creep

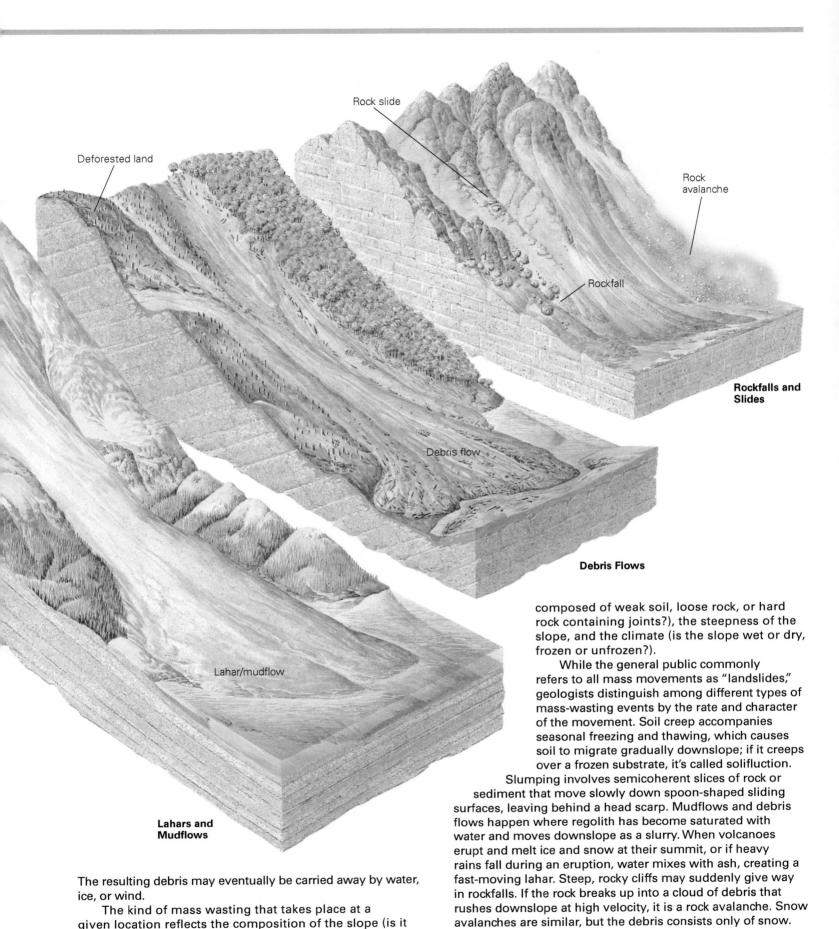

Rock slide

Deforested land

Rock
avalanche

Rockfall

**Rockfalls and
Slides**

Debris flow

Debris Flows

Lahar/mudflow

**Lahars and
Mudflows**

The resulting debris may eventually be carried away by water,
ice, or wind.

The kind of mass wasting that takes place at a
given location reflects the composition of the slope (is it
composed of weak soil, loose rock, or hard
rock containing joints?), the steepness of the
slope, and the climate (is the slope wet or dry,
frozen or unfrozen?).

While the general public commonly
refers to all mass movements as "landslides,"
geologists distinguish among different types of
mass-wasting events by the rate and character
of the movement. Soil creep accompanies
seasonal freezing and thawing, which causes
soil to migrate gradually downslope; if it creeps
over a frozen substrate, it's called solifluction.
Slumping involves semicoherent slices of rock or
sediment that move slowly down spoon-shaped sliding
surfaces, leaving behind a head scarp. Mudflows and debris
flows happen where regolith has become saturated with
water and moves downslope as a slurry. When volcanoes
erupt and melt ice and snow at their summit, or if heavy
rains fall during an eruption, water mixes with ash, creating a
fast-moving lahar. Steep, rocky cliffs may suddenly give way
in rockfalls. If the rock breaks up into a cloud of debris that
rushes downslope at high velocity, it is a rock avalanche. Snow
avalanches are similar, but the debris consists only of snow.

creating a 300-m-high (1,200-foot) splash that washed forests off the slopes bordering the bay and carried fishing boats anchored in the bay many kilometers out to sea. The vibrations of an earthquake break bonds that hold a mass in place and/or cause the mass and the slope to separate slightly, thereby decreasing friction. As a consequence, the resistance force decreases, and the downslope force sets the mass in motion.

In certain types of wet sediment, shaking can cause **liquefaction**, meaning that it turns what seems to be a solid layer into a slurry. For example, **quick clay**, which consists of damp clay flakes, behaves like a solid when still, for surface tension holds water-coated flakes together—shaking separates the flakes from one another and suspends them in the water, thereby transforming the clay into wet mud that flows like a fluid (Fig. 16.16). And in wet sand, shaking causes the sand grains to shift slightly relative to one another, which then causes the water pressure in pores between the grains to increase, thus pushing the grains apart such that they become suspended in water. As a result, the wet sand becomes a sandy slurry with virtually no strength. If a layer of sediment at depth below a hillslope undergoes liquefaction, the layer becomes a failure surface, permitting collapse of the hillslope.

Changing Slope Loads, Steepness, and Support

As we have seen, the stability of a slope at a given time depends on the balance between downslope force and resistance force. Factors that change one or the other of these forces can lead to failure. Examples include changes in slope loads, failure-surface strength, slope steepness, and the support provided by material at the base of the slope.

Slope loads change when the weight of the material above a potential failure plane changes. If the load increases, due to the addition of fill, the construction of buildings, or saturation of regolith with water due to heavy rains, the downslope force will increase and may exceed the resistance force. For example, the devastating Oso mudslide of 2014 happened after a 6-week period during which rainfall was 200% greater than average, so the sandy ground underlying the hillslopes of the region had become saturated. Seepage of water into the ground may also trigger failure in bedrock. An example of such failure triggered the huge Gros Ventre Slide, which took place in 1925 on the flank of Sheep Mountain, near Jackson Hole, Wyoming (Fig. 16.17). The surface of Sheep Mountain is parallel to the bedding in underlying bedrock. Heavy rains saturated the permeable sandstone beds of the Tensleep Formation, which lay above the weak Amsden Shale, making the bedrock much heavier. On June 27, the downslope force exceeded the restraining force, and 40 million cubic meters of rock, as well as the overlying soil and forest, detached from the side of the mountain and slid 600 m downslope, with the Amsden Shale serving as the failure surface. The debris filled the valley below and built a 75-m-high natural dam across the Gros Ventre River.

Slope steepness may change over time, when rivers cut valleys, or construction engineers pile up debris or cut into slopes (Fig. 16.18). An increase in steepness causes an increase in the downslope force but does not change the resistance force. If the slope becomes too steep, it becomes unstable and may fail. Removing support at the base of a slope has a similar effect, and plays a major role in triggering slope failures. In effect, the material at the base of a slope acts like a retaining wall or "dam" holding back the material farther up the slope. When natural erosion, or bulldozer excavations, takes away this "dam," the upslope material can start to move. Such a process contributed to setting the stage for both Oso Mudslide (see Fig. 16.5), and the Gros Ventre Slide—in both cases, the river flowing at the base of what would become the slide had been cutting into the base of the hill. Cutting terraces into hillslopes for road building can have the same effect, as can wave erosion at the base of a slope along a coast. In some cases, erosion by a river or by waves eats into the base of a cliff and produces an overhang. When such **undercutting** has occurred, rock making up the overhang eventually breaks away from the slope and falls (Fig. 16.19).

FIGURE 16.16 Quick clay mudslides.

 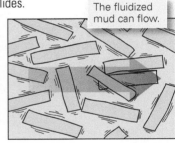

The fluidized mud can flow.

(a) Before shaking, clay flakes stick together.

(b) During shaking, clays separate and become suspended in water.

(c) A mudslide near Namsos, Norway, destroyed ten houses. Movement may have been triggered by nearby blasting.

FIGURE 16.17 Stages leading to the 1925 Gros Ventre Slide in Wyoming.

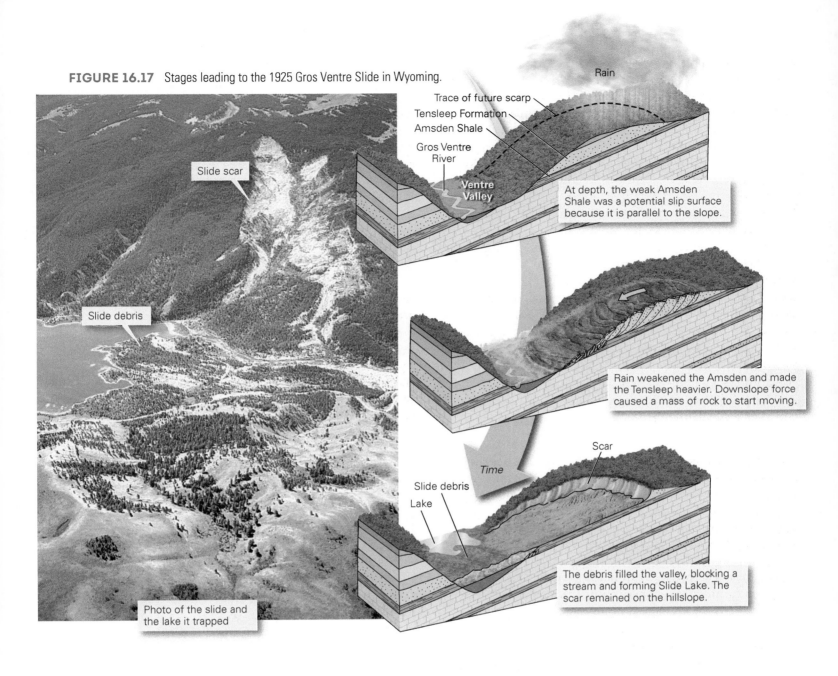

Slide scar

Slide debris

Photo of the slide and the lake it trapped

Rain

Trace of future scarp
Tensleep Formation
Amsden Shale
Gros Ventre River

Ventre Valley

At depth, the weak Amsden Shale was a potential slip surface because it is parallel to the slope.

Rain weakened the Amsden and made the Tensleep heavier. Downslope force caused a mass of rock to start moving.

Time

Scar

Slide debris

Lake

The debris filled the valley, blocking a stream and forming Slide Lake. The scar remained on the hillslope.

FIGURE 16.18 Processes that can steepen slopes and make them unstable.

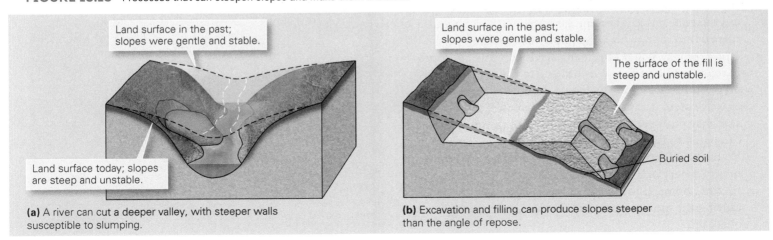

Land surface in the past; slopes were gentle and stable.

Land surface in the past; slopes were gentle and stable.

The surface of the fill is steep and unstable.

Land surface today; slopes are steep and unstable.

Buried soil

(a) A river can cut a deeper valley, with steeper walls susceptible to slumping.

(b) Excavation and filling can produce slopes steeper than the angle of repose.

FIGURE 16.19 Undercutting and collapse of a sea cliff.

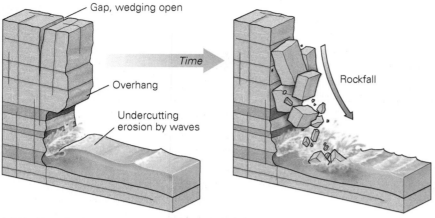

Gap, wedging open

Overhang

Undercutting erosion by waves

Time

Rockfall

(a) Undercutting by waves removes the support beneath an overhang.

(b) Eventually, the overhang breaks off along joints, and a rockfall takes place.

Take-Home Message

Weathering and fragmentation weaken slope materials and make them more susceptible to mass movement. The stability of a slope reflects the relative sizes of downslope force and resistance force. Failure occurs when downslope force exceeds resistance force, perhaps due to shocks, changing slope angles and strength, changing water content, and changing slope support.

QUICK QUESTION: If the slope of a sand pile is less than the angle of repose, will the slope of the pile fail?

Changing the Slope Strength The stability of a slope depends on the strength of the material constituting it. If the material weakens with time, the slope becomes weaker and eventually collapses. Three factors influence the strength of slopes: weathering, vegetation cover, and water:

- *Weathering:* With time, chemical weathering produces weaker minerals, and physical weathering breaks rocks apart. Thus, a formerly intact rock composed of strong minerals is transformed into a weaker rock or into regolith.
- *Vegetation cover:* In the case of slopes underlain by regolith, vegetation tends to strengthen the slope because the roots hold otherwise unconsolidated grains together. Also, plants absorb water from the ground, thus keeping it from turning into slippery mud. The removal of vegetation therefore has the net result of making slopes more susceptible to downslope mass movement. Deforestation, for example, can lead to catastrophic mass wasting of the forest's substrate (Fig. 16.20). And terrifying wildfires, stoked by strong winds, can destroy ground-covering vegetation. If heavy rains fall on burned regions, the unprotected soil can became saturated with water and turned into mud, which then flows downslope.
- *Water content:* Water affects materials comprising slopes in many ways. Surface tension, due to the film of water on grain surfaces, may help hold regolith together. But, as we've seen, if the water content increases, water pressure may push grains apart so that regolith liquefies and can begin to flow or may make the substrate heavier. Water infiltration may make weak surfaces underground more slippery or may push surfaces apart and decrease friction. Some kinds of clays absorb water and expand, causing the ground surface to rise and, as a consequence, break up.

16.4 Where Do Mass Movements Occur?

The Importance of Relief, Climate, and Substrate

The single most important factor in determining whether a locality is susceptible to mass movements is the relief (elevation

FIGURE 16.20 Deforestation decreases slope stability. A large slump has formed on this deforested hill in Brazil.

Slump scar

difference) of a region, for mass wasting does not occur without slopes. Further, regions with steeper slopes tend to be more susceptible to mass movements than are regions with gentle slopes. Thus, locations where rivers or glaciers have cut valleys, mountains have risen, or ocean waves have eaten into the shores to form sea cliffs are places where mass movements are more likely.

Slope is not the only factor affecting the character and frequency of mass movements, though. Climate also affects mass movements. For example, regions with heavy seasonal rainfalls are subject to mudflows and landslides, especially if fire or deforestation has removed vegetation. In these regions, the climate has led to deep weathering and weakening of the substrate, and rainfalls increase slope loads and weaken failure surfaces. Desert and alpine regions, where slopes tend to be underlain by unweathered bedrock, tend to host rare but dramatic rock falls.

The Importance of the Tectonic Setting

Most unstable ground on Earth ultimately owes its existence to the activity of plate tectonics. As we've seen, plate tectonics causes uplift, generates relief, and causes faulting, which fragments the crust. And, of course, earthquakes on plate boundaries trigger devastating landslides. Spend a day along the steep slopes of the Southern Alps, a mountain range now uplifting along plate boundary that transects New Zealand, and you can hear mass movement in progress—during heavy rains, rockfalls and landslides clatter with astounding frequency, as if the mountains were falling down around you.

A Case Study: Southern California

To see the interplay of plate tectonics and other factors, let's consider a case study in southern California. Contractors have built expensive homes on cliffs overlooking the Pacific so that homeowners can enjoy spectacular sunset views from their backyard patios. But the landscape is not ideal from the standpoint of stability. Slumps and mudflows on coastal cliffs have consumed some of these homes over the years, with a cost to their owners (or insurance companies) of millions of dollars. What is special about southern California that makes it so susceptible to mass wasting?

First, California lies along an active plate boundary, the San Andreas fault. Repeated slip events along the fault over millions of years have shattered the rock of California's crust. Fractures not only act as planes of weakness but can provide paths for water to seep into bedrock and cause chemical weathering, producing slippery clay that weakens the rock. Also, the rocks in many areas are weak to begin with

Did you ever wonder...

why parts of the California coast slip into the sea?

because they formed as part of an accretionary prism, a chaotic mass of sediment that was scraped off subducting oceanic lithosphere during the Mesozoic Era.

Though most of the movement on the boundary between the North American and Pacific plates involves strike-slip displacement, there is a component of compression across the boundary. This compression leads to uplift and slope formation in California (see Box 16.1). Since the uplifted region borders the coast, wave erosion steepens and, in some places, undercuts cliffs. And because it is a plate boundary, numerous earthquakes rock the region, thus shaking regolith loose.

California is also susceptible to mass movements because of its climate. In general, the region is hot and dry and thus supports only semidesert flora. Brush fires remove much of this cover, leaving large areas with no dense vegetation. But since the region lies on the Pacific coast, it endures occasional heavy winter rains. The water sinks quickly into the sparsely vegetated ground, adds weight to the mass on the slope, and weakens failure surfaces.

Development of cities and suburbs also contributes to triggering mass movements in southern California. Development has oversteepened and overloaded slopes and has caused the water content of regolith to change. The consequences can be seen in the Portuguese Bend Slide of the Palos Verdes area near Los Angeles (Fig. 16.21). The Portuguese Bend region is underlain with a thick, seaward-dipping layer of weak volcanic ash (now altered to weak clay) resting on shale. The weak ash has served as a failure plane a few times during the past few thousand years. In 1956, developers deposited a 23-m-thick layer of fill over the ground surface and built homes on top. Residents began to water their lawns and to use septic tanks that were susceptible to leaking. The water seeped into the ground and decreased the

SEE FOR YOURSELF...

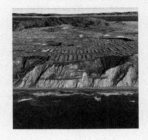

Slumps near San Francisco

LATITUDE
37°40'47.33"N

LONGITUDE
122°29'46.14"W

Zoom to 2.5 km (~8200 ft.) and rotate the view so north is on the left (top photo). Then tilt, to look obliquely east (bottom photo) from 550 m.

You are seeing the coast near San Francisco, where waves erode sea cliffs at the base of a terrace. Occasionally, slumps along the cliffs carry debris to the beach. The bowls cut into the terrace are places where slumps have occurred in the past.

strength of the ash layer. Because of the decrease in strength, the added weight, and the erosion of the toe of the hill by the sea, the upper 30 m of land began to move once again. Between 1956 and 1985, the Portuguese Bend Slide moved at rates of up to 2.5 cm per day. Eventually, portions of a 260-acre region slid by over 200 m, and in the process more than 150 homes were destroyed.

Take-Home Message

Mass movement can occur where slopes have developed, particularly if the substrate has undergone weathering and fragmentation, for these processes weaken slope materials. Failure occurs when the downslope force exceeds resistance force due to shocks (such as earthquakes), changing slope angles and strength, changing water content, and changing slope support. Climate can impact the susceptibility of a region to mass wasting because it affects the character of vegetation and the amount and distribution of rainfall.

QUICK QUESTION: Are mass movements likely to be frequent on the surface of the Moon? Why or why not?

16.5 How Can We Protect against Mass-Movement Disasters?

Identifying Regions at Risk

Clearly, landslides, mudflows, and slumps are natural hazards that we cannot ignore. Too many of us live in regions where mass wasting has the potential to kill people and destroy property. In many cases, the best solution is avoidance: don't build, live, or work on slopes or below slopes where mass movement is likely to take place. But avoidance is possible only if we know where the hazards are greater.

To pinpoint regions that are particularly susceptible to mass movements, and thus are regions of elevated risk, geologists look for landforms known to result from mass movements, for where mass movements have happened in the past, they might happen again in the future. Features such as slump head scarps, swaths of forest in which trees have been tilted, piles of loose debris at the base of hills, and hummocky land surfaces all indicate recent mass wasting.

Geologists may also be able to detect regions that are beginning to move (Fig. 16.22). For example, roads, buildings, and pipes begin to crack over unstable ground. Power lines may be too tight or too loose because the poles to which they are attached move together or apart. Visible cracks form on the ground at the potential head of a slump, while the ground may bulge up at the toe of the slump. In some cases, subsurface cracks may drain the water from an area and kill off vegetation, whereas in other areas land may sink and form a swamp. Even if mass wasting takes place too slowly to be perceptible to people, it can be documented with sensitive instruments that can detect a subtle tilt of the ground or changes in distance between nearby points. Specifically, measurements with satellite data, with laser surveys, and with tiltmeters permit geologists to identify movements of just a few millimeters that, while small, may indicate the reactivation of a slump.

If various clues indicate that a landmass is beginning to move, and if conditions make accelerating movement likely (e.g., persistent rain, rising floodwaters, or continuing earthquake aftershocks), then officials may order an evacuation. Evacuations have saved lives, and ignored warnings have cost lives.

FIGURE 16.21 The Portuguese Bend Slide viewed from the air.

Head scarp

Approximate edge of slump

Hummocky slump surface

FIGURE 16.22 Surface features warn that a large slump is beginning to develop. Cracks that appear at the head scarp may drain water and kill trees. Power-line poles tilt and the lines become tight. Fences, roads, and houses on the slump begin to crack.

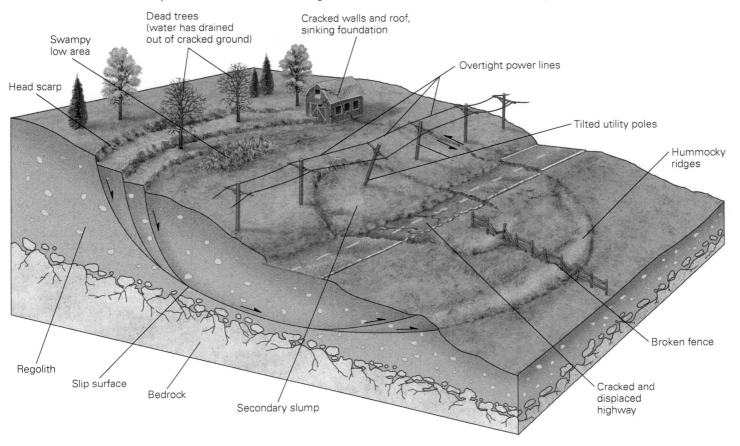

But unfortunately, some mass movements happen without any warning, and some evacuations prove costly but unnecessary.

In places that are being directly monitored, warnings can be quite precise. For example, an immense landslide that happened within the Bingham Canyon Mine of Utah was predicted with enough advance warning to evacuate the miners before the landslide happened. Thus, the debris flow, which carried material almost 2 km at speeds of up to 100 km per hour (Fig. 16.23), destroyed some buildings and equipment but did not cause any injury.

Even if there is no evidence of recent movement, a danger may still exist: just because a steep slope hasn't collapsed in the recent past doesn't mean it won't in the future. In recent years, geologists have begun to identify such potential hazards by using computer programs that evaluate factors that trigger mass wasting. With these data, they create maps that portray the degree of risk for a certain location. These factors include the following: slope steepness; strength of substrate; degree of water saturation; orientation of bedding, joints, or foliation relative to the slope; nature of vegetation cover; potential for heavy rains; potential for undercutting to occur; and likelihood of earthquakes. From such hazard-assessment studies, geologists compile **landslide-potential maps**, which rank regions according to the likelihood that a mass movement will occur (Fig. 16.24). Officials may restrict construction in landslide-prone areas.

FIGURE 16.23 A huge landslide took away one of the walls of the Bingham open-pit copper mine in Utah. No lives were lost because engineers detected the instability of the slope and evacuated the mine in time.

FIGURE 16.24 A landslide hazard map of the Seattle area.

Preventing Mass Movements

In areas where a hazard exists, people can take certain steps to remedy the problem and stabilize the slope (Fig. 16.25).

- *Revegetation:* Since bare ground is more vulnerable to downslope movement than is vegetated ground, stability in deforested areas will be greatly enhanced if land owners replant the region with vegetation that sends down deep roots.
- *Regrading:* An oversteepened slope can be regraded or terraced so that it does not exceed the angle of repose.
- *Reducing subsurface water:* Because water weakens material beneath a slope and adds weight to the slope, an unstable situation may be remedied either by improving drainage so that water does not enter the subsurface in the first place or by removing water from the ground.
- *Preventing undercutting:* In places where a river undercuts a cliff face, engineers can divert the river. Similarly, along coastal regions they may build an offshore breakwater or pile **riprap** (loose boulders or concrete) along the beach to

absorb wave energy before it strikes the cliff face.

- *Constructing safety structures:* In some cases, the best way to prevent mass wasting is to build a structure that stabilizes a potentially unstable slope or protects a region downslope from debris if a mass movement does occur. For example, civil engineers can build retaining walls or bolt loose slabs of rock to more coherent masses in the substrate in order to stabilize highway embankments. The danger from rock falls can be decreased by covering a road cut with chain-link fencing or by spraying road cuts with "shotcrete," a cement that coats the wall and prevents water infiltration and consequent freezing and thawing. Highways at the base of an avalanche chute can be covered by an avalanche shed, whose roof keeps debris off the road.
- *Controlled blasting of unstable slopes:* When it is clear that unstable ground or snow threatens a particular region, the best solution may be to blast the unstable ground or snow loose at a time when its movement can do no harm.

Clearly, the cost of preventing mass-wasting calamities is high, and people might not always be willing to pay the price. In such cases, they have a choice of avoiding the risky area, taking the chance that a calamity will not happen while they are around, buying appropriate insurance, or counting on relief agencies to help if disaster does strike. Once again, geology and society cross paths.

Take-Home Message

Various features of the landscape may help geologists to identify unstable slopes and estimate risk. Systematic study allows production of landslide-potential maps. Engineers can use a variety of techniques to stabilize slopes.

QUICK QUESTION: Why is mass movement of major concern during production of large road cuts?

FIGURE 16.25 A variety of remedial steps can stabilize unstable ground.

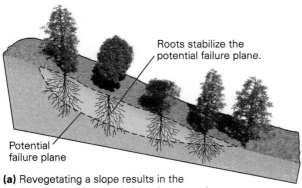

Roots stabilize the potential failure plane.

Potential failure plane

(a) Revegetating a slope results in the growth of roots that can hold a slope together.

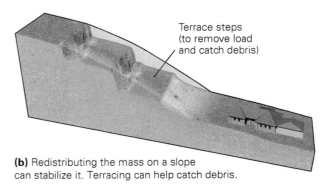

Terrace steps (to remove load and catch debris)

(b) Redistributing the mass on a slope can stabilize it. Terracing can help catch debris.

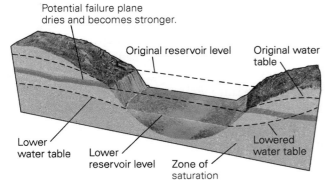

Potential failure plane dries and becomes stronger.

Original reservoir level

Original water table

Lower water table

Lower reservoir level

Zone of saturation

Lowered water table

(c) Lowering the level of the water table can strengthen a potential failure surface.

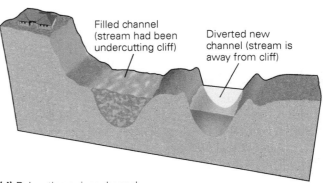

Filled channel (stream had been undercutting cliff)

Diverted new channel (stream is away from cliff)

(d) Relocating a river channel can prevent undercutting.

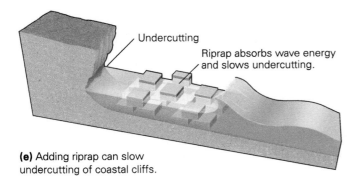

Undercutting

Riprap absorbs wave energy and slows undercutting.

(e) Adding riprap can slow undercutting of coastal cliffs.

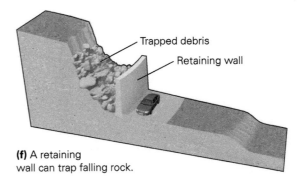

Trapped debris

Retaining wall

(f) A retaining wall can trap falling rock.

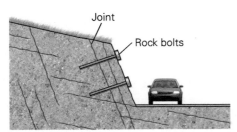

Joint

Rock bolts

(g) Bolting or screening a cliff face can hold loose rocks in place.

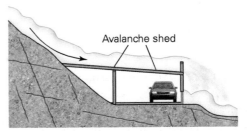

Avalanche shed

(h) An avalanche shed diverts debris or snow over a roadway.

CHAPTER SUMMARY

- Rock or regolith on unstable slopes has the potential to move downslope under the influence of gravity. This process, called mass movement or mass wasting, plays an important role in the shaping of landforms and transport of sediment.

- Though in everyday language people refer to most mass movements as landslides, geologists distinguish among different types of mass movements based on factors such as the composition of the moving materials and the rate of movement.

- Slow mass movement, caused by the freezing and thawing of regolith, is called creep. In places where slopes are underlain with permafrost, solifluction causes a melted layer of regolith to flow down slopes. During slumping, a semicoherent mass of material moves down a spoon-shaped failure surface. Mudflows and debris flows occur where regolith has become saturated with water and moves downslope as a slurry.

- Rock and debris slides move very rapidly down a slope; the rock or debris breaks apart and tumbles. During avalanches, snow or debris mixes with air and moves downslope as a turbulent cloud. And in a debris fall or rockfall, the material free-falls down a vertical cliff.

- Mass movements of various types occur undersea and can trigger tsunamis.

- Intact, fresh rock is too strong to undergo mass movement. Thus, for mass movement to be possible, rock must be weakened by fracturing (joint formation) and/or weathering.

- Unstable slopes start to move when the downslope force exceeds the resistance force that holds material in place. The steepest angle at which a slope of unconsolidated material can remain without collapsing is the angle of repose.

- Downslope movement can be triggered by shocks and vibrations, a change in the steepness of a slope, removal of support from the base of the slope, a change in the strength of a slope, deforestation, weathering, or heavy rain.

- Geologists produce landslide-potential maps to identify areas susceptible to mass movement. Engineers can help detect incipient mass movements and can help prevent mass movements by using a variety of techniques.

GUIDE TERMS

angle of repose (p. 601)	lahar (p. 593)	natural hazard (p. 588)	solifluction (p. 588)
avalanche (p. 588)	landslide (p. 588)	quick clay (p. 604)	submarine debris flow (p. 596)
creep (p. 588)	landslide-potential map (p. 609)	riprap (p. 610)	
debris flow (debris slide) (p. 591)		rock glacier (p. 588)	submarine slump (p. 596)
	liquefaction (p. 604)	rockslide (p. 594)	substrate (p. 588)
debris slide (p. 594)	mass movement (mass wasting) (p. 588)	slope failure (p. 600)	talus (p. 595)
failure surface (p. 590)		slump (p. 590)	turbidity current (p. 596)
head scarp (p. 591)	mudflow (mudslide) (p. 591)	snow avalanche (p. 594)	undercutting (p. 604)

REVIEW QUESTIONS

1. What factors do geologists use to distinguish among various types of mass movements?

2. Identify the key differences among a slump, a debris flow, a lahar, an avalanche, a rockslide, and a rockfall.

3. Explain the process of creep, and discuss how it differs from solifluction.

4. Distinguish among different types of submarine mass movements. Which of these types can trigger a major tsunami, and why?

5. Why is intact bedrock stronger than fractured bedrock? Why is it stronger than regolith?

6. Explain the difference between a stable and unstable slope. What factors determine the angle of repose of a material? What features are likely to serve as failure surfaces?

7. Discuss the variety of phenomena that can cause a stable slope to become so unstable that it fails.

8. How can ground shaking cause fairly solid layers or sand or mud to become weak slurries capable of flowing?

9. Discuss the role of vegetation in slope stability. Why can fires and deforestation lead to slope failure?

10. Identify the various factors that make the coast of California susceptible to mass movements.

11. What factors do geologists take into account when producing a landslide-potential map, and how can geologists detect the beginning of mass movement in an area? What steps can people take to avoid landslide disasters?

ON FURTHER THOUGHT

12. Imagine that you have been asked by the World Bank to determine whether it makes sense to build a dam in a steep-sided, east-west-trending valley in a small central Asian nation. The local government has lobbied for the dam because the climate of the country has gradually been getting drier and the farms of the area are running out of water, and construction of the dam would employ thousands of now-jobless people. Initial investigation shows that the rock of the valley floor consists of schist containing a strong foliation that dips south. Outcrop studies reveal that abundant fractures occur in the schist along the valley floor; the surfaces of most fractures are coated with slickensides. Moderate earthquakes have rattled the region. What would you advise the bank? Explain the hazards and what might happen if the reservoir were filled.

smartwork smartwork.wwnorton.com

This chapter's Smartwork features:

- Labeling exercise on types of mass movements.
- What A Geologist Sees activity on slump features.
- Video questions on microgravity measurement.

GEOTOURS

This chapter's GeoTour exercise (M) features:

- Portuguese Bend Landslide, CA
- La Conchita Mudslide, CA
- Gros Ventre Slide, WY
- Vaiont Dam Slide, Italy

Another View The huge Ganges Chasma landslide, which formed along the Valles Marineris, a canyon wall on Mars, has taken part of a meteorite crater with it. The field of view is about 60 km across.

A small glacier, all that remains of what was once a large ice cap, clings to the side of a mountain in the Canadian Rockies. Flow of glaciers contributed to carving this rugged landscape.

CHAPTER 22

Amazing Ice:
Glaciers and Ice Ages

> I seemed to vow to myself that some day I would go to the region of ice and snow and go on and on till I came to one of the poles of the earth.
>
> —*Ernest Shackleton (British polar explorer, 1874–1922)*

22.1 Introduction

There's nothing like a good mystery, and one of the most puzzling in the annals of geology came to light in northern Europe early in the 19th century. When farmers of the region prepared their land for spring planting, they occasionally broke their plows by inadvertently running them into large boulders that were buried randomly through otherwise fine-grained sediment. Many of these boulders did not consist of local bedrock but rather came from outcrops hundreds of kilometers away. Because the boulders had apparently traveled so far, they came to be known as **erratics** (from the Latin *errare*, to wander).

The mystery of the wandering boulders became a subject of great interest to early-19th-century geologists, who realized that such deposits of extremely unsorted sediment, meaning sediment that contains a great variety of different clast sizes, could not be examples of typical stream alluvium, for running water sorts sediment by size. Most attributed the deposits to a vast flood, during which a slurry of boulders, sand, and mud spread across the continent. In 1837, however, a young Swiss geologist named Louis Agassiz proposed a radically different interpretation. Agassiz often hiked in the Alps near his home,

where he could study **glaciers**, rivers or sheets of recrystallized ice that last all year long and flow slowly under the influence of gravity. He observed that glacial ice could carry enormous boulders as well as sand and mud, because ice is a solid and has enough strength to support the weight of rock. Agassiz realized that because ice does not sort sediment as it flows, glaciers leave behind extremely unsorted sediment when they melt. On the basis of this observation, he proposed that the mysterious sediment and erratics of Europe were deposits left by **continental ice sheets**, vast glaciers that cover large areas of a continent (Fig. 22.1). In Agassiz's view, Europe had once been in the grip of an **ice age**, a time when the climate was significantly colder and glaciers grew to be immensely larger than they are today.

FIGURE 22.1 Agassiz's thoughts about the Ice Age.

(a) Agassiz found boulders protruding from the ground in places that are not currently glaciated. He proposed that the boulders are erratics left by now-vanished glaciers.

(b) Agassiz envisoned that vast areas of the northern hemisphere were once covered by vast ice sheets comparable to the one covering Antarctica today.

Agassiz's radical proposal faced intense criticism for the next two decades. But he didn't back down and instead challenged opponents to visit the Alps and examine the sedimentary deposits that alpine glaciers had left behind. By the late 1850s, most doubters had changed their minds, and the geological community concluded that the notion that Europe once had Arctic-like climates was correct. Later in life, Agassiz traveled to the United States and documented many glacier-related features in North America's landscape, proving that an ice age had affected vast areas of the planet.

Glaciers cover only about 10% of the land on Earth today, but during the most recent ice age, which ended less than 12,000 years ago, as much as 30% of continental land surface had a coating of ice. New York City, Montreal, and many of the great cities of Europe occupy land that once lay beneath hundreds of meters to a few kilometers of ice. The work of Louis Agassiz brought the subject of glaciers and ice ages into the realm of geologic study and led people to recognize that major climate changes have happened during Earth history. In this chapter, after considering the nature of ice, we see how glaciers form, why they move, and how they modify landscapes by erosion and deposition. A substantial portion of the chapter concerns the most recent ice age, known as the **Pleistocene Ice Age**, for its impact on the landscape can still be seen today, but we briefly introduce ice ages that happened earlier in Earth history, too. We conclude by considering hypotheses to explain why ice ages happen.

22.2 Ice and the Nature of Glaciers

What Is Ice?

Ice consists of solid water, formed when liquid water cools below its freezing point. We can consider a single ice crystal to be analogous to a mineral specimen: it is a naturally occurring, inorganic solid, with a definite chemical composition (H_2O) and a regular crystal structure. Ice crystals have a hexagonal form, so snowflakes grow into six-pointed stars (**Fig. 22.2a**). We can think of a layer of fresh snow as a layer of sediment, and a layer of snow that has been compacted so that its grains stick together as a bed of sedimentary rock (**Fig. 22.2b**). We can think of a coating of ice that appears on the surface of a pond in winter as an igneous rock, for it forms when molten ice—liquid water—solidifies. Glacier ice, in this context, is a metamorphic rock. It develops when pre-existing ice recrystallizes, meaning that the molecules in solid water rearrange to form new crystals (**Fig. 22.2c**).

Pure new ice has the transparency of glass, but if ice contains tiny air bubbles or cracks that disperse light, it becomes milky. Like glass, ice has a high **albedo**, meaning that it reflects light well—so well, in fact, that if you walk on ice without eye protection, you risk blindness from the glare. Ice differs from most other familiar materials in that its solid form is not as dense as its liquid form, for the architecture of an ice crystal holds water molecules apart. Ice, therefore, floats on water. This unusual characteristic prevents the oceans from freezing solid when it gets cold. If ice didn't float, ice in oceans would sink, leaving room for new ice to form above.

Ice also has the unusual property of being slippery—that's why skaters can skate! Surprisingly, researchers still don't completely understand this property. An older explanation—that skaters can glide on ice because a film of liquid water forms on the surface of the ice beneath their skates in response to frictional heating or to pressure-induced melting—can't explain how ice remains slippery even when it's so cold that water can't exist as liquid. Modern studies suggest that ice remains slippery at very low temperatures because the surface of ice consists of a layer of water molecules that are not completely fixed within a crystal lattice. The existence of unattached bonds permits the surface molecules to behave somewhat like a liquid, even while attached to the solid.

How Does a Glacier Form?

In order for a glacier to form, four conditions must be met. First, the local climate must be sufficiently cold that winter snow does not melt away entirely during the summer; second, there must be or must have been sufficient snowfall for a large amount of snow to accumulate; third, the surface on which the snow accumulates must have a gentle slope so that snow falling on it does not slide away in avalanches; and fourth, the area where snow falls must be protected enough so that snow doesn't blow away.

Glaciers develop in polar regions because even though relatively little snow falls today, temperatures remain so low that most ice and snow survive all year. Glaciers develop in mountains, even at low latitudes, because temperature decreases with elevation. Thus, at high elevations, the mean temperature stays low enough for ice and snow to survive all year. Since the temperature of a region depends on latitude, the specific elevation at which glaciers form in mountains depends on latitude. In Earth's present-day climate, glaciers form only at elevations above 5 km at latitudes of between 0° and 30°, but they can flow down to sea level at latitudes of between 60° to 90°. Thus, you can see high-latitude glaciers from a cruise ship, but at the equator you have to climb way up into the mountains to find glaciers. Mountain glaciers tend to develop on the side of mountains that receives less wind and on the side that receives less sunlight. Glaciers do not form on slopes greater than about 30°, because avalanches clear such slopes.

FIGURE 22.2 The nature of ice and the formation of glaciers. Snow falls like sediment and metamorphoses to ice when buried.

(a) The hexagonal shape of snowflakes. No two are alike.

A boundary between layers

The layers in the photo at left are part of this glacier in the Alps.

(b) Layers of snow accumulate. They recrystallize to become ice.

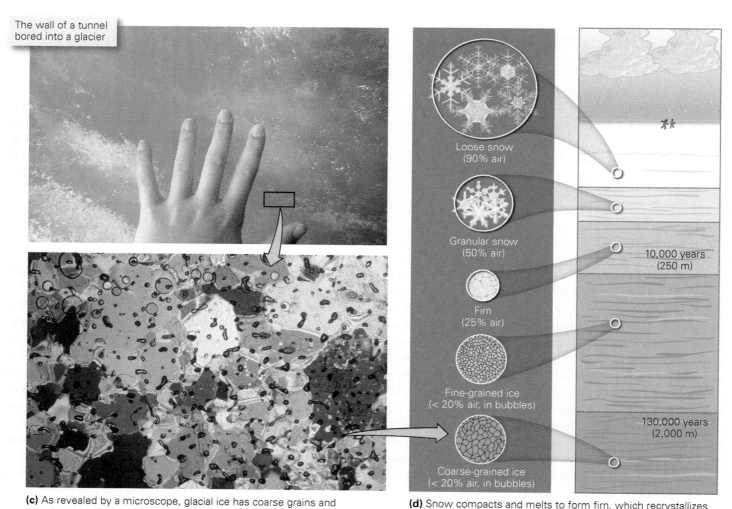

The wall of a tunnel bored into a glacier

Loose snow (90% air)

Granular snow (50% air)

Firn (25% air)

Fine-grained ice (< 20% air, in bubbles)

Coarse-grained ice (< 20% air, in bubbles)

10,000 years (250 m)

130,000 years (2,000 m)

(c) As revealed by a microscope, glacial ice has coarse grains and contains air bubbles.

(d) Snow compacts and melts to form firn, which recrystallizes into ice. Crystal size increases with depth.

The transformation of snow to glacier ice takes place slowly, as younger snow progressively buries older snow. Freshly fallen snow consists of delicate hexagonal crystals with sharp points. The crystals do not fit together tightly, so this snow contains about 90% air. With time, the points of the snowflakes become blunt because they either **sublimate** (evaporate directly into vapor) or melt, and the snow packs more tightly. As snow becomes buried, the weight of the overlying snow increases pressure, which causes any remaining points of contact between snowflakes to melt. This process of melting at points of contact, where the pressure is greatest, is another example of *pressure solution* (see Chapter 8). Gradually, the snow transforms into a packed granular material called **firn**, which contains only about 25% air (Fig. 22.2d). Melting of firn grains at contact points produces water that crystallizes in the spaces between grains until eventually the firn transforms into a solid mass of glacial ice composed of interlocking ice crystals. Such glacial ice, which may still contain up to 20% air trapped in bubbles, tends to absorb red light and thus has a bluish color (see Fig. 22.2c). The transformation of fresh snow to glacier ice can take as little as tens of years in regions with abundant snowfall or as long as thousands of years in regions with little snowfall.

Categories of Glaciers

Today glaciers highlight coastal and mountain scenery in Alaska, the Cordillera of western North America, the Alps of Europe, the Southern Alps of New Zealand, the Himalayas of Asia, and the Andes of South America, and they cover most of Greenland and Antarctica. Geologists distinguish between two main categories: mountain glaciers and continental glaciers.

Mountain glaciers (also called *alpine glaciers*) exist in or adjacent to mountainous regions (Fig. 22.3a). Overall, mountain glaciers flow from higher elevations to lower elevations. Mountain glaciers include *cirque glaciers*, which fill bowl-shaped depressions, or **cirques**, on the flank of a mountain; *valley glaciers*, rivers of ice that flow down valleys; mountain *ice caps*, mounds of ice that submerge peaks and ridges at the crest of a mountain range; and *piedmont glaciers*, fans or lobes of ice that form where a valley glacier emerges from a valley and spreads out into the adjacent plain (Fig. 22.3b–f). Mountain glaciers range in size from a few hundred meters to a few hundred kilometers long.

Continental glaciers are vast ice sheets that spread over thousands of square kilometers of continental crust. Today they exist only on Antarctica and Greenland (Fig. 22.4), but during ice ages they have covered other continental areas. Keep in mind that Antarctica is a continent, so the ice beneath the South Pole rests mostly on solid ground. We say *mostly* because new research reveals that at least three lakes underlie the glacier—the largest of these, Lake Vostok, has an area of 5,400 km².

The ice beneath the North Pole, in contrast, forms part of a thin sheet of sea ice floating on the Arctic Ocean. Continental glaciers flow outward from their thickest point (up to 3.5 km thick) and thin toward their margins, where they may be only a few hundred meters thick. The front edge of the glacier may divide into several tongue-shaped lobes, because not all of the glacier flows at the same speed. Of note, Earth is not alone in hosting polar ice sheets—Mars has them too (Box 22.1).

Geologists also find it valuable to distinguish between types of glaciers based on thermal conditions in the glacier. **Temperate glaciers** occur where atmospheric temperatures become warm enough for the glacial ice to be at or near its melting temperature during part or all of the year, so they contain some liquid water, in films between grains in the glacier, or in lenses and streams at the base of the glacier. Because of this water, a temperate glacier can also be called a *wet-based glacier*. **Polar glaciers** occur in regions where atmospheric temperatures stay so cold all year long that the glacial ice remains below melting temperature throughout the year—they are solid ice through and through. Geologists may also refer to a polar glacier as a *dry-based glacier*, because no liquid water collects at the base of the glacier.

The Movement of Glacial Ice

When Louis Agassiz became fascinated by glaciers, he decided to find out how fast the ice in them moved, so he hammered stakes into an Alpine glacier and watched the stakes change position during the year. More recently, researchers have observed glacial movement with the aid of time-lapse photography, which shows the evolution of a glacier over several years in a movie that lasts a few minutes. In such movies, the glacial ice seems to flow across the screen. How does this movement occur? Geologists have found that glacial flow involves two mechanisms—plastic deformation and basal sliding.

Did you ever wonder... how a glacier moves?

At conditions found below depths of about 60 m in a glacier, ice deforms by **plastic deformation**, meaning the grains within it change shape very slowly, and/or new grains grow while old ones disappear (Fig. 22.5a, b). Simplistically, we can picture such changes to be a consequence of the rearrangement of water molecules within a crystal lattice as some chemical bonds break and new ones form. If ice becomes warm enough for thin water films to form along grain boundaries, plastic deformation may also involve the microscopic slip of ice grains past their neighbors along water films.

In some cases, significant quantities of liquid water collect at the base of a glacier. This water can occur as a lens of liquid under the ice, but commonly it mixes with subglacial sediment

FIGURE 22.3 A great variety of glaciers form in mountainous areas.

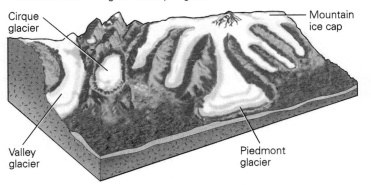

(a) Mountain glaciers are classified based on shape and position.

(d) A valley glacier and cirque glaciers in Switzerland.

(b) An ice cap in Alaska.

(e) A large trunk valley glacier and tributary glaciers in Pakistan.

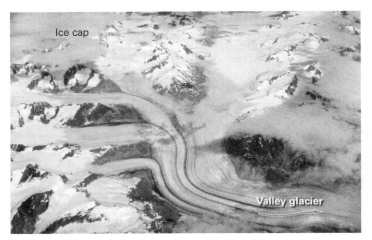

(c) Valley glaciers draining a mountain ice cap in Alaska.

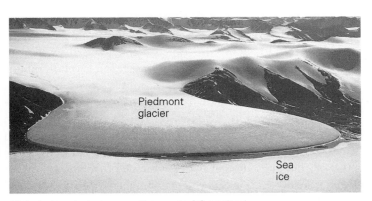

(f) A piedmont glacier near the coast of Greenland.

to form a slurry. The presence of liquid water or a wet slurry beneath a glacier allows the glacier to move by **basal sliding**. During this process, friction or bonding between the ice and its substrate has diminished the glacier so much that it effectively glides along on a wet cushion (**Fig. 22.5c**).

Where does the liquid water at the base of glaciers come from? Some forms when sunlight and atmospheric warming heats the glacier sufficiently to produce meltwater, either on the surface of the glacier or within the glacier. Recent studies show that surface meltwater ponds may drain in a matter of minutes to hours into cracks or tunnels that provide a conduit between the surface and the base of the glacier. Melting may also occur due to the trapping of heat rising from the ground beneath the glacier (for ice is an insulator) or due to the weight of overlying ice (for at elevated pressures, ice can melt even if its temperature remains below 0°C).

FIGURE 22.4 Two major continental glaciers exist today—one on Antarctica and one on Greenland.

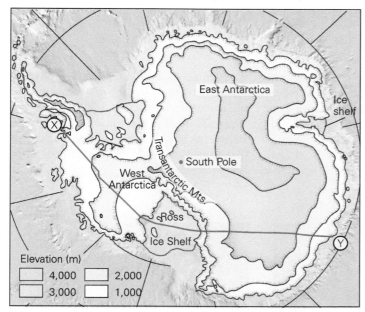

(a) A contour map of the Antarctic ice sheet. Valley glaciers carry ice from the ice sheet of East Antarctica down to the Ross Ice Shelf.

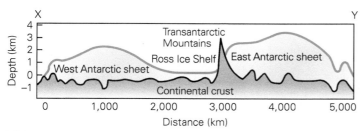

(b) A cross section X to Y of the Antarctic ice sheet. The Transantarctic Mountains separate East Antarctica from West Antarctica.

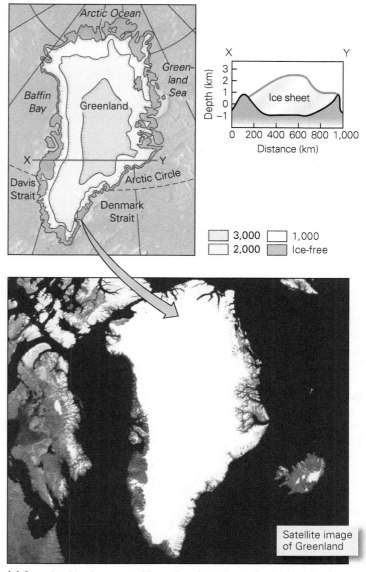

(c) Greenland is also covered by an ice sheet that at its thickest is 1 km thinner than Antarctica's.

In the case of polar glaciers, which are so cold that they have no internal water films and have a dry base, flow takes place generally by plastic deformation alone. In the case of temperate glaciers, which contain some intergranular water and/or have a wet base, flow can involve both plastic deformation and basal sliding. Note that not all parts of a given glacier necessarily flow in the same way. For example, imagine a continental glacier that originates in a very cold polar realm but eventually flows into temperate realms at lower latitudes. Near its cold origin, the glacier has a dry base and moves only by plastic deformation, but near its warmer margin, it becomes wet based and moves by both plastic deformation and basal sliding. Similarly, a long valley glacier may be dry based and flow only plastically at higher, colder elevations, but it may become wet based and flow by both plastic deformation and basal sliding at lower, warmer elevations.

As we noted earlier, plastic deformation takes place only at depths of greater than about 60 meters in a glacier—above this depth, known as the *brittle–plastic transition*, ice is too brittle to

flow. (Note that, by comparison, plastic deformation in silicate rocks of the Earth's crust occurs primarily under metamorphic temperatures greater than about 300°C; thus, the brittle–plastic transition in continental crust occurs at depths of about 10 to 15 km; see Chapter 11.) As a glacier overall undergoes movement, its upper 60 meters of ice deform predominantly by cracking. A crack that develops by brittle deformation of a glacier is called a **crevasse** (Fig. 22.6). In large glaciers, crevasses can be hundreds of meters long and tens of meters deep, and they may open into gashes that are many meters across. Tragically, explorers, hikers, and skiers have died by falling into crevasses, whose openings sometimes become covered

BOX 22.1 CONSIDER THIS . . .

Polar Ice Caps on Mars

The discovery that Mars has polar ice caps dates back to 1666, when the first telescopes allowed astronomers to resolve details of the red planet's surface. By 1719, astronomers had detected that Martian polar caps change in area with the season, suggesting that they partially melt and then refreeze. You can see these changes on modern images (Fig. Bx22.1). The question of what the ice caps consist of remained a puzzle until fairly recently. Early studies revealed that the atmosphere of Mars consists mostly of carbon dioxide, so researchers first assumed that the ice caps consisted of frozen carbon dioxide. But data from modern spacecraft led to the conclusion that this initial assumption is wrong. It now appears that the Martian ice caps consist mostly of water ice, mixed with dust, in layers from 1 to 3 km thick. During the winter, atmospheric carbon dioxide freezes and covers the north polar cap with a 1-m-thick layer of dry ice. During the summer this layer melts away. The south polar cap is different, for its dry ice blanket is 8 m thick and doesn't melt away entirely in the summer. The difference between the north and south

poles may reflect elevation for the south pole is 6 km higher and therefore remains colder.

High-resolution photographs reveal that distinctive canyons, up to 10 km wide and 1 km deep, spiral outward from the center of the north polar ice cap. Why did this pattern form? Recent calculations suggest that

if the ice sublimates (transforms into gas) on the sunny side of a crack and refreezes on the shady side, the crack will migrate sideways over time. If the cracks migrate more slowly closer to the pole, where it's colder, than they do farther away, they will naturally evolve into spirals.

FIGURE Bx22.1 The ice caps of Mars.

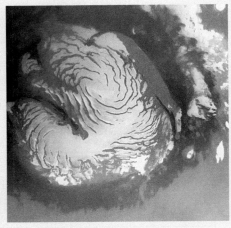

(a) During the winter, the ice caps expand to lower latitudes.

(b) A close-up of the northern polar cap in summer.

FIGURE 22.5 Mechanisms of glacial movement.

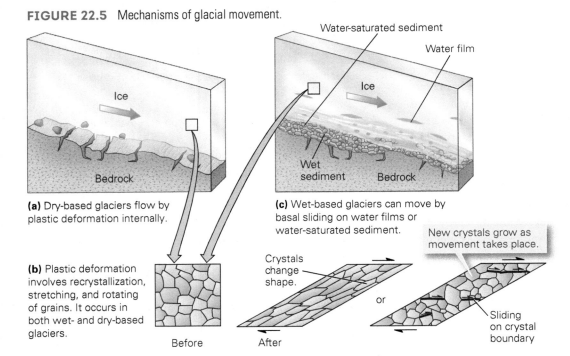

(a) Dry-based glaciers flow by plastic deformation internally.

(b) Plastic deformation involves recrystallization, stretching, and rotating of grains. It occurs in both wet- and dry-based glaciers.

(c) Wet-based glaciers can move by basal sliding on water films or water-saturated sediment.

by a bridge of weak, windblown snow. Crevasse formation typically localizes in regions where a glacier flows over steps or hills in the underlying bedrock surface, for the ice of the glacier must bend to accommodate the surface shape of the substrate.

Why do glaciers move? Ultimately, because the pull of gravity exceeds the strength of ice and can cause the ice to flow (Fig. 22.7a). A glacier flows in the direction in which its top surface slopes. Thus, valley glaciers flow down their valleys, and continental ice sheets spread outward from their thickest point. Note that it is the slope of the top surface that matters in

FIGURE 22.6 Crevasses form in the upper layer of a glacier, in which the ice is brittle. Commonly, cracking takes place where the glacier bends while flowing over steps or ridges in its substrate.

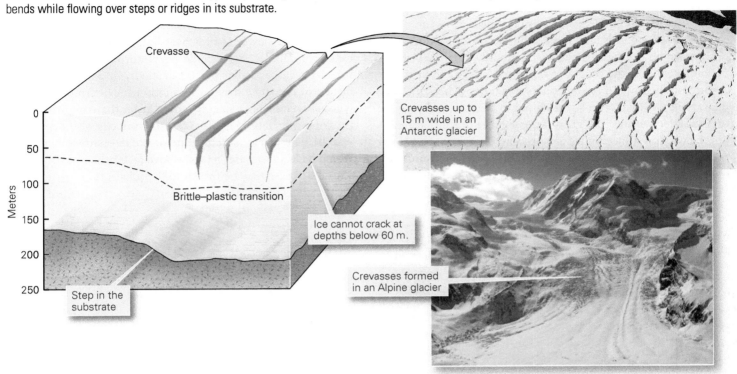

Crevasse

Meters
0
50
100
150
200
250

Brittle–plastic transition

Ice cannot crack at depths below 60 m.

Step in the substrate

Crevasses up to 15 m wide in an Antarctic glacier

Crevasses formed in an Alpine glacier

FIGURE 22.7 Forces that drive the movement of glaciers.

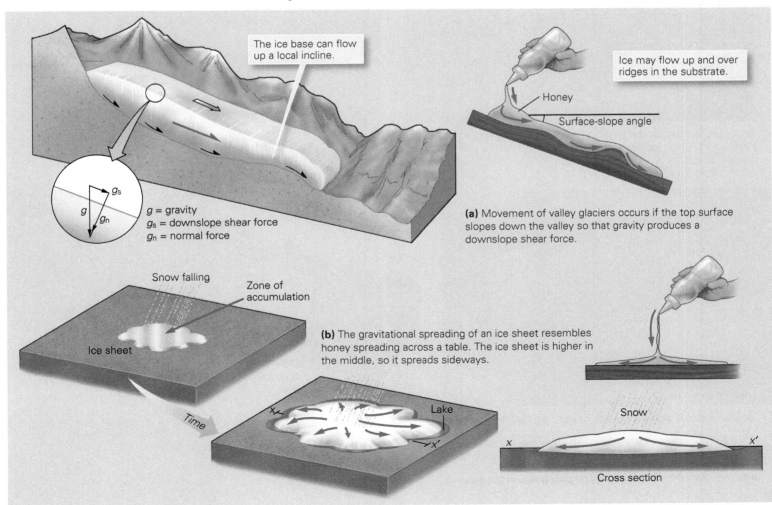

The ice base can flow up a local incline.

g = gravity
g_s = downslope shear force
g_n = normal force

Ice may flow up and over ridges in the substrate.

Honey

Surface-slope angle

(a) Movement of valley glaciers occurs if the top surface slopes down the valley so that gravity produces a downslope shear force.

Snow falling

Zone of accumulation

Ice sheet

Time

Lake

(b) The gravitational spreading of an ice sheet resembles honey spreading across a table. The ice sheet is higher in the middle, so it spreads sideways.

Snow

x   x'

Cross section

driving ice forward—at its base, ice can flow up and over hills or ridges in the substrate.

To picture the movement of an ice sheet, imagine that a thick pile of ice builds up. Gravity causes the top of the pile to push down on the ice at the base. Eventually, the basal ice can no longer support the weight of the overlying ice and begins to deform plastically and/or slide on its substrate. When this happens, the basal ice starts squeezing out to the side, carrying the overlying ice with it. The greater the volume of ice that builds up, the wider the sheet of ice can become. You've seen a similar process of *gravitational spreading* if you've ever poured honey onto a plate. The honey can't build up into a narrow column because it's too weak; rather, it flows laterally away from the point where it lands to form a wide, thin layer (Fig. 22.7b).

Glaciers generally flow at rates of between 10 and 300 m per year—far slower than a river but far faster than a silicate rock even under high-grade metamorphic conditions. The velocity of a particular glacier depends, in part, on the magnitude of the force driving its motion. For example, a glacier whose surface slopes steeply moves faster than one with a gently sloping surface (Fig. 22.8a). Flow velocity also depends on whether the glacier is temperate or polar—temperate glaciers, which have a wet base, tend to move faster than polar glaciers, whose dry base may be frozen to the substrate.

FIGURE 22.8 Glacial flow, accumulation, and ablation.

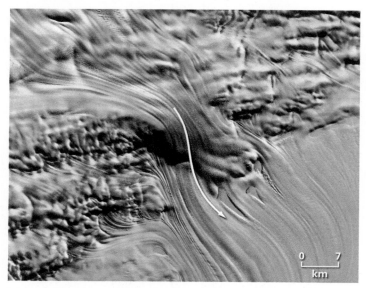

(a) A satellite image of ice flowing from the Polar Plateau of Antarctica, down a 400-m-high ice fall to the Lambert Glacier. Curving lines indicate the flow directions.

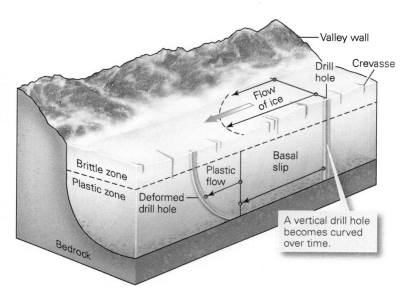

(b) Different parts of a glacier flow at different velocities due to friction with the substrate. The top and center regions flow fastest.

(c) Blocks of blue glacial ice, which calved off a glacier in the Alps.

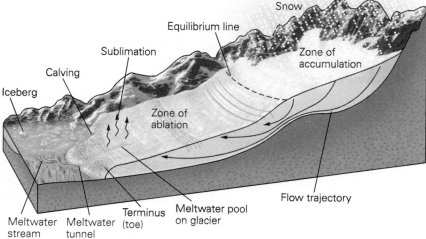

(d) The equilibrium line separates the zone of accumulation from the zone of ablation. As indicated by arrows, ice flows down in the zone of accumulation and up in the zone of ablation.

Not all parts of a glacier move at the same rate. For example, friction or bonding between rock and ice slows a glacier, so the center of a valley glacier moves faster than its margins and the top of a glacier moves faster than its base (Fig. 22.8b). Because water at the base of a glacier allows it to travel more rapidly, wet-based portions of a continental glacier can become *ice streams* that travel 10 to 100 times faster than adjacent dry-based portions of the glacier. The volume of water at the bottom of a wet-based glacier may change over time. If water suddenly builds up beneath a glacier to the point where a large area lifts the glacier off its substrate, basal sliding starts and the glacier undergoes a **surge** and flows much faster for a limited time (rarely more than a few months). During surges, glaciers have been clocked at speeds of 10 to 110 m per day! Sudden surges may generate **ice quakes**, because of the cracking that occurs in the brittle portion of the glacier. A surge stops when the water escapes, so basal sliding slows.

Glacial Advance and Retreat

Glaciers resemble bank accounts. Snowfall adds to the account, while **ablation**—the removal of ice—subtracts from the account. Ablation involves three processes: *sublimation* (the evaporation of ice into water vapor); *melting* (the transformation of ice into liquid water); and *calving* (the breaking off of chunks of ice at the end of the glacier) (Fig. 22.8c). Snowfall adds ice to a glacier in the **zone of accumulation**, whereas ablation subtracts ice from the glacier in the **zone of ablation**—the boundary between these two zones is the **equilibrium line** (Fig. 22.8d). The zone of accumulation occurs where the temperature remains cold enough year-round so that winter snow does not melt or sublimate away entirely during the summer. Therefore, elevation and latitude control the position of the equilibrium line.

The leading edge or margin of a glacier is called its **toe**, or *terminus* (Fig. 22.9a). If the rate at which ice builds up in the zone of accumulation exceeds the rate at which ablation occurs below the equilibrium line, then the toe moves forward into previously unglaciated regions, a change called a **glacial advance** (Fig. 22.9b). In mountain glaciers, the position of a toe moves downslope during an advance, and in continental glaciers, the toe moves outward, away from the glacier's origin. If the rate of ablation below the equilibrium line equals the rate of accumulation, then the position of the toe remains fixed. But if the rate of ablation exceeds the rate of accumulation, then the position of the toe moves back toward the origin of the glacier—such a change is called a **glacial retreat** (Fig. 22.9c). During a mountain glacier's retreat, the position of the toe moves upslope. But it's important to realize that when a glacier retreats, it's only the position of the toe that moves back toward the origin. Even during glacial retreat, ice continues to flow toward the toe as long as the surface of the glacier slopes

FIGURE 22.9 Glacial advance and retreat.

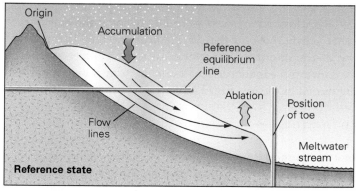

(a) The position of the toe represents a balance between addition by accumulation and loss by ablation.

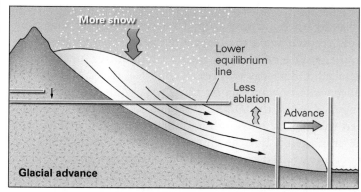

(b) If accumulation exceeds ablation, the glacier advances, the toe moves farther from the origin, and the ice thickens.

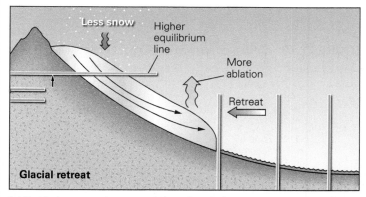

(c) If ablation exceeds accumulation, the glacier retreats and thins. The toe moves back, even though ice continues to flow toward the toe.

toward the toe—glacial ice cannot flow upslope, back toward the glacier's origin.

One final point before we leave the subject of glacial flow: Note that beneath the zone of accumulation a given volume of ice gradually moves down toward the base of the glacier as new ice accumulates above it. In contrast, beneath the zone of ablation, a given volume of ice gradually moves up toward the surface of the glacier as overlying ice ablates. Thus, as a glacier flows, ice volumes overall follow curved trajectories (see Fig. 22.9). For this reason, rocks picked up by ice at the base of the glacier slowly move to the surface near the toe. The upward flow of ice where the Antarctic ice sheet collides with the Transantarctic Mountains, for example, brings up meteorites long buried in the ice (Fig. 22.10).

Ice in the Sea

On the moonless night of April 14, 1912, the great ocean liner *Titanic* plowed through the calm but frigid waters of the North Atlantic on her maiden voyage from Southampton, England, to New York. Although radio broadcasts from other ships warned that **icebergs**, large blocks of ice floating in the water, had been sighted in the area and might pose a hazard, the ship sailed on, its crew convinced that they could see and avoid the biggest bergs and that smaller ones would not be a problem for the steel hull of this "unsinkable" vessel. But in a story now retold countless times, their confidence was fatally wrong. At 11:40 P.M., while first-class passengers danced, the *Titanic* struck an iceberg. Lookouts had seen the ghostly mass only minutes earlier and had alerted the ship's pilot, but the ship had been unable to turn fast enough to avoid disaster. The force of the blow split the steel hull spanning 5 of the ship's 16 watertight compartments. The ship could stay afloat if 4 compartments flooded, but the flooding of 5 meant it would sink. At about 2:15 A.M., the

bow disappeared below the water, and the stern rose until the ship protruded nearly vertically from the water. Without water to support its weight, the hull buckled and split in two. The stern section fell back down onto the water and momentarily bobbed horizontally before following the bow, settling downward through over 3.5 km of water to the silent sea floor below. Because of an inadequate number of lifeboats, only 705 passengers survived; 1,500 expired in the frigid waters of the Atlantic. The *Titanic* remained lost until 1985, when a team of oceanographers located the sunken hull and photographed its eerie form.

Where do icebergs, such as the one responsible for the *Titanic*'s demise, originate? In high latitudes, mountain glaciers and continental ice sheets flow down to the shore. Glaciers that flow out into the sea along the coast become **tidewater glaciers**. Large valley glaciers may protrude several kilometers out into the ocean as elongate *ice tongues* (Fig. 22.11a). Continental glaciers entering the sea become broad, flat sheets called **ice shelves** (Fig. 22.11b). In shallow water, glacial ice remains grounded in that the base of the glacier rests on the sea floor (Fig. 22.11c). But where the water is deep enough, the ice floats with four-fifths of the ice below the water's surface. At the boundary between glacier and ocean, blocks of ice calve off and tumble into the water with an impressive splash, producing large waves. If a free-floating chunk rises 6 m above the water and is at least 15 m long, mariners refer to it as an *iceberg*. Smaller pieces, formed when ice blocks fragment before entering the water or after icebergs have had time to melt, include *bergy bits*, rising

FIGURE 22.10 Meteorites accumulate along the Transantarctic Mountains.

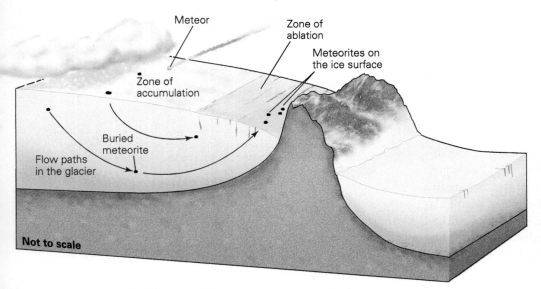

(a) Meteorites landing in the zone of accumulation are buried and incorporated in the flowing ice. They return to the ice surface in the zone of ablation.

(b) Researchers document a new meteorite discovery.

FIGURE 22.11 Ice along the edge of continents—shelves, tongues, and bergs.

(a) An ice tongue protruding into the Ross Sea along the coast of Antarctica.

(b) The Larsen Ice Shelf along the coast of Antarctica, as viewed from a satellite in 2002.

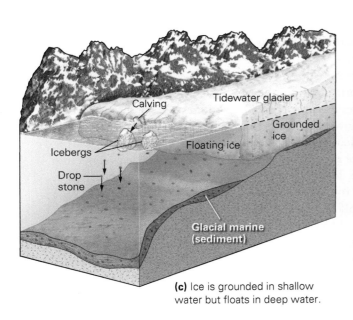

(c) Ice is grounded in shallow water but floats in deep water.

(e) This artist's rendition of an iceberg emphasizes that most of the ice is underwater.

(f) In summer, some of the sea ice of Antarctica breaks up to form tabular icebergs.

(d) A "growler" of floating ice off Alaska. Note the layering in the ice.

(g) Sea ice covers most of the Arctic Ocean (left) and surrounds Antarctica (right).

1 to 5 m above the water and covering an area of 100 to 300 m², and *growlers* (Fig. 22.11d), rising less than 1 m above the water and covering an area of about 20 m²—still big enough to damage a ship. Growlers get their name because of the sound they make as they bob in the sea and grind together.

Most large icebergs form along the western coast of Greenland or along the coast of Antarctica. Icebergs that calve off valley glaciers tend to be irregularly shaped with pointed peaks rising upward. Such glaciers are called castle bergs or *pinnacle bergs*—one of the largest on record protruded about 180 m above the sea. Since four-fifths of the ice lies below the surface of the sea, the base of a large iceberg may actually be a few hundred meters below the surface (Fig. 22.11e). Icebergs that originate in Greenland float into the "iceberg alley" region of the North Atlantic. These are the bergs that threaten ships, although the danger has diminished in modern times because of less ice and because of ice patrols that report the locations of floating ice. Blocks that calve off the vast ice shelves of Antarctica tend to have flat tops and nearly vertical sides—such glaciers are called *tabular bergs*. Some of the tabular bergs in the Antarctic are truly immense—air photos have revealed individual bergs over 160 km across.

Not all ice floating in the sea originates as glaciers on land. In polar climates, the surface of the sea itself freezes, forming **sea ice** (Fig. 22.11f, g). Some sea ice, such as that covering the interior of the Arctic Ocean, floats freely, but some protrudes outward from the shore (Fig. 22.11d). Icebreakers can crunch through sea ice that is up to 2.5 m thick; the icebreaker rides up on the ice, and its weight crushes the ice below. Vast areas of sea ice have been melting in recent years in association with global warming (see Chapter 23). For example, open regions develop in the Arctic Ocean during the summers, and the ice shelf in Antarctica has been decreasing rapidly in area. In some locations, large openings known as *polynyas* have developed in the sea ice of Antarctica. Some sea ice forms in winter and melts away in summer, but at high latitudes sea ice may last for several years. For example, in the Arctic Ocean, sea ice may last long enough to make the 7- to 10-year voyage around the Arctic Ocean, in response to currents, at least once.

The existence of icebergs leaves a record in the stratigraphy of the seafloor, for icebergs carry *ice-rafted sediment*. Larger rocks that drop from the ice to the sea floor are called **drop stones** (see Fig. 22.11c). In ancient glacial deposits, drop stones appear as isolated blocks surrounded by mud. Icebergs and smaller fragments also drop sand and gravel, derived by the erosion of continents, onto the seafloor. In cores extracted by drilling into seafloor sediment, horizons of such land-derived sediment, sandwiched between layers of sediment formed from marine plankton shells, indicate times in Earth history when glaciers were breaking up and icebergs became particularly abundant.

Take-Home Message

Glaciers form when buried snow lasts all year, turns to ice, and gradually recrystallizes. Glacial ice flows by plastic deformation or by basal sliding. Mountain glaciers form at high elevation and flow to lower elevations. Ice sheets form in high latitudes and spread over continents. The balance of accumulation to ablation controls glacial advance or retreat. Where glaciers reach the sea, they may spall off icebergs. In polar regions, sea ice covers large areas.

QUICK QUESTION: Does ice actually flow uphill during a glacial retreat?

22.3 Carving and Carrying by Ice

The Process of Glacial Erosion

The Sierra Nevada range of California consists largely of granite that formed during the Mesozoic Era in the crust beneath a volcanic arc. During the past 10 million years or more, the land surface slowly rose, and erosion stripped away overlying rock and yielded rounded, dome-like granite mountains. During the last ice age, valley glaciers cut deep, steep-sided valleys into the range. In the process, some of the domes were cut in half, leaving a rounded surface on one side and a steep cliff on the other. Half Dome in Yosemite National Park formed in this way (Fig. 22.12a). Such glacial erosion has also produced the knife-edge ridges and pointed spires of high mountains (Fig. 22.12b) and broad expanses of land where rock outcrops have been stripped of overlying sediment. Glacial erosion can keep pace with tectonic uplift—in fact, glacial erosion is so efficient at grinding away mountain peaks that geologists sometimes refer to the phenomenon as the "glacial buzz saw." Glaciers similarly strip material from the surface of continents—at least 30 m of rock was removed from the Canadian Shield during the last glaciation.

How does glacial erosion take place? In part, erosion in glaciated mountains takes place by landslides or rockfalls of debris onto glaciers, which then carry the debris away. Freezing and thawing in glacial environments may accelerate the mechanical weathering that sets the stage for such mass wasting. But erosion also takes place where the glacial ice flows along the land surface, for as ice moves, clasts embedded in the ice act like the teeth of a giant rasp and grind away the substrate. This process, **glacial abrasion**, produces very fine sediment called *rock flour*, just as sanding wood produces sawdust.

FIGURE 22.12 Products of glacial erosion. Ice is a very aggressive agent of erosion.

(a) Half Dome in Yosemite National Park, California.

(b) Examples of a cirque and an arête in the Swiss Alps.

(c) Glacially polished outcrop in Central Park, New York City.

(d) Small striations on an outcrop in Scotland.

(e) Glacial mega-striations in Victoria, British Columbia.

(f) Close-up of striations and chatter marks, Switzerland.

Rasping by embedded sand can smooth rock faces and produce **glacially polished surfaces** (Fig. 22.12c). Individual hard clasts protruding from moving ice yield grooves or scratches called **glacial striations** (1 to 10 cm across) in the bedrock below (Fig. 22.12d). These striations trend parallel to the flow direction of the glacier. In some cases, striations may be up to half a meter across and tens of meters long (Fig. 22.12e). Geologists don't fully understand the origin of such mega-striations, but they may be due to streamlined trains of sediment embedded in the ice, which can carve into bedrock along the same line for an extended period of time. Locally, when boulders entrained in the base of the ice strike bedrock below as the ice moves, asymmetric wedges of bedrock break off, leaving behind indentations called *chatter marks* (Fig. 22.12f). In regions of wet-based glaciers, sediment-laden water rushing through tunnels at the base of the glaciers can carve substantial subglacial channels.

Glaciers pick up fragments of their substrate in several ways. During *glacial incorporation*, ice surrounds loose debris so the debris starts to move with the ice (Fig. 22.13a). During *glacial plucking* (or glacial quarrying), a glacier breaks off fragments of

Glaciated Peaks, Montana

LATITUDE
48°56'33.66"N

LONGITUDE
113°49'54.59"W

Looking down from 8 km (~5 mi).

You can see three cirques bounding a horn in the Rocky Mountains, north of Glacier National Park. Note the knife-edged arêtes between the cirques. The glaciers that carved the cirques have melted away.

bedrock. Plucking occurs when ice freezes around rock that has just started to separate from its substrate; movement of the ice lifts off pieces of the rock. At the toe of an advancing glacier, ice may actually bulldoze sediment slightly before flowing over it (Fig. 22.13b).

Landforms Produced by Glacial Erosion

Let's now look more closely at the erosional features associated with mountain glaciers. If the glacier builds into an ice cap that completely covers the mountain, it smooths and rounds peaks (see the Chapter 6 opening photo). But, if the glacier's head (the top edge of the ice) lies below the peak of the mountain, then the ice carves rugged topography. Freezing and thawing during the fall and spring

help fracture the rock bordering the head of the glacier. This rock falls on the ice or gets picked up at the base of the ice and moves downslope with the glacier. As a consequence, a bowl-shaped depression, or *cirque*, develops on the side of the mountain at the head of a glacier (see Fig. 22.12b). If the ice later melts, a lake called a tarn may remain at the base of the cirque, filling the base of the depression. An **arête** (French for "ridge"), a residual knife-edge ridge of rock, separates two adjacent cirques (see Fig. 22.12b), and a pointed mountain peak surrounded by at least three cirques is a **horn** (Fig. 22.14a). The Matterhorn, a famous peak in Switzerland, serves as a particularly beautiful example of a horn; each of its four faces originated as a cirque (Fig. 22.14b).

Glacial erosion severely modifies the shape of valleys. To see how, compare a river-eroded valley with a glacially eroded valley. If you look along the length of a river in unglaciated mountains, you'll see that it flows down a V-shaped valley, with the river channel forming the point of the V. The V develops because river erosion occurs only in the channel, and mass wasting causes the valley slopes to approach the angle of repose. But if you look down the length of a glacially eroded valley, you'll see that it resembles a U, with steep walls. A **U-shaped valley** (Fig. 22.14c) forms because the combined processes of glacial abrasion and plucking not only lower the floor of the valley but also bevel its sides. Remember that mountain faces above the ice level of a valley glacier erode as mechanical weathering breaks rock apart, and landslides carry debris onto the surface of the glacier below.

Glacial erosion in mountains also modifies the intersections between tributaries and the trunk valley. In a river system, the trunk stream serves as the local base level for tributaries (see Chapter 17), so the mouths of the tributary valleys lie at the same elevation as the trunk valley. The ridges (spurs) between valleys taper to a point when they join the trunk valley floor. During glaciation, tributary glaciers flow down side valleys into a trunk glacier. But the trunk glacier cuts the floor of its valley down to a depth that far exceeds the depth cut by the tributary glaciers. Thus, when the glaciers melt away, the mouths of the tributary valleys perch at a higher elevation than the floor of the trunk valley. Such side valleys are called **hanging valleys**. The water in post-glacial streams that flow down a hanging valley cascades over a spectacular waterfall to reach the post-glacial trunk stream (Fig. 22.14d). As they erode, trunk glaciers also remove the ends of spurs between valleys, producing *truncated spurs*.

FIGURE 22.13 The processes of incorporation and plowing.

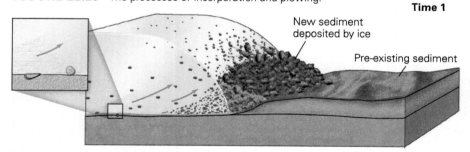

Time 1

New sediment deposited by ice

Pre-existing sediment

(a) Glacial ice can pluck, pick up, and incorporate chunks of rock that it flows over. The chunks then move with the ice, following the ice's flow trajectories, until deposition at the toe of the glacier.

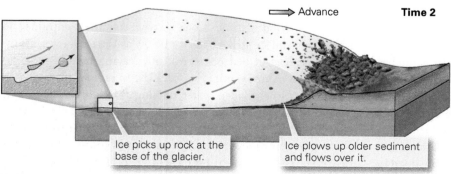

Advance   **Time 2**

Ice picks up rock at the base of the glacier.

Ice plows up older sediment and flows over it.

(b) At the toe of the glacier, ice can flow up and over pre-existing sediment. Locally, it bulldozes sediment, pushing it up into a ridge.

FIGURE 22.14 Landscape features formed by the glacial erosion of a mountainous landscape.

Before glaciation, valleys are V-shaped, and tributary mouths are the same elevation as the trunk stream.

V-shaped valley
Tributary valley
Trunk valley
Trunk valley
Tributary valley

During glaciation, the valleys fill with ice.

Time

Mt. Snowdon, Wales
Cirque
Tarn

After glaciation, the region contains U-shaped valleys, hanging valleys, truncated spurs, and horns.

Cirque
Arête
Horn
Hanging valley
U-shaped valley
Truncated spur

(a) Stages in the development of a glacially carved mountainous landscape.

(b) The Matterhorn in Switzerland. The first ascent was in 1865.

(c) A U-shaped glacial valley in the Tongass National Forest, Alaska.

(d) A waterfall spilling out of a U-shaped hanging valley in the Sierra Nevada.

FIGURE 22.15 The sculpting of hills by glacial erosion.

(a) Polished and striated bedrock in Ontario.

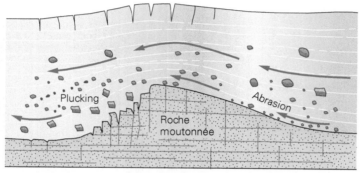

(c) Abrasion rasps the upstream side, and plucking carries away fracture-bounded blocks on the downstream side.

(b) Rounded hills in the highlands of Scotland formed when the entire region was covered by an ice sheet.

(d) An example of a roche moutonnée. The glacier flowed from right to left.

Now let's look at the erosional features produced by continental ice sheets. To a large extent, these depend on the nature of the pre-glacial landscape. Where an ice sheet spreads over a region of low relief, such as in Canada (Fig. 22.15a), glacial erosion creates a vast region of polished, flat, striated surfaces. Where an ice sheet spreads completely over a hilly area, it smooths hills (Fig. 22.15b). In Maine, for example, glaciers smoothed and streamlined the granite and metamorphic rock hills of Acadia National Park. Glacially eroded hills may become elongate in the direction of flow, and because glacial rasping smooths and bevels the upstream part of the hill, creating a gentle slope—whereas glacial plucking eats away at the downstream part, making a steep slope—the hills may become asymmetric. Ultimately, the hill's profile resembles that of a sheep lying in a meadow—such a hill is called a **roche moutonnée**, from the French for "sheep rock" (Fig. 22.15c, d). In some cases, a glacier erodes three sides of a hill, but deposits debris on the downstream or wake side of the hill. This process produces a *crag and tail*, with a steep cliff on the upstream side and a long ramp on the downflow side. The castle of Edinburgh,

Scotland, was build on a crag. The steep scarps on three sides were easier to defend, while the tail provided a site for the growth of a town.

Fjords: Submerged Glacial Valleys

If the floor of a glacially carved valley lies below sea level along the coast, or beneath the water table inland, the floor of the valley becomes submerged with water. Geologists refer to any glacial valley that has filled partially or entirely with water as a **fjord**—marine fjords occur along the coast and have filled with seawater, whereas freshwater fjords lie inland (Fig. 22.16).

Spectacular examples of marine fjords can be found along the coasts of Norway, New Zealand, Chile, Alaska, and Greenland—in some cases, the walls of submerged U-shaped valleys rise straight from the sea as vertical cliffs up to 1,000 m high, and the

SEE FOR YOURSELF . . .

Baffin Island, Canada

LATITUDE
67°8'27.56"N

LONGITUDE
64°49'49.31"W

Looking down from 40 km (~25 mi).

You can see two valley glaciers draining the Baffin Island ice cap. They merge into a trunk glacier that flows NE and then into a fjord, partly filing a U-shaped valley. Note the lateral and medial moraines.

water depth just offshore may exceed a few hundred meters. How do such dramatic fjords develop? As noted earlier, where a valley glacier meets the sea, the glacier's base remains in contact with the ground until the water depth exceeds about four-fifths of the glacier's thickness. Further, during an ice age, water extracted from the sea becomes locked in the ice sheets on land, so sea level drops significantly. Therefore, the floors of valleys cut by coastal glaciers during the Pleistocene Ice Age could be cut much deeper than present sea level.

Take-Home Message

A glacier scrapes up and plucks rock from its substrate and carries debris that falls on its surface. Glacial erosion polishes and scratches rock and carves distinctive landforms, such as U-shaped valleys, cirques, and striations. An elongate bay or lake formed when water partially fills a glacial valley is a fjord.

QUICK QUESTION: Why do we find hanging valleys spilling waterfalls into trunk valleys, in regions that have been eroded by mountain glaciers?

22.4 Deposition Associated with Glaciation

The Glacial Conveyor and Glacial Moraines

Glaciers can carry sediment of any size and, like a conveyor belt, transport it in the direction of flow (Fig. 22.17a). Remember that ice flows toward the toe regardless of whether the glacier is advancing or retreating, so the transport of sediment always progresses in the direction of the toe. Where does the sediment come from? The sediment load either falls onto the surface of the glacier from bordering cliffs or gets plucked and lifted from the substrate and incorporated into the moving ice.

Sediment dropped on the glacier's surface from its margins becomes a stripe of debris, known as a **lateral moraine**, along the side edge of the glacier. When a glacier melts, its lateral moraines will be stranded along the side of the glacially carved valley, like bathtub rings. In places where two valley glaciers merge, the debris constituting two lateral moraines merges to become a **medial moraine**, running as a stripe down the interior of the composite glacier (Fig. 22.17b, c). Trunk glaciers created by the merging of many tributary glaciers contain several medial moraines. Sediment transported to a glacier's toe by the glacial conveyor accumulates in a pile

FIGURE 22.16 Examples of fjords.

(a) The Finger Lakes of central New York State are freshwater fjords.

(b) One of the many spectacular fjords of Norway. The water is an arm of the sea that fills a glacially carved valley. Tourists are standing on Pulpit Rock (Prekestolen).

at the toe and builds up to form an **end moraine**. If the glacier recedes, the end moraine will remain as a low ridge, outlining the former position of the toe. The name *moraine* originated from a term used by Alpine farmers and shepherds for any pile of rock and dirt. The word now applies exclusively to debris piles carried by or left by glaciers.

FIGURE 22.17 The glacial conveyor and the formation of lateral and medial moraines on glaciers.

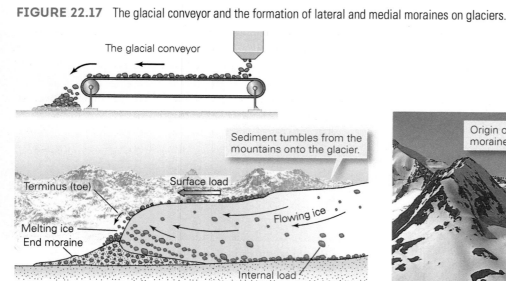

(a) Sediment falls on a glacier from bordering mountains and gets plucked up from below. Glaciers are like conveyor belts, moving sediment toward the toe of the glacier.

(b) This glacier in the French Alps carries lots of sediment.

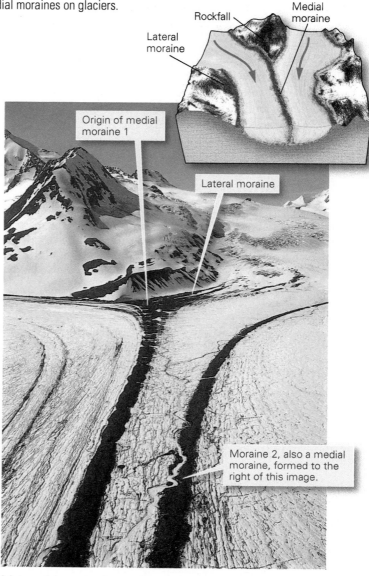

(c) A medial moraine forms where lateral moraines of two valley glaciers merge.

Types of Glacial Sedimentary Deposits

If you drill into the soil throughout much of the upper midwestern and northeastern United States and adjacent parts of Canada, the drill penetrates a layer of sediment deposited during the Pleistocene Ice Age. A similar story holds true for much of northern Europe. Thus, many of the world's richest agricultural regions rely on soil derived from sediment deposited by glaciers during the Ice Age. This sediment buries a pre–Ice Age landscape, as frosting fills the irregularities on a cake. Pre-glacial valleys may be completely filled with sediment.

Several different types of sediment can be deposited in glacial environments; all of these types together constitute **glacial drift**. (The term dates from pre-Agassiz studies of glacial deposits, when geologists thought that the sediment had "drifted" into place during an immense flood.) Glacial sediment, carried and deposited by ice, contains no layering, so geologists refer to it as *unstratified drift*. In contrast, glacial sediment that has been redistributed by flowing water, or settled through water, tends to contain layering and is called *stratified drift*. In detail, glacial drift includes the following features.

- *Till:* Sediment transported by ice and deposited beneath, at the side, or at the toe of a glacier is called **glacial till**. Glacial till is unsorted, so it's a type of diamicton (see Chapter 7), because the solid ice of glaciers can carry clasts of all sizes (**Fig. 22.18a**).
- *Erratics:* Boulders that have been dropped by a glacier are called *glacial erratics* (**Fig. 22.18b**). Some erratics protrude from till piles, and others rest on glacially polished surfaces.
- *Glacial marine:* Where a sediment-laden glacier flows into the sea, icebergs calve off the toe and raft clasts out to sea. As the icebergs melt, they drop the clasts, which settle into the muddy sediment on the seafloor. Pebble- and larger-size clasts deposited in this way, as we have seen, are called *dropstones*. Sediment consisting of ice-rafted clasts mixed with marine sediment makes up *glacial marine*. Glacial marine can also consist of sediment carried into the sea by water flowing at the base of a glacier.
- *Glacial outwash:* Till deposited by a glacier at its toe may be picked up and transported by meltwater streams that sort the sediment. The clasts are deposited by a braided stream network in a broad area of gravel and sandbars called an outwash plain. This sediment is known as **glacial outwash** (**Fig. 22.18c**).
- *Loess:* When the warmer air above ice-free land beyond the toe of a glacier rises, the cold, denser air from above the glacier rushes in to take its place; a strong wind, called *katabatic wind*, therefore blows at the margin of a glacier. This wind picks up fine silt and clay and transports it away from the glacier's toe. Where the winds die down, the sediment settles and forms a thick layer. This sediment, called **loess**, tends to stick together, so steep escarpments can develop by erosion of loess deposits (**Fig. 22.18d**).
- *Glacial lake-bed sediment:* Streams transport fine clasts, including rock flour, away from the glacial front. This sediment eventually settles in meltwater lakes, forming a thick layer of glacial lake-bed sediment. This sediment commonly contains varves. A **varve** is a pair of thin layers deposited during a single year. One layer consists of silt brought in during spring floods and the other of clay deposited in winter when the lake's surface freezes over and the water becomes still (**Fig. 22.18e**).
- *Kame deposits:* A *kame deposit* is an accumulation of sediment transported on the surface of a glacier by flowing meltwater. Because the sediment in a kame was in a current, the sediment in kame deposits tends to be somewhat sorted. Some kame deposits form along the sides of glaciers, created by water sorting of lateral moraines, whereas others form in the interior of a glacier, as meltwater transports sediments into basins on the surface of the glacier.
- *Esker deposits:* In temperate glacial environments, the flowing water at the base of the glacier, moving through channels, transports much of the sediment load. Some of this water, along with its sedimentary load, exits the glacier through tunnels in the glacier's toe. But some never makes it out of the glacier and accumulates in sub-ice tunnels. This sediment is called an *esker deposit*.

Depositional Landforms of Glacial Environments

Picture a hunter, dressed in deerskin, standing at the toe of a continental glacier in what is now southern Canada, waiting for an unwary woolly mammoth to wander by. It's about 12,000 years ago, and the glacier has been receding for at least a millennium. Milky, sediment-laden streams gush from tunnels and channels at the base of the glacier and pour off the top as the ice melts. No mammoths venture by today, so the bored hunter climbs to the top of the glacier for a view. The climb isn't easy, partly because of the incessant katabatic wind and partly because deep crevasses interrupt his path. Reaching the top of the ice sheet, the hunter looks northward, and the glare almost blinds him. Squinting, he sees the white of snow, and where the snow has blown away, he sees the rippled, glassy surface of bluish ice (see Fig. 22.1b). Here and there, a rock protrudes from the ice. Now looking southward, he surveys a stark landscape of low, sinuous ridges separated by hummocky (bumpy) plains (see **Geology at a Glance**, pp. 820–821). Braided streams, which carry meltwater out across this landscape, flow through the hummocky plains and supply a number of lakes. Dust fills the air because of the wind.

All of the landscape features that the hunter observes as he looks southward were formed by deposition in glacial environments (**Fig. 22.19a, b**). The low, sinuous ridges that outline the former edge of the ice are end moraines, developed when the toe of a glacier stalls in one position for a while. The specific end moraine at the farthest limit of glaciation is called the **terminal moraine**. (The ridge of sediment that makes up Long Island, New York, and continues east-northeast into Cape Cod, Massachusetts, forms part of the terminal moraine of the ice sheet that covered New England and eastern Canada during the Pleistocene Ice Age; **Fig. 22.19c**.) End moraines that form when a glacier stalls temporarily as it recedes overall are **recessional moraines**.

FIGURE 22.18 Sedimentation processes and products associated with glaciation. Glacial sediment is distinctive.

(a) This glacial till in Ireland is unsorted, because ice can carry sediment of all sizes.

(b) Glacial erratics resting on a glacially polished surface in Wyoming.

(c) Braided streams choked with glacial outwash in Alaska. The streams carry away finer sediment and leave the gravel behind.

(d) Thick loess deposits underlie parts of the prairie in Illinois.

(e) In the quiet water of an Alaskan glacial lake, fine-grained sediments accumulate. Alternating layers in the sediment (varves), now exposed in an outcrop near Puget Sound, Washington, reflect seasonal changes.

FIGURE 22.19 The formation of depositional landforms associated with continental glaciation.

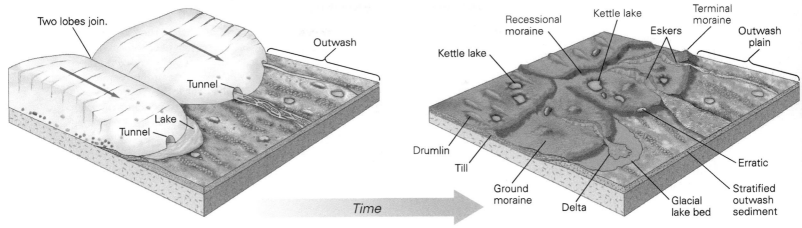

(a) The ice in continental glaciers flows toward the toe; sediment accumulates at the base and at the toe of the ice sheet.

(b) Several distinct depositional landforms form during glaciation; some developed under the ice and some at the toe.

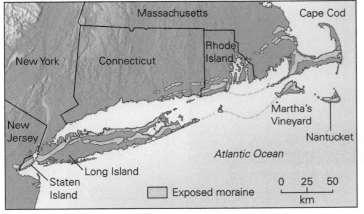

(c) Cape Cod, Long Island, and other landforms in the northeastern United States formed at the end of the continental ice sheet.

The till contains large boulders; finer sediment became soil.

(d) This glacial moraine, in Wyoming, formed when glaciers covered the region between the moraine and the mountains in the distance.

Till that has been released from the ice at the base of a flowing glacier and remains after the glacier has melted away makes up *lodgment till* (Fig. 22.19d). Clasts in lodgment till may be aligned and scratched during glacial flow. The till left behind during rapid recession forms a thin, hummocky layer on the land surface. This till, together with lodgment till, forms a landscape feature known as *ground moraine*. The flow of the glacier may mold till and other subglacial sediment into a streamlined, elongate hill called a **drumlin** (from the Gaelic word for hills). Drumlins tend to be asymmetric along their length, with a gentle downstream slope, tapered in the direction of flow, and a steeper upstream slope (Fig. 22.20a, b).

The hummocky surface of moraines reflects partly the variations in the amount of sediment supplied by the glacier and partly the formation of kettle holes, circular depressions made when blocks of ice calve off the toe of the glacier, become

buried by till or kame deposits, and then melt to leave a depression (Fig. 22.20c, d). A land surface with many kettle holes separated by round hills of till displays *knob-and-kettle topography* (Fig. 22.20e).

As we've noted, ice does not directly deposit all of the sediment associated with glacial landscapes, for meltwater also carries and deposits sediment. Water-transported sediment, in contrast to till, tends to be sorted and stratified. When the underlying ice melts away, kame deposits become a small hill or ridge known as a *kame*; kames may comprise some of the knobs in knob-and-kettle topography. Esker deposits, filling meltwater tunnels beneath a glacier, may remain as a narrow sinuous ridge, known as an **esker,** when the glacier melts away; eskers tend to trend at a high angle to the toe of the glacier (Fig. 22.21). Braided meltwater streams that flow beyond the end of a glacier deposit layers of sand and gravel over a broad area, yielding a **glacial outwash plain**. Meltwater collecting adjacent to the glacier's toe forms an *ice-margin lake*. Additional lakes and swamps may form in low areas on the ground moraine. Sediments deposited in eskers, kames, and glacial outwash plains serve as important sources of sand and gravel for construction, and the fine sediment of former glacial lake beds evolves into fertile soil for agriculture.

Take-Home Message

Glaciers carry sediment of all sizes toward the toe. Along the surface of the glacier, this sediment becomes lateral or medial moraines. When ice melts, it deposits unsorted till in an end moraine or ground moraine. Meltwater streams and wind transport and sort the sediment to form outwash-plain gravels and loess deposits, respectively. Sediment carried to the sea by glaciers settles on the seafloor when the ice melts. Deposition by glaciers produces distinctive landforms, such as moraines, eskers, kames, and kettle holes.

QUICK QUESTION: How does knob-and-kettle topography develop?

FIGURE 22.20 Drumlins and knob-and-kettle topography characterize some areas that were once glaciated.

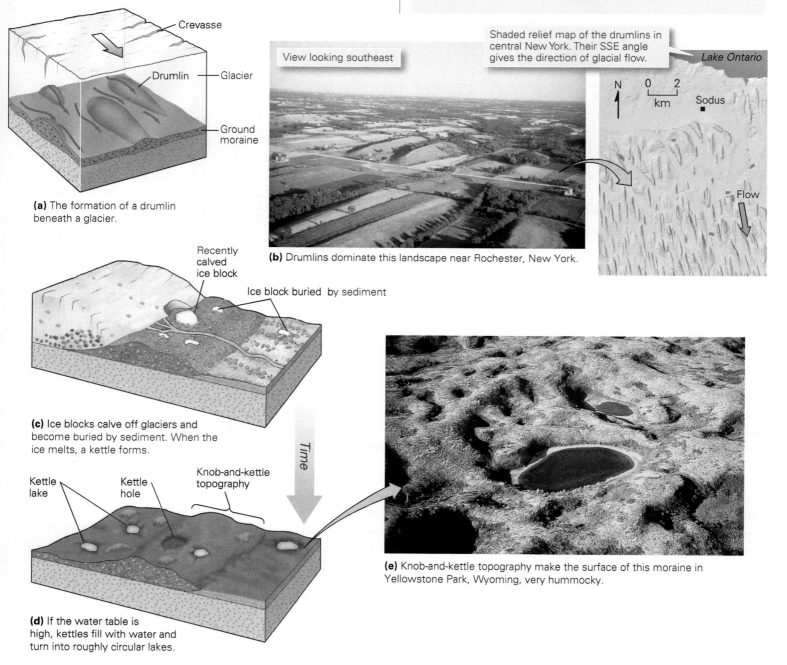

(a) The formation of a drumlin beneath a glacier.

(b) Drumlins dominate this landscape near Rochester, New York.

(c) Ice blocks calve off glaciers and become buried by sediment. When the ice melts, a kettle forms.

(d) If the water table is high, kettles fill with water and turn into roughly circular lakes.

(e) Knob-and-kettle topography make the surface of this moraine in Yellowstone Park, Wyoming, very hummocky.

FIGURE 22.21 Eskers are snake-like ridges of sand and gravel that form when sediment fills meltwater tunnels at the base of a glacier.

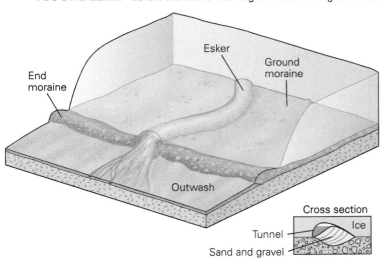

(a) At the time of formation, an esker develops beneath an ice sheet. In cross section (inset), wedges of sand accumulate in the tunnel.

(b) An example of an esker in an area once glaciated but now farmed.

22.5 Other Consequences of Continental Glaciation

Ice Loading and Glacial Rebound

When a large ice sheet (more than 50 km in diameter) grows on a continent, its weight causes the surface of the lithosphere to sink. In other words, ice loading causes **glacial subsidence**. Lithosphere, the relatively rigid outer shell of the Earth, can sink because the underlying asthenosphere is soft enough to flow slowly out of the way (Fig. 22.22a). As an analogy, imagine this simple experiment: Fill a bowl with honey and then place a thin rubber sheet over the honey. The rubber represents the lithosphere, and the honey represents the asthenosphere. If you place an ice cube on the rubber sheet, the sheet sinks because the weight of the ice pushes it down; the honey flows out of the way to make room. Because of ice loading, the rock surface underlying large areas of Antarctica's and Greenland's ice sheets now lie below sea level (see Fig. 22.4), so if the ice were instantly to melt away, these continents would be flooded by a shallow sea.

What happens when continental ice sheets do melt away? Gradually, the surface of the underlying continent rises back up to re-achieve isostasy (see Interlude D), by a process called **post-glacial rebound**. As this happens, the asthenosphere flows back underneath to fill the space (Fig. 22.22b). Where

rebound affects coastal areas, beaches along the shoreline rise several meters above sea level and become terraces (Fig. 22.22c). In the honey and rubber analogy, when you remove the ice cube, the rubber sheet slowly returns to its original shape. This process doesn't take place instantly because the honey can only flow slowly. Similarly, because the asthenosphere flows so slowly, it takes thousands of years for ice-depressed continents to rebound. Thus, glacial rebound is still taking place in some regions that were burdened by ice during the Pleistocene Ice Age. Recently, researchers in North America have documented this movement by using GPS measurements (Fig. 22.22d). Regions north of a line passing through the Great Lakes are now rising, relative to sea level.

Sea-Level Changes: The Glacial Reservoir

More of the Earth's surface and near-surface freshwater is stored in glacial ice than in any other reservoir. In fact, glacial ice accounts for 2.15% of Earth's total water supply, while lakes, rivers, soil, and the atmosphere together contain only 0.03%. The melting of glacial ice would transfer this water back into the ocean, causing sea level to rise. In fact, if today's ice sheets in Antarctica and Greenland were to melt, large areas of the coastal plain along the east coast and Gulf Coast of North America would become submerged, as would much of the Ganges Delta of Bangladesh.

During the last ice age, when glaciers covered almost three times as much land area as they do today, they held almost three times more water (70 million km^3, as opposed to 25 million km^3 today). In effect, during the ice age, water

Glaciers and Glacial Landforms

Continental ice sheet

Crevasses

Ice shelf

Higher sea level

Lower sea level

Drop stones

Iceberg

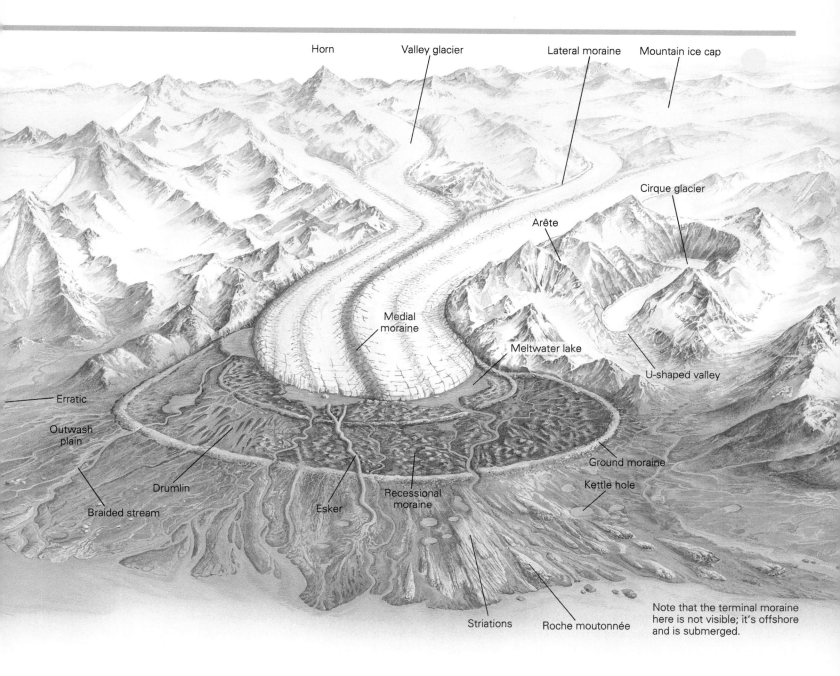

Horn · Valley glacier · Lateral moraine · Mountain ice cap · Cirque glacier · Arête · Medial moraine · Meltwater lake · U-shaped valley · Erratic · Outwash plain · Drumlin · Braided stream · Esker · Recessional moraine · Ground moraine · Kettle hole · Striations · Roche moutonnée

Note that the terminal moraine here is not visible; it's offshore and is submerged.

Glaciers are rivers or sheets of ice that last all year and slowly flow. Continental glaciers, vast sheets of ice up to a few kilometers thick, covered extensive areas of land during times when Earth had a colder climate. At the peak of the last ice age, ice sheets covered almost all of Canada, much of the United States, northern Europe, and parts of Russia.

The upper part of a sheet is brittle and may crack to form crevasses. Because ice sheets store so much of the Earth's water, sea level becomes lower during an ice age. When a glacier reaches the sea, it becomes an ice shelf. Rock that the glacier has plucked up along the way is carried out to sea with the ice; when the ice melts, the rocks fall to the sea floor as drop stones. At the edge of the shelf, icebergs calve off and float away.

Mountain or alpine glaciers grow in mountainous areas because snow can last all year at high elevations. During an ice age, mountain glaciers grow and flow out onto the land surface beyond the mountain front. Glacial recession may happen when the climate warms, so ice melts away faster at the toe (terminus) of the glacier than it can be added at the source. Consequences of glacial erosion and deposition remain when a glacier melts away. Erosion features include striations on bedrock and roches moutonnées. Deposition features include glacial moraines, glacial outwash, and esker deposits. Even when the toe remains fixed in position for a while, the ice continues to flow and thus molds underlying sediment into drumlins. Ice blocks buried in till melt to form kettle holes. In the mountains, glaciers fill valleys or form ice caps. Sediment falling from the mountains creates lateral and medial moraines. Glaciers carve distinct landforms in the mountains, such as cirques, arêtes, horns, and U-shaped valleys.

FIGURE 22.22 The concept of subsidence and rebound due to continental glaciation and deglaciation. (Not to scale)

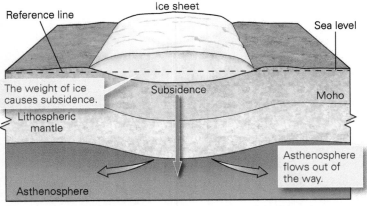

(a) The weight of the ice sheet causes the surface of the lithosphere to sink (subside).

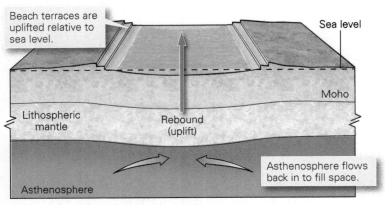

(b) After the glacier melts, the land surface rebounds and rises. This process uplifts beaches relative to sea level.

(c) Uplifted beaches along the coast of Arctic Canada form as the land undergoes post-glacial rebound.

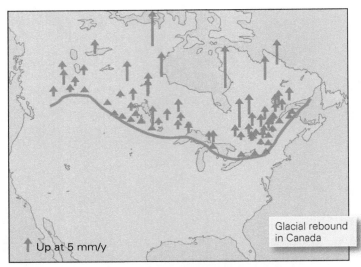

(d) GPS measurements show that the region north of the green line is rebounding. Different rates of uplift occur at different locations.

from the ocean reservoir was transferred from the ocean reservoir to the glacial reservoir, and remained trapped on land. As a consequence, sea level dropped by as much as 100 m, and extensive areas of continental shelves became exposed as the coastline migrated seaward, in places by more than 100 km (Fig. 22.23). People and animals migrated into the newly exposed ice-age coastal plains. In fact, fishermen dragging their nets along the Atlantic Ocean floor off New England today occasionally recover human artifacts. The drop in sea level also created land bridges across the Bering Strait between North America and northeastern Asia and between Australia and Indonesia, providing convenient migration routes for early people.

Effect on Drainage and Lakes

Continental glaciation can significantly modify the location and character of rivers and streams draining the land. For example, locally, the growth of a glacier, and/or the deposition of a moraine by glaciers, can block an individual stream. Diverted flow finds a new route and can carve a new valley. By the time the glacier melts away, these new streams have become so well established that pre-glacial channels remain abandoned.

At a regional scale, glaciation during the Pleistocene Ice Age profoundly modified North America's interior drainage. Before this ice age, several major rivers drained much of the interior of the continent to the north, into the Arctic Ocean (Fig. 22.24a, b). The ice sheet buried this drainage network and diverted the flow into the Mississippi–Missouri network, which became larger.

When ice-age glaciers receded, new lakes appeared on the land. For example, kettles in regions covered by knob-and-kettle topography turned into small lakes, as now occur in central and southern Minnesota by the thousands. In the Canadian Shield, scouring left innumerable depressions that have now become lakes.

FIGURE 22.23 The link between sea level and global glaciation: glaciers store water on land, so when glaciers grow, sea level falls, and when glaciers melt, sea level rises.

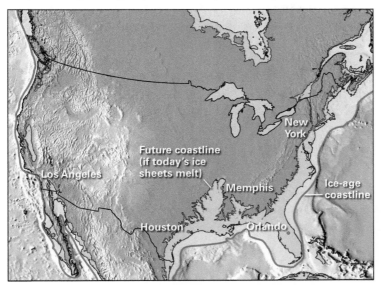

(a) The red line shows the coastline during the last ice age; much of the continental shelf was dry. If present-day ice sheets melt, coastal lands will flood.

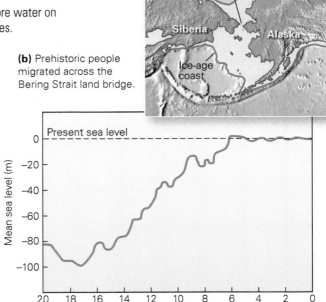

(b) Prehistoric people migrated across the Bering Strait land bridge.

(c) Sea-level rise between 17,000 and 7,000 B.C.E. was due to the melting of ice-age glaciers.

FIGURE 22.24 Ice-age glaciation changed the position of the divide between north-draining and south-draining river networks.

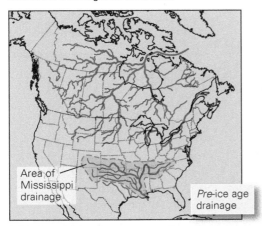

(a) Before the last ice age, more rivers flowed north; the Mississippi network was smaller.

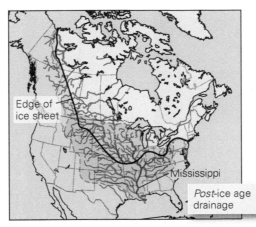

(b) Glaciation blocked northward drainage; the Mississippi network grew larger.

Erosion by glacial meltwater can carve valleys. Especially dramatic examples of this process result when the ice dams that held back large ice-margin lakes melted and broke. In a matter of hours to days, the contents of lakes could drain, yielding an immense flood called an outburst flood or *torrent*. Torrents can carve huge valleys and steep cliffs, strip the land of soil, and leave behind immense ripple marks (Fig. 22.24c). For example, when the ice dam holding back Glacial Lake Missoula in Montana broke, it released an immense torrent—known as the Great Missoula Flood—that scoured eastern Washington, creating a barren, soil-free landscape called the *channeled scablands* (see Chapter 17). Recent evidence suggests that this process repeated several times. Another torrent flowed down the channel of what is now the Illinois River and, in northern Illinois, carved a broad, steep-sided valley that is much too large to have been cut by the present-day Illinois River.

The largest known ice-margin lake covered portions of Manitoba and Ontario in south-central Canada and North Dakota and Minnesota in the United States (Fig. 22.25a).

(c) Giant ripple marks formed during the Great Missoula Flood.

This body of water, Glacial Lake Agassiz, existed between 11,700 and 9,000 years ago, a time during which the most recent phase of the last ice age came to a close and the continental glacier retreated north. At its largest, the lake covered over 250,000 square km (100,000 square miles), an area greater than that of all the present Great Lakes combined. Eventually, the ice sheet receded from the north shore of Glacial Lake Agassiz, so near the end of its life, the lake was surrounded by ice-free land. Field evidence suggests that the lake's demise came when it drained catastrophically, sending a torrent down what is now the St. Lawrence Seaway.

Pluvial Features

During the Pleistocene Ice Age, regions to the south of continental glaciers were wetter than they are today. Fed by enhanced rainfall, lakes accumulated in low-lying land even at a great distance from the ice front. The largest of these **pluvial lakes** (from the Latin *pluvia*, meaning rain) in North America flooded interior basins of the Basin and Range Province in Utah and Nevada (Fig. 22.25b). Examples include glacial Lake Bonneville, which covered almost a third of western Utah. When this lake suddenly drained after a natural dam holding it back broke,

FIGURE 22.25 Ice-age lakes in North America.

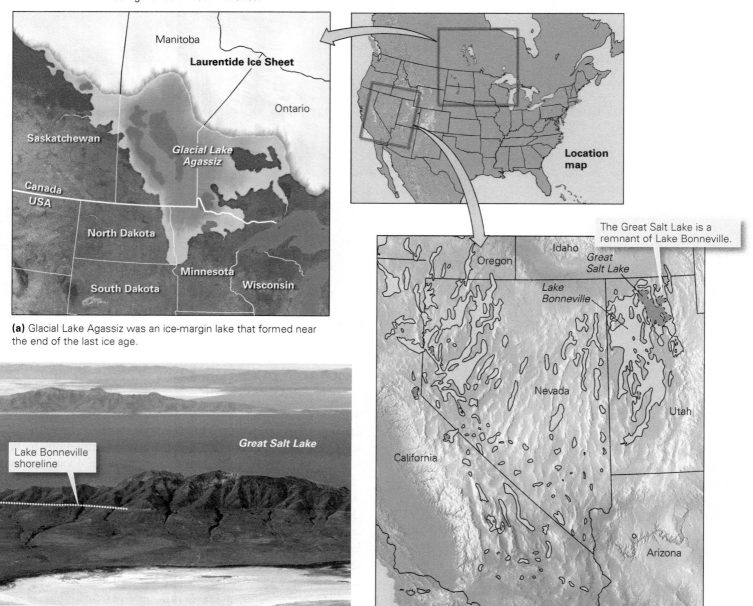

(a) Glacial Lake Agassiz was an ice-margin lake that formed near the end of the last ice age.

(b) Pluvial lakes occurred throughout the Basin and Range Province during the last ice age due to the wetter climate. The largest of these was Lake Bonneville. Subtle horizontal terraces define the remnants of beaches, now over 100 m above the present level of the Great Salt Lake.

FIGURE 22.26 Periglacial regions are not ice covered but do include substantial areas of permafrost.

(a) The distribution of periglacial environments in North America.

(b) An example of patterned ground near a pond in Manitoba, Canada.

(c) Stone circles of Spitzbergen form due to repeated freeze and thaw that separates gravel from silt.

it left a bathtub ring of shoreline rimming the mountains near Salt Lake City (see Fig. 22.25b). Today's Great Salt Lake itself is but a small remnant of Lake Bonneville.

Periglacial Environments

In polar latitudes today, and in regions adjacent to the fronts of continental glaciers during the last ice age, the mean annual temperature stays low enough (below −5°C) that soil moisture and groundwater freeze and, except in the upper few meters, stay solid all year. Such permanently frozen ground, or **permafrost**, may extend to depths of 1,500 m below the ground surface. Regions with widespread permafrost that do not have a cover of snow or ice are called *periglacial environments* (the Greek *peri* means around, or encircling; periglacial environments appear around the edges of glacial environments; Fig. 22.26a).

The upper few meters of permafrost may melt during the summer months, only to refreeze again when winter comes. As a consequence of the freeze-thaw process, the ground of some permafrost areas splits into pentagonal or hexagonal shapes, creating a landscape called **patterned ground** (Fig. 22.26b). Water fills the gaps between the cracks and freezes to create wedge-shaped walls of ice. In some places, freeze-and-thaw cycles in permafrost gradually push cobbles and pebbles up from the subsurface. Because the expansion of the ground is not even, the stones gradually collect between adjacent bulges to form stone rings (Fig. 22.26c). Some stone rings may also form when mud at depth pushes up from beneath a permafrost layer and forces stones aside.

Permafrost presents a unique challenge to people who live in polar regions or who work to extract resources from these regions. For example, heat from a building may warm and melt underlying permafrost, creating a mire into which the building settles. For this reason, buildings in permafrost regions must be placed on stilts so that cold air can circulate beneath them to keep the ground frozen. When geologists discovered oil on the northern coast of Alaska, oil companies faced the challenge of shipping the oil to markets outside of Alaska. After much debate over the environmental impact, the Trans Alaska Pipeline was built, and now it carries oil for 1,000 km to a seaport in southern Alaska (see Chapter 14). The oil must be warm during transport or it would be too viscous to flow; thus, to prevent the warm pipeline from melting underlying permafrost, it had to be built on a frame that holds it above the ground for most of its length.

22.6 The Pleistocene Ice Age

The Pleistocene Glaciers

Today most of the land surface in New York City lies hidden beneath concrete and steel, but in Central Park it's still possible to see land in a seminatural state. If you stroll through the park and study the rock outcrops, you'll find that their top surfaces are smooth and polished (see Fig. 22.12c) and in places have been grooved and scratched. You can also find numerous erratics. You are seeing evidence that an ice sheet once scraped along this now-urban ground. Geologists estimate that the ice sheet that overrode the New York City area may have been 250 m thick, enough to engulf the Empire State Building up to the 75th floor.

Glacial features such as those on display in Central Park first led Louis Agassiz to propose the idea that vast continental glaciers advanced over substantial portions of North America, Europe, and Asia during a great ice age. Since Agassiz's day, geologists, by mapping out the distribution of glacial deposits and landforms, have gradually defined the extent of ice-age glaciers and a history of their movement (Box 22.2).

The fact that glacially modified landscapes decorate the surface of the Earth today means that the most recent ice age occurred fairly recently during Earth history. This ice age, responsible for the glacial landforms of North America and Eurasia, happened mostly during the Pleistocene Epoch, which began about 2.6 million years ago (Ma) (see Chapter 13), so as we've noted earlier, it is commonly known as the *Pleistocene Ice Age*. Geologists use the term *Holocene* for about the last 12,000 years, the time since the last Pleistocene ice sheet melted away.

Based on mapping of glacial striations and deposits, geologists have determined where the great Pleistocene ice sheets originated and flowed. In North America, the *Laurentide ice sheet* started to grow over northeastern Canada, then merged with the *Keewatin ice sheet*, which originated in northwestern Canada. Together these ice sheets eventually covered all of Canada east of the Rocky Mountains and extended southward across the border as far as southern Illinois (Fig. 22.27a). At their maximum, the ice sheets attained a thickness of 2 to 3 km; each thinned toward its toe. In northeastern Canada, the ice sheet eroded the land surface, but farther south and west it deposited sediment (Fig. 22.27b, c). These ice sheets eventually merged with the Greenland ice sheet to the northeast and the Cordilleran ice sheet to the west. The Cordilleran ice sheet covered the mountains of western Canada as well as the southern third of Alaska.

During the Pleistocene Ice Age, mountain ice caps and valley glaciers also grew in the southern Rocky Mountains, the Sierra Nevada, and the Cascade Mountains, elevated regions to the south of the continental glacier. In Eurasia, a large ice sheet formed in northernmost Europe and adjacent Asia, and it gradually covered all of Scandinavia and northern Russia. This ice sheet flowed southward across France until it reached the Alps and merged with Alpine mountain glaciers. Ice also covered almost all of Ireland and the United Kingdom. Notably, even the highest mountains of Scotland were completely submerged beneath ice, so the peaks have been rounded by glacial erosion. A smaller ice sheet grew in eastern Siberia, and glaciers expanded in the mountains of central Asia. In the southern hemisphere, Antarctica remained ice covered, and mountain ice caps expanded in the Andes, but there were no continental glaciers in South America, Africa, or Australia.

In addition to continental ice sheets, sea ice in the northern hemisphere covered all of the Arctic Ocean and parts of the North Atlantic during the Pleistocene. Sea ice surrounded Iceland, approached Scotland, and also fringed most of western Canada and southeastern Alaska.

Life and Climate in the Pleistocene World

During the Pleistocene Ice Age, all climatic belts of the northern hemisphere shifted southward (Fig. 22.28a, b). Geologists can document this shift by examining fossil pollen, which can survive for thousands of years if preserved in the sediment of bogs. Presently, the southern boundary of North America's **tundra**, a treeless region supporting only low shrubs, moss, and lichen capable of living on permafrost, lies at a latitude of 68° N—during the Pleistocene Ice Age, it moved down to 48° N. Much of the interior of the United States, which now has temperate, deciduous forest, harbored cold-weather spruce and pine forest. Ice-age climates also changed the distribution

BOX 22.2   CONSIDER THIS . . .

So You Want to See Glaciation?

Though the Pleistocene continental ice sheet that once covered much of North America vanished about 6,000 years ago, you can find evidence of its power quite easily. The Great Lakes, along the U.S.–Canada border, the Finger Lakes and drumlins of New York, the low-lying moraines and outwash plains of Illinois, and the polished outcrops of the southern Canadian Shield all formed in response to the existence of this glacier. But if you want to see continental glaciers in action today, you must trek to Greenland or Antarctica.

Mountain glaciers are easier to reach. A trip to the mountains of western North America (including Alaska), the Alps of France or Switzerland, the Andes of South America, or the mountains of southern New Zealand will bring you in contact with active glaciers. You can even spot glaciers from the comfort of a cruise ship. Some of the most spectacular glacial landscapes in North America formed during the Pleistocene Epoch, when mountain glaciers were more widespread. These are now on display in national parks.

- **Glacier National Park (Montana):** This park, which borders Waterton Lakes National Park in Canada, displays giant cirques, U-shaped valleys, hanging valleys, and terminal moraines. In 1850, there were about 150 glaciers in the park, and some of these were quite large. Now only 25 active relicts of formerly larger glaciers remain, all in a mountainous terrain that reaches elevations of over 3 km. Unfortunately, these glaciers are melting away quickly and may vanish entirely by 2030.
- **Yosemite National Park (California):** A huge U-shaped valley carved into the Sierra Nevada granite batholith makes up the centerpiece of this park. Waterfalls spill out of hanging valleys bordering the valley.
- **Voyageurs National Park (Minnesota):** This park lacks the high peaks of mountainous parks but shows the dramatic consequences of glacial scouring and deposition on the Canadian Shield. The low-lying landscape, dotted with lakes, contains abundant polished surfaces, glacial striations, and erratics, along with moraines, glacial lake beds, and outwash plains.
- **Acadia National Park (Maine):** During the last ice age, the continental ice sheet overrode low bedrock hills and flowed into the sea along the coast of Maine. This park provides some of the best examples of the consequences. Its hills were scoured and shaped into large roches moutonnées by glacial flow. Some of the deeper valleys have now become small fjords.
- **Glacier Bay National Park (Alaska):** In Glacier Bay, huge tidewater glaciers fringe the sea, creating immense ice cliffs from which icebergs calve off. Cruise ships bring tourists up to the toes of these glaciers. More adventurous visitors can climb the coastal peaks and observe lateral and medial moraines, crevasses, and the erosional and depositional consequences of glaciers that have already retreated up the valley.

---

of rainfall on the planet. As we noted earlier, rainfall increased in North America, south of the glaciers, leading to the filling of pluvial lakes in Utah and Nevada. In contrast, rainfall decreased in equatorial regions, leading to shrinkage of the rainforest. Overall, the contrast between colder, glaciated regions and warmer, unglaciated regions created windier conditions worldwide. These winds sent glacial rock flour skyward, creating a dusty atmosphere (and, presumably, spectacular sunsets). The dust settled to create extensive deposits of loess. And because glaciers trapped so much water, as we have seen, sea level dropped.

Numerous species of now-extinct large mammals inhabited the Pleistocene world (Fig. 22.28c). Giant mammoths and mastodons, relatives of the elephant, along with woolly rhinos, musk oxen, reindeer, giant ground sloths, bison, lions, saber-toothed cats, and giant cave bears wandered forests and tundra in North America. Early human-like species were already foraging in the woods by the beginning of the Pleistocene Epoch, and by the end modern *Homo sapiens* lived on every continent except Antarctica and had discovered fire and invented tools.

Rapidly changing climates may have triggered a global migration of early humans, who gained access to the Americas, Indonesia, and Australia via land bridges that became exposed when sea level dropped.

Timing of the Pleistocene Ice Age

Louis Agassiz assumed that only one ice age had affected the planet. But close examination of the stratigraphy of glacial deposits on land revealed that *paleosols* (ancient soils preserved in the stratigraphic record), as well as beds containing fossils of warmer-weather animals and plants, separate distinct layers of glacial sediment. This observation suggested that between episodes of glacial deposition, glaciers receded and temperate climates prevailed. In the second half of the 20th century, when modern methods for dating geological materials became available, the difference in ages between the different layers of glacial sediment could be confirmed. Clearly, glaciers had advanced and then retreated more than once during the Pleistocene. Times during which the glaciers grew and

FIGURE 22.27 Pleistocene ice sheets and their consequences.

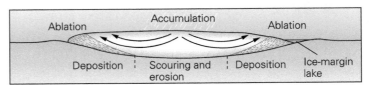

(b) Erosion dominates beneath the interior of the glacier, and deposition dominates along its margins.

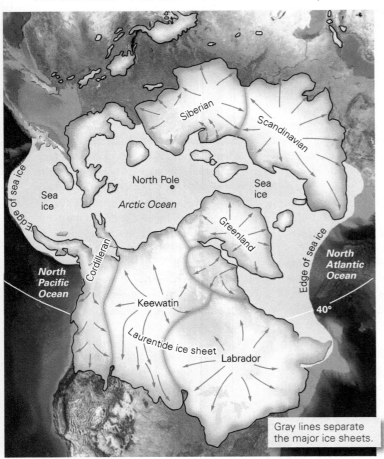

(a) During the Pleistocene, several distinct ice sheets formed. In several places, neighboring sheets came in contact.

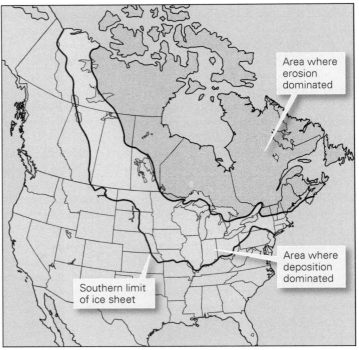

(c) Erosion dominated in northern and eastern Canada; deposition dominated in the Great Plains.

covered substantial areas of the continents are called glacial periods, or **glaciations**, and times between glacial periods are called interglacial periods, or **interglacials**.

Using the on-land sedimentary record, geologists recognized five Pleistocene glaciations in Europe (named, in order of increasing age, Würm, Riss, Mindel, Gunz, and Donau) and, traditionally, four in the midwestern United States (Wisconsinan, Illinoian, Kansan, and Nebraskan, named after the southernmost states in which their till was deposited; Fig. 22.29). Since the mid-1980s, geologists no longer distinguish the Nebraskan from the Kansan—they are lumped together as "pre-Illinoian." With the advent of radiometric dating in the mid-20th century, the ages of the younger glaciations were determined by dating wood trapped in glacial deposits. Geologists estimate the ages of the older glaciations by identifying fossils in the deposits.

The four- or five-stage chronology of glaciations was turned on its head in the 1960s, when geologists began to study submarine sediment containing the fossilized shells of microscopic marine plankton. Because the assemblage of plankton species living in warm water is not the same as the assemblage living in cold water, geologists can track changes in the temperature of the ocean by studying plankton fossils. Researchers found that in post-2.6-Ma sediment, assuming that cold water indicates a glacial period and warm water an interglacial period, there is a record of 20 to 30 different glacial advances during the Pleistocene Epoch. The four or five traditionally recognized glaciations possibly represent only the largest of these. Sediments deposited on land by other glaciations were eroded and redistributed during subsequent glaciations or were eroded away by streams and wind during interglacials.

Geologists refined their conclusions about the frequency of Pleistocene glaciations by examining the isotopic composition of fossil shells. Shells of many plankton species consist of calcite ($CaCO_3$). The oxygen in the shells includes two isotopes, a heavier one (^{18}O) and a lighter one (^{16}O). The ratio of

FIGURE 22.28 Climate belts during the Pleistocene.

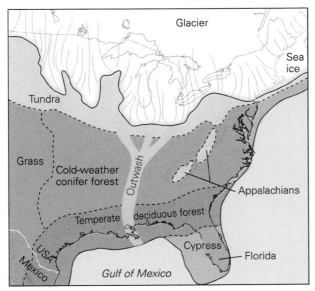

(a) Tundra covered parts of the United States, and southern states had forests like those of New England's today.

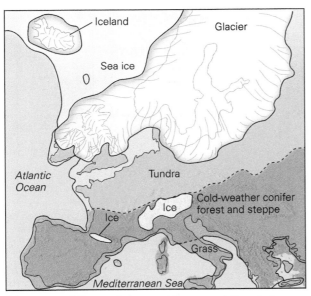

(b) Regions of Europe that support large populations today would have been barren tundra during the Pleistocene.

(c) Cold-adapted, now-extinct, large mammals roamed regions that are now temperate.

FIGURE 22.29 Pleistocene glacial deposits in the north-central United States. Curving moraines reflect the shape of glacial lobes.

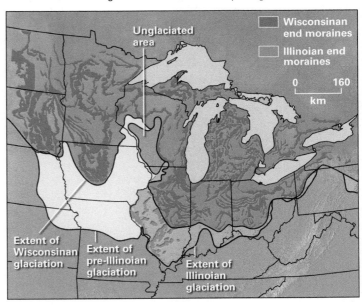

these isotopes tells us about the water temperature in which the plankton grew, for as water gets colder, plankton incorporate a higher proportion of ^{18}O into their shells (see Chapter 23). Thus, intervals in the stratigraphic record during which plankton shells have a large ratio of ^{18}O to ^{16}O define times when Earth had a colder, glacial climate. The isotope record confirms that 20 to 30 glaciations occurred during the last 2.6 Ma (Fig. 22.30a).

> **Did you ever wonder...**
>
> how many ice ages have happened during Earth history?

Older Ice Ages during Earth History

So far, we've focused on the Pleistocene Ice Age because of its importance in developing Earth's present landscape. Was this the only ice age during Earth history, or do ice ages happen frequently? To answer such questions, geologists study the stratigraphic record and search both for glacially striated and polished surfaces that have been buried by ancient strata, and for ancient deposits of till that have hardened into rock. Ancient, lithified till deposits are called **tillites** and consist of larger clasts distributed throughout a matrix of sandstone and mudstone.

By using the stratigraphic principles described in Chapter 12, geologists have determined that the most recent pre-Pleistocene widespread striated and polished surfaces and tillites formed in Permian time, about 280 Ma (Fig. 22.30b).

FIGURE 22.30 The timing of glaciations. Ice ages have occurred at several times in the geologic past.

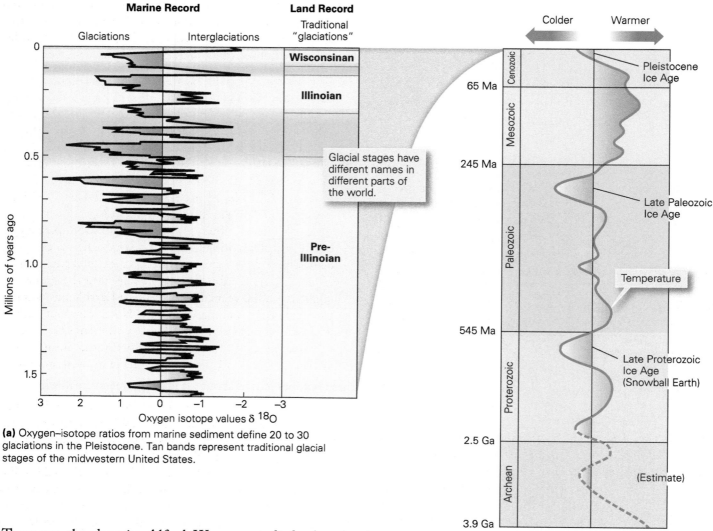

(a) Oxygen–isotope ratios from marine sediment define 20 to 30 glaciations in the Pleistocene. Tan bands represent traditional glacial stages of the midwestern United States.

(b) The Pleistocene is not the only ice-age time in Earth history. Glacial events happened in colder intervals of earlier eras, too.

These are the deposits Alfred Wegener studied when he developed the concept of continental drift, for on a reconstruction of Pangaea, the Permian glaciated areas are adjacent (see Chapter 3). Tillites were also deposited about 600 to 700 Ma (at the end of the Proterozoic Eon), about 2.2 billion years ago (Ga) (near the beginning of the Proterozoic), and perhaps about 2.7 Ga (in the Archean Eon). Strata deposited at other times in Earth history do not contain tillites. Thus, it appears that glacial advances and retreats have not occurred steadily throughout Earth history but rather are restricted to specific time intervals—*ice ages*—of which there were four or five: Pleistocene, Permian, late Proterozoic, early Proterozoic, and perhaps Archean.

Of particular note, some tillites of the late Proterozoic event were deposited at equatorial latitudes, suggesting that for at least a short time the continents worldwide were largely glaciated, and the sea may have been covered worldwide by ice. Geologists refer to the ice-encrusted planet as **snowball Earth** (see Chapter 13).

Take-Home Message

The most recent ice age, responsible for continental glacial landscapes of today, occurred during the past 2.6 Ma. The land record shows four to five discrete glaciations, but the marine record reveals that, in fact, ice sheets advanced and retreated about 20 to 30 times. Ice ages also happened earlier in Earth history. Proterozoic glaciers and sea ice may have covered all of "snowball Earth."

QUICK QUESTION: What's the evidence for multiple Pleistocene glaciations?

22.7 The Causes of Ice Ages

Ice ages occur only during restricted intervals of Earth history, hundreds of millions of years apart. But within an ice age, glaciers advance and retreat with a frequency measured in tens of thousands to hundreds of thousands of years. Thus, there must be both long-term and short-term controls on glaciation.

Long-Term Causes

Plate tectonics exercises long-term control over glaciation for several reasons. First, continental drift due to plate tectonics determines the distribution of continents relative to the equator. If all continents straddled the equator, none could become cold enough to host continental glaciations—ice ages can happen only when substantial continental area lies at high latitudes. Second, the distribution of continents relative to upwelling and downwelling zones of the mantle may influence overall land elevation and thus land-surface temperature. Third, the global volume of mid-ocean ridges, which reflects seafloor-spreading rates, influences global sea level—at times when continents are relatively low and sea level is relatively high, large areas of continents flood and cannot host glaciers. Finally, global climate can be affected by heat redistributed by oceanic currents—growth of island arcs and drift of continents can influence the configuration of currents and determine whether high-latitude regions can become cold enough to host ice sheet formation.

The concentration of carbon dioxide in the atmosphere may also play a key role in determining whether an ice age can or can't occur. As we've noted, carbon dioxide (CO_2) is a greenhouse gas—it traps infrared radiation rising from the Earth—so if the concentration of CO_2 increases, the atmosphere becomes warmer. Ice sheets cannot form during periods when the atmosphere has a relatively high concentration of CO_2, even if other factors favor glaciation. But what might cause long-term changes in CO_2 concentration? Possibilities include changes in the number of marine organisms that extract CO_2 to make shells; changes in the amount of chemical weathering on land, caused by growth of mountain ranges (weathering absorbs CO_2); changes in the amount of volcanic activity; and changes in the distribution and volume of photosynthetic organisms (these organisms remove CO_2 from the air). Of note, the widespread appearance of coal swamps may have triggered Permian glaciations of Pangaea.

Short-Term Causes

Now we've seen how the stage could be set for an ice age to occur, but why do glaciers advance and retreat periodically during an ice age? In 1920, Milutin Milanković, a Serbian astronomer and geophysicist, came up with an explanation. Milanković studied how the Earth's orbit changes shape and how its axis changes orientation through time, and he calculated the frequency of these changes. In particular, he evaluated three aspects of Earth's movement around the Sun.

- *Orbital eccentricity:* The Earth's orbit gradually changes from a more circular shape to a more elliptical shape. The degree to which an orbit deviates from a perfect circle is called the orbital eccentricity. Earth's eccentricity cycle takes around 100,000 years (**Fig. 22.31a**).
- *Tilt of Earth's axis:* We have seasons because the Earth's axis is not perpendicular to the plane of its orbit. Over time, the tilt angle varies between 22.5° and 24.5°, with a frequency of 41,000 years (**Fig. 22.31b**).
- *Precession of Earth's axis:* If you've ever set a top spinning, you've probably noticed that its axis gradually traces a conical path. This motion, or wobble, is called *precession* (**Fig. 22.31c**). The Earth's axis wobbles over the course of about 23,000 years. Right now, the Earth's axis points toward Polaris, making Polaris the North Star, but 12,000 years ago the axis pointed to Vega, a different star. Precession determines the relationship between the timing of the seasons and the position of Earth along its orbit around the Sun.

Milanković showed that precession, along with variations in orbital eccentricity and tilt, combine to affect the total annual amount of *insolation* (exposure to the Sun's rays) and the seasonal distribution of insolation that the Earth receives at the mid- to high-latitudes (such as 65° N) by as much as 25%. For example, such regions receive more insolation when the Earth's axis is almost perpendicular to its orbital plane than when its axis is greatly tilted. According to Milanković, glaciers tend to advance during times of cool summers at 65° N, which occur periodically (**Fig. 22.31d**). When geologists began to study the climate record, they found climate cycles with the frequency predicted by Milanković. These climate cycles, controlled by "orbital forcing," are now called **Milankovitch cycles**.

The discovery of Milankovitch cycles in the geologic record strongly supports the contention that changes in the Earth's orbit and tilt help trigger short-term advances and retreats during an ice age. But orbit and tilt changes cannot be the whole story because they could cause only about a 4°C temperature decrease (relative to today's temperature), and during glaciations the temperature decreased 5° to 7°C along coasts and 10° to 13°C inland. Geologists suggest that several other factors may come into play in order to trigger a glacial advance.

- *A changing albedo:* When snow remains on land throughout the year, or clouds form in the sky, the albedo (reflectivity) of the Earth increases, so Earth's surface reflects incoming sunlight and thus becomes even cooler.

FIGURE 22.31 Milankovitch cycles influence the amount of insolation received at high latitudes.

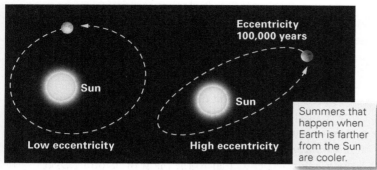

(a) Variations caused by changes in orbital shape.

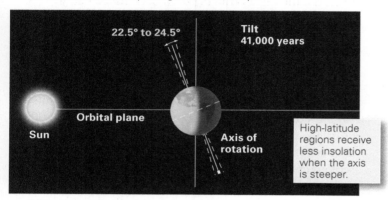

(b) Variations caused by changes in axis tilt.

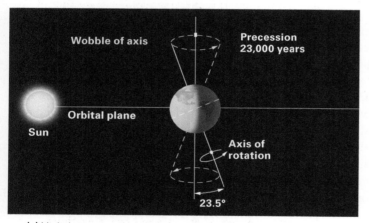

(c) Variations caused by the precession of Earth's axis.

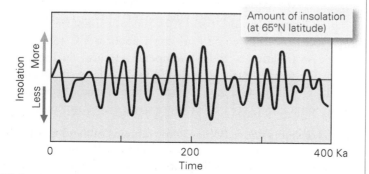

(d) Combining the effects of eccentricity, tilt, and precession produces distinct periods of more or less insolation.

• *Interrupting the global heat conveyor:* As the climate cools, evaporation rates from the sea decrease, so seawater does not become as salty. Decreasing salinity might stop the system of thermohaline currents that brings warm water to high latitudes (see Chapter 18). Thus, the high latitudes become even colder than they would otherwise.

• *Biological processes that change CO_2 concentration:* Several kinds of biological processes may have amplified climate changes by altering the concentration of CO_2 in the atmosphere. For example, a greater amount of plankton growing in the oceans could absorb more CO_2 and thus remove it from the atmosphere. A bloom of plankton might reflect an addition of nutrients to the oceans, perhaps because of changing patterns of upwelling or changing amounts of runoff.

The above processes represent *positive feedback* in that they enhance the effects of the phenomenon that causes them. Because of positive feedback, the Earth could cool more than it would otherwise during the cooler stage of a Milankovitch cycle, and this could trigger a glacial advance. Variations in the radiation output of the Sun could also affect the amount of energy the Earth receives, but the long-term periodicity of such variability remains unclear, so the effect is hard to evaluate.

A Model for Pleistocene Ice Age History

Long-Term Cooling in the Cenozoic Era Taking all of the above causes into account, we can now propose a scenario for the events that led to the Pleistocene glacial advances. Our story begins in the Eocene Epoch, about 55 Ma (Fig. 22.32). At that time, climates were warm and balmy not only in the tropics but even above the Arctic Circle. At the end of the Middle Eocene (37 Ma), the climate began to cool, and by Early Oligocene time (33 Ma), Antarctica became glaciated. The Antarctic ice sheet came and went until the middle of the Miocene Epoch (15 Ma), when an ice sheet formed that has lasted ever since. Ice sheets did not appear in the Arctic, however, until 2 to 3 Ma, when the Pleistocene Ice Age began.

Cenozoic long-term climate changes may have been caused, in part, by changes in the pattern of oceanic currents that happened, in turn, because of plate tectonics. For example, in the Eocene, the collision of India with Asia cut off warm equatorial currents that had been flowing in the Tethys Sea. And in the Miocene and Oligocene, Australia and South America drifted away from Antarctica, allowing the cold circum-Antarctic current to develop. This new current prevented warm southward-flowing currents from reaching Antarctica, allowing ice to form and survive in the region. Without the warm currents, the climate of Antarctica overall underwent cooling,

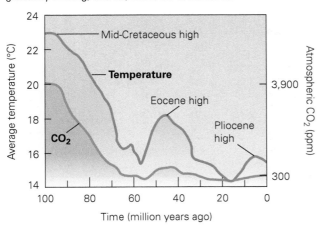

FIGURE 22.32 Until recently, Earth's atmosphere has been gradually cooling, overall, since the Cretaceous.

retreat of the Laurentide ice sheet. (Such models remain the subject of vigorous debate.)

- *Stage 1:* During the overall cooler climates of the late Cenozoic Era, the Earth reaches a point in the Milankovitch cycle when the average mean temperature in temperate latitudes drops. Because of glacial rebound, the ice-free surface of northern Canada has risen to an altitude of several hundred meters above sea level. With lower temperatures and higher elevations, not all of winter's snow melts away during the summer. Eventually, snow covers the entire region of northern Canada, even during the summer. Because of the snow's high albedo, it reflects sunlight, so the region grows still colder (a positive feedback) and even more snow accumulates. Precipitation rates are high, because evaporation off the Gulf Stream provides moisture. Finally, the snow at the base of the pile turns to ice, and the ice begins to spread outward under its own weight. A new continental glacier has been born.
- *Stage 2:* The ice sheet continues to grow as more snow piles up in the zone of accumulation. And as the ice sheet grows, the atmosphere continues to cool because of the albedo effect. But now the weight of the ice loads the continent and makes it sink, so the elevation of the glacier decreases and its surface approaches the equilibrium line. Also, the temperature becomes cold enough that in high latitudes the Atlantic Ocean begins to freeze. As the sea ice covers the ocean, the amount of evaporation decreases, so the source of snow is cut off and the amount of snowfall diminishes. The glacial advance basically chokes on its own success. The decrease in the glacier's elevation (leading to warmer summer temperatures) on the ice surface, as well as the decrease in snowfall, causes ablation to occur faster than accumulation, and the glacier begins to retreat.
- *Stage 3:* As the glacier retreats, temperatures gradually increase and the sea ice begins to melt. The supply of water to the atmosphere from evaporation increases once again, but with the warmer temperatures and lower elevations, this water precipitates as rain during the summer. The rain drastically accelerates the rate of ice melting, and the retreat progresses quite rapidly.

and this could have cooled the global ocean. Changes to atmospheric circulation and temperature may also have happened at this time. Models suggest that the uplift of the Himalayas and Tibet diverted winds in a way that cooled the climate. Further, this uplift exposed more rock to chemical weathering, perhaps leading to extraction of CO_2 from the atmosphere (as noted, chemical weathering reactions absorb CO_2). A decrease in the concentration of this greenhouse gas would contribute to atmospheric cooling.

So far, we've examined hypotheses that explain long-term cooling since about 40 Ma, but what caused the sudden appearance of the Laurentide ice sheet about 2.6 Ma? This event may coincide with other plate-tectonic events. For example, the gap between North and South America closed when the Isthmus of Panama grew and separated the waters of the Caribbean from those of the tropical Pacific for the first time. When this happened, warm currents that previously flowed out of the Caribbean into the Pacific were blocked and diverted northward to merge with the Gulf Stream. This current transfers warm water from the Caribbean up the Atlantic Coast of North America and ultimately to the British Isles. As the warm water moves up the Atlantic Coast, it generates warm, moisture-laden air that provides a source for the snow that falls over New England, eastern Canada, and Greenland. In other words, the Arctic has long been cold enough for ice caps, but until the Gulf Stream was diverted northward by the growth of Panama, there was no source of moisture to make abundant snow and ice needed for glacial growth.

Short-term Advances and Retreats in the Pleistocene Epoch

Once the Earth's climate had cooled overall, short-term processes such as the Milankovitch cycles led to periodic advances and retreats of the glaciers. To understand how, let's look at a possible case history of a single advance and

Will There Be Another Glacial Advance?

What does the future hold? Considering the periodicity of glacial advances and retreats during the Pleistocene Epoch, we may be living in an interglacial period. Pleistocene interglacials lasted about 10,000 years, and since the present interglacial began about 12,000 years ago, the time seems ripe for

FIGURE 22.33 The Little Ice Age and its demise. Glaciers that advanced between 1550 and 1850 have since retreated.

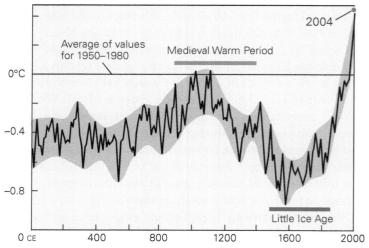

(a) A model of global temperature for the past 2,000 years. Overall trends display the Medieval Warm Period followed by the Little Ice Age. Since 1850, temperatures have warmed.

(b) Skaters (ca. 1600) on the frozen canals of the Netherlands during the Little Ice Age.

(c) During the Little Ice Age, a glacier filled this valley. In this 2003 photo, most of the glacier has vanished. Most of the retreat has happened in the last century.

a new glaciation. If a glacier on the scale of the Laurentide ice sheet were to develop, major cities and agricultural belts would be overrun by ice, and their populations would have to migrate southward. Long before the ice front arrived, though, the climate would become so hostile that northern cities would already be abandoned.

The Earth actually had a brush with ice-age conditions between the 1300s and the mid-1800s, when average annual temperatures in the northern hemisphere fell sufficiently for mountain glaciers to advance significantly. During this period, now known as the **Little Ice Age**, sea ice surrounded Iceland and canals froze in the Netherlands, leading to that country's tradition of skating (Fig. 22.33a, b). Some researchers speculate that the depopulation of the western hemisphere, in the wake of European conquest, which brought devastating epidemics, caused temporary reforestation, for without inhabitants, farmlands went untended and new forests, which absorbed CO_2, grew. This process caused atmospheric concentrations of CO_2 to decrease, leading to the cooler conditions that triggered the Little Ice Age. Others speculate that the change reflects increased cloud cover, not a change in CO_2 concentration. Researchers will likely propose additional ideas as work on this problem continues.

During the past 150 years, temperatures have warmed, and most mountain glaciers have retreated significantly (Fig. 22.33c). Large slabs have been calving off Antarctic ice shelves. In fact, the Larsen B Ice Shelf of Antarctica, an area larger than Rhode Island, disintegrated in 2002 over a period of only one month. Greenland's glaciers, in particular, are showing signs of accelerating retreat (Fig. 22.34). Large meltwater ponds are forming on the surface of the ice sheet, and some of these drain abruptly through cracks to the base of the glacier a kilometer below. The vast majority of researchers suggest that this global-warming trend is due to increased CO_2 in the atmosphere from the burning of fossil fuels (see Chapter 23). Global warming could conceivably cause a "super-interglacial," meaning that the next glaciation could be substantially delayed or might never happen.

FIGURE 22.34 Greenland's melting glaciers. Melting has accelerated in the last few decades.

(a) Lakes of meltwater accumulate on the surface of the ice sheet during the summer.

(c) Where glaciers meet the sea, huge masses calve off and crash into the water. This is happening so fast that the ice front is retreating.

(b) Lakes suddenly drain through cracks that carry the water to the base of the glacier, 1 km down. Addition of liquid water to the base allows the glacier to move faster, causing a "surge."

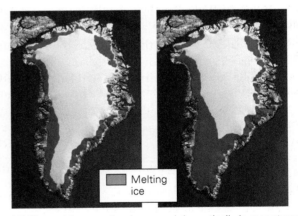

Melting ice

(d) The melting area has increased dramatically in recent years.

Current trends of global warming have led to concern that the ice sheet of West Antarctica might begin to float and then break up rapidly. If all of today's ice caps melted, global sea level would rise by 70 m (230 ft), extensive areas of coastal plains would be flooded, and major coastal cities such as New York, Miami, and London would be submerged (see Fig. 22.23). Instead of protruding from ice, the tip of the Empire State Building would protrude from the sea. Icehouse or greenhouse? We may not know which scenario will play out in the future until it happens. However, researchers have voiced concern that, at least in the near term, glacial melting will be the order of the day, as global temperatures seem to be rising. The next chapter addresses such change.

Take-Home Message

Ice ages occur when the distribution of continents, ocean currents, and the concentration of atmospheric CO_2 are appropriate. Advances and retreats during an ice age are controlled by Milankovitch cycles that take into account variations in Earth's orbit and rotation axis. Because of global warming, we may be living in a super-interglacial period.

QUICK QUESTION: How does positive feedback contribute to a glaciation during an ice age, and why does the glaciation eventually cease?

CHAPTER SUMMARY

- Glaciers are streams or sheets of recrystallized ice that survive for the entire year and flow in response to gravity. Mountain glaciers exist in high regions and fill cirques and valleys. Continental glaciers (ice sheets) spread over substantial areas of the continents.

- Glaciers form when snow accumulates over a long period of time. With progressive burial, the snow first turns to firn and then to ice.

- Ice in temperate glaciers melts during at least part of the year. Polar glaciers are frozen solid. Glaciers move by basal sliding over water or wet sediment, and/or by plastic deformation of ice grains. In general, glaciers move tens of meters per year.

- Glaciers move because of gravitational pull; they flow in the direction of their surface slope.

- Whether the toe of a glacier stays fixed in position, advances farther from the glacier's origin, or retreats back toward the origin depends on the balance between the rate at which snow builds up in the zone of accumulation and the rate at which glaciers melt or sublimate in the zone of ablation.

- Icebergs break off glaciers that flow into the sea. Continental glaciers that flow out into the sea along a coast make ice shelves. Sea ice forms where the ocean's surface freezes.

- As glacial ice flows over sediment, it incorporates clasts. The clasts embedded in glacial ice act like a rasp that abrades the substrate.

- Mountain glaciers carve numerous landforms, including cirques, arêtes, horns, U-shaped valleys, hanging valleys, and truncated spurs. Fjords are glacially carved valleys that filled with water.

- Glaciers can transport sediment of all sizes. Glacial drift includes till, glacial marine, glacial outwash, lake-bed mud, and loess. Lateral moraines accumulate along the sides of valley glaciers, and medial moraines form down the middle of two glaciers. End moraines accumulate at a glacier's toe.

- Glacial depositional landforms include moraines, knob-and-kettle topography, drumlins, kames, eskers, meltwater lakes, and outwash plains.

- Continental crust subsides as a result of ice loading. When the glacier melts away, the crust rebounds.

- When water is stored in continental glaciers, sea level drops. When glaciers melt, sea level rises.

- During past ice ages, the climate in regions south of the continental glaciers was wetter, and pluvial lakes formed. Permafrost (permanently frozen ground) exists in periglacial environments.

- During the Pleistocene Ice Age, large continental glaciers covered much of North America, Europe, and Asia.

- The stratigraphy of Pleistocene glacial deposits preserved on land records five European and four North American glaciations, times during which ice sheets advanced. The record preserved in marine sediments records 20 to 30 such events. The land record, therefore, is incomplete.

- Long-term causes of ice ages include plate tectonics and changes in the concentration of CO_2 in the atmosphere. Short-term causes include the Milankovitch cycles (caused by periodic changes in Earth's orbit and tilt).

GUIDE TERMS

REVIEW QUESTIONS

1. What evidence did Louis Agassiz offer to support the idea of an ice age?
2. How do mountain glaciers and continental glaciers differ in terms of dimensions, thickness, and patterns of movement?
3. Describe the transformation from snow to glacial ice.
4. Explain how arêtes, cirques, and horns form.
5. Describe the mechanisms that enable glaciers to move, and explain why they move.
6. How fast do glaciers normally move? How fast can they move during a surge?
7. Explain how the balance between ablation and accumulation determines whether a glacier advances or retreats.
8. How can a glacier continue to flow toward its toe even though its toe is retreating?
9. How does a glacier transform a V-shaped river valley into a U-shaped valley? Discuss how hanging valleys develop.
10. Describe the various kinds of glacial deposits. Be sure to note the materials from which the deposits are made and the landforms that result from deposition.
11. How do the crust and mantle respond to the weight of glacial ice?
12. How was the world different during the glacial advances of the Pleistocene Ice Age? Be sure to mention the relation between glaciations and sea level.
13. How was the standard four-stage chronology of North American glaciations developed? Why is it so incomplete? How was it modified with the study of marine sediment?
14. Were there ice ages before the Pleistocene? If so, when?
15. What are some of the long-term causes that lead to ice ages? What are the short-term causes that trigger glaciations and interglacials?

ON FURTHER THOUGHT

16. If you fly over the barren cornfields of central Illinois during the early spring, you will see slight differences in soil color due to variations in moisture content—wetter soil is darker. These variations outline the shapes of polygons that are tens of meters across. What do these patterns represent, and how might they have formed? What do they tell us about the climate of central Illinois at the end of the last ice age?

17. An unusual late Precambrian rock unit crops out in the Flinders Range, a small mountain belt in South Australia near Adelaide. Structures in the belt formed at the beginning of the Paleozoic. This unit consists of clasts of granite and gneiss, in a wide range of sizes, suspended through a matrix of slate. What is this unusual rock?

smartwork

smartwork.wwnorton.com

This chapter's Smartwork features:

- Labeling exercise on identifying mountain glaciers.
- Interactive ranking activity on the transformation from ice to snow.
- Art-based, interactive exercises on glacial movements.

GEOTOURS

This chapter's GeoTour exercise (R) features:

- Continental glacier features in the northeastern U.S.
- Alpine-valley glacial features around the world
- Piedmont glacial features in Alaska

Rice paddies and villages cover the countryside near Shanghai, China. The landscape here would have looked vastly different before the arrival of humanity. Land-use change affects many aspects of the Earth System.

CHAPTER 23

Global Change in the Earth System

All we in one long caravan
are journeying since the world began,
we know not whither, we know . . . all must go.

—*Bhartrihari (Indian poet, ca. 500 C.E.)*

23.1 Introduction

Did the Earth's surface look the same in the Jurassic Period as it does today? Definitely not! Two hundred million years ago, the North Atlantic Ocean was just a narrow sea, and the South Atlantic Ocean didn't exist at all, so most dry land connected to form a single vast supercontinent (Fig. 23.1). Today the Atlantic is a wide ocean and the Earth has seven separate continents. Moreover, during the Jurassic, the call of the wild rumbled from the throats of dinosaurs, whereas today the largest land animals are mammals. In essence, what we see of the Earth today is just a snapshot, an instant in the life story of a constantly changing planet. This idea arguably stands as geology's greatest philosophical contribution to humanity's understanding of our Universe.

Why has the Earth changed so much over geologic time, and why does it continue to change? Ultimately, change happens because the Earth's internal heat keeps the asthenosphere

weak enough to flow and because the Sun's heat keeps most of the Earth's surface at temperatures above the freezing point of water. Flow in the asthenosphere permits plate tectonics, which leads to continental drift, volcanism, and mountain building. Solar heat, together with gravity, keeps streams, glaciers, waves, and wind in motion, thereby causing erosion and deposition. Solar heat also makes the Earth's surface and near-surface regions hospitable to life. If the Earth did not have just the right mix of tectonic activity and solar heat, it would be a frozen dust bowl like Mars, a crater-pocked wasteland like the Moon, or a cloud-choked oven like Venus.

Many of the changes that take place on Earth reflect complex interactions among geologic and biological phenomena. For example, photosynthetic organisms affect the composition of the atmosphere by providing oxygen, and atmospheric composition, in turn, determines the nature of chemical weathering reactions that take place in rocks. We've referred to the global interconnecting web of physical and biological phenomena on Earth as the **Earth System** (see **Geology at a Glance**, pp. 840–841). We can now define **global change**, in a general sense, as transformations or modifications of physical and biological components in the Earth System through time.

FIGURE 23.1 The map of Earth's surface changes over time because of plate motions.

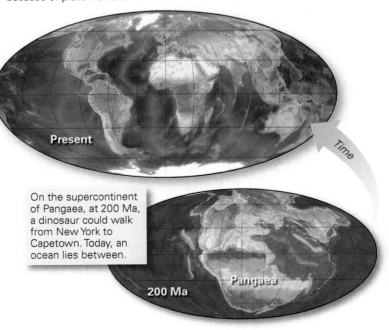

Present

Time

On the supercontinent of Pangaea, at 200 Ma, a dinosaur could walk from New York to Capetown. Today, an ocean lies between.

200 Ma   **Pangaea**

The Earth System

External
energy

Sun

Thunderhead

Lightning

Rain and
snow

Mountain
uplift

Continental
glacier

City

Ocean

Rocky coastline

Desert

Valley

Arid mountains

Mining

Lakes

Deciduous forest

Field pattern

Beach

Forested mountains

Tropical
rain forest

Coral reef

Shark

Internal
energy

The Earth's surface is the interface among the solid Earth (lithosphere); the liquid water of oceans, lakes, streams, groundwater (the hydrosphere); the solid water of glaciers and permafrost (the cryosphere); and the planet's gaseous envelope (the atmosphere). Countless species of life, ranging from nearly invisible bacteria to giant whales and trees, populate complex ecosystems (the biosphere). These components, and the interactions among them, constitute the Earth System. Two key sources of energy fuel the dynamic Earth System. External energy comes from solar radiation, and internal energy comes from the Earth's interior and drives tectonic processes.

Various materials cycle among living and nonliving components of the Earth System during the hydrologic cycle, the rock cycle, and various biogeochemical cycles (such as the carbon cycle).

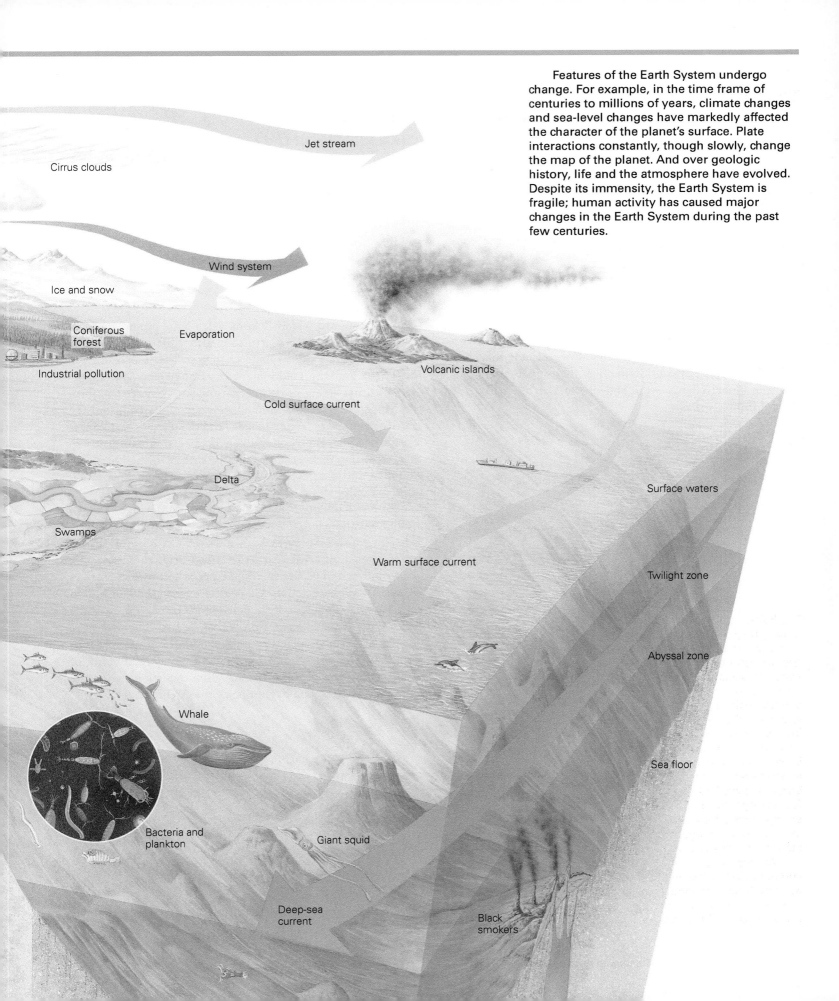

Features of the Earth System undergo change. For example, in the time frame of centuries to millions of years, climate changes and sea-level changes have markedly affected the character of the planet's surface. Plate interactions constantly, though slowly, change the map of the planet. And over geologic history, life and the atmosphere have evolved. Despite its immensity, the Earth System is fragile; human activity has caused major changes in the Earth System during the past few centuries.

Cirrus clouds

Jet stream

Wind system

Ice and snow

Coniferous forest

Evaporation

Industrial pollution

Volcanic islands

Cold surface current

Delta

Surface waters

Swamps

Warm surface current

Twilight zone

Abyssal zone

Whale

Sea floor

Bacteria and plankton

Giant squid

Deep-sea current

Black smokers

Geologists distinguish among different types of global change, on the basis of the rate or way in which change progresses with time. Specifically, *gradual change* takes place over long periods of geologic time (millions to billions of years); *catastrophic change* takes place relatively rapidly in the context of geologic time (seconds to millennia); *unidirectional change* involves transformations that never repeat; and *cyclic change* repeats the same steps over and over, though not necessarily with the same results or at the same rate.

In this chapter, we begin by reviewing examples of global change involving phenomena discussed earlier in the book. Then we introduce the concept of a *biogeochemical cycle*, the exchange of chemicals among living and nonliving reservoirs, for certain kinds of global change reflect an alteration in the proportion of chemicals held in different reservoirs. Finally, we focus on *global climate change*, transformations or modifications in Earth's climate over time, some of which have been attributed to the actions of human society. We conclude this chapter, and this book, by considering hypotheses that describe the ultimate global change—the end of the Earth—in the very distant future.

23.2 Unidirectional Changes

The Evolution of the Solid Earth

Recall from Chapter 1 that Earth began as a fairly homogenous mass formed by the coalescence of planetesimals. The homogeneous proto-Earth did not last long, for within about 10 to 100 million years of its birth, the planet began to melt, yielding liquid iron alloy that sank to the center to form the core (Fig. 23.2a). This process of **differentiation** represents a major unidirectional change in the Earth System—it produced a layered, onion-like planet with an iron alloy core surrounded by a rocky mantle.

According to a widely held model, a large protoplanet collided with the newborn Earth soon after differentiation. This collision caused a catastrophic change in that much of both the Earth and the colliding object fragmented and vaporized, creating a ring of debris that quickly coalesced to form the Moon (Fig. 23.2b). Immediately after this collision, the Earth's mantle was largely molten, and the planet's surface was a sea of magma. But cooling likely happened fairly quickly so that, according to recent research, the surface of the Earth had solidified and may even have hosted liquid water before 4.0 billion years ago (Ga).

The Earth underwent another catastrophic change between around 4.0 and 3.9 Ga, when it endured pummeling by asteroids and comets, an event known as the *late heavy bombardment*. Almost all crust that had formed prior to 3.9 Ga was largely pulverized or melted—in fact, no whole rock older than 4.0 Ga has yet been found. Geologists refer to the half-billion years between the birth of the Earth and the beginning of the rock record as the Hadean Eon. When bombardment slowed, our planet changed again, cooling enough for a new crust to form, new seas to accumulate, and probably an early form of plate tectonics to begin operating. This transition marks the end of the Hadean and beginning of the Archean.

FIGURE 23.2 Examples of major unidirectional change in Earth history.

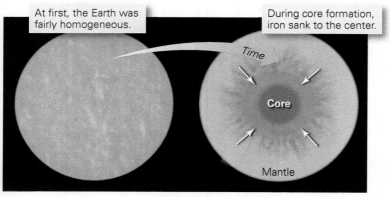

(a) When the Earth became hot enough inside, rock comprising it started to melt, and droplets of iron sank to the center, accumulating to form a core. Once core formation happened, it could not happen again.

(b) Moon formation happened early during Earth history but probably after core formation. According to a popular theory, the Moon coalesced from debris resulting from the collision of a Mars-sized protoplanet with the Earth.

During the Archean, another type of unidirectional change then began when partial melting, perhaps associated with subduction and/or the upwelling of mantle plumes, started to produce relatively low-density rocks, such as granite. Low-density rocks could not be subducted and thus remained at or near the surface to constitute relatively buoyant blocks of crust. Eventually, these blocks sutured together to form the first continents. Effectively, partial melting "distilled" the crust out of the mantle. The amount of continental crust progressively increased as the process continued until by the end of the Archean, continental crust covered about 25% of the Earth's surface. Subsequently, continental area has continued to grow but at a slower pace—today continental crust underlies about 30% of the surface.

Overall, therefore, the transition from the Hadean Eon to the Archean Eon saw a remarkable unidirectional change in the nature of the Earth. By early Archean time, our planet had distinct continents and ocean basins, and thus looked radically different from the way it did when it was first formed (see Chapter 13).

The Evolution of the Atmosphere and Oceans

The Earth's atmosphere has also undergone major unidirectional change over time. Changes in atmospheric composition are so profound that researchers distinguish among first, second, and third atmospheres. As discussed in Chapter 20, the "first atmosphere" consisted of gases from the protoplanetary disk that had been trapped by our planet's gravity. These gases eventually escaped and were replaced by gases belched from volcanoes, perhaps mixed with gases brought to the Earth by comets, and the Earth accumulated a "second atmosphere" composed dominantly of carbon dioxide (CO_2) and water (H_2O). Other gases, such as nitrogen (N_2), composed only a minor proportion of the second atmosphere. When the Earth's surface cooled, however, water condensed and fell as rain, collecting in low areas to form oceans. Gradually, CO_2 dissolved in the oceans and was absorbed by chemical-weathering reactions on land, so its concentration in the atmosphere decreased. N_2, which doesn't react with other chemicals, was left behind. Thus, the atmosphere's composition changed to become the "third atmosphere," dominated by N_2. Photosynthetic organisms appeared early in the Archean. But it probably wasn't until between 2.5 and 2.0 Ga, the early Proterozoic, that oxygen (O_2) became a significant proportion of the atmosphere, and it didn't reach breathable concentrations for another billion years.

Did you ever wonder . . .

whether the Earth's atmosphere has always been breathable?

The Evolution of Life

During its earliest stages, Earth's surface was probably lifeless, for carbon-based organisms could not survive the high temperatures of the time. The fossil record indicates that life had appeared at least by 3.8 Ga and has undergone evolution, a unidirectional change, in fits and starts ever since (see Interlude E). Though simple organisms such as archaea and bacteria still exist, life evolution during the late Proterozoic and early Phanerozoic yielded multicellular plants and animals (Fig. 23.3). Life now

FIGURE 23.3 New species of life have evolved over geologic time. Though some of the simplest still exist, more complex organisms have appeared more recently.

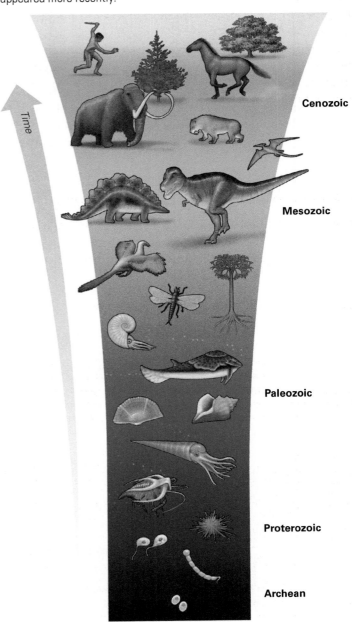

inhabits regions from a few kilometers below the surface to a few kilometers above, yielding a diverse and complex biosphere.

23.3 Cyclic Changes

In *cyclic changes*, a sequence of stages may be repeated over time. Some cyclic changes are periodic in that the cycles happen with a definable frequency, but others are not. Below we look at several examples of cyclic change—you'll see that some involve movements of physical components of the Earth, whereas others involve transfer of chemicals among both living and nonliving reservoirs.

The Supercontinent Cycle

During Earth history, the map of the planet's surface has constantly changed. At times, almost all continental crust merged to form a supercontinent, but usually the crust is distributed among several smaller continents. The process of change during which a supercontinent forms and later breaks apart is called the **supercontinent cycle** (Fig. 23.4). Geologists have found evidence that supercontinents existed at least three or four times during the past 3 billion years of Earth history—no two included exactly the same arrangement of smaller continents. The most recent supercontinent, Pangaea, formed 300 million years ago (Ma) at the end of the Paleozoic Era and survived until it broke up to form today's continents, beginning about 200 Ma.

The Sea-Level Change Cycle

Global sea level rose and fell by as much as 300 m during the Phanerozoic and likely did the same in the Precambrian. When sea level rises, the shoreline migrates inland, and low-lying plains in the continental interiors become submerged. In fact, during periods of particularly high sea level, more than half of Earth's continental area was covered by shallow seas. At such times, shallow marine sediment buries continental regions (Fig. 23.5a, b). When sea level falls, the continents become dry again, and regional unconformities develop. We can see the record of this sea-level change cycle preserved in the sedimentary beds of the midwestern United States. Here a succession of strata record at least six continent-wide advances and retreats of the sea, each of which left behind a blanket of sediment called a **sedimentary sequence**. Unconformities define the boundaries between the sequences (Fig. 23.5c). Of note, the sequence deposited during the Pennsylvanian contains at least 30 shorter repeated intervals, called *cyclothems*,

FIGURE 23.4 The stages of the supercontinent cycle.

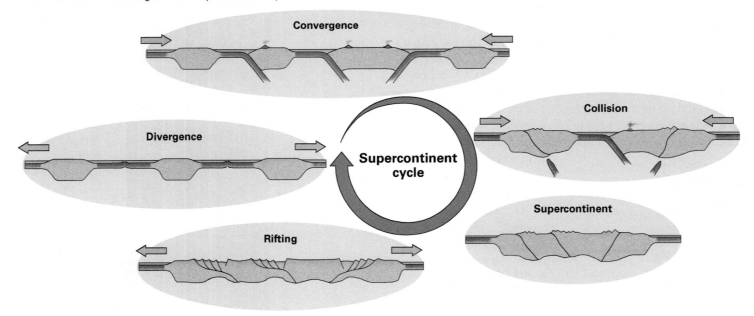

FIGURE 23.5 Sea-level change, and its manifestations, over geologic time.

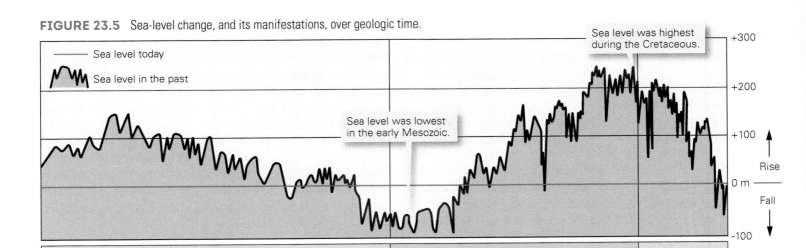

(a) This chart provides one interpretation of sea-level change during the past half-billion years, based on the stratigraphic record. There is not full agreement about this interpretation; it remains the subject of research.

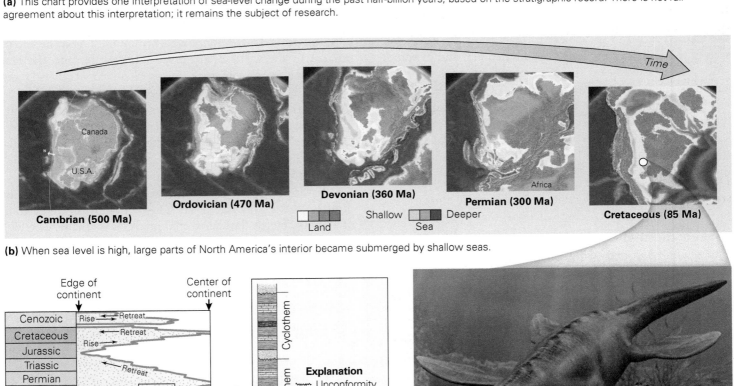

Cambrian (500 Ma)　**Ordovician (470 Ma)**　**Devonian (360 Ma)**　**Permian (300 Ma)**　**Cretaceous (85 Ma)**

Shallow ▭▭▭ Deeper
Land ▭▭ Sea

(b) When sea level is high, large parts of North America's interior became submerged by shallow seas.

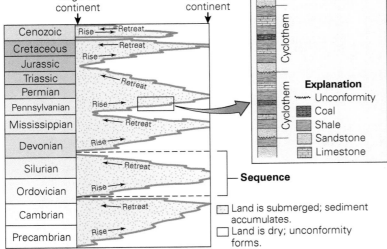

Explanation
～～ Unconformity
▨ Coal
▨ Shale
▨ Sandstone
▨ Limestone

Sequence

▭ Land is submerged; sediment accumulates.
▭ Land is dry; unconformity forms.

(c) Sea-level rise and fall left sedimentary sequences separated by unconformities. Pennsylvanian sequences contain cyclothems.

A plesiosaur searches for food in the Cretaceous seaway of North America.

each of which contains a layer of coal. Cyclothems represent short-term cycles of sea-level rise and fall.

After studying sedimentary sequences around the world, geologists pieced together a chart defining the succession of global transgressions and regressions during the Phanerozoic Eon. The global sedimentary cycle chart may largely reflect the cycles of *eustatic* (worldwide) *sea-level change*. However, the chart probably does not give us an exact image of sea-level change because the sedimentary record reflects other factors as well, such as changes in sediment supply. Eustatic sea-level changes may be due to advances and retreats of continental glaciers, changes in the volume of mid-ocean ridge systems, and changes in continental elevation and area. Note that while we refer to the repeated rise and fall of sea level over time as a "cycle," stages in the cycle are not periodic; that is, the time intervals between successive events of sea-level rise are not constant.

The Rock Cycle

We learned early in this book that the crust of the Earth consists of three rock types: igneous, sedimentary, and metamorphic. Atoms making up the minerals of one rock type may later become part of another rock type. As we learned in Interlude C, this process is the *rock cycle*. In effect, we can think of rocks as, simply, reservoirs of atoms—during the rock cycle, atoms move from reservoir to reservoir over time. Each stage in the rock cycle changes the Earth by redistributing and modifying material.

Biogeochemical Cycles

A **biogeochemical cycle** involves the passage of a chemical among nonliving and living reservoirs in the Earth System, mostly on or near the surface. Nonliving reservoirs include the atmosphere, the crust, and the ocean, whereas living reservoirs include plants, animals, and microbes. Some stages in a biogeochemical cycle may take only hours, some may take thousands of years, and others may take millions of years. The transfer of a chemical from reservoir to reservoir during these cycles doesn't really seem like a change in the Earth in the way that the movement of continents or the metamorphism of rock seems like a change, because for intervals of time biogeochemical cycles attain a **steady-state condition**, meaning the proportions of a chemical in different reservoirs remain fairly constant even though there is a constant flux (flow) of the chemical among reservoirs. When we speak of global change in a biogeochemical cycle, we mean a change in the relative proportions of a chemical held in different reservoirs at a given time—in other words, a change in the steady-state condition. Although a great variety of chemicals (water, carbon, oxygen, sulfur, ammonia, phosphorus, and nitrogen) participate in biogeochemical cycles, here we look at only two: water (H_2O) and carbon (C).

Hydrologic Cycle As we learned in Interlude F, the hydrologic cycle involves the movement of water from reservoir to reservoir on or near the surface of the Earth. The hydrologic cycle is an example of a biogeochemical cycle in that a chemical (H_2O) passes through both nonliving and living entities—the oceans, the atmosphere, surface water, groundwater, glaciers, soil, and living organisms. Global change in the hydrologic cycle occurs when a change in climate alters the ratio between the amount of water held in the ocean relative to the amount held in continental ice sheets. When continental glaciers grow, water that had been stored in oceans moves into glacial reservoirs, so sea level drops. When the glaciers melt, water returns to the oceans, so sea level rises.

The Carbon Cycle Most carbon in the near-surface realm of Earth originally bubbled out of the mantle in the form of CO_2 gas released by volcanoes (Fig. 23.6). Once it enters the atmosphere, it moves through various reservoirs of the Earth system in the **carbon cycle**. Some dissolves in seawater to form bicarbonate (HCO_3^-) ions, which may later become incorporated in the shells of organisms that settle onto the seafloor. Some reacts with rock during chemical weathering and becomes incorporated in minerals. And some gets absorbed by photosynthetic organisms (microbes and plants), which convert it into sugar and other organic chemicals—this carbon enters the food chain and ultimately makes up the flesh of animals. Of note, about 63 billion tons of carbon move from the atmosphere into life forms every year.

Of the carbon incorporated in organisms, some returns directly to the atmosphere (as CO_2) through the respiration of animals, by the flatulence of animals (as methane, or CH_4), or by the decay of dead organisms. But some can be stored for long periods of time in fossil fuels (oil, gas, and coal), in organic shale, in methane hydrates (ice containing CH_4), or in limestone ($CaCO_3$). This carbon can return to the atmosphere (as CO_2) due to the burning of fossil fuels, the melting of methane hydrates, production of cement, or the metamorphism of limestone. Or it can return to the sea after undergoing chemical weathering followed by dissolution in river water or groundwater.

Take-Home Message

Some changes in the Earth System are cyclic in that they have stages that may be repeated. Examples include the supercontinent cycle, the sea-level cycle, the rock cycle, the hydrologic cycle, and biogeochemical cycles. During the carbon cycle, carbon can be stored in both living and nonliving reservoirs.

QUICK QUESTION: What evidence indicates that sea level rises and falls over time?

FIGURE 23.6 In the carbon cycle, carbon transfers among various reservoirs at or near the Earth's surface. Red arrows indicate release to the air, and green arrows indicate absorption from air.

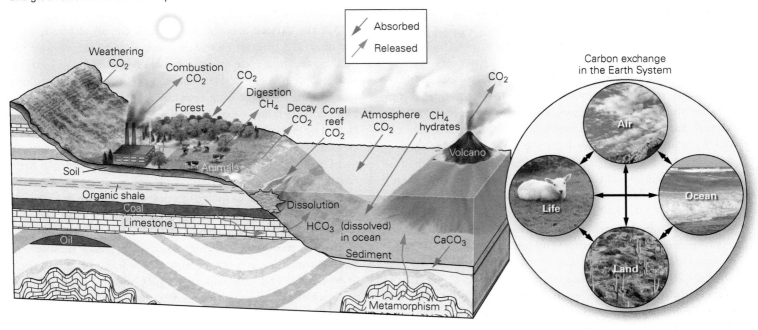

23.4 Global Climate Change

What Is Climate Change?

How often have you seen a newspaper proclaim "Record High Temperatures!" when thermometers register temperatures several degrees above "normal" for days on end. Do such headlines mean that "climate" is changing? To start addressing this question, we first need to distinguish between two common terms: weather and climate.

As discussed in Chapter 20, atmospheric conditions during a specific time interval in a given region define the region's **weather** for the time interval. The weather may be "windy, rainy, and cool" in the morning and "calm, sunny, and dry" in the afternoon. The term **climate**, in contrast, refers to overall range of weather conditions, as well as the typical daily to seasonal variability of weather conditions, as observed over a period of decades for a region. We can contrast, for example, a "tropical climate" with a "temperate climate"—the former tends to have hot, humid days all year, whereas the latter tends to have contrasting seasons and a wide range of temperature and humidity. So a newspaper's headline about a single hot spell or cold snap does not mean that the climate is changing. But if a new set of conditions—say, an overall increase in average temperature, a rising snow line, a longer growing season, or a change in storm frequency or intensity—becomes the new

norm for a region, then climate change has occurred. And if such changes happen worldwide, then **global climate change** has occurred.

The stratigraphic record clearly shows that global climate change has taken place repeatedly throughout Earth's long history for natural reasons. As we described in Chapter 13, for example, the Cretaceous was a time of relatively warm temperatures during which no polar ice caps existed, while the late Proterozoic may have seen "snowball Earth," when all oceans were frozen over and glaciers covered all continents. This well-established principle has been recognized since geologists first learned how to interpret the stratigraphic record, so it's not news. But global climate change has become a staple of the news media in recent years, and that's because research of the past few decades led to the conclusion that global climate change is now taking place, not at the slow pace typical of most geologic phenomena but at rates fast enough to have potential impacts in the next few decades. In other words, readers of this book may see the effects of contemporary global climate change in their lifetimes.

In this section, we begin our study of global climate change by first reviewing the fundamental role that greenhouse gases play in regulating atmospheric temperature, then by describing how researchers study past climates, and finally by defining different rates at which climate has changed over geologic time. For purpose of our discussion, we distinguish between *long-term climate change*, which takes place over millions to tens of millions of years, and *short-term climate change*, which takes place over tens to hundreds of thousands of years. If average atmospheric and sea-surface temperature rises, we have **global warming**, and if they fall we have **global cooling**.

The Role of Greenhouse Gases

The Sun constantly bathes the Earth in visible light. Some of this energy reflects off the atmosphere or off the Earth's surface, so that our planet shines when viewed from space. The Earth's surface absorbs the remainder of the incoming visible light and then releases it in the form of thermal energy (infrared radiation) that radiates upward. If the Earth had no atmosphere, all of this thermal energy would escape back into space. But our planet does have an atmosphere, and certain of its gases (H_2O, CO_2, CH_4, NO_2 [nitrogen dioxide], and O_3 [ozone]) absorb thermal radiation and re-radiate it. Some of the re-radiated energy continues up into space, but some heads downward and warms the lower atmosphere (Fig. 23.7; see Chapter 20). In effect, these gases trap infrared radiation and keep the lower atmosphere warm, somewhat as glass traps heat in a greenhouse. Thus, the overall trapping process is known as the **greenhouse effect**, and the gases that cause it are **greenhouse gases**.

Researchers estimate that were it not for the greenhouse effect, global average surface temperature of the Earth would be about 33°C (91.4°F) lower than it is today. Put another way, an Earth without greenhouse gases would have an average global temperature of about –19°C (–2.2°F), and our planet's surface would be a frozen wasteland—it is the presence of greenhouse gases that make the Earth habitable! Because greenhouse gases trap heat, any process that transfers these gases from underground, oceanic, or biomass reservoirs into the atmospheric reservoir will cause the climate to warm. Similarly, any process

that removes greenhouse gases from the atmospheric reservoir and transfers them in biomass, or into oceanic or underground reservoirs, will cause the climate to cool.

Of the various greenhouse gases in the atmosphere, H_2O occurs in the greatest concentration and plays the biggest role in the greenhouse effect—it causes between 30% and 70% of the greenhouse effect. But researchers emphasize that global temperature changes over time are not driven by changes in H_2O concentration—rather, changes in H_2O concentration are caused by global temperature changes. That's because water concentration in the atmosphere, as represented by relative humidity (see Chapter 20), varies radically from place to place, and if the relative humidity gets too high at a location, excess water simply rains out. In fact, H_2O molecules that enter the atmosphere stay there for a very short time, generally less than nine days.

Of the other greenhouse gases, CO_2 and CH_4 play the most significant role in influencing changes in global atmospheric temperature. This is partly because CO_2 molecules are 20 times as efficient as H_2O molecules, and CH_4 molecules are about 70 times as efficient as CO_2 molecules, in absorbing and re-radiating infrared radiation. So even though these gases occur in very low concentrations, they can contribute significantly to the greenhouse effect (9% to 30%, and 4% to 9%, respectively). Also, CO_2 and CH_4 mix thoroughly with other gases in the lower atmosphere and remain in the atmosphere for a long time. So if new CO_2 or CH_4 enters the atmosphere from a surface or subsurface reservoir, it adds to the existing quantities of these gases and causes the overall concentration of these gases to increase—the excess doesn't simply rain back to Earth. The increase in the concentration of these gases causes an increase in the greenhouse effect and, therefore, global temperature increases.

Warming or cooling due to changes in the concentration of greenhouse gases can be amplified by positive or negative

FIGURE 23.7 The greenhouse effect shows how thermal energy can be trapped in the atmosphere.

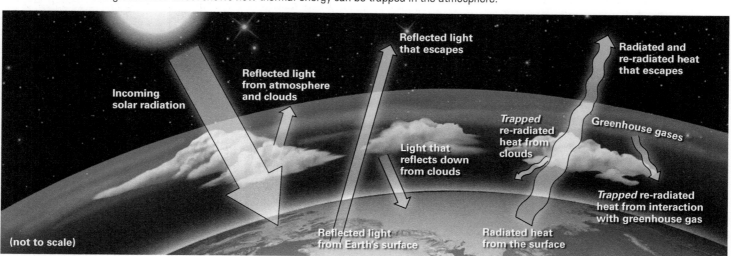

feedback mechanisms. *Negative* feedback slows a process down or even reverses it, whereas *positive* feedback enhances a process and amplifies its consequences. Let's consider an example of how positive feedback affects climate. Imagine that global average atmospheric temperature has increased due to an increase in CO_2. This increase will, in turn, cause the oceans to warm and evaporate more, so more water transfers into the atmospheric reservoir globally and increases the greenhouse effect due to water vapor. The increase also causes some of the CO_2 dissolved in the oceans to come out of solution and return to the atmosphere, and it causes CH_4 to enter the atmosphere from decay of organic matter in melting permafrost and perhaps from the melting of gas hydrates (ice containing dissolved CH_4). Thus, the warming due to the initial addition of CO_2 can cause the concentration of other greenhouse gases to increase overall, forcing the atmosphere to warm even more than it would have in the first place.

Methods of Studying Climate Change

Geologists and climatologists are working hard to define the nature of climate change, the rates at which change can take place, and the effects that change may have on our planet. There are three basic approaches to studying global climate change: (1) measure past climate change, as recorded by stratigraphy, to document the magnitude of changes that are possible and the rate at which such changes occurred; (2) conduct experiments and calculations to see how changes in the concentration of atmospheric components, such as CO_2 or dust, might affect climate; (3) develop computer programs (called *general circulation models*, or GCMs) to simulate how factors such as atmospheric composition, topography, ocean currents, and Earth's orbit affect the circulation of the atmosphere and, therefore, the distribution of climate belts. Researchers use GCMs to develop broader **climate-change models** that seek to provide insight into when and why changes took place in the past and whether they will happen in the future. Climate-change models try to predict changes in rainfall, sea level, ice cover, and other physical features that may be influenced by the warming or cooling of the atmosphere.

Let's look more closely at how geologists study the **paleoclimate** (past climate) so as to document climate changes throughout Earth history. Any feature whose character depends on the climate, and whose age can be determined, provides a clue to defining paleoclimate. Examples include:

Did you ever wonder . . .

how researchers study past climates on Earth?

- *Stratigraphic record:* The nature of sedimentary strata deposited at a certain location reflects the climate at that location. For example, an outcrop exposing cross-bedded sandstone, overlain successively by coal and glacial till, indicates that the site of the outcrop has endured different climates (desert, then tropical, then glacial) over time.

- *Paleontological evidence:* Different assemblages of species survive in different climatic belts. Thus, the succession of fossils in a sedimentary sequence provides clues to the changes in climate at that site. For example, a record of short-term climate change can be obtained by studying the succession of plankton fossils in seafloor sediments, because cold-water species of plankton are different from warm-water species. Fossil plant pollen preserved in the mud of bogs also provides information about paleoclimate since different plant species live in different climates (Fig. 23.8a). Pollen studies show, for example, that spruce forests, indicative of cool climates, have slowly migrated north since the last ice age (Fig. 23.8b).

- *Oxygen–isotope ratios:* Geologists have found that the ratio of ^{18}O to ^{16}O in glacial ice indicates the atmospheric temperature in which the snow that made up the ice formed: simplistically, the ratio is larger in snow that forms in warmer air, and smaller in snow that forms in colder air. Because of this relationship, the isotope ratio of the oxygen in H_2O measured in a succession of ice layers in a glacier indicates temperature change over time. Researchers have now obtained ice cores down to a depth of almost 3 km in Antarctica and in Greenland, a record that spans over 720,000 years (Fig. 23.9a). The $^{18}O/^{16}O$ ratio in the $CaCO_3$ making up plankton shells also gives geologists an indication of past temperatures. Thus, measurement of oxygen-isotope ratios in drill cores of marine sediment extends the record of temperature change back over millions of years (Fig. 23.9b, c).

- *Bubbles in ice:* Bubbles in ice trap the air present at the time the ice forms. By analyzing these bubbles, geologists can measure the concentration of CO_2 in the atmosphere back through time. This information can be used to correlate CO_2 concentration with past atmospheric temperature.

- *Growth rings:* If you've ever looked at a tree stump, you will have noticed the concentric rings visible in the wood. Each ring represents one year of growth, and the thickness of the ring indicates the rate of growth in a given year. Trees grow faster during warmer, wetter years and more slowly during cold, dry years (Fig. 23.10a). Thus, the succession of ring widths provides a calibrated record of climate during the lifetime of the tree. Bristlecone pines supply a record back through 4,000 years. To go further into the past, dendrochronologists (scientists who study tree rings) look at the record of rings in logs dated by the radiocarbon technique or in logs whose ages overlap with that of the oldest living tree. Growth rings in corals and shells can provide similar information.

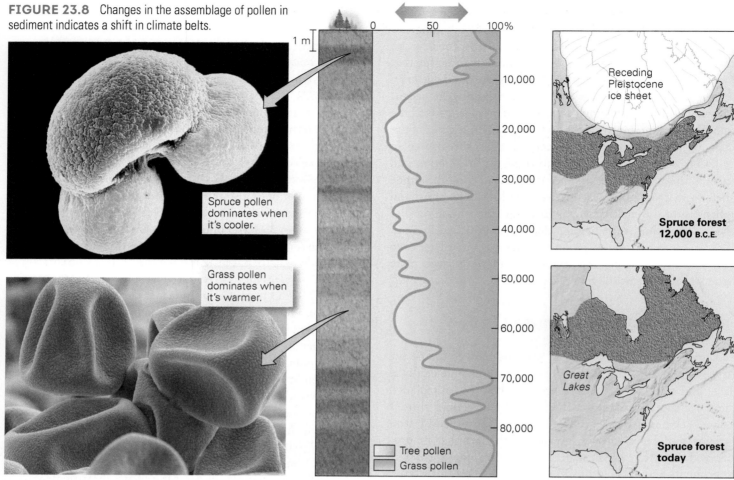

FIGURE 23.8 Changes in the assemblage of pollen in sediment indicates a shift in climate belts.

Spruce pollen dominates when it's cooler.

Grass pollen dominates when it's warmer.

Receding Pleistocene ice sheet

Spruce forest 12,000 B.C.E.

Great Lakes

Spruce forest today

Tree pollen
Grass pollen

(a) The proportion of tree pollen relative to grass pollen can change in a sedimentary sequence through time. Researchers plot changes in the proportion of pollen types over time by examining samples from a column of sediment.

(b) Spruce forests (green) grew farther south 12,000 years ago than they do today.

• *Human history:* Researchers have been able to make careful, direct measurements of climate changes only for the past few decades. This record is not long enough to document long-term climate change. But history, both written and archaeological, contains important clues to climates at times centuries or millennia in the past. Periods of unusual cold or drought leave an impression on people, who record them in paintings, stories, and records of crop success or failure (**Fig. 23.10b; Box 23.1**).

Long-Term Climate Change

Using the variety of techniques described above, geologists have reconstructed an approximate record of global climate, represented by the Earth's mean atmospheric temperature, for geologic time. The record shows that, with the exception of snowball Earth intervals (see Chapter 13), temperature has stayed between the freezing point of water and the boiling point of water since the beginning of the Archean. But the temperature has not always been the same—at some times in the past, the Earth's atmosphere was significantly warmer than it is today, and at other times it was significantly cooler. The warmer periods have come to be known as **greenhouse** (or **hothouse**) **periods** and the colder as **icehouse periods**. (The more familiar term, *ice age*, refers to portions of an icehouse period when the Earth was cold enough for ice sheets to advance and cover substantial areas of the continents.) As the chart in **Figure 23.11a** shows, there have been at least five major icehouse periods during geologic time.

Let's look a little more closely at the climate record of the last 100 million years, for this time interval includes the transition between a greenhouse and an icehouse period. Paleontological and other data suggest that the climate of the Mesozoic Era, the Age of Dinosaurs, was much warmer than the climate of today. At the equator, average annual temperatures

FIGURE 23.9 The proportion of isotopes transferred between reservoirs during evaporation or precipitation depends on temperature. The $^{18}O/^{16}O$ ratio can be studied in glacial ice (H_2O) and fossil shells ($CaCO_3$).

(a) A researcher examines an ice core in the field. Lab photos reveal annual layers.

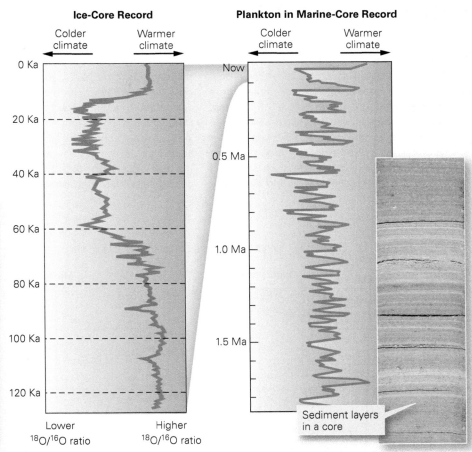

Ice-Core Record

Colder climate ← → Warmer climate

0 Ka
20 Ka
40 Ka
60 Ka
80 Ka
100 Ka
120 Ka

Lower $^{18}O/^{16}O$ ratio   Higher $^{18}O/^{16}O$ ratio

(b) The $^{18}O/^{16}O$ ratios in an ice core represent temperature changes.

Plankton in Marine-Core Record

Colder climate ← → Warmer climate

Now
0.5 Ma
1.0 Ma
1.5 Ma

Sediment layers in a core

(c) Studies of $^{18}O/^{16}O$ ratios in deep-sea cores also provide a climate record.

FIGURE 23.10 Records of recent climate change.

Researchers extract cores to see rings in living trees without damaging the tree.

(a) Tree rings provide a record of climate; more growth happens in wet years than in dry years.

(b) Historical archives provide records of floods and droughts.

BOX 23.1 CONSIDER THIS . . .

Global Climate Change and the Birth of Legends

Some of the myths passed down from the early days of civilization may have their roots in global climate change. For example, recent evidence suggests that before 7,600 years ago, the region that is now the Black Sea contained a much smaller freshwater lake surrounded by settlements. When the most recent ice-age glaciers retreated, sea level rose, and the Mediterranean Sea eventually broke through a natural dam at the site of the present Bosporus Strait. Researchers suggest that seawater from the Mediterranean spilled into the Black Sea basin via a waterfall 200 times larger than Niagara Falls. This influx of water caused the lake level to rise by as much as 10 cm per day, and within a year 155,000 square km (60,000 square miles) of populated land had become submerged beneath hundreds of meters of water. This traumatic flooding presumably forced many people to migrate, and its timing has led some researchers to speculate that it may have inspired the Epic of Gilgamesh (written in Babylonia ca. 2000 B.C.E.) and, later, the biblical epic of Noah's Ark.

FIGURE 23.11 Estimates of global temperature change over geologic time, relative to a reference value.

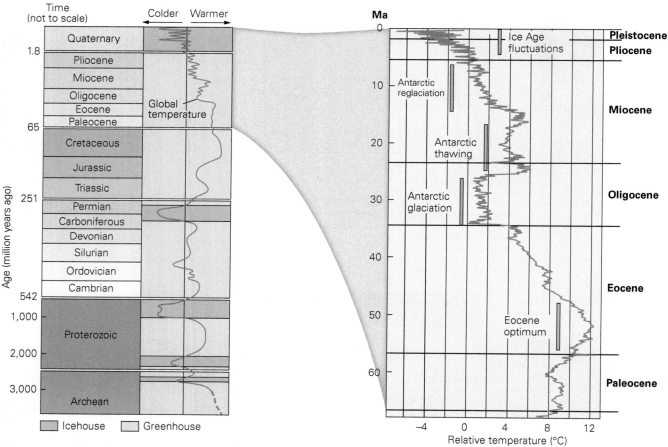

(a) Geologic data suggest the occurrence of icehouse and greenhouse phases at various times during Earth history.

(b) During the Cenozoic, there was an overall cooling trend; climate alternately warmed and cooled dramatically during the Pleistocene Ice Age.

may have been 2° to 6°C warmer, while at the poles temperatures may have been 20° to 60°C warmer. In fact, during the Cretaceous Period, dinosaurs could live at high latitudes, and there were no polar ice caps on Earth. But starting about 80 Ma, the Earth's atmosphere began to cool. The cooling trend continued, except for an interval of about 10 million years, a time now called the "Eocene climatic optimum" (**Fig. 23.11b**), and at about 33 Ma, our planet entered an icehouse period.

Temperatures in polar regions dropped below freezing, and the Antarctic ice sheet formed, and beginning at about 2.6 Ma, the Pleistocene Ice Age began.

What caused long-term global climate changes? The answer may lie in the complex relationships among the various solar, geologic, and biogeochemical cycles of the Earth System (Box 23.2). Factors that may have played a role include the following.

- *Positions of continents:* Continental drift influences the climate by controlling the pattern of oceanic currents, which redistribute heat around the planet's surface (Fig. 23.12a). Drift also determines whether the land is at high or low latitudes (and thus how much solar radiation strikes it), whether or not there are large continental interior regions where extremely cold winter temperatures can develop, and/or whether there is a lot of rainfall, which could cause weathering.

- *Volcanic activity:* A long-term global increase in volcanic activity may contribute to long-term global warming, if it increases the concentration of CO_2 in the atmosphere. For example, when Pangaea broke up during the Cretaceous Period, numerous rifts formed, and seafloor-spreading rates were particularly high, so volcanoes were more abundant than they are today. Such voluminous volcanic activity may have triggered Cretaceous greenhouse conditions.

- *Uplift of land surfaces:* Tectonic events that lead to the long-term uplift of the land affect atmospheric CO_2 concentration, because such events expose land to weathering, and chemical-weathering reactions absorb CO_2. Thus, uplift potentially decreases the greenhouse effect and causes global cooling. For example, uplift of the Himalayas and Tibet may have triggered Cenozoic icehouse conditions (Fig. 23.12b). Such uplift will also affect atmospheric circulation and rainfall rates (see Chapter 20).

FIGURE 23.12 Changes in the distribution and elevation of landmasses can affect climate.

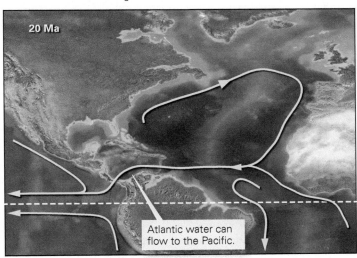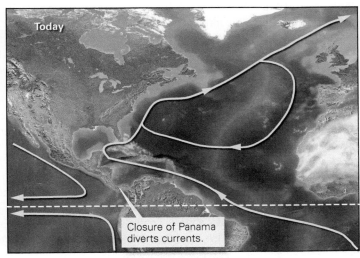

(a) When the Isthmus of Panama, a volcanic arc, formed during the Miocene, the patterns of oceanic currents in the North Atlantic changed. The white dashed line is the equator.

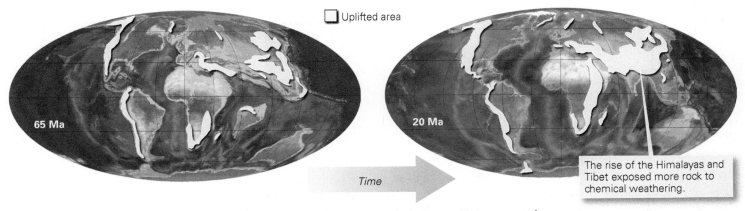

(b) The percentage of elevated land increased between 65 Ma and 20 Ma because of orogeny. The exposure of more rock leads to more weathering, potentially affecting the concentration of greenhouse gases in the atmosphere.

BOX 23.2   CONSIDER THIS . . .

Goldilocks and the Faint Young Sun

Like Baby Bear's porridge in the tale of *Goldilocks and the Three Bears*, Earth is not too hot, and it's not too cold . . . it's just right for liquid water and, therefore, for life, to exist (**Fig. Bx23.2**). Researchers informally refer to the two related factors that make the Earth "just right" as the **Goldilocks effect**.

What factors keep Earth's surface habitable? The first is our planet's distance from the Sun, which determines the intensity of radiation that reaches the surface, and the second is the concentration of CO_2 and other greenhouse gases, which governs how much of that radiation remains trapped in the atmosphere. If the Earth orbited too close to the Sun, solar radiation would be so intense that water could not exist in liquid form, regardless of atmospheric composition. And without seas of liquid water, most CO_2 emitted by volcanoes could not have dissolved in the sea, so the atmosphere would contain so much water and CO_2 that the greenhouse effect would make surface temperatures on Earth way too hot for life. In contrast, if the Earth orbited too far from the Sun, temperatures would remain so cold that, regardless of atmospheric composition, any water present would freeze solid and life could not have evolved.

Astronomers define the distance from the Sun at which the Goldilocks effect is possible as the **habitable zone** of the Solar System.

The habitable zone currently extends roughly from 0.8 AU to 1.3 AU. (An AU, or astronomical unit, represents the mean distance between the Earth and the Sun.) Notably, the distance of the habitable zone from the Sun has increased over the history of the solar system. That's because the intensity of radiation emitted by the Sun has increased over time. This change has taken place because the Sun's energy comes from the fusion of four hydrogen atoms to form one helium atom, and one helium atom takes up less space than four hydrogen atoms. So, over time, production of helium has caused the Sun to contract. The resulting increase in internal pressure and temperature within the Sun, in turn, has caused the rate of fusion reactions to increase, and the Sun may be about 30% brighter today than it was when the Earth first formed.

If the Sun's intensity were the only factor controlling Earth's temperature, our planet should have been over 20°C cooler during the Archean than it is today, and all water should have been frozen. But this wasn't the case. Stratigraphic and fossil records indicate that water has existed in liquid form on our planet's surface at least since the early Archean (~ 3.8 Ga). Researchers refer to this apparent contradiction between the calculated temperature and the observed temperature of the early Earth as the **faint young Sun paradox**. Most researchers agree that

the paradox can be resolved by keeping in mind that earlier in Earth history, before the widespread appearance of photosynthetic life, the atmosphere contained more CO_2 than it does today. The greenhouse effect caused by the additional CO_2 increased the temperature of the Earth's atmosphere enough to counteract the lack of radiation from the faint young Sun, and this kept surface temperatures above freezing.

With the faint young Sun paradox in mind, astronomers speculate that when the Solar System was younger, Venus may also have orbited within the habitable zone and may have hosted liquid water. But as the Sun became brighter, Venus warmed up until its surface water evaporated. Addition of water to Venus's atmosphere caused the planet's surface to warm even more, leading to a drastic positive feedback that could not be stopped. Such a situation is called the *runaway greenhouse effect*. As a consequence, Venus's atmosphere eventually became so hot that water molecules broke apart, forming hydrogen atoms that escaped to space and oxygen atoms that reacted with rocks on the planet's surface to produce iron-oxide minerals. Volcanic CO_2 became the dominant gas of Venus's atmosphere, forming a dense blanket that now keeps the surface temperature of the planet at about 460°C, hot enough to melt lead.

FIGURE Bx23.2 The "Goldilocks effect," as applied to the Earth and its neighbors.

Venus is too hot.

Mars is too cold.

Earth is just right.

- *Formation of fossil fuels:* At various times during Earth history, environments suitable for the growth, accumulation, and burial of abundant organic material become particularly widespread. Once buried, the organic material transforms into coal or oil and can remain trapped underground. This overall process removes CO_2 from the atmosphere and thus may result in global cooling. The cooling that occurred in the late Paleozoic, a time when coal swamps were widespread, may be a manifestation of this process.
- *Life evolution:* The appearance or extinction of certain life forms may have affected climate significantly. For example, some researchers speculate that the appearance of lichens in the late Proterozoic may have decreased atmospheric CO_2 concentration and thus could have triggered icehouse conditions. Similarly, the appearance of grasses at around 30 to 35 Ma may have triggered Cenozoic icehouse conditions.

Natural Short-Term Climate Change

So far, we've focused on climate change that takes place on a time scale of millions to tens or even hundreds of millions of years. The geologic record of the past few million years provides enough detail to allow geologists to detect cycles of climate change that have durations of centuries to hundreds of thousands of years. Such *short-term climate change* must be a consequence of factors that can operate quickly in the context of geologic time. We can get a sense of short-term climate change by examining the Pleistocene stratigraphic record. Changes in fossil assemblages, sediment composition, and isotopic ratios indicate that continental glaciers advanced and retreated about 20 to 30 times in the northern hemisphere during the past 2.5 million years. Each advance (glaciation) represents an interval of global cooling, and each retreat (interglacial) represents an interval of global warming.

If we focus on the last 15,000 years, a period that includes all of the Holocene, we see trends of cooling or warming that last thousands of years, within which there are climate-change events whose duration lasts centuries or less (Fig. 23.13a). For example, the time between about 15,000 and 10,500 B.C.E. was a warming period during which the last ice-age glaciers retreated. At 10,500 B.C.E., the Earth entered the *Younger Dryas,* an interval of cooler temperatures named for an Arctic flower that became widespread at the time. Then climate warmed again, reaching a peak at 5,000 to 6,000 years ago, a period called the *Holocene maximum,* when average temperatures peaked at about 2°C above temperatures of today. This warming peak led to increased evaporation and therefore precipitation, making the Middle East region unusually wet and fertile—conditions that may partially account for the rise of civilization in Mesopotamia. The temperature dipped to a low about 3,000 years ago, before returning to a high during the Middle Ages, a time called the *Medieval Warm Period.* During this time, Vikings landed on the coast of Greenland and established settlements which could be self-supporting because of the relatively mild climate (Fig. 23.13b). The temperature dropped again from 1500 C.E. to about 1800 C.E., a period known as the *Little Ice Age,* when Alpine glaciers advanced and the canals of the Netherlands froze over in winter (Fig. 23.13c; see Fig. 22.33b). Overall, the climate has warmed since the end of the Little Ice Age, and today global temperature is comparable to that of the Medieval Warm Period.

What factors might control short-term climate change? There may be many, but geologists speculate that the following phenomena may have played the most important role.

- *Changes in Earth's orbit and tilt:* As Milanković first recognized in 1920, the tilt of Earth's axis changes over a period of 41,000 years, the Earth's axis undergoes precession over a period of 23,000 years, and the eccentricity of the Earth's orbit changes over a period of 100,000 years. Together these phenomena cause the amount of summer insolation and, therefore, the temperature in high latitudes to vary (see Chapter 22).
- *Changes in ocean currents:* Recent studies suggest that the configuration of currents can change quite quickly and that this configuration could affect the climate. The Younger Dryas, for example, may have resulted when a layer of freshwater from melting glaciers spread out over the North Atlantic and prevented thermohaline circulation in the ocean, thereby shutting down the Gulf Stream (see Chapter 18).
- *Large eruptions of volcanic aerosols:* Not all of the sunlight that reaches the Earth penetrates its atmosphere and warms the ground. Some gets reflected by the atmosphere. The degree of reflectivity, or **albedo,** of the atmosphere increases not only if cloud cover increases, as we have noted, but also if the concentration of volcanic aerosols in the atmosphere increases. Very large eruptions can emit enough aerosols (particularly SO_2) to affect global temperature for months to years. For example, the year following the 1815 eruption of Mt. Tambora in the western Pacific became known as the "year without a summer," for sulfur aerosols that erupted encircled the Earth and blocked the Sun. Snow fell in Europe throughout the spring, and the entire summer was cold. Recent studies suggest that the immense eruption of Toba (in Indonesia) 70,000 years ago disrupted climate for so many years that it caused worldwide extinctions and nearly eliminated *Homo sapiens.* (Note that the effect of volcanic aerosol emission is global cooling, the opposite of the effect of volcanic CO_2

FIGURE 23.13 Climate during the Holocene. Measurements suggest that temperature has varied significantly.

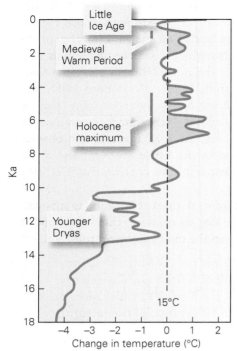

(a) There were several temperature highs and lows during the Holocene.

At the end of the Little Ice Age, this tributary glacier in France reached the main valley floor.

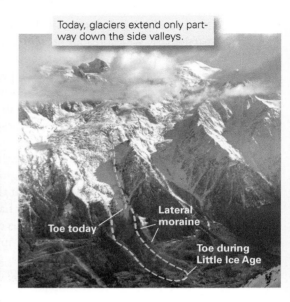

Today, glaciers extend only part-way down the side valleys.

Lateral moraine

Toe today

Toe during Little Ice Age

(c) Glaciers advanced in Europe during the Little Ice Age.

(b) During the Medieval Warm Period, Vikings settled in Greenland, where the climate was warm enough for agriculture.

emission, which causes global warming. Aerosols tend to impact climate for a relatively short time, but CO_2 can have effects for a relatively long time.)

• *Fluctuations in solar radiation:* The amount of energy produced by the Sun varies with the **sunspot cycle**. At peaks during the cycle, there are many sunspots (black spots thought to be magnetic storms on the Sun's surface), and at lulls in the cycle, there are few sunspots (**Fig. 23.14a, b**). Sunspots correlate with the amount of solar energy (irradiance) reaching the Earth, in that when there are many sunspots, more energy reaches the Earth (**Fig. 23.14c**).

A reliable record of sunspot activity can be taken back for about 400 years and reveals that cycles last 9 to 11.5 years, too fast to correlate with the rates of climate change observed in the geological record. There may be, however, longer-term cycles that have not yet been identified.

• *Fluctuations in cosmic rays:* Some researchers have speculated that changes in the rate of influx of cosmic rays may affect climate, perhaps by generating clouds. Specifically, recent research suggests that cosmic rays striking the atmosphere produce clusters of ions that become condensation nuclei around which water molecules congregate, thus forming the mist droplets making up clouds. But how cloud formation changes climate remains uncertain. High-elevation clouds could reflect incoming solar radiation and would cool the planet, whereas low-elevation clouds could absorb infrared rays rising from the Earth's surface and would warm the planet.

• *Changes in surface albedo:* Regional-scale changes in the nature of continental vegetation cover, and/or the proportion of snow and ice on the Earth's surface, and/or the sudden deposition of reflective volcanic ash could affect our planet's albedo. Increasing albedo causes cooling, whereas decreasing albedo causes warming. Of note, the Toba volcanic eruption covered vast areas of land with reflective white ash, which may have contributed to the global cooling that occurred after the event.

• *Abrupt changes in concentrations of greenhouse gases:* A relatively sudden change in greenhouse gas concentration in the atmosphere could affect climate. One such change might happen if sea temperature warmed or sea level

FIGURE 23.14 The abundance of sunspots varies with time and affects the radiation emitted by the Sun.

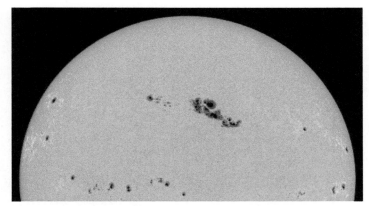

(a) Sunspots are magnetic storms that slow convection at the Sun's surface, producing a cooler area that appears as a dark patch.

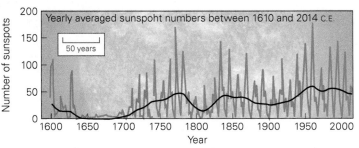

(b) The abundance of sunspots varies cyclically. When there are more sunspots, the Sun radiates less heat.

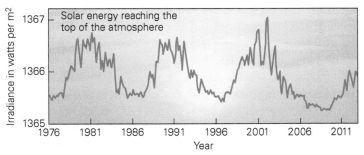

(c) Measurements since 1978 suggest that the solar energy reaching the atmosphere fluctuates periodically over time.

dropped, causing some of the methane hydrate that crystallized in sediment on the seafloor to melt suddenly. Such melting would release CH_4 to the atmosphere. Similarly, algal blooms and reforestation (or deforestation) conceivably could change CO_2 concentrations.

Catastrophic Climate Change and Mass-Extinction Events

Changes that happen on Earth almost instantaneously are called *catastrophic changes*. For example, a volcanic explosion,

an earthquake, a tsunami, or a landslide can change a local landscape in seconds or minutes. But such events affect only relatively small areas. Can such catastrophes happen on a global scale? In recent decades, geoscientists have come to the conclusion that the answer is yes. The stratigraphic record shows that Earth history includes several **mass-extinction events** (see Interlude E and Chapter 13), during which large numbers of species abruptly vanished (**Fig. 23.15a**). Some of these events define boundaries between geologic periods. A mass-extinction event decreases the *biodiversity*, the number of different species that exist at a given time, of life on Earth. It takes millions of years after a mass-extinction event for biodiversity to increase again, and the new species that appear differ from those that vanished, for evolution is unidirectional.

Geologists speculate that some mass-extinction events reflect a catastrophic change in the planet's climate, brought about by incredibly voluminous volcanic eruptions or by the impact of a comet or an asteroid with the Earth (**Fig. 23.15b**). Either of these events could eject enough debris into the atmosphere to block sunlight. Without the warmth of the Sun, winter-like or night-like conditions would last for weeks to years, long enough to disrupt the food chain. In addition, either event could eject aerosols that would turn into global acid rain, scatter hot debris that would ignite forest fires, or give off chemicals that when dissolved in the ocean would make the ocean either toxic, killing marine life, or so nutritious that oxygen-consuming algae could thrive.

Let's examine possible causes for two of the more profound mass-extinction events in Earth history. The first event marks the boundary between the Permian and Triassic periods and thus defines the boundary between the Paleozoic and Mesozoic Eras). During the Permian-Triassic extinction event, over two-thirds of the species on Earth became extinct. In fact, this boundary was first defined in the 19th century, precisely because the assemblage of fossils from rocks below the boundary differs so markedly from the assemblage in rocks above. Isotopic dating suggests that the extinction event roughly coincided with the eruption of vast quantities of basalt in Siberia. So much basalt erupted that geologists attribute its source to a "superplume," a mantle plume many times larger than the one currently beneath Hawaii. Because of the correlation between the time of the basalt eruptions and the time of the mass extinction, geologists suggest that the former caused the latter. Still controversial evidence suggests that, alternatively, a large asteroid collided with the Earth at the Permian-Triassic boundary and caused the mass extinction.

The second event, called the K-T boundary event, caused the mass extinction that marks the boundary between the Cretaceous and Tertiary Periods and, therefore, the boundary between the Mesozoic and Cenozoic Eras. The time of this event correlates well with the time at which an asteroid collided with the Earth at a site now called the Chicxulub crater

FIGURE 23.15 Life evolution has proceeded in fits and starts. During geologic time, there have been several catastrophic extinction events in which a larger percentage of the genera on Earth went extinct and biodiversity abruptly decreased.

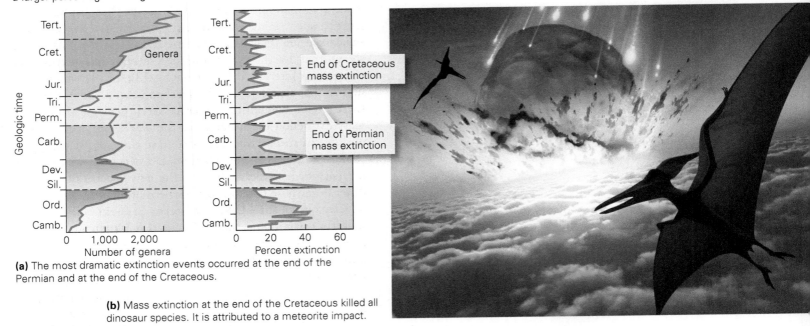

(a) The most dramatic extinction events occurred at the end of the Permian and at the end of the Cretaceous.

(b) Mass extinction at the end of the Cretaceous killed all dinosaur species. It is attributed to a meteorite impact.

in Yucatán, Mexico. Thus, most geologists suggest that the mass extinction is the aftermath of this collision. A minority of researchers emphasize that the extinction is comparable in age to the eruption of extensive basalt flows in India and suggest that volcanic activity caused or at least contributed to causing the mass extinction.

Take-Home Message

Geologic study, using the stratigraphic record and fossils, shows that the climate has alternated between greenhouse and icehouse conditions over geologic time. Factors including life evolution, uplift of mountain belts, and continental drift may cause long-term change. Orbital cycles, eruption of volcanic aerosols, and perhaps solar radiation changes contribute to short-term change. Supervolcanoes or giant meteorite impacts can cause catastrophic change.

QUICK QUESTION: How does continental drift contribute to climate change?

23.5 Human Impact on Land and Life

According to some estimates, perhaps only 2,000 to 20,000 people lived on Earth after the catastrophic eruption of the Toba volcano about 70,000 years ago, and by the dawn of civilization at 4000 B.C.E., the human population was still, at most, a few tens of millions. But by the beginning of the 19th century, revolutions in industrial methods, agriculture, medicine, and hygiene had substantially lowered death rates and raised living standards, so the human population began to grow at accelerating rates and reached 1 billion in 1850. It took only 80 years for the population to double, reaching 2 billion in 1930. Now the doubling time is only 44 years, so the population passed the 6 billion mark just before the year 2000 (**Fig. 23.16**), and surpassed the 7.25 billion mark in 2014.

As the population grows and the standard of living improves, per capita usage of geologic resources increases. We use land for agriculture and grazing, forests for wood, rock and dirt for construction, oil and coal for energy or plastics, and ores for metals (see Chapter 12). Without a doubt, our usage of resources has affected the Earth System profoundly, and thus humanity has become a major agent of global change. Here we examine some of these anthropogenic (human-induced) impacts to the land surface, the environment, and finally to near-term climate.

The Modification of Landscapes

Every time we pick up a shovel and move a pile of rock or soil, we redistribute a portion of the Earth's crust, an activity that prior to humanity was accomplished only by rivers, the wind, rodents, and worms. In the last century, the pace of human-driven Earth movement has accelerated, for now we

FIGURE 23.16 Population now doubles about every 44 years. The Black Death pandemic caused an abrupt drop that lasted for a few decades.

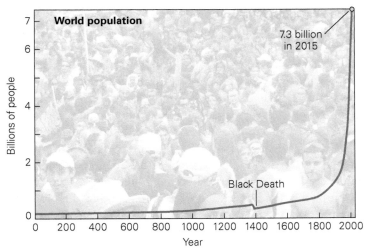

have shovels in coal mines that can move 300 cubic meters of coal in a single scoop, trucks that can carry 200 tons of ore in a single load, and tankers that can transport 500 million liters (about 3 million barrels) of oil during a single journey. In North America, human activity now moves more sediment each year than rivers do. The extraction of rock during mining, the building of levees and dams along rivers or of sea walls along the coast, and the construction of highways and cities all involve the redistribution of Earth materials (Fig. 23.17). In addition, people clear and plow fields, drain and fill wetlands, and pave over the land surface. All these activities change the landscape, the water table, and the supply of sediment.

Landscape modification has side effects. For example, it may make the ground unstable and susceptible to landslides. It may expose the land to erosion, thereby changing the volume of sediment transported by natural agents, such as running water and wind. Locally, flood-control projects may diminish the sediment supply downstream, with unfortunate consequences. For example, the damming of the Nile by the Aswan High Dam cut off the sediment supply to the Nile Delta, so ocean waves along the Mediterranean coast of the delta now eat into the coastline by more than 1 m per year.

The Modification of Ecosystems

In undisturbed areas, the **ecosystem**—meaning an interconnected network of organisms, together with the physical environment in which they live—is the product of evolution for an extended period of time. The ecosystem's flora (plant life) include

FIGURE 23.17 Excavation, agriculture, and construction modify topography, drainage, infiltration, and ecology.

Humans move vast amounts of rock.

Agriculture eliminates diverse ecosystems.

Urbanization changes the water table.

species that have adapted to living together in that particular climate and on the substrate available, and its fauna (animal life) can survive local climate conditions and utilize local food supplies. Human-caused deforestation, overgrazing, agriculture, and urbanization disrupt ecosystems and lead to a decrease in biodiversity.

Archaeological studies have found that the earliest major example of human modification of an ecosystem took place in the Stone Age (pre-6,000 B.C.E.). Spear-bearing hunters, over a relatively short time, caused the mass extinction of mammoths and other large mammals. With the advent of agriculture and deforestation, and the growth of towns and cities, modification of the land accelerated, and today less than 5% of the landscapes in Europe and the United States retain their original ecosystems. In the developing world, landscape modification has claimed more than half of the area once occupied by tropical rainforests, and such forests are now disappearing at a rate of about 1.8% per year (Fig. 23.18a, b)—much of this loss comes from slash-and-burn agriculture, in which farmers and ranchers destroy forest to make open land for farming and grazing (Fig. 23.18c, d).

Some of the changes we make to the land have permanent consequences in a human time frame. For example, the heavy rainfall of tropical regions removes nutrients from the soil, making the soil useless in just a few years, so forests cannot regrow quickly even if farming or grazing of the land stops. Overgrazing by domesticated animals can remove vegetation so completely that some grasslands have undergone desertification. And urbanization replaces the natural land surface with concrete or asphalt, a process that not only completely destroys ecosystems but also radically changes the amount of rain that infiltrates the land surface to become groundwater.

Human-caused changes to ecosystems affect the broader Earth System because they modify biogeochemical cycles and the Earth's albedo. For example, deforestation increases the CO_2 concentration in the atmosphere, for the carbon stored

FIGURE 23.18 The area of forests has been shrinking. For example, tropical rainforests are being logged or burned.

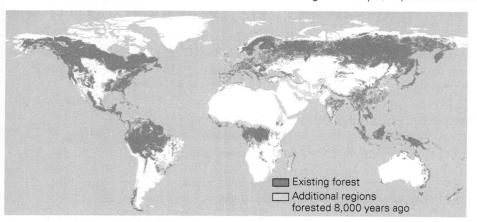

Existing forest
Additional regions forested 8,000 years ago

(a) Remaining forests today are much smaller than forests of 8,000 years ago.

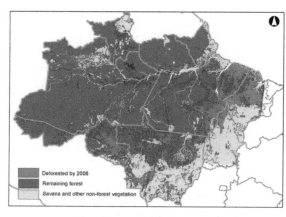

Deforested by 2008
Remaining forest
Savana and other non-forest vegetation

(b) A significant percentage of the Amazon rainforest has been lost in the past few decades.

(c) Part of the Amazon rainforest's destruction is due to slash-and-burn agriculture.

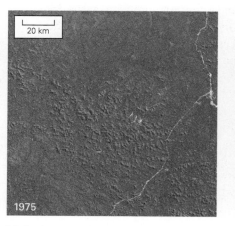
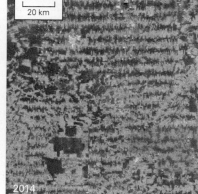

1975

2014

(d) Comparison of satellite imagery highlights areas that have undergone deforestation, such as this one near Ariquemes, Brazil.

in trees returns to the atmosphere when the trees burn. Further, the replacement of forest cover with concrete or fields increases the Earth's albedo.

Pollution

The environment has always contained various natural contaminants such as soot, dust, chemical run-off from sulfide minerals, and waste produced by organisms. In general, ecosystems could manage such contaminants naturally, by absorbing them, by breaking them down, or by locking them into accumulating strata so that the contaminants didn't damage the environment. The nearly exponential growth of human population, coupled with urbanization, industrialization, mining, expansion of farming and ranching, and a switch to engine-driven transportation has changed this situation. We've greatly increased both the quantity and the diversity of contaminants that enter the air, surface water, and groundwater. Some of these contaminants can be considered **pollution**, in that they yield poisonous or harmful effects. This pollution includes both natural and synthetic materials—in liquid, solid, or gaseous form—and has become a major problem because there is too much of it for the Earth System to accommodate. Pollution of the Earth System is a type of global change because it represents a redistribution and reformulation of materials. The following are key problems associated with this change.

- *Smog:* This term was originally coined to refer to the dank, dark air that resulted when smoke from the burning of coal mixed with fog in London and other industrial cities from the early 19th to mid-20th centuries. Beginning in the mid-20th century, another kind of smog, *photochemical smog*, has plagued cities. It forms when exhaust from cars and trucks reacts with air in the presence of sunlight to produce an ozone-rich brown haze. When this haze gets trapped in the lower kilometer or so of the air, it can make the air dangerous to breathe. In cities where photochemical smog has become a common problem, authorities publicize the *air-quality index*, a number representing the degree to which the air has become dangerous to breathe.
- *Water contamination:* Society dumps vast quantities of chemicals into surface water and groundwater. Examples include gasoline, other organic chemicals, radioactive waste, acids, fertilizers—the list could go on for pages. These chemicals can make groundwater supplies undrinkable and in some cases can kill off species in ecosystems where springs return the groundwater to the surface.
- *Acid runoff and acid rain:* When sulfide minerals remain buried in bedrock at depth, water and air can't reach them. But in mines and tailings piles, where rocks are exposed

and broken up, the minerals do come into contact with oxygen and water. The minerals may then react in the water to produce sulfuric acid. This *acid runoff,* which may flow out of mined areas, can be toxic to life. Similarly, when rain passes through air that contains sulfur-containing aerosols (emitted from power plants or factories), the water dissolves the sulfur and yields *acid rain.* Wind can carry aerosols far from their source, so acid rain can damage a broad region (Fig. 23.19).
- *Radioactive materials:* The by-products of producing nuclear weapons, nuclear energy, and medical-imaging equipment can all yield radioactive materials, including new radioactive isotopes, some of which have relatively short half-lives (see Chapter 14). Thus, society has changed the distribution and composition of radioactive material worldwide. Radioactive pollution arises when radioactive material escapes into the air or into rivers or groundwater.
- *Ozone depletion:* When emitted into the atmosphere, human-produced chemicals, most notably chlorofluorocarbons (CFCs), react with ozone in the stratosphere. This reaction, which happens most rapidly on the surfaces of tiny ice crystals in polar stratospheric clouds, destroys ozone molecules, thus creating an **ozone hole** over high-latitude regions, particularly during the spring (Fig. 23.20). Note that the "hole" is not really an area where no ozone is present but rather is a region where atmospheric ozone has been reduced substantially. The ozone hole is more prominent in the Antarctic than in the Arctic because a current of air circulates around the landmass of Antarctica and traps the air, with its CFCs, above the continent, preventing it from mixing with air from elsewhere. Ozone holes have dangerous consequences, for they affect the ability of the atmosphere to shield the Earth's surface from harmful ultraviolet radiation. In 1987, a summit conference in Montreal proposed a global reduction of ozone-destroying CFC emissions. As a consequence, reductions of such emissions have decreased, and the ozone hole has become smaller.

Take-Home Message

Human activities impact the landscape and ecosystems significantly by moving earth, paving the surface, and changing the character of land cover. Society also introduces contaminants into the environment at rates that cannot be accommodated by the Earth System, leading to pollution of land, air, surface water, and groundwater.

QUICK QUESTION: What is the ozone hole, and why did it form?

FIGURE 23.19 Acid rain forms when the sulfur dioxide in industrial smoke dissolves in water and produces sulfuric acid. Acid rain is a problem in all industrialized countries.

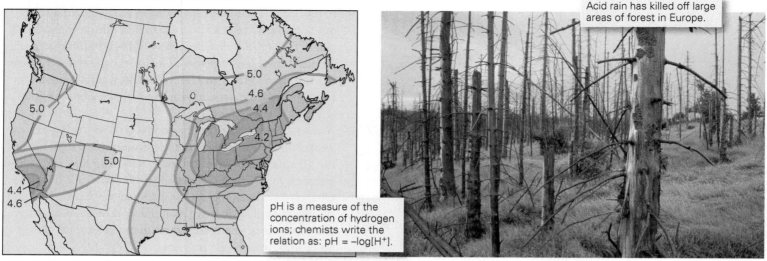

Acid rain has killed off large areas of forest in Europe.

5.0
4.6
4.4
4.2

5.0

5.0

5.0

4.4
4.6

pH is a measure of the concentration of hydrogen ions; chemists write the relation as: $pH = -\log[H^+]$.

(a) Acid rain in North America occurs downwind of major industrial cities. We can specify the acidity of rainwater by stating its pH.

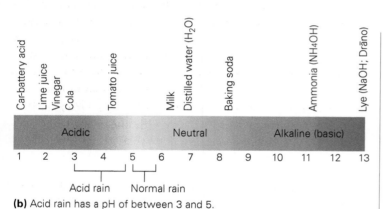

Car-battery acid
Lime juice
Vinegar
Cola
Tomato juice
Milk
Distilled water (H_2O)
Baking soda
Ammonia (NH_4OH)
Lye (NaOH; Drāno)

| Acidic | Neutral | Alkaline (basic) |

1   2   3   4   5   6   7   8   9   10   11   12   13

Acid rain   Normal rain

(b) Acid rain has a pH of between 3 and 5.

23.6 Recent Climate Change

Observed Changes in Atmospheric CO_2 and CH_4

We've seen that greenhouse gases, most notably CO_2 and CH_4, play a major role in the regulation of the Earth's surface temperatures—without these gases, the Earth could not be a home for life. Both CO_2 and CH_4 cycle through various biogeochemical reservoirs of the Earth System, and the rate of movement between reservoirs determines the amount in any given reservoir at any given time. For most of geologic time, the concentration of greenhouse gases in the atmosphere was governed by natural processes—volcanic eruptions, life-evolution events, forest fires, weathering of mountain belts, warming and cooling due to the Milankovitch cycles, changes

in solar activity or cosmic-ray flux, and/or meteor impact. But beginning around 8,000 years ago, human society began to significantly modify the environment, first with the invention of agriculture and then, during the past two centuries, with the advent of industrialization.

Both industry and agriculture produce greenhouse gases and in effect transfer carbon that had been stored in underground reservoirs or biomass reservoirs into the atmospheric reservoir. For example: the burning of fossil fuels oxidizes vast quantities of carbon, which had previously been locked for millions of years in fossil fuel underground, to yield CO_2, which mixes into the atmosphere; the heating of calcite ($CaCO_3$) to produce the lime (CaO) of cement takes carbon that had been locked for millions of years in limestone underground and produces CO_2, which also mixes into the air; the clear-cutting of forests to make way for grazing land or fields replaces high-biomass vegetation (trees) with low-biomass vegetation (grasses or crops), thereby leaving CO_2 in the atmosphere; the decay of organic material in soggy rice paddies or melting permafrost, as well as the flatulence of cattle herds, produces significant quantities of CH_4 that would otherwise remain locked in biomass; and the melting of gas hydrates in the sediment of warming oceans releases CH_4 that would otherwise be locked in ice.

It may seem strange that human society's input of greenhouse gases can be so significant, but a comparison of human production of greenhouse gas relative to volcanic production shows that it indeed is. Specifically, researchers estimate that all volcanic eruptions together in a given year—including both submarine and subaerial eruptions—emit about 0.15 to 0.26 gigatons of CO_2. By comparison, activities of humanity emit about 35 gigatons of CO_2 every year (about 135 times as much).

FIGURE 23.20 The ozone hole over Antarctica.

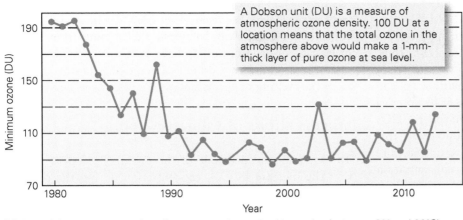

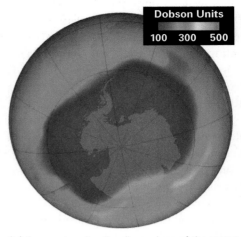

(a) The minimum concentration of ozone over Antarctica (the region between 60° and 90°S) diminished from 1980 to 2006 and has been increasing subsequently.

(b) A map showing the dimensions of the ozone hole in 2006—the largest hole ever recorded.

Put another way, human activities now produce more CO_2 in three days than do all of the volcanoes on Earth in a typical year. A large volcanic explosion, such as that of Mt. Pinatubo in 1991, emits only about as much CO_2 as society produces in one day, and a supervolcanic explosion (see Chapter 9), which happens only once every 100,000 to 300,000 years, produces about as much CO_2 as society produces in one year. About 85% of the CO_2 that we send into the atmosphere comes from burning fossil fuels and producing cement, while about 15% is a consequence of deforestation.

Significantly, not all of the greenhouse gases that society sends into the atmosphere stay there. In the case of CO_2, some dissolves in the ocean, some reacts with minerals in rocks during chemical weathering, and some gets incorporated into plants during photosynthesis. Before about 1900, natural "sinks" (the ocean, rock weathering, plants) could absorb most anthropogenic CO_2. But since then, the amount of CO_2 has exceeded the ability of natural sinks to absorb it (Fig. 23.21). In fact, calculations and isotopic studies suggest that only about 40% to 50% of the CO_2 that society produces—what researchers refer to as *anthropogenic CO_2*—gets reabsorbed by oceans, organisms or land during biogeochemical cycles. The remainder stays in the atmosphere.

Can we detect increases in atmospheric CO_2 concentration? In the early 1960s, a chemist named Charles Keeling decided to find out, and he set out to measure the concentration of CO_2 in the atmosphere using the most accurate methods available. To avoid areas with urban pollution, he collected air samples every month at the summit of Mauna Kea volcano in Hawaii. After completing many years of measurements, Keeling showed not only that distinct

seasonal variations occur (CO_2 concentration goes down in the warm summer when rates of photosynthesis increase, and it goes up in the winter when organic matter dies and decays) but also that the average annual concentration of CO_2 steadily rises (Fig. 23.22a). Specifically, he demonstrated that average yearly CO_2 concentration went from 320 parts per million (ppm) in 1965 to 360 ppm in 1995. Keeling died in 2005, but measurements at Mauna Kea have continued. On May 9, 2013, the daily CO_2 concentration surpassed 400 ppm for the first time in probably over 3 million years, and the average for the

FIGURE 23.21 Until about 1900, anthropogenic CO_2 could be absorbed by natural sinks. Since then, about 50% of anthropogenic CO_2 remains in the atmosphere.

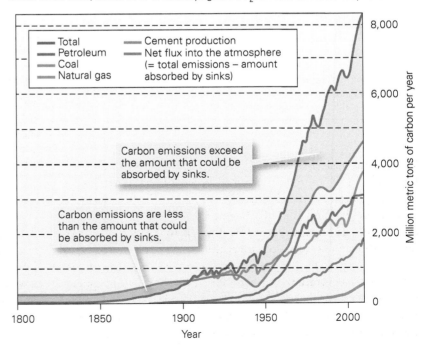

year was 396.5 ppm. (At the time this book went to press in 2014, CO_2 concentration was 401.24 ppm.) Using records in ice cores, researchers have extended the record of CO_2 concentration further back in time and have found that in 1750, CO_2 concentration was only 280 ppm (Fig. 23.22b). Thus, atmospheric CO_2 concentration has increased by over 120 ppm (40%) since the beginning of the industrial revolution.

Studies of gas bubbles trapped in glaciers of Antarctica allow researchers to extend the record of atmospheric CO_2 concentration back through almost the last 800,000 years. This record demonstrates that during the alternating glacial and interglacial periods of the Late Pleistocene CO_2 concentration varied between about 180 and 300 ppm (Fig. 23.22c). Thus, the increases that have happened since the beginning of the industrial revolution are beyond the range of natural fluctuations that occurred during the last 800,000 years. Have CO_2 concentrations ever been higher than they are today? Yes. For example, CO_2 concentration during the Eocene climatic optimum (49 to 56 Ma) was over 1,000 ppm, about 2.5 times what it is today.

CO_2 is not the only greenhouse gas whose concentration has increased in the past two centuries. CH_4 (methane) concentrations have also risen (Fig. 23.22d). Some of this gas comes from combustion of fossil fuels, some from venting or leakage of gas from oil and gas fields, some from decay of organic matter in rice paddies and in melting tundra, and some from the melting of gas hydrates.

Observations of Climate Change

The fundamental principle of the greenhouse effect requires that the increase in CO_2 concentration during the past 200 years has caused atmospheric warming. Has warming taken place during the past 200 years? Researchers have published thousands of observations suggesting that it has. For example:

- Large ice shelves, such as the Larsen B Ice Shelf, along the Antarctic Peninsula, and the Ayles Ice Shelf, along Ellesmere Island in northernmost Canada, are breaking up rapidly (Fig. 23.23a).

FIGURE 23.22 Changes in carbon dioxide (CO_2) and methane (CH_4) concentrations over time.

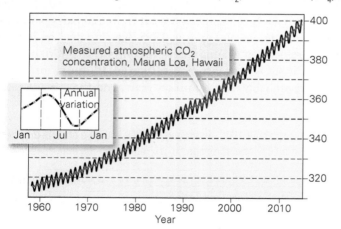

(a) Monthly measurements begin in 1960. There is an annual cycle, related to seasons, but the overall increase is clear; CO_2 will soon reach 402 ppm.

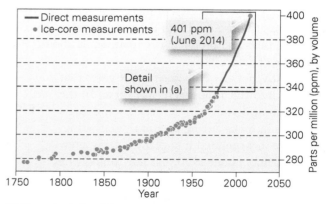

(b) Since the industrial revolution, CO_2 concentration has steadily increased.

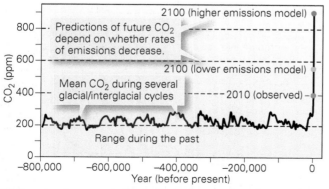

(c) Based on ice-core studies in glaciers, researchers find that CO_2 concentration varied between 180 and 300 ppm throughout glacial advances and retreats. The current value, 400 ppm, is above this range.

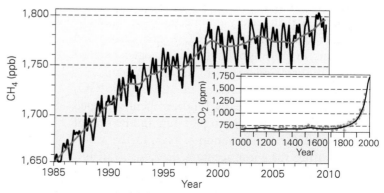

(d) Methane, another greenhouse gas, has been increasing, too.

- The area covered by sea ice in the Arctic Ocean has decreased substantially (**Fig. 23.23b**). Some estimates place the rate of ice-cover loss at about 3% per decade. But the trends are not simple—a graph of ice area from 1979 to 2013 shows many ups and downs lasting a few years (**Fig. 23.23c**), but the overall average appears to be in the direction of decreasing ice, and if this trend continues, it may be possible to sail across the Arctic Ocean within decades. Support for this prediction comes from studies of the age of the sea ice—the area of "old ice" (ice over 5 years old) has decreased by about 50% over the last 25 years (**Fig. 23.23d**).

- The Greenland ice sheet is melting at an accelerating pace. Studies suggest that the rate of ice loss has increased from 90 to 220 cubic km per year in the last 10 years and that in places the sheet is thinning by about 1 m per year. Warming has caused the number of days during the year when melting takes place to increase (**Fig. 23.24a**). In addition, the annual melt zone along the margins of the ice sheet has widened dramatically, because the elevation of the equilibrium line (see Chapter 22) has risen (**Fig. 23.24b**). Further indication of melting comes from observing the flow rates of valley glaciers draining the ice sheet—they flowed 50% faster in 2003 than they did in 1992.

- Valley glaciers worldwide have been retreating rapidly, so that areas that were once ice covered are now bare. The change is truly dramatic in many locations (**Fig. 23.25a**).

- Worldwide, glacial volumes have been diminishing. About 400 km³ of ice disappears every year (**Fig. 23.25b**).

- The area of permafrost in high latitudes has substantially decreased, and melt ponds have formed on the surface of once-frozen land (**Fig. 23.25c**). In fact, large regions that once stayed frozen all year are now melting in the summer.

- Average annual water vapor in the atmosphere has been increasing due to evaporation of warmer seas. This trend is hard to characterize, however, because humidity can vary significantly around the world at a given time.

- Biological phenomena that are sensitive to climate are being disrupted. For example: the time at which sap in the maple trees of

FIGURE 23.23 The melting of sea ice.

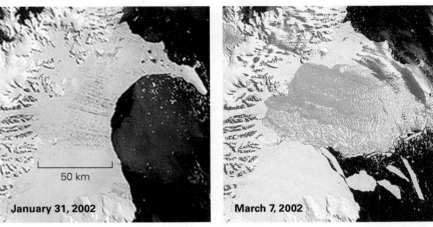

(a) In 2002, the Larson B Ice Shelf of Antarctica disintegrated over the course of a month.

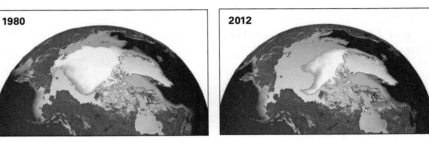

(b) Between 1980 and 2012, the coverage of sea ice in the Arctic decreased.

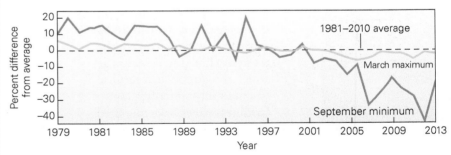

(c) The area of sea ice in the Arctic has gone up and down yearly, but on average it is decreasing.

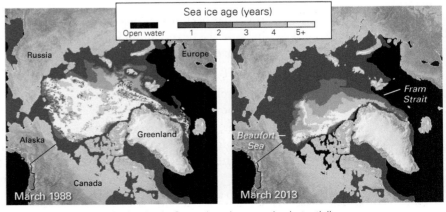

(d) The age of sea ice in the Arctic Ocean has decreased substantially during the past 25 years.

FIGURE 23.24 Melting of the Greenland Ice Sheet.

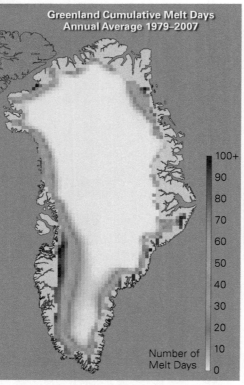
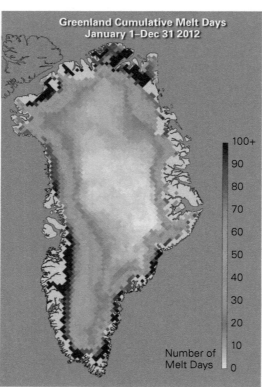

(a) The number of days during which melting of the Greenland Ice Sheet takes place has increased.

The gray area, spotted with puddles, is the melt zone.

June 13, 2002

June 17, 2003

(b) The summer melt line has risen to higher elevations. Each photo shows the same area.

the northeastern United States starts to flow has changed; the mosquito line (the elevation at which mosquitoes can survive) has risen substantially; plant hardiness zones have migrated northward in the United States, which means that at a given location it's possible to plant earlier in the year (Fig. 23.26); and the average weight of polar bears has been decreasing, because the bears can no longer walk over pack ice to reach their hunting grounds in the sea.

Researchers consider the observations above to be substantive evidence that, averaged over decades, average global atmospheric temperature near the Earth's surface is rising, a phenomenon widely referred to as *global warming*. Direct measurements of temperatures, collected at recording stations around the world since about 1880, support this proposal. Specifically, global mean atmospheric temperature has risen by almost 1°C during the last century and is higher now than it has been at any time during the past 2,000 years (Fig. 23.27a, b). Although such a change may seem small, the magnitude of temperature change between the last ice age and now, by comparison, was only 3° to 5°C. A small change in average temperature may have major consequences. Significantly, temperature change is not uniform around the world—some regions appear to be warming more than others, and some areas have been cooling (Fig. 23.27c). Because of the increase in atmospheric temperature, average measured values of near-surface ocean-water temperatures have also been rising (Fig. 23.28).

Interpretations and Potential Consequences of Climate Change

Climate data are not easy to obtain or to interpret, for individual measurements may have large uncertainties, and plots of measurements may show significant scatter. And, as is to be expected in any scientific endeavor, in some cases measurements and conclusions based on them do not stand the test of time and turn out to be incorrect, to be replaced by the results of newer studies. In the case of climate-change studies,

FIGURE 23.25 Global change in glaciers and permafrost.

(a) The Muir Glacier in Alaska retreated 12 km between 1941 and 2004.

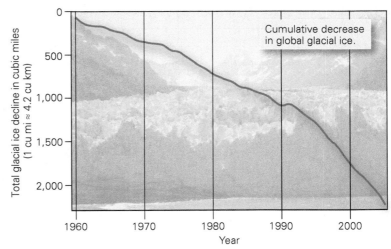

Cumulative decrease in global glacial ice.

(b) Global glacial ice volume has been decreasing by 400 km³ (about 100 mile³) per year.

(c) Lakes and puddles forming when permafrost melts along the coast of the Arctic Ocean.

the data show ups and downs from year to year and in some cases from decade to decade. This fact can lead to confusion in interpreting the data, because a trend that lasts for, say, 5 years, does not necessarily represent a trend that lasts for 100 years. Further, because so many variables control climate change, and because so many feedbacks are likely involved in climate change, it's not easy to associate specific individual effects with specific individual causes. In an attempt to make sense of overwhelming volumes of sometimes contradictory data and interpretations relevant to climate change, a group of leading scientists founded the *Intergovernmental Panel on Climate Change* (IPCC), whose purpose is to evaluate published climate studies from a broad perspective

FIGURE 23.26 Plant hardiness zones have been migrating northward.

1990

2012

Zone
2 3 4 5 6 7 8 9 10

FIGURE 23.27 Measurements of global warming and global temperature anomalies.

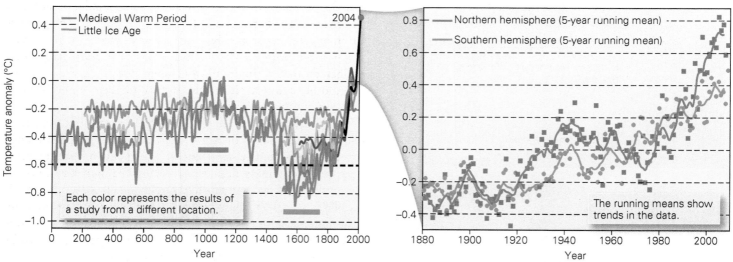

(a) Reconstructions of temperature during the past 2,000 years. Each color is a published estimate from a research team. The black line is the average of direct measurements.

(b) Graphs showing the change in global average temperature since 1880 relative to a reference value. Note that both the northern and southern hemispheres show a temperature increase.

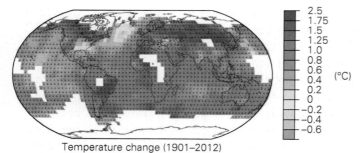

Temperature change (1901–2012)

(c) Colors represent change in average atmospheric temperature at the Earth's surface, for the time period of 1901 to 2012. Redder areas are warm, and blue areas are cold.

and provide assessments of conclusions from the studies. This assessment has societal significance because climate change can have major implications for society and for global policy decisions. The IPCC, sponsored by the World Meteorological Organization and the United Nations, summarizes its conclusions in a report that is revised and published every 5 years. The language describing the likelihood that global warming is happening, and that humans have contributed significantly to causing it, has become progressively less equivocal in successive editions of the report. The *Fifth Assessment Report*, published in 2013, states:

FIGURE 23.28 The difference in global temperature of shallow ocean water relative to the average temperature between 1961 and 2006.

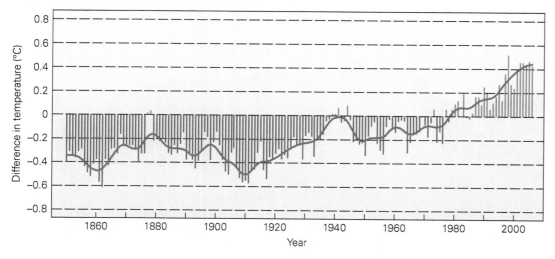

Warming of the climate system is unequivocal, and since the 1950s, many of the observed changes are unprecedented over decades to millennia. The atmosphere and ocean have warmed, the amounts of snow and ice have diminished, sea level has risen, and the concentrations of greenhouse gases have increased . . . It is extremely likely that human influence has been the dominant cause of the observed warming since the mid-20th century.

FIGURE 23.29 Model comparing the consequences of natural forcing both to natural plus anthropogenic forcing and to observed changes in temperature.

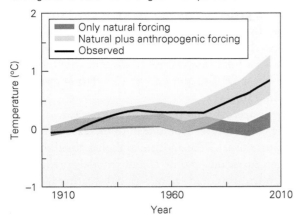

This wording means that the vast majority of climate researchers have concluded that global warming is real, and the activities of people (anthropogenic forcing)—the burning of fossil fuels, the production of cement, and changes in land use such as the cutting down of forests—have played a significant role in causing the change. Non-anthropogenic forcing, such as changes in solar radiation or cosmic-ray flux, do not appear to be of sufficient magnitude to have caused all observed warming. Calculations suggest that the rate of temperature change during the past 50 years is greater than the rate for the previous 50 years.

Some researchers suggest that human impact on climate became noticeable as far back as 8,000 years ago and that climate has been trending toward warmer conditions ever

since. Deviations from the warming trend have been attributed, speculatively, to times when human population abruptly decreased (due to pandemics). During these times, the production of greenhouse gas slowed and forests returned. But deviations have been relatively short-lived, so overall, researchers conclude that without anthropogenic forcing, Earth's climate would be significantly cooler, and we might even be heading toward another ice age (Fig. 23.29).

If the fifth assessment of the IPCC proves to be correct, then society faces the challenge of either slowing climate change or dealing with its consequences. The effects of global warming over the coming decades to centuries remain the subject of intense debate because predictions depend on computer models and not all researchers agree on how to construct or interpret these models. The role of clouds in climate change, for example, remains poorly understood and inadequately addressed by such models. But newer models, running on faster computers, provide increasingly reliable constraints on future trends. In a worst-case scenario, global warming will continue into the future at the present rate, so that by 2050—within the lifetime of many readers of this book—the average annual temperature will have increased in some parts of the world by 1.5° to 2.0°C. At these rates, by the end of the century, temperatures could be over 4°C warmer depending on the model used (Fig. 23.30a), and by 2150 global temperatures may be 5° to 11°C warmer than at present—the warmest since the Eocene Epoch, 40 million years ago. Models predict that warming will not be the same everywhere—the greatest impact will be in the Arctic (Fig. 23.30b). The effects of such a change are controversial, but according to many climate models, the following events might happen.

FIGURE 23.30 Model predictions of future global warming.

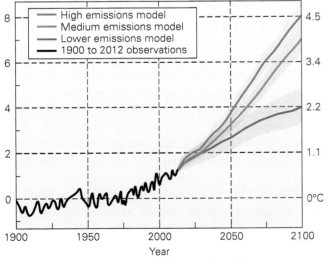

(a) Model calculations of global warming. Different models assume different rates of CO_2 emissions. All suggest significant global temperature increase by 2100.

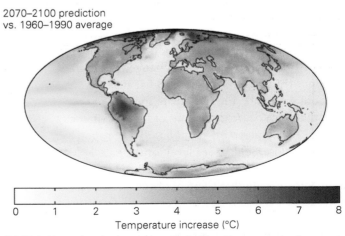

(b) Global warming does not mean that all locations warm by the same amount. This map shows a model prediction of how temperature may vary with location for the time period 2070–2100.

- *Shift in climate belts:* As the climate overall warms, temperate and desert regions would occur at higher latitudes. Thus, regions that are now agricultural areas may dry out and become unfarmable (Fig. 23.31a). The change in climate would also affect the amount and distribution of precipitation (rain and snow) that falls. For example, in North America summers would become drier and winters would become wetter (Fig. 23.31b). One way to picture this change is to think of how the "climatic latitude" of a state in the United States might change over time. Models suggest that if current warming rates continue, the future climate of Illinois would be like the present climate of Texas, and the future climate of New Hampshire might be like the current climate of North Carolina (Fig. 23.31c). Models also suggest that global warming would dramatically increase the number of health-threatening *heat waves* (loosely defined as a prolonged period of excessively hot weather, i.e., above 32°C, or 90°F) that would affect particular regions (Fig. 23.31d).

- *Ice retreat and snow-line rise:* We've already seen evidence that the volume of glacial ice worldwide is decreasing. This is manifested by the shrinkage and retreat of most glaciers, exposing land that was once buried by ice. Of note, some glaciers are advancing. Current glacial advance could be a consequence either of surging due to addition of liquid water to the base of the glacier (see Chapter 22) or of local increases in snowfall due to the addition of moisture to the atmosphere as the oceans warm. As temperatures increase, the snow line in mountains rises to higher latitudes and higher elevations. This change affects ecosystems and may even impact tourism by shortening the ski season at resorts.

- *Melting permafrost:* Warming climates will cause areas of unglaciated land that previously had remained frozen most of the year to thaw during the summer. Such melting of permafrost will permit organic matter that had been stored in frozen form to decompose and release methane.

- *Rise in sea level:* Water expands when heated, so warming of the global oceans will cause sea level to rise. Glacial melting due to global warming will add to the rise. These two processes together have already changed sea level notably. Since the last ice age, sea level has risen by about 120 m (about 400 feet). The rise due to melting of the ice sheets that once covered portions of North America, Europe, and Asia tapered off about 8,000 years ago (Fig. 23.32a). But a closer look at sea level for the past 130 years shows that it is continuing to rise (Fig. 23.32b). In fact, measurements indicate that there has been a rise of almost 12 cm in the past century. Sea-level rise is already causing flooding of coastal wetlands and has submerged some islands, and it has led some nations to begin investing in new coastal flood-control measures. This rise correlates with warming of ocean water (Fig. 23.32c) and with the melting of glaciers (see Fig. 23.25b).

The amount of sea-level rise in the future depends on the rate of global warming. Models suggest that by 2100, it may rise by an additional 20 to 60 cm (Fig. 23.33a). A map showing the elevations of coastal areas emphasizes that a meter or two of sea-level rise could inundate regions of the world where 20% of the human population currently lives (Fig. 23.33b).

- *Stronger storms:* An increase in average ocean and atmospheric temperatures would lead to increased evaporation from the sea. The additional moisture might nourish stronger hurricanes. Some climate models predict that global warming could change global weather patterns and/or cause more intense flooding or drought.

- *Increase in wildfires:* Warmer temperatures may lead to an increase in the frequency of wildfires because the moisture content of plants is lower.

- *Interruption of the oceanic heat conveyor:* Oceanic currents play a major role in transferring heat across latitudes. According to some models, if global warming melts enough polar ice, the resulting freshwater would dilute surface ocean water at high latitudes. This water could not sink, and thus thermohaline circulation would be shut off (see Chapter 18), preventing the water from conveying heat.

The potential changes described above, along with other studies that estimate the large economic cost of global warming, imply that the issue needs to be addressed seriously and soon. But what can be done? The 160 nations that signed the 1997 Kyoto Accord, at a summit meeting held in Japan, propose that the first step would be to slow the input of greenhouse gases into the atmosphere by decreasing the burning of fossil fuels. This could be accomplished by switching to alternative energy sources, or by encouraging energy conservation. While some countries have succeeded in decreasing emissions, globally, emissions continue to rise primarily due to rapid industrialization in the developing world. Another approach involves collecting CO_2 produced at power plants, so that it can be condensed and then injected down deep wells into pore space underground—this overall process is called *carbon capture and sequestration* (CCS). Motivating such actions, needless to say, involves challenging economic, political, and lifestyle decisions.

Some researchers suggest that more aggressive solutions to climate change may be possible. Speculations include the intentional addition of sulfur dioxide to the atmosphere in order to increase the amount of sunlight reflected back to space or the intentional addition of iron to the sea to encourage algal blooms that would absorb CO_2. But the feasibility and potential risks of such approaches remains very uncertain.

FIGURE 23.31 Model predictions of changes that may happen if current global warming continues.

Tundra | Deciduous forest | Evergreen forest | Boreal forest | Shrub and grassland | Sparse vegetation

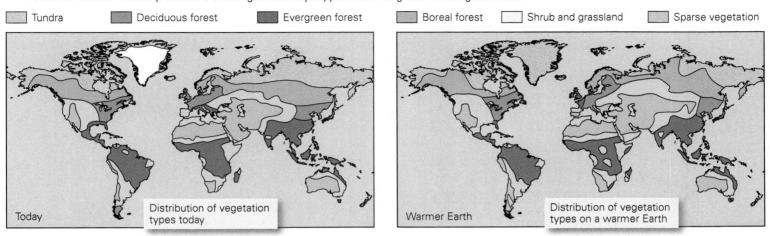

Today — Distribution of vegetation types today

Warmer Earth — Distribution of vegetation types on a warmer Earth

(a) Model predictions of changes that may happen if current global warming continues.

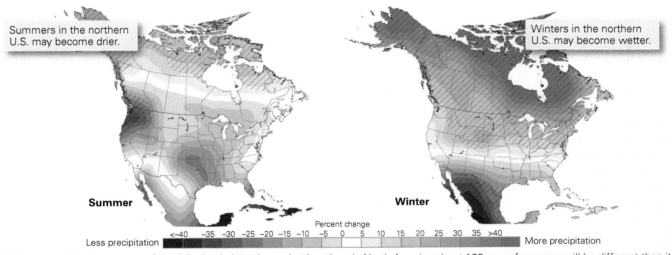

Summers in the northern U.S. may become drier.

Winters in the northern U.S. may become wetter.

Summer

Winter

Percent change

Less precipitation | <−40 −35 −30 −25 −20 −15 −10 −5 0 5 10 15 20 25 30 35 >40 | More precipitation

(b) Models suggest that the amount of precipitation (rain and snow) at locations in North America about 100 years from now will be different than it is today.

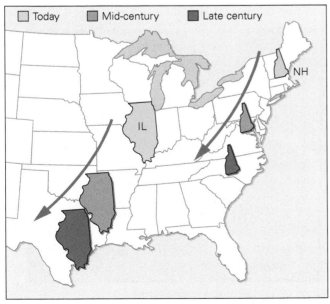

Today | Mid-century | Late century

NH

IL

(c) This map represents, symbolically, how the climate of a given state may change if the climate warms, according to models. At the end of the century, northern states (such as Illinois) may have climates that are like those of southern states today.

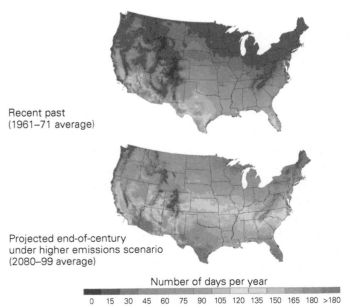

Recent past (1961–71 average)

Projected end-of-century under higher emissions scenario (2080–99 average)

Number of days per year

0 15 30 45 60 75 90 105 120 135 150 165 180 >180

(d) A prediction of the increase in the number of days above 32°C (90°F) at the end of the century, in comparison to today, in the United States.

FIGURE 23.32 Sea-level rise of the recent past and possible sea-level rise of the future.

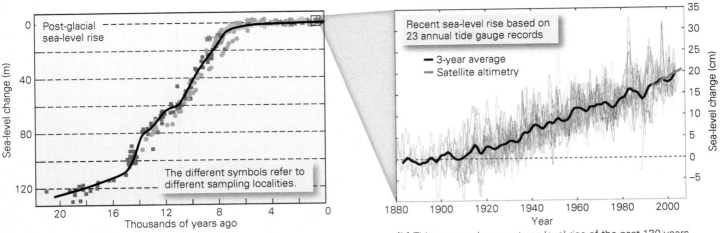

(a) Sea level rose rapidly after the last ice age due to melting of continental glaciers.

(b) Tide gauges document sea-level rise of the past 130 years.

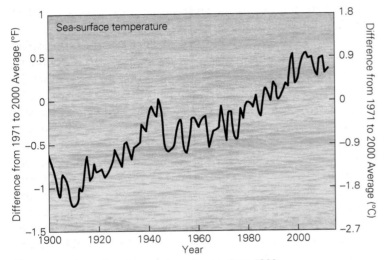

(c) Average sea-surface temperature change since 1900.

Take-Home Message

Growing evidence indicates that greenhouse gases (CO_2 and CH_4) being introduced into the atmosphere by activities of society are causing global warming of both the air and sea that might not otherwise have happened. This change is associated with glacial melting, shifting climate belts, sea-level rise, and other phenomena.

QUICK QUESTION: How do researchers develop predictions of future climate change?

FIGURE 23.33 Estimates and consequences of future sea-level rise.

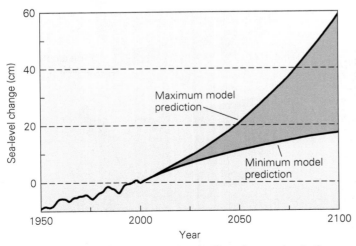

(a) If global warming continues, sea level will continue to rise, both because of the addition of glacial meltwater and the expansion of water that happens when water becomes warmer.

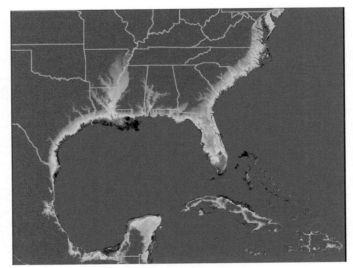

Height above sea level (m)

0   1   2   3   5   8   12   20   35   60   80

(b) The red and black areas of this map are so low that they could be flooded if sea level rose a few meters.

23.7 The Future of the Earth

Most of the discussion in this book has focused on the past, for the geologic record preserved in rocks tells us of earlier times. Let's now bring this book to a close by facing in the opposite direction and speculating what the world might look like in geologic time to come.

In the geologic near term, the future of the world likely depends largely on human activities. Whether the Earth System shifts to a new equilibrium, whether a mass-extinction event takes place, or whether society achieves **sustainable growth** (an ability to prosper within the constraints of the Earth System) will depend on our own foresight and ingenuity. Projecting thousands of years into the future, we might well wonder if the Earth will return to ice-age conditions, with glaciers growing over major cities and the continental shelf becoming dry land, or if the ice age is over for good because of global warming. No one really knows for sure. If we project millions of years into the future, it is clear that the map of the planet will change significantly because of the continuing activity of plate tectonics. For example, during the next 50 million years or so, the Atlantic Ocean will probably become bigger, the Pacific Ocean will shrink, and the western part of California will migrate northward. Eventually, Australia may crush against the southern margin of Asia, and the islands of Indonesia will be flattened in between.

Predicting the map of the Earth beyond that is hard, because we can't predict where new subduction zones will develop. Perhaps subduction of the Pacific Ocean will lead to the collision of the Americas with Asia, to produce a new supercontinent ("Amasia"). A subduction zone eventually will form on one side (or both sides) of the Atlantic Ocean, and the ocean will be consumed. As a consequence, the eastern margin of the Americas will collide with the western margin of Europe and/or Africa. The sites of major cities—New York, Miami, Rio de Janeiro, Buenos Aires, and London—will be incorporated in a collisional mountain belt and likely will be subjected to metamorphism and igneous intrusion before being uplifted and eroded. Shallow seas may once again cover the interiors of continents and then later retreat, and glaciers may once again cover the continents—it happened in the past, so it could happen again! And if the past is the key to the future, we *Homo sapiens* might not be around to watch our cities enter the rock cycle, for biological evolution may have introduced new species to the biosphere, and there is no way to predict what these species will be like. Perhaps 100 million years from now, the stratigraphic record of our time might be several centimeters of strata containing anomalous isotopes and unusual chemicals, trace fossils of concrete structures, and a record of widespread extinctions.

And what of the end of the Earth? Geologic catastrophes resulting from asteroid and comet collisions will undoubtedly occur in the future as they have in the past. We can't predict when the next strike will come, but unless the object can be diverted, Earth is in for another radical readjustment of surface conditions. It's not likely, however, that such collisions will destroy our planet. Rather, astronomers predict that the end of the Earth will occur some 5 billion years from now, when the Sun begins to run out of nuclear fuel. When this happens, outward-directed thermal pressure caused by fusion reactions will no longer be able to prevent the Sun from collapsing inward, because of the immense gravitational pull of its mass. Were the Sun a few times larger than it is, the collapse would trigger a supernova explosion that would blast matter out into space to form a new nebula, perhaps surrounding a black hole. But since the Sun is not that large, the thermal energy generated when

FIGURE 23.34 In about 5 billion years, the Sun will become a red giant.

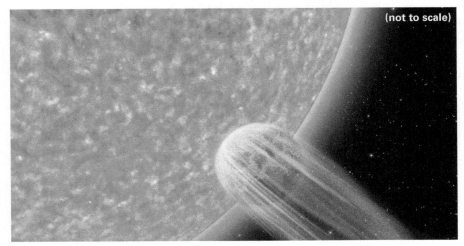

(not to scale)

(a) As the surface of the red giant approaches the Earth, the Earth will evaporate like a giant comet.

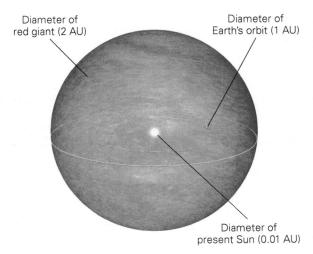

Diameter of red giant (2 AU)

Diameter of Earth's orbit (1 AU)

Diameter of present Sun (0.01 AU)

(b) At full size, the red giant will have a diameter twice that of the Earth's orbit, so atoms of the Earth will become part of the star.

its interior collapses inward will heat the gases of its outer layers sufficiently to cause them to expand. As a result, the Sun will become a red giant, a huge star whose radius would grow beyond the orbit of Earth (Fig. 23.34). Our planet will then vaporize, and its atoms will join an expanding ring of gas—the ultimate global change. If this happens, the atoms that once formed Earth and all its inhabitants through geologic time may eventually be incorporated in a future solar system, where the cycle of planetary formation and evolution will begin anew.

Take-Home Message

In the near term, Earth's surface will be affected by decisions of human society. Over longer time scales, the map of the Earth will change due to plate interactions and sea-level change.

QUICK QUESTION: What might happen to the atoms that make up the Earth long after the red-giant stage of Solar System evolution?

CHAPTER SUMMARY

- We refer to the global interconnecting web of physical and biological phenomena on Earth as the Earth System. Global change involves transformations or modifications of physical and biological components of the Earth System through time. Unidirectional change results in transformations that never repeat, whereas cyclic change involves repetition of the same steps over and over.

- Examples of unidirectional change include differentiation of the solid Earth, growth of continents, formation of the oceans, change in atmospheric composition, and life evolution.

- Examples of physical cycles that take place on Earth include the supercontinent cycle, the sea-level cycle, and the rock cycle.

- A biogeochemical cycle involves the passage of a chemical among nonliving and living reservoirs. Examples include the hydrologic cycle and the carbon cycle. Global change occurs when the relative proportions of the chemicals in different reservoirs change.

- Tools for documenting global climate change include the stratigraphic record, paleontology, oxygen-isotope ratios, bubbles in ice, growth rings in trees, and human history.

- Studies of long-term climate change show that at some times in the past the Earth experienced greenhouse (warmer) periods, while at other times there were icehouse (cooler) periods. Factors leading to long-term climate change include the positions of continents, volcanic activity, the uplift of land, and the formation of materials that remove CO_2.

- Short-term climate change can be seen in the record of the last million years. In fact, during only the past 15,000 years, we see that the climate has warmed and cooled several times. Causes of short-term climate change include changes in Earth's orbit and tilt, changes in surface albedo, changes in ocean currents, and perhaps fluctuations in solar radiation and cosmic rays.

- Mass extinction, a catastrophic change in biodiversity, may be caused by the impact of a comet or asteroid or by intense volcanic activity associated with a superplume.

- During the last two centuries, humans have changed landscapes and modified ecosystems and have added pollutants to the land, air, and water at rates faster than the Earth System can process.

- The addition of greenhouse gases (CO_2 and CH_4) to the atmosphere appears to be causing global warming, which could shift climate belts and lead to a rise in sea level. Sources for the added CO_2 include fossil-fuel burning, cement production, and deforestation.

- In the future, in addition to climate change, the Earth will witness a continued rearrangement of continents resulting from plate tectonics and will likely suffer the impact of asteroids and comets. The end of the Earth may come in about 5 billion years when the Sun runs out of fuel and becomes a red giant.

GUIDE TERMS

albedo (p. 855)
biogeochemical cycle (p. 846)
carbon cycle (p. 846)
climate (p. 847)
climate-change model (p. 849)
differentiation (p. 842)
Earth System (p. 839)
ecosystem (p. 859)
faint young Sun paradox (p. 854)
feedback mechanism (p. 849)

global change (p. 839)

global climate change (p. 847)

global cooling (p. 848)

global warming (p. 848)

Goldilocks effect (p. 854)

greenhouse effect (p. 848)

greenhouse gas (p. 848)

greenhouse (hothouse) period (p. 850)

habitable zone (p. 854)

icehouse period (p. 850)

mass-extinction event (p. 857)

ozone hole (p. 861)

paleoclimate (p. 849)

pollution (p. 861)

sedimentary sequence (p. 844)

steady-state condition (p. 846)

sunspot cycle (p. 856)

supercontinent cycle (p. 844)

sustainable growth (p. 873)

weather (p. 847)

REVIEW QUESTIONS

1. What does the term *Earth System* refer to?

2. How have the Earth's interior, crust, and atmosphere changed since the planet first formed?

3. What processes control the rise and fall of sea level on Earth?

4. Describe the various reservoirs that play a role in the carbon cycle and how carbon transfers among these reservoirs.

5. How do paleoclimatologists study ancient climate change?

6. Contrast icehouse and greenhouse conditions. Have icehouse conditions happened prior to the most recent ice age?

7. What are the possible causes of long-term climatic change?

8. What factors explain short-term climatic change?

9. Give some examples of events that cause catastrophic change.

10. Give some examples of how humans have changed the solid Earth.

11. What are pollutants, and why are they a problem? What is the ozone hole, and why did it form?

12. What is the evidence that researchers use to argue that global warming has been taking place during the past few centuries in response to human activities? What effects might global warming have on the Earth System?

13. What approaches could be employed to decrease CO_2 emissions?

14. What are some likely scenarios for the long-term future of the Earth?

ON FURTHER THOUGHT

15. If global warming continues, how will the distribution of grain crops change? Might this affect national economies, and if so, why? How will the distribution of spruce forests change?

16. Currently, tropical rainforests are being cut down at a rate of 1.8% per year. At this rate, how many more years will the forests survive? In the eastern United States, the proportion of land with forest cover today has increased over the past century. In fact, most of the farmland that

existed in New York State in 1850 is forestland today. Why? How might this change affect erosion rates in the region?

17. Using the library or the Web, examine the change in the nature of world fisheries that has taken place in the last 50 years. Is the world's fish biomass sustainable if these patterns continue? What has happened to whale populations during the past 50 years?

smartwork   smartwork.wwnorton.com

This chapter's Smartwork features:

• Labeling exercise on the Carbon Cycle.
• Animation-based problem on the Milankovitch Cycles.
• Comprehensive questions dealing with climate change.

GEOTOURS

This chapter's GeoTour exercise (S) features:

• Effects of global warming
• Effects of deforestation
• Water use in arid regions
• Preservation of natural habitats

Additional Maps and Charts

This appendix contains several maps and charts for general reference. We list the purpose of each below.

The *Periodic Table of Elements* (Fig. a.1) has been provided as a reference since certain key topics of chemistry are an essential background to this text.

Mineral Identification Flowcharts: Geologists use these charts to identify unknown mineral specimens (Fig. a.2a, b). A mineral flowchart is simply an organized series of questions concerning the mineral's physical properties. The questions are arranged in a sequence such that appropriate answers ultimately lead you on a path to a specific mineral. To understand this concept, let's imagine that we are trying to identify a shiny, bronze- or gold-colored, metallic-looking mineral specimen. We start by observing the specimen's luster. It is metallic, so we follow the path on the chart for metallic-luster minerals (see Fig. a.2a). Next, we determine if the mineral is magnetic or nonmagnetic. If it is nonmagnetic, we follow the path for nonmagnetic minerals. Then, we look at the mineral's color. Since it is bronze- or gold-colored, our path ends at pyrite.

Notice that one of the flowchart questions in Fig. a.2b asks about the reaction of the specimen with hydrochloric acid (HCl). Only calcite and dolomite react, so the question allows definitive identification of these minerals. Another question pertains to striations, faint parallel lines on cleavage planes. Only plagioclase has striations.

World Magnetic Declination Map: This map shows the variation of magnetic declination with location on the surface of the Earth (Fig. a.3a). Declination exists because the position of the Earth's magnetic pole does not coincide exactly with that of the geographic pole. In fact, the magnetic pole location constantly moves, currently at a rate of about 20 km per year. It now lies off the north coast of Canada, and in the not too distant future, it may lie along the coast of Siberia. For a compass to give an accurate indication of direction, it must be adjusted to accommodate for the declination at the location of measurement.

US Magnetic Declination Map: This map shows the magnetic declination for the United States (Fig. a.3b).

The North America Tapestry of Time and Terrain: Another map provided by USGS superimposes a digital elevation map of North America over a geologic map of the same to get a full geologic picture of our continent (Fig. a.4).

Metric Conversion Chart: This chart shows the correlation between U.S. standard units and metric units for length, area, volume, mass, pressure, and temperature (including formulas for converting temperatures between Fahrenheit, Celsius, and Kelvin).

Symbol → He | 2 ← Atomic number
Name → Helium
Atomic weight → 4.002

Alkali metals

Nonmetals

Inert gases

Transition elements (metals)

Symbol	Atomic number	Name	Atomic weight
H	1	Hydrogen	1.007
He	2	Helium	4.002
Li	3	Lithium	6.941
Be	4	Beryllium	9.0121
B	5	Boron	10.811
C	6	Carbon	12.011
N	7	Nitrogen	14.006
O	8	Oxygen	15.999
F	9	Fluorine	18.998
Ne	10	Neon	20.179
Na	11	Sodium	22.989
Mg	12	Magnesium	24.305
Al	13	Aluminum	26.981
Si	14	Silicon	28.085
P	15	Phosphorus	30.973
S	16	Sulfur	32.066
Cl	17	Chlorine	35.452
Ar	18	Argon	39.948
K	19	Potassium	39.098
Ca	20	Calcium	40.078
Sc	21	Scandium	44.955
Ti	22	Titanium	47.88
V	23	Vanadium	50.941
Cr	24	Chromium	51.996
Mn	25	Manganese	54.938
Fe	26	Iron	55.847
Co	27	Cobalt	58.933
Ni	28	Nickel	58.693
Cu	29	Copper	63.546
Zn	30	Zinc	65.39
Ga	31	Gallium	69.723
Ge	32	Germanium	72.61
As	33	Arsenic	74.921
Se	34	Selenium	78.96
Br	35	Bromine	79.904
Kr	36	Krypton	83.80
Rb	37	Rubidium	85.467
Sr	38	Strontium	87.62
Y	39	Yttrium	88.905
Zr	40	Zirconium	91.224
Nb	41	Niobium	92.906
Mo	42	Molybdenum	95.94
Tc	43	Technetium	98.907
Ru	44	Ruthenium	101.07
Rh	45	Rhodium	102.905
Pd	46	Palladium	106.42
Ag	47	Silver	107.868
Cd	48	Cadmium	112.411
In	49	Indium	114.82
Sn	50	Tin	118.710
Sb	51	Antimony	121.757
Te	52	Tellurium	127.60
I	53	Iodine	126.904
Xe	54	Xenon	131.29
Cs	55	Cesium	132.905
Ba	56	Barium	137.327
La	57	Lanthanum	138.905
Hf	72	Hafnium	178.49
Ta	73	Tantalum	180.947
W	74	Tungsten	183.85
Re	75	Rhenium	186.207
Os	76	Osmium	190.2
Ir	77	Iridium	192.22
Pt	78	Platinum	195.08
Au	79	Gold	196.966
Hg	80	Mercury	200.59
Tl	81	Thallium	204.383
Pb	82	Lead	2072
Bi	83	Bismuth	208.980
Po	84	Polonium	208.982
At	85	Astatine	209.987
Rn	86	Radon	222.017
Fr	87	Francium	223.019
Ra	88	Radium	226.025
Ac	89	Actinium	227.027

Symbol	Atomic number	Name	Atomic weight
Ce	58	Cerium	140.115
Pr	59	Praseodymium	140.907
Nd	60	Neodymium	144.24
Pm	61	Promethium	144.912
Sm	62	Samarium	150.36
Eu	63	Europium	151.965
Gd	64	Gadolinium	157.25
Tb	65	Terbium	158.925
Dy	66	Dysprosium	162.50
Ho	67	Holmium	164.930
Er	68	Erbium	167.26
Tm	69	Thulium	168.934
Yb	70	Ytterbium	173.04
Lu	71	Lutetium	174.967
Th	90	Thorium	232.038
Pa	91	Protactinium	231.035
U	92	Uranium	238.028
Np	93	Neptunium	237.048
Pu	94	Plutonium	244.064
Am	95	Americium	243.061
Cm	96	Curium	247.070
Bk	97	Berkelium	247.070
Cf	98	Californium	251.079
Es	99	Einsteinium	252.083
Fm	100	Fermium	257.095
Md	101	Mendelevium	258.10
No	102	Nobelium	259.100
Lr	103	Lawrencium	262.11

FIGURE a.1 The modern periodic table of the elements. Each column groups elements with related properties. For example, inert gases are listed in the column on the right. Metals are found in the central and left parts of the chart.

FIGURE a.2 Simplified mineral identification flowcharts

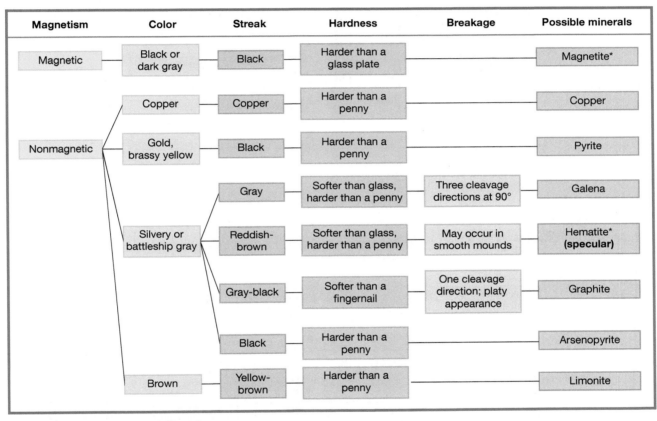

Magnetism	Color	Streak	Hardness	Breakage	Possible minerals
Magnetic	Black or dark gray	Black	Harder than a glass plate		Magnetite*
Nonmagnetic	Copper	Copper	Harder than a penny		Copper
	Gold, brassy yellow	Black	Harder than a penny		Pyrite
	Silvery or battleship gray	Gray	Softer than glass, harder than a penny	Three cleavage directions at 90°	Galena
		Reddish-brown	Softer than glass, harder than a penny	May occur in smooth mounds	Hematite* **(specular)**
		Gray-black	Softer than a fingernail	One cleavage direction; platy appearance	Graphite
		Black	Harder than a penny		Arsenopyrite
	Brown	Yellow-brown	Harder than a penny		Limonite

*Hematite is sometimes weakly magnetic.

(a) Minerals with metallic luster.

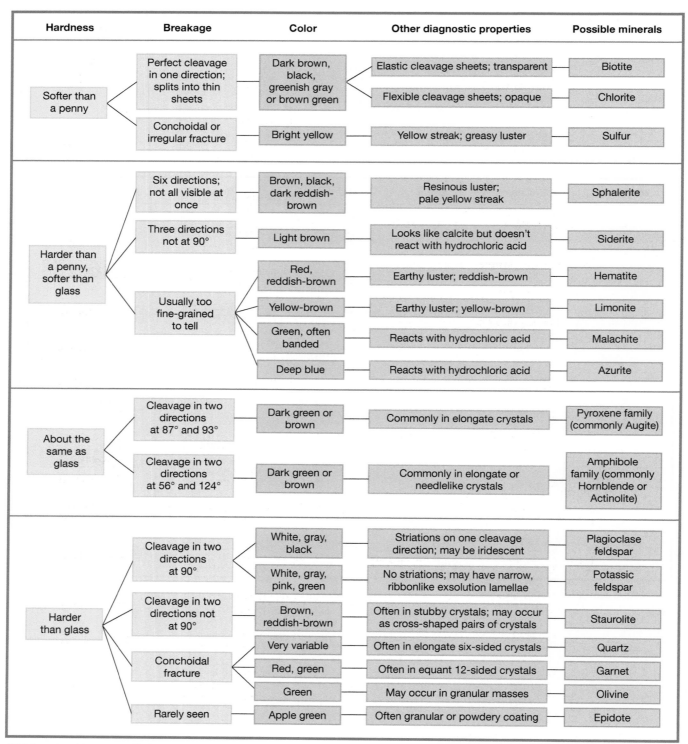

Hardness	Breakage	Color	Other diagnostic properties	Possible minerals
Softer than a penny	Perfect cleavage in one direction; splits into thin sheets	Dark brown, black, greenish gray or brown green	Elastic cleavage sheets; transparent	Biotite
			Flexible cleavage sheets; opaque	Chlorite
	Conchoidal or irregular fracture	Bright yellow	Yellow streak; greasy luster	Sulfur
Harder than a penny, softer than glass	Six directions; not all visible at once	Brown, black, dark reddish-brown	Resinous luster; pale yellow streak	Sphalerite
	Three directions not at 90°	Light brown	Looks like calcite but doesn't react with hydrochloric acid	Siderite
	Usually too fine-grained to tell	Red, reddish-brown	Earthy luster; reddish-brown	Hematite
		Yellow-brown	Earthy luster; yellow-brown	Limonite
		Green, often banded	Reacts with hydrochloric acid	Malachite
		Deep blue	Reacts with hydrochloric acid	Azurite
About the same as glass	Cleavage in two directions at 87° and 93°	Dark green or brown	Commonly in elongate crystals	Pyroxene family (commonly Augite)
	Cleavage in two directions at 56° and 124°	Dark green or brown	Commonly in elongate or needlelike crystals	Amphibole family (commonly Hornblende or Actinolite)
Harder than glass	Cleavage in two directions at 90°	White, gray, black	Striations on one cleavage direction; may be iridescent	Plagioclase feldspar
		White, gray, pink, green	No striations; may have narrow, ribbonlike exsolution lamellae	Potassic feldspar
	Cleavage in two directions not at 90°	Brown, reddish-brown	Often in stubby crystals; may occur as cross-shaped pairs of crystals	Staurolite
	Conchoidal fracture	Very variable	Often in elongate six-sided crystals	Quartz
		Red, green	Often in equant 12-sided crystals	Garnet
		Green	May occur in granular masses	Olivine
	Rarely seen	Apple green	Often granular or powdery coating	Epidote

(b) Minerals with nonmetallic luster, dark-colored.

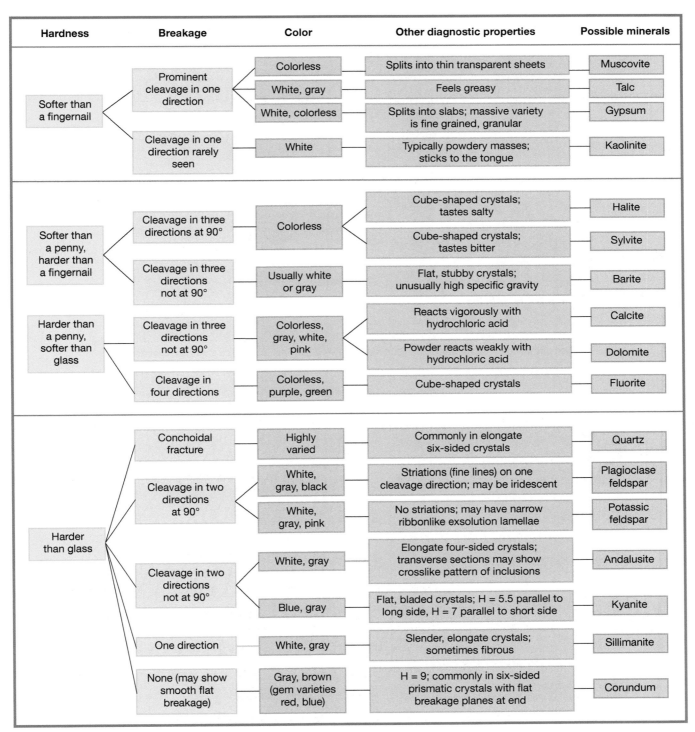

Hardness	Breakage	Color	Other diagnostic properties	Possible minerals
Softer than a fingernail	Prominent cleavage in one direction	Colorless	Splits into thin transparent sheets	Muscovite
		White, gray	Feels greasy	Talc
		White, colorless	Splits into slabs; massive variety is fine grained, granular	Gypsum
	Cleavage in one direction rarely seen	White	Typically powdery masses; sticks to the tongue	Kaolinite
Softer than a penny, harder than a fingernail	Cleavage in three directions at 90°	Colorless	Cube-shaped crystals; tastes salty	Halite
			Cube-shaped crystals; tastes bitter	Sylvite
	Cleavage in three directions not at 90°	Usually white or gray	Flat, stubby crystals; unusually high specific gravity	Barite
Harder than a penny, softer than glass	Cleavage in three directions not at 90°	Colorless, gray, white, pink	Reacts vigorously with hydrochloric acid	Calcite
			Powder reacts weakly with hydrochloric acid	Dolomite
	Cleavage in four directions	Colorless, purple, green	Cube-shaped crystals	Fluorite
Harder than glass	Conchoidal fracture	Highly varied	Commonly in elongate six-sided crystals	Quartz
	Cleavage in two directions at 90°	White, gray, black	Striations (fine lines) on one cleavage direction; may be iridescent	Plagioclase feldspar
		White, gray, pink	No striations; may have narrow ribbonlike exsolution lamellae	Potassic feldspar
	Cleavage in two directions not at 90°	White, gray	Elongate four-sided crystals; transverse sections may show crosslike pattern of inclusions	Andalusite
		Blue, gray	Flat, bladed crystals; H = 5.5 parallel to long side, H = 7 parallel to short side	Kyanite
	One direction	White, gray	Slender, elongate crystals; sometimes fibrous	Sillimanite
	None (may show smooth flat breakage)	Gray, brown (gem varieties red, blue)	H = 9; commonly in six-sided prismatic crystals with flat breakage planes at end	Corundum

(c) Minerals with nonmetallic luster, light-colored.

FIGURE a.3 Magnetic declination charts.

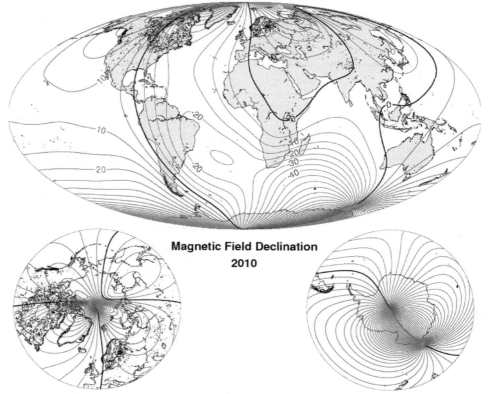

Magnetic Field Declination
2010

(a) A simplified declination map for the world. Blue areas are west declination and red areas are east declination.

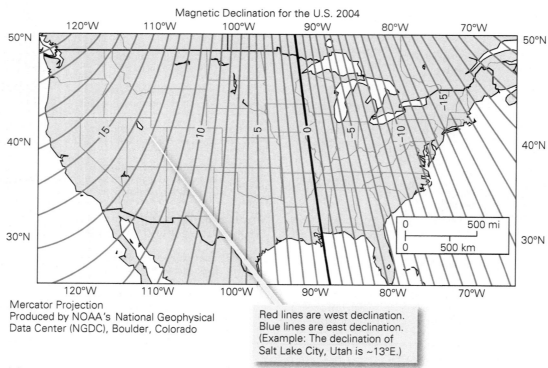

Magnetic Declination for the U.S. 2004

Mercator Projection
Produced by NOAA's National Geophysical
Data Center (NGDC), Boulder, Colorado

Red lines are west declination.
Blue lines are east declination.
(Example: The declination of
Salt Lake City, Utah is ~13°E.)

(b) A simplified declination map of the United States for 2004. Because of changes in the field, most of the lines are drifting westward at about 5' (minutes) per year. (Note: 1° = 60')

The North American
Tapestry of Time and Terrain

Quaternary
Neogene
Paleogene
Cretaceous
Jurassic
Triassic
Permian
Pennsylvanian
Mississippian
Devonian
Silurian
Ordovician
Cambrian
Later Proterozoic
Middle Proterozoic
Early Proterozoic
Later Archean
Middle Archean
Early Archean

Glacial ice
Age unknown

USGS
science for a changing world
U.S. DEPARTMENT OF THE INTERIOR
U.S. GEOLOGICAL SURVEY

0   1,000 mi

0   1,500 km

FIGURE a.4   Geologic map of North America, superimposed on a digital elevation map.

Metric Conversion Chart

Length

1 kilometer (km) = 0.6214 mile (mi)
1 meter (m) = 1.094 yards = 3.281 feet
1 centimeter (cm) = 0.3937 inch
1 millimeter (mm) = 0.0394 inch
1 mile (mi) = 1.609 kilometers (km)
1 yard = 0.9144 meter (m)
1 foot = 0.3048 meter (m)
1 inch = 2.54 centimeters (cm)

Area

1 square kilometer (km^2) = 0.386 square mile (mi^2)
1 square meter (m^2) = 1.196 square yards (yd^2)
= 10.764 square feet (ft^2)
1 square centimeter (cm^2) = 0.155 square inch (in^2)
1 square mile (mi^2) = 2.59 square kilometers (km^2)
1 square yard (yd^2) = 0.836 square meter (m^2)
1 square foot (ft^2) = 0.0929 square meter (m^2)
1 square inch (in^2) = 6.4516 square centimeters (cm^2)

Volume

1 cubic kilometer (km^3) = 0.24 cubic mile (mi^3)
1 cubic meter (m^3) = 264.2 gallons
= 35.314 cubic feet (ft^3)
1 liter (1) = 1.057 quarts
= 33.815 fluid ounces
1 cubic centimeter (cm^3) = 0.0610 cubic inch (in^3)
1 cubic mile (mi^3) = 4.168 cubic kilometers (km^3)
1 cubic yard (yd^3) = 0.7646 cubic meter (m^3)
1 cubic foot (ft^3) = 0.0283 cubic meter (m^3)
1 cubic inch (in^3) = 16.39 cubic centimeters (cm^3)

Mass

1 metric ton = 2,205 pounds
1 kilogram (kg) = 2.205 pounds
1 gram (g) = 0.03527 ounce
1 pound (lb) = 0.4536 kilogram (kg)
1 ounce (oz) = 28.35 grams (g)

Pressure

1 kilogram per
square centimeter (kg/cm^2)* = 0.96784 atmosphere (atm)
= 0.98066 bar
= 9.8067 × 10^4 pascals (Pa)
1 bar = 0.1 megapascals (Mpa)
= 1.0 × 10^5 pascals (Pa)
= 29.53 inches of mercury (in a barometer)
= 0.98692 atmosphere (atm)
= 1.02 kilograms per square centimeter (kg/cm^2)
1 pascal (Pa) = 1 kg/m/s^2
1 pound per square inch = 0.06895 bars
= 6.895 × 10^3 pascals (Pa)
= 0.0703 kilogram per square centimeter

Temperature

To change from Fahrenheit (F) to Celsius (C):
$$°C = \frac{(°F - 32°)}{1.8}$$
To change from Celsius (C) to Fahrenheit (F):
$$°F = (°C \times 1.8) + 32°$$
To change from Celsius (C) to Kelvin (K):
$$K = °C + 273.15$$
To change from Fahrenheit (F) to Kelvin (K):
$$K = \frac{(°F - 32°)}{1.8} + 273.15$$

*Note: Because kilograms are a measure of mass whereas pounds are a unit of weight, pressure units incorporating kilograms assume a given gravitational constant (g) for Earth. In reality, the gravitational for Earth varies slightly with location.

a'a A lava flow with a rubbly surface.

abandoned meander A meander that dries out after it was cut off.

ablation The removal of ice at the toe of a glacier by melting, sublimation (the evaporation of ice into water vapor), and/or calving.

abrasion The process in which one material (such as sand-laden water) grinds away at another (such as a stream channel's floor and walls).

absolute age Numerical age (the age specified in years).

absolute plate velocity The movement of a plate relative to a fixed point in the mantle.

absolute zero The lowest temperature possible (−273.15°C); at absolute zero, vibrations and movements of atoms in a material cease.

abyssal plain A broad, relatively flat region of the ocean that lies at least 4.5 km below sea level.

Acadian orogeny A convergent mountain-building event that occurred around 400 million years ago, during which continental slivers accreted to the eastern edge of the North American continent.

accreted terrane A block of crust that collided with a continent at a convergent margin and stayed attached to the continent.

accretionary coast A coastline that receives more sediment than erodes away.

accretionary lapilli Hailstone-like clumps of wet ash that fall from a volcanic eruptive cloud.

accretionary orogen An orogen formed by the attachment of numerous buoyant slivers of crust to an older, larger continental block.

accretionary prism A wedge-shaped mass of sediment and rock scraped off the top of a downgoing plate and accreted onto the overriding plate at a convergent plate margin.

acid mine runoff A dilute solution of sulfuric acid, produced when sulfur-bearing minerals in mines react with rainwater, that flows out of a mine.

acid rain Precipitation in which air pollutants react with water to make a weak acid that then falls from the sky.

active continental margin A continental margin that coincides with a plate boundary.

active fault A fault that has moved recently or is likely to move in the future.

active sand The top layer of beach sand, which moves daily because of wave action.

active volcano A volcano that has erupted within the past few centuries and will likely erupt again.

adiabatic cooling The cooling of a body of air or matter without the addition or subtraction of thermal energy (heat).

adiabatic heating The warming of a body of air or matter without the addition or subtraction of heat.

advection A process of heat transfer in which heat is carried into a solid by a liquid or gas moving through fractures or pores in the solid.

aerosols Tiny solid particles or liquid droplets that remain suspended in the atmosphere for a long time.

aftershocks The series of smaller earthquakes that follow a major earthquake.

air The mixture of gases that make up the Earth's atmosphere.

air-fall tuff Tuff formed when ash settles gently from the air.

air mass A body of air, about 1,500 km across, that has recognizable physical characteristics.

air pressure The push that air exerts on its surroundings.

albedo The reflectivity of a surface.

Alleghenian orogeny The orogenic event that occurred about 270 million years ago when Africa collided with North America.

alloy A metal containing more than one type of metal atom.

alluvial fan A gently sloping apron of sediment dropped by an ephemeral stream at the base of a mountain in arid or semiarid regions.

alluvium Sorted sediment deposited by a stream.

alluvium-filled valley A valley whose floor fills with sediment.

Alpine-Himalayan chain The largest orogenic belt on Earth today, formed by collisions of the former Gondwana continents with the southern margins of Europe and Asia.

amber Hardened (fossilized) ancient sap or resin.

amphibolite facies A set of metamorphic mineral assemblages formed under intermediate pressures and temperatures.

amplitude The height of a wave from crest to trough.

Ancestral Rockies The late Paleozoic uplifts of the Rocky Mountain region; they eroded away long before the present Rocky Mountains formed.

angiosperm A flowering plant.

angle of repose The angle of the steepest slope that a pile of uncemented material can attain without collapsing from the pull of gravity.

angularity The degree to which grains have sharp or rounded edges or corners.

angular unconformity An unconformity in which the strata below were tilted or folded before the unconformity developed; strata below the unconformity therefore have a different tilt than strata above.

anhedral grains Crystalline mineral grains without well-formed crystal faces.

anion A negatively charged ion.

annual probability The likelihood that a flood of a given size or larger will happen at a specified locality during any given year.

Antarctic bottom water mass The mass of cold, dense water that sinks along the coast of Antarctica.

antecedent stream A stream that cuts across an uplifted mountain range; the stream must have existed before the range uplifted and must then have been able to downcut as fast as the land was rising.

anthracite coal Shiny black coal formed at temperatures between 200°C and 300°C. A high-rank coal.

anticline A fold with an arch-like shape in which the limbs dip away from the hinge.

anticyclone The clockwise flow of air around a high-pressure mass.

anticyclonic flow A circulation of air around a high-pressure region in the atmosphere; it rotates clockwise in the northern hemisphere.

Antler orogeny The Late Devonian mountain-building event in which slices of deep-marine strata were pushed eastward, up and over the shallow-water strata on the western coast of North America.

anvil cloud A large cumulonimbus cloud that spreads laterally at the tropopause to form a broad, flat top.

aphanitic A textural term for fine-grained igneous rock.

apparent polar-wander path A path on the globe along which a magnetic pole appears to have wandered over time; in fact, the continents drift, while the magnetic pole stays fairly fixed.

aquiclude Sediment or rock that transmits no water.

aquifer Sediment or rock that transmits water easily.

aquitard Sediment or rock that does not transmit water easily and therefore retards the motion of the water.

archaea A kingdom of "old bacteria," now commonly found in extreme environments like hot springs. (Also called archaeobacteria.)

Archean Eon The middle Precambrian eon (4.0–2.5 Ga).

Archimedes' principle The mass of the water displaced by a block of material equals the mass of the whole block of material.

arête A residual knife-edge ridge of rock that separates two adjacent cirques.

argillaceous sedimentary rock Sedimentary rock that contains abundant clay.

arkose A clastic sedimentary rock containing both quartz and feldspar grains.

arroyo The channel of an ephemeral stream; dry wash; wadi.

artesian spring A location where the ground surface intersects a natural fracture (joint) that taps a confined aquifer in which the pressure can drive the water to the surface.

artesian well A well in which water rises on its own.

artificial levee A man-made retaining wall to hold back a river from flooding.

ash *See* Volcanic ash.

ash fall Ash that falls to the ground out of an ash cloud.

ash flow An avalanche of ash that tumbles down the side of an explosively erupting volcano.

assimilation The process of magma contamination in which blocks of wall rock fall into a magma chamber and dissolve.

asteroid One of the fragments of solid material, left over from planet formation or produced by collision of planetesimals, that resides between the orbits of Mars and Jupiter.

asthenosphere The layer of the mantle that lies between 100–150 km and 350 km deep; the asthenosphere is relatively soft and can flow when acted on by force.

atm A unit of air pressure that approximates the pressure exerted by the atmosphere at sea level.

atmosphere A layer of gases that surrounds a planet.

atoll A coral reef that develops around a circular reef surrounding a lagoon.

atom The smallest piece of an element that has the properties of the element; it consists of a nucleus surrounded by an electron cloud.

atomic mass The amount of matter in an atom; roughly, it is the sum of the number of protons plus the number of neutrons in the nucleus.

atomic number The number of protons in the nucleus of a given element.

atomic weight The number of protons plus the number of neutrons in the nucleus of a given element. (Also known as atomic mass.)

aurora australis The same phenomenon as the aurora borealis, but in the southern hemisphere.

aurora borealis A ghostly curtain of varicolored light that appears across the night sky in the northern hemisphere when charged particles from the Sun interact with the ions in the ionosphere.

avalanche A turbulent cloud of debris mixed with air that rushes down a steep hill slope at high velocity; the debris can be rock and/or snow.

avalanche chute A downslope hillside pathway along which avalanches repeatedly fall, consequently clearing the pathway of mature trees.

avulsion The process in which a river overflows a natural levee and begins to flow in a new direction.

axial plane The imaginary surface that encompasses the hinges of successive layers of a fold.

axial trough A narrow depression that runs along a mid-ocean ridge axis.

axis An imaginary line around which an object spins.

backscattered light Atmospheric scattered sunlight that returns to space.

backshore zone The zone of beach that extends from a small step cut by high-tide swash to the front of the dunes or cliffs that lie farther inshore.

backswamp The low marshy region between the bluffs and the natural levees of a floodplain.

backwash The gravity-driven flow of water back down the slope of a beach.

bacteria A type of tiny prokaryotic single-celled organism.

bajada An elongate wedge of sediment formed by the overlap of several alluvial fans emerging from adjacent valleys.

Baltica A Paleozoic continent that included crust that is now part of today's Europe.

banded-iron formation (BIF) Iron-rich sedimentary layers consisting of alternating gray beds of iron oxide and red beds of iron-rich chert.

bar (1) A sheet or elongate lens or mound of alluvium; (2) a unit of air-pressure measurement approximately equal to 1 atm.

barchan dune A crescent-shaped dune whose tips point downwind.

barrier island An offshore sand bar that rises above the mean high-water level, forming an island.

barrier reef A coral reef that develops offshore, separated from the coast by a lagoon.

basal sliding The phenomenon in which meltwater accumulates at the base of a glacier, so that the mass of the glacier slides on a layer of water or on a slurry of water and sediment.

basalt A fine-grained, mafic, igneous rock.

base level The lowest elevation a stream channel's floor can reach at a given locality.

basement Older igneous and metamorphic rocks making up the Earth's crust beneath sedimentary cover.

basement uplift Uplift of basement rock by faults that penetrate deep into the continental crust.

base metals Metals that are mined but not considered precious. Examples include copper, lead, zinc, and tin.

basin A fold or depression shaped like a right-side-up bowl.

Basin and Range Province A broad, Cenozoic continental rift that has affected a portion of the western United States in Nevada, Utah, and Arizona; in this province, tilted fault blocks form ranges, and alluvium-filled valleys are basins.

batholith A vast composite, intrusive, igneous rock body up to several hundred km long and 100 km wide, formed by the intrusion of numerous plutons in the same region.

bathymetric map A map illustrating the shape of the ocean floor.

bathymetric profile A cross section showing ocean depth plotted against location.

bathymetry Variation in depth.

bauxite A residual mineral deposit rich in aluminum.

baymouth bar A sandspit that grows across the opening of a bay.

beach A gently sloping fringe of sediment along the shore.

beach drift The gradual migration of sand along a beach.

beach erosion The removal of beach sand caused by wave action and long-shore currents.

beach face A steeply concave part of the foreshore zone formed where the swash of the waves actively scours the sand.

bedding Layering or stratification in sedimentary rocks.

bed load Large particles, such as sand, pebbles, or cobbles, that bounce or roll along a streambed.

bedrock Rock still attached to the Earth's crust.

Bergeron process Precipitation involving the growth of ice crystals in a cloud at the expense of water droplets.

berm A horizontal or landward-sloping terrace in the backshore zone of a beach that receives sediment during a storm.

Big Bang A cataclysmic explosion that scientists suggest represents the formation of the Universe; before this event, all matter and all energy were packed into one volumeless point.

biochemical sedimentary rock Sedimentary rock formed from material (such as shells) produced by living organisms.

biodiversity The number of different species that exist at a given time.

biofuel Gas or liquid fuel made from plant material (biomass). Examples of biofuel include alcohol (from fermented sugar), biodiesel from vegetable oil, and wood.

biogenic minerals Substances that meet the definition of a mineral and are produced naturally by organisms (e.g., calcite in shells).

biogeochemical cycle The exchange of chemicals between living and nonliving reservoirs in the Earth System.

biomass The amount of organic material in a specified volume.

bioremediation The injection of oxygen and nutrients into a contaminated aquifer to foster the growth of bacteria that will ingest or break down contaminants.

biosphere The region of the Earth and atmosphere inhabited by life; this region stretches from a few km below the Earth's surface to a few km above.

bioturbation The mixing of sediment by burrowing animals such as clams and worms.

bituminous coal Dull, black intermediate-rank coal formed at temperatures between 100°c and 200°C.

black-lung disease Lung disease contracted by miners from the inhalation of too much coal dust.

black smoker The cloud of suspended minerals formed where hot water spews out of a vent along a mid-ocean ridge; the dissolved sulfide components of the hot water instantly precipitate when the water mixes with seawater and cools.

blind fault A fault that does not intersect the ground surface.

block Large, angular pyroclastic fragments consisting of volcanic rock, broken up during the eruption.

blocking temperature The temperature below which isotopes in a mineral are no longer free to move, so the radiometric clock starts.

blocky lava Lava that is so viscous that it breaks into boulder-like blocks as it moves; typically, such lavas are andesitic or rhyolitic.

blowout A deep, bowl-like depression scoured out of desert terrain by a turbulent vortex of wind.

blue shift The phenomenon in which a source of light moving toward you appears to have a higher frequency.

body fossil A relict of an organism's body, preserved in rock.

body waves Seismic waves that pass through the interior of the Earth.

bog A wetland dominated by moss and shrubs.

bolide A solid extraterrestrial object such as a meteorite, comet, or asteroid that explodes in the atmosphere.

bornhardt An inselberg with a loaf geometry, like that of Uluru (Ayers Rock) in central Australia.

Bowen's reaction series The sequence in which different silicate minerals crystallize during the progressive cooling of a melt.

braided stream A sediment-choked stream consisting of entwined subchannels.

breaker A water wave in which water at the top of the wave curves over the base of the wave.

breakwater An offshore wall, built parallel or at an angle to the beach, that prevents the full force of waves from reaching a harbor.

breccia Coarse sedimentary rock consisting of angular fragments; or rock broken into angular fragments by faulting.

breeder reactor A nuclear reactor that produces its own fuel.

brine Water that is not fresh but is less salty than seawater; brine may be found in estuaries.

brittle deformation The cracking and fracturing of a material subjected to stress.

brittle-ductile transition (brittle-plastic transition) The depth above which materials behave brittlely and below which materials behave ductilely (plastically); this transition typically lies between a depth of 10 and 15 km in continental crustal rock, and 60 m deep in glacial ice.

buoyancy The upward force acting on an object immersed or floating in fluid; the tendency of an object to float when placed in a fluid.

burial metamorphism Metamorphism due only to the consequences of very deep burial.

butte A medium-sized, flat-topped hill in an arid region.

caldera A large circular depression with steep walls and a fairly flat floor, formed after an eruption as the center of the volcano collapses into the drained magma chamber below.

caliche A solid mass created where calcite cements the soil together. (Also called calcrete.)

calorie A unit of energy approximately equal to 4.2 joules; 1 calorie can raise the temperature of 1 gm of water by 1°C.

calving The breaking off of chunks of ice at the edge of a glacier.

Cambrian explosion of life The remarkable diversification of life, indicated by the fossil record, that occurred at the beginning of the Cambrian Period.

Canadian Shield A broad, low-lying region of exposed Precambrian rock in the Canadian interior.

canyon A trough or valley with steeply sloping walls, cut into the land by a stream.

capacity (of a stream) The total quantity of sediment a stream can carry.

capillary fringe The thin subsurface layer in which water molecules seep up from the water table by capillary action to fill pores.

carbonate rocks Rocks containing calcite and/or dolomite.

carbon-14 A radioactive isotope of the element carbon; the ratio of C14 to C12 can provide an isotopic date of organic carbon.

carbon-14 dating A radiometric dating process that can tell us the age of organic material containing carbon originally extracted from the atmosphere.

carbon sequestration The process of extracting carbon dioxide from sources (e.g., power plants) and sending it back underground to keep it out of the atmosphere and diminish the greenhouse effect.

cast Sediment that preserves the shape of a shell it once filled before the shell dissolved or mechanically weathered away.

catabatic winds Strong winds that form at the margin of a glacier where the warmer air above ice-free land rises and the cold, denser air from above the glaciers rushes in to take its place.

catastrophic change Change that takes place either instantaneously or rapidly in geologic time.

catchment *See* Drainage network.

cation A positively charged ion.

Celsius scale A metric-system measure of temperature in which the difference between the freezing point (0°C) and boiling point (100°C) of water is divided into 100 units; equivalent to centigrade scale.

cement Mineral material that precipitates from water and fills the spaces between grains, holding the grains together.

cementation The phase of lithification in which cement, consisting of minerals that precipitate from groundwater, partially or completely fills the spaces between clasts and attaches each grain to its neighbor.

Cenozoic Era The most recent era of the Phanerozoic Eon, lasting from 66 Ma up until the present.

chain reaction A self-perpetuating process in a nuclear reaction, whereby neutrons released during the fission trigger more fission.

chalk Very fine-grained limestone consisting of weakly cemented plankton shells.

change of state The process in which a material changes from one phase (liquid, gas, or solid) to another.

channel A trough dug into the ground surface by flowing water.

channeled scablands A barren, soil-free landscape in eastern Washington, scoured clean by a flood unleashed when a large glacial lake drained.

chatter marks Wedge-shaped indentations left on rock surfaces by glacial plucking.

chemical A material consisting of a distinct element or compound.

chemical bond The invisible link that holds together atoms in a molecule and/or in a crystal.

chemical formula The "recipe" that specifies the elements and their proportions in a compound.

chemical fossil Distinctive molecules or molecular fragments, formed from the remains of living organisms, that can be preserved in rock.

chemical reaction Interactions among atoms and/or molecules involving breaking or forming chemical bonds.

chemical sedimentary rocks Sedimentary rocks made up of minerals that precipitate directly from water solution.

chemical weathering The process in which chemical reactions alter or destroy minerals when rock comes in contact with water solutions and/or air.

chert A sedimentary rock composed of very fine-grained silica (cryptocrystalline quartz).

Chicxulub crater A circular excavation buried beneath younger sediment on the Yucatán Peninsula; geologists suggest that a meteorite landed there 65 Ma.

chimney (1) A conduit in a magma chamber in the shape of a long vertical pipe through which magma rises and erupts at the surface; (2) an isolated column of strata in an arid region.

chron The time interval between successive magnetic reversals.

cinder cone A subaerial volcano consisting of a cone-shaped pile of tephra whose slope approaches the angle of repose for tephra.

cinders Fragments of glassy rock ejected from a volcano.

cirque A bowl-shaped depression carved by a glacier on the side of a mountain.

cirrus cloud A wispy cloud that tapers into delicate, feather-like curls.

clast A fragment or grain produced by the physical or chemical weathering of a pre-existing rock.

clastic (detrital) sedimentary rock Sedimentary rock consisting of cemented-together detritus derived from the weathering of preexisting rock.

cleavage (1) The tendency of a mineral to break along preferred planes; (2) a type of foliation in low-grade metamorphic rock.

cleavage planes A series of surfaces on a crystal that form parallel to the weakest bonds holding the atoms of the crystal together.

cliff (scarp) retreat The change in the position of a cliff face caused by erosion.

climate The average weather conditions, along with the range of conditions, of a region over a year.

climate-change model A computer-generated model designed to provide insight into how climate changed in the past and may change in the future, and what the consequences of climate change may be.

cloud A mist of tiny water droplets in the sky.

coal A black, organic rock consisting of greater than 50% carbon; it forms from the buried and altered remains of plant material.

coalbed methane Natural gas created during the formation of coal, that gets trapped within the coal.

coal gasification The process of producing relatively clean-burning gases from solid coal.

coal rank A measurement of the carbon content of coal; higher-rank coal forms at higher temperatures.

coal reserve The quantities of discovered, but not yet mined, coal in sedimentary rock of the continents.

coal swamp A swamp whose oxygen-poor water allows thick piles of woody debris to accumulate; this debris transforms into coal upon deep burial.

coast The belt of land bordering the sea.

coastal plain Low-relief regions of land adjacent to the coast.

coastal wetland A flat-lying coastal area that floods during high tide and drains during low tide, and hosts salt-resistant plants.

cold front The boundary at which a cold air mass pushes underneath a warm air mass.

collision The process of two buoyant pieces of lithosphere converging and squashing together.

color The characteristic of a material due to the spectrum of light emitted or reflected by the material, as perceived by eyes or instruments.

columnar jointing A type of fracturing that yields roughly hexagonal columns of basalt; columnar joints form when a dike, sill, or lava flow cools.

comet A ball of ice and dust, probably remaining from the formation of the Solar System, that orbits the Sun.

compaction The phase of lithification in which the pressure of the overburden on the buried rock squeezes out water and air that was trapped between clasts, and the clasts press tightly together.

competence (of a stream) The maximum particle size a stream can carry.

composite volcano *See* Stratovolcano.

compositional banding A type of metamorphic foliation, found in gneiss, defined by alternating bands of light and dark minerals.

compound A material composed of two or more elements that cannot be separated mechanically; the smallest piece is a molecule.

compressibility The degree to which a material's volume changes in response to squashing.

compression A push or squeezing felt by a body.

compressional waves Waves in which particles of material move back and forth parallel to the direction in which the wave itself moves.

concentration The proportion of one substance (the solute) dissolved within another (the solvent).

conchoidal fractures Smoothly curving, clamshell-shaped surfaces along which materials with no cleavage planes tend to break.

condensation The process of gas molecules linking together to form a liquid.

condensation nuclei Preexisting solid or liquid particles, such as aerosols, onto which water condenses during cloud formation.

conduction A process of heat transfer involving progressive migration of thermal energy from cooler to warmer regions in a material, without the physical flow of the material itself.

cone of depression The downward-pointing, cone-shaped surface of the water table in a location where the water table is experiencing drawdown because of pumping at a well.

confined aquifer An aquifer that is separated from the Earth's surface by an overlying aquitard.

conglomerate Very coarse-grained sedimentary rock consisting of rounded clasts.

consuming boundary *See* Convergent plate boundary.

contact The boundary surface between two rock bodies (as between two stratigraphic formations, between an igneous intrusion and adjacent rock, between two igneous rock bodies, or between rocks juxtaposed by a fault).

contact metamorphism *See* Thermal metamorphism.

contaminant plume A cloud of contaminated groundwater that moves away from the source of the contamination.

continental crust The crust beneath the continents.

continental divide A highland separating drainage that flows into one ocean from drainage that flows into another.

continental-drift hypothesis The idea that continents have moved and are still moving slowly across the Earth's surface.

continental glacier A vast sheet of ice that spreads over thousands of square km of continental crust.

continental-interior desert An inland desert that develops because by the time air masses reach the continental interior, they have lost all of their moisture.

continental lithosphere Lithosphere topped by continental crust; this lithosphere reaches a thickness of 150 km.

continental margin A continent's coastline.

continental rift A linear belt along which continental lithosphere stretches and pulls apart.

continental rifting The process by which a continent stretches and splits along a belt; if it is successful, rifting separates a larger continent into two smaller continents separated by a divergent boundary.

continental rise The sloping sea floor that extends from the lower part of the continental slope to the abyssal plain.

continental shelf A broad, shallowly submerged fringe of a continent; ocean-water depth over the continental shelf is generally less than 200 meters; the widest continental shelves occur over passive margins.

continental slope The slope at the edge of a continental shelf, leading down to the deep sea floor.

continental volcanic arc A long, curving chain of subaerial volcanoes on the margin of a continent adjacent to a convergent plate boundary.

contour lines Lines on a map along which a parameter has a constant value; for example, all points along a contour line on a topographic map are at the same elevation.

control rod Rods that absorb neutrons in a nuclear reactor and thus decrease the number of collisions between neutrons and radioactive atoms.

convection Heat transfer that results when warmer, less dense material rises while cooler, denser material sinks.

convective cell A distinct flow configuration for a volume of material that is moving during convective heat transport; simplistically, the material rises when warm and sinks when cool, and thus follows a loop-like path.

convergence zone A place where two surface air flows meet so that air has to rise.

convergent margin *See* Convergent plate boundary.

convergent plate boundary A boundary at which two plates move toward each other so that one plate sinks (subducts) beneath the other; only oceanic lithosphere can subduct.

coral reef A mound of coral and coral debris forming a region of shallow water.

core The dense, iron-rich center of the Earth.

core-mantle boundary An interface 2,900 km below the Earth's surface separating the mantle and core.

Coriolis effect The deflection of objects, winds, and currents on the surface of the Earth owing to the planet's rotation.

cornice A huge, overhanging drift of snow built up by strong winds at the crest of a mountain ridge.

correlation The process of defining the age relations between the strata at one locality and the strata at another.

cosmic rays Nuclei of hydrogen and other elements that bombard the Earth from deep space.

cosmology The study of the overall structure of the Universe.

country rock (wall rock) The preexisting rock into which magma intrudes.

covalent bonding The attachment of one atom to another that develops when the atoms share electrons; one type of chemical bond.

crater (1) A circular depression at the top of a volcanic mound; (2) a depression formed by the impact of a meteorite.

craton A long-lived block of durable continental crust commonly found in the stable interior of a continent.

cratonic platform A province in the interior of a continent in which Phanerozoic strata bury most of the underlying Precambrian rock.

creep The gradual downslope movement of regolith.

crevasse A large crack that develops by brittle deformation in the top 60 m of a glacier.

critical mass A sufficiently dense and large mass of radioactive atoms in which a chain reaction happens so quickly that the mass explodes.

cross bed Internal laminations in a bed, inclined at an angle to the main bedding; cross beds are a relict of the slip face of dunes or ripples.

cross section A diagram depicting the geometry of materials underground as they would appear on an imaginary vertical slice through the Earth.

crude oil Oil extracted directly from the ground.

crust The rock that makes up the outermost layer of the Earth.

crustal root Low-density crustal rock that protrudes downward beneath a mountain range.

crustal thickening The process by which the continental crust increases in thickness, becoming up to 70 km thick (vs. normal thickness of about 35–40 km); it can occur during continental collision.

crystal A single, continuous piece of a mineral bounded by flat surfaces that formed naturally as the mineral grew.

crystal face The flat surfaces of a crystal, formed during the crystal's growth.

crystal form The geometric shape of a crystal, defined by the arrangement of crystal faces.

crystal habit The general shape of a crystal or cluster of crystals that grew unimpeded.

crystal lattice The orderly framework within which the atoms or ions of a mineral are fixed.

crystal structure The arrangement of atoms in a crystal.

crystalline Containing a crystal lattice.

crystalline igneous rock A rock that consists of minerals that grew when a melt solidified, and eventually interlock like pieces of a jigsaw puzzle.

cuesta An asymmetric ridge formed by tilted layers of rock, with a steep cliff on one side cutting across the layers and a gentle slope on the other side; the gentle slope is parallel to the layering.

cumulonimbus cloud A rain-producing, puffy cloud.

cumulus cloud A puffy, cotton-ball-shaped cloud.

current (1) A well-defined stream of ocean water; (2) the moving flow of water in a stream.

cut bank The outside bank of the channel wall of a meander, which is continually undergoing erosion.

cutoff A straight reach in a stream that develops when erosion eats through a meander neck.

cyanobacteria Blue-green algae; a type of archaea.

cycle A series of interrelated events or steps that occur in succession and can be repeated, perhaps indefinitely.

cyclone (1) The counterclockwise flow of air around a low-pressure mass; (2) the equivalent of a hurricane in the Indian Ocean.

cyclonic flow A circulation of air around a low-pressure region in the atmosphere; it rotates counterclockwise in the northern hemisphere.

cyclothem A repeated interval within a sedimentary sequence that contains a specific succession of sedimentary beds.

Darcy's law A mathematical equation stating that a volume of water, passing through a specified area of material at a given time, depends on the material's permeability and hydraulic gradient.

daughter isotope The decay product of radioactive decay.

day The time it takes for the Earth to spin once on its axis.

debris avalanche An avalanche in which the falling debris consists of rock fragments and dust.

debris flow A downslope movement of mud mixed with larger rock fragments.

debris slide A sudden downslope movement of material consisting only of regolith.

decompression melting The kind of melting that occurs when hot mantle rock rises to shallower depths in the Earth so that pressure decreases while the temperature remains unchanged.

deep current An ocean current at a depth greater than 100 m.

deep-focus earthquake An earthquake that occurs at a depth between 300 and 670 km; below 670 km, earthquakes do not happen.

deflation The process of lowering the land surface by wind abrasion.

deformation A change in the shape, position, or orientation of a material, by bending, breaking, or flowing.

dehydration Loss of water.

delamination (plate tectonics) The process by which dense litho-spheric mantle separates from the base of a plate and sinks into the mantle.

delta A wedge of sediment formed at a river mouth when the running water of the stream enters standing water, the current slows, the stream loses competence, and sediment settles out.

delta plain The low, swampy land on the surface of a delta.

delta-plain flood A flood in which water submerges a delta plain.

dendritic network A drainage network whose interconnecting streams resemble the pattern of branches connecting to a deciduous tree.

dendrochronologist A scientist who analyzes tree rings to determine the geologic age of features.

density Mass per unit volume.

denudation The removal of rock and regolith from the Earth's surface.

deposition The process by which sediment settles out of a transporting medium.

depositional environment A setting in which sediments accumulate; its character (fluvial, deltaic, reef, glacial, etc.) reflects local conditions.

depositional landform A landform resulting from the deposition of sediment where the medium carrying the sediment evaporates, slows down, or melts.

desert A region so arid that it contains no permanent streams, except for those that bring water in from elsewhere, and has very sparse vegetation cover.

desertification The process of transforming nondesert areas into desert.

desert pavement A mosaic-like stone surface forming the ground in a desert.

desert varnish A dark, rusty-brown coating of iron oxide and magnesium oxide that accumulates on the surface of the rock.

detachment fault A nearly horizontal fault at the base of a fault system.

detritus The chunks and smaller grains of rock broken off outcrops by physical weathering.

dewpoint temperature The temperature at which air becomes saturated so that dew can form.

diagenesis All of the physical, chemical, and biological processes that transform sediment into sedimentary rock and that alter the rock after the rock has formed.

differential stress A condition causing a material to experience a push or pull in one direction of a greater magnitude than the push or pull in another direction; in some cases, differential stress can result in shearing.

differential weathering What happens when different rocks in an outcrop undergo weathering at different rates.

differentiation (of a planet) A process early in a planet's history during which dense iron alloy melted and sank downward to form the core, leaving less-dense mantle behind.

diffraction The splitting of light into many tiny beams that interfere with one another.

digital elevation map (DEM) A computer-produced portrayal of elevation differences commonly using shading to simulate shadows; the data used to produce the map assigns elevations to each point on the map.

dike A tabular (wall-shaped) intrusion of rock that cuts across the layering of country rock.

dimension stone An intact block of granite or marble to be used for architectural purposes.

dip The angle of a plane's slope as measured in a vertical plane perpendicular to the strike.

dipole A magnetic field with a north and south pole, like that of a bar magnet.

dipole field (for Earth) The part of the Earth's magnetic field, caused by the flow of liquid iron alloy in the outer core, that can be represented by an imaginary bar magnet with a north and south pole.

dip-slip fault A fault in which sliding occurs up or down the slope (dip) of the fault.

dip slope A hill slope underlain by bedding parallel to the slope.

directional drilling The process of controlling the trajectory of a drill bit to make sure that the drill hole goes exactly where desired.

disappearing stream A stream that intersects a crack or sinkhole leading to an underground cavern, so that the water disappears into the subsurface and becomes an underground stream.

discharge The volume of water in a conduit or channel passing a point in 1 second.

discharge area A location where groundwater flows back up to the surface and may emerge at springs.

disconformity An unconformity parallel to the two sedimentary sequences it separates.

displacement (offset) The amount of movement or slip across a fault plane.

disseminated deposit A hydrothermal ore deposit in which ore minerals are dispersed throughout a body of rock.

dissolution A process during which materials dissolve in water.

dissolved load Ions dissolved in a stream's water.

distillation column A vertical pipe in which crude oil is separated into several components.

distributaries The fan of small streams formed where a river spreads out over its delta.

divergence zone A place where sinking air separates into two flows that move in opposite directions.

divergent plate boundary A boundary at which two lithosphere plates move apart from each other; they are marked by mid-ocean ridges.

diversification The development of many different species.

DNA (deoxyribonucleic acid) The complex molecule, shaped like a double helix, containing the code that guides the growth and development of an organism.

doldrums A belt with very slow winds along the equator.

dome Folded or arched layers with the shape of an overturned bowl.

Doppler effect The phenomenon in which the frequency of wave energy appears to change when a moving source of wave energy passes an observer.

dormant volcano A volcano that has not erupted for hundreds to thousands of years but does have the potential to erupt again in the future.

downcutting The process in which water flowing through a channel cuts into the substrate and deepens the channel relative to its surroundings.

downdraft   Downward-moving air.

downgoing plate (slab)   A lithosphere plate that has been subducted at a convergent margin.

downslope force   The component of the force of gravity acting in the downslope direction.

downslope movement   The tumbling or sliding of rock and sediment from higher elevations to lower ones.

downwelling zone   A place where near-surface water sinks.

drag fold   A fold that develops in layers of rock adjacent to a fault during or just before slip.

drainage divide   A highland or ridge that separates one watershed from another.

drainage network (basin)   An array of interconnecting streams that together drain an area.

drainage reversal   When the overall direction of flow in a drainage network becomes the opposite of what it once had been.

drawdown   The phenomenon in which the water table around a well drops because the users are pumping water out of the well faster than it flows in from the surrounding aquifer.

drilling mud   A slurry of water mixed with clay that oil drillers use to cool a drill bit and flush rock cuttings up and out of the hole.

dripstone   Limestone (travertine in a cave) formed by the precipitation of calcium carbonate out of groundwater.

dropstone   A rock that drops to the sea floor once the iceberg that was carrying the rock melts.

drumlin   A streamlined, elongate hill formed when a glacier overrides glacial till.

dry-bottom (polar) glacier   A glacier so cold that its base remains frozen to the substrate.

dry wash   The channel of an ephemeral stream when empty of water.

dry well   (1) A well that does not supply water because the well has been drilled into an aquitard or into rock that lies above the water table; (2) a well that does not yield oil, even though it has been drilled into an anticipated reservoir.

ductile (plastic) deformation   The bending and flowing of a material (without cracking and breaking) subjected to stress.

dune   A pile of sand generally formed by deposition from the wind.

dust storm   An event in which strong winds hit unvegetated land, strip off the topsoil, and send it skyward to form rolling dark clouds that block out the Sun.

dynamic metamorphism   Metamorphism that occurs as a consequence of shearing alone, with no change in temperature or pressure.

dynamo   A power plant generator in which water or wind power spins an electrical conductor around a permanent magnet.

dynamothermal metamorphism   Metamorphism that involves heat, pressure, and shearing.

earthquake   A vibration caused by the sudden breaking or frictional sliding of rock in the Earth.

earthquake belt   A relatively narrow, distinct belt of earthquakes that defines the position of a plate boundary.

earthquake engineering   The design of buildings that can withstand shaking.

earthquake warning system   A communications network that provides an alert within microseconds after the first earthquake waves arrive at a seismograph near the epicenter, but before damaging vibrations reach population centers.

earthquake zoning   The determination of where land is relatively stable and where it might collapse because of seismicity.

Earth System   The global interconnecting web of physical and biological phenomena involving the solid Earth, the hydrosphere, and the atmosphere.

ebb tide   The falling tide.

eccentricity cycle   The cycle of the gradual change of the Earth's orbit from a more circular to a more elliptical shape; the cycle takes around 100,000 years.

ecliptic   The plane defined by a planet's orbit.

ecosystem   An environment and its inhabitants.

eddy   An isolated, ring-shaped current of water.

Ediacaran fauna   Multicellular invertebrate organisms that lived perhaps as early as 620 Ma and certainly by 565 Ma. They were named for a region in southern Australia.

effusive eruption   An eruption that yields mostly lava, not ash.

Ekman spiral   The change in flow direction of water with depth, caused by the Coriolis effect.

Ekman transport   The overall movement of a mass of water, resulting from the Eckman spiral, in a direction 90° to the wind direction.

elastic-rebound theory   The concept that earthquakes happen because stress builds up, causing rock adjacent to a fault to bend elastically until breaking and slip on a fault occurs; the slip relaxes the elastic bending and decreases stress.

elastic strain   A change in shape of a material; the change disappears instantly when stress is removed.

electromagnet   An electrical device that produces a magnetic field.

electron   A negatively charged subatomic particle that orbits the nucleus of an atom; electrons are about $0.0005 \times$ the size of a proton.

electron microprobe   A laboratory instrument that can focus a beam of electrons on a small part of a mineral grain in order to create a signal that defines its chemical composition.

element   A material consisting entirely of one kind of atom; elements cannot be subdivided or changed by chemical reactions.

El Niño   The flow of warm water eastward from the Pacific Ocean that reverses the upwelling of cold water along the western coast of South America and causes significant global changes in weather patterns.

embayment   A low area of coastal land.

emergent coast   A coast where the land is rising relative to sea level or sea level is falling relative to the land.

end moraine (terminal moraine)   A low, sinuous ridge of till that develops when the terminus (toe) of a glacier stalls in one position for a while.

energy   The capacity to do work.

energy resource   Something that can be used to produce work; in a geologic context, a material (such as oil, coal, wind, flowing water) that can be used to produce energy.

eon   The largest subdivision of geologic time.

epeirogenic movement   The gradual uplift or subsidence of a broad region of the Earth's surface.

epeirogeny   An event of epeirogenic movement; the term is usually used in reference to the formation of broad mid-continent domes and basins.

ephemeral (intermittent) stream   A stream whose bed lies above the water table, so that the stream flows only when the rate at which water enters the stream from rainfall or meltwater exceeds the rate at which water infiltrates the ground below.

epicenter   The point on the surface of the Earth directly above the focus of an earthquake.

epicontinental sea   A shallow sea overlying a continent.

epoch   An interval of geologic time representing the largest subdivision of a period.

equant   A term for a grain that has the same dimensions in all directions.

equatorial low   The area of low pressure that develops over the equator because of the intertropical convergence zone.

equilibrium line (of a glacier)   The boundary between the zone of accumulation and the zone of ablation.

equinox One of two days out of the year (September 22 and March 21) in which the Sun is directly overhead at noon at the equator.

era An interval of geologic time representing the largest subdivision of the Phanerozoic Eon.

erg Sand seas formed by the accumulation of dunes in a desert.

erosion The grinding away and removal of Earth's surface materials by moving water, air, or ice.

erosional coast A coastline where sediment is not accumulating and wave action grinds away at the shore.

erosional landform A landform that results from the breakdown and removal of rock or sediment.

erratic A boulder or cobble that was picked up by a glacier and deposited hundreds of kilometers away from the outcrop from which it detached.

eruptive style The character of a particular volcanic eruption; geologists name styles based on typical examples (e.g., Hawaiian, Strombolian).

esker A ridge of sorted sand and gravel that snakes across a ground moraine; the sediment of an esker was deposited in subglacial meltwater tunnels.

estuary An inlet in which seawater and river water mix; created when a coastal valley is flooded because of either rising sea level or land subsidence.

Eubacteria The kingdom of "true bacteria."

euhedral crystal A crystal whose faces are well formed and whose shape reflects crystal form.

eukaryote An organism whose cells contain a nucleus; all plants and animals consist of eukaryotic cells.

eukaryotic cell A cell with a complex internal structure, capable of building multicellular organisms.

eustatic sea-level change A global rising or falling of the ocean surface.

evaporate To change from liquid to vapor.

evaporite Thick salt deposits that form as a consequence of precipitation from saline water.

evapotranspiration The sum of evaporation from bodies of water and the ground surface and transpiration from plants and animals.

exfoliation The process by which an outcrop of rock splits apart into onion-like sheets along joints that lie parallel to the ground surface.

exhumation The process (involving uplift and erosion) that returns deeply buried rocks to the surface.

exotic terrane A block of land that collided with a continent along a convergent margin and attached to the continent; the term exotic implies that the land was not originally part of the continent to which it is now attached.

expanding Universe theory The theory that the whole Universe must be expanding because galaxies in every direction seem to be moving away from us.

explosive eruptions Violent volcanic eruptions that produce clouds and avalanches of pyroclastic debris.

external process A geomorphologic process—such as downslope movement, erosion, or deposition—that is the consequence of gravity or of the interaction between the solid Earth and its fluid envelope (air and water). Energy for these processes comes from gravity and sunlight.

extinction The death of the last members of a species so that there are no parents to pass on their genetic traits to offspring.

extinct volcano A volcano that was active in the past but has now shut off entirely and will not erupt in the future.

extraordinary fossil A rare fossilized relict, or trace, of the soft part of an organism.

extratropical cyclone (wave cyclone, mid-latitude cyclone) A large, rotating storm system, in mid-latitudes, associated with a regional-scale low-pressure zone.

extrusive igneous rock Rock that forms by the freezing of lava above ground, after it flows or explodes out (extrudes) onto the surface and comes into contact with the atmosphere or ocean.

eye The relative calm in the center of a hurricane.

eye wall A rotating vertical cylinder of clouds surrounding the eye of a hurricane.

facet (of a gem) The ground and polished surface of a gem, produced by a gem cutter using a grinding lap.

facies (1) Sedimentary: a group of rocks and primary structures indicative of a given depositional environment; (2) metamorphic: a set of metamorphic mineral assemblages formed under a given range of pressures and temperatures.

Fahrenheit scale An English-system measure of temperature in which the difference between the freezing point (32°F) and the boiling point (212°F) is divided into 180 units.

failure surface A weak surface that forms the base of a landslide.

faint young Sun paradox The apparent contradiction implied by the fact that much of the Earth's surface temperature has remained above the melting point of water during the past 4 Ga, even though calculations indicate that the Sun produced much less energy when young.

fault A fracture on which one body of rock slides past another.

fault-block mountains An outdated term for a narrow, elongate range of mountains that develops in a continental-rift setting as normal faulting drops down blocks of crust or tilts blocks.

fault breccia Fragmented rock in which angular fragments were formed by brittle fault movement; fault breccia occurs along a fault.

fault creep Gradual movement along a fault that occurs in the absence of an earthquake.

fault gouge Pulverized rock consisting of fine powder that lies along fault surfaces; gouge forms by crushing and grinding.

faulting Slip events along a fault.

fault scarp A small step on the ground surface where one side of a fault has moved vertically with respect to the other.

fault system A grouping of numerous related faults.

fault trace (fault line) The intersection between a fault and the ground surface.

feedback mechanism A condition that arises when the consequence of a phenomenon influences the phenomenon itself.

felsic An adjective used in reference to igneous rocks that are rich in elements forming feldspar and quartz.

Ferrel cells The name given to the middle-latitude convection cells in the atmosphere.

fetch The distance across a body of water along which a wind blows to build waves.

field force A push or pull that applies across a distance (i.e., without contact between objects); examples are gravity and magnetism.

fine-grained A textural term for rock consisting of many fine grains or clasts.

firn Compacted granular ice (derived from snow) that forms where snow is deeply buried; if buried more deeply, firn turns into glacial ice.

fission A nuclear reaction during which the nucleus of a large atom splits to form two nuclei of smaller atoms; the process also releases neutrons and energy.

fission track A line of damage formed in the crystal lattice of a mineral by the impact of an atomic particle ejected during the decay of a radioactive isotope.

fissure A conduit in a magma chamber in the shape of a long crack through which magma rises and erupts at the surface.

fjord A deep, glacially carved, U-shaped valley flooded by rising sea level.

flank eruption An eruption that occurs when a secondary chimney, or fissure, breaks through the flank of a volcano.

flash flood A flood that occurs during unusually intense rainfall or as the result of a dam collapse, during which the floodwaters rise very fast.

flexing The process of folding in which a succession of rock layers bends and slip occurs between the layers.

flocculation The clumping together of clay suspended in river water into bunches that are large enough to settle out.

flood An event during which the volume of water in a stream becomes so great that it covers areas outside the stream's normal channel.

flood basalt Vast sheets of basalt that spread from a volcanic vent over an extensive surface of land; they may form where a rift develops above a continental hot spot, and where lava is particularly hot and has low viscosity.

flood-hazard map A representation of a portion of the Earth's surface that is designed to show how the danger of flooding varies with location.

floodplain The flat land on either side of a stream that becomes covered with water during a flood.

floodplain flood A flood during which a floodplain is submerged.

flood stage The stage when water reaches the top of a stream channel.

flood tide The rising tide.

floodway A mapped region likely to be flooded, in which people avoid constructing buildings.

flow fold A fold that forms when the rock is so soft that it behaves like weak plastic.

flowstone A sheet of limestone that forms along the wall of a cave when groundwater flows along the surface of the wall.

fluvial deposit Sediment deposited in a stream channel, along a stream bank, or on a floodplain.

flux Flow.

flux melting The transformation of hot solid to liquid that occurs when a volatile material injects into the solid.

focus The location where a fault slips during an earthquake (hypocenter).

fog A cloud that forms at ground level.

fold A bend or wrinkle of rock layers or foliation; folds form as a consequence of ductile deformation.

fold axis An imaginary line that, when moved parallel to itself, can trace out the shape of a folded surface.

fold-thrust belt An assemblage of folds and related thrust faults that develop above a detachment fault.

foliation Layering formed as a consequence of the alignment of mineral grains, or of compositional banding in a metamorphic rock.

foraminifera Microscopic plankton with calcitic shells, components of some limestones.

foreland sedimentary basin A basin located under the plains adjacent to a mountain front, which develops as the weight of the mountains pushes the crust down, creating a depression that traps sediment.

foreshocks The series of smaller earthquakes that precede a major earthquake.

foreshore zone The zone of beach regularly covered and uncovered by rising and falling tides.

formation *See* Stratigraphic formation.

fossil The remnant, or trace, of an ancient living organism that has been preserved in rock or sediment.

fossil assemblage A group of fossil species found in a specific sequence of sedimentary rock.

fossil correlation A determination of the stratigraphic relation between two sedimentary rock units, reached by studying fossils.

fossil fuel An energy resource such as oil or coal that comes from organisms that lived long ago and thus stores solar energy that reached the Earth then.

fossiliferous limestone Limestone consisting of abundant fossil shells and shell fragments.

fossilization The process of forming a fossil.

fractional crystallization The process by which a magma becomes progressively more silicic as it cools, because early-formed crystals settle out.

fracture zone A narrow band of vertical fractures in the ocean floor; fracture zones lie roughly at right angles to a mid-ocean ridge, and the actively slipping part of a fracture zone is a transform fault.

fragmental igneous rock A rock consisting of igneous chunks and/or shards that are packed together, welded together, or cemented together after having solidified.

frequency The number of waves that pass a point in a given time interval.

fresh rock Rock whose mineral grains have their original composition and shape.

friction Resistance to sliding on a surface.

fringing reef A coral reef that forms directly along the coast.

front The boundary between two air masses.

frost wedging The process in which water trapped in a joint freezes, forces the joint open, and may cause the joint to grow.

fuel rod A metal tube that holds the nuclear fuel in a nuclear reactor.

Fujita scale A scale that distinguishes among tornadoes on the basis of wind speed, path dimensions, and possible damage.

fusion A type of nuclear reaction during which nuclei collide and bond; fusion occurs in stars and hydrogen bombs.

Ga Billions of years ago (abbreviation).

gabbro A coarse-grained, intrusive, mafic igneous rock.

Gaia The term used for the Earth System, with the implication that it resembles a complex living entity.

galaxy An immense system of hundreds of billions of stars.

gem A finished (cut and polished) gemstone ready to be set in jewelry.

gemstone A mineral that has special value because it is rare and people consider it beautiful.

gene An individual component of the DNA code that guides the growth and development of an organism.

general circulation model A numerical calculation that simulates the flow of the atmosphere and resulting phenomena, due to changes in atmospheric temperature and other parameters.

genetics The study of genes and how they transmit information.

geocentric Universe concept An ancient Greek idea suggesting that the Earth sat motionless in the center of the Universe while stars and other planets and the Sun orbited around it.

geochronology The science of dating geologic events in years.

geode A cavity in which euhedral crystals precipitate out of water solutions passing through a rock.

geographical pole The locations (north and south) where the Earth's rotational axis intersects the planet's surface.

geologic column A composite stratigraphic chart that represents the entirety of the Earth's history.

geologic history The sequence of geologic events that has taken place in a region.

geologic map A map showing the distribution of rock units and structures across a region.

geologic time The span of time since the formation of the Earth.

geologic time scale A scale that describes the intervals of geologic time.

geology The study of the Earth, including our planet's composition, behavior, and history.

geotherm The change in temperature with depth in the Earth.

geothermal energy Heat and electricity produced by using the internal heat of the Earth.

geothermal gradient The rate of change in temperature with depth.

geothermal region A region of current or recent volcanism in which magma or very hot rock heats up groundwater, which may discharge at the surface in the form of hot springs and/or geysers.

geyser A fountain of steam and hot water that erupts periodically from a vent in the ground in a geothermal region.

giant planets The four outer, or Jovian, planets of our Solar System, which are significantly larger than the rest of the planets and consist largely of gas and/or ice.

glacial abrasion The process by which clasts embedded in the base of a glacier grind away at the substrate as the glacier flows.

glacial advance The forward movement of a glacier's toe when the supply of snow exceeds the rate of ablation.

glacial drift Sediment deposited in glacial environments.

glacial incorporation The process by which flowing ice surrounds and incorporates debris.

glacial marine Sediment consisting of ice-rafted clasts mixed with marine sediment.

glacial outwash Coarse sediment deposited on a glacial outwash plain by meltwater streams.

glacially polished surface A polished rock surface created by the glacial abrasion of the underlying substrate.

glacial plucking (glacial quarrying) The process by which a glacier breaks off and carries away fragments of bedrock.

glacial rebound The process by which the surface of a continent rises back up after an overlying continental ice sheet melts away and the weight of the ice is removed.

glacial retreat The movement of a glacier's toe back toward the glacier's origin; glacial retreat occurs if the rate of ablation exceeds the rate of supply.

glacial striation Grooves or scratches cut into bedrock when clasts embedded in the moving glacier act like the teeth of a giant rasp.

glacial subsidence The sinking of the surface of a continent caused by the weight of an overlying glacial ice sheet.

glacial till Sediment transported by flowing ice and deposited beneath a glacier or at its toe.

glaciation (glacial period) A portion of an ice age during which huge glaciers grew and covered substantial areas of the continents.

glacier A river or sheet of ice that slowly flows across the land surface and lasts all year long.

glass A solid in which atoms are not arranged in an orderly pattern.

glassy igneous rock Igneous rock consisting entirely of glass, or of tiny crystals surrounded by a glass matrix.

glide horizon The surface along which a slump slips.

global change The transformations or modifications of both physical and biological components of the Earth System through time.

global circulation The movement of volumes of air in paths that ultimately take it around the planet.

global climate change Transformations or modifications in Earth's climate over time.

global cooling A fall in the average atmospheric temperature.

global positioning system (GPS) A satellite system people can use to measure rates of movement of the Earth's crust relative to one another, or simply to locate their position on the Earth's surface.

global warming A rise in the average atmospheric temperature.

gneiss A compositionally banded metamorphic rock typically composed of alternating dark- and light-colored layers.

Gondwana A supercontinent that consisted of today's South America, Africa, Antarctica, India, and Australia. (Also called Gondwanaland.)

graben A down-dropped crustal block bounded on either side by a normal fault dipping toward the basin.

grade (of an ore) The concentration of a useful metal in an ore—the higher the concentration, the higher the grade.

graded bed A layer of sediment, deposited by a turbidity current, in which grain size varies from coarse at the bottom to fine at the top.

graded stream A stream that has attained an equilibrium longitudinal profile in which the sediment input into an area equals sediment removal.

gradualism The theory that evolution happens at a constant, slow rate.

grain A fragment of a mineral crystal or of a rock.

grain rotation The process by which rigid, inequant mineral grains distributed through a soft matrix may rotate into parallelism as the rock changes shape owing to differential stress.

granite A coarse-grained, intrusive, silicic igneous rock.

granulite facies A set of metamorphic mineral assemblages formed at very high pressures and temperatures.

gravitational spreading A process of lateral spreading that occurs in a material because of the weakness of the material; gravitational spreading causes continental glaciers to grow and mountain belts to undergo orogenic collapse.

gravity The attractive force that one mass exerts on another; the magnitude depends on the size of the objects and the distance between them.

graywacke An informal term used for sedimentary rock consisting of sand-sized up to small-pebble-sized grains of quartz and rock fragments all mixed together in a muddy matrix; typically, graywacke occurs at the base of a graded bed.

great oxygenation event The time in Earth's history, about 2.4 Ga, when the concentration of oxygen in the atmosphere increased dramatically.

greenhouse conditions (greenhouse period) Relatively warm global climate leading to the rising of sea level for an interval of geologic time.

greenhouse effect The trapping of heat in the Earth's atmosphere by carbon dioxide and other greenhouse gases, which absorb infrared radiation; somewhat analogous to the effect of glass in a greenhouse.

greenhouse gases Atmospheric gases, such as carbon dioxide and methane, that regulate the Earth's atmospheric temperature by absorbing infrared radiation.

greenschist facies A set of metamorphic mineral assemblages formed under relatively low pressures and temperatures.

greenstone A low-grade metamorphic rock formed from basalt; if foliated, the rock is called greenschist.

Greenwich mean time (GMT) The time at the astronomical observatory in Greenwich, England; time in all other time zones is set in relation to GMT.

Grenville orogeny The orogeny that occurred about 1 billion years ago and yielded the belt of deformed and metamorphosed rocks that underlie the eastern fifth of the North American continent.

groin A concrete or stone wall built perpendicular to a shoreline in order to prevent beach drift from removing sand.

ground moraine A thin, hummocky layer of till left behind on the land surface during a rapid glacial recession.

groundwater Water that resides under the surface of the Earth, mostly in pores or cracks of rock or sediment.

groundwater contamination Addition of chemicals or microbes (e.g., from agricultural and industrial activities, and landfills or septic tanks) to the groundwater supply.

group A succession of stratigraphic formations that have been lumped together, making a single, thicker stratigraphic entity.

growth ring A rhythmic layering that develops in trees, travertine deposits, and shelly organisms as a consequence of seasonal changes.

gusher A fountain of oil formed when underground pressure causes the oil to rise on its own out of a drilled hole.

guyot A seamount that had a coral reef growing on top of it, so that it is now flat-crested.

gymnosperm A plant whose seeds are "naked," not surrounded by a fruit.

gyre A large, circular flow pattern of ocean surface currents.

habitable zone (astronomy) The region in the Solar System where the intensity of radiation is sufficient to allow water to exist in liquid form on the surface of a planet.

Hadean Eon The oldest of the Precambrian eons; the time between Earth's origin and the formation of the first rocks that have been preserved.

Hadley cells The name given to the low-latitude convection cells in the atmosphere.

hail Falling ice balls from the sky, formed when ice crystallizes in turbulent storm clouds.

hail streak An approximately 2-by-10-km stretch of ground, elongate in the direction of a storm, onto which hail has fallen.

half-graben A wedge-shaped basin in cross section that develops as the hanging-wall block above a normal fault slides down and rotates; the basin develops between the fault surface and the top surface of the rotated block.

half-life The time it takes for half of a group of a radioactive element's isotopes to decay.

halocline The boundary in the ocean between surface-water and deep-water salinities.

hamada Barren, rocky highlands in a desert.

hanging valley A glacially carved tributary valley whose floor lies at a higher elevation than the floor of the trunk valley.

hanging wall The rock or sediment above an inclined fault plane.

hardness (of a mineral) A measure of the relative ability of a mineral to resist scratching; it represents the resistance of bonds in the crystal structure from being broken.

hard water Groundwater that contains dissolved calcium and magnesium, usually after passing through limestone or dolomite.

head (1) The elevation of the water table above a reference horizon; (2) the edge of ice at the origin of a glacier.

headland A place where a hill or cliff protrudes into the sea.

head scarp The distinct step along the upslope edge of a slump where the regolith detached.

headward erosion The process by which a stream channel lengthens up its slope as the flow of water increases.

headwaters The beginning point of a stream.

heat Thermal energy resulting from the movement of molecules.

heat capacity A measure of the amount of heat that must be added to a material to change its temperature.

heat flow The rate at which heat rises from the Earth's interior up to the surface.

heat-transfer melting Melting that results from the transfer of heat from a hotter magma to a cooler rock.

heliocentric Universe concept An idea proposed by Greek philosophers around 250 B.C.E. suggesting that all heavenly objects including the Earth orbited the Sun.

heliosphere A bubble-like region in space in which solar wind has blown away most interstellar atoms.

Hercynian orogen The late Paleozoic orogen that affected parts of Europe; a continuation of the Alleghenian orogen.

heterosphere A term for the upper portion of the atmosphere, in which gases separate into distinct layers on the basis of composition.

hiatus The interval of time between deposition of the youngest rock below an unconformity and deposition of the oldest rock above the unconformity.

high-altitude westerlies Westerly winds at the top of the troposphere.

high-grade metamorphic rocks Rocks that metamorphose under relatively high temperatures.

high-level waste Nuclear waste containing greater than 1 million times the safe level of radioactivity.

hinge The portion of a fold where curvature is greatest.

hogback A steep-sided ridge of steeply dipping strata.

Holocene The period of geologic time since the last glaciation.

Holocene climatic maximum The period from 5,000 to 6,000 years ago, when Holocene temperatures reached a peak.

homosphere The lower part of the atmosphere, in which the gases have stirred into a homogenous mixture.

hoodoo The local name for the brightly colored shale and sandstone chimneys found in Bryce Canyon National Park in Utah.

horn A pointed mountain peak surrounded by at least three cirques.

hornfels Rock that undergoes metamorphism simply because of a change in temperature, without being subjected to differential stress.

horse latitudes The region of the subtropical high in which winds are weak.

horst The high block between two grabens.

hot spot A location at the base of the lithosphere, at the top of a mantle plume, where temperatures can cause melting.

hot-spot track A chain of now-dead volcanoes transported off the hot spot by the movement of a lithosphere plate.

hot-spot volcano An isolated volcano not caused by movement at a plate boundary, but rather by the melting of a mantle plume.

hot spring A spring that emits water ranging in temperature from about 30°C to 104°C.

hummocky surface An irregular and lumpy ground surface.

hurricane A huge rotating storm, resembling a giant spiral in map view, in which sustained winds blow over 119 km per hour.

hurricane track The path a hurricane follows.

hyaloclastite A rubbly extrusive rock consisting of glassy debris formed in a submarine or sub-ice eruption.

hydration The absorption of water into the crystal structure of minerals; a type of chemical weathering.

hydraulic conductivity The coefficient K in Darcy's law; hydraulic conductivity takes into account the permeability of the sediment or rock as well as the fluid's viscosity.

hydraulic gradient The slope of the water table.

hydraulic head The potential energy available to drive the flow of a given volume of groundwater at a location; it can be measured as an elevation above a reference.

hydrocarbon A chain-like or ring-like molecule made of hydrogen and carbon atoms; petroleum and natural gas are hydrocarbons.

hydrocarbon generation A process in which oil shale warms to temperatures of greater than about 90°C so kerogen molecules transform into oil and natural gas molecules.

hydrocarbon reserve A known supply of oil and gas held underground.

hydrocarbon system The association of source rock, migration pathway, reservoir rock, seal, and trap geometry that leads to the occurrence of a hydrocarbon reserve.

hydrofracturing ("fracking") A process by which drillers generate new fractures or open preexisting ones underground, by pumping a high-pressure fluid into a portion of the drill hole, in order to increase the permeability of surrounding hydrocarbon-bearing rocks.

hydrogen bond The attraction of a hydrogen atom to a negatively charged atom or molecule (e.g., hydrogen bonds attach water molecules to each other).

hydrologic cycle The continual passage of water from reservoir to reservoir in the Earth System.

hydrolysis The process in which water chemically reacts with minerals and breaks them down.

hydrosphere The Earth's water, including surface water (lakes, rivers, and oceans), groundwater, and liquid water in the atmosphere.

hydrothermal deposit An accumulation of ore minerals precipitated from hot-water solutions circulating through a magma or through the rocks surrounding an igneous intrusion.

hydrothermal metamorphism When very hot water passes through the crust and causes metamorphism of rock.

hypocenter (focus) The place within the Earth where earthquake energy originates; commonly, the hypocenter is the place on a fault where slip took place.

hypsometric curve A graph that plots surface elevation on the vertical axis and the percentage of the Earth's surface on the horizontal axis.

ice age An interval of time in which the climate was colder than it is today, glaciers occasionally advanced to cover large areas of the continents, and mountain glaciers grew; an ice age can include many glacials and interglacials.

iceberg A large block of ice that calves off the front of a glacier and drops into the sea.

icehouse period A period of time when the Earth's temperature was cooler than it is today and ice ages could occur.

ice-margin lake A meltwater lake formed along the edge of a glacier.

ice-rafted sediment Sediment carried out to sea by icebergs.

ice sheet A vast glacier that covers the landscape.

ice shelf A broad, flat region of ice along the edge of a continent formed where a continental glacier flowed into the sea.

ice stream A portion of a glacier that travels much more quickly than adjacent portions of the glacier.

ice tongue The portion of a valley glacier that has flowed out into the sea.

igneous rock Rock that forms when hot molten rock (magma or lava) cools and freezes solid.

ignimbrite Rock formed when deposits of pyroclastic flows solidify.

inactive fault A fault that last moved in the distant past and probably won't move again in the near future, yet is still recognizable because of displacement across the fault plane.

inactive sand The sand along a coast that is buried beneath a layer of active sand and moves only during severe storms or not at all.

incised meander A meander that lies at the bottom of a steep-walled canyon.

index minerals Minerals that serve as good indicators of metamorphic grade.

induced seismicity Seismic events caused by the actions of people (e.g., filling a reservoir that lies over a fault with water).

industrial minerals Minerals that serve as the raw materials for manufacturing chemicals, concrete, and wallboard, among other products.

inequant A term for a mineral grain whose length and width are not the same.

inertia The tendency of an object at rest to remain at rest.

infiltrate Seep down into.

injection well A well in which a liquid is pumped down into the ground under pressure so that it passes from the well back into the pore space of the rock or regolith.

inner core The inner section of the core, extending from 5,155 km deep to the Earth's center at 6,371 km and consisting of solid iron alloy.

inselberg An isolated mountain or hill in a desert landscape created by progressive cliff retreat, so that the hill is surrounded by a pediment or an alluvial fan.

insolation Exposure to the Sun's rays.

intensity (seismology) A measure of the relative size of an earthquake (the severity of ground shaking) at a location, as determined by examining the amount of damage caused.

interglacial A period of time between two glaciations.

interior basin A basin with no outlet to the sea.

interlocking texture The texture of crystalline rocks in which mineral grains fit together like pieces of a jigsaw puzzle.

internal process A process in the Earth System, such as plate motion, mountain building, or volcanism, ultimately caused by Earth's internal heat.

intertidal zone The area of coastal land across which the tide rises and falls.

intertropical convergence zone The equatorial convergence zone in the atmosphere.

intraplate earthquakes Earthquakes that occur away from plate boundaries.

intrusive contact The boundary between country rock and an intrusive igneous rock.

intrusive igneous rock Rock formed by the freezing of magma underground.

ion A version of an atom that has lost or gained electrons, relative to an electrically neutral version, so that it has a net electrical charge.

ionic bond The attachment of one atom to another that happens when one atom transfers electrons to another; one type of chemical bond.

ionosphere The interval of Earth's atmosphere, at an elevation between 50 and 400 km, containing abundant positive ions.

iron catastrophe The proposed event very early in Earth history when the Earth partly melted and molten iron sank to the center to form the core.

isobar A line on a map along which the air has a specified pressure.

isograd (1) A line on a pressure-temperature graph along which all points are taken to be at the same metamorphic grade; (2) a line on a map making the first appearance of a metamorphic index mineral.

isostasy (isostatic equilibrium) The condition that exists when the buoyancy force pushing lithosphere up equals the gravitational force pulling lithosphere down.

isostatic compensation The process in which the surface of the crust slowly rises or falls to reestablish isostatic equilibrium after a geologic event changes the density or thickness of the lithosphere.

isotherm Lines on a map or cross section along which the temperature is constant.

isotopes Different versions of a given element that have the same atomic number but different atomic weights.

jet stream A fast-moving current of air that flows at high elevations.

jetty A man-made wall that protects the entrance to a harbor.

joints Naturally formed cracks in rocks.

joint set A group of systematic joints.

Jovian A term used to describe the outer gassy, Jupiter-like planets (gas-giant planets).

kame A stratified sequence of lateral-moraine sediment that's sorted by water flowing along the edge of a glacier.

karst landscape A region underlain by caves in limestone bedrock; the collapse of the caves creates a landscape of sinkholes separated by higher topography, or of limestone spires separated by low areas.

Kelvin (K) scale A measure of temperature in which 0 K is absolute zero and the freezing point of water is 273.15 K; divisions in the Kelvin scale have the same value as those in the Celsius scale.

kerogen The waxy molecules into which the organic material in shale transforms on reaching about 100°C. At higher temperatures, kerogen transforms into oil.

kettle hole A circular depression in the ground made when a block of ice calves off the toe of a glacier, becomes buried by till, and later melts.

knob-and-kettle topography A land surface with many kettle holes separated by round hills of glacial till.

K-T boundary event The mass extinction that happened at the end of the Cretaceous Period, 66 million years ago, possibly due to the collision of an asteroid with the Earth.

Kuiper Belt A diffuse ring of icy objects, remnants of Solar System formation, that orbit our Sun outside the orbit of Neptune.

laccolith A blister-shaped igneous intrusion that forms when magma injects between layers underground in a manner that pushes overlying layers upward to form a dome.

lag deposit The coarse sediment left behind in a desert after wind erosion removes the finer sediment.

lagoon A body of shallow seawater separated from the open ocean by a barrier island.

lahar A thick slurry formed when volcanic ash and debris mix with water, either in rivers or from rain or melting snow and ice on the flank of a volcano.

landslide A sudden movement of rock and debris down a nonvertical slope.

landslide-potential map A map on which regions are ranked according to the likelihood that a mass movement will occur.

land subsidence Sinking elevation of the ground surface; the process may occur over an aquifer that is slowly draining and decreasing in volume because of pore collapse.

La Niña Years in which the El Niño event is not strong.

lapilli Any pyroclastic particle that is 2 to 64 mm in diameter (i.e., marble-sized); the particles can consist of frozen lava clots, pumice fragments, or ash clumps.

Laramide orogeny The mountain-building event that lasted from about 80 Ma to 40 Ma, in western North America; in the United States, it formed the Rocky Mountains as a result of basement uplift and the warping of the younger overlying strata into large monoclines.

large igneous province (LIP) A region in which huge volumes of lava and/or ash erupted over a relatively short interval of geologic time.

latent heat of condensation The heat released during condensation, which comes only from a change in state.

lateral moraine A strip of debris along the side margins of a glacier.

laterite soil A hard, brick-red, soil formed from iron-rich rock in a tropical environment; it consists primarily of insoluble iron and aluminum oxide and hydroxide and forms due to extreme leaching.

Laurentia A continent in the early Paleozoic Era composed of today's North America and Greenland.

Laurentide ice sheet An ice sheet that spread over northeastern Canada during the Pleistocene ice age(s).

lava Molten rock that has flowed out onto the Earth's surface.

lava dome A dome-like mass of rhyolitic lava that accumulates above the eruption vent.

lava flows Sheets or mounds of lava that flow onto the ground surface or sea floor in molten form and then solidify.

lava lake A large pool of lava produced around a vent when lava fountains spew forth large amounts of lava in a short period of time.

lava tube The empty space left when a lava tunnel drains; this happens when the surface of a lava flow solidifies while the inner part of the flow continues to stream downslope.

leach To dissolve and carry away.

leader A conductive path stretching from a cloud toward the ground, along which electrons leak from the base of the cloud, and which provides the start for a lightning flash to the ground.

lightning bolt (lightning flash, lightning stroke) A giant spark or pulse of current that jumps across a gap of charge separation.

light year The distance that light travels in one Earth year (about 6 trillion miles or 9.5 trillion km).

lignite Low-rank coal that consists of 50% carbon.

limb The side of a fold, showing less curvature than at the hinge.

limestone Sedimentary rock composed of calcite.

liquefaction The process by which saturated, unconsolidated sediments are transformed into a substance that acts like a liquid as a result of ground shaking.

liquidus The lowest temperature at which all the components of a material have melted and transformed into liquid.

liquification The process by which wet sediment becomes a slurry; liquification may be triggered by earthquake vibrations.

lithification The transformation of loose sediment into solid rock through compaction and cementation.

lithologic correlation A correlation based on similarities in rock type.

lithosphere The relatively rigid, nonflowable, outer 100- to 150-km-thick layer of the Earth, constituting the crust and the top part of the mantle.

lithosphere plate One of many distinct pieces of the lithosphere (Earth's relatively rigid shell) that are separated from one another by breaks (plate boundaries).

little ice age A period of cooler temperatures, between 1500 and 1800 C.E., during which many glaciers advanced.

loam A type of soil consisting of roughly equal parts of sand, silt, and clay; it tends to be good for growth of crops.

local base level A base level upstream from a drainage network's mouth.

lodgment till A flat layer of till smeared out over the ground when a glacier overrides an end moraine as it advances.

loess Layers of fine-grained sediments deposited from the wind; large deposits of loess formed from fine-grained glacial sediment blown off outwash plains.

longitudinal (seif) dune A dune formed when there is abundant sand and a strong, steady wind, and whose axis lies parallel to the wind direction.

longitudinal profile A cross-sectional image showing the variation in elevation along the length of a river.

longshore current The flow of water parallel to the shore just off a coast, because of the diagonal movement of waves toward the shore.

longshore drift The movement of sediment laterally along a beach; it occurs when waves wash up a beach diagonally.

lower mantle The deepest section of the mantle, stretching from 670 km down to the core-mantle boundary.

low-grade metamorphic rocks Rocks that underwent metamorphism at relatively low temperatures.

low-velocity zone The asthenosphere underlying oceanic lithosphere in which seismic waves travel more slowly, probably because rock has partially melted.

luster The way a mineral surface scatters light.

L-waves (Love waves) Surface seismic waves that cause the ground to ripple back and forth, creating a snake-like movement.

Ma Millions of years ago (abbreviation).

macrofossil A fossil large enough to be seen with the naked eye.

mafic A term used in reference to magmas or igneous rocks that are relatively poor in silica and rich in iron and magnesium.

magma Molten rock beneath the Earth's surface.

magma chamber A space below ground filled with magma.

magma contamination The process in which flowing magma incorporates components of the country rock through which it passes.

magmatic deposit An ore deposit formed when sulfide ore minerals accumulate at the bottom of a magma chamber.

magnetic anomaly The difference between the expected strength of the Earth's magnetic field at a certain location and the actual measured strength of the field at that location.

magnetic declination The angle between the direction a compass needle points at a given location and the direction of true north.

magnetic dipole An imaginary vector that points from the north magnetic pole to the south magnetic pole of a magnetic field.

magnetic field The region affected by the force emanating from a magnet.

magnetic field lines The trajectories along which magnetic particles would align, or charged particles would flow, if placed in a magnetic field.

magnetic force The push or pull exerted by a magnet.

magnetic inclination The angle between a magnetic needle free to pivot on a horizontal axis and a horizontal plane parallel to the Earth's surface.

magnetic poles The ends of a magnetic dipole; all magnetic dipoles have a north pole and a south pole.

magnetic reversal The change of the Earth's magnetic polarity; when a reversal occurs, the field flips from normal to reversed polarity, or vice versa.

magnetic-reversal chronology The history of magnetic reversals through geologic time.

magnetism An attractive or repulsive field force generated by permanent magnets or by an electrical current.

magnetization The degree to which a material can exert a magnetic force.

magnetometer An instrument that measures the strength of the Earth's magnetic field.

magnetosphere The region protected from the electrically charged particles of the solar winds by Earth's magnetic field.

magnetostratigraphy The comparison of the pattern of magnetic reversals in a sequence of strata, with a reference column showing the succession of reversals through time.

magnitude (of an earthquake) The number that represents the maximum amplitude of ground motion that would be measured by a seismometer placed at a specified distance from the epicenter.

manganese nodules Lumpy accumulations of manganese-oxide minerals precipitated onto the sea floor.

mantle The thick layer of rock below the Earth's crust and above the core.

mantle plume A column of very hot rock rising up through the mantle.

marble A metamorphic rock composed of calcite and transformed from a protolith of limestone.

mare The broad, darker areas on the Moon's surface; they consist of flood basalts that erupted over 3 billion years ago and spread out across the Moon's lowlands.

marginal sea A small ocean basin created when sea-floor spreading occurs behind an island arc.

marine magnetic anomaly The difference between the *expected* strength of the Earth's main dipole field at a certain location on the sea floor and the *actual* measured strength of the magnetic field at that location.

maritime tropical air mass A mass of air that originates over tropical or subtropical oceanic regions.

marker bed A particularly unique layer that provides a definitive basis for correlation.

marsh A wetland dominated by grasses.

mass The amount of matter in an object; mass differs from weight in that its value does not depend on the strength of gravity.

mass-extinction event A time when vast numbers of species abruptly vanish.

mass movement (mass wasting) The gravitationally caused downslope transport of rock, regolith, snow, or ice.

matter The material substance of the universe; it consists of atoms and has mass.

matrix Finer-grained material surrounding larger grains in a rock.

meander A snake-like curve along a stream's course.

meandering stream A reach of stream containing many meanders (snake-like curves).

meander neck A narrow isthmus of land separating two adjacent meanders.

mean sea level The average level between the high and low tide over a year at a given point.

mechanical force A push, pull, or shear applied by one object on another; it can be applied only if the objects are in contact.

mechanical weathering *See* Physical weathering.

medial moraine A strip of sediment in the interior of a glacier, parallel to the flow direction of the glacier, formed by the lateral moraines of two merging glaciers.

Medieval Warm Period A period of high temperatures in the Middle Ages.

melt Molten (liquid) rock.

meltdown The melting of the fuel rods in a nuclear reactor that occurs if the rate of fission becomes too fast and the fuel rods become too hot.

melting curve The line defining the range of temperatures and pressures at which a rock melts.

melting temperature The temperature at which the thermal vibration of the atoms or ions in the lattice of a mineral is sufficient to break the chemical bonds holding them to the lattice, so a material transforms into a liquid.

meltwater lake A lake fed by glacial meltwater.

mesa A large, flat-topped hill (with a surface area of several square km) in an arid region.

mesopause The boundary that marks the top of the mesosphere of Earth's atmosphere.

mesosphere The cooler layer of atmosphere overlying the stratosphere.

Mesozoic Era The middle of the three Phanerozoic eras; it lasted from 252 Ma to 66 Ma.

metaconglomerate A metamorphic rock produced by metamorphism of a conglomerate; typically, it contains flattened pebbles and cobbles.

metal A solid composed almost entirely of atoms of metallic elements; it is generally opaque, shiny, smooth, malleable, and can conduct electricity.

metallic bond A chemical bond in which the outer atoms are attached to each other in such a way that electrons flow easily from atom to atom.

metamorphic aureole The region around a pluton, stretching tens to hundreds of meters out, in which heat transferred into the country rock and metamorphosed the country rock.

metamorphic facies A set of metamorphic mineral assemblages indicative of metamorphism under a specific range of pressures and temperatures.

metamorphic foliation A fabric defined by parallel surfaces or layers that develop in a rock as a result of metamorphism; schistocity and gneissic layering are examples.

metamorphic grade A representation of the intensity of metamorphism, meaning the amount or degree of metamorphic change.

metamorphic mineral New minerals that grow in place within a solid rock under metamorphic temperatures and pressures.

metamorphic mineral assemblage A group of minerals that form in a rock as a result of metamorphism.

metamorphic rock Rock that forms when preexisting rock changes into new rock as a result of an increase in pressure and temperature and/or shearing under elevated temperatures; metamorphism occurs without the rock first becoming a melt or a sediment.

metamorphic texture A distinctive arrangement of mineral grains produced by metamorphism.

metamorphic zone The region between two metamorphic isograds, typically named after an index mineral found within the region.

metamorphism The process by which one kind of rock transforms into a different kind of rock.

metasomatism The process by which a rock's overall chemical composition changes during metamorphism because of reactions with hot water that bring in or remove elements.

meteor A streak of bright, glowing gas created as a meteoroid vaporizes in the atmosphere due to friction.

meteoric water Water that falls to Earth from the atmosphere as either rain or snow.

meteorite A piece of rock or metal alloy that fell from space and landed on Earth.

micrite Limestone consisting of lime mud (i.e., very fine-grained limestone).

microfossil A fossil that can be seen only with a microscope or an electron microscope.

mid-ocean ridge A 2-km-high submarine mountain belt that forms along a divergent oceanic plate boundary.

migmatite A rock formed when gneiss is heated high enough so that it begins to partially melt, creating layers, or lenses, of new igneous rock that mix with layers of the relict gneiss.

Milanković cycles Climate cycles that occur over tens to hundreds of thousands of years because of changes in Earth's orbit and tilt.

mine A site at which ore is extracted from the ground.

mineral A homogenous, naturally occurring, solid inorganic substance with a definable chemical composition and an internal structure characterized by an orderly arrangement of atoms, ions, or molecules in a lattice. Most minerals are inorganic.

mineral classes Groups of minerals distinguished from each other on the basis of chemical composition.

mineralogist A geoscientist specializing in the study of minerals.

mineral resources The minerals extracted from the Earth's upper crust for practical purposes.

Mississippi Valley–type (MVT) ore An ore deposit, typically in dolostone, containing lead- and zinc-bearing minerals that precipitated from groundwater that had moved up from several km depth in the upper crust; such deposits occur in the upper Mississippi Valley.

mixture A material consisting of two or more substances that can be separated mechanically (i.e., without chemical reactions).

Modified Mercalli scale An earthquake characterization scale based on the amount of damage that the earthquake causes.

Moho The seismic-velocity discontinuity that defines the boundary between the Earth's crust and mantle. Named for Andrija Mohorovičić.

Mohs hardness scale A list of ten minerals in a sequence of relative hardness, with which other minerals can be compared.

mold A cavity in sedimentary rock left behind when a shell that once filled the space weathers out.

molecule The smallest piece of a compound that has the properties of the compound; it consists of two or more atoms attached by chemical bonds.

monocline A fold in the land surface whose shape resembles that of a carpet draped over a stair step.

monsoon A seasonal reversal in wind direction that causes a shift from a very dry season to a very rainy season in some regions of the world.

moon A sizable solid body locked in orbit around a planet.

moraine A sediment pile composed of till deposited by a glacier.

mountain front The boundary between a mountain range and adjacent plains.

mountain (alpine) glacier A glacier that exists in or adjacent to a mountainous region.

mountain ice cap A mound of ice that submerges peaks and ridges at the crest of a mountain range.

mouth The outlet of a stream where it discharges into another stream, a lake, or a sea.

mudflow A downslope movement of mud at slow to moderate speed.

mud pot A viscous slurry that forms in a geothermal region when hot water or steam rises into soils rich in volcanic ash and clay.

mudstone Very fine-grained sedimentary rock that will not easily split into sheets.

mylonite Rock formed during dynamic metamorphism and characterized by foliation that lies roughly parallel to the fault (shear zone) involved in the shearing process; mylonites have very fine grains formed by the nonbrittle subdivision of larger grains.

native metal A naturally occurring pure mass of a single metal in an ore deposit.

natural arch An arch that forms when erosion along joints leaves narrow walls of rock; when the lower part of the wall erodes while the upper part remains, an arch results.

natural hazard A natural feature of the environment that can cause injury to living organisms and/or damage to buildings and the landscape.

natural levees A pair of low ridges that appear on either side of a stream and develop as a result of the accumulation of sediment deposited naturally during flooding.

natural selection The process by which the fittest organisms survive to pass on their characteristics to the next generation.

neap tide An especially low tide that occurs when the angle between the direction of the Moon and the direction of the Sun is 90°.

nebula A cloud of gas or dust in space.

nebular theory of planet formation The concept that planets grow out of rings of gas, dust, and ice surrounding a newborn star.

negative anomaly An area where the magnetic field strength is less than expected.

negative feedback Feedback that slows a process down or reverses it.

neocrystallization The growth of new crystals, not in the protolith, during metamorphism.

neutron A subatomic particle, in the nucleus of an atom, that has a neutral charge.

Nevadan orogeny A convergent-margin mountain-building event that took place in western North America during the Late Jurassic Period.

nonconformity A type of unconformity at which sedimentary rocks overlie basement (older intrusive igneous rocks and/or metamorphic rocks).

nonflowing artesian well An artesian well in which water rises on its own up to a level that lies below the ground surface.

nonfoliated metamorphic rock Rock containing minerals that recrystallized during metamorphism but has no foliation.

nonmetallic mineral resources Mineral resources that do not contain metals; examples include building stone, gravel, sand, gypsum, phosphate, and salt.

nonplunging fold A fold with a horizontal hinge.

nonrenewable resource A resource that nature will take a long time (hundreds to millions of years) to replenish or may never replenish.

nonsystematic joints Short cracks in rocks that occur in a range of orientations and are randomly placed and oriented.

nor'easter A large, midlatitude North American cyclone; when it reaches the east coast, it produces strong winds that come out of the northeast.

normal fault A fault in which the hanging-wall block moves down the slope of the fault.

normal force The component of the gravitational force acting perpendicular to a slope.

normal polarity Polarity in which the paleomagnetic dipole has the same orientation as it does today.

normal stress The push or pull that is perpendicular to a surface.

North Atlantic deep-water mass The mass of cold, dense water that sinks in the north polar regions.

northeast tradewinds Surface winds that come out of the northeast and occur in the region between the equator and 30°N.

nuclear bond The force that attaches subatomic particles to each other within the nucleus of an atom.

nuclear fuel Pellets of concentrated uranium oxide or a comparable radioactive material that can provide energy in a nuclear reactor.

nuclear fusion The process by which the nuclei of atoms fuse together, thereby creating new, larger atoms.

nuclear reaction   A process that results in changing the nucleus of an atom by breaking or forming nuclear bonds.

nuclear reactor   The part of a nuclear power plant where the fission reactions occur.

nuclear waste   The radioactive material produced as a byproduct in a nuclear plant that must be disposed of carefully due to its dangerous radioactivity.

nucleus   The central ball of an atom that consists of protons and neutrons (except for hydrogen, whose nuclei contains only a proton).

nuée ardente   *See* Pyroclastic flow.

numerical age   (in older literature, "absolute age") The age of a geologic feature given in years.

oasis   A verdant region surrounded by desert, occurring at a place where natural springs provide water at the surface.

oblique-slip fault   A fault in which sliding occurs diagonally along the fault plane.

obsidian   An igneous rock consisting of a solid mass of volcanic glass.

occluded front   A front that no longer intersects the ground surface.

oceanic crust   The crust beneath the oceans; composed of gabbro and basalt, overlain by sediment.

oceanic plateau   A region of oceanic floor that is higher than surrounding areas; such regions have particularly thick oceanic crust and are relics of submarine large igneous provinces.

oceanic lithosphere   Lithosphere topped by oceanic crust; it reaches a thickness of 100 km.

offshore bar   A narrow ridge of sand that forms off the shore of a beach; some offshore bars rise above sea level, and separate a lagoon on one side from the open ocean on the other.

oil   (geology) A liquid hydrocarbon that can be burned as a fuel.

Oil Age   The period of human history, including our own, so named because the economy depends on oil.

oil field   A region containing a significant amount of accessible oil underground.

oil reserve   The known supply of oil held underground.

oil shale   Shale containing kerogen.

oil trap   A geologic configuration that keeps oil underground in the reservoir rock and prevents it from rising to the surface.

oil window   The narrow range of temperatures under which oil can form in a source rock.

olistotrome   A large, submarine slump block, buried and preserved.

Oort Cloud   A cloud of icy objects, left over from Solar System formation, that orbit the Sun in a region outside of the heliosphere.

ophiolite   A slice of oceanic crust that has been thrust onto continental crust.

ordinary well   A well whose base penetrates below the water table and can thus provide water.

ore   Rock containing native metals or a concentrated accumulation of ore minerals.

ore deposit   An economically significant accumulation of ore.

ore minerals   Minerals that have metal in high concentrations and in a form that can be easily extracted.

organic carbon   Carbon that has been incorporated in an organism.

organic chemical   A carbon-containing compound that occurs in living organisms, or that resembles such compounds; it consists of carbon atoms bonded to hydrogen atoms along with varying amounts of oxygen, nitrogen, and other chemicals.

organic coast   A coast along which living organisms control landforms along the shore.

organic sedimentary rock   Sedimentary rock (such as coal) formed from carbon-rich relicts of organisms.

organic shale   Lithified, muddy, organic-rich ooze that contains the raw materials from which hydrocarbons eventually form.

orogen (orogenic belt)   A linear range of mountains.

orogenic collapse   The process in which mountains begin to collapse under their own weight and spread out laterally.

orogeny   A mountain-building event.

orographic barrier   A landform that diverts air flow upward or laterally.

outcrop   An exposure of bedrock.

outer core   The section of the core, between 2,900 and 5,150 km deep, that consists of liquid iron alloy.

outwash plain   A broad area of gravel and sandbars deposited by a braided stream network, fed by the melt water of a glacier.

overburden   The weight of overlying rock on rock buried deeper in the Earth's crust.

overriding plate (slab)   The plate at a subduction zone that overrides the downgoing plate.

oversaturated solution   A solution that contains so much solute (dissolved ions) that precipitation begins.

oversized stream valley   A large valley with a small stream running through it; the valley formed earlier when the flow was greater.

oxbow lake   A meander that has been cut off yet remains filled with water.

oxidation reaction   A reaction in which an element loses electrons; an example is the reaction of iron with air to form rust.

ozone O_3, an atmospheric gas that absorbs harmful ultraviolet radiation from the Sun.

ozone hole   An area of the atmosphere, over polar regions, from which ozone has been depleted.

pahoehoe   A lava flow with a surface texture of smooth, glassy, ropelike ridges.

paleoclimate   The past climate of the Earth.

paleomagnetism   The record of ancient magnetism preserved in rock.

paleopole   The supposed position of the Earth's magnetic pole in the past, with respect to a particular continent.

paleosol   Ancient soil preserved in the stratigraphic record.

Paleozoic Era   The oldest era of the Phanerozoic Eon (541–252 Ma).

Pangaea   A supercontinent that assembled at the end of the Paleozoic Era.

Pannotia   A supercontinent that may have existed sometime between 800 Ma and 600 Ma.

parabolic dunes   Dunes formed when strong winds break through transverse dunes to make new dunes whose ends point upwind.

parallax   The apparent movement of an object seen from two different points not on a straight line from the object (e.g., from your two different eyes).

parallax method   A trigonometric method used to determine the distance from the Earth to a nearby star.

parent isotope   A radioactive isotope that undergoes decay.

partial melting   The melting in a rock of the minerals with the lowest melting temperatures, while other minerals remain solid.

passive margin   A continental margin that is not a plate boundary.

passive-margin basin   A thick accumulation of sediment along a tectonically inactive coast, formed over crust that stretched and thinned when the margin first began.

patterned ground   A polar landscape in which the ground splits into pentagonal or hexagonal shapes.

pause   An elevation in the atmosphere where temperature stops decreasing and starts increasing, or vice versa.

peat   Compacted and partially decayed vegetation accumulating beneath a swamp.

pedalfer soil A temperate-climate soil characterized by well-defined soil horizons and an organic A-horizon.

pediment The broad, nearly horizontal bedrock surface at the base of a retreating desert cliff.

pedocal soil Thin soil, formed in arid climates. It contains very little organic matter, but significant precipitated calcite.

pegmatite A coarse-grained igneous rock containing crystals of up to tens of centimeters across and occurring in dike-shaped intrusions.

pelagic sediment Microscopic plankton shells and fine flakes of clay that settle out and accumulate on the deep-ocean floor.

Pelé's hair Droplets of basaltic lava that mold into long, glassy strands as they fall.

Pelé's tears Droplets of basaltic lava that mold into tear-shaped, glassy beads as they fall.

peneplain A nearly flat surface that lies at an elevation close to sea level; thought to be the product of long-term erosion.

perched water table A quantity of groundwater that lies above the regional water table because an underlying lens of impermeable rock or sediment prevents the water from sinking down to the regional water table.

percolation The process by which groundwater meanders through tiny, crooked channels in the surrounding material.

peridotite A coarse-grained ultramafic rock.

periglacial environment A region with widespread permafrost but without a blanket of snow or ice.

period An interval of geologic time representing a subdivision of a geologic era.

permafrost Permanently frozen ground.

permanent magnet A special material that behaves magnetically for a long time all by itself.

permanent stream A stream that flows year-round because its bed lies below the water table, or because more water is supplied from upstream than can infiltrate the ground.

permeability The degree to which a material allows fluids to pass through it via an interconnected network of pores and cracks.

permineralization The fossilization process in which plant material becomes transformed into rock by the precipitation of silica from groundwater.

petrified A term used by geologists to describe plant material that has transformed into rock by permineralization.

petroglyph Drawings formed by chipping into the desert varnish of rocks to reveal the lighter rock beneath.

petroleum *See* Oil.

phaneritic A textural term used to describe coarse-grained igneous rock.

Phanerozoic Eon The most recent eon, an interval of time from 542 Ma to the present.

phenocryst A large crystal surrounded by a finer-grained matrix in an igneous rock.

photochemical smog Brown haze that blankets a city when exhaust from cars and trucks reacts in the presence of sunlight.

photosynthesis The process during which chlorophyll-containing plants remove carbon dioxide from the atmosphere, form tissues, and expel oxygen back to the atmosphere.

phreatomagmatic eruption An explosive eruption that occurs when water enters the magma chamber and turns into steam.

phyllite A fine-grained metamorphic rock with a foliation caused by the preferred orientation of very fine-grained mica.

phyllitic luster A silk-like sheen characteristic of phyllite, a result of the rock's fine-grained mica.

phylogenetic tree A chart representing the ideas of paleontologists showing which groups of organisms radiated from which ancestors.

physical weathering The process in which intact rock breaks into smaller grains or chunks.

piedmont glacier A fan or lobe of ice that forms where a valley glacier emerges from a valley and spreads out into the adjacent plain.

pillow basalt Glass-encrusted basalt blobs that form when magma extrudes on the sea floor and cools very quickly.

placer deposit Concentrations of metal grains in stream sediment that develop when rocks containing native metals erode and create a mixture of sand grains and metal fragments; the moving water of the stream carries away lighter mineral grains.

planet An object that orbits a star, is roughly spherical, and has cleared its neighborhood of other objects.

planetesimal Tiny, solid pieces of rock and metal that collect in a planetary nebula and eventually accumulate to form a planet.

plankton Tiny plants and animals that float in sea or lake water.

plastic deformation The deformational process in which mineral grains behave like plastic and, when compressed or sheared, become flattened or elongate without cracking or breaking.

plate One of about 20 distinct pieces of the relatively rigid lithosphere.

plate boundary The border between two adjacent lithosphere plates.

plate-boundary earthquakes The earthquakes that occur along and define plate boundaries.

plate-boundary volcano A volcanic arc or mid-ocean ridge volcano, formed as a consequence of movement along a plate boundary.

plate interior A region away from the plate boundaries that consequently experiences few earthquakes.

plate tectonics *See* Theory of plate tectonics.

playa The flat, typically salty lake bed that remains when all the water evaporates in drier times; forms in desert regions.

Pleistocene Epoch The period of time from about 2 Ma to 14,000 years ago, during which the Earth experienced an ice age.

plunge pool A depression at the base of a waterfall scoured by the energy of the falling water.

plunging fold A fold with a tilted hinge.

pluton An irregular or blob-shaped intrusion; can range in size from tens of m across to tens of km across.

pluvial lake A lake formed to the south of a continental glacier as a result of enhanced rainfall during an ice age.

point bar A wedge-shaped deposit of sediment on the inside bank of a meander.

polar cell A high-latitude convection cell in the atmosphere.

polar easterlies Prevailing winds that come from the east and flow from the polar high to the subpolar low.

polar front The convergence zone in the atmosphere at latitude 60°.

polar glacier *See* Dry-bottom glacier.

polar high The zone of high pressure in polar regions created by the sinking of air in the polar cells.

polarity The orientation of a magnetic dipole.

polarity chron The time interval between polarity reversals of Earth's magnetic field.

polarity subchron The time interval between magnetic reversals if the interval is of short duration (less than 200,000 years long).

polarized light A beam of filtered light waves that all vibrate in the same plane.

polar wander The phenomenon of the progressive changing through time of the position of the Earth's magnetic poles relative to a location on a continent; significant polar wander probably doesn't occur—in fact, poles seem to remain fairly fixed, while continents move.

polar-wander path The curving line representing the apparent progressive change in the position of the Earth's magnetic pole, relative to a locality X, assuming that the position of X on Earth has been fixed through time (in fact, poles stay fixed while continents move).

pollen Tiny grains involved in plant reproduction.

pollution Natural and synthetic contaminant materials introduced to the Earth's environment by the activities of humans.

polymorphs Two minerals that have the same chemical composition but a different crystal lattice structure.

pore A small, open space within sediment or rock.

pore collapse The closer packing of grains that occurs when groundwater is extracted from pores, thus eliminating the support holding the grains apart.

porosity The total volume of empty space (pore space) in a material, usually expressed as a percentage.

porphyritic A textural term for igneous rock that has phenocrysts distributed throughout a finer matrix.

Portland cement Cement made by mechanically mixing limestone, sandstone, and shale in just the right proportions, before heating in a kiln, to provide the correct chemical makeup of cement.

positive anomaly An area where the magnetic field strength is stronger than expected.

positive-feedback mechanism A mechanism that enhances the process that causes the mechanism in the first place.

potentiometric surface The elevation to which water in an artesian system would rise if unimpeded; where there are flowing artesian wells, the potentiometric surface lies above ground.

pothole A bowl-shaped depression carved into the floor of a stream by a long-lived whirlpool carrying sand or gravel.

Precambrian Period The interval of geologic time between Earth's formation about 4.57 Ga and the beginning of the Phanerozoic Eon 542 Ma.

precession The gradual conical path traced out by Earth's spinning axis; simply put, it is the "wobble" of the axis.

precious metals Metals (like gold, silver, and platinum) that have high value.

precipitate (chemistry, n.) A solid substance formed when atoms attach and settle out of a solution, or attach to the walls of the container holding the solution; (chemistry, v.) the action of forming a solid substance from a solution; (meteorology, v.) the dropping of snow or rain from the sky.

precipitation (1) The process by which atoms dissolved in a solution come together and form a solid; (2) rainfall or snow.

preferred mineral orientation The metamorphic texture that exists where platy grains lie parallel to one another and/or elongate grains align in the same direction.

pressure Force per unit area, or the "push" acting on a material in cases where the push (compressional stretch) is the same in all directions.

pressure gradient The rate of pressure change over a given horizontal distance.

pressure solution The process of dissolution at points of contact, between grains, where compression is greatest, producing ions that then precipitate elsewhere, where compression is less.

prevailing winds Surface winds that generally flow in the same direction for long time periods.

primary porosity The space that remains between solid grains or crystals immediately after sediment accumulates or rock forms.

principal aquifer The geologic unit that serves as the primary source of groundwater in a region.

principle of baked contacts When an igneous intrusion "bakes" (metamorphoses) surrounding rock, the rock that has been baked must be older than the intrusion.

principle of cross-cutting relations If one geologic feature cuts across another, the feature that has been cut is older.

principle of fossil succession In a stratigraphic sequence, different species of fossil organisms appear in a definite order; once a fossil species disappears in a sequence of strata, it never reappears higher in the sequence.

principle of inclusions If a rock contains fragments of another rock, the fragments must be older than the rock containing them.

principle of original continuity Sedimentary layers, before erosion, formed fairly continuous sheets over a region.

principle of original horizontality Layers of sediment, when originally deposited, are fairly horizontal.

principle of superposition In a sequence of sedimentary rock layers, each layer must be younger than the one below, for a layer of sediment cannot accumulate unless there is already a substrate on which it can collect.

principle of uniformitariansim The physical processes we observe today also operated in the past in the same way, and at comparable rates.

product (chemistry, n.) materials produced or formed by a chemical reaction.

prograde metamorphism Metamorphism that occurs as temperatures and pressures are increasing.

prokaryote An organism whose cells do not contain a nucleus; archaea and bacteria consist of prokaryotic cells.

Proterozoic Eon The most recent of the Precambrian eons (2,500–541 Ma).

protocontinent A block of crust composed of volcanic arcs and hotspot volcanoes sutured together.

protolith The original rock from which a metamorphic rock formed.

proton A positively charged subatomic particle in the nucleus of an atom.

protoplanet A body that grows by the accumulation of planetesimals but has not yet become big enough to be called a planet.

protoplanetary nebula A ring of gas and dust that surrounded the newborn Sun, from which the planets were formed.

protostar A dense body of gas that is collapsing inward because of gravitational forces and that may eventually become a star.

pumice A glassy igneous rock that forms from felsic frothy lava and contains abundant (over 50%) pore space.

pumice lapilli Marble-sized chunks consisting of frothy, siliceous igneous rock that fall from a volcanic eruptive cloud.

punctuated equilibrium The hypothesis that evolution takes place in fits and starts; evolution occurs very slowly for quite a while and then, during a relatively short period, takes place very rapidly.

P-waves Compressional seismic waves that move through the body of the Earth.

P-wave shadow zone A band between 103° and 143° from an earthquake epicenter, as measured along the circumference of the Earth, inside which P-waves do not arrive at seismograph stations.

pycnocline The boundary between layers of water of different densities.

pyroclastic debris Fragmented material that sprayed out of a volcano and landed on the ground or sea floor in solid form.

pyroclastic flow A fast-moving avalanche that occurs when hot volcanic ash and debris mix with air and flow down the side of a volcano.

pyroclastic rock Rock made from fragments that were blown out of a volcano during an explosion and were then packed or welded together.

quarry A site at which stone is extracted from the ground.

quartzite A metamorphic rock composed of quartz and transformed from a protolith of quartz sandstone.

quenching A sudden cooling of molten material to form a solid.

quick clay Clay that behaves like a solid when still (because of surface tension holding the water-coated clay flakes together) but that flows like a liquid when shaken.

radial network A drainage network in which the streams flow outward from a cone-shaped mountain and define a pattern resembling spokes on a wheel.

radiation (physics) Electromagnetic energy traveling away from a source through a medium or space.

radioactive decay   The process by which a radioactive atom undergoes fission or releases particles, thereby being transformed into a new element.

radioactive isotope   An unstable isotope of a given element.

radiometric dating   The science of dating geologic events in years by measuring the ratio of parent radioactive atoms to daughter product atoms.

rain band   A spiraling arm of a hurricane radiating outward from the eye.

rain shadow   The inland side of a mountain range, which is arid because the mountains block rain clouds from reaching the area.

range (for fossils)   The interval of a sequence of strata in which a specific fossil species appears.

rapids   A reach of a stream in which water becomes particularly turbulent; as a consequence, waves develop on the surface of the stream.

rare earth element   One of a group of 17 elements including the lanthanides, scandium, and yttrium; they are essential in the production of high-tech devices.

reach   A specified segment of a stream's path.

reactant   (chemistry) The starting materials of a chemical reaction.

recessional moraine   The end moraine that forms when a glacier stalls for a while as it recedes.

recharge area   A location where water enters the ground and infiltrates down to the water table.

recrystallization   The process in which ions or atoms in minerals rearrange to form new minerals.

rectangular network   A drainage network in which the streams join each other at right angles because of a rectangular grid of fractures that breaks up the ground and localizes channels.

recurrence interval   The average time between successive geologic events.

red giant   A huge red star that forms when Sun-sized stars start to die and expand.

red shift   The phenomenon in which a source of light moving away from you very rapidly shifts to a lower frequency; that is, toward the red end of the spectrum.

reef bleaching   The death and loss of color of a coral reef.

reflected ray   A ray that bounces off a boundary between two different materials.

refracted ray   A ray that bends as it passes through a boundary between two different materials.

refraction   The bending of a ray as it passes through a boundary between two different materials.

refractory materials   Substances that have a relatively high melting point and tend to exist in solid form.

reg   A vast stony plain in a desert.

regional metamorphism   *See also* Dynamothermal metamorphism; metamorphism of a broad region, usually the result of deep burial during an orogeny.

regolith   Any kind of unconsolidated debris that covers bedrock.

regression   The seaward migration of a shoreline caused by a lowering of sea level.

relative age   The age of one geologic feature with respect to another.

relative humidity   The ratio between the measured water content of air and the maximum possible amount of water the air can hold at a given condition.

relative plate velocity   The movement of one lithosphere plate with respect to another.

relief   The difference in elevation between adjacent high and low regions on the land surface.

renewable resource   A resource that can be replaced by nature within a short time span relative to a human life span.

reservoir rock   Rock with high porosity and permeability, so it can contain an abundant amount of easily accessible oil.

residence time   The average length of time that a substance stays in a particular reservoir.

residual mineral deposit   Soils in which the residuum left behind after leaching by rainwater is so concentrated in metals that the soil itself becomes an ore deposit.

resonance   (seismology) A situation that arises when earthquake waves of a particular frequency cause particularly large-amplitude movements because energy input happens at just the right time.

resurgent dome   The new mound, or cone, of igneous rock that grows within a caldera as an eruption begins anew.

retrograde metamorphism   Metamorphism that occurs as pressures and temperatures are decreasing; for retrograde metamorphism to occur, water must be added.

return stroke   An upward-flowing electric current from the ground that carries positive charges up to a cloud during a lightning flash.

reversed polarity   Polarity in which the paleomagnetic dipole points north.

reverse fault   A steeply dipping fault on which the hanging-wall block slides up.

rhythmic layering   Banding in sediments, shells, trees, corals, or ice that repeats periodically; it may be correlated to annual cycles.

Richter magnitude scale   A scale that defines earthquakes on the basis of the amplitude of the largest ground motion recorded on a seismogram.

ridge axis   The crest of a mid-ocean ridge; the ridge axis defines the position of a divergent plate boundary.

ridge-push force   A process in which gravity causes the elevated lithosphere at a mid-ocean ridge axis to push on the lithosphere that lies farther from the axis, making it move away.

right-lateral strike-slip fault   A strike-slip fault in which the block on the opposite fault plane from a fixed spot moves to the right of that spot.

rip current   A strong, localized seaward flow of water perpendicular to a beach.

ripple mark   Relatively small elongated ridges that form on a sedimentary bed surface at right angles to the direction of current flow.

riprap   Loose boulders or concrete piled together along a beach to absorb wave energy before it strikes a cliff face.

roche moutonnée   A glacially eroded hill that becomes elongate in the direction of flow and asymmetric; glacial rasping smoothes the upstream part of the hill into a gentle slope, while glacial plucking erodes the downstream edge into a steep slope.

rock   A coherent, naturally occurring solid, consisting of an aggregate of minerals or a mass of glass.

rock burst   A sudden explosion of rock off the ceiling or wall of an underground mine.

rock cycle   The succession of events that results in the transformation of Earth materials from one rock type to another, then another, and so on.

rockfall   A mass of rock that separates from a cliff, typically along a joint, and then free-falls downslope.

rock flour   Fine-grained sediment produced by glacial abrasion of the substrate over which a glacier flows.

rock glacier   A slow-moving mixture of rock fragments and ice.

rockslide   A sudden downslope movement of rock.

rocky coast   An area of coast where bedrock rises directly from the sea, so beaches are absent.

Rodinia   A proposed Precambrian supercontinent that existed around 1 billion years ago.

rogue wave   Waves that are two to five times the size of most of the large waves passing a locality in a given time interval.

rotational axis   The imaginary line through the center of the Earth around which the Earth spins.

running water   Water that flows down the surface of sloping land in response to the pull of gravity.

R-waves (Rayleigh waves)   Surface seismic waves that cause the ground to ripple up and down, like water waves in a pond.

sabkah   A region of formerly flooded coastal desert in which stranded seawater has left a salt crust over a mire of mud that is rich in organic material.

salinity   The degree of concentration of salt in water.

saltation   The movement of a sediment in which grains bounce along their substrate, knocking other grains into the water column (or air) in the process.

salt dome   A rising bulbous dome of salt that bends up the adjacent layers of sedimentary rock.

salt wedging   The process in arid climates by which dissolved salt in groundwater crystallizes and grows in open pore spaces in rocks and pushes apart the surrounding grains.

sand dune   A relatively large ridge of sand built up by a current of wind (or water); cross bedding typically occurs within the dune.

sandspit   An area where the beach stretches out into open water across the mouth of a bay or estuary.

sandstone   Coarse-grained sedimentary rock consisting almost entirely of quartz.

sand volcano (sand blow)   A small mound of sand produced when sand layers below the ground surface liquify as a result of seismic shaking, causing the sand to erupt onto the Earth's surface through cracks or holes in overlying clay layers.

saprolite   A layer of rotten rock created by chemical weathering in warm, wet climates.

Sargasso Sea   The center of North Atlantic Gyre, named for the tropical seaweed sargassum, which accumulates in its relatively noncirculating waters.

saturated solution   Water that carries as many dissolved ions as possible under given environmental conditions.

saturated zone   The region below the water table where pore space is filled with water.

scattering   The dispersal of energy that occurs when light interacts with particles in the atmosphere.

schist   A medium-to-coarse-grained metamorphic rock that possesses schistosity.

schistosity   Foliation caused by the preferred orientation of large mica flakes.

scientific method   A sequence of steps for systematically analyzing scientific problems in a way that leads to verifiable results.

scoria   A glassy, mafic, igneous rock containing abundant air-filled holes.

scoria cone   An accumulation of lapilli-sized or larger fragments formed from a volcanic eruption that spatters clots of basaltic lava. (Also called cinder cone.)

scouring   A process by which running water removes loose fragments of sediment from a streambed.

sea arch   An arch of land protruding into the sea and connected to the mainland by a narrow bridge.

sea-floor spreading   The gradual widening of an ocean basin as new oceanic crust forms at a mid-ocean ridge axis and then moves away from the axis.

sea ice   Ice formed by the freezing of the surface of the sea.

seal   A relatively impermeable rock, such as shale, salt, or unfractured limestone, that lies above a reservoir rock and stops the oil from rising further.

seam   A sedimentary bed of coal interlayered with other sedimentary rocks.

seamount   An isolated submarine mountain.

seasonal floods   Floods that appear almost every year during seasons when rainfall is heavy or when winter snows start to melt.

seasonal well   A well that provides water only during the rainy season when the water table rises below the base of the well.

sea stack   An isolated tower of land just offshore, disconnected from the mainland by the collapse of a sea arch.

seawall   A wall of riprap built on the landward side of a backshore zone in order to protect shore cliffs from erosion.

second   The basic unit of time measurement, now defined as the time it takes for the magnetic field of a cesium atom to flip polarity 9,192,631,770 times, as measured by an atomic clock.

secondary enrichment   The process by which a new ore deposit forms from metals that were dissolved and carried away from preexisting ore minerals.

secondary porosity   New pore space in rocks, created some time after a rock first forms.

secondary recovery technique   A process used to extract the quantities of oil that will not come out of a reservoir rock with just simple pumping.

sediment   An accumulation of loose mineral grains, such as boulders, pebbles, sand, silt, or mud, that are not cemented together.

sediment liquefaction   When pressure in the water in the pores push sediment grains apart so that they become surrounded by water and no longer rest against each other, and the sediment becomes able to flow like a liquid.

sedimentary basin   A depression, created as a consequence of subsidence, that fills with sediment.

sedimentary rock   Rock that forms either by the cementing together of fragments broken off preexisting rock or by the precipitation of mineral crystals out of water solutions at or near the Earth's surface.

sedimentary sequence   A grouping of sedimentary units bounded on top and bottom by regional unconformities.

sediment budget   The proportion of sand supplied to sand removed from a depositional setting.

sediment load   The total volume of sediment carried by a stream.

sediment maturity   The degree to which a sediment has evolved from a crushed-up version of the original rock into a sediment that has lost its easily weathered minerals and become well sorted and rounded.

sediment sorting   The segregation of sediment by size.

seep   A place where oil-filled reservoir rock intersects the ground surface, or where fractures connect a reservoir to the ground surface, so that oil flows out onto the ground on its own.

seiche   Rhythmic movement in a body of water caused by ground motion.

seismic belts (seismic zones)   The relatively narrow strips of crust on Earth under which most earthquakes occur.

seismicity   Earthquake activity.

seismic-moment magnitude scale   A scale that defines earthquake size on the basis of calculations involving the amount of slip, length of rupture, depth of rupture, and rock strength.

seismic ray   The changing position of an imaginary point on a wave front as the front moves through rock.

seismic-reflection profile   A cross-sectional view of the crust made by measuring the reflection of artificial seismic waves off boundaries between different layers of rock in the crust.

seismic retrofitting   The strengthening of an already existing structure (building, bridge, etc.) so that it can withstand earthquake vibrations.

seismic tomography   Analysis by sophisticated computers of global seismic data in order to create a three-dimensional image of variations in seismic-wave velocities within the Earth.

seismic velocity   The speed at which seismic waves travel.

seismic-velocity discontinuity   A boundary in the Earth at which seismic velocity changes abruptly.

seismic (earthquake) waves   Waves of energy emitted at the focus of an earthquake.

seismogram   The record of an earthquake produced by a seismograph.

seismometer (seismograph) An instrument that can record the ground motion from an earthquake.

semipermanent pressure cell A somewhat elliptical zone of high or low atmospheric pressure that lasts much of the year; it forms because high-pressure zones tend to be narrower over land than over sea.

Sevier orogeny A mountain-building event that affected western North America between about 150 Ma and 80 Ma, a result of convergent margin tectonism; a fold-thrust belt formed during this event.

shale Very fine-grained sedimentary rock that breaks into thin sheets.

shale gas Gas that comes directly from a source rock (organic shale).

shatter cones Small, cone-shaped fractures formed by the shock of a meteorite impact.

shear When one part of a material moves sideways, relative to another.

shear strain A change in shape of an object that involves the movement of one part of a rock body sideways past another part so that angular relationships within the body change.

shear stress A stress that moves one part of a material sideways past another part.

shear waves Seismic waves in which particles of material move back and forth perpendicular to the direction in which the wave itself moves.

shear zone A fault in which movement has occurred ductilely.

sheetwash A film of water less than a few mm thick that covers the ground surface during heavy rains.

shell (biology) A relatively hard, protective structure formed of minerals and surrounding the soft part of an invertebrate organism.

shield An older, interior region of a continent.

shield volcano A subaerial volcano with a broad, gentle dome, formed either from low-viscosity basaltic lava or from large pyroclastic sheets.

shocked quartz Grains of quartz that have been subjected to intense pressure such as occurs during a meteorite impact.

shock metamorphism The changes that can occur in a rock due to the passage of a shock wave, generally resulting from a meteorite impact.

shoreline The boundary between the water and land.

shortening The process during which a body of rock or a region of crust becomes shorter.

short-term climate change Climate change that takes place over hundreds to thousands of years.

Sierran arc A large continental volcanic arc along western North America that was initiated at the end of the Jurassic Period and lasted until about 80 million years ago.

silica SiO2.

silicate rock Rock composed of silicate minerals.

silicates (silicate minerals) Minerals built from silicon-oxygen tetrahedra arranged in chains, sheets, or 3-D networks; they make up most of the Earth's crust and mantle.

siliceous sedimentary rock Sedimentary rock that contains abundant quartz.

silicon-oxygen tetrahedron The SiO44– anionic group, in which four oxygen atoms surround a single silicon atom, thereby defining the corners of a tetrahedron.

silicic Rich in silica with relatively little iron and magnesium.

sill A nearly horizontal tabletop-shaped tabular intrusion that occurs between the layers of country rock.

siltstone Fine-grained sedimentary rock generally composed of very small quartz grains.

sinkhole A circular depression in the land that forms when an underground cavern collapses.

slab-pull force The force that downgoing plates (or slabs) apply to oceanic lithosphere at a convergent margin.

slate Fine-grained, low-grade metamorphic rock, formed by the metamorphism of shale.

slaty cleavage The foliation typical of slate, and reflective of the preferred orientation of slate's clay minerals, that allows slate to be split into thin sheets.

slickensides The polished surface of a fault caused by slip on the fault; lineated slickensides also have grooves that indicate the direction of fault movement.

slip face The leeward slope of a dune; sand that builds up at the crest of the dune slides down this face; slip faces are preserved as cross beds within sandstone layers.

slip lineations Linear marks on a fault surface created during movement on the fault; some slip lineations are defined by grooves, some by aligned mineral fibers.

slope failure The downslope movement of material on an unstable slope.

slumping Downslope movement in which a mass of regolith detaches from its substrate along a spoon-shaped, sliding surface and slips downward semicoherently.

smelting The heating of a metal-containing rock to high temperatures in a fire so that the rock will decompose to yield metal plus a nonmetallic residue (slag).

snottite A long gob of bacteria that slowly drips from the ceiling of a cave.

snowball Earth A model proposing that, at times during Earth history, glaciers covered all land, and the entire ocean surface froze.

snow line The boundary above which snow remains all year.

soda straw A hollow stalactite in which calcite precipitates around the outside of a drip.

soil Sediment that has undergone changes at the surface of the Earth, including reaction with rainwater and the addition of organic material.

soil erosion The removal of soil by wind and runoff.

soil horizon Distinct zones within a soil, distinguished from each other by factors such as chemical composition and organic content.

soil moisture Underground water that wets the surface of the mineral grains and organic material making up soil, but lies above the water table.

soil profile A vertical sequence of distinct zones of soil.

Solar System Our Sun and all the materials that orbit it (including planets, moons, asteroids, Kuiper Belt objects, and Oort Cloud objects).

solar wind A stream of particles with enough energy to escape from the Sun's gravity and flow outward into space.

solid-state diffusion The slow movement of atoms or ions through a solid.

solidus The highest temperature at which all the components of a material are solid; at the solidus temperature, the material begins to melt.

solifluction The type of creep characteristic of tundra regions; during the summer, the uppermost layer of permafrost melts, and the soggy, weak layer of ground then flows slowly downslope in overlapping sheets.

solstice A day on which the polar ends of the terminator (the boundary between the day hemisphere and the night hemisphere) lie 23.5° away from the associated geographic poles.

solution A material containing dissolved ions.

Sonoma orogeny A convergent-margin mountain-building event that took place on the western coast of North America in the Late Permian and Early Triassic periods.

sorting (1) The range of clast sizes in a collection of sediment; (2) the degree to which sediment has been separated by flowing currents into different-sized fractions.

source rock A rock (organic-rich shale) containing the raw materials from which hydrocarbons eventually form.

southeast tradewinds Tradewinds in the southern hemisphere, which start flowing northward, deflect to the west, and end up flowing from southeast to northwest.

southern oscillation The movement of atmospheric pressure cells back and forth across the Pacific Ocean, in association with El Niño.

specific gravity A number representing the density of a mineral, as specified by the ratio between the weight of a volume of the mineral and the weight of an equal volume of water.

speleothem A formation that grows in a limestone cave by the accumulation of travertine precipitated from water solutions dripping in a cave or flowing down the wall of a cave.

sphericity The measure of the degree to which a clast approaches the shape of a sphere.

spreading boundary *See* Divergent plate boundary.

spreading rate The rate at which sea floor moves away from a mid-ocean ridge axis, as measured with respect to the sea floor on the opposite side of the axis.

spring A natural outlet from which groundwater flows up onto the ground surface.

spring tide An especially high tide that occurs when the Sun is on the same side of the Earth as the Moon.

stable air Air that does not have a tendency to rise rapidly.

stable slope A slope on which downward sliding is unlikely.

stalactite An icicle-like cone that grows from the ceiling of a cave as dripping water precipitates limestone.

stalagmite An upward-pointing cone of limestone that grows when drips of water hit the floor of a cave.

standing wave A wave whose crest and trough remain in place as water moves through the wave.

star An object in the Universe in which fusion reactions occur pervasively, producing vast amounts of energy; our Sun is a star.

star dune A constantly changing dune formed by frequent shifts in wind direction; it consists of overlapping crescent dunes pointing in many different directions.

steady state condition The condition when proportions of a chemical in different reservoirs remain fairly constant even though there is a constant flux (flow) of the chemical among the reservoirs.

stellar nucleosynthesis The production of new, larger atoms by fusion reactions in stars; the process generates more massive elements that were not produced by the Big Bang.

stellar wind The stream of atoms emitted from a star into space.

stick-slip behavior Stop-start movement along a fault plane caused by friction, which prevents movement until stress builds up sufficiently.

stone rings Ridges of cobbles between adjacent bulges of permafrost ground.

stoping A process by which magma intrudes; blocks of wall rock break off and then sink into the magma.

storm An episode of severe weather in which winds, precipitation, and in some cases lightning become strong enough to be bothersome and even dangerous.

storm-center velocity A storm's (hurricane's) velocity along its track.

storm surge Excess seawater driven landward by wind during a storm; the low atmospheric pressure beneath the storm allows sea level to rise locally, increasing the surge.

strain The change in shape of an object in response to deformation (i.e., as a result of the application of a stress).

strata A succession of several layers or beds together.

stratified drift Glacial sediment that has been redistributed and stratified by flowing water.

stratigraphic column A cross-section diagram of a sequence of strata summarizing information about the sequence.

stratigraphic formation A recognizable layer of a specific sedimentary rock type or set of rock types, deposited during a certain time interval, that can be traced over a broad region.

stratigraphic group Several adjacent stratigraphic formations in a succession.

stratigraphic sequence An interval of strata deposited during periods of relatively high sea level, and bounded above and below by regional unconformities.

stratopause The temperature pause that marks the top of the stratosphere.

stratosphere The stable, stratified layer of atmosphere directly above the troposphere.

stratovolcano A large, cone-shaped subaerial volcano consisting of alternating layers of lava and tephra.

stratus cloud A thin, sheet-like, stable cloud.

streak The color of the powder produced by pulverizing a mineral on an unglazed ceramic plate.

stream A ribbon of water that flows in a channel.

streambed The floor of a stream.

stream capacity The total quantity of sediment a stream carries.

stream capture (stream piracy) The situation in which headward erosion causes one stream to intersect the course of another, previously independent stream, so that the intersected stream starts to flow down the channel of the first stream.

stream competence The maximum particle size that a stream can carry.

stream gradient The slope of a stream's channel in the downstream direction.

stream piracy A process that happens when headward erosion by one stream causes the stream to intersect the course of another stream and capture its flow.

stream rejuvenation The renewed downcutting of a stream into a floodplain or peneplain, caused by a relative drop of the base level.

stream terrace When a stream downcuts through the alluvium of a floodplain so that a new, lower floodplain develops and the original floodplain becomes a step-like platform.

stress The push, pull, or shear that a material feels when subjected to a force; formally, the force applied per unit area over which the force acts.

stretching The process during which a layer of rock or a region of crust becomes longer.

striations Linear scratches in rock.

strike-slip fault A fault in which one block slides horizontally past another (and therefore parallel to the strike line), so there is no relative vertical motion.

strip mining The scraping off of all soil and sedimentary rock above a coal seam in order to gain access to the seam.

stromatolite Layered mounds of sediment formed by cyanobacteria; cyanobacteria secrete a mucous-like substance to which sediment sticks, and as each layer of cyanobacteria gets buried by sediment, it colonizes the surface of the new sediment, building a mound upward.

structural control The condition in which geologic structures, such as faults, affect the distribution and drainage of water or the shape of the land surface.

subaerial Pertaining to land regions above sea level (i.e., under air).

subduction The process by which one oceanic plate bends and sinks down into the asthenosphere beneath another plate.

subduction zone The region along a convergent boundary where one plate sinks beneath another.

sublimation The evaporation of ice directly into vapor without first forming a liquid.

submarine canyon A narrow, steep canyon that dissects a continental shelf and slope.

submarine fan   A wedge-shaped accumulation of sediment at the base of a submarine slope; fans usually accumulate at the mouth of a submarine canyon.

submarine slump   The underwater downslope movement of a semicoherent block of sediment along a weak mud detachment.

submergent coast   A coast at which the land is sinking relative to sea level.

subpolar low   The rise of air where the surface flow of a polar cell converges with the surface flow of a Ferrel cell, creating a low-pressure zone in the atmosphere.

subsidence   The vertical sinking of the Earth's surface in a region, relative to a reference plane.

substrate   A general term for material just below the ground surface.

subtropical high (subtropical divergence zone)   A belt of high pressure in the atmosphere at 30° latitude formed where the Hadley cell converges with th Ferrel cell, causing cool, dense air to sink.

subtropics   Desert climate regions that lie on either side of the equatorial tropics between the lines of 20° and 30° north or south of the equator.

summit eruption   An eruption that occurs in the summit crater of a volcano.

sunspot cycle   The cyclic appearance of large numbers of sunspots (black spots thought to be magnetic storms on the Sun's surface) every 9 to 11.5 years.

supercontinent cycle   The process of change during which supercontinents develop and later break apart, forming pieces that may merge once again in geologic time to make yet another supercontinent.

supernova   A short-lived, very bright object in space that results from the cataclysmic explosion marking the death of a very large star; the explosion ejects large quantities of matter into space to form new nebulae.

superplume   A huge mantle plume.

superposed stream   A stream whose geometry has been laid down on a rock structure and is not controlled by the structure.

superrotation   The faster rotation of the core, relative to the rest of the Earth.

supervolcano   A volcano that erupts a vast amount (more than 1,000 cubic km) of volcanic material during a single event; none have erupted during recorded human history.

surface current   An ocean current in the top 100 m of water.

surface load   (bed load)   Sediment that rolls and bounce along the ground (under the air) or along a stream bed (under water).

surface water   Liquid or seasonally frozen water that resides at the surface of the Earth in oceans, lakes, streams, and marshes.

surface waves   Seismic waves that travel along the Earth's surface.

surface westerlies   The prevailing surface winds in North America and Europe, which come out of the west or southwest.

surf zone   A region of the shore in which breakers crash onto the shore.

surge (glacial)   A pulse of rapid flow in a glacier.

suspended load   Tiny solid grains carried along by a stream without settling to the floor of the channel.

sustainable growth   The ability of society to prosper without depleting the supply of natural resources, and without destroying the environment.

swamp   A wetland dominated by trees.

swash   The upward surge of water that flows up a beach slope when breakers crash onto the shore.

S-waves   Seismic shear waves that pass through the body of the Earth.

S-wave shadow zone   A band between 103° and 180° from the epicenter of an earthquake inside of which S-waves do not arrive at seismograph stations.

swelling clay   Clay possessing a mineral structure that allows it to absorb water between its layers and thus swell to several times its original size.

symmetry   The condition in which the shape of one part of an object is a mirror image of the other part.

syncline   A trough-shaped fold whose limbs dip toward the hinge.

systematic joints   Long planar cracks that occur fairly regularly throughout a rock body.

tabular intrusions   Sheet intrusions that are planar and of roughly uniform thickness.

Taconic orogeny   A convergent mountain-building event that took place around 400 million years ago, in which a volcanic island arc collided with eastern North America.

tailings pile   A pile of waste rock from a mine.

talus   A sloping apron of fallen rock along the base of a cliff.

tar   Hydrocarbons that exist in solid form at room temperature.

tarn   A lake that forms at the base of a cirque on a glacially eroded mountain.

tar sand   Sandstone reservoir rock in which less viscous oil and gas molecules have either escaped or been eaten by microbes, so that only tar remains.

taxonomy   The study and classification of the relationships among different forms of life.

tectonic foliation   A planar fabric, such as cleavage, schistocity, or gneissic banding, that develops in rocks; caused by compression or shearing during deformation (e.g., during mountain building).

temperature   A measure of the hotness or coldness of a material.

tension   A stress that pulls on a material and could lead to stretching.

tephra   Unconsolidated accumulations of pyroclastic grains.

terminal moraine   The end moraine at the farthest limit of glaciation.

terminator   The boundary between the half of the Earth that has daylight and the half experiencing night.

terrace   The elevated surface of an older floodplain into which a younger floodplain had cut down.

terrestrial planets   Planets that are of comparable size and character to the Earth and consist of a metallic core surrounded by a rock mantle.

thalweg   The deepest part of a stream's channel.

theory   A scientific idea supported by an abundance of evidence that has passed many tests and failed none.

theory of plate tectonics   The theory that the outer layer of the Earth (the lithosphere) consists of separate plates that move with respect to one another.

thermal energy   The total kinetic energy in a material due to the vibration and movement of atoms in the material.

thermal metamorphism   Metamorphism caused by heat conducted into country rock from an igneous intrusion.

thermocline   A boundary between layers of water with differing temperatures.

thermohaline circulation   The rising and sinking of water driven by contrasts in water density, which is due in turn to differences in temperature and salinity; this circulation involves both surface and deep-water currents in the ocean.

thermosphere   The outermost layer of the atmosphere, containing very little gas.

thin section   A 3/100-mm-thick slice of rock that can be examined with a petrographic microscope.

thin-skinned deformation   A distinctive style of deformation characterized by displacement on faults that terminate at depth along a subhorizontal detachment fault.

thrust fault   A gently dipping reverse fault; the hanging-wall block moves up the slope of the fault.

tidal bore   A visible wall of water that moves toward shore with the rising tide in quiet waters.

tidal flat   A broad, nearly horizontal plain of mud and silt, exposed or nearly exposed at low tide but totally submerged at high tide.

tidal power   Energy produced by the daily rise and fall of the tides; people can utilize this energy, for example, by damming a bay or estuary, so that water passes through turbines when the tide changes.

tidal range   The difference in sea level between high tide and low tide at a given point.

tide　The daily rising or falling of sea level at a given point on the Earth.

tide-generating force　The force, caused in part by the gravitational attraction of the Sun and Moon and in part by the centrifugal force created by the Earth's spin, that generates tides.

tidewater glacier　A glacier that has entered the sea along a coast.

till　A mixture of unsorted mud, sand, pebbles, and larger rocks deposited by glaciers.

tillite　A rock formed from hardened ancient glacial deposits and consisting of larger clasts distributed through a matrix of sandstone and mudstone.

toe (terminus)　The leading edge or margin of a glacier.

tombolo　A narrow ridge of sand that links a sea stack to the mainland.

topographical map　A map that uses contour lines to represent variations in elevation.

topography　Variations in elevation.

topsoil　The top soil horizons, which are typically dark and nutrient-rich.

tornado　A near-vertical, funnel-shaped cloud in which air rotates extremely rapidly around the axis of the funnel.

tornado swarm　Dozens of tornadoes produced by the same storm.

tower karst　A karst landscape in which steep-sided residual bedrock towers remain between sinkholes.

trace fossil　Fossilized imprints or debris that an organism leaves behind while moving on or through sediment; examples include footprints, burrows, and fecal matter.

transform fault　A fault marking a transform plate boundary; along mid-ocean ridges, transform faults are the actively slipping segment of a fracture zone between two ridge segments.

transform plate boundary　A boundary at which one lithosphere plate slips laterally past another.

transgression　The inland migration of shoreline resulting from a rise in sea level.

transition zone　The middle portion of the mantle, from 400 to 670 km deep, in which there are several jumps in seismic velocity.

transpiration　The release of moisture as a metabolic by-product.

transverse dune　A simple, wave-like dune that appears when enough sand accumulates for the ground surface to be completely buried, but only moderate winds blow.

trap　A subsurface configuration of seal rocks and structures that keep oil and/or gas underground, so it doesn't seep out at the surface.

travel-time curve　A graph that plots the time since an earthquake began on the vertical axis and the distance to the epicenter on the horizontal axis.

travertine　A rock composed of crystalline calcium carbonate ($CaCO_3$) formed by chemical precipitation from groundwater that has seeped out at the ground surface.

trellis network　A drainage system that develops across a landscape of parallel valleys and ridges so that major tributaries flow down the valleys and join a trunk stream that cuts through the ridge; the resulting map pattern resembles a garden trellis.

trench　A deep, elongate trough bordering a volcanic arc; a trench defines the trace of a convergent plate boundary.

triangulation　The method for determining the map location of a point from knowing the distance between that point and three other points; this method is used to locate earthquake epicenters.

tributary　A smaller stream that flows into a larger stream.

triple junction　A point where three lithosphere plate boundaries intersect.

tropical depression　A tropical storm with winds reaching up to 61 km per hour; such storms develop from tropical disturbances, and may grow to become hurricanes.

tropical disturbance　Cyclonic winds that develop in the tropics.

tropopause　The temperature pause marking the top of the troposphere.

troposphere　The lowest layer of the atmosphere, where air undergoes convection and where most wind and clouds develop.

truncated spur　A spur (elongate ridge between two valleys) whose end was eroded off by a glacier.

trunk stream　The single larger stream into which an array of tributaries flow.

tsunami　A large wave along the sea surface triggered by an earthquake or large submarine slump.

tuff　A pyroclastic igneous rock composed of volcanic ash and fragmented pumice, formed when accumulations of the debris cement together.

tundra　A cold, treeless region of land at high latitudes, supporting only species of shrubs, moss, and lichen capable of living on permafrost.

turbidite　A graded bed of sediment built up at the base of a submarine slope and deposited by turbidity currents.

turbidity current　A submarine avalanche of sediment and water that speeds down a submarine slope.

turbulence　The chaotic twisting, swirling motion in flowing fluid.

typhoon　The equivalent of a hurricane in the western Pacific Ocean.

ultimate base level　Sea level; the level below which a trunk stream cannot cut.

ultramafic　A term used to describe igneous rocks or magmas that are rich in iron and magnesium and very poor in silica.

unconfined aquifer　An aquifer that intersects the surface of the Earth.

unconformity　A boundary between two different rock sequences representing an interval of time during which new strata were not deposited and/or were eroded.

unconsolidated　Consisting of unattached grains.

undercutting　Excavation at the base of a slope that results in the formation of an overhang.

undersaturated　A term used to describe a solution capable of holding more dissolved ions.

Universe　All of space and all the matter and energy within it.

unsaturated zone　The region of the subsurface above the water table.

unstable air　Air that is significantly warmer than air above and has a tendency to rise quickly.

unstable ground　Land capable of slumping or slipping downslope in the near future.

unstable slope　A slope on which sliding will likely happen.

updraft　Upward-moving air.

upper mantle　The uppermost section of the mantle, reaching down to a depth of 400 km.

upwelling zone　A place where deep water rises in the ocean, or where hot magma rises in the asthenosphere.

U-shaped valley　A steep-walled valley shaped by glacial erosion into the form of a U.

vacuum　Space that contains very little matter in a given volume (e.g., a region in which air has been removed).

valley　A trough with sloping walls, cut into the land by a stream.

valley glacier　A river of ice that flows down a mountain valley.

Van Allen radiation belts　Belts of solar wind particles and cosmic rays that surround the Earth, trapped by Earth's magnetic field.

van der Waals bonding　The relatively weak attachment of two elements or molecules due to their polarity and not due to covalent or ionic bonding.

varve　A pair of thin layers of glacial lake-bed sediment, one consisting of silt brought in during the spring floods and the other of clay deposited during the winter when the lake's surface freezes over and the water is still.

vascular plant　A plant with woody tissue and seeds and veins for transporting water and food.

vein A seam of minerals that forms when dissolved ions carried by water solutions precipitate in cracks.

vein deposit A hydrothermal deposit in which the ore minerals occur in veins that fill cracks in preexisting rocks.

velocity-versus-depth curve A graph that shows the variation in the velocity of seismic waves with increasing depth in the Earth.

ventifact (faceted rock) A desert rock whose surface has been faceted by the wind.

vesicles Open holes in igneous rock formed by the preservation of bubbles in magma as the magma cools into solid rock.

viscosity The resistance of material to flow.

volatiles (volatile materials) Elements or compounds such as H_2O and CO_2 that evaporate at relatively low temperatures and can exist in gaseous forms at the Earth's surface.

volatility A specification of the ease with which a material evaporates.

volcanic agglomerate An accumulation consisting dominantly of volcanic bombs and other relatively large chunks of igneous material.

volcanic arc A curving chain of active volcanoes formed adjacent to a convergent plate boundary.

volcanic ash Tiny glass shards formed when a fine spray of exploded lava freezes instantly upon contact with the atmosphere.

volcanic bomb A large piece of pyroclastic debris thrown into the atmosphere during a volcanic eruption.

volcanic breccia A pyroclastic igneous rock that consists of fragments of volcanic debris, which either fall through the air and accumulate, or form when solidfying lava breaks up during flow.

volcanic danger-assessment map A map delineating areas that lie in the path of potential lava flows, lahars, debris flows, or pyroclastic flows of an active volcano.

volcanic debris flow A mixture of water and pyroclastic debris that moves downslope like wet concrete.

volcanic gas Elements or compounds that bubble out of magma or lava in gaseous form.

volcanic island arc The volcanic island chain that forms on the edge of the overriding plate where one oceanic plate subducts beneath another oceanic plate.

volcaniclastic deposit An accumulation of large quantities of fragmental igneous material (including both pyroclastic debris, and water-transported debris).

volcaniclastic rock A material composed of cemented-together grains of volcanic material; it includes both pyroclastic rocks and rocks formed from accumulations of water-transported volcanic debris.

volcano (1) A vent from which melt from inside the Earth spews out onto the planet's surface; (2) a mountain formed by the accumulation of extrusive volcanic rock.

V-shaped valley A valley whose cross-sectional shape resembles the shape of a V; the valley probably has a river running down the point of the V.

Wadati-Benioff zone A sloping band of seismicity defined by intermediate- and deep-focus earthquakes that occur in the downgoing slab of a convergent plate boundary.

wadi The name used in the Middle East and North Africa for a dry wash.

warm front A front in which warm air rises slowly over cooler air in the atmosphere.

waste rock Rock dislodged by mining activity yet containing no ore minerals.

waterfall A place where water drops over an escarpment.

water gap An opening in a resistant ridge where a trunk river has cut through the ridge.

watershed The region that collects water that feeds into a given drainage network.

water table The boundary, approximately parallel to the Earth's surface, that separates substrate in which groundwater fills the pores from substrate in which air fills the pores.

wave A disturbance that transmits energy from one point to another in the form of periodic motions.

wave base The depth, approximately equal in distance to half a wavelength in a body of water, beneath which there is no wave movement.

wave-cut bench A platform of rock, cut by wave erosion, at the low-tide line that was left behind a retreating cliff.

wave-cut notch A notch in a coastal cliff cut out by wave erosion.

wave erosion The combined effects of the shattering, wedging, and abrading of a cliff face by waves and the sediment they carry.

wave front The boundary between the region through which a wave has passed and the region through which it has not yet passed.

wavelength The horizontal difference between two adjacent wave troughs or two adjacent crests.

wave refraction (ocean) The bending of waves as they approach a shore so that their crests make no more than a 5° angle with the shoreline.

weather Local-scale conditions as defined by temperature, air pressure, relative humidity, and wind speed.

weathered rock Rock that has reacted with air and/or water at or near the Earth's surface.

weathering The processes that break up and corrode solid rock, eventually transforming it into sediment.

weather system A specific set of weather conditions, reflecting the configuration of air movement in the atmosphere, that affects a region for a period of time.

welded tuff Tuff formed by the welding together of hot volcanic glass shards at the base of pyroclastic flows.

well A hole in the ground dug or drilled in order to obtain water.

Western Interior Seaway A north-south-trending seaway that ran down the middle of North America during the Late Cretaceous Period.

wet-bottom (temperate) glacier A glacier with a thin layer of water at its base, over which the glacier slides.

wetted perimeter The area in which water touches a stream channel's walls.

wind abrasion The grinding away at surfaces in a desert by windblown sand and dust.

wind gap An opening through a high ridge that developed earlier in geologic history by stream erosion, but that is now dry.

xenolith A relict of wall rock surrounded by intrusive rock when the intrusive rock freezes.

yardang A mushroom-like column with a resistant rock perched on an eroding column of softer rock; created by wind abrasion in deserts where a resistant rock overlies softer layers of rock.

yazoo stream A small tributary that runs parallel to the main river in a floodplain because the tributary is blocked from entering the main river by levees.

Younger Dryas An interval of cooler temperatures that took place 4,500 years ago during a general warming/glacier-retreat period.

zeolite facies The metamorphic facies just above diagenetic conditions, under which zeolite minerals form.

zone of ablation The area of a glacier in which ablation (melting, sublimation, calving) subtracts from the glacier.

zone of accumulation (1) The layer of regolith in which new minerals precipitate out of water passing through, thus leaving behind a load of fine clay; (2) the area of a glacier in which snowfall adds to the glacier.

zone of aeration *See* Unsaturated zone.

zone of leaching The layer of regolith in which water dissolves ions and picks up very fine clay; these materials are then carried downward by infiltrating water.

Title page: Stephen Marshak
Author photo: Kurt Burmeister
Table of Contents (in chronological order): Stephen Marshak; NASA; Stephen Marshak; © Julius T. Csotonyi; Images provided by Google Earth mapping services/NASA, © DigitalGlobe, © Terra Metrics, © GeoEye, © Europa Technologies, Copyright 2014; Mark Schneider/Visuals Unlimited/Corbis; Photos 12 / Alamy; Stephen Marshak (5 photos); Richard Roscoe/Stocktrek Images/Corbis; AP Photo/Natacha Pisarenko; USGS; Stephen Marshak (6 photos); NOAA; Reuters/Newscom; Stephen Marshak (2 photos); Emma Marshak; Stephen Marshak (4 photos).

PRELUDE

Page 1: Stephen Marshak; **p. 2 (both):** Stephen Marshak; **p. 3 (all):** Stephen Marshak; **p. 4 (both):** Stephen Marshak; **p. 5 (a):** AP Photo/Hurriyet; **(b):** Stephen Marshak; **p. 7:** Stephen Marshak.

CHAPTER 1

Page 10: NASA; **p. 12:** NASA; **p. 13:** NASA; **p. 14 (a):** Deyan Georgiev Creative collection / Alamy; **(b):** Gordon Garradd/Science Source; **(c):** Nasa/JPL-Caltech; **p. 15(a):** Peter Apian, *Cosmographia*, Antwerp, 1524; **(b):** Picture Library/Alamy; **p. 16 (all):** Stephen Marshak; **p. 17 (a):** © Miloslav Druckmuller; **(b):** NASA; **(c):** NASA/JPL-Caltech; **p. 20 (left):** 2/Christoph Wilhelm /Ocean/Corbis; **(right):** Stephen Marshak; **p. 23:** Moonrunner Design; **p. 26:** NASA, ESA, and M. Livio and the Hubble 20th Anniversary Team (STScI); **p. 27 (a):** SOHO (ESA & NASA); **(b):** J. Hester and P. Scowen/NASA; **p. 29 (a):** NASA; **(b):** R. Pelisson, © SaharaMet; **(c):** NASA; **p. 32:** Images provided by Google Earth mapping services/NASA, © DigitalGlobe, ©Terra Metrics, © GeoEye, © Europa Technologies, Copyright 2014; **p. 33:** Images provided by Google Earth mapping services/NASA, © DigitalGlobe, © Terra Metrics, © GeoEye, © Europa Technologies, Copyright 2014; **p. 35 (a):** NASA/ESA; **(b):** © Robert Gendler.

CHAPTER 2

Page 36: Stephen Marshak; **p. 39 (a):** NASA/JPL/Cal Tech; **(b):** Science Source; **(c):** NASA/JPL-Caltech/UMD; **p. 40 (all but Mars):** JPL/NASA; **(Mars):** NASA and The Hubble Heritage Team (STScI/AURA); **p. 41:** NASA/Science Source; **p. 42:** NASA; **p. 44 (both):** Images provided by Google Earth mapping services/NASA, © DigitalGlobe, © Terra Metrics, © GeoEye, © Europa Technologies, Copyright 2014; **p. 45:** Images provided by Google Earth mapping services/NASA, © DigitalGlobe, © Terra Metrics, © GeoEye, © Europa Technologies, Copyright 2014; **p. 47:** Tate Gallery, London/ Art Resource, N.Y; **p. 48:** Stephen Marshak; **p. 50 (a):** Fred Espenak / Science Source; **(b):** ©Tom Bean; Marli Miller/Visuals Unlimited, Inc.; **(d):** AP Photo; **p. 52 (from left to right):** Susan E. Degginger / Alamy (3 photos); The Natural History Museum/Alamy (2 photos); **p. 54:** Stephen Marshak; **p. 60:** NASA/JPL-Caltech.

CHAPTER 3

Page 61: © Julius T. Csotonyi; **p. 63 (a):** Alfred Wegener Institute for Polar and Marine Research; **(b):** Ron Blakey, Colorado Plateau Geosystems; **(bottom):** Images provided by Google Earth mapping services/NASA, © DigitalGlobe, © Terra Metrics, © GeoEye, © Europa Technologies, Copyright 2014; **p. 64:** Images provided by Google Earth mapping services/NASA, © DigitalGlobe, © Terra Metrics, © GeoEye, © Europa Technologies, Copyright 2014; **p. 65 (a):** Pete M. Wilson / Alamy; **(c):** Courtesy of Thomas N. Taylor; **p. 66:** Ron Blakey, Colorado Plateau Geosystems; **p. 73:** NOAA; **p. 74:** Images provided by Google Earth mapping services/NASA, © DigitalGlobe, © Terra Metrics, © GeoEye, © Europa Technologies, Copyright 2014; **p. 78 (all):** Images Courtesy of Gary A.Glatzmaier (University of California, Santa Cruz) And Paul H. Roberts (University of California, Los Angeles), Taken from their computer simulation; **p. 82:** Magnetic Anomaly Map of the World, 2007 Equatorial scale: 1: 50 000 000; © CCGM-CGMW; Authors: J.V. Korhonen,J. Derek Fairhead, M. Hamoudi, K. Hemant, V. Lesur, M. Mandea, S. Maus, M. Purucker, D. Ravat, T. Sazonova & E. Thébault; **p. 85:** Christoph Hormann.

CHAPTER 4

Page 86: Images provided by Google Earth mapping services/NASA, © DigitalGlobe, © Terra Metrics, © GeoEye, © Europa Technologies, Copyright 2014; **p. 89:** Images provided by Google Earth mapping services/NASA, © DigitalGlobe, © Terra Metrics, © GeoEye, © Europa Technologies, Copyright 2014; **p. 92:** Images provided by Google Earth mapping services/NASA, © DigitalGlobe, © Terra Metrics, © GeoEye, © Europa Technologies, Copyright 2014; **p. 93:** EOS TRANSACTIONS, AMERICAN GEOPHYSICAL UNION, VOL. 78, PAGE 265, JULY 1, 1997, D. Smith et al: Viewing the Morphology of the Mid-Atlantic Ridge from a New perspective; **p. 94 (both):** NOAA / University of Washington; **p. 95:** J.R. Delaney and D.S. Kelley, University of Washington; **p. 97:** Images provided by Google Earth mapping services/NASA, © DigitalGlobe, © Terra Metrics, © GeoEye, © Europa Technologies, Copyright 2014; **p. 99:** Images provided by Google Earth mapping services/NASA, © DigitalGlobe, © Terra Metrics, © GeoEye, © Europa Technologies, Copyright 2014; **p. 100:** Kevin Schafer / Alamy; **p. 104 (d):** Johnson Space Center, NASA; **p. 105:** Images provided by Google Earth mapping services/NASA, © DigitalGlobe, © Terra Metrics, © GeoEye, © Europa Technologies, Copyright 2014; **p. 107:** Tomography shear velocity model SAVANI by Ludwig Auer (ETH Zurich) and Lapo Boschi (Université Pierre et Marie Curie Paris).

CHAPTER 5

Page 114: Stephen Marshak; **p. 116:** Mark Schneider/Visuals Unlimited/Corbis; **p. 117:** Yakub88/Dreamstime.com; **p. 118 (left):** Ken Lucas/ Visuals Unlimited; **(right):** Stephen Marshak; **p. 119 (left):** Mark A. Schneider/Science Source; **(center):** incamerastock / Alamy; **(right):** Darryl Brooks/Dreamstime; **p. 123 (a):** Erich Schrempp/Science Source; **(c):** Courtesy of Prof. Huifang Xu, Dept. of Geology and Geophysics, University of Wisconsin, Madison; **p. 125 (a):** Charles O'Rear /Corbis; **(b):** John A. Jaszczak, Michigan Technological University; **(a-d):** Stephen Marshak; **(e):** Wikimedia Commons; pd; **p. 126:** ©1996 Jeff Scovil; **p. 128 (a-b, d, f):** Richard P. Jacobs /JLM Visuals; **(c):** Breck P. Kent/JLM Visuals; **(e top):** Stephen Marshak; **(e bottom):** Andrew Silver/USGS; **(g):** Scientifica/Visuals Unlimited/Corbis; **p. 130 (a):** Richard P. Jacobs/JLM Visuals; **(b):** 1992 Jeff Scovil; **(c):** Marli Miller/Visuals Unlimited, Inc.; **(d-e):** Richard P. Jacobs/JLM Visuals; **(h, left):** Arco Images GmbH/Alamy; **(h, right):** Ann Bryant www.Geology.com; **(g):** Stephen Marshak; **p. 131:** Javier Trueba/MSF/Science Source; **p. 132 (a):** Farbled/Dreamstime.com; **(b):** Huguette Roe/Dreamstime.com; **(c):** Dennis Kunkel Microscopy, Inc./Visuals Unlimited/Corbis; **p. 132 (d):** Construction Photography/Alamy; **p. 134 (a-b):** Stephen Marshak; **p. 134:** Images provided by Google Earth mapping services/NASA, © DigitalGlobe, © Terra Metrics, © GeoEye, © Europa Technologies, Copyright 2014; **p. 135 (left):** Michael Langford/Gallo Images/Getty Images; **(right):** Ken Lucas/Visuals Unlimited; **p. 136: (left):** Images provided by Google Earth mapping services/NASA, © DigitalGlobe, © Terra Metrics, © GeoEye, © Europa Technologies, Copyright 2014; **(right):** 1996 Smithsonian Institution; **p. 138 (a):** Albert Copley/Visuals Unlimited; **(d):** © 1998 Jeff Scovil; **(inset):** Stephen J. Krasemann/Science Source; **p. 140:** Chip Clark / Smithsonian Institution.

INTERLUDE A

Page 141: Photos 12 / Alamy; **p. 142 (both):** Stephen Marshak; **p. 143 (a, left):** Richard P. Jacobs/JLM Visuals; **(a, center):** Courtesy David W. Houseknecht, USGS; **(b, left):** sciencephotos/Alamy; **(b, center):** Courtesy of Kent Ratajeski, Dept. of Geology and Geophysics, U of Wisconsin, Madison; **p. 145 (all):** Stephen Marshak; **p. 146 (all):** Stephen Marshak; **p. 148 (a):** © Tom Bean; **(b):** Stephen Marshak; **p. 149 (all):** Stephen Marshak; **p. 150 top: (c):** Stephen Marshak; **(d):**

Scenics & Science / Alamy; **(bottom, a):** Product photo courtesy of JEOL, USA; **(bottom, b):** Courtesy of Joseph H. Reibenspies, Texas A & M University.

CHAPTER 6

Page 152: Stephen Marshak; **p. 154 (a):** Liysa/Pacific Stock/Agefotostock; **(b):** J.D. Griggs/ U.S. Geological Survey; **(c):** Stephen Marshak; **p. 155 (top left):** Images provided by Google Earth mapping services/NASA, © DigitalGlobe, © Terra Metrics, © GeoEye, © Europa Technologies, Copyright 2014; **(bottom, b-c):** Stephen Marshak; **p. 158:** USGS; **p. 162:** Stephen Marshak; **p. 163 (a):** USGS; **(b-e):** Stephen Marshak; **p. 165 (both):** Stephen Marshak; **p. 166:** Stephen Marshak; **p. 167:** Stephen Marshak; **p. 168:** Stephen Marshak; **p. 169 (both):** Stephen Marshak; **p. 170 (top, left to right):** Dr. Kent Ratajeski; Omphacite. 2006. Wikimedia; http://en.wikipedia.org/wiki/Public_domain; Dr. Matthew Genge; **(bottom, from left to right):** Stephen Marshak; **(b):** Mark A. Schneider/ Science Source; **(c):** Doug Sokell/Visuals Unlimited; **p. 173: (clockwise from top left):** geoz / Alamy; Stephen Marshak; Siim Sepp /Alamy; Wally Eberhart/Visuals Unlimited/Corbis; Joyce Photographics/Science Source; Mark A. Schneider/ Science Source; **p. 174 (all):** Stephen Marshak; **p. 176:** Images provided by Google Earth mapping services/NASA, © DigitalGlobe, © Terra Metrics, © GeoEye, © Europa Technologies, Copyright 2014; **p. 177 (both):** Stephen Marshak; **p. 179 (both):** Stephen Marshak; **p. 182 (top):** Tony Linck/SuperStock; **(bottom):** Jacques Descloitres, MODIS team, NASA Visible Earth.

INTERLUDE B

Page: 183: Stephen Marshak; **p. 184:** Corbis; **p. 185 (a-b, bottom):** Stephen Marshak; **(c):** Emma Marshak; **p. 186 (all):** Stephen Marshak; **p. 187 (top, both):** Stephen Marshak; **(middle right):** Visuals Unlimited; **(bottom, both):** Stephen Marshak; **p. 188 (all):** Stephen Marshak; **p. 189 (a):** Stephen Marshak; **(b):** Carlo Giovanella, UBC, 1997-2005; **(c):** British Geology Survey; **p. 190:** Stephen Marshak; **p. 192 (both):** Stephen Marshak; **p. 193 (all):** Stephen Marshak; **p. 194 (all):** Stephen Marshak; **p. 195:** Stephen Marshak; **p. 198:** US Dept. of Agriculture, Natural Resources Conservation Services; **p. 199:** Stephen Marshak; **p. 200 (both):** Stephen Marshak; **p. 201:** Jim Richardson/Corbis.

CHAPTER 7

Page 202: Stephen Marshak; **p. 204:** Stephen Marshak; **p. 205 (all):** Stephen Marshak; **p. 208 (all but bottom right):** Stephen Marshak; **(bottom right):** Scottsdale Community College; **p. 209 (top left):** Stephen Marshak; **(top right):** E.R. Degginger/Color-Pic, Inc.; **(bottom left):** Stephen Marshak; **(center both):** Stephen Marshak; **(bottom right):** D. G. F. Long; p. 211; **(a-c, e):** Stephen Marshak; **(d):** Emma Marshak; **p. 212 (both):** Stephen Marshak; **p. 213 (a):** Visuals Unlimited; **(inset):** Stephen Marshak; **(c):** Jason Bye / Alamy; **p. 214 (a):** Marli Miller; **(b):** Photo by Yukinobu Zengame, 2005. http://commons.wikimedia.org/ wiki/File:Limestone_towers_at_Mono_Lake,_California.jpg; http://creative-commons.org/licenses/by/2.0/deed.en; **(c):** M.W. Schmidt; **p. 215 (all):** Stephen Marshak; **p. 216:** Images provided by Google Earth mapping services/NASA, © DigitalGlobe, © Terra Metrics, © GeoEye, © Europa Technologies, Copyright 2014; **p. 217 (both):** Stephen Marshak; **p. 218 (inset):** Stephen Marshak; **(a):** All Canada Photos / Alamy; **(b):** 1980 Grand Canyon Natural History Association; **p. 219 (both):** Stephen Marshak; **p. 220 (a):** Imagina Photography /Alamy; **(b-c):** Stephen Marshak; **p. 221 (top, a, b):** Stephen Marshak; **(c):** Marli Miller/ Visuals Unlimited; **p. 222:** Stephen Marshak; **p. 225 (a):** Emma Marshak; **(b):** Stephen Marshak; **(c):** Marli Miller/Visuals Unlimited; **(d):** Stephen Marshak; **(e):** Stephen Marshak; **(f):** John S. Shelton; **p. 226:** Images provided by Google Earth mapping services/NASA, © DigitalGlobe, © Terra Metrics, © GeoEye, © Europa Technologies, Copyright 2014; **p. 227 (a):** Stephen Marshak; **(b):** Corbis; p. 228: **(a):** Belgian Federal Science Policy Office; **(b):** G.R. "Dick" Roberts © / Natural Sciences Image Library; **p. 232:** Corbis.

CHAPTER 8

Page 233: Stephen Marshak; **p. 235:** Stephen Marshak; **p. 236 (top left):** Stephen Marshak; **(top right):** Visuals Unlimited; **(bottom, all):** Stephen Marshak; **p. 237 (left):** Corbis; **(inset):** Stephen Marshak; **(right):** Kurt Freihauf; **p. 240:** Stephen Marshak; **p. 242 (inset):** Emma Marshak; **(a):** Corbis; **(b):** Stephen Marshak; **p. 243 (both, left):** Stephen Marshak; **(top right):** Dr. Jane A. Gilotti; **(bottom right):** Stephen Marshak; **(bottom, c):** Visuals Unlimited/Corbis; **p. 245:** Stephen Marshak; **p. 246 (all):** Stephen Marshak; **p. 252 (all):** Stephen Marshak; **p. 253:** Stephen Marshak; **p. 256 (top):** Dr. Terry Wright; (bottom, both): Images provided by Google Earth mapping services/NASA, © DigitalGlobe, © Terra Metrics, © GeoEye, © Europa Technologies, Copyright 2014; **p. 258 (both):** Stephen Marshak; **p. 260:** Stephen Marshak.

INTERLUDE C

Page 261 (all): Stephen Marshak; **p. 265:** Stephen Marshak; **p. 269:** Stephen Marshak.

CHAPTER 9

Page 270: Stephen Marshak; **p. 272:** Richard Roscoe/Stocktrek Images/Corbis; **p. 273 (left):** Bridgeman Art Library; **(right):** Source: ZeroOne Animation in association with Museum Victoria; **p. 274 (a):** Images provided by Google Earth mapping services/NASA, © DigitalGlobe, © Terra Metrics, © GeoEye, © Europa Technologies, Copyright 2014; **(b-c, e1):** Stephen Marshak; **(d, e2 3):** Jack Repcheck; **p. 275 (b):** Images provided by Google Earth mapping services/NASA, © DigitalGlobe, © Terra Metrics, © GeoEye, © Europa Technologies, Copyright 2014; **(c):** Marli Miller / Visuals Unlimited; **p. 277 (a):** Robert Francis/Agefotostock; **(b, d-f):** Stephen Marshak; **(c):** USGS; **p. 278 (a):** Thomas Hallstein / Alamy; **(b):** Stephen Marshak; **p. 279 (top, a):** AP Photo; **(top, b):** Stephen Weaver; **(top, c):** Stephen Marshak; **(bottom, a):** AFP/Getty Images; **(bottom, b):** Photo by Suzanne MacLachlan, British Ocean Sediment Core Research Facility, National Oceanography Centre, Southampton; **(bottom, c-d):** Stephen Marshak; **p. 280 (a-b, d, f):** Stephen Marshak; **(c):** USGS; **(e):** Anthony Phelps/Reuters/Corbis; **p. 281:** Images provided by Google Earth mapping services/NASA, © DigitalGlobe, © Terra Metrics, © GeoEye, © Europa Technologies, Copyright 2014; **p. 282 (top, both):** Stephen Marshak; **(right, a):** Sunshine Pics /Alamy; **(right, b):** USGS; **p. 283 (a):** John J. Bangma/Getty Images; **(bottom):** Marli Miller/ Visuals Unlimited; **p. 284 (a):** Marli Miller/Visuals Unlimited; **(b):** © Tom Bean 1985; **(c):** Robert Harding World Imagery / Alamy; **p. 288 (a):** USGS; **(b):** George Dimijian/Science Source; **p. 289 (a):** Westend61 GmbH / Alamy; **(b):** © Tom Pfeiffer / www.volcanodiscovery.com; **(c):** AFP/Getty Images; **(d):** USGS; **p. 291 (top):** Gary Braasch/Corbis; **(bottom):** Stephen Marshak; **p. 292 (b):** USGS; **(c):** AFP/Getty Images; **p. 294 (b):** Images provided by Google Earth mapping services/NASA, © DigitalGlobe, © Terra Metrics, © GeoEye, © Europa Technologies, Copyright 2014; **p. 295:** Images provided by Google Earth mapping services/NASA, © DigitalGlobe, © Terra Metrics, © GeoEye, © Europa Technologies, Copyright 2014; **p. 296:** Arctic Images / Alamy; **p. 297:** Stephen Marshak; **p. 298:** Stephen Marshak; **p. 300 (a):** USGS; **(b):** Vittoriano Rastelli/Corbis; **(c):** AP Photo; **(d):** Roy Whiddon; **(e):** Alberto Garcia / Corbis; **(f):** Philippe Bourseiller/Getty Images; **(g):** Photo: Magnus T. Gudmundsson, University of Iceland; **(h):** USGS; **p. 301 (b):** Thierry Orban/Sygma/Corbis; **(c):** Peter Turnley/Corbis; **p. 302:** Stephen Marshak; **p. 304:** Jennifer L. Lewicki , USGS; **p. 305 (a):** Vittoriano Rastelli/Corbis; **(b):** Sigurgeir Jonasson/Frank Lane Picture Agency/Corbis; **p. 306:** NASA; **p. 307 (a):** Gail Mooney/Corbis; **(b):** Santorini Caldera. Photo by Steve Jurvetson. 2012. http://creativecommons. org/licenses/by/2.0/deed.en; **(c):** Earth Sciences and Image Analysis Laboratory, NASA; **p. 308 (a):** Julian Baum / Science Source; **(b-e):** NASA/JPL; **p. 311 (left):** Reuters/Landov; **(right):** Arctic Images/Corbis.

CHAPTER 10

Page 312: AP Photo/Natacha Pisarenko; **p. 314 (a):** AFP/Getty Images; **(b):** JIJI Press / AFP / Getty Images; **(c):** AP Photo/ Kyodo News; **p. 317 (both):** Photo Courtesy of Paul ""Kip"" Otis-Diehl, USMC, 29 Palms CA; **p. 319 (a):** Created by Lou Estey with UNAVCO's Jules Verne Voyager, Earth edition, using the "Face of the Earth" dataset from ARC Science Simulations and U.S. Geological Survey earthquake hypocenters (2011). Credit: UNAVCO/NSF; **(left):** Images provided by Google Earth mapping services/NASA, © DigitalGlobe, © Terra Metrics, © GeoEye, © Europa Technologies, Copyright 2014; **p. 321:** Peltzer et al. (1999), Evidence of nonlinear elasticity of the Crust. *Science*, v. 286. Copyright © 1999, AAAS; **p. 322:** Created by Lou Estey with UNAVCO's Jules Verne Voyager, Earth edition, using the "Face of the Earth" dataset from ARC Science Simulations and U.S. Geological Survey earthquake hypocenters (2011). Credit: UNAVCO/NSF; **p. 326:** Inga Spence/Visuals Unlimited; **p. 334 (b):** Corbis; **(c):** George Hall/Corbis; **p. 335:** Patrick Robert/Corbis Sygma; **p. 338:** New Madrid earthquake woodcut from Deven's Our First Century (1877); **p. 340 (from top down):** AP Photo; Pacific Press Service / Alamy; M. Celebi, U.S. Geographical Survey; Reuters; **p. 341 (a):** Barry Lewis / Alamy; **(b):** Bettmann/Corbis; **p. 342 (a):** NOAA / National Geophysical Data Center (NGDC); **(b):** Rob Grange/ Getty Images; **(c):** James Mori, Research Center for Earthquake Prediction, Disaster Prevention Institute Kyoto University; **(e):** Courtesy of the National Information Service for Earthquake Engineering, PEER-NISEE, University of California, Berkeley; **p. 343 (a):** Karl V. Steinbrugge Collection, University of California, Berkeley; **(b):** National Geophysical Data Center (NGDC); p. 346: Images provided by Google Earth mapping services/NASA, © DigitalGlobe, © Terra Metrics, © GeoEye, © Europa Technologies, Copyright 2014; **p. 347**

(a): Vasily V. Titov, Associate Director, Tsunami Inundation Mapping Efforts (TIME), NOAA/PMEL-UW/JISAO, USA; (b): AFP/ Getty images; (c): Photo by David Rydevik. 2004. Wikimedia http://en.wikipedia.org/wiki/Public_domain; (d): Ikonos images copyright Centre for Remote Imaging, Sensing and Processing, National University of Singapore and Space Imaging; p. 348: National Geophysical Data Center (NGDC); p. 349 (a-b): Reuters/Eduardo Munoz; (c): Images provided by Google Earth mapping services/NASA, © DigitalGlobe, © Terra Metrics, © GeoEye, © Europa Technologies, Copyright 2014; (d): USGS; p. 350 (a): AP Photo/Kyodo News; (b): EPA/The Tokyo Electric Power Company /Landov; (c): Air Photo Service/Reuters /Landov; p. 356: NOAA/NOA Center for Tsunami Research; p. 358: NOAA Center for Tsunami Research.

INTERLUDE D

Page 359: USGS; p. 362: George Resch / Fundamental Photographs, NYC; p. 365: Jennifer Jackson, Caltech and Jay Bass, University of Illinois; p. 368: Matthew Fouch, Arizona State University; p. 369 (a): Adapted/Reproduced from Naliboff and Kellogg, "(2006. Dynamic effects of a step-wise increase in thermal conductivity and viscosity in the lowermost mantle," Geophysical Research Letters, 33. Copyright 2006 by the American Geophysical Union; (b): Courtesy of Allen K. McNamara, School of Earth and Space Exploration, Arizona State University; p. 370: Sarah Robinson, EarthScope National Office. EarthScope is a National Science Foundation funded project; p. 371 (a, c): John Q. Thompson, courtesy of Dawson Geophysical Co.; (b): Shell Oil Company; (inset): Courtesy Sercel and CGG Veritas; (d): Courtesy of Greg Moore, University of Hawaii and Nathan Bangs, University of Texas; p. 372: Stephen Marshak; p. 373 (top, both): Figure provided courtesy F. Lemoine & J. Frawley, NASA Goddard Space Flight Center; (bottom): USGS; p. 377: USGS.

CHAPTER 11

Page 379: Stephen Marshak; pp. 380-381: NOAA/ETOPO1382; p. 383 (both): Stephen Marshak; p. 384 (all): Stephen Marshak; p. 385 (both): Stephen Marshak; p. 387 (a): Galen Rowell/Corbis; (b-c): Stephen Marshak; (top): Images provided by Google Earth mapping services/NASA, © DigitalGlobe, © Terra Metrics, © GeoEye, © Europa Technologies, Copyright 2014; p. 389 (both): Stephen Marshak; p. 392 (a): John S. Shelton; (b): USGS; (c): Lloyd Cluff/Corbis; p. 393 (all): Stephen Marshak; p. 394: © Doug Sherman; (e): Stephen Marshak; p. 396: (a-d): Stephen Marshak; (e): John S. Shelton; p. 397 (a, c): Stephen Marshak; (b): John S. Shelton; p. 398 (both): Stephen Marshak; (right): Images provided by Google Earth mapping services/NASA, © DigitalGlobe, © Terra Metrics, © GeoEye, © Europa Technologies, Copyright 2014; p. 399 (b): Stephen Marshak; (bottom): © Marli Miller; p. 400: Stephen Marshak; p. 401: USGS; p. 404: Stephen Marshak; p. 406: Stephen Marshak; p. 407: Stephen Marshak; p. 409 (both): Stephen Marshak; p. 413 (a): USGS; (b): Modified from the original, Miles, C.E., compiler (2008). Geologic shaded-relief of Pennsylvania. Pennsylvania Geologic Society Survey.

INTERLUDE E

Page 416: Photo courtesy of Fred Delcomyn; p. 418: Stephen Marshak; p. 419 (a-c): Stephen Marshak; (d): Photo by William L. Jones from the Stones & Bones Collection, http://www.stones-bones.com; p. 420: John Reader/ Science Source; p. 421 (b): Richard T. Nowitz / Corbis; (c): Photo by Stephen Marshak; museum display courtesy of Amherst College, Massachusetts; p. 422 (a): Sovfoto/UIG via Getty Images; (b,d,f): Stephen Marshak; (c): Dirk Wiersma / Science Source; (e): Kevin Schafer/Corbis; p. 423 (all): Stephen Marshak; p. 424: UCL Micropalaeontology Collections, UCL Museums & Collections; p. 426 (a): Courtesy of Senckenberg, Messel Research Department; (b): Humboldt-Universität zu Berlin Museum für Naturkunde. Photo by W. Harre; (c): O. Louis Mazzatenta, National Geographic / Getty Images; (d): Illustration by Karen Carr and Karen Carr Studio, Inc. © Smithsonian Institution; p. 427 (a): Eye of Science/Science Source; (b): Shutterstock; p. 429 (all): Stephen Marshak; p. 430: This tree is based on the Tree of Life appendix in Life: The Science of Biology, 9th ed., by D. Sadava, D. M. Hillis, H. C. Heller, and M. Berenbaum (Sinauer Associates and W. H. Freeman, 2011). Image courtesy of David M. Hillis, University of Texas at Austin.

CHAPTER 12

Page 434: Stephen Marshak; p. 435: Granger Collection; p. 436: Stephen Marshak; p. 439 (all but b, left): Stephen Marshak; (b, left): Tom Pfeiffer / www.volcanodiscovery.com; p. 440: Stephen Marshak; p. 442: Layne Kennedy/ Corbis; p. 443 (both): Stephen Marshak; p. 445 (left): Stephen Marshak; (right): Images provided by Google Earth mapping services/NASA, © DigitalGlobe, ©Terra Metrics, © GeoEye, © Europa Technologies, Copyright 2014; p. 447: Stephen Marshak; p. 449 (left): Jenning, C.W., 1997, California Dept. of Mines

& Geology/ USGS; (right): Paul Karabinos, Williams College and USGS; p. 452 (all): Stephen Marshak; p. 453: Images provided by Google Earth mapping services/NASA, © DigitalGlobe, ©Terra Metrics, © GeoEye, © Europa Technologies, Copyright 2014; p. 457: Stephen Marshak; p. 459 (a): Damon Runberg, USGS; p. 459 (b-c): Stephen Marshak; p. 460: Courtesy of Yong Il Lee, School of Earth and Environment Sciences, Seoul National University; p. 462: Adapted from the International Commission on Stratigraphy 2013 Chronostratigraphic Chart, and from Walker, et al., 2013, Geological Society of America Bulletin; p. 463: Northwest Territories Geoscience Office; p. 466: (both): Stephen Marshak.

CHAPTER 13

Page 467: Stephen Marshak; p. 469 (both): Stephen Marshak; p. 472 (both): artwork copyright Don Dixon / cosmographica.com; p. 474: Stephen Marshak; p. 475 (a): Courtesy of Dr. J. William Schopf/UCLA; (b): Stephen Marshak; (c): Frans Lanting/Corbis; p. 476: USGS; p. 479 (a): Lisa-Ann Gershwin/U.C. Museum of Paleontology; (b): Stephen Marshak; (c): Courtesy of Dr. Paul Hoffman, Harvard University; p. 482 (b-c): Ronald C. Blakey; Colorado Plateau Geosystems, Inc.; p. 483: Tom McHugh/Science Source; p. 484 (b): Ronald C. Blakey Colorado Plateau Geosystems, Inc.; (c): Stephen Marshak; (d): Ted Daeschler, PhD.; p. 485: Ronald C. Blakey; Colorado Plateau Geosystems, Inc.; p. 488 (b): Mackenzie, J. 2012. Hillshaded Digital Elevation Model of the Continental US. http://www.udel.edu/johnmack/data_library/usa_dem.png; (c): Images provided by Google Earth mapping services/ DigitalGlobe, © Terra Metrics, NASA, © Europa Technologies, Copyright 2014; p. 488 (bottom): E.R. Degginger/Color-Pic, Inc; (bottom, inset): Dan Osipov; p. 489 (inset): Ronald C. Blakey; Colorado Plateau Geosystems, Inc.; (left): Stephen Marshak; p. 490 (a): Roger Harris/Science Source; (b): Stocktrek Images, Inc. / Alamy; (c): Richard Bizley; (right): Images provided by Google Earth mapping services/NASA, © DigitalGlobe, © Terra Metrics, © GeoEye, © Europa Technologies, Copyright 2014; p. 491 (both): Ronald C. Blakey; Colorado Plateau Geosystems, Inc.; p. 492 (b): Ronald C. Blakey; Colorado Plateau Geosystems, Inc.; p. 493 (both): Stephen Marshak; p. 494 (a): NASA, JPL; (a, inset): Ron Blakey, Colorado Plateau Geosystems, Inc.; (b): Images provided by Google Earth mapping services/NASA, © DigitalGlobe, © Terra Metrics, © GeoEye, © Europa Technologies, Copyright 2014; p. 494 (c): Image Credit: Virgil L. Sharpton, Lunar and Planetary Institute; p. 495: Images provided by Google Earth mapping services/NASA, © DigitalGlobe, © Terra Metrics, © GeoEye, © Europa Technologies, Copyright 2014; p. 498 (all): Ron Blakey, Colorado Plateau Geosystems, Inc.; p. 499 (all): Ron Blakey, Colorado Plateau Geosystems, Inc.

CHAPTER 14

Page 502: Stephen Marshak; p. 504: Stephen Marshak; p. 505 (a): Stephen Marshak; (b): Wikipedia, 1800, http://commons.wikimedia.org/wiki/Public_domain#Material_in_the_public_domain; p. 509: Department of Defense; p. 513 (a): Stephen Marshak; (b): Photo by Tormod Sandtorv. Sept 30, 2011, https://creativecommons.org/licenses/by-sa/2.0/515; (b): Data courtesy of Fugro. Credit: Virtual Seismic Atlas http://www.seismicatlas.org; p. 516 (b): Courtesy of the West Kern Oil Museum; (c): Stephen Marshak; (d): Accent Alaska.com / Alamy; (top left): Images provided by Google Earth mapping services/NASA, © DigitalGlobe, © Terra Metrics, © GeoEye, © Europa Technologies, Copyright 2014; p. 518 (a, c-d): Stephen Marshak; (b): AP Photo/Franship/HO; p. 519: Ron Blakey, Colorado Plateau Geosystems, Inc.; p. 520: U.S. Energy Information Administration; p. 521 (a): AP Photo/Jeff McIntosh; (b): Aurora Photos/Alamy; (c): William J.Winters, USGS; p. 523 (b): Andrew Harrer /Bloomberg via Getty Images; p. 524: Field Museum Library/Getty Images; p. 525: Department of Natural Resources, Alaska; p. 527 (a, c): Stephen Marshak; (d): Cultura Creative (RF) / Alamy; p. 529 (a): Philadelphia Inquirer; (b): Courtesy of Anupma Prakahs, Geophysical Institute; p. 530: James Blank/Photophile; p. 531: Images provided by Google Earth mapping services/NASA, © DigitalGlobe, © Terra Metrics, © GeoEye, © Europa Technologies, Copyright 2014; p. 532: G.R. 'Dick' Roberts © Natural Sciences Image Library; p. 533 (both): Stephen Marshak; p. 534: Stephen Marshak; p. 539 (a): AP Photo/Stapleton; (b): AFP/Getty Images; p. 541 (a): iStockphoto; (b, e): NASA; (c): US Coast Guard/Handout/Corbis; (d): Reuters / Landov; p. 544: Heino Kalis/Corbis

CHAPTER 15

Page 545: Stephen Marshak; p. 546 (both): Wikimedia Commons, pd; p. 547: Courtesy of Nightflyer; (inset): Stephen Marshak; p. 548 (a): Stephen Marshak; (inset): Layne Kennedy/Corbis; (b): Stephen Marshak; (bottom): Science VU-ASIS/Visual Unlimited; p. 549 (both): Richard P. Jacobs/JLM Visuals; p. 550 (both): Stephen Marshak; p. 553 (a): Stephen Marshak; (b): K.L. Smith Jr.

(MBARI) and S.E. Beaulieu (WHOI); **p. 554 (center):** Art Directors & TRIP / Alamy; (bottom): Hemis / Alamy; **p. 555:** Images provided by Google Earth mapping services/NASA, © DigitalGlobe, © Terra Metrics, © GeoEye, © Europa Technologies, Copyright 2014; **p. 556 (a):** Robert W. Gerling/ Visual Unlimited; **(b):** USGS; **(d):** Stephen Marshak; **p. 558:** Rodrigo Arangua / AFP / Getty Images; **p. 559 (a):** Richard P. Jacobs/JLM Visuals; **(b-d):** Stephen Marshak; **p. 560 (all):** Stephen Marshak; **p. 561 (a):** Stephen Marshak; **(b):** Bloomberg/ Getty Images; **p. 566 (a):** Stephen Marshak; **(b):** Doug Sokell/Visuals Unlimited; **(c):** A.J. Copley/Visual Unlimited; **p. 569:** Lucidio Studio, Inc/Getty Images.

INTERLUDE F

Page 570: Stephen Marshak; **p. 572:** NOAA; **p. 573 (all):** Stephen Marshak; **p. 574: (a):** KennethTownsend (artist); http://www.shadedreliefarchive.com/Europe_townsend.html http://www.shadedreliefarchive.com/Kenneth_Townsend.html **p. 574 (b):** JLP/NASA; **p. 576 (both):** Stephen Marshak; **p. 577 (a):** G.R. 'Dick' Roberts © Natural Sciences Image Library; **(b):** Photo by Davie Pierson/ St. Petersburg Times; **p. 578: (all):** Stephen Marshak; **p. 579:** Stephen Marshak; **p. 583 (a):** NASA; **p. 583 (b):** JSC/NASA; **(c):** Dr. David Smith, NASA Goddard Space Flight Center/MOLA Science Team; **(d):** NASA/USGS Flagstaff; **p. 584 (a):** ESA/DLR/FU Berlin (G. Neukum); **(b):** ESA/DLR/FU Berlin; **(c):** AP Photo/NASA; **p. 585 (left):** NASA/JPL/Space Science Institute; **(right):** NASA/JPL/University of Arizona.

CHAPTER 16

Page 586: Reuters/Newscom; **p. 587 (both):** Lloyd Cluff/Corbis; **p. 589 (inset):** Stephen Marshak; **(d):** Marli Miller/Visuals Unlimited, Inc.; **(e):** George Herben Photo/ Visuals Unlimited; **p. 590 (all):** Stephen Marshak; **p. 591 (a):** Shana Reis/ EPA /Landov; **(b):** Cascades Volcano Observatory /USGS; **(c):** Stephen Marshak; **(left):** Images provided by Google Earth mapping services/NASA, © DigitalGlobe, © Terra Metrics, © GeoEye, © Europa Technologies, Copyright 2014; **p. 592 (a):** Bob Schuster, USGS; **(b):** National Geographic Image Collection / Alamy; **(c):** Ron Varela/Ventura County Star; **p. 593 (top, a):** AP Photo/Ted S. Warren; **(bottom, a):** Stephen Marshak; **(bottom, b):** Guido Alberto Rossi/Age Fotostock; **p. 594:** Images provided by Google Earth mapping services/NASA, © DigitalGlobe, © Terra Metrics, © GeoEye, © Europa Technologies, Copyright 2014; **p. 595:** Stephen Marshak; **p. 596: (a):** AFP Photos; **(b):** Stephen Marshak; **(c):** Alaska Stock/Alamy; **p. 597 (a-c):** Stephen Marshak; **(d):** AP Photo; **p. 598 (a):** USGS/Barry W. Eakins; **(b):** USGS, Geologic Investigations Series I-2809 by Barry W. Eakins, Joel E. Robinson, Toshiya Kanamatsu, Jiro Naka, John R. Smith, Eiichi Takahashi, and David A. Clague; **(c):** Jerome Neufeld and Stephen Morris, Nonlinear Physics, University of Toronto; **p. 600:** Stephen Marshak; **p. 604:** Gorm Kallestad/Scan Pix/Sipa USA; **p. 605:** Breck P.Kent/JLM Visuals; **p. 606:** Stephen Marshak; **p. 607 (both):** Images provided by Google Earth mapping services/NASA, © DigitalGlobe, © Terra Metrics, © GeoEye, © Europa Technologies, Copyright 2014; **p. 608:** Stephen Marshak; **p. 609:** AP Photo/The Deseret News, Ravell Call, File; **p. 610:** © 2008, All Rights Reserved, City of Seattle; **p. 613:** Heino Kalis/Reuters/Corbis.

CHAPTER 17

Page 614: Stephen Marshak; **p. 616 (a):** Helen H. Richardson/ The Denver Post/ Getty Images; **(b):** John Gibson/Getty Images; **(c):** Andy Clark/Reuters/Corbis; **p. 617 (b):** Stephen Marshak; **(left):** Images provided by Google Earth mapping services/NASA, © DigitalGlobe, © Terra Metrics, © GeoEye, © Europa Technologies, Copyright 2014; **p. 618 (left):** Images provided by Google Earth mapping services/NASA, © DigitalGlobe, © Terra Metrics, © GeoEye, © Europa Technologies, Copyright 2014; **(right):** Stephen Marshak; **p. 619:** Stephen Marshak; **p. 620:** NASA; **p. 621 (both):** Stephen Marshak; **p. 623:** Stephen Marshak; **p. 624 (a):** Stephen Marshak; **(b):** © Ron Niebrugge; **p. 625 (all):** Stephen Marshak; **p. 628 (a, c):** Stephen Marshak; **(b):** Amar and Isabelle Guillen - Guillen Photography / Alamy; **p. 630:** Stephen Marshak; **p. 631: (all):** Stephen Marshak; **p. 632 (top, b):** Stephen Marshak; **(d):** courtesy of Jenny Jackson, Caltech; **(bottom, a):** Marti Miller/Visuals Unlimited; **(bottom, b):** Stephen Marshak; **p. 633 (a):** 1998 Tom Bean; **(b, e):** Stephen Marshak; **p. 634 (top):** NASA Earth Observatory; **(bottom):** NASA/GSFC/meti/ersdac/jaros, and US/Japan ASTER Science Team; **p. 635:** James Parker; **p. 638:** 1997 Tom Bean; **p. 640 (a):** Stephen Marshak; **(b):** AP Photo/Binsar Bakkara; **(c):** Mike Hollingshead/Corbis; **p. 641 (a, b):** NASA images created by Jesse Allen, Earth Observatory, using data provided courtesy of the Landsat Project Science Office- copyright 2008; **(b):** AP Photo/ United Nations, Evan Schneider; **p. 642 (all):** Stephen Marshak; **p. 643 (both):** Stephen Marshak; **p. 644 (a):** Reuters/Yoray Cohen/Eilat Rescue Unit /Landov; **(b):** USGS; **p. 645 (left):** Courtesy Johnstown Area Heritage Association; **(right):**

Mary Evans Picture Library / The Image Works; **p. 646:** ©Tom Foster; **p. 647 (both):** Stephen Marshak; **p. 648 (b):** AP Photo/The News-Star, Margaret Croft; **(c):** NASA; **p. 649: (a):** Fred Lynch/Southeast Missourian; **(b):** Scott Olson/Getty Images; **p. 652:** Photo courtesy of the Bureau of Reclamation.

CHAPTER 18

Page 655: Stephen Marshak; **p. 656 (a):** Rod Catanach, Woods Hole Oceanographic Institution; **(b):** Topham/ The Image Works; **(c, left):** Woods Hole Oceanographic Institution; **(c, right):** © Harbor Branch Oceanographic Institution; **(e):** Photo by Chris Griner, Woods Hole Oceanographic Institution; **p. 657:** NOAA; **p. 660 (all):** NOAA; **p. 661 (b):** © 2007 MBARI; **(c):** Hannes Grobe / Alfred Wegener Institute for Polar and Marine Research; **(bottom):** Images provided by Google Earth mapping services/NASA, © DigitalGlobe, © Terra Metrics, © GeoEye, © Europa Technologies, Copyright 2014; **p. 662:** U.S. Embassy/ Wikimedia; **p. 664:** NASA; **p. 665:** NASA/ SeaWIFS; **p. 668 (c):** Stephen Marshak; **(e-f):** www.michaelmarten.com; **p. 669 (a):** Wikimedia; http://en.wikipedia.org/wiki/Public_domain; **(b):** Imaginechina/Corbis; **p. 673 (b):** NOAA; **p. 674 (both):** Stephen Marshak; **p. 675 (inset):** NOAA; **(a-c):** Stephen Marshak; **(d):** Manfred Gottschalk / Alamy; **p. 677 (a, b, f):** Stephen Marshak; **(e):** NASA; **p. 679:** Stephen Marshak; **p. 680 (a):** G.R. 'Dick' Roberts © Natural Sciences Image Library; **(b, e1):** Stephen Marshak; **(e2):** Emma Marshak; **p. 681:** Cody Duncan / Alamy; **p. 682 (a-b):** Stephen Marshak; **(bottom):** Images provided by Google Earth mapping services/NASA, © DigitalGlobe, © Terra Metrics, © GeoEye, © Europa Technologies, Copyright 2014; **p. 683 (inset):** Steve Bloom Images / Alamy; **(b):** Stephen Marshak; **p. 689 (both, left):** USGS; **(b):** Stephen Marshak; **(top right):** Images provided by Google Earth mapping services/NASA, © DigitalGlobe, © Terra Metrics, © GeoEye, © Europa Technologies, Copyright 2014; **p. 690 (both):** Stephen Marshak.

CHAPTER 19

Page 694: Emma Marshak; **p. 695:** Images provided by Google Earth mapping services/NASA, © DigitalGlobe, © Terra Metrics, © GeoEye, © Europa Technologies, Copyright 2014; **p. 696 (a):** GeoPhoto Publishing Company; **(c):** Images provided by Google Earth mapping services/NASA, © DigitalGlobe, © Terra Metrics, © GeoEye, © Europa Technologies, Copyright 2014; **(d):** Red Huber/ Orlando Sentinel/MCT via Getty Images; **p. 697 (b):** Photo courtesy of Eric Prokacki and Jim Best, University of Illinois; **(d):** Stephen Marshak; **p. 702 (a):** Stephen Marshak; **(b):** Larry W. Smith/EPA/Alamy; **p. 707:** Stephen Marshak; **p. 708:** Vince Streano/ Corbis; **p. 709:** Food and Agriculture Organization of the United Nations; **p. 710:** Stephen Marshak; **p. 711 (a):** Allan Tuchman; **(b):** Stephen Marshak; **(c):** Emma Marshak; **(d):** Stephen Marshak; **p. 712 (a-c):** Allan Tuchman; **(d):** Stephen Marshak; **p. 713 (both):** Stephen Marshak; **p. 714:** Döll, P., Fiedler, K. (2008): Global-scale modeling of groundwater recharge. Hydrol. Earth Syst. Sci., 12, 863-885; http://creativecommons.org/licenses/by-sa/3.0/deed.en; **p. 717 (all):** Stephen Marshak; **p. 721 (a, c):** Stephen Marshak; **(b):** Francesco Tomasinelli / Science Source; **p. 722 (top, both):** Stephen Marshak; **(a):** George Steinmetz/Corbis; **(b):** Stephen Marshak; Images provided by Google Earth mapping services/NASA, © DigitalGlobe, © Terra Metrics, © GeoEye, © Europa Technologies, Copyright 2014; **p. 723 (a):** Kjell B. Sandyed /Visuals Unlimited; **(b):** Photo by Jim Pisarowicz/NPS; **p. 724 (left):** Paul F. Hudson, University of Texas; **(right):** ML Sinibaldi / Corbis; **(top):** Lois Kent; **p. 725 (left):** Lois Kent; **(right):** Ashley Cooper/Corbis.

CHAPTER 20

Page 728: Stephen Marshak; **p. 729:** AFP/Getty images; **p. 732:** Reuters News-Media Inc./Corbis; **p. 733:** Stephen Marshak; **p. 734 (a):** Stephen Marshak; **(b):** Kathryn Marshak; **p. 737:** Stocktrek Images, Inc. / Alamy; **p. 741:** CIMSS; **p. 742 (both):** NASA; **p. 747:** Stephen Marshak; **p. 748:** Stephen Marshak; **p. 749:** Stephen Marshak; **p. 750:** Stephen Marshak; **p. 753 (a):** Eric Nguyen/Corbis; **(b):** NOAA, photo by Brian Bill; **(c):** AFP/Getty images; **(d):** Photo By Miami Herald/Getty Images; **(e):** FEMA Photo by Greg Henshall; **(f):** NOAA; **p. 755 (b):** NASA; **(c):** NOAA; **p. 756 (b):** Photograph by Robert Simmon, ASA Earth Observatory and NASA/NOAA GOES Project Science team; **p. 758 (a):** NOAA; **(b):** AP Photo; **(c):** Images & Stories / Alamy; **(d):** Universal Images Group/Getty Images; **p. 759 (left, both):** Images provided by Google Earth mapping services/NASA, © DigitalGlobe, © Terra Metrics, © GeoEye, © Europa Technologies, Copyright 2014; **(right):** NASA; **p. 760 (a):** NOAA; **(b):** AP Photo/Susan Walsh; **(c):** New York Times Photos & Graphics; **(d):** Vincent Laforet /Pool /Reuters / Corbis; **(e):** Stephen Marshak; **p. 761 (both):** Images provided by Google Earth mapping services/NASA, © DigitalGlobe, © Terra Metrics, © GeoEye, ©

Europa Technologies, Copyright 2014; **p. 764 (a):** FAO-SDRN Agrometeorology Group; **(b):** NASA/ GSFC.

CHAPTER 21

Page 768: Stephen Marshak; **p. 770 (top):** Stephen Marshak; **(bottom):** O. Alamany & E. Vicens / Corbis; **p. 771:** Stephen Marshak; **p. 772:** Professor Andre Danderfer; **p. 773:** Stephen Marshak; **p. 774 (all):** Stephen Marshak; **p. 775 (all):** Stephen Marshak; **p. 776 (a):** Liba Taylor/Corbis; **(b):** Shannon Arledge / USMC / Getty Images; **(c):** Mike Olbinski; **p. 777 (left):** Stephen Marshak; **(a):** Stephen Marshak; **(b):** O. Alamany & E. Vicens / Corbis; **p. 778 (left):** JPL/ NASA; **(right):** Images provided by Google Earth mapping services/NASA, © DigitalGlobe, © Terra Metrics, © GeoEye, © Europa Technologies, Copyright 2014; **p. 779 (all):** Stephen Marshak; **p. 780 (a-b, d, inset):** Stephen Marshak; **(c):** Amar and Isabelle Guillen - Guillen Photography / Alamy; **p. 781:** Stephen Marshak; **p. 782 (b-c):** Stephen Marshak; **(d):** Photo by Flicka. Sept 2007. Wikimedia. http://creativecommons.org/licenses/by-sa/3.0/deed.en; **p. 783 (both):** Stephen Marshak; **p. 786:** Stephen Marshak; **p. 787 (all):** Stephen Marshak; **p. 788 (c-d):** Stephen Marshak; **(bottom right):** Images provided by Google Earth mapping services/NASA, © DigitalGlobe, © Terra Metrics, © GeoEye, © Europa Technologies, Copyright 2014; **p. 790 (top a-c):** Stephen Marshak; **(bottom, a):** Eitan Simanor / Alamy; **(bottom, b):** Stephen Marshak; **p. 791 (a):** Mark Phillips / Alamy; **(c):** Charles & Josette Lenars / Corbis; **p. 792 (top, both):** USGS; **(bottom, left):** BDR / Alamy; **(bottom, right):** Stocktrek Images, Inc. / Alamy; **p. 793 (left):** Library of Congress; **(right):** Image courtesy Jacques Descloitres MODIS Rapid Response Team; **p. 797:** USGS.

CHAPTER 22

Page 795: Stephen Marshak; **p. 796 (a):** Stephen Marshak; **(b):** Tom Bean/Corbis; **p. 798 (a):** Shutterstock; **(b, both):** Stephen Marshak; **(c, center):** Emma Marshak; **(c, bottom):** Ted Spiegel/National Geographic Creative; **p. 800 (b-d):** Stephen Marshak; **(e):** Galen Rowell/Corbis; **(f):** 1996 Galen Rowell; **p. 801:** NASA; **p. 802 (a):** NASA-JPL; **(b):** NASA; **p. 803 (top):** Stephen Marshak; **(bottom):** National Geophysical Data Center/NOAA; **p. 804 (a):** NASA/USGS Landsat 7; **(c):** Emma Marshak; **p. 806:** Antarctic Search for Meteorites Program, Linda Martel; **p. 807 (a):** Stephen Marshak; **(b):** Ted Scambos, National Snow and Ice Data Center, Clevenger/ Corbis; **(d):** Ralph A. Clevenger /Corbis; **(e-f):** Stephen Marshak; **(g, both):** ESA; **p. 809 (a):** Shutterstock; **(b-f):** Stephen Marshak; **p. 810:** Images provided by Google Earth mapping services/NASA, © DigitalGlobe, © Terra Metrics, © GeoEye, © Europa Technologies, Copyright 2014; **p. 811 (a-c):** Stephen Marshak; **(d):** 1986 Keith S. Walklet/Quietworks; **p. 812: (a-b):** Stephen Marshak; **(d):** Marli Miller/Visuals Unlimited, Inc.; **p. 812:** Images provided by Google Earth mapping services/NASA, © DigitalGlobe, © Terra Metrics, © GeoEye, © Europa Technologies, Copyright 2014; **p. 813 (a):** Stephen

Marshak; **(b):** Wolfgang Meier/zefa/Corbis; **p. 814 (both):** Stephen Marshak; **p. 816 (a-e1):** Stephen Marshak; **(e2):** Kevin Schafer/Alamy; **p. 817:** Stephen Marshak; **p. 818: (b):** Stephen Marshak; **(e):** Glenn Oliver/Visuals Unlimited; **p. 819:** Tom Bean/Corbis; **p. 822:** Michael Beauregard; **p. 823:** © Tom Foster; **p. 824:** Stephen Marshak; **p. 825 (b):** Lynda Dredge /Geological Survey of Canada; **(c):** Shutterstock; **p. 834: (b):** Hendrick Averkamp, Winter Scene with Ice Skaters, ca. 1600. Courtesy of Rijksmusuem, Amsterdam; **(c):** Stephen Marshak; **p. 835 (a):** Ed Stockard; **(b):** Roger J. Braithwaite; **(c):** Michael Melford / Getty Images; **(d):** NASA.

CHAPTER 23

Page 838: Stephen Marshak; **p. 845: (all, b):** Ron Blakey, Colorado Plateau Geosystems, Inc.; (c): Bournemouth News and Picture Service; **p. 847 (all):** Stephen Marshak; **p. 850: (top):** ISM/PhotoTakeUSA.com; **(bottom):** Bob Sacha/Corbis; **(inset):** NOAA; **p. 851 (a):** Nick Cobbing / Alamy; **(c):** Core Repository Lab at Lamont-Doherty Geological Observatory of Columbia University; **(inset):** NOAA; **(bottom, a):** Stephen Marshak; **(bottom, inset):** Provided courtesy of JRTC & Fort Polk. Photography by Bruce Martin, Natural Resources Management Branch, ENRMD; **(bottom, b):** Courtesy of the Climatic Research Unit, University of East Anglia; **p. 853: (all):** Ron Blakey, Colorado Plateau Geosystems, Inc.; **p. 854 (all):** NASA; **p. 856 (b):** Crown Copyright. Reproduced courtesy of Historic Scotland, Edinburgh; **(both, c):** Stephen Marshak; **p. 857 (a):** NASA; **(b-c):** Stephen Marshak; **p. 858:** Mark Garlick / Science Source; **p. 859 (top, left):** Stephen Marshak; **(top, right):** Images provided by Google Earth mapping services/NASA, © DigitalGlobe, © Terra Metrics, © GeoEye, © Europa Technologies, Copyright 2014; **(bottom, left):** Courtesy P&H Mining Equipment; **(center):** Richard Hamilton Smith/Corbis; **(right):** Stephen Marshak; **p. 860 (b):** Fearnside, P. M. 2008. The roles and movements of actors in the deforestation of Brazilian Amazonia. Ecology and Society 13(1): 23, Deforestation data from Brazil's National Institute for Space Research (INPE); **(c):** Nigel Dickinson / Alamy; **(d, both):** Images provided by Google Earth mapping services/NASA, © DigitalGlobe, © Terra Metrics, © GeoEye, © Europa Technologies, Copyright 2014; **p. 862:** Oliver Strewe / Getty Images; **p. 863:** NASA; **p. 865 (a, both):** NASA/Goddard Space Flight Center Scientific Visualization Studio; **p. 866 (a, both):** National Snow and Ice Data Center; **(b, all):** Jacques Descloitres, MODIS Rapid Response Team, NASA/GSFC; (bottom): Images provided by Google Earth mapping services/NASA, © DigitalGlobe, © Terra Metrics, © GeoEye, © Europa Technologies, Copyright 2014; **p. 867 (a, top):** USGS; **(b, bottom):** USGS photograph by Bruce Molnia; **(b):** Stephen Marshak; **(c):** Steven Kaziowski/Alamy; **p. 868:** IPCC; **p. 872 (c):** Stephen Marshak.

APPENDIX

Page A-6 (both): NOAA / NGDC; **A-7** USGS.